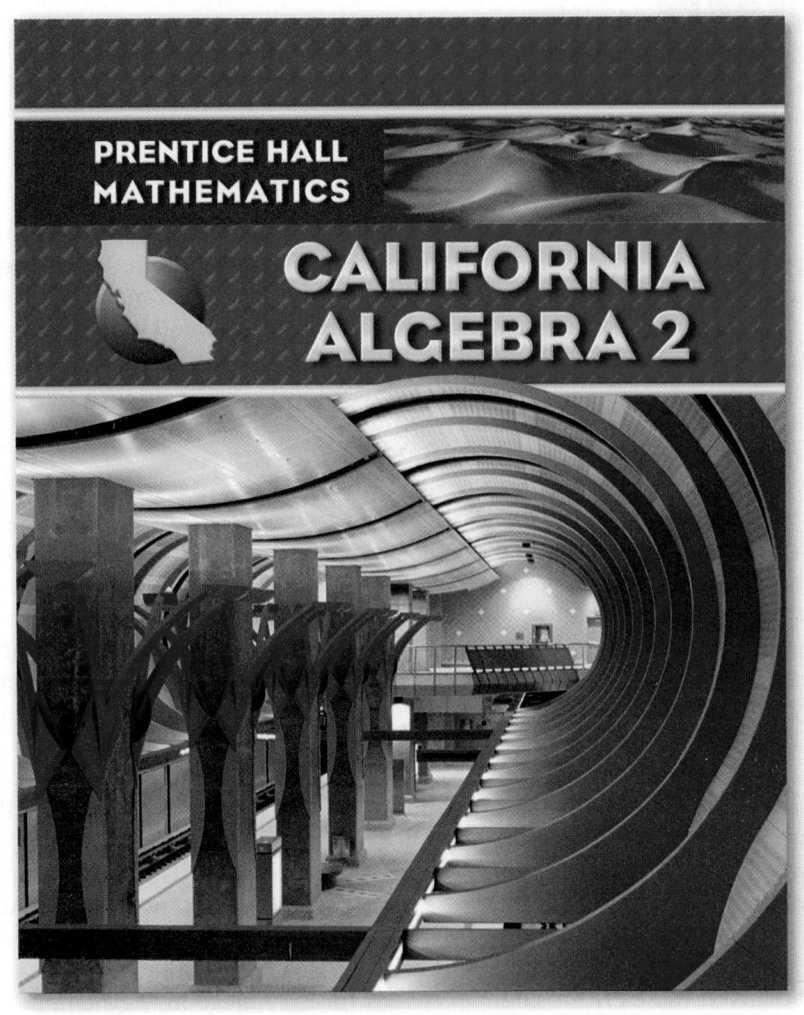

PRENTICE HALL
MATHEMATICS

CALIFORNIA ALGEBRA 2

Allan E. Bellman
Sadie Chavis Bragg
Randall I. Charles
Basia Hall
William G. Handlin, Sr.
Dan Kennedy

PEARSON

Prentice
Hall

Boston, Massachusetts
Upper Saddle River, New Jersey

Authors

Series Authors

Dan Kennedy, Ph.D., is a classroom teacher and the Lupton Distinguished Professor of Mathematics at the Baylor School in Chattanooga, Tennessee. A frequent speaker at professional meetings on the subject of mathematics education reform, Dr. Kennedy has conducted more than 50 workshops and institutes for high school teachers. He is coauthor of textbooks in calculus and precalculus, and from 1990 to 1994 he chaired the College Board's AP Calculus Development Committee. He is a 1992 Tandy Technology Scholar and a 1995 Presidential Award winner.

Randall I. Charles, Ph.D., is Professor Emeritus in the Department of Mathematics and Computer Science at San Jose State University, San Jose, California. He began his career as a high school mathematics teacher, and he was a mathematics supervisor for five years. Dr. Charles has been a member of several NCTM committees and is the former Vice President of the National Council of Supervisors of Mathematics. Much of his writing and research has been in the area of problem solving. He has authored more than 75 mathematics textbooks for kindergarten through college.

Basia Hall currently serves as Manager of Instructional Programs for the Houston Independent School District. With 30 years teaching experience, Ms. Hall has served as a department chair, instructional specialist, instructional supervisor, a school improvement facilitator, and a professional development (TEXTEAMS) trainer. Ms. Hall has developed curriculum for Algebra 1, Geometry, and Algebra 2 and contributed to the development of the Texas Essential Knowledge and Skills. A recipient of the 1992 Presidential Award for Excellence in Mathematics Teaching, Ms. Hall is also a past president of the Texas Association of Supervisors of Mathematics, and she is a state representative for the National Council of Supervisors of Mathematics (NCSM).

Acknowledgments appear on pages 1065–1067, which constitutes an extension of this copyright page.

PEARSON
Prentice Hall

ISBN 0-13-203124-8
3 4 5 6 7 8 9 10   11 10 09 08

Algebra 1 and Algebra 2 Authors

Allan E. Bellman is a Lecturer/Supervisor in the School of Education at the University of California, Davis. Before coming to Davis, he was a mathematics teacher for 31 years in Montgomery County, Maryland. He has been an instructor for both the Woodrow Wilson National Fellowship Foundation and the T^3 program. Mr. Bellman has a particular expertise in the use of technology in education and speaks frequently on this topic. He was a 1992 Tandy Technology Scholar.

Sadie Chavis Bragg, Ed.D., is Senior Vice President of Academic Affairs at the Borough of Manhattan Community College of the City University of New York. A former professor of mathematics, she is a past president of the American Mathematical Association of Two-Year Colleges (AMATYC), co-director of the AMATYC project to revise the standards for introductory college mathematics before calculus, and an active member of the Benjamin Banneker Association. Dr. Bragg has coauthored more than 50 mathematics textbooks for kindergarten through college.

William G. Handlin, Sr., is a classroom teacher and Department Chairman of Technology Applications at Spring Woods High School in Houston, Texas. Awarded Life Membership in the Texas Congress of Parents and Teachers for his contributions to the well-being of children, Mr. Handlin is also a frequent workshop and seminar leader in professional meetings throughout the world.

Geometry Authors

Laurie E. Bass is a classroom teacher at the 9–12 division of the Ethical Culture Fieldston School in Riverdale, New York. Ms. Bass has a wide base of teaching experience, ranging from grade 6 through Advanced Placement Calculus. She was the recipient of a 2000 Honorable Mention for the RadioShack National Teacher Awards. She has been a contributing writer of a number of publications, including software-based activities for the Algebra 1 classroom. Among her areas of special interest are cooperative learning for high school students and geometry exploration on the computer. Ms. Bass has been a presenter at a number of local, regional, and national conferences.

Art Johnson, Ed.D., is a professor of mathematics education at Boston University. He is a mathematics educator with 32 years of public school teaching experience, a frequent speaker and workshop leader, and the recipient of a number of awards. Dr. Johnson received the Tandy Prize for Teaching Excellence in 1995, a Presidential Award for Excellence in Mathematics Teaching in 1992, and New Hampshire Teacher of the Year, also in 1992. He was profiled by the Disney Corporation in the American Teacher of the Year Program.

California Mathematics Program Advisors

Prentice Hall wishes to thank the following educators for their ongoing advice in the development of this California Edition of Prentice Hall Mathematics. Their valuable insights have helped ensure that this mathematics series meets the needs of California students and their teachers.

Danelle Almaraz
Pre-Algebra Teacher
East Whittier City School District
Whittier, California

Catherine Barker
Algebra Teacher
Los Angeles USD
Long Beach, California

Eric Bitter
Pre-Algebra & Algebra Teacher
Clovis USD
Clovis, California

Joe Brumfield
Consultant
Pasadena, California

Lynn Cevallos
Consultant
Hacienda Heights, California

Manuel E. Chavez
AP Calculus Teacher/Math Coach
Los Angeles USD
Huntington Park, California

Edward Ford
Consultant
Escondido, California

Courtney Glass
Algebra 2 & Pre-Calculus Teacher
Monrovia City USD
Monrovia, California

Bernice Levens
Former Teacher/Consultant
Hacienda Heights, California

Sia Lux
Algebra & Calculus Teacher
Coachella Valley USD
Indio, California

Shawn Neal
Pre-Algebra & Algebra Teacher
Visalia USD
Visalia, California

Christy McAloney
Algebra & Calculus Teacher
Grossmont Union High School
    District
Spring Valley, California

Brian McElfish
Pre-Algebra & Algebra Teacher
Saddleback Valley USD
Lake Forest, California

Paul Dennis McLaughlin
Algebra Teacher
Wainut Valley USD
Wainut, California

Jason Rose
Algebra Teacher
Temple City USD
Temple City, California

Keith Smith
Pre-Algebra & Algebra Teacher
Grant Joint USD
Sacramento, California

Sarah Thomson
Calculus Teacher & Math Coach
San Bernardino City USD
San Bernardino, California

Contents in Brief

California Mathematics Student Handbook

CHAPTER 1

Tools of Algebra

California Standards

Algebra 2
1.0

Page 22

Functions, Equations, and Graphs

California Standards

Algebra 2
1.0

Standards Mastery and Assessment

Page 80

Linear Systems

California Standards

Algebra 2
1.0, 2.0

Mathematical Analysis
7.0

Page 148

CHAPTER 4

Matrices

California Standards

Algebra 2
2.0
Linear Algebra
4.0, 5.0, 9.0, 10.0, 11.0

Page 189

CHAPTER 5

Quadratic Equations and Functions

Student Support

California Standards

Algebra 2
4.0, 5.0, 6.0, 8.0, 9.0, 10.0

Standards Mastery and Assessment

Polynomials and Polynomial Functions

Student Support

California Check System

Check Your Readiness 310

Check Skills You'll Need 312, 319, 326, 333, 341, 347, 351, 359

CA Standards Check 313, 314, 315, 319, 320, 321, 322, 327, 328, 329, 333, 334, 335, 336, 342, 343, 344, 348, 349, 351, 352, 353, 360, 361

Checkpoint Quiz 332, 357

Vocabulary 🔊

New Vocabulary 312, 319, 326, 333, 341, 347, 351, 359

Vocabulary Tip 313, 316, 320, 321, 322, 326, 328, 335, 341, 348

Vocabulary Builder 340

Vocabulary Review 365

GO Online

Video Tutor Help 327, 353

Active Math 322, 329

Homework Video Tutor 316, 324, 331, 338, 345, 349, 355, 362

Lesson Quizzes 317, 325, 331, 337, 345, 349, 357, 363

Vocabulary Quiz 365

Chapter Test 368

Algebra at Work 332

California Standards

Algebra 2
3.0, 4.0, 5.0, 6.0, 8.0, 10.0, 18.0, 19.0, 20.0

Mathematical Analysis
4.0

Page 355

Radical Functions and Rational Exponents

Standards Mastery and Assessment

Student Support

California Check System

Vocabulary

GO Online

California Standards

Algebra 2
8.0, 11.2, 12.0, 15.0, 24.0, 25.0

Page 378

CHAPTER 8

Exponential and Logarithmic Functions

California Standards

Algebra 2
11.0, 11.1, 11.2, 12.0, 13.0, 14.0, 15.0

Probability and Statistics
8.0

Page 479

Rational Functions

Student Support

Standards Mastery and Assessment

California Standards

Algebra 2
7.0

Probability and Statistics
1.0

Mathematical Analysis
6.0, 8.0

Page 527

Quadratic Relations and Conic Sections

Standards Mastery and Assessment

California Standards

Algebra 2
8.0, 16.0, 17.0

Mathematical Analysis
5.0, 5.2, 7.0

Page 573

CHAPTER 11

Sequences and Series

 California Standards

Algebra 2
21.0, 22.0, 23.0

Mathematical Analysis
3.0, 8.0

Page 619

Probability and Statistics

Standards Mastery and Assessment

 California Standards

Algebra 2
18.0, 19.0

Probability and Statistics
2.0, 3.0, 4.0, 5.0, 6.0, 7.0, 8.0

Page 694

CHAPTER 13

Periodic Functions and Trigonometry

Student Support

California Check System

Vocabulary

GO Online

Standards Mastery and Assessment

California Standards

Trigonometry
1.0, 2.0, 4.0, 5.0, 6.0, 9.0

Page 725

CHAPTER 14

Trigonometric Identities and Equations

Student Support

 California Check System

Check Your Readiness 790

Check Skills You'll Need 792, 797, 806, 815, 822, 828, 835

CA Standards Check 793, 794, 797, 798, 799, 800, 807, 808, 809, 815, 816, 817, 823, 824, 829, 830, 831, 836, 837

Checkpoint Quiz 813, 834

Vocabulary 🔊

New Vocabulary 792, 806, 815, 822

Vocabulary Tip 793, 794, 798, 807, 812, 815, 816, 829

Vocabulary Review 841

GO Online

Video Tutor Help 808

Active Math 793, 831

Homework Video Tutor 795, 802, 811, 819, 825, 832, 838

Lesson Quizzes 795, 803, 813, 819, 825, 833, 839

Vocabulary Quiz 841

Chapter Test 844

Algebra at Work 827

California Standards

Trigonometry
3.0, 3.2, 7.0, 8.0, 9.0, 10.0, 11.0, 12.0, 13.0, 14.0, 19.0

Mathematical Analysis
7.0

Page 807

Learning the
California Standards

Your *Prentice Hall Algebra 2* textbook is designed to help you fully understand and learn the California Mathematics Standards. Here are some features of your textbook that will support your learning throughout the year.

California Check System

Look for the ☑ in each lesson. These questions are opportunities for you and your teacher to make sure you understand the mathematics – so you can be successful with each day's lesson.

GO for Help

Look for this Go for Help arrow throughout every lesson to point you to where you can get help or review important concepts. Be an independent learner – and go for help when you're having trouble.

Get Ready to Learn

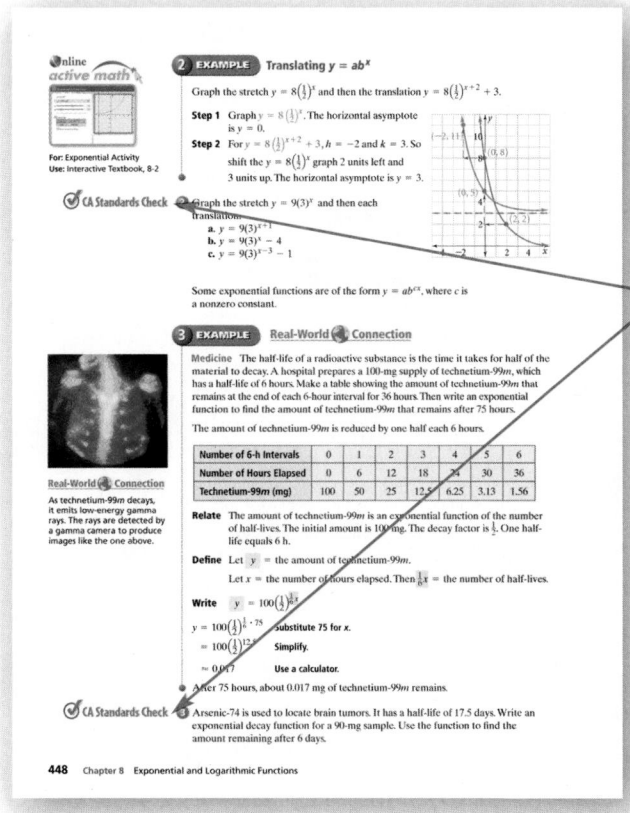

California Content Standards

Your textbook identifies which California standards you'll be covering each day. You'll also know whether you are being introduced to this standard for the first time, developing your understanding of it, or showing your mastery of it.

Check Skills You'll Need

These questions make sure you're ready to start the lesson by reviewing important skills and vocabulary words you'll need. Need help? Go for Help points you to the lesson you can review.

CA Standards Check

These questions, after every example, help you and your teacher make sure you understand the example – and the California Standards being taught.

Practicing the
California Standards

Your *Prentice Hall Algebra 2* textbook gives you plenty of opportunities to practice, with plenty of homework help along the way.

Standards Practice

Each lesson's Standards Practice gives you different levels of exercises.

A Practice by Example: These exercises give you practice with the examples you just learned. Go for Help points you back to the example for easy reference.

B Apply Your Skills: These exercises give you a chance to practice everything you learned in the day's lesson.

C Challenge: This problem extends your learning and gives you a more challenging problem.

Homework Video Tutor

What if you need help with your homework? These tutorials show real teachers reviewing each lesson. Your Prentice Hall textbook gives you a unique source for more help – called Homework Video Tutors. Log on to PHSchool.com and enter the Web Code provided – you'll get the homework help you need!

Mastering the California Standards

Your *Prentice Hall Algebra 2* textbook provides opportunities for you to ensure you've mastered the standards after every lesson and every chapter in your textbook.

Standards Mastery After Every Lesson

 Multiple Choice Practice and Mixed Review

The final part of each day's exercises includes practice with multiple choice problems and a chance to review skills you learned earlier in your course. This will help keep your skills sharp and help you receive lots of practice with multiple choice questions. All questions are correlated to the California Standards.

 for Help

The Go for Help arrow points to the lesson you can review. You can also go online and take a lesson quiz – another chance to make sure you've mastered the California Standards you learned.

Standards Mastery after Every Chapter

After every chapter, Standards Mastery Cumulative Practice provides an opportunity to demonstrate your understanding of all the California Standards covered so far.

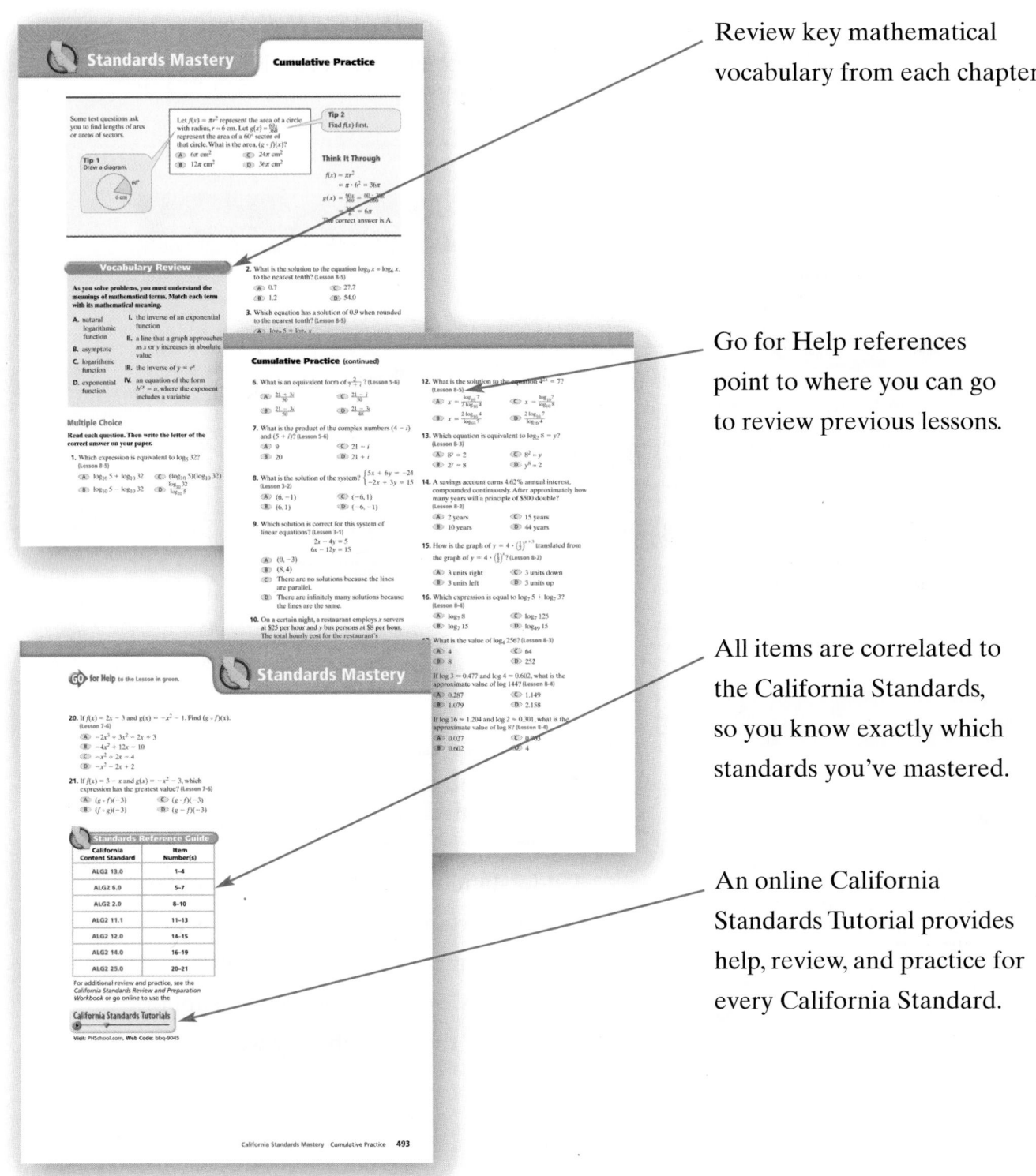

Review key mathematical vocabulary from each chapter.

Go for Help references point to where you can go to review previous lessons.

All items are correlated to the California Standards, so you know exactly which standards you've mastered.

An online California Standards Tutorial provides help, review, and practice for every California Standard.

Mastering the California Standards

> There are other types of features in your *Prentice Hall Algebra 2* textbook that will help you learn the mathematics and be successful in your class.

These features provide opportunities for you to engage with the mathematics being taught. Each feature states the California Standards being covered.

Vocabulary Builder

Understanding mathematical vocabulary is an important part of your success in any mathematics class. These features give you even more practice and support in learning these vocabulary words.

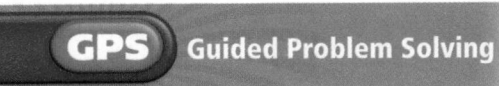

Guided Problem Solving

These features give you more support in becoming a good problem solver.

- We provide a great model for talking through the problem-solving process.
- "Think It Through" questions get more in-depth.

- The first two exercises present the steps you should take to solve the problem. They often contain a visual model of the problem.
- The remaining exercises provide independent practice.

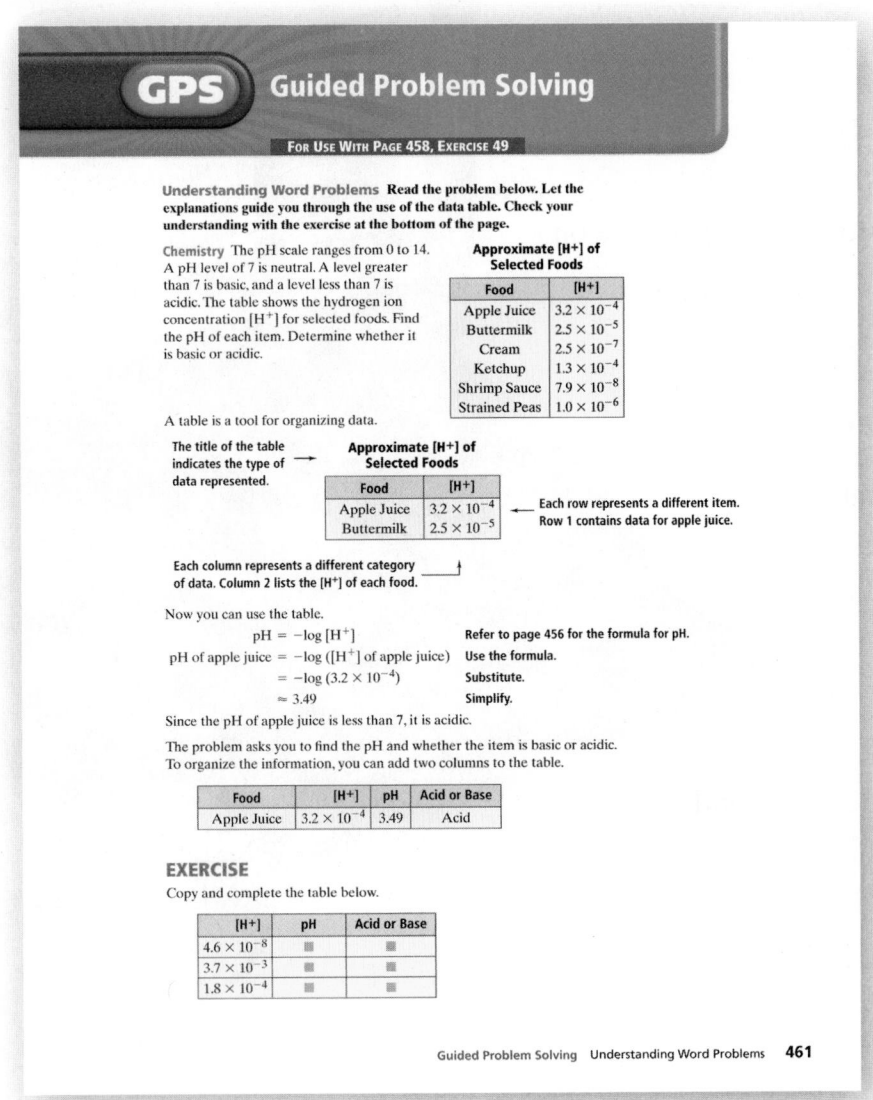

GPS Guided Problem Solving

FOR USE WITH PAGE 458, EXERCISE 49

Understanding Word Problems Read the problem below. Let the explanations guide you through the use of the data table. Check your understanding with the exercise at the bottom of the page.

Chemistry The pH scale ranges from 0 to 14. A pH level of 7 is neutral. A level greater than 7 is basic, and a level less than 7 is acidic. The table shows the hydrogen ion concentration [H$^+$] for selected foods. Find the pH of each item. Determine whether it is basic or acidic.

Approximate [H$^+$] of Selected Foods

Food	[H$^+$]
Apple Juice	3.2×10^{-4}
Buttermilk	2.5×10^{-5}
Cream	2.5×10^{-7}
Ketchup	1.3×10^{-4}
Shrimp Sauce	7.9×10^{-8}
Strained Peas	1.0×10^{-6}

A table is a tool for organizing data.

The title of the table indicates the type of data represented. →

Approximate [H$^+$] of Selected Foods

Food	[H$^+$]
Apple Juice	3.2×10^{-4}
Buttermilk	2.5×10^{-5}

← Each row represents a different item. Row 1 contains data for apple juice.

Each column represents a different category of data. Column 2 lists the [H$^+$] of each food.

Now you can use the table.

$$pH = -\log [H^+]$$ Refer to page 456 for the formula for pH.
$$pH \text{ of apple juice} = -\log ([H^+] \text{ of apple juice})$$ Use the formula.
$$= -\log (3.2 \times 10^{-4})$$ Substitute.
$$\approx 3.49$$ Simplify.

Since the pH of apple juice is less than 7, it is acidic.

The problem asks you to find the pH and whether the item is basic or acidic. To organize the information, you can add two columns to the table.

Food	[H$^+$]	pH	Acid or Base
Apple Juice	3.2×10^{-4}	3.49	Acid

EXERCISE

Copy and complete the table below.

[H$^+$]	pH	Acid or Base
4.6×10^{-8}	▪	▪
3.7×10^{-3}	▪	▪
1.8×10^{-4}	▪	▪

Guided Problem Solving   Understanding Word Problems   **461**

California
Student Center

Your Prentice Hall Student Center is your one-stop spot for reviewing the math you learned in class and completing your homework.

Interactive Text

Your complete textbook – electronically! Also includes:

- Stepped examples for you to review
- Activities and Videos to review your lesson
- Self-Check tests to make sure you're on the right track.

Student Worksheets

All the additional resources your teacher might assign you to extend your learning.

Web Resources

Links out to helpful sites to extend your understanding of math concepts.

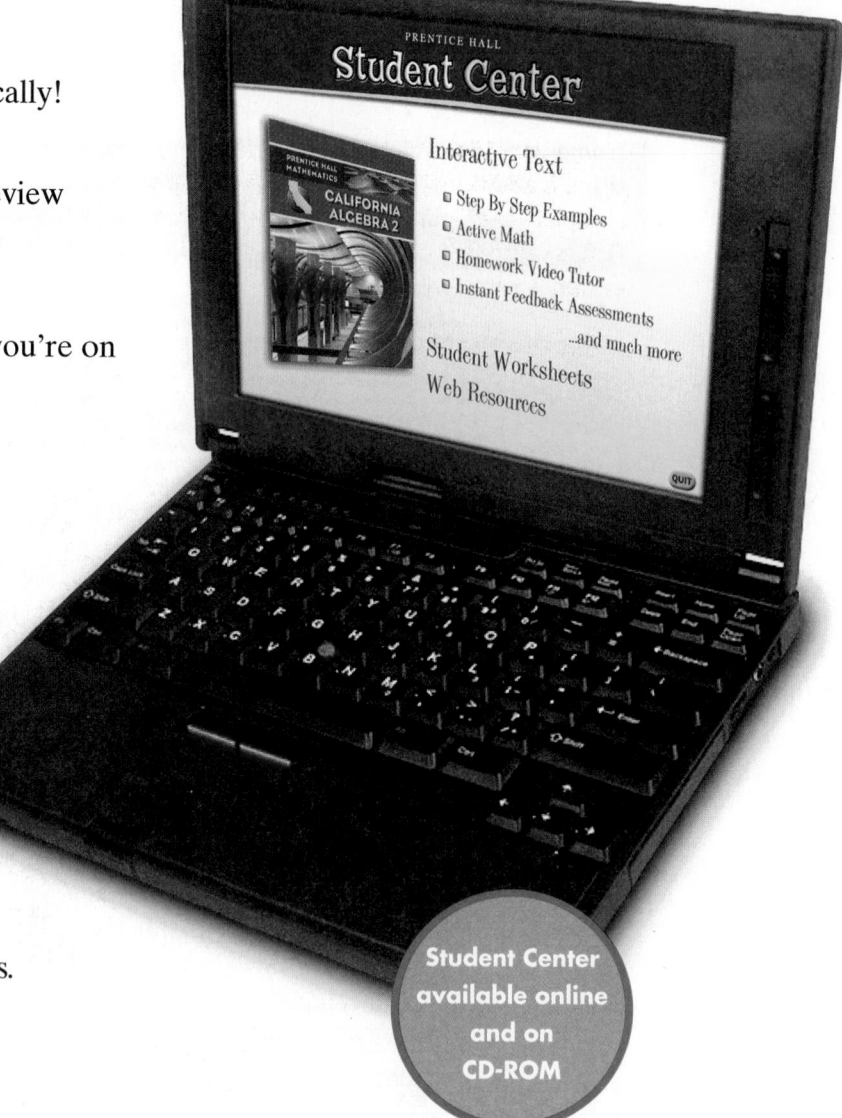

Student Center available online and on CD-ROM

Go Online

Throughout this book you will find links to the Prentice Hall Web site. Use the Web Codes provided with each link to gain direct access to online material. Here's how to *Go Online*:

1. **Go to PHSchool.com**
2. **Enter the Web Code**
3. **Click Go!**

Lesson Web Codes

Lesson Quiz Web Codes: There is an online quiz for every lesson. Access these quizzes with Web Codes bba-0101 through bba-1407 for Lesson 1-1 through Lesson 14-7.

Lesson Quizzes
Web Code format: bba-0204
02 = Chapter 2   04 = Lesson 4

Homework Video Tutor Web Codes: For every lesson, there is additional support online to help students complete their homework. Access the Homework Video Tutors with Web Codes bbe-0101 through bbe-1407 for Lesson 1-1 through Lesson 14-7.

Homework Video Tutor
Web Code format: bbe-0605
06 = Chapter 6   05 = Lesson 5

Chapter Web Codes

Chapter	Vocabulary Quizzes	Chapter Tests	California Standards Tutorial
1	bbj-0151	bba-0152	bbq-9045
2	bbj-0251	bba-0252	bbq-9045
3	bbj-0351	bba-0352	bbq-9045
4	bbj-0451	bba-0452	bbq-9045
5	bbj-0551	bba-0552	bbq-9045
6	bbj-0651	bba-0652	bbq-9045
7	bbj-0751	bba-0752	bbq-9045
8	bbj-0851	bba-0852	bbq-9045
9	bbj-0951	bba-0952	bbq-9045
10	bbj-1051	bba-1052	bbq-9045
11	bbj-1151	bba-1152	bbq-9045
12	bbj-1251	bba-1252	bbq-9045
13	bbj-1351	bba-1352	bbq-9045
14	bbj-1451	bba-1452	bbq-9045

Additional Web Codes

Video Tutor Help:
Use Web Code bbe-0775 to access engaging online instructional videos to help bring math concepts to life.

Data Updates:
Use Web Code bbg-9041 to get up-to-date government data for use in examples and exercises.

Math at Work:
For information about each Math at Work feature, use Web Code bbb-2031.

Your Guide to the Standards

California Mathematics Content Standards

Here is a list of the Mathematics Content Standards for Algebra 2, Probability and Statistics, and Trigonometry. The Algebra 2 standards are organized around four major strands: Polynomials and Rational Expressions; Quadratics, Conics, and Complex Numbers; Exponents and Logarithms; and Series, Combinatorics, and Probability and Statistics. Use this section as a reference guide as you explore the topics in each chapter.

Algebra 2

1.0 Students solve equations and inequalities involving absolute value.

2.0 Students solve systems of linear equations and inequalities (in two or three variables) by substitution, with graphs, or with matrices.

3.0 Students are adept at operations on polynomials, including long division.

4.0 Students factor polynomials representing the difference of squares, perfect square trinomials, and the sum and difference of two cubes.

5.0 Students demonstrate knowledge of how real and complex numbers are related both arithmetically and graphically. In particular, they can plot complex numbers as points in the plane.

6.0 Students add, subtract, multiply, and divide complex numbers.

7.0 Students add, subtract, multiply, divide, reduce, and evaluate rational expressions with monomial and polynomial denominators and simplify complicated rational expressions, including those with negative exponents in the denominator.

What You'll Learn

In Chapter 3 you will learn how to solve systems of equations, as in the following problem.

In a mayoral election, the number of votes for the incumbent was 25% more than the number for the opponent. Altogether, the two candidates received 5175 votes. How many votes did the incumbent mayor receive?

Where You'll Learn This

You will study these standards in Chapters 1, 2, 3, 4, 5, 6, and 9.

Algebra 2 (continued)

8.0 Students solve and graph quadratic equations by factoring, completing the square, or using the quadratic formula. Students apply these techniques in solving word problems. They also solve quadratic equations in the complex number system.

9.0 Students demonstrate and explain the effect that changing a coefficient has on the graph of quadratic functions; that is, students can determine how the graph of a parabola changes as a, b, and c vary in the equation $y = a(x - b)^2 + c$.

10.0 Students graph quadratic functions and determine the maxima, minima, and zeros of the function.

11.0 Students prove simple laws of logarithms.

11.1 Students understand the inverse relationship between exponents and logarithms, and use this relationship to solve problems involving logarithms and exponents.

11.2 Students judge the validity of an argument according to whether the properties of real numbers, exponents, and logarithms have been applied correctly at each step.

12.0 Students know the laws of fractional exponents, understand exponential functions, and use these functions in problems involving exponential growth and decay.

13.0 Students use the definition of logarithms to translate between logarithms in any base.

14.0 Students understand and use the properties of logarithms to simplify logarithmic numeric expressions and to identify their approximate values.

15.0 Students determine whether a specific algebraic statement involving rational expressions, radical expressions, or logarithmic or exponential functions is sometimes true, always true, or never true.

What You'll Learn

In Chapter 5, you will write equations for parabolas like the one at the right.

Write the equation of the parabola in vertex form.

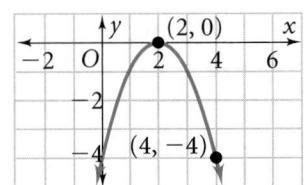

Where You'll Learn This

You will study these standards in Chapters 5, 6, 7, and 8.

Algebra 2 (continued)

16.0 Students demonstrate and explain how the geometry of the graph of a conic section (e.g., asymptotes, foci, eccentricity) depends on the coefficients of the quadratic equation representing it.

17.0 Given a quadratic equation of the form $ax^2 + by^2 + cx + dy + e = 0$, students can use the method for completing the square to put the equation into standard form and can recognize whether the graph of the equation is a circle, ellipse, parabola, or hyperbola. Students can then graph the equation.

18.0 Students use fundamental counting principles to compute combinations and permutations.

19.0 Students use combinations and permutations to compute probabilities.

20.0 Students know the binomial theorem and use it to expand binomial expressions that are raised to positive integer powers.

21.0 Students apply the method of mathematical induction to prove general statements about the positive integers.

What You'll Learn

In Chapter 10, you will learn about the geometry of conic sections. For example, you will find the eccentricity of an ellipse.

The eccentricity of an ellipse is a measure of how nearly circular it is. Eccentricity is defined as $\frac{c}{a}$, where c is the distance from the center to a focus and a is the distance from the center to a vertex.

a. Find the eccentricity of an ellipse with foci $(\pm 9, 0)$ and vertices $(\pm 10, 0)$. Sketch the graph.

b. Find the eccentricity of an ellipse with foci $(1, 0)$ and vertices $(\pm 10, 0)$. Sketch the graph.

c. Describe the shape of an ellipse that has an eccentricity close to 0.

d. Describe the shape of an ellipse that has an eccentricity close to 1.

Where You'll Learn This

You will study these standards in Chapters 6, 10, 11, and 12.

Algebra 2 (continued)

22.0 Students find the general term and the sums of arithmetic series and of both finite and infinite geometric series.

23.0 Students derive the summation formulas for arithmetic series and for both finite and infinite geometric series.

24.0 Students solve problems involving functional concepts, such as composition, defining the inverse function and performing arithmetic operations on functions.

25.0 Students use properties from number systems to justify steps in combining and simplifying functions.

What You'll Learn

You will explore sequences and series in Chapter 11. Understanding the pattern of a series enables you to find the sum of that series.

Consider the finite arithmetic series $10 + 13 + 16 + \ldots + 31$. How many terms are in it? Evaluate the series.

Where You'll Learn This

You will study these standards in Chapters 7 and 11.

Probability and Statistics

1.0 Students know the definition of the notion of *independent events* and can use the rules for addition, multiplication, and complementation to solve for probabilities of particular events in finite sample spaces.

2.0 Students know the definition of *conditional probability* and use it to solve for probabilities in finite sample spaces.

3.0 Students demonstrate an understanding of the notion of *discrete random variables* by using them to solve for the probabilities of outcomes, such as the probability of the occurrence of five heads in 14 coin tosses.

What You'll Learn

You can use formulas or tree diagrams to solve problems involving probability.

Make a tree diagram based on the survey results below. Then find *P*(a female respondent is left-handed) and *P*(a respondent is both male and right-handed).

- Of all the respondents, 17% are male.

- Of the male respondents, 33% are left-handed.

- Of female respondents, 90% are right-handed.

Where You'll Learn This

You will study these standards in Chapters 9 and 12.

Probability and Statistics (continued)

4.0 Students are familiar with the standard distributions (normal, binomial, and exponential) and can use them to solve for events in problems in which the distribution belongs to those families.

5.0 Students determine the mean and standard deviation of a normally distributed random variable.

6.0 Students know the definitions of the *mean*, *median*, and *mode* of a distribution of data and can compute each in particular situations.

7.0 Students compute the variance and the standard deviation of a distribution of data.

8.0 Students organize and describe distributions of data by using a number of different methods, including frequency tables, histograms, standard line and bar graphs, stem-and-leaf displays, scatterplots, and box-and-whisker plots.

What You'll Learn

The method you choose for organizing data depends on the type of data you are dealing with. Box-and-whisker plots clearly display the minimum and maximum values of a data set.

The table shows the high temperatures for one day at different locations on the island of Maui, Hawaii. Make a box-and-whisker plot of the data.

High Temperatures on Maui

Location	Temperature
Kahului	88°F
Kihei	85°F
Lahaina	86°F
Hana	82°F
Haleakala	66°F
Kula	75°F

Where You'll Learn This

You will study these standards in Chapters 8 and 12.

Trigonometry

1.0   Students understand the notion of angle and how to measure it, in both degrees and radians. They can convert between degrees and radians.

2.0   Students know the definition of sine and cosine as y- and x- coordinates of points on the unit circle and are familiar with the graphs of the sine and cosine functions.

3.0   Students know the identity $\cos^2(x) + \sin^2(x) = 1$.

3.1   Students prove that this identity is equivalent to the Pythagorean theorem (i.e., students can prove this identity by using the Pythagorean theorem and, conversely, they can prove the Pythagorean theorem as a consequence of this identity).

3.2   Students prove other trigonometric identities and simplify others by using the identity $\cos^2(x) + \sin^2(x) = 1$. For example, students use this identity to prove that $\sec^2(x) = \tan^2(x) + 1$.

4.0   Students graph functions of the form $f(t) = A \sin(Bt + C)$ or $f(t) = A \cos(Bt + C)$ and interpret A, B, and C in terms of amplitude, frequency, period, and phase shift.

5.0   Students know the definitions of the tangent and cotangent functions and can graph them.

6.0   Students know the definitions of the secant and cosecant functions and can graph them.

7.0   Students know that the tangent of the angle that a line makes with the x-axis is equal to the slope of the line.

8.0   Students know the definitions of the inverse trigonometric functions and can graph the functions.

9.0   Students compute, by hand, the values of trigonometric functions and the inverse trigonometric functions at various standard points.

10.0 Students demonstrate an understanding of the addition formulas for sines and cosines and their proofs and can use those formulas to prove and/or simplify other trigonometric identities.

What You'll Learn

In Chapter 13, you will explore the graphs of sine, cosine, and tangent functions. Graph the function $y = 3 \sin \frac{1}{2} x$ in the interval from 0 to 2π.

Where You'll Learn This

You will study these standards in Chapters 13 and 14.

Trigonometry (continued)

11.0 Students demonstrate an understanding of half-angle and double-angle formulas for sines and cosines and can use those formulas to prove and/or simplify other trigonometric indentities.

12.0 Students use trigonometry to determine unknown sides of angles in right triangles.

13.0 Students know the law of sines and the law of cosines and apply those laws to solve problems.

14.0 Students determine the area of a triangle, given one angle and the two adjacent sides.

19.0 Students are adept at using trigonometry in a variety of applications and word problems.

What You'll Learn

The Pythagorean theorem can be used to solve many real world problems, like the one below.

A transit is 330 ft from the base of a building. The angles of elevation of the top and bottom of a flagpole situated on top of the building are 55° and 53°. Find the height of the flagpole.

Where You'll Learn This

You will study these standards in Chapter 14.

Entry-Level Assessment

Read each question. Then write the letter of the correct answer on your paper.

1. If $y = 1$, then $(x + 5) \cdot y = x + 5$. This is an application of which property?

   (A) Inverse Property of Multiplication

   (B) Identity Property of Multiplication

   (C) Associative Property of Addition

   (D) Commutative Property of Addition

2. Give the solution to $|3x - 2| \geq 5$.

   (A) $x \leq -1$ or $x \geq \frac{7}{3}$

   (B) $x \geq \frac{7}{3}$

   (C) $-5 \leq x \leq 5$

   (D) $x \leq 3$ or $x \geq 7$

3. The graph of which equation would be perpendicular to a line with a slope of $\frac{1}{5}$?

   (A) $y = -5x + 2$

   (B) $y = -\frac{1}{5}x + 3$

   (C) $y = 5x - 2$

   (D) $5y + x = 2$

4. On a car trip, Kai wants to travel at least 436 miles in 8 hours of driving. What must be Kai's average rate of travel?

   (A) 54.5 mi/h

   (B) less than 54.5 mi/h

   (C) more than 54.5 mi/h

   (D) at least 54.5 mi/h

5. The pattern $x^2 \cdot x^5 = x^{10}$ is true for __?__.

   (A) $x = 2$ only

   (B) $x = 1$ and $x = 0$ only

   (C) $x = -1$ only

   (D) all real numbers

6. Mike and Jane leave their home on bikes traveling in opposite directions on a straight road. Mike rides five miles per hour faster than Jane. After 4 hours they are 228 miles apart. At what rate does Mike ride his bike?

   (A) 5 mi/h

   (B) 26 mi/h

   (C) 31 mi/h

   (D) 57 mi/h

7. Which is not true about the data in the table?

Hiking	
Time (min)	Distance (mi)
10	0.50
35	1.75
20	1.00
5	0.25
40	2.00

   (A) The domain is $\{5, 10, 20, 35, 40\}$.

   (B) The range is $\{0.25, 0.5, 1, 1.75, 2\}$.

   (C) The independent variable is distance.

   (D) The relationship is a function.

8. Divide and simplify.

   $$\frac{2x}{5y^2} \div \frac{3x^3}{10y}$$

   (A) $\dfrac{3x^4}{25y^3}$

   (B) $\dfrac{20xy}{15x^3y^2}$

   (C) $3x^3y^2$

   (D) $\dfrac{4}{3x^2y}$

9. Solve $x^2 + 2x - 3 = 0$ by factoring.

   (A) $x = -3$ and $x = 1$

   (B) $x = -1$ and $x = 3$

   (C) $x = 0$

   (D) $x = -3$ and $x = 0$

10. Which function would pass through $(3,0)$?

   (A) $y = -|x + 3|$

   (B) $y = |x| + 3$

   (C) $y = |x| - 3$

   (D) $y = |x + 3|$

11. Which of the following is true?

   Ⓐ $\sqrt{85} < 9$

   Ⓑ $8 < \sqrt{62}$

   Ⓒ $\sqrt{\dfrac{16}{25}} > \sqrt{\dfrac{16}{4}}$

   Ⓓ $\sqrt{121} < \sqrt{144}$

12. Determine which relation is a function.

Ⓐ

x	−2	0	1	2
y	0	−2	−3	−4

Ⓑ

x	0	0	0	0
y	0	1	2	3

Ⓒ

x	3	3	2	0
y	1	5	5	−3

Ⓓ

x	6	4	6	−1
y	0	3	2	−2

13. Use inductive reasoning to describe the pattern.

   $2, -6, 18, -54$

   Ⓐ Multiply the previous term by -2 and add -1.

   Ⓑ Multiply the previous term by -3.

   Ⓒ Add -3 to the previous term.

   Ⓓ Add -4 to the previous term.

14. If you use the quadratic formula to solve the equation $6x^2 + 5x = 21$, you will get the solution $\frac{3}{2}$ and

   Ⓐ $\frac{7}{3}$.   Ⓒ 7.

   Ⓑ $-\frac{7}{3}$.   Ⓓ $\frac{1}{2}$.

15. Which of the following is a product of $5y\,(y^2 + 7y - 5)$?

   Ⓐ $5y^3 + 35y - 25$

   Ⓑ $5y + 35$

   Ⓒ $5y^3 + 35y^2 - 25y$

   Ⓓ $6y^2 + 35y - 25$

16. Factor by grouping.

   $6x^3 - 27x^2 + 2x - 9$

   Ⓐ $(2x + 9)(3x^2 - 1)$

   Ⓑ $3(2x^2 + 1)(x - 3)$

   Ⓒ $3(x + 3)(2x^2 - 1)$

   Ⓓ $(3x^2 + 1)(2x - 9)$

17. Which is *not* a solution of $5(2x + 4) \geq 2(x + 34)$?

   Ⓐ 48 Ⓒ 6

   Ⓑ 8 Ⓓ 3

18. Write an equation of the line that passes through the point $(-6, 4)$ with slope -2.

   Ⓐ $y = 2x + 4$

   Ⓑ $y = -2x - 8$

   Ⓒ $y = -2x + 4$

   Ⓓ $y = 2x - 8$

19. Which of the following represents the system shown in the graph below?

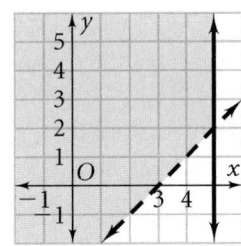

   Ⓐ $y = x - 3$
      $x \geq 5$

   Ⓑ $y \leq x - 3$
      $x > 5$

   Ⓒ $y < x - 3$
      $x = 5$

   Ⓓ $y > x - 3$
      $x \leq 5$

20. What is the number of x-intercepts of the parabola with equation $y = 6x^2 - 4x - 3$?

   Ⓐ 0 Ⓒ 3

   Ⓑ 2 Ⓓ 1

21. Which is the graph of a line with slope of -2 and y-intercept of 4?

 A

 C

B

D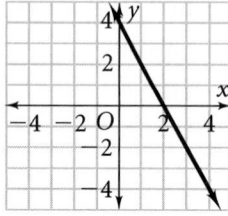

22. Which relation is not a function?

- **A** $\{(1, -5), (2, -4), (1, -4)\}$
- **B** $\{(1, -5), (2, -4), (3, -3)\}$
- **C** $\{(1, -5), (2, -4), (3, 2)\}$
- **D** $\{(1, -5), (2, -4), (3, -4)\}$

23. Factor.

$6x^2 - 216$

- **A** $6(x - 6)(x + 6)$
- **B** $(6x - 36)(6x + 36)$
- **C** $6(x - 6)$
- **D** $6(x - 36)(x + 6)$

24. Evaluate the discriminant of this equation.

$2x^2 + 2x - 15 = 0$

Which statement best describes the graph of the equation?

- **A** It lies on the x-axis.
- **B** It does not cross the x-axis.
- **C** It crosses the x-axis once.
- **D** It crosses the x-axis twice.

25. Simplify.

$(-6y^{-4})^5$

- **A** $7776y^{20}$
- **C** $-7776y^{20}$
- **B** $\dfrac{7776}{y^{20}}$
- **D** $-\dfrac{7776}{y^{20}}$

26. Simply $x^{\frac{1}{4}} \cdot x^{\frac{2}{3}}$.

- **A** $x^{\frac{11}{12}}$
- **B** $x^{\frac{1}{6}}$
- **C** $x^{-\frac{5}{12}}$
- **D** $x^{\frac{3}{8}}$

27. Solve.

$x^2 - 4x + 3 = 0$

- **A** $x = 1$
- **B** $x = 3$
- **C** $x = -1$ and $x = -3$
- **D** $x = 1$ and $x = 3$

28. Subtract and simplify.

$\dfrac{2}{4x} - \dfrac{3 - 2x}{x^2}$

- **A** $\dfrac{-1 + 2x}{4x - x^2}$
- **C** $\dfrac{5x - 6}{2x^2}$
- **B** $\dfrac{-1 + 2x}{4x^2}$
- **D** $\dfrac{10x - 12}{4x^2}$

29. What is (are) the solution(s) of the graphed function when the value of the function is 0?

- **A** -1 and 2
- **C** 2
- **B** 1 and -2
- **D** 2.2

30. Solve.

$$3x + y = -7$$
$$4x - y = -14$$

- Ⓐ $(-3, -2)$
- Ⓑ $(3, 2)$
- Ⓒ $(-3, 2)$
- Ⓓ no solution

31. Add:

$(7x^2 - 8x^3 + 4) + (9x^3 + 2x^2 + 7)$

- Ⓐ $-x^3 + 9x^2 + 11$
- Ⓑ $16x^5 - 6x + 11$
- Ⓒ $x^3 + 9x^2 + 11$
- Ⓓ $x^3 + 9x^2 - 3$

32. Which of the following represents the equation of the line that is parallel to the line $y = 5x + 2$ and passes through the point $(1, -3)$?

- Ⓐ $y = -5x + 2$
- Ⓒ $y = \frac{1}{5}x - 8$
- Ⓑ $y = 5x + 8$
- Ⓓ $y = 5x - 8$

33. The graph relates the height of a ball tossed in the air to the time after the ball is tossed. What does the y-intercept represent?

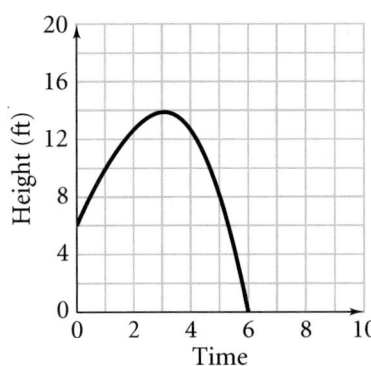

- Ⓐ The maximum height of the ball was 6 feet.
- Ⓑ The ball was tossed from 6 feet above the ground.
- Ⓒ The ball landed after 6 seconds.
- Ⓓ The minimum height of the ball was 6 feet.

34. Which expression represents the volume of the figure shown?

- Ⓐ $x^2 + 2x$
- Ⓑ $x^2 + 2x + 6$
- Ⓒ $x^3 + 6x^2 + 8x$
- Ⓓ $x^3 + 6x^2 + 8$

35. Solve the equation using the quadratic formula.

$$6x^2 - 10x + 3 = 0$$

- Ⓐ $\dfrac{5 \pm \sqrt{7}}{6}$
- Ⓑ $\dfrac{3 \pm \sqrt{5}}{6}$
- Ⓒ -2 and 5
- Ⓓ $\frac{3}{4}$ and $\frac{2}{3}$

36. A car travels 217 miles in 3.5 hours. Traveling at this average rate, how far will the car travel in one hour?

- Ⓐ 6.2 miles
- Ⓒ 62 miles
- Ⓑ 21.7 miles
- Ⓓ 350 miles

37. Which of the following best describes the graph of a quadratic equation with one real root?

- Ⓐ It has 2 x-intercepts.
- Ⓑ It does not cross the x-axis.
- Ⓒ Its vertex lies on the x-axis.
- Ⓓ Its vertex lies on the y-axis.

38. If $b \neq 0$, which exponents or powers property is *not* written correctly?

- Ⓐ $\dfrac{a^n}{b^n} = \left(\dfrac{a}{b}\right)^n$
- Ⓒ $b^0 = 1$
- Ⓑ $\dfrac{1}{b^n} = b^{-n}$
- Ⓓ $b^m \cdot b^n = b^{mn}$

Tools of Algebra

 What You've Learned

California Content Standards

AF 1.0 Students express quantitative relationships by using algebraic terminology, expressions, equations, inequalities, and graphs. *Grade 7*

AF 1.2 Students use the correct order of operations to evaluate algebraic expressions. *Grade 7*

 Check Your Readiness   **GO for Help** to the Lesson in green.

Adding Rational Numbers (Skills Handbook page 871)

Find each sum.

1. $6 + (-6)$ **2.** $-8 + 6$ **3.** $5.31 + (-7.40)$ **4.** $-1.95 + 10$

5. $7\frac{3}{4} + \left(-8\frac{1}{2}\right)$ **6.** $-2\frac{1}{3} + 3\frac{1}{4}$ **7.** $6\frac{2}{5} + \left(4\frac{3}{10}\right)$ **8.** $-1\frac{5}{6} + 5\frac{1}{3}$

Subtracting Rational Numbers (Skills Handbook page 871)

Find each difference.

9. $-28 - 14$ **10.** $61 - (-11)$ **11.** $-16 - (-25)$ **12.** $-6.2 - 3.6$

13. $-5\frac{2}{3} - \left(-2\frac{1}{3}\right)$ **14.** $-2\frac{1}{4} - 3\frac{1}{4}$ **15.** $2\frac{2}{3} - 7\frac{1}{3}$ **16.** $\frac{5}{2} - \frac{13}{4}$

Multiplying and Dividing Rational Numbers (Skills Handbook page 871)

Find each product or quotient.

17. $-3 \cdot 7$ **18.** $-2.1 \cdot (-3.5)$ **19.** $-\frac{2}{3} \div 4$ **20.** $-\frac{3}{8} \div \frac{5}{8}$

Using the Order of Operations (Skills Handbook page 871)

Simplify each expression.

21. $8 \cdot (-3) + 4$ **22.** $3 \cdot 4 - 8 \div 2$ **23.** $1 \div 2^2 - 0.54 + 1.26$

24. $9 \div (-3) - 2$ **25.** $5(3 \cdot 5 - 4)$ **26.** $1 - (1 - 5)^2 \div (-8)$

What You'll Learn Next

▲ Most kayaks have a weight limit between 200 and 600 pounds. This limit can be expressed as a compound inequality.

California Content Standards

4.0 Students simplify expressions before solving linear equations and inequalities in one variable. *Alg1*

5.0 Students solve multistep problems, including word problems, involving linear equations and linear inequalities in one variable and provide justification for each step. *Alg1*

1.0 Students solve equations and inequalities involving absolute value.

New Vocabulary

🔊 **English and Spanish Audio Online**

- **absolute value** (p. 33)
- **absolute value of a real number** (p. 8)
- **additive inverse** (p. 7)
- **algebraic expression** (p. 12)
- **coefficient** (p. 13)
- **compound inequality** (p. 28)

- **evaluate** (p. 12)
- **experimental probability** (p. 40)
- **extraneous solution** (p. 34)
- **multiplicative inverse** (p. 7)
- **opposite** (p. 7)
- **reciprocal** (p. 7)
- **sample space** (p. 41)

- **simulation** (p. 40)
- **solution of an equation** (p. 18)
- **term** (p. 13)
- **theoretical probability** (p. 41)
- **tolerance** (p. 36)
- **variable** (p. 12)
- **variable expression** (p. 12)

Properties of Real Numbers

What You'll Learn

- To graph and order real numbers
- To identify and use properties of real numbers

. . . And Why

To classify the numbers used in managing an amusement park, as in Example 1

 Check Skills You'll Need

Simplify.

1. $-(-7.2)$

3. $-9 + (-4.5)$

5. $-15 \div 3$

2. $1 - (-3)$

4. $(-3.4)(-2)$

6. $\frac{-2}{5} + \frac{3}{-5}$

GO **for Help** Skills Handbook page 871

New Vocabulary
- opposite
- reciprocal
- absolute value of a real number
- additive inverse
- multiplicative inverse

---

1 **Graphing and Ordering Real Numbers**

 Real-World **Connection**

Artists frequently use geometric figures in their work. Juan Gris (1887–1927) used right triangles in this portrait of Picasso.

Activity: Estimating Square Roots

1. Use the Pythagorean Theorem to calculate *PB, PC, PD,* and so on, in the figure below.

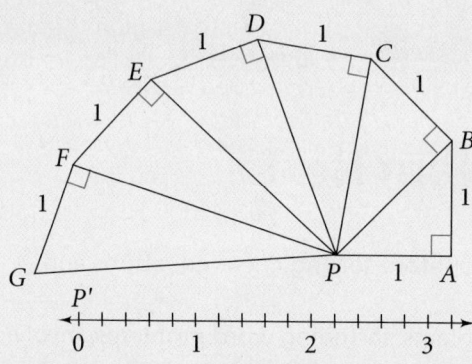

2. Copy the number line above. Mark point *B'* so that $P'B' = PB$. Similarly mark points *C', D',* and so on, on your number line.

3. Estimate the decimal coordinates of *B', C', D',* and so on. Copy and complete the table below.

Leg 1	1	$\sqrt{2}$	■	■	■	■
Leg 2	1	1	1	1	1	1
Hypotenuse	$\sqrt{2} \approx ?$	■	■	■	■	■

4. Evaluate each square root in the table using your calculator. Does the calculator give you exact answers? How do you know?

Algebra deals with operations and relations among numbers, including real numbers and imaginary numbers. Listed below are some of the subsets of the real numbers. Imaginary numbers will be introduced in Chapter 5.

 Key Concepts

Summary	Subsets of Real Numbers

Natural numbers $1, 2, 3, 4, \ldots$
- Natural numbers are the numbers used for counting.

Whole numbers $0, 1, 2, 3, 4, \ldots$
- Whole numbers are the natural numbers and 0.

Integers $\ldots -3, -2, -1, 0, 1, 2, 3, 4, \ldots$
- The integers are the natural numbers (also called positive integers), their opposites (also called negative integers), and zero.

Rational numbers   Examples: $\frac{7}{5}, \frac{-3}{2}, -\frac{4}{5}, 0, 0.3, -1.2, 9$
- Rational numbers are all the numbers that can be written as quotients of integers. Each quotient must have a nonzero denominator.
- Some rational numbers can be written as terminating decimals. For example, $\frac{1}{8} = 0.125$.
- All other rational numbers can be written as repeating decimals. For example, $\frac{1}{3} = 0.\overline{3}$.

Irrational numbers   Examples: $\sqrt{2}, \sqrt{7}, \sqrt{\frac{2}{3}}, \pi, 1.011011101111011111\ldots$
- Irrational numbers are numbers that cannot be written as quotients of integers.
- Their decimal representations neither terminate nor repeat.
- If a positive rational number is not a perfect square such as 25 or $\frac{4}{9}$, then its square root is irrational.

This diagram shows how the above sets of numbers are related.

Real Numbers   Examples: $-5, -\sqrt{3}, -\frac{1}{2}, 1, \sqrt{5}, \frac{8}{3}$

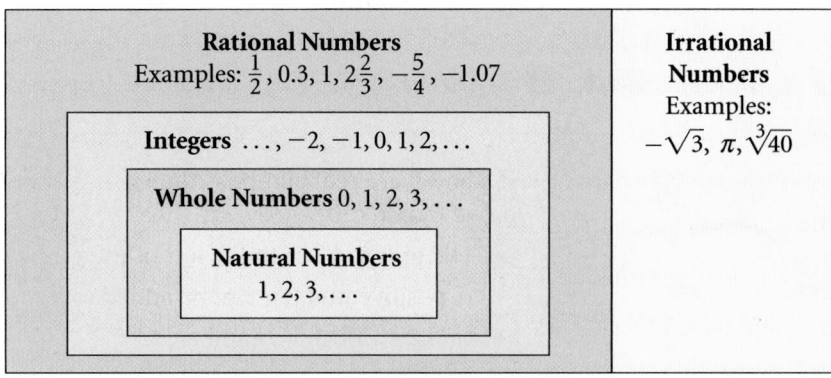

For example, the diagram shows the following:
- The set of whole numbers is a subset of the set of integers, the set of rational numbers, and the set of real numbers.
- The set of rational numbers and the set of irrational numbers do not intersect.
- Integers are not irrational numbers.
- The rational numbers and irrational numbers form the set of real numbers.

1 EXAMPLE Real-World Connection

Recreation Many mathematical relationships involving variables are related to amusement parks. Which set of numbers best describes the values for each variable?

a. the cost C in dollars of admission for n people

The cost C of admission is a rational number (such as $7.25), and the number n of people is a whole number.

b. the maximum speed s in meters per second on a roller coaster of height h in meters (Use the formula in the caption of the photograph.)

The height h is measured in rational numbers. Since the speed s is calculated using a formula with a square root, s is an irrational number unless h is the square of a rational number.

c. the park's profit (or loss) P in dollars for each week w of the year

The week number w is one of the first 52 natural numbers, and the profit (or loss) P is a rational number.

Real-World Connection

The maximum speed of a roller coaster is given by the formula $s = \frac{1200}{\sqrt{h}}$.

✓ **CA Standards Check** ❶ The number r is the ratio of the number of adult tickets sold to the number of children's tickets sold. Which set of numbers best describes the values of r? Which set of numbers best describes the average cost c per family for tickets?

Real numbers are graphed as points on the number line.

2 EXAMPLE Graphing Numbers on the Number Line

Graph the numbers $-\frac{3}{2}$, $1.\overline{7}$, and $\sqrt{5}$.

Since $-\frac{3}{2} = -1\frac{1}{2}$, $-\frac{3}{2}$ is between -1 and -2. Round $1.\overline{7}$ to 1.8. Use a calculator to find that $\sqrt{5} \approx 2.2$.

✓ **CA Standards Check** ❷ Graph the numbers $-\sqrt{2}$, $0.\overline{3}$, and $-2\frac{1}{4}$.

If a and b are real numbers, then $a = b$, $a < b$, or $a > b$. There are several ways to prove that $a < b$:

- The graph of a is to the left of the graph of b on a number line.
- A positive number can be added to a to get b.
- $b - a$ is a positive number.

Online active math

For: Real Number Line Activity
Use: Interactive Textbook, 1-1

3 EXAMPLE Ordering Real Numbers

Compare $-\sqrt{0.25}$ and $-\sqrt{0.01}$. Use the symbols $<$ and $>$.

$-\sqrt{0.25} = -0.5$, and $-\sqrt{0.01} = -0.1$. Since $-0.1 - (-0.5)$ is positive, $-0.5 < -0.1$. So $-\sqrt{0.25} < -\sqrt{0.01}$ and $-\sqrt{0.01} > -\sqrt{0.25}$.

✓ **CA Standards Check** ❸ Compare $-\sqrt{0.08}$ and $-\sqrt{0.1}$ using the symbols $<$ and $>$.

The **opposite** or **additive inverse** of any number a is $-a$.
The sum of opposites is 0.

The **reciprocal** or **multiplicative inverse** of any nonzero number a is $\frac{1}{a}$.
The product of reciprocals is 1.

4 EXAMPLE Finding Inverses

Find the opposite and the reciprocal of each number.

a. -3.2

Opposite $-(-3.2) = 3.2$

Reciprocal $\frac{1}{-3.2} = \frac{10}{-32}$
$= -\frac{5}{16}$, or -0.3125

b. $\frac{3}{5}$

Opposite $-\left(\frac{3}{5}\right) = -\frac{3}{5}$

Reciprocal $\frac{1}{\frac{3}{5}} = 1 \cdot \frac{5}{3} = \frac{5}{3}$

Vocabulary Tip

Read $-(-3.2)$ as "the opposite of negative 3.2."

 CA Standards Check ❹ Find the opposite and the reciprocal of each number.

a. 400   **b.** $4\frac{1}{5}$ **c.** -0.002 **d.** $-\frac{4}{9}$

You can summarize the properties of real numbers in terms of addition and multiplication.

 Key Concepts

| **Summary** | **Properties of Real Numbers** | |

Let a, b, and c represent real numbers.

Property	Addition	Multiplication
Closure	$a + b$ is a real number.	ab is a real number.
Commutative	$a + b = b + a$	$ab = ba$
Associative	$(a + b) + c = a + (b + c)$	$(ab)c = a(bc)$
Identity	$a + 0 = a, 0 + a = a$	$a \cdot 1 = a, 1 \cdot a = a$
Inverse	$a + (-a) = 0$	$a \cdot \frac{1}{a} = 1, a \neq 0$
Distributive	$a(b + c) = ab + ac$	

5 EXAMPLE Identifying Properties of Real Numbers

Which property is illustrated?
a. $6 + (-6) = 0$

Inverse Property of Addition

b. $(-4 \cdot 1) - 2 = -4 - 2$

Identity Property of Multiplication

CA Standards Check ❺ Which property is illustrated?
a. $(3 + 0) - 5 = 3 - 5$ **b.** $-5 + [2 + (-3)] = (-5 + 2) + (-3)$

The **absolute value of a real number** is its distance from zero on the number line.

6 **EXAMPLE** **Finding Absolute Value**

Find $|-4|$, $|0|$, and $|-1 \cdot (-2)|$.

$|-1 \cdot (-2)| = |2|$ **Simplify within absolute value symbols first.**

Graph -4, 0, and 2 on a number line.

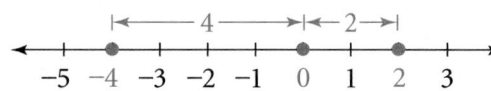

The distances from the origin are $4, 0,$ and 2. So,

$$|-4| = 4 \qquad |0| = 0 \qquad |-1 \cdot (-2)| = |2| = 2$$

 CA Standards Check **6** **a.** Simplify $|-10|$, $|1.5|$, and $|0 - 3|$.
b. Critical Thinking For what values of x does $|x| = -x$?

EXERCISES For more exercises, see *Extra Skill and Word Problem Practice*.
Standards Practice

A **Practice by Example** **To which sets of numbers does each number belong?**

Example 1
(page 6)

1. 4   **2.** $\sqrt{6}$ **3.** π **4.** -6

5. 0   **6.** $0.\overline{6}$ **7.** $-\sqrt{0.04}$ **8.** $\sqrt{0.4}$

Which set of numbers best describes the values of each variable?

9. the number of times n a cricket chirps; the outdoor temperature T in tenths of a degree

10. the year y; the median selling price p for a house that year

11. the time t in seconds an object takes to fall d feet, where $t = \frac{\sqrt{d}}{4}$

Example 2
(page 6)

Graph each number on a number line.

12. 0   **13.** $-\sqrt{24}$ **14.** -2 **15.** $2\frac{1}{2}$ **16.** $-4\frac{2}{3}$

Example 3
(page 6)

Replace each ■ with the symbol <, >, or = to make the sentence true.

17. -7 ■ -9 **18.** 3 ■ 3   **19.** 14 ■ $\sqrt{14}$

20. $\sqrt{6}$ ■ $\sqrt{10}$ **21.** 0 ■ $0.\overline{3}$ **22.** 0.8 ■ $\frac{4}{5}$

23. -18 ■ -82 **24.** 0.72737475 . . . ■ 0.73737373 . . .

Compare each pair of numbers. Use < and >.

25. $-\frac{1}{4}, -\frac{1}{3}$ **26.** 0.075, 0.39   **27.** $-2.\overline{3}, 2.\overline{1}$

28. $-5.2, -4.8$ **29.** $3.0\overline{4}, 3.4$ **30.** 0.4, $\sqrt{0.4}$

31. $-4, -\sqrt{4}$ **32.** $\sqrt{5}, \sqrt{7}$ **33.** $-\sqrt{3}, -\sqrt{5}$

Vocabulary Tip

Read $|2|$ as
"the absolute value of 2."

Example 4
(page 7)

Find the opposite and the reciprocal of each number.

34. 200   **35.** $3\frac{3}{5}$ **36.** -0.01 **37.** $-\frac{7}{2}$

38. $\sqrt{3}$ **39.** 2π **40.** -2.34 **41.** $\pi - 3$

Example 5
(page 7)

Name the property of real numbers illustrated by each equation.

42. $\pi(a + b) = \pi a + \pi b$ **43.** $-7 + 4 = 4 + (-7)$

44. $(2\sqrt{10}) \cdot \sqrt{3} = 2(\sqrt{10} \cdot \sqrt{3})$ **45.** $29\pi = \pi \cdot 29$

46. $-\sqrt{5} + 0 = -\sqrt{5}$ **47.** $\frac{4}{7} \cdot \frac{7}{4} = 1$

Example 6
(page 8)

Simplify each expression.

48. $|10.3|$ **49.** $|-0.06|$ **50.** $-|-25|$ **51.** $0.2|-8|$

52. $\left|-\frac{1}{3}\right|$ **53.** $|7 - 10|$ **54.** $|10 - 7|$ **55.** $|5| - |-7|$

B   **Apply Your Skills**

Estimate the numbers graphed at the labeled points.

$$
\begin{array}{ccccccccc}
A & B & & C & D & E & & F\,G\,H \\
\end{array}
$$

$\leftarrow\!|\!\bullet\!|\!\bullet\!|\!\!-\!\!|\!\bullet\!|\!\!-\!\!|\!\bullet\!|\!\bullet\!|\!\!-\!\!|\!\bullet\!|\!\bullet\!|\!\bullet\!|\!\rightarrow$

$\quad -5\ -4\ -3\ -2\ -1\quad 0\quad 1\quad 2\quad 3\quad 4\quad 5$

56. point A **57.** point B **58.** point C **59.** point D

60. point E **61.** point F **62.** point G **63.** point H

64. Multiple Choice The length of a side of an equilateral triangle is 4. Which type of number best describes the length of the altitude of the triangle?

    Ⓐ whole number   Ⓒ rational number

    Ⓑ integer   Ⓓ irrational number

Label indicates power in watts *W*.

Tungsten filament creates resistance *R*.

Current *I* enters through base.

Electric Circuits The electric current I in amperes that flows through an appliance is given by the formula $I = \sqrt{\dfrac{W}{R}}$, where W is the power in watts and R is the resistance in ohms. Which sets of numbers contain the value of I for the given values of W and R?

65. $W = 100, R = 25$ **66.** $W = 100, R = 50$ **67.** $W = 500, R = 100$

68. $W = 50, R = 200$ **69.** $W = 250, R = 100$ **70.** $W = 240, R = 100$

Replace each ■ with the symbol $<$, $>$, or $=$ to make the sentence true.

71. 0 ■ -4 **72.** -4 ■ -9 **73.** -5.2 ■ -4.8 **74.** $|-8|$ ■ $|3|$

75. $|2|$ ■ $|-6|$ **76.** $|7|$ ■ $|-8|$ **77.** $-|6|$ ■ $|6|$ **78.** $-|-6|$ ■ $|-6|$

Reasoning Show that each statement is false by finding a counterexample (an example that makes the statement false).

79. The reciprocal of each whole number is a whole number.

80. The opposite of each natural number is a natural number.

81. There is no whole number that has an opposite that is a whole number.

82. There is no integer that has a reciprocal that is an integer.

83. The product of two irrational numbers is an irrational number.

84. Open-Ended Write an example of each of the 11 properties of real numbers listed on page 7.

Homework Video Tutor

Visit: PHSchool.com
Web Code: bbe-0101

Critical Thinking Review the eleven properties on page 7. Which ones still hold true if *real numbers* is replaced by each of the following?

85. natural numbers   **86.** whole numbers   **87.** integers

88. rational numbers   **89.** irrational numbers

 90. Writing Are there two integers with a product of -12 and a sum of -3? Explain.

Multiple Choice Practice

For California Standards and CAHSEE Tutorials, visit PHSchool.com. Web Code: bbq-9045

CAHSEE
Alg1 6.0

91. Which equation best represents the line at the right?

    (A) $4x + 3y = 12$

    (B) $4x - 3y = 12$

    (C) $4x + 3y = -12$

    (D) $3x - 4y = -12$

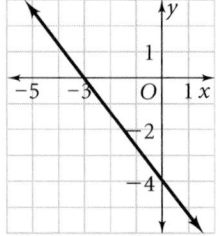

CAHSEE
7AF 4.2

92. Josh rode his bike m miles to his friend's house in 20 minutes. He made the trip back in 15 minutes. Which of the following expressions represents Josh's average speed riding his bike?

   (A) $\frac{2m}{35}$ (B) $\frac{7m}{60}$ (C) $\frac{35}{m}$ (D) $\frac{m}{35}$

CAHSEE
7MG 2.1

93. Robin needs a cover for her circular pool. The diameter of the pool is 20 feet. She calculates that she needs about 314 square feet of material to cover the pool. Which formula can be used to confirm that Robin's answer is correct?

    (A) Circumference of a circle

    (B) Surface area of a cylinder

    (C) Area of a circle

    (D) Volume of a cylinder

Mixed Review

Skills Handbook

 GO for Help

Simplify each expression.

94. $3.6 + (-1.7)$ **95.** $1.2 - 5$ **96.** $(-3)(-9)$

97. $0(-8)$ **98.** $-2.8 \div 7$ **99.** $-35 \div (-5)$

Skills Handbook

Use the order of operations to simplify each expression.

100. $3 \div 4 + 6 \div 4$ **101.** $5[(2 + 5) \div 3]$

102. $\frac{8 + 5 \cdot 2}{12}$ **103.** $(40 + 24) \div 8 - (2^2 - 1)$

104. $40 + 24 \div 8 - 2^2 - 1$ **105.** $40 + 24 \div (8 - 2^2) - 1$

Activity Lab

Writing Expressions From Tables

You can sometimes describe data in a table by writing an expression.

1 ACTIVITY

Study the polygons below. You can cut each polygon into triangles by connecting one vertex with each of the other nonadjacent vertices.

1. a. The sum of the angle measures for each triangle is 180. Fill in the data missing from the table.
  b. Describe the relationship between the number of sides in a polygon and the number of triangles.
  c. Describe the relationship between the number of triangles and the sum of the angle measures of the polygon.
  d. Complete the sentence: The sum of the angle measures of a polygon is the number of sides of the polygon less __?__, times __?__.
  e. The number of sides of a polygon is *n*. Write the number of triangles in terms of *n*.
  f. Write the sum of the angle measures of the *n*-sided polygon in terms of *n*.

Number of Sides	Number of Triangles	Sum of Angle Measures
3	1	180
4	2	360
5	3	■
6	4	■
7	■	■
8	■	1080
9	■	■

2 ACTIVITY

The diagrams below show arrangements of tables and chairs. Each small table can seat 6 people. When you join tables, you lose space for some chairs. So, an arrangement of two tables has 10 chairs rather than 12 chairs.

Number of tables: 1   2   3   4

2. a. Make a table that lists the number of tables and the number of chairs in each arrangement shown in the diagram.
  b. Find the number of chairs needed for arrangements of 5 tables and 6 tables.
  c. Write an expression for the number of chairs needed for *n* tables. (*Hint:* How many new chairs are needed for each new table?)

3. You can arrange the tables and chairs differently. One possible pattern is shown at the right. Write an expression for the number of chairs needed to make one large table out of *k* tables in this way.

1   2   3

Algebraic Expressions

What You'll Learn

- To evaluate algebraic expressions
- To simplify algebraic expressions

. . . And Why

To use an expression for the number of voters in U.S. elections, as in Example 3

☑ **Check Skills You'll Need**

GO for Help Skills Handbook page 871

Use the order of operations to simplify each expression.

1. $8 \cdot 3 - 2 \cdot 4$
2. $8 - 4 + 6 \div 3$
3. $24 \div 12 \cdot 4 \div 3$
4. $3 \cdot 8^2 + 12 \div 4$
5. $27 + 18 \div 9 - 3^2 + 1$
6. $(40 + 24) \div 8 - (2^3 + 1)$

 New Vocabulary
- variable
- algebraic expression
- variable expression
- evaluate
- term
- coefficient

---

1 Evaluating Algebraic Expressions

A **variable** is a symbol, usually a letter, that represents one or more numbers. An expression that contains one or more variables is an **algebraic expression** or a **variable expression.** When you substitute numbers for the variables in an expression and follow the order of operations, you **evaluate** the expression.

1 EXAMPLE Evaluating an Algebraic Expression

GO for Help

To review the order of operations, go to page 871.

Evaluate $a - 2b + ab$ for $a = 3$ and $b = -1$.

$$a - 2b + ab = 3 - 2(-1) + 3(-1) \quad \textbf{Substitute 3 for } a \textbf{ and } -1 \textbf{ for } b.$$
$$= 3 - (-2) + (-3) \quad \textbf{Multiply first.}$$
$$= 3 + 2 + (-3) \quad \textbf{To subtract, add the opposite.}$$
$$= 5 + (-3) \quad \textbf{Add from left to right.}$$
$$= 2 \quad \textbf{Add.}$$

☑ **CA Standards Check** **1** Evaluate each expression for $x = 4$ and $y = -2$.
a. $x + y \div x$ **b.** $3x - 4y + x - y$ **c.** $x + 2x \div y - 2y$

2 EXAMPLE Evaluating an Algebraic Expression with Exponents

Problem Solving Hint

Note that $-3^2 \ne (-3)^2$.
$-3^2 = -(3 \cdot 3) = -9$
$(-3)^2 = (-3)(-3) = 9$

Evaluate $-x^2 - 2(x + 1)$ for $x = 3$.

$$-x^2 - 2(x + 1) = -3^2 - 2(3 + 1) \quad \textbf{Substitute 3 for } x.$$
$$= -9 - 2(4) \quad \textbf{Simplify the power } 3^2. \textbf{ Add within the parentheses.}$$
$$= -9 - 8 \quad \textbf{Multiply.}$$
$$= -17 \quad \textbf{Subtract.}$$

☑ **CA Standards Check** **2** Evaluate each expression for $c = -3$ and $d = 5$.
a. $c^2 - d^2$ **b.** $c(3 - d) - c^2$ **c.** $-d^2 - 4(d - 2c)$

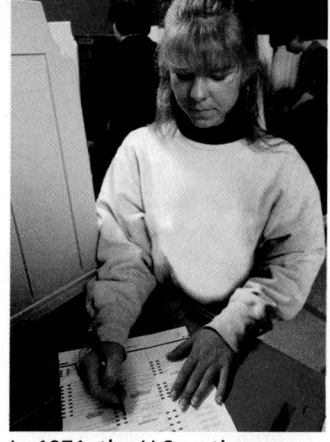

In 1971, the U.S. voting age was lowered from 21 to 18.

3 EXAMPLE **Real-World Connection**

Elections The expression $-0.3y + 61$ models the percent of eligible voters who voted in presidential elections from 1960 to 2000. In the expression, y represents the number of years since 1960. Find the approximate percent of eligible voters who voted in 1988.

Since $1988 - 1960 = 28$, $y = 28$ represents the year 1988.

$-0.3y + 61 = -0.3(28) + 61$ **Substitute 28 for y.**

≈ 53

● About 53% of the eligible voters voted in the 1988 presidential election.

✓ CA Standards Check **3** **a.** Assume that the model in Example 3 holds for future years. What percent of the eligible voters will vote in 2012? In 2020?

b. Critical Thinking Give some reasons that the model may not hold in future years.

---

2 Simplifying Algebraic Expressions

In an algebraic expression such as $-4x + 10$, the parts that are added are called terms. A **term** is a number, a variable, or the product of a number and one or more variables. The numerical factor in a term is the **coefficient.** Think of an expression such as $a - 2b$ as the sum $a + (-2b)$ to determine that the coefficient of b is -2.

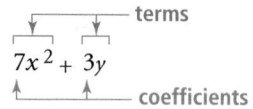

Like terms have the same variables raised to the same powers.

Like terms: $3r^2$ and $-r^2$ $-2xy^3$ and $3xy^3$

You can simplify expressions by combining like terms using the basic properties on page 7 and other properties that can be derived from them. The simplified expressions are equivalent to the original expressions; that is, their values are equal for any replacement of the variables.

Key Concepts

Summary	Properties for Simplifying Algebraic Expressions

Let a, b, and c represent real numbers.

Definition of Subtraction	$a - b = a + (-b)$
Definition of Division	$a \div b = \frac{a}{b} = a \cdot \frac{1}{b}, b \neq 0$
Distributive Property for Subtraction	$a(b - c) = ab - ac$
Multiplication by 0	$0 \cdot a = 0$
Multiplication by -1	$-1 \cdot a = -a$
Opposite of a Sum	$-(a + b) = -a + (-b)$
Opposite of a Difference	$-(a - b) = b - a$
Opposite of a Product	$-(ab) = -a \cdot b = a \cdot (-b)$
Opposite of an Opposite	$-(-a) = a$

Simplify by combining like terms.

a. $3k - k$

$$3k - k = 3k - 1k \quad \text{**Identity Property of Multiplication**}$$
$$= (3 - 1)k \quad \text{**Distributive Property**}$$
$$= 2k \quad \text{**Simplify.**}$$

b. $5z^2 - 10z - 8z^2 + z$

$$5z^2 - 10z - 8z^2 + z = 5z^2 - 8z^2 + (-10z) + z \quad \begin{array}{l}\text{**Commutative Property**}\\\text{**of Addition**}\end{array}$$
$$= (5 - 8)z^2 + (-10 + 1)z \quad \text{**Distributive Property**}$$
$$= -3z^2 - 9z$$

c. $-(m + n) + 2(m - 3n)$

$$-(m + n) + 2(m - 3n)$$
$$= -m + (-n) + 2m + (-6n) \quad \text{**Opposite of a Sum, Distributive Property**}$$
$$= -m + 2m + (-n) + (-6n) \quad \text{**Commutative Property of Addition**}$$
$$= -1 \cdot m + 2m + (-1 \cdot n) + (-6n) \quad \text{**Multiplication by** -1}$$
$$= (-1 + 2)m + [-1 + (-6)]\, n \quad \text{**Distributive Property**}$$
$$= m - 7n$$

✓ **CA Standards Check** **4** Simplify by combining like terms.

a. $2x^2 + 5x - 4x^2 + x - x^2$ **b.** $-2(r + s) - (2r + 2s)$

5 **EXAMPLE** **Finding Perimeter**

Multiple Choice Which expression represents the perimeter of the figure at the right?

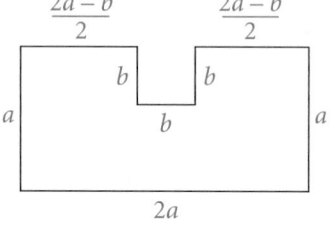

  Ⓐ $8a + b$ Ⓒ $6a + 2b$

  Ⓑ $6a + b$ Ⓓ $4a + 3b$

$$\frac{2a - b}{2} + b + b + b + \frac{2a - b}{2} + a + 2a + a$$
$$= \frac{2a - b}{2} + \frac{2a - b}{2} + 3b + 4a$$
$$= \frac{2(2a - b)}{2} + 3b + 4a$$
$$= 2a - b + 3b + 4a$$
$$= 6a + 2b$$

Test-Taking Tip

You can check your answer by substituting values. In Example 5, let $a = 2$ and $b = 1$. The perimeter is 14. Also, $6a + 2b = 6(2) + 2(1)$ $= 14$.

An expression for the perimeter is $6a + 2b$. The correct choice is C.

✓ **CA Standards Check** **5** Find an expression for the perimeter of each figure. Simplify the answer.

a.

b.

EXERCISES
Standards Practice

For more exercises, see *Extra Skill and Word Problem Practice.*

A **Practice by Example**

Examples 1 and 2
(page 12)

 for Help

Evaluate each expression for the given values of the variables.

1. $4a + 7b + 3a - 2b + 2a$; $a = -5$ and $b = 3$

2. $5y - 3z + 4y - 1z - 3y$; $y = 3$ and $z = -2$

3. $12a^2 - 3ab + 2b$; $a = -5$ and $b = 4$

4. $-k^2 - (3k - 5n) + 4n$; $k = -1$ and $n = -2$

5. $3y - (4y + 6x)$; $x = 3$ and $y = -2$

6. $3(2c + d) - d$; $c = 5$ and $d = -1$

7. $-5(x + 2y) + 15(x + 2y)$; $x = 7$ and $y = -7$

8. $4(2m - n) - 3(2m - n)$; $m = -15$ and $n = -18$

Example 3
(page 13)

Physics The expression $16t^2$ models the distance in feet that an object falls during t seconds after being dropped. Find the distance of an object falls during each time.

9. 0.25 second

10. 0.5 second

11. 2 seconds

12. 10 seconds

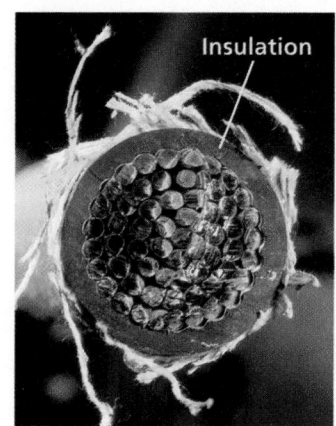

Insulation

Electrical Engineering The expression $0.01E + 0.003E^2$ gives the thickness in millimeters of the insulation needed for the high voltage cable shown at the left. E is the number of kilovolts carried by the cable. Find the thickness of insulation material needed for each voltage.

13. 1 kilovolt   **14.** 2 kilovolts   **15.** 10 kilovolts   **16.** 20 kilovolts

Investing The expression $1000(1.1)^t$ represents the value of a $1000 investment that earns 10% interest per year, compounded annually for t years. Find the value of a $1000 investment at the end of each period.

17. 2 years   **18.** 3 years   **19.** 4 years   **20.** 5 years

Example 4
(page 14)

Simplify by combining like terms.

21. $5a - a$

22. $5 + 10s - 8s$

23. $-5a - 4a + b$

24. $2a + 3b + 4a$

25. $6r + 3s + 2s + 4r$

26. $w + 3z + 5w + 2z$

27. $x^2 + x^2 + x$

28. $xy + 2x + x$

29. $0.5x - x$

30. $3(2x + 1) - 8$

31. $2(5y - 2) + x$

32. $3y - (4y + 6x)$

33. $7b - (3a - 8b)$

34. $5 + (4g - 7)$

35. $-(3x - 4y + z)$

Example 5
(page 14)

Geometry **Find an expression for the perimeter. Simplify the answer.**

36.

37.

Evaluate each expression for the given value of the variable.

38. $|x| + |2x| - |x - 1|; x = 2$

39. $|2z + 3| + |5 - 3z|; z = -3$

40. $3|2a + 5| + 2|3 - a|; a = 4$

41. $6|4b - 5| + 3|2 - 2b|; b = -1$

42. $\dfrac{3(2x + 1) - 2(x - 3)}{x + 6}; x = -3$

43. $\dfrac{5(2k - 3) - 3(k + 4)}{3k + 2}; k = -2$

44. $y^2 + 3; y = \sqrt{7}$

45. $5c^3 - 6c^2 - 2c; c = -5$

46. Elections The expression $2.6y + 107$ models the number of eligible voters in millions in the United States from 1960 to 2000. In the expression, y represents the number of years since 1960.
   a. Find the approximate number of eligible voters in 1988.
   b. Assume that the model continues to hold for future years. How many eligible voters will there be in 2012? In 2020?
   c. The expression $-0.3y + 61$ models the *percent* of eligible voters who voted in presidential elections from 1960 to 2000. (See Example 3.) Write an expression that models the *number* of voters in presidential elections from 1960 to 2000.
   d. Use your model from (c) to find the approximate number of voters who voted for president in 1980.

Simplify by combining like terms.

47. $-a^2 + 2b^2 + \frac{1}{4}a^2$

48. $x + \frac{x^2}{2} + 2x^2 - x$

49. $\frac{y^2}{4} + \frac{y}{3} + \frac{y^2}{3} - \frac{y}{5}$

50. $-(2x + y) - 2(-x - y)$

51. $x(3 - y) + y(x + 6)$

52. $4(2x + y) - 2(2x + y)$

53. $\frac{1}{2}(x^2 - y^2) - \frac{5}{2}(x^2 - y^2)$

Match the property name with the appropriate equation.

54. Definition of Subtraction   **A.** $2(s - t) = 2s - 2t$

55. Definition of Division   **B.** $-(a - b) = (-1)(a - b)$

56. Distributive Property   **C.** $(7 - y) \div (2y) = \dfrac{7 - y}{2y}$

57. Multiplication by 0   **D.** $-[-(x - 10)] = x - 10$

58. Multiplication by -1 **E.** $-(2t - 11) = 11 - 2t$

59. Opposite of a Sum   **F.** $2t - 11 = 2t + (-11)$

60. Opposite of a Difference   **G.** $(4a^2 - 9a)(0) + 5a = 0 + 5a$

61. Opposite of a Product   **H.** $-[3 + (-y)] = -3 + [-(-y)]$

62. Opposite of an Opposite   **I.** $-(4z^2) = 4(-z^2)$

Justifying Steps **Name the property used in each step of simplification.**

63. $(3x + y) + x = 3x + (y + x)$
$\qquad\qquad\quad = 3x + (x + y)$
$\qquad\qquad\quad = (3x + x) + y$
$\qquad\qquad\quad = (3x + 1x) + y$
$\qquad\qquad\quad = (3 + 1)x + y$
$\qquad\qquad\quad = 4x + y$

64. $2(5 + x) + 4(5 + x) = (2 + 4)(5 + x)$
$\qquad\qquad\qquad\qquad = 6(5 + x)$
$\qquad\qquad\qquad\qquad = 30 + 6x$

65. Open-Ended Write four different expressions that simplify to $x^2 - x$. Each expression must have five terms.

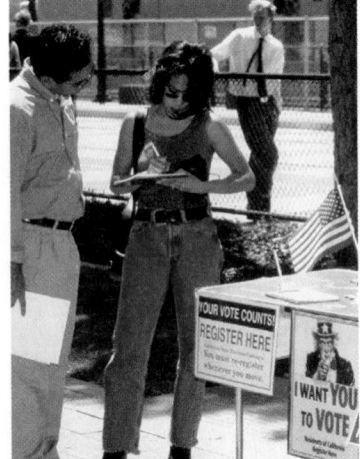

Real-World **Connection**

Each year, millions of U.S. citizens turn 18 and become eligible to vote. Unfortunately, fewer than half of them register.

Homework Video Tutor

Visit: PHSchool.com
Web Code: bbe-0102

C Challenge

66. Simplify $2(b - a) + 5(b - a)$ and explain each step in your simplification.

67. a. Evaluate the expression $2(2x^2 - x) - 3(x^2 - x) + x^2 - x$ for $x = 3$. Do *not* simplify the expression before evaluating it.

  b. Simplify the expression in (a) and then evaluate your answer for $x = 3$.

  c. Writing Explain why the values in (a) and (b) should be the same.

  d. Error Analysis A student simplified $2x(x - 6)$ to $2x^2 - 6x$. Should the student check his work by evaluating both expressions for $x = 0$? Explain.

Multiple Choice Practice

For California Standards and CAHSEE Tutorials, visit PHSchool.com. Web Code: bbq-9045

CAHSEE 7MR 1.1

68. Use the graph at the right to decide which statement is true.

  Ⓐ If $x > 0$, then $\sqrt{x} < x$.

  Ⓑ If $0 < x < 1$, then $\sqrt{x} < x$.

  Ⓒ If $x > 1$, then $\sqrt{x} > x$.

  Ⓓ If $0 < x < 1$, then $\sqrt{x} > x$.

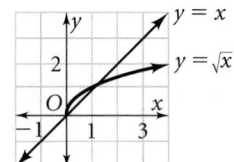

CAHSEE 7AF 1.2

69. Which expression is equivalent to $2(x - 1) - 2x + 2 - 3(x + 1) + 4x$?

  Ⓐ $x - 3$ Ⓑ $x + 3$ Ⓒ $5x - 7$ Ⓓ $5x + 7$

CAHSEE 7AF 1.1

70. A rectangular farm has an area of n acres and is x miles long. If 1 square mile = 640 acres, which expression represents the width of the farm, in miles?

  Ⓐ $\dfrac{nx}{640}$ Ⓑ $\dfrac{x}{640n}$ Ⓒ $\dfrac{n}{640x}$ Ⓓ $\dfrac{640n}{x}$

CAHSEE 7MG 2.1

71. The shaded region in the circle at the right represents a slice of pizza. Which is the approximate area of the slice of pizza?

  Ⓐ 8 in.^{2} Ⓒ 50 in.^{2}

  Ⓑ 34 in.^{2} Ⓓ 134 in.^{2}

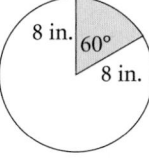

CAHSEE 7AF 2.1

72. Which expression best represents the simplified form of $(4m^{-3}n^2)(-3m^5n^{-5})$?

  Ⓐ $-12m^2n^3$ Ⓒ $-12\dfrac{m^2}{n^{-3}}$

  Ⓑ $\dfrac{-1m^2}{12n^3}$ Ⓓ $\dfrac{-12m^2}{n^3}$

Mixed Review

 for Help

Lesson 1-1

Order the numbers from least to greatest.

73. $-1.5, -0.5, -\sqrt{2}, -1.4$ **74.** $|-4.3|, -4.3, -|3.4|, |-3.4|$

75. $-\dfrac{3}{8}, \dfrac{1}{2}, -\dfrac{3}{4}, -\dfrac{5}{6}$ **76.** $\sqrt{\dfrac{1}{4}}, \sqrt{\dfrac{1}{16}}, -\sqrt{\dfrac{1}{8}}, -\sqrt{\dfrac{1}{10}}$

Lesson 1-1

Replace each ▣ with the symbol <, >, or = to make the sentence true.

77. $|-11|$ ▣ $|9|$ **78.** $|11|$ ▣ $|9|$ **79.** $|-11|$ ▣ $|-9|$

80. $-|-7|$ ▣ $|7|$ **81.** $-|7|$ ▣ $|-7|$ **82.** $-|-7|$ ▣ $-|7|$

Solving Equations

 California Content Standards

Prepares for ALG2 2.0 Students solve systems of linear equations (in two or three variables) by substitution, with graphs, or with matrices.

What You'll Learn

• To solve equations

• To solve problems by writing equations

. . . And Why

To solve a problem about aeronautics, as in Example 7

✓ **Check Skills You'll Need**

Simplify each expression.

1. $5x - 9x + 3$

2. $2y + 7x + y - 1$

3. $10h + 12g - 8h - 4g$

4. $\frac{x}{3} + \frac{y}{3} + \frac{2y}{3} - y$

5. $(x + y) - (x - y)$

6. $-(3 - c) - 4(c - 1)$

GO for Help Lesson 1-2

◀)) **New Vocabulary** • solution of an equation

---

1 Solving Equations

An equation that contains a variable may be true for some replacements of the variable and false for others. A number that makes the equation true is a **solution of the equation.** You can use the properties of equality to solve equations.

 Key Concepts

Summary	Properties of Equality
Let a, b, and c represent real numbers.	
Reflexive Property	$a = a$
Symmetric Property	If $a = b$, then $b = a$.
Transitive Property	If $a = b$ and $b = c$, then $a = c$.
Addition Property	If $a = b$, then $a + c = b + c$.
Subtraction Property	If $a = b$, then $a - c = b - c$.
Multiplication Property	If $a = b$, then $ac = bc$.
Division Property	If $a = b$ and $c \neq 0$, then $\frac{a}{c} = \frac{b}{c}$.
Substitution Property	If $a = b$, then b may be substituted for a in any expression to obtain an equivalent expression.

Video Tutor Help

Visit: PHSchool.com
Web Code: bbe-0775

1 EXAMPLE **Solving an Equation With a Variable on Both Sides**

Solve $13y + 48 = 8y - 47$.

$13y + 48 = 8y - 47$

$5y + 48 = -47$ **Subtract 8y from each side.**

$5y = -95$ **Subtract 48 from each side.**

$y = -19$ **Divide each side by 5.**

Check $13y + 48 = 8y - 47$

$13(-19) + 48 \stackrel{?}{=} 8(-19) - 47$

$-199 = -199$ ✓

CA Standards Check ① Solve each equation. Check your answers.

a. $8z + 12 = 5z - 21$ **b.** $2t - 3 = 9 - 4t$

---

② **EXAMPLE** **Using the Distributive Property**

Solve $3x - 7(2x - 13) = 3(-2x + 9)$.

$3x - 7(2x - 13) = 3(-2x + 9)$

$3x - 14x + 91 = -6x + 27$ **Distributive Property**

$-11x + 91 = -6x + 27$ **Combine like terms.**

$-5x + 91 = 27$ **Add 6x to each side.**

$-5x = -64$ **Subtract 91 from each side.**

$x = \frac{64}{5}$, or 12.8   **Divide each side by −5.**

Vocabulary Tip

Literally, <u>to solve</u> means "to set apart." Think of solving an equation as setting apart the variable.

CA Standards Check ② Solve each equation. Check your answers.

a. $2(y - 3) + 6 = 70$ **b.** $6(t - 2) = 2(9 - 2t)$

When you have a formula or equation that has more than one variable, you can solve for any one of the variables.

③ **EXAMPLE** **Solving a Formula for One of Its Variables**

Geometry The formula for the area of a trapezoid is $A = \frac{1}{2}h(b_1 + b_2)$. Solve the formula for h.

$A = \frac{1}{2}h(b_1 + b_2)$

$2A = h(b_1 + b_2)$ **Multiply each side by 2.**

$\frac{2A}{b_1 + b_2} = h$ **Divide each side by $b_1 + b_2$.**

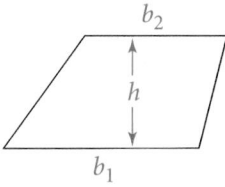

CA Standards Check ③ Solve the formula for the area of a trapezoid for b_1.

---

④ **EXAMPLE** **Solving an Equation for One of Its Variables**

Solve $\frac{x}{a} + 1 = \frac{x}{b}$ for x. Find any restrictions on a and b.

$\frac{x}{a} + 1 = \frac{x}{b}$

$ab\left(\frac{x}{a}\right) + ab(1) = ab\left(\frac{x}{b}\right)$ **Multiply each side by the least common denominator (LCD).**

$bx + ab = ax$ **Simplify.**

$ab = ax - bx$ **Collect terms with x on one side.**

$ab = (a - b)x$ **Distributive Property**

$x = \frac{ab}{a - b}$ **Divide each side by $a - b$.**

The denominators cannot be 0, so $a \neq 0$ and $b \neq 0$. Also $a - b \neq 0$, so $a \neq b$.

CA Standards Check ④ Solve each equation for x. Find any restrictions.

a. $ax + bx - 15 = 0$ **b.** $d = \frac{2x}{a} + b$

You can write an equation to model and solve a real-world problem.

5   EXAMPLE   Real-World 🌐 Connection

Construction   A dog kennel owner has 100 ft of fencing to enclose a rectangular dog run. She wants it to be 5 times as long as it is wide. Find the dimensions of the dog run.

Relate   2 · width + 2 · length = perimeter

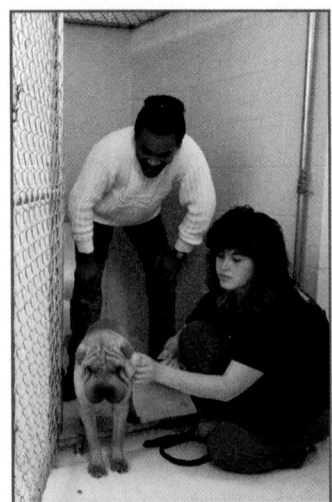

x

5*x*

Define   Let x = the width.

Then $5x$ = the length.

Write

$$2x + 2(5x) = 100$$
$$2x + 10x = 100 \quad \textbf{Multiply.}$$
$$12x = 100 \quad \textbf{Combine like terms.}$$
$$x = 8\tfrac{1}{3} \quad \textbf{Divide each side by 12.}$$
$$5x = 41\tfrac{2}{3} \quad \textbf{Find the length.}$$

The width is $8\tfrac{1}{3}$ ft and the length is $41\tfrac{2}{3}$ ft.

Check   Is the answer reasonable? Since the dimensions are about 8 ft and 42 ft, and 2 · 8 + 2 · 42 = 100, the answer is reasonable.

Real-World 🌐 Connection

Some states regulate the minimum amount of floor space for animals in kennels.

✅ **CA Standards Check**   **5**   A rectangle is twice as long as it is wide. Its perimeter is 48 cm. Find its dimensions.

Many geometry problems require writing and solving equations.

6   EXAMPLE   Using Ratios

Geometry   The lengths of the sides of a triangle are in the ratio 3 : 4 : 5. The perimeter of the triangle is 18 in. Find the lengths of the sides.

Relate   Perimeter equals the sum of the lengths of the three sides.

Define   Let $3x$ = the length of the shortest side.
Then $4x$ = the length of the second side.
Then $5x$ = the length of the third side.

5*x*   3*x*

4*x*

Write

$$18 = 3x + 4x + 5x$$
$$18 = 12x \quad\quad\quad \textbf{Combine like terms.}$$
$$1.5 = x$$
$$3x = 3(1.5) \quad 4x = 4(1.5) \quad 5x = 5(1.5) \quad \textbf{Find the length of each side.}$$
$$= 4.5 \quad\quad\quad = 6 \quad\quad\quad = 7.5$$

The lengths of the sides are 4.5 in., 6 in., and 7.5 in.

Check   Is the answer reasonable? Since 5 + 6 + 8 = 19, the answer is reasonable.

✅ **CA Standards Check**   **6**   The sides of a triangle are in the ratio 12 : 13 : 15. The perimeter is 120 cm. Find the lengths of the sides of the triangle.

The F-117 is nearly invisible to radar. The faceted construction deflects most radar energy away from the radar receiver.

7 EXAMPLE <u>Real-World Connection</u>

Aeronautics Radar detected an unidentified plane 5000 mi away, approaching at 700 mi/h. Fifteen minutes later an interceptor plane was dispatched, traveling at 800 mi/h. How long did the interceptor take to reach the approaching plane?

Relate distance for interceptor + distance for approaching plane = 5000 mi

Define Let t = the time in hours for the interceptor.
Then $t + 0.25$ = the time in hours for the approaching plane.

Write
$$800t + 700(t + 0.25) = 5000$$
$$800t + 700t + 175 = 5000 \quad \textbf{Distributive Property}$$
$$1500t = 4825 \quad \textbf{Solve for } t.$$
$$t \approx 3.217 \text{ or } 3 \text{ h } 13 \text{ min}$$

Check Is the answer reasonable? In $3\frac{1}{4}$ h, the interceptor flies 2600 mi. In $3\frac{1}{2}$ h, the approaching plane flies 2450 mi. $2600 + 2450 \approx 5000$, so the answer is reasonable.

✓ **CA Standards Check** ⑦ A space probe leaves Earth at the rate of 3 km/s. After 100 days, a radio signal is sent to the probe. Radio signals travel at the speed of light, about 3×10^5 km/s. About how long does the signal take to reach the probe?

For more exercises, see *Extra Skill and Word Problem Practice*.

Standards Practice

Ⓐ **Practice by Example**

Example 1
(page 18)

GO for Help

Solve each equation. Check your answers.

1. $7w + 2 = 3w + 94$ **2.** $15 - g = 23 - 2g$

3. $43 - 3d = d + 9$ **4.** $5y + 1.8 = 4y - 3.2$

5. $6a - 5 = 4a + 2$ **6.** $7y + 4 = 3 - 2y$

7. $5c - 9 = 8 - 2c$ **8.** $4y - 8 - 2y + 5 = 0$

Example 2
(page 19)

9. $6(n - 4) = 3n$ **10.** $2 - 3(x + 4) = 8$

11. $5(2 - g) = 0$ **12.** $2(x + 4) = 8$

13. $6(t - 2) = 2(9t - 2)$ **14.** $4w - 2(1 - w) = -38$

15. $4(k + 5) = 2(9k - 4)$ **16.** $10(1 - 2y) = -5(2y - 1)$

Example 3
(page 19)

Solve each formula for the indicated variable.

17. $A = \frac{1}{2}bh$, for h **18.** $s = \frac{1}{2}gt^2$, for g **19.** $V = \ell wh$, for w

20. $I = prt$, for r **21.** $S = 2\pi rh$, for r **22.** $V = \pi r^2 h$, for h

Example 4
(page 19)

Solve each equation for x. Find any restrictions.

23. $ax + bx = c$ **24.** $bx - cx = -c$ **25.** $\frac{x}{a} + b = c$

26. $\frac{x}{a} - 5 = b$ **27.** $\frac{x - 2}{2} = m + n$ **28.** $\frac{2}{5}(x + 1) = g$

Lesson 1-3 Solving Equations **21**

Buses reduce travel time by
using high occupancy vehicle
(HOV) lanes.

Write an equation to solve each problem.

29. Two buses leave Fresno at the same time and travel in opposite directions. One bus averages 55 mi/h and the other bus averages 45 mi/h. When will they be 400 mi apart?

30. Two planes left an airport at noon. One flew east at a certain speed and the other flew west at twice the speed. The planes were 2700 mi apart in 3 h. How fast was each plane flying?

31. Geometry The length of a rectangle is 3 cm greater than its width. The perimeter is 24 cm. Find the dimensions of the rectangle.

x

$x + 3$

32. Geometry One side of a triangle is 1 in. longer than the shortest side and is 1 in. shorter than the longest side. The perimeter is 17 in. Find the dimensions of the triangle.

33. Geometry The sides of a rectangle are in the ratio $3 : 2$. What is the length of each side if the perimeter of the rectangle is 55 cm?

34. Geometry The sides of a triangle are in the ratio $3 : 4 : 5$. What is the length of each side if the perimeter of the triangle is 30 cm?

35. The sum of three consecutive integers is 90.
 a. Find the three numbers by letting x represent the first integer.
 b. Find the three numbers by letting x represent the second integer.

B **Apply Your Skills**

Solve each equation.

36. $0.2(x + 3) - 4(2x - 3) = 3.4$

37. $12 - 3(2w + 1) = 7w - 3(7 + w)$

38. $3(m - 2) - 5 = 8 - 2(m - 4)$

39. $7(a + 1) - 3a = 5 + 4(2a - 1)$

40. $\frac{x}{2} + \frac{x}{5} + \frac{x}{3} = 31$

41. $0.5\left(2x + \frac{3}{4}\right) - \frac{1}{3}(0.1 + x) = 1$

Solve each formula for the indicated variable.

42. $R(r_1 + r_2) = r_1 r_2$, for R

43. $R(r_1 + r_2) = r_1 r_2$, for r_2

44. $S = 2\pi r^2 + 2\pi r h$, for h

45. $h = vt - 5t^2$, for v

46. $v = s^2 + \frac{1}{2}sh$, for h

47. $A = \frac{1}{2}h(b_1 + b_2)$, for b_2

48. Geometry The measure of the supplement of an angle is 20° more than three times the measure of the original angle. Find the measures of the angles.

49. Geometry The measures of an angle and its complement differ by 22°. Find the measures of the angles.

50. Michael drove to a friend's house at a rate of 40 mi/h. He returned by the same route at a rate of 45 mi/h. The driving time for the round trip was 4 h. What is the distance Michael traveled?

51. Sports In the 2004 Olympics, a runner from Belarus won the gold medal in the 100-meter race. Her time was 10.93 seconds. In 1988, Florence Griffith Joyner of the United States set a world record of 10.49 seconds for the 100-meter race. If these two athletes had run in the same race with their respective times above, by how many meters would Griffith Joyner have won?

52. Investments Suppose you have $5000 to invest. A certificate of deposit (CD) earns 6% annual interest, while bonds, which are riskier, earn 8% annual interest. You decide to invest $2000 in a CD and the rest in bonds. How much interest will you have earned at the end of one year? Of two years, compounded annually?

Homework Video Tutor

53. Find 4 consecutive odd integers with a sum of 184.

54. Find 4 consecutive even integers such that the sum of the second and fourth is 76.

Solve for x. State any restrictions on the variables.

55. $\frac{x + a}{b} + b = a$

56. $bx + a = dx + c$

57. $cx - b = ax + d$

58. $a(x - 3) + 8 = b(x - 1)$

59. $c(x + 2) - 5 = b(x - 3)$

60. $a(3tx - 2b) = c(dx - 2)$

61. $b(5px - 3c) = a(qx - 4)$

62. $\frac{a}{b}(2x - 12) = \frac{c}{d}$

63. $\frac{3ax}{5} - 4c = \frac{ax}{5}$

64. $\frac{a - c}{x - a} = m$

 Challenge

65. a. The speed of sound in air s, in ft/s, is given by the formula $s = 1055 + 1.1t$, where t is the temperature in degrees Fahrenheit. Solve the formula for t.
  b. Find the Fahrenheit temperature at which the speed of sound is 1100 ft/s.
  c. The relationship between the temperature in degrees Fahrenheit F and degrees Celsius C is given by the formula $F = \frac{9}{5}C + 32$. Solve the formula for C.
  d. Find the Celsius temperature at which the speed of sound is 1100 ft/s.

66. There are 40 cows and chickens in the farmyard. One quiet afternoon, Jack counted and found that there were 100 legs in all. How many cows and how many chickens are there?
  a. Solve this problem by writing and solving an equation.
  b. Critical Thinking This problem can also be solved by reasoning. Suppose all 40 animals are chickens. How many legs would there be? How many too few legs is that? If one chicken is replaced by one cow, by how many would the number of legs be increased? How many cows would have to replace chickens to get the required 100 legs?
  c. Open-Ended Write a problem about the number of wheels in a group of bicycles and tricycles. Solve your problem.

67. Assume that a, b, and c are integers and $a \neq 0$.
  a. Proof Prove that the solution of the linear equation $ax - b = c$ must be a rational number.

  b. Writing Describe the values of a, b, and c for which the solutions of $ax^2 + b = c$ are rational.

68. A tortoise crawling at the rate of 0.1 mi/h passes a resting hare. The hare wants to rest another 30 min before chasing the tortoise at the rate of 5 mi/h. How many feet must the hare run to catch the tortoise?

Multiple Choice Practice

For California Standards and CAHSEE Tutorials, visit PHSchool.com. Web Code: bbq-9045

CAHSEE
6SDAP 1.1

69. A clothing store sells small, medium, and large T-shirts. Which measure describes the T-shirt size that sells most often?
  Ⓐ Mean Ⓑ Median Ⓒ Mode Ⓓ Range

CAHSEE
7AF 4.2

70. Marco drove for 1 hour at 57 miles per hour and for $\frac{1}{2}$ hour at 60 miles per hour. Which equation can be used to find his average speed s for the entire trip?
  Ⓐ $s = \frac{57 + 30}{1.5}$
  Ⓒ $s = 57 + \frac{1}{2}(60)$
  Ⓑ $s = \frac{57 + 60}{1.5}$
  Ⓓ $s = 57 + \frac{60}{0.5}$

Lesson 1-2

Evaluate each expression for $x = -4$ and $y = 3$.

71. $x - 2y + 3$ **72.** $x + x \div y$ **73.** $3x - 4y - x$ **74.** $x + 2y \div x$

Lesson 1-2

Simplify each expression.

75. $2x^2 + x + 5x^2 - 3x$ **76.** $ab - a - 5a$ **77.** $-(3x - y + 4x - y)$

78. $2(5x - 3) + x$ **79.** $5 - 2(3x + 5)$ **80.** $4r + 2s - (6r + 7s)$

✓ Checkpoint Quiz 1   Lessons 1-1 through 1-3

1. Simplify the expressions and arrange them in order from least to greatest.

$|4 - 11|$ $0.1|-3|$ $|1 - \frac{1}{3}|$ $|3| - |4|$

2. What three properties of real numbers are needed to simplify $3x + (2 + 5x)$?

Simplify each expression.

3. $-(a + 2b) + 4(a + 2b) - 2(a + 2b)$ **4.** $-3(a^2 + a + 1) - 4(-a^2 - a + 1)$

Solve each equation.

5. $2(4x + 1) = 3(4 + 2x)$ **6.** $12 - 2(3x + 1) = 4x - 5$

7. $\frac{1}{2}(4b + 1) = 7 - \frac{1}{4}(6b - 2)$

Solve for the indicated variable. Find any restrictions.

8. $A = p(1 + rt)$, for r **9.** $8ax - b = 3b + ax$, for x

10. The perimeter of Sportsland Park is 624 yd. The length of the rectangular park is 8 yd more than 3 times the width. Find the dimensions of the park.

Algebra at Work

Wildlife biologists can model changes in an animal population. An animal population increases rapidly when conditions are good. However, as the number of animals increases, the food supplies decrease. Hunger and disease then lower the population.

Wildlife biologists take a special interest in extremes of animal populations. If the population of one species becomes too large, it may reduce the population of another species. A continuing decrease may cause the species to become endangered or extinct.

Go Online
PHSchool.com

For: Information about wildlife biology
Web Code: bbb-2031

Activity Lab

Spreadsheets

Suppose that you buy an electronic keyboard and sound system for $500 using a credit card. When you get your first monthly statement, the minimum payment is $25. The minimum payment is either $15 or 5% of your balance, whichever is greater. Interest is calculated at 1.8% per month. You pay the minimum each month.

ACTIVITY

You can examine the situation described above with a spreadsheet. Write cell formulas for row 3 of the spreadsheet.

	A	B	C	D	E	F	G
1	Month	Balance	Interest	Payment	New Balance	Total Interest	Total Paid
2	1	$500.00	$9.00	$25.00	$484.00	$9.00	$25.00
3	2	$484.00	$8.71	$24.20	$468.51	$17.71	$49.20
4	3	$468.51	$8.43	$23.43	$453.52	$26.15	$72.63

Month	$A3 = A2 + 1$	**Increase the month by 1.**
Balance	$B3 = E2$	**balance from the previous month**
Interest	$C3 = B3 \cdot 0.018$	**1.8% of the month's balance**
Payment	$D3 = B3 \cdot 0.05$	**5% of the month's balance**
New Balance	$E3 = B3 + C3 - D3$	**Add the interest and subtract the payment.**
Total Interest	$F3 = F2 + C3$	**Add the month's interest to the previous total interest.**
Total Paid	$G3 = G2 + D3$	**Add the month's payment to the previous total.**

EXERCISES

1. Create a spreadsheet for the situation in the Example.
   a. In which month will the minimum payment first be $15?
   b. After how many months will the balance reach zero?
   c. What is the total interest paid?
   d. What is the total amount you will pay?
   e. How many payments are required to reduce the balance to $400?
   f. Rewrite the right side of $E3 = B3 + C3 - D3$ in terms of B3.

2. Create a new spreadsheet for an account that charges 14.9% annual interest. Use a minimum payment of 10% or $20, whichever is greater. What is the total interest paid for the keyboard and sound system?

3. Writing Why is it better to pay off a credit card debt as soon as you can rather than pay just the minimum each month?

Solving Inequalities

 California Content Standards

Prepares for ALG2 2.0 Students solve systems of linear inequalities (in two variables).

What You'll Learn

• To solve and graph inequalities

• To solve and write compound inequalities

. . . And Why

To analyze quality control, as in Example 6

 Check Skills You'll Need

 for Help   Lessons 1-1 and 1-3

State whether each inequality is true or false.

1. $5 < 12$ **2.** $5 < -12$ **3.** $5 \geq 12$

4. $5 \leq -12$ **5.** $5 \leq 5$ **6.** $5 \geq 5$

Solve each equation.

7. $3x + 3 = 2x - 3$ **8.** $5x = 9(x - 8) + 12$

◀)) **New Vocabulary** • compound inequality

---

1 Solving and Graphing Inequalities

As with an equation, the solutions of an inequality are the numbers that make it true.

An equation such as $-2x = 10$ has only one solution, -5. On the other hand, the inequality $-2x < 10$ is true for many values of x, such as $-4.99, -1,$ and 100. The solutions of $-2x < 10$ are all the numbers x such that $x > -5$, as shown in the graph at the right.

$x > -5$

GO for Help

To review the properties of equality, go to p. 18.

The properties for solving inequalities are similar to the properties for solving equations. The exception occurs when you multiply or divide each side by a negative quantity. Notice that you can obtain $x > -5$ from $-2x < 10$ by dividing each side by -2 and *reversing* the inequality symbol.

The following properties are for $\leq$. There are similar properties for $<, >,$ and $\geq$.

 Key Concepts

Property	Properties of Inequalities

Let $a, b,$ and c represent real numbers.

Transitive Property	If $a \leq b$ and $b \leq c$, then $a \leq c$.
Addition Property	If $a \leq b$, then $a + c \leq b + c$.
Subtraction Property	If $a \leq b$, then $a - c \leq b - c$.
Multiplication Property	If $a \leq b$ and $c > 0$, then $ac \leq bc$.
	If $a \leq b$ and $c < 0$, then $ac \geq bc$.
Division Property	If $a \leq b$ and $c > 0$, then $\frac{a}{c} \leq \frac{b}{c}$.
	If $a \leq b$ and $c < 0$, then $\frac{a}{c} \geq \frac{b}{c}$.

← You must reverse the inequality symbol when *c* is negative.

1 EXAMPLE Solving and Graphing Inequalities

Solve each inequality. Graph the solution.

a. $3x - 12 < 3$

$3x - 12 < 3$

$\quad\quad 3x < 15$ **Add 12 to each side.**

$\quad\quad\quad x < 5$ **Divide each side by 3.**

Graph the solution.

$$\xleftarrow{\quad\;+\;\;+\;\;+\;\;+\;\;+\;\;+\;\;\oplus\;\;+\;\;}\rightarrow$$
$$-1\;\;0\;\;1\;\;2\;\;3\;\;4\;\;5\;\;6$$

Check First check the boundary point: $3(5) - 12 = 3.$ ✓
Then check another point on the graph, such as 4: $3(4) - 12 < 3.$ ✓

b. $6 + 5(2 - x) \leq 41$

$\quad 6 + 10 - 5x \leq 41$ **Distributive Property**

$\quad\quad 16 - 5x \leq 41$ **Simplify.**

$\quad\quad\quad -5x \leq 25$ **Subtract 16 from each side.**

$\quad\quad\quad\quad x \geq -5$ **Divide each side by −5 and reverse the inequality.**

Graph the solution.

$$\xleftarrow{\quad+\;\;\bullet\;\;+\;\;+\;\;+\;\;+\;\;+\;\;+\;\;}\rightarrow$$
$$-6\,-5\,-4\,-3\,-2\,-1\;\;0\;\;1$$

Check First check the boundary point: $6 + 5[2 - (-5)] = 41.$ ✓
Then check another point, such as −4: $6 + 5[2 - (-4)] \leq 41.$ ✓

 CA Standards Check **1** Solve each inequality. Graph the solution.
a. $3x - 6 < 27$ **b.** $12 \geq 2(3n + 1) + 22$

Some inequalities have no solution, and some are true for all real numbers.

2 EXAMPLE No Solutions or All Real Numbers as Solutions

Solve each inequality. Graph the solution.

a. $2x - 3 > 2(x - 5)$

$\quad 2x - 3 > 2x - 10$ **Distributive Property**

$\quad\quad 2x > 2x - 7$ **Add 3 to each side.**

$\quad\quad\quad 0 > -7$ **Subtract 2x from each side.**

The last inequality is always true, so $2x - 3 > 2(x - 5)$ is always true. All real numbers are solutions.

$$\xleftarrow{\;+\;\;+\;\;+\;\;+\;\;+\;\;+\;\;+\;\;}\rightarrow$$
$$-3\,-2\,-1\;\;0\;\;1\;\;2\;\;3$$

b. $7x + 6 < 7(x - 4)$

$\quad 7x + 6 < 7x - 28$ **Distributive Property**

$\quad\quad 6 < -28$ **Subtract 7x from each side.**

The last inequality is always false, so $7x + 6 < 7(x - 4)$ is always false. It has no solution.

 CA Standards Check **2 a.** Solve $2x < 2(x + 1) + 3$. Graph the solution.
b. Solve $4(x - 3) + 7 \geq 4x + 1$. Graph the solution.
c. **Critical Thinking** If possible, find values of a such that $2x + a > 2x$ has no solution. Then find values of a such that all real numbers are solutions.

3 EXAMPLE **Real-World Connection**

Revenue The band shown at the left agrees to play for $200 plus 25% of the ticket sales. Find the ticket sales needed for the band to receive at least $500.

Relate $200 + 25\%$ of ticket sales $\geq \$500$

Define Let x = ticket sales (in dollars).

Write $200 + 0.25x \geq 500$

$\qquad\qquad 0.25x \geq 300$ **Subtract 200 from each side.**

$\qquad\qquad\quad\ x \geq 1200$ **Divide each side by 0.25.**

The ticket sales must be greater than or equal to $1200.

✅ **CA Standards Check** ③ A salesperson earns a salary of $700 per month plus 2% of the sales. What must the sales be if the salesperson is to have a monthly income of at least $1800?

2 Compound Inequalities

A **compound inequality** is a pair of inequalities joined by *and* or *or*.

Examples:
- $-1 < x$ and $x \leq 3$, which you can also write as $-1 < x \leq 3$
- $x < -1$ or $x \geq 3$

Online active math

For: Inequalities Activity
Use: Interactive Textbook, 1-4

To solve a compound inequality containing *and*, find all values of the variable that make both inequalities true.

4 EXAMPLE **Compound Inequality Containing *And***

Graph the solution of $3x - 1 > -28$ and $2x + 7 < 19$.

$3x - 1 > -28$ and $2x + 7 < 19$

$\quad 3x > -27 \qquad\qquad 2x < 12$

$\quad\ x > -9$ and $\qquad x < 6$

This compound inequality can be rewritten as $-9 < x < 6$.

✅ **CA Standards Check** ④ Graph the solution of $2x > x + 6$ and $x - 7 < 2$.

To solve a compound inequality containing *or*, find all values of the variable that make at least one of the inequalities true.

5 EXAMPLE **Compound Inequality Containing *Or***

Graph the solution of $4y - 2 \geq 14$ or $3y - 4 \leq -13$.

$4y - 2 \geq 14 \quad$ or $\quad 3y - 4 \leq -13$

$\quad 4y \geq 16 \qquad\qquad 3y \leq -9$

$\quad\ y \geq 4 \quad$ or $\quad\ y \leq -3$

✅ **CA Standards Check** ⑤ Solve the compound inequality $x - 1 < 3$ or $x + 3 > 8$. Graph the solution.

6 EXAMPLE **Real-World** 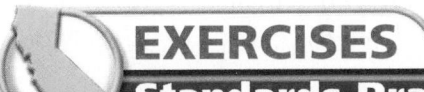 **Connection**

Multiple Choice The ideal length of a bolt is 13.48 cm. The length can vary from the ideal by at most 0.03 cm. A machinist finds one bolt that is 13.67 cm long. By how much should the machinist decrease the length so the bolt can be used?

Ⓐ between 13.45 cm and 13.51 cm   Ⓒ between 0.16 cm and 0.22 cm

Ⓑ between 13.64 cm and 13.70 cm   Ⓓ between 0.13 cm and 0.19 cm

Test-Taking Tip

When you multiply by a negative number across a compound inequality, remember to reverse both inequality symbols.

Relate   minimum length $\leq$ final length $\leq$ maximum length

Define   Let x = number of centimeters to remove.

Write

$13.48 - 0.03 \leq 13.67 - x \leq 13.48 + 0.03$	
$13.45 \leq 13.67 - x \leq 13.51$	**Simplify.**
$-0.22 \leq -x \leq -0.16$	**Subtract 13.67.**
$0.22 \geq x \geq 0.16$	**Multiply by -1.**

The machinist must remove at least 0.16 cm and no more than 0.22 cm.
The answer is C.

 CA Standards Check ⑥ The plans for a circular plastic part in a medical instrument require the diameter to be within 0.2 in. of 1.5 in. A machinist finds that the diameter is now 1.73 in. By how much should the machinist decrease the diameter?

EXERCISES

For more exercises, see *Extra Skill and Word Problem Practice.*

Standards Practice

Ⓐ Practice by Example

Examples 1 and 2
(page 27)

 GO for Help

Solve each inequality. Graph the solution.

1. $-12 \geq 24x$ **2.** $-7k < 63$ **3.** $8a - 15 > 73$

4. $57 - 4t \geq 13$ **5.** $-18 - 5y \geq 52$

6. $14 - 4y \geq 38$ **7.** $4(x + 3) \leq 44$

8. $2(m - 3) + 7 < 21$ **9.** $4(n - 2) - 6 > 18$

10. $9(x + 2) > 9(x - 3)$ **11.** $6x - 13 < 6(x - 2)$

12. $-6(2x - 10) + 12x \leq 180$ **13.** $-7(3x - 7) + 21x \geq 50$

Example 3
(page 28)

Solve each problem by writing an inequality.

14. The length of a picture frame is 3 in. greater than the width. The perimeter is less than 52 in. Describe the dimensions of the frame.

15. The lengths of the sides of a triangle are in the ratio $5 : 6 : 7$. Describe the length of the longest side if the perimeter is less than 54 cm.

16. Find the lesser of two consecutive integers with a sum greater than 16.

17. The cost of a field trip is $220 plus $7 per student. If the school can spend at most $500, how many students can go on the field trip?

Example 4
(page 28)

Solve each compound inequality. Graph the solution.

18. $2x > -10$ and $9x < 18$ **19.** $3x \geq -12$ and $8x \leq 16$

20. $6x \geq -24$ and $9x < 54$ **21.** $7x > -35$ and $5x \leq 30$

Example 5
(page 28)

Solve each compound inequality. Graph the solution.

22. $4x < 16$ or $12x > 144$

23. $3x \geq 3$ or $9x < 54$

24. $8x > -32$ or $-6x \leq 48$

25. $9x \leq -27$ or $4x \geq 36$

Example 6
(page 29)

Solve each problem by writing a compound inequality.

26. A baker needs between 40 lb and 50 lb of a flour-sugar mixture that contains ten times as much flour as sugar. What are the possible weights of flour the baker can use?

27. Between 15,000 yd^3 and 16,000 yd^3 of earth must be trucked away from a construction site. The trucks can remove 1000 yd^3 per day, and 10,500 yd^3 has already been removed. How many days are needed?

28. By how much should a machinist decrease the length of a rod that is 4.78 cm long if the length must be within 0.02 cm of 4.5 cm?

 Apply Your Skills

Solve each inequality. Graph the solution.

29. $2 - 3z \geq 7(8 - 2z) + 12$

30. $17 - 2y \leq 5(7 - 3y) - 15$

31. $\frac{2}{3}(x - 12) \leq x + 8$

32. $\frac{3}{5}(x - 12) > x - 24$

33. $3[4x - (2x - 7)] < 2(3x - 5)$

34. $6[5y - (3y - 1)] \geq 4(3y - 7)$

 35. Writing Write a problem that can be solved using the inequality $x + 0.5x \leq 60$.

GO for Help

For a guide to solving
Exercise 36, see page 32.

36. Geometry The sum of the lengths of any two sides of a triangle is greater than the length of the third side. In $\triangle ABC$, $BC = 4$ and $AC = 8 - AB$. What can you conclude about AB?

37. a. Error Analysis Suppose a classmate writes $y \leq 20$ as the solution of $\frac{1}{2}(y - 16) \geq y + 2$. Prove that your classmate's answer is wrong by checking a number that is less than 20. Choose a number that makes the computation easy.
b. Solve $\frac{1}{2}(y - 16) \geq y + 2$.

38. Construction A contractor estimated that her expenses for a construction project would be between $700,000 and $750,000. She has already spent $496,000. How much more can she spend and remain within her estimate?

Justifying Steps Justify each step by identifying the property used.

39. $3x \leq 4(x - 1) - 8$
$3x \leq 4x - 4 - 8$
$3x \leq 4x - 12$
$-x \leq -12$
$x \geq 12$

40. $\frac{1}{2}(y + 3) > \frac{1}{3}(4 - y)$
$3(y + 3) > 2(4 - y)$
$3y + 9 > 8 - 2y$
$5y + 9 > 8$
$5y > -1$
$y > -0.2$

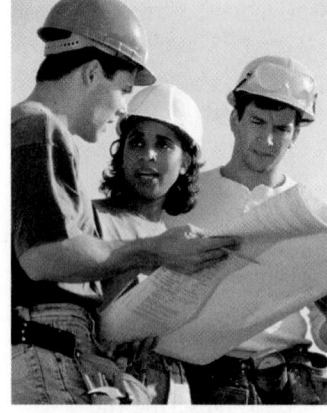

Solve each compound inequality. Graph the solutions.

41. $-6 < 2x - 4 < 12$

42. $11 < 3y + 2 < 20$

43. $-18 > 4x - 3 > -15$

44. $36 \geq 1 - 5z > -21$

45. $5a - 4 > 16$ or $3a + 2 < 17$

46. $6b + 3 < 15$ or $4b - 2 > 18$

47. $6c \leq 18$ or $-5c \leq 15$

48. $8d < -64$ and $5d > 25$

49. $4x \leq 12$ or $-7x \leq 21$

50. $15x > 30$ and $18x < -36$

Open-Ended Write an inequality with a solution that matches the graph. At least two steps should be needed to solve your inequality.

51.
$$-3\ -2\ -1\ \ 0\ \ 1\ \ 2\ \ 3$$

52.
$$-3\ -2\ -1\ \ 0\ \ 1\ \ 2\ \ 3$$

53.
$$-3\ -2\ -1\ \ 0\ \ 1\ \ 2\ \ 3$$

54.
$$-3\ -2\ -1\ \ 0\ \ 1\ \ 2\ \ 3$$

55. Critical Thinking Consider the compound inequality $x < 8$ and $x > a$.
  a. Are there any values of a such that all real numbers are solutions of the compound inequality? If so, what are they?
  b. Are there any values of a such that no real numbers are solutions of the compound inequality? If so, what are they?
  c. Repeat parts (a) and (b) for the compound inequality $x < 8$ or $x > a$.

Multiple Choice Practice

For California Standards and CAHSEE Tutorials, visit PHSchool.com. Web Code: bbq-9045

CAHSEE
Alg1 4.0

56. Solve $3(x - 4) + 2x = x - 8$.
  (A) -1 (B) 1 (C) 3 (D) 5

CAHSEE
7SDAP 1.1

57. The results of a survey about favorite sports are shown in the table at the right. For a circle graph to show these results, what central angle should be used for the sector representing soccer?

  (A) $54°$
  (B) $81°$
  (C) $99°$
  (D) $108°$

Favorite Sports

Sport	Responses
Baseball	55
Basketball	30
Football	60
Soccer	45
Other	10

CAHSEE
7MG 2.1

58. A rectangular swimming pool, 20 feet long and 14 feet wide, is surrounded by a deck that is 4 feet wide. What is the area of the deck?
  (A) $152\ \text{ft}^2$
  (B) $280\ \text{ft}^2$
  (C) $336\ \text{ft}^2$
  (D) $432\ \text{ft}^2$

Mixed Review

Lesson 1-3

Solve each equation. Check your answers.

59. $7x - 6(11 - 2x) = 10$
60. $10x - 7 = 2(13 + 5x)$
61. $4y - \frac{1}{10} = 3y + \frac{4}{5}$
62. $0.4x + 1.18 = -3.1(2 - 0.01x)$

Lesson 1-2

Simplify each expression.

63. $(2a - 4) + (5a + 9)$
64. $3(x + 3y) - 5(x - y)$
65. $\frac{1}{3}(b + 12) - \frac{1}{4}(b + 12)$
66. $0.4(k - 0.1) + 0.5(3.3 - k)$

Understanding Math Problems Read the problem below. Then let Malik's thinking guide you through the solution. Check your understanding with the exercises at the bottom of the page.

Geometry The sum of the lengths of any two sides of a triangle is greater than the length of the third side. In $\triangle ABC$, $BC = 4$ and $AC = 8 - AB$. What can you conclude about AB?

What Malik Thinks

$\triangle ABC$ has three sides, so I can write three inequalities, each with AB.

I also know that $BC = 4$ and $AC = 8 - AB$.

I can substitute for BC and AC in each of the three inequalities and simplify.

Here's the first inequality.

Here's the second.

Here's the third.

I can combine $2 < AB$ and $AB < 6$ into a compound inequality.

What Malik Writes

$$AC + BC > AB$$
$$AB + BC > AC$$
$$AB + AC > BC$$

$$BC = 4 \text{ and } AC = 8 - AB.$$

$$(8 - AB) + 4 > AB$$
$$12 - AB > AB$$
$$12 > 2AB$$
$$6 > AB, \text{ or } AB < 6.$$

$$AB + 4 > 8 - AB$$
$$2AB > 4$$
$$AB > 2, \text{ or } 2 < AB.$$

$$AB + (8 - AB) > 4$$
$$8 > 4$$

$$2 < AB < 6$$

EXERCISES

The sum of the lengths of any two sides of a triangle is greater than the length of the third side. What can you conclude about AC in $\triangle ABC$?

1. $AB = 6$; $BC + 2AC = 18$

2. $BC = 7$; $AC = 2 + AB$

3. $AB + AC = 5$; $AC + BC = 4$

4. $BC + AC = 22$; $AB + BC = 12$

1-5

Absolute Value Equations and Inequalities

 California Content Standards

ALG2 1.0 Students solve equations and inequalities involving absolute value. *Introduce*

What You'll Learn

- To solve absolute value equations
- To solve absolute value inequalities

. . . And Why

To write specifications for a basketball, as in Example 6

✓ **Check Skills You'll Need**

GO for Help Lessons 1-3 and 1-4

Solve each equation.

1. $5(x - 6) = 40$ **2.** $5b = 2(3b - 8)$ **3.** $2y + 6y = 15 - 2y + 8$

Solve each inequality.

4. $4x + 8 > 20$ **5.** $3a - 2 \geq a + 6$ **6.** $4(t - 1) < 3t + 5$

🔊 **New Vocabulary** • absolute value • extraneous solution • tolerance

---

▼ **1**   **Absolute Value Equations**

The **absolute value** of a number is its distance from zero on the number line and distance is nonnegative. So the absolute value of a negative number such as -5 is its opposite, $-(-5)$. For $x < 0, |x| = -x$.

 Key Concepts

Definition	**Algebraic Definition of Absolute Value**
• If $x \geq 0$, then $|x| = x$.	• If $x < 0$, then $|x| = -x$.

An absolute value equation such as $|2y - 4| = 12$ has two solutions, since the expression $2y - 4$ can equal 12 or -12.

1 EXAMPLE   **Solving Absolute Value Equations**

Solve $|2y - 4| = 12$.

$|2y - 4| = 12$

$2y - 4 = 12$ or $2y - 4 = -12$ **The value of 2y − 4 can be 12 or −12 since |12| and |−12| both equal 12.**

$2y = 16$ $2y = -8$ **Add 4 to each side of both equations.**

$y = 8$ or $y = -4$ **Divide each side of both equations by 2.**

Check $|2y - 4| = 12$

$|2(8) - 4| \stackrel{?}{=} 12$ $|2(-4) - 4| \stackrel{?}{=} 12$

$|12| = 12$ ✓ $|-12| = 12$ ✓

 CA Standards Check   **1** Solve $|3x + 2| = 7$. Check your answer.

You will find it easier to solve a multi-step absolute value equation if you first isolate the absolute value expression on one side of the equation.

2 EXAMPLE **Solving Multi-Step Absolute Value Equations**

Solve $3|4w - 1| - 5 = 10$.

$3|4w - 1| - 5 = 10$

$\quad 3|4w - 1| = 15$ **Add 5 to each side.**

$\quad\quad |4w - 1| = 5$ **Divide each side by 3.**

$\quad\quad 4w - 1 = 5$ or $4w - 1 = -5$ **Rewrite as two equations.**

$\quad\quad\quad 4w = 6$ | $4w = -4$ **Add 1 to each side of both equations.**

$\quad\quad\quad\quad w = \frac{3}{2}$ or $w = -1$ **Divide each side of both equations by 4.**

Check $3|4w - 1| - 5 = 10$ $3|4w - 1| - 5 = 10$

$\quad\quad 3|4(\frac{3}{2}) - 1| - 5 \overset{?}{=} 10$ $3|4(-1) - 1| - 5 \overset{?}{=} 10$

$\quad\quad\quad\quad 3|5| - 5 \overset{?}{=} 10$ $3|-5| - 5 \overset{?}{=} 10$

$\quad\quad\quad\quad\quad 10 = 10 \checkmark$ $10 = 10 \checkmark$

 CA Standards Check **2** Solve $2|3x - 1| + 5 = 33$. Check your answer.

The equation $|2x + 7| = -2$ has no solution because $|2x + 7|$ cannot be negative. It is important to check possible solutions in the original equation. One or more may be extraneous solutions.

 Key Concepts

Definition	**Extraneous Solution**

An **extraneous solution** is a solution of an equation derived from an original equation that is not a solution of the original equation.

3 EXAMPLE **Checking for Extraneous Solutions**

Solve $|2x + 5| = 3x + 4$.

$|2x + 5| = 3x + 4$

$\quad 2x + 5 = 3x + 4$ or $2x + 5 = -(3x + 4)$ **Rewrite as two equations.**

$\quad\quad -x = -1$ | $2x + 5 = -3x - 4$ **Solve each equation.**

$\quad\quad\quad x = 1$ | $5x = -9$

$\quad\quad\quad x = 1$ or $x = -\frac{9}{5}$

Check $|2x + 5| = 3x + 4$ $|2x + 5| = 3x + 4$

$\quad |2(1) + 5| \overset{?}{=} 3(1) + 4$ $|2(-\frac{9}{5}) + 5| \overset{?}{=} 3(-\frac{9}{5}) + 4$

$\quad\quad\quad |7| \overset{?}{=} 7$ $|\frac{7}{5}| \overset{?}{=} -\frac{7}{5}$

$\quad\quad\quad 7 = 7 \checkmark$ $\frac{7}{5} \neq -\frac{7}{5}$

The only solution is 1. $-\frac{9}{5}$ is an extraneous solution.

Vocabulary Tip

Extraneous is pronounced ek-STRAY-nee-us.

 CA Standards Check **3** **a.** Solve $|2x + 3| = 3x + 2$. Check for extraneous solutions.
    b. Solve $|x| = x - 1$. Check for extraneous solutions.
    c. **Critical Thinking** Find a value for a such that $|x| = x + a$ has exactly one solution.

If $|x| > 3$, then x is more than 3 units from 0 on the number line.

$$-4\ -3\ -2\ -1\ \ 0\ \ 1\ \ 2\ \ 3\ \ 4$$

This is also the graph of $x < -3$ or $x > 3$. So the absolute value inequality $|x| > 3$ can be rewritten as the compound inequality $x < -3$ or $x > 3$.

4 **EXAMPLE** **Solving Absolute Value Inequalities, $|A| \geq b$**

Solve $|3x + 6| \geq 12$. Graph the solution.

$|3x + 6| \geq 12$

$3x + 6 \leq -12$ or $3x + 6 \geq 12$ **Rewrite as a compound inequality.**

$\qquad 3x \leq -18$ $\qquad\qquad 3x \geq 6$

$\qquad\quad x \leq -6$ or $\qquad x \geq 2$

$$-7\ -6\ -5\ -4\ -3\ -2\ -1\ \ 0\ \ 1\ \ 2\ \ 3$$ **Graph the solution.**

CA Standards Check **4** Solve $|2x - 3| > 7$. Graph the solution.

If $|x| < 2$, then x is less than 2 units from 0 on the number line.

$$-3\ -2\ -1\ \ 0\ \ 1\ \ 2\ \ 3$$

This is also the graph of $-2 < x < 2$. So the absolute value inequality $|x| < 2$ can be written as the compound inequality $-2 < x < 2$.

Key Concepts

Properties	**Absolute Value Inequalities**
Let k represent a positive real number.	
$|x| \geq k$ is equivalent to	$x \leq -k$ or $x \geq k$.
$|x| \leq k$ is equivalent to	$-k \leq x \leq k$.

When an absolute value is combined with other operations, first isolate the absolute value expression on one side of the inequality.

5 **EXAMPLE** **Solving Absolute Value Inequalities, $|A| < b$**

Solve $3|2x + 6| - 9 < 15$. Graph the solution.

$3|2x + 6| - 9 < 15$

$\qquad 3|2x + 6| < 24$ **Isolate the absolute value expression. Add 9 to each side.**

$\qquad\quad |2x + 6| < 8$ **Divide each side by 3.**

$-8 < 2x + 6 < 8$ **Rewrite as a compound inequality.**

$-14 < \quad 2x \quad < 2$ **Solve for x.**

$-7 < \quad x \quad < 1$

$$-8\ -7\ -6\ -5\ -4\ -3\ -2\ -1\ \ 0\ \ 1\ \ 2$$

GO for Help

To review the properties of inequalities, go to p. 26.

CA Standards Check **5** Solve $|5z + 3| - 7 < 34$. Graph the solution.

You can use absolute value inequalities and compound inequalities to specify allowable ranges in measurements. The difference between a desired measurement and its maximum and minimum allowable values is the tolerance. The **tolerance** equals one half of the difference between the maximum and the minimum values.

For example, if a manufacturing specification calls for a dimension d of 10 cm with a tolerance of 0.1 cm, then the allowable difference between d and 10 is less than or equal to 0.1. This specification can be expressed in the following ways.

$\lvert d - 10 \rvert \le 0.1$	**absolute value inequality**
$d - 10 \le 0.1$ and $d - 10 \ge -0.1$	**equivalent compound inequality**
$-0.1 \le d - 10 \le 0.1$	**equivalent compound inequality**
$9.9 \le d \le 10.1$	**simplified compound inequality**

6 EXAMPLE   Real-World Connection

Basketball The specification for the circumference C in inches of a basketball is $29.5 \le C \le 30$. Write the specification as an absolute value inequality.

$\dfrac{30 - 29.5}{2} = \dfrac{0.5}{2} = 0.25$	**Find the tolerance.**
$\dfrac{29.5 + 30}{2} = 29.75$	**Find the average of the maximum and minimum values.**
$-0.25 \le C - 29.75 \le 0.25$	**Write an inequality.**
$\lvert C - 29.75 \rvert \le 0.25$	**Rewrite as an absolute value inequality.**

✓ CA Standards Check ⑥ The specification for the circumference C in inches of a basketball for junior high school is $27.75 \le C \le 28.5$. Write the specification as an absolute value inequality.

EXERCISES

For more exercises, see *Extra Skill and Word Problem Practice*.

Standards Practice   ALG2 1.0

A Practice by Example

Examples 1 and 2
(pages 33, 34)

GO for Help

Solve each equation. Check your answers.

1. $\lvert 3x \rvert = 18$ **2.** $\lvert -4x \rvert = 32$ **3.** $\lvert x - 3 \rvert = 9$

4. $2\lvert 3x - 2 \rvert = 14$ **5.** $\lvert 3x + 4 \rvert = -3$ **6.** $\lvert 2x - 3 \rvert = -1$

7. $\lvert x + 4 \rvert + 3 = 17$ **8.** $\lvert y - 5 \rvert - 2 = 10$ **9.** $\lvert 4 - z \rvert - 10 = 1$

Example 3
(page 34)

Solve each equation. Check for extraneous solutions.

10. $\lvert x - 1 \rvert = 5x + 10$ **11.** $\lvert 2z - 3 \rvert = 4z - 1$ **12.** $\lvert 3x + 5 \rvert = 5x + 2$

13. $\lvert 2y - 4 \rvert = 12$ **14.** $3\lvert 4w - 1 \rvert - 5 = 10$ **15.** $\lvert 2x + 5 \rvert = 3x + 4$

Example 4
(page 35)

Solve each inequality. Graph the solution.

16. $\lvert x + 3 \rvert > 9$ **17.** $\lvert x - 5 \rvert \ge 8$ **18.** $\lvert y - 3 \rvert \ge 12$

19. $\lvert 2x + 1 \rvert \ge -9$ **20.** $3\lvert 2x - 1 \rvert \ge 21$ **21.** $\lvert 3z \rvert - 4 > 8$

Example 5
(page 35)

22. $3\lvert y - 9 \rvert < 27$ **23.** $\lvert 6y - 2 \rvert + 4 < 22$ **24.** $\lvert 3x - 6 \rvert + 3 < 15$

25. $\frac{1}{4}\lvert x - 3 \rvert + 2 < 1$ **26.** $4\lvert 2w + 3 \rvert - 7 \le 9$ **27.** $3\lvert 5t - 1 \rvert + 9 \le 23$

Example 6
(page 36)

Write each specification as an absolute value inequality.

28. $1.3 \le h \le 1.5$ **29.** $50 \le k \le 51$ **30.** $27.25 \le C \le 27.75$

31. $50 \le b \le 55$ **32.** $1200 \le m \le 1300$ **33.** $0.1187 \le d \le 0.1190$

 Apply Your Skills

Solve each equation.

34. $-|4 - 8b| = 12$ **35.** $4|3x + 4| = 4x + 8$

36. $|3x - 1| + 10 = 25$ **37.** $\frac{1}{2}|3c + 5| = 6c + 4$

38. $5|6 - 5x| = 15x - 35$ **39.** $7|8 - 3h| = 21h - 49$

40. $2|3x - 7| = 10x - 8$ **41.** $6|2x + 5| = 6x + 24$

42. $\frac{1}{4}|4x + 7| = 8x + 16$ **43.** $\frac{2}{3}|3x - 6| = 4(x - 2)$

Homework Video Tutor

Visit: PHSchool.com
Web Code: bbe-0105

Solve each inequality. Graph the solutions.

44. $|3x - 4| + 5 \le 27$ **45.** $|2x + 3| - 6 \ge 7$

46. $-2|x + 4| < 22$ **47.** $2|4t - 1| + 6 > 20$

48. $|3z + 15| \ge 0$ **49.** $|-2x + 1| > 2$

50. $\frac{1}{9}|5x - 3| - 3 \ge 2$ **51.** $\frac{1}{11}|2x - 4| + 10 \le 11$

52. $\left|\frac{x - 3}{2}\right| + 2 < 6$ **53.** $\left|\frac{x + 5}{3}\right| - 3 > 6$

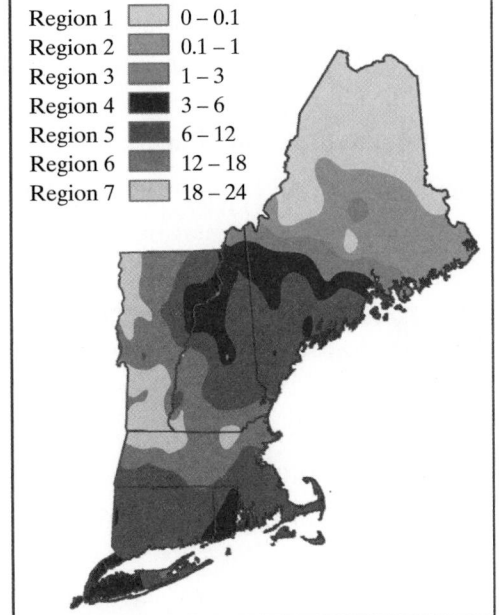

A March Snowfall (inches)

Region 1   0 – 0.1
Region 2   0.1 – 1
Region 3   1 – 3
Region 4   3 – 6
Region 5   6 – 12
Region 6   12 – 18
Region 7   18 – 24

Source: Northeast River Forecast Center/NOAA

54. Meteorology Write a compound inequality and an absolute value inequality for the snowfall in regions 1, 2, 3, and 4 in the figure at the left.

55. Multiple Choice The circumference of a basketball for college women must be from 28.5 in. to 29.0 in. Which absolute value inequality best represents the circumference of the ball?

  Ⓐ $|C - 0.25| \ge 28.5$ Ⓒ $|C - 28.75| \le 0.25$

  Ⓑ $|C - 0.25| \le 29.0$ Ⓓ $|C - 28.75| \ge 0.25$

56. Writing Describe the differences in the graphs of $|x| < a$ and $|x| > a$, where a is a positive real number.

57. Open-Ended Write an absolute value inequality for which every real number is a solution. Write an absolute value inequality that has no solution.

Write an absolute value inequality and a compound inequality for each length x with the given tolerance.

58. a length of 36.80 mm with a tolerance of 0.05 mm

59. a length of 9.55 mm with a tolerance of 0.02 mm

60. a length of 100 yd with a tolerance of 4 in.

Ⓒ **Challenge**

Solve each equation for x.

61. $|ax| - b = c$ **62.** $|cx - d| = ab$ **63.** $a|bx - c| = d$

Graph each solution.

64. $|x| \ge 5$ and $|x| \le 6$ **65.** $|x| \ge 6$ or $|x| < 5$ **66.** $|x - 5| \le x$

Multiple Choice Practice

For California Standards and CAHSEE Tutorials, visit PHSchool.com. **Web Code: bbq-9045**

ALG2 1.0

67. What is the complete solution to the equation $|1 + 2x| + 3 = 22$?

    Ⓐ $x = 9, x = 10$ Ⓒ $x = -9, x = 10$

    Ⓑ $x = 9, x = -10$ Ⓓ $x = -9, x = -10$

**CAHSEE
7AF 1.2**

68. Which expression is equivalent to $3n(2n + 3) - (n + 1)(2n + 3)$?

    Ⓐ $2n - 1$ Ⓒ $4n^2 + 4n - 3$

    Ⓑ $2n + 1$ Ⓓ $4n^2 + 14n + 3$

**CAHSEE
7NS 1.7**

69. Amanda bought a television that was on sale for 25% off the list price. She paid \$252.63, which included a 5% sales tax. What was the list price of the television?

    Ⓐ   \$282.63   Ⓑ   \$303.16   Ⓒ   \$320.80   Ⓓ   \$331.58

Mixed Review

Lesson 1-4

Solve each inequality. Graph the solution.

70. $5y - 10 < 20$ **71.** $-5(4s + 1) < 23$ **72.** $4a + 6 \geq 2a + 14$

73. $0.5x + 5 \geq x - 1$ **74.** $3(4x - 1) \geq 2(4 - x)$ **75.** $4(3t + 2) \leq 43 + 7t$

Lesson 1-2

Evaluate each expression for the given value.

76. $3|4x - 6| - 2x^2$, for $x = -3$ **77.** $\frac{5r - r^2}{1 - 4r}$, for $r = 4$

Lesson 1-1

Name the property of real numbers illustrated by each of the following.

78. $16x + (-16x) = 0$ **79.** 5π is a real number.   **80.** $4(x - 9) = (x - 9)4$

✓ Checkpoint Quiz 2   Lessons 1-4 through 1-5

Solve each inequality. Graph the solution.

1. $3x + 10 \leq 25$ **2.** $8x + 15 > 15x - 24$

3. $5z > 2z - 18$ and $3 - 9z < 12$ **4.** $4w > 1 + 3w$ or $12w + 18 < 11w + 15$

5. $2|x + 4| \leq 22$ **6.** $|2x| + 8 > 12$

Solve each equation.

7. $7|3 - 2y| = 56$ **8.** $\frac{1}{4}|4x + 2| = 1 - 2x$

9. Write and solve an inequality to find three consecutive whole numbers with a sum between 13 and 16.

 10. Geometry The length of any side of a triangle is less than the sum of the lengths of the other two sides. In $\triangle PQR$, $PR = RQ + 4$ and $RQ < 11$. Write and solve an inequality for PQ.

1-6 Probability

California Content Standards
Prepares for PS 1.0 Students can use the rules for addition, multiplication, and complementation to solve for probabilities in finite sample spaces.

What You'll Learn

- To find experimental probabilities
- To find theoretical probabilities

...And Why

To find the probabilities of inherited traits, as in Example 4

 Check Skills You'll Need

GO for Help Skills Handbook page 868

Write each number as a percent.

1. $\frac{3}{8}$

2. $1\frac{5}{6}$

3. 0.0043

4. $\frac{1}{400}$

5. 1.04

6. 3

New Vocabulary
- experimental probability
- simulation • sample space
- theoretical probability

---

1 Experimental Probability

Hands-On Activity: Experimental Probability

Fold an index card slightly off center, as shown at the left. When you drop the card from a height of several feet, how will it land?

1. Drop the card 50 times. Record the number of times the card lands in each position.

2. What percent of the time does the card land on its short side? Find the percents for the other positions.

3. In what position is the card most likely to land? Least likely to land?

4. Suppose that you drop the card another 20 times. Predict how many times it will land in each position.

5. a. Drop the card another 20 times. Record your results.
   b. Compare the results with your prediction from Question 4. Are they close? How could you improve your prediction?

Probability measures how likely it is for an event to occur. You can express probabilities as percents (0% through 100%) or as real numbers (0 through 1).

The probability of an impossible event is 0 or 0%. The probability of a certain event, which must happen, is 1 or 100%.

When you gather data from observations, you can calculate an experimental probability. Each observation is called an experiment or a trial.

 Key Concepts

Definition	Experimental Probability

experimental probability of event = P(event)
$$= \frac{\text{number of times the event occurs}}{\text{number of trials}}$$

1 EXAMPLE Finding Experimental Probability

Vocabulary Tip

Read P(completion) as "probability of a completion."

When the University of Texas won college football's national championship in the 2006 Rose Bowl game, its quarterback completed 30 of 40 passes. Find the experimental probability of the quarterback completing a pass.

P(completion) $= \frac{30}{40} = 0.75$, or 75%.

✓ **CA Standards Check** ❶ In the same game, the University of Southern California quarterback completed 29 of 40 passes. Find the experimental probability of this player completing a pass.

When actual trials are difficult to conduct, you can find experimental probabilities by using a **simulation,** which is a model of one or more events.

2 EXAMPLE Using a Simulation

Suppose you take a true-or-false quiz and guess four answers at random. What is an experimental probability that you will get at least three correct answers?

```
rand
        .8767044746
        .7208728315
        .6495877886
        .3462435756
        .8958229562
        .4615208491
■


        .1214849574
        .5070685798
        .5584414289
        .9071019949
        .1991062533
        .4761581612
        .4792397345
■


        .6388889895
        .5466561294
        .2840659518
        .2096111775
        .7827769142
        .7787959459
        .6958584068
■
```

Step 1 Define how you will do the simulation.
- Generate random numbers on a calculator.
- Since you answer true or false at random, you have a 50% chance of guessing correctly on each question. So let half of the digits represent correct answers. For example, let even digits represent correct answers.
- Since there are four questions, group the random digits in groups of four. List 50 groups to represent taking the test 50 times.

Step 2 Conduct the simulation. Underline groups with at least three even digits.

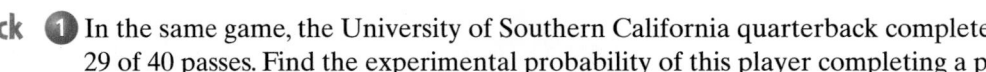

8767	<u>0447</u>	<u>4672</u>	<u>0872</u>	8315	6495	8778	<u>8634</u>	<u>6243</u>	5756
8958	2295	<u>6246</u>	1520	8491	1214	8495	7450	<u>7068</u>	5798
5584	<u>4142</u>	8990	7101	9949	1991	<u>0625</u>	3347	6158	1612
4792	3973	4563	<u>8888</u>	9895	<u>5466</u>	5612	<u>9428</u>	<u>4065</u>	9518
<u>2096</u>	1117	7578	2776	9142	7787	9594	5969	5858	<u>4068</u>

Step 3 Interpret the simulation. Since 15 of the 50 groups represent at least three correct answers, P(at least 3 correct) $= \frac{15}{50} = 0.3$.

This experimental probability of getting at least three correct answers is 30%.

✓ **CA Standards Check** ❷ What is the experimental probability of getting all four answers correct?

When you roll a number cube, the possible outcomes are 1, 2, 3, 4, 5, and 6. The set of all possible outcomes is called the **sample space.** You can calculate theoretical probability as a ratio of outcomes.

 Key Concepts

| **Definition** | **Theoretical Probability** |

If a sample space has n equally likely outcomes and an event A occurs in m of these outcomes, then the **theoretical probability** of event A is $P(A) = \frac{m}{n}$.

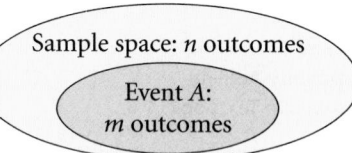

Sample space: n outcomes

Event A: m outcomes

3 EXAMPLE **Finding Theoretical Probability**

Find the theoretical probability of getting an even number when you roll a number cube.

The even outcomes are 2, 4, and 6.

3 outcomes result in an even number. → $\frac{3}{6}$ ← **6 equally likely outcomes are in the sample space.**

$= \frac{1}{2}$

✓ **CA Standards Check** ③ Find the theoretical probability of getting a prime number when you roll a number cube.

4 EXAMPLE **Real-World 🌐 Connection**

**gg
Right thumb on top**

**GG or Gg
Left thumb on top**

Biology Fold your hands so your fingers interlace. Do you naturally place your left or right thumb on top? Placing your left thumb on top is a dominant genetic trait.

When a parent has both a dominant and a recessive gene, then the two genes are equally likely to be passed to a child. If you have one or two dominant genes, you normally place your left thumb on top.

Suppose a child has parents who both have just one dominant gene. What is the theoretical probability that the child will naturally place the left thumb on top?

Make a table. Let G represent the dominant gene (left thumb on top). Let g represent the recessive gene (right thumb on top).

The sample space {GG, Gg, Gg, gg} contains four equally likely outcomes. Three outcomes have at least one G. So P(left thumb on top) $= \frac{3}{4}$.

		Gene from Mother	
		G	**g**
Gene from Father	**G**	GG	Gg
	g	Gg	gg

The theoretical probability that the child will naturally place the left thumb on top is $\frac{3}{4}$, or 75%.

✓ **CA Standards Check** ④ What is the theoretical probability that a child of the parents in Example 4 places the right thumb on top?

Sometimes you can use areas to find theoretical probability.

For: Probability Activity
Use: Interactive Textbook, 1-6

5 EXAMPLE Finding Geometric Probability

Geometry Suppose that all the points on the circular dartboard shown at the right are equally likely to be hit by a dart you have thrown. Find the probability of scoring at least ten points.

P(at least 10 points)

$$= \frac{\text{area of circle with radius } 2r}{\text{area of circle with radius } 4r}$$

$$= \frac{\pi(2r)^2}{\pi(4r)^2}$$

$$= \frac{4\pi r^2}{16\pi r^2} = \frac{1}{4}$$

● The theoretical probability of scoring at least ten points is $\frac{1}{4}$, or 25%.

CA Standards Check   5 Use the dartboard from Example 5. Find each probability.
a. P(scoring 20 points)   **b.** P(scoring 5 points)

EXERCISES

Standards Practice

For more exercises, see *Extra Skill and Word Problem Practice*.

 Practice by Example

Example 1
(page 40)

 for Help

1. A class tossed coins and recorded 161 heads and 179 tails. What is the experimental probability of heads? Of tails?

2. Another class rolled number cubes. Their results are shown in the table. What is the experimental probability of rolling each number?

Number	1	2	3	4	5	6
Occurrences	42	44	45	44	47	46

Example 2
(page 40)

For Exercises 3–5, define a simulation by telling how you represent correct answers, incorrect answers, and the quiz. Use your simulation to find each experimental probability.

Graphing Calculator Hint

To generate random numbers, press
[MATH] ◄ 1 [ENTER].

3. If you guess the answers at random, what is the probability of getting at least two correct answers on a five-question true-or-false quiz?

4. If you guess the answers at random, what is the probability of getting at least three correct answers on a five-question true-or-false quiz?

5. A five-question multiple-choice quiz has five choices for each answer. What is the probability of correctly guessing at random exactly one correct answer? Exactly two correct answers? Exactly three correct answers? (*Hint:* You could let any two digits represent correct answers, and the other digits represent wrong answers.)

Example 3
(page 41)

A jar contains 30 red marbles, 50 blue marbles, and 20 white marbles. You pick one marble from the jar at random. Find each theoretical probability.

6. P(red)   7. P(blue)   8. P(not white)   9. P(red or blue)

A bag contains 36 red, 48 green, 22 yellow, and 19 purple blocks. You pick one block from the bag at random. Find each theoretical probability.

10. P(green) **11.** P(purple) **12.** P(not yellow)

13. P(green or yellow) **14.** P(yellow or not green)

Example 4
(page 41)

For each situation, find the sample space and the theoretical probability that a child will naturally place the left thumb on top.

15. The father has gene pair gg and the mother has Gg.

16. The father has gene pair gg and the mother has GG.

Example 5
(page 42)

Geometry Suppose that a dart lands at random on the dartboard shown at the right. Find each theoretical probability.

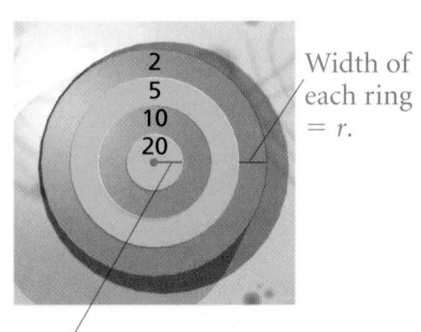

Width of each ring = r.

17. The dart lands in the bull's-eye.

18. The dart lands in a green region.

19. The dart scores at least 10 points.

20. The dart scores less than 10 points.

 Apply Your Skills

21. The common interpretation of Murphy's Law is, If something can go wrong, it will. Assume that Murphy's Law applies to the following situations, and estimate each probability as either 0 or 1.
  a. P(your dog chews up your homework after you've finished it)
  b. P(your teacher accepts your excuse for not having your homework)

22. Multiple Choice A caterer knows that, on average, there will be one broken egg in every 3 cartons. A carton contains 12 eggs. The caterer plans to serve 1200 eggs at a breakfast. What is the best estimate for the number of cartons the caterer should buy?
  Ⓐ 97 cartons Ⓑ 100 cartons Ⓒ 103 cartons Ⓓ 112 cartons

23. Use the random number table at the left to simulate tossing a coin 50 times. Find the experimental probability that the outcome of a coin toss is heads.

Random Number Table		
31504	51648	40613
79321	80927	42404
15594	84675	68591
34178	00460	31754
49676	58733	00884
85400	72294	22551
22547	86066	93114
85211	07790	20890
21339	09414	51549
13843	18407	87043
34990	16214	46849
11390	01322	82656
45950	37521	77417

In a class of 147 students, 95 are taking math (M), 73 are taking science (S), and 52 are taking both math and science. One student is picked at random. Find each probability.

24. P(taking math or science or both)

25. P(not taking math)

26. P(taking math but not science)

27. P(taking neither math nor science)

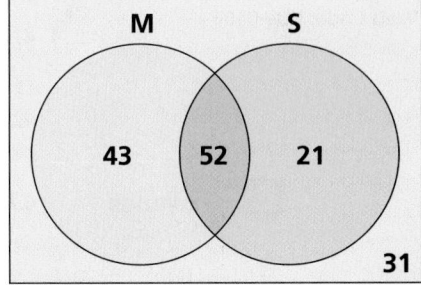

Suppose you roll a number cube. Find each theoretical probability.

28. P(5) **29.** P(an even number)

30. P(a number less than 5) **31.** P(8)

32. P(a number greater than 5) **33.** P(a number less than 8)

Suppose you select a number at random from the sample space {1, 2, 3, 4, 5, 6, 7, 8, 9}. Find each theoretical probability.

34. P(the number is a multiple of 3)   **35.** P(the number is less than 5)

36. P(the number is prime)   **37.** P(the number is even)

38. Suppose you roll two number cubes.
   a. What is the sample space?
   b. How many outcomes are there?
   c. What is the theoretical probability of getting a sum of 12?
   d. What is the theoretical probability of getting a sum of 7?

39. Sports The batter's strike zone depends on the height and stance of the batter. Find the geometric probability that a baseball thrown at random within the batter's strike zone as shown in the figure below will be a high-inside strike. This is one of the hardest pitches to hit!

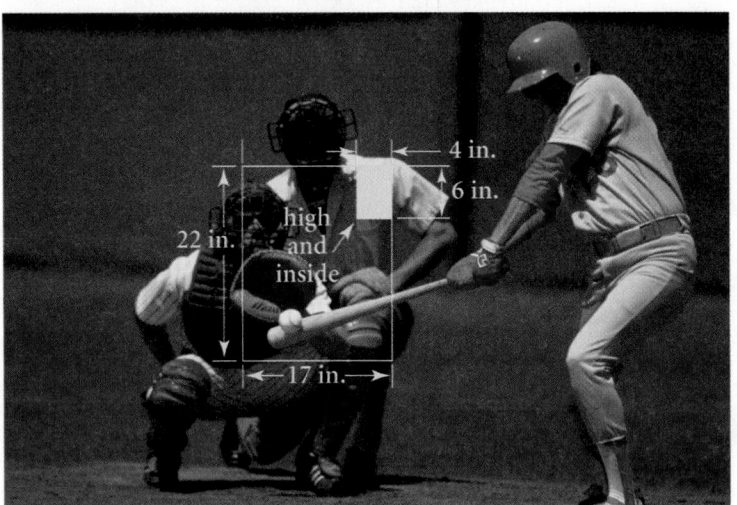

40. a. Sports Team A has won one game and team B has won three games in a World Series. What is the experimental probability that team A wins the next game? That team B wins the next game?
   b. Critical Thinking Do you think that experimental probability is a good predictor of the winner of the next game? Explain.

41. Writing Explain what you would need to know to determine the theoretical probability that a five-digit postal ZIP code ends in 1.

42. Suppose you choose a two-digit number at random. What is the theoretical probability that its square root is an integer?

Homework Video Tutor

Visit: PHSchool.com
Web Code: bbe-0106

C Challenge

43. Assume that an event is neither certain nor impossible. Then the odds in favor of the event are the ratio of the number of favorable outcomes to the number of unfavorable outcomes.
   a. If the odds in favor of the event are a to b or $\frac{a}{b}$, what is the probability of the event?
   b. If the probability of the event is $\frac{a}{b}$, what are the odds in favor of the event?
   c. Would you rather play a game where your odds of winning are $\frac{1}{2}$, or a game where your probability of winning is $\frac{1}{2}$? Explain.

44. Open-Ended Use a telephone book. Select 50 telephone numbers at random and record the first three digits (the "exchange") of each number. Summarize your results using probability statements.

45. On a TV game show, you want to win a prize that is hidden behind one of three doors. You choose one door, but before it is opened the host opens another door and shows that the prize is not there. Now you can switch to the other unopened door or stick with your original choice.
a. Find the experimental probability of winning the prize if you stick with your original choice. (*Hint:* Simulate the doors with index cards and the prize with a mark on one side of one card. One person can act as the host and another as the contestant.)
b. Find the experimental probability of winning if you switch to the other door.

Multiple Choice Practice

For California Standards and CAHSEE Tutorials, visit PHSchool.com. Web Code: bbq-9045

ALG2 1.0

46. Solve $3|2x - 4| = 21$.

Ⓐ $-1.5, 5.5$ Ⓑ $-7, 7$ Ⓒ $7, 11$ Ⓓ $2.5, 5.5$

ALG2 1.0

47. Which is equivalent to the compound inequality $x < 2$ or $x > 4$?

Ⓐ $|x - 3| > 1$ Ⓑ $|x - 2| > 4$ Ⓒ $|x - 1| > 3$ Ⓓ $|x - 3| < 1$

CAHSEE 7MG 2.3

48. What is the volume of a 3-dimensional object with the dimensions shown in the 3 views below?

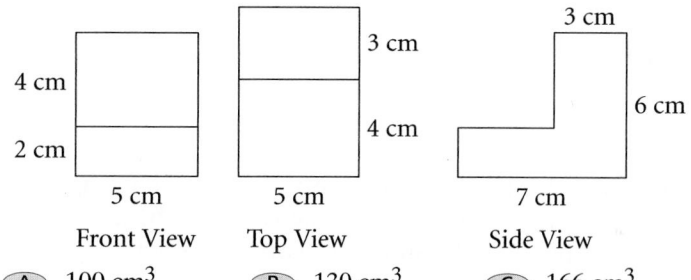

Ⓐ 100 cm^3 Ⓑ 130 cm^3 Ⓒ 166 cm^3 Ⓓ 186 cm^3

CAHSEE 7SDAP 1.1

49. The scores on Mr. Nathan's algebra exam were 54, 58, 62, 67, 69, 70, 75, 75, 77, 79, 80, 81, 81, 84, 85, 89, 90, 92, 95, and 96. Mr. Nathan displayed the data in a histogram. He used equal intervals, starting with 50–59, and ending with 90–99. How many scores were represented by the tallest bar in the histogram?

Ⓐ 3   Ⓑ 4   Ⓒ 5   Ⓓ 6

Mixed Review

Lesson 1-5

Solve each absolute value equation. Check your answers.

50. $|x + 3| = 9$ **51.** $|3x - 5| = 10$ **52.** $|2x + 7| + 3 = 22$

53. $|3x - 6| - 7 = 14$ **54.** $|2x + 3| - 9 = 14$ **55.** $|6 - 5x| = 18$

Lesson 1-5

Solve each absolute value inequality.

56. $2|x| - 3 \geq 5$ **57.** $|2x - 4| + 16 \leq 24$ **58.** $|3x - 5| - 2 > 0$

59. $|2x + 4| - 6 < 0$ **60.** $2|x + 3| \geq 10$ **61.** $6|x + 9| \leq 36$

Not all questions ask you to find the solution to a problem. Some questions instead ask *how* you would solve a problem. To answer these questions, you must choose a process.

EXAMPLE

Samantha is designing a container in the shape of a triangular prism like the one shown below. She wants to find a height that will give the container a volume of 84 cubic centimeters. Which of the following is a reasonable first step?

4 cm   6 cm

   Ⓐ Multiply 84 and 6
   Ⓑ Multiply 4 and 6.
   Ⓒ Divide 6 by 84.
   Ⓓ Subtract 10 from 84.

The volume of a prism is the product of the base area B and the height h, or $V = Bh$. To find the height Samantha needs to divide the volume V by the base area B. The base area is half of the product of 4 and 6. The correct answer is B.

EXERCISES

1. Jack is graphing the line represented by the equation $3x - 5y = 12$. Which of the following steps should he use to find the coordinates of the *x*-intercept?

   Ⓐ Substitute 0 for *x* and solve for *y*.
   Ⓑ Substitute 5 from 3.
   Ⓒ Add 12 to each side of the equation.
   Ⓓ Substitute 0 for *y* and solve for *x*.

2. Marianna surveyed students in her class to find out what their favorite lunch is in the school cafeteria. Based on the responses, she wants to predict how many students of the 140 in her grade would choose pizza as their favorite lunch. Which of the following should be her first step?

Lunch	Number of Students
Hamburger	9
Pizza	13
Chicken	6

   Ⓐ Divide 140 by 13.
   Ⓑ Subtract 13 from 140.
   Ⓒ Add 9, 13, and 6.
   Ⓓ Multiply 13 and 3.

Chapter 1 Review

Vocabulary Review

🔊)) **English and Spanish Audio Online**

absolute value (p. 33)	evaluate (p. 12)	simulation (p. 40)
absolute value of a real number (p. 8)	experimental probability (p. 40)	solution of an equation (p. 18)
additive inverse (p. 7)	extraneous solution (p. 34)	term (p. 13)
algebraic expression (p. 12)	multiplicative inverse (p. 7)	theoretical probability (p. 41)
coefficient (p. 13)	opposite (p. 7)	tolerance (p. 36)
compound inequality (p. 28)	reciprocal (p. 7)	variable (p. 12)
	sample space (p. 41)	variable expression (p. 12)

For: Vocabulary quiz
Web Code: bbj-0151

Choose the correct vocabulary term to complete each sentence.

1. The opposite of a number is also called its __?__ .

2. The __?__ is the set of all possible outcomes of an experiment.

3. The __?__ makes an equation true.

4. A pair of inequalities joined by *and* or *or* is called a(n) __?__ .

5. __?__ is another name for a multiplicative inverse of a number.

6. The __?__ of an event is the ratio of occurrences to trials.

7. The __?__ of an event is the ratio of possible event outcomes to total possible outcomes.

8. A possible solution that does not satisfy the original equation is a(n) __?__ .

9. You can use a(n) __?__ to find experimental probabilities.

10. A number's distance from zero on the number line is its __?__ .

Skills and Concepts

Lesson 1-1

- To graph and order real numbers (p. 4)
- To identify and use properties of real numbers (p. 7)

The natural numbers, whole numbers, integers, rational numbers, and irrational numbers are all subsets of the real numbers. Each real number corresponds to a point on the number line. A real number's distance from zero on the number line is its absolute value.

For both addition and multiplication, real numbers satisfy the properties of closure, associativity, and commutativity. Real numbers have **additive inverses (opposites)**. Nonzero real numbers have **multiplicative inverses (reciprocals)**. They also have additive and multiplicative identities. Real numbers satisfy the Distributive Property.

To which sets of numbers does each number belong?

11. 8.1π **12.** -79 **13.** $\sqrt{121}$ **14.** $\sqrt{200}$ **15.** $12\frac{7}{8}$

Compare each pair of numbers. Use < or >.

16. $-\frac{2}{3}, -\frac{3}{2}$ **17.** $\sqrt{6}, 2.\overline{3}$ **18.** $0.45, 0.405$ **19.** $-7, |-7|$

Find the opposite and reciprocal of each number. Then graph all three numbers on a number line.

20. -3.4 **21.** $4 + \pi$ **22.** $1\frac{7}{8}$ **23.** $\sqrt{12}$

Open-Ended Write an equation that illustrates each property of real numbers.

24. The Identity Property of Multiplication

25. The Associative Property of Addition

26. The Distributive Property

27. The Commutative Property of Multiplication

28. The Identity Property of Addition

Lessons 1-2, 1-3

- To evaluate algebraic expressions (p. 12)
- To simplify algebraic expressions (p. 13)
- To solve equations (p. 18)
- To solve problems by writing equations (p. 20)

You **evaluate** an **algebraic expression** by substituting numbers for the **variables.** You simplify an algebraic expression by combining like **terms,** using the appropriate properties. To find the **solutions of an equation,** use the properties of equality. To check for **extraneous solutions,** substitute in the original equation. Some equations may have no solutions. Some equations are true for all real numbers.

29. Evaluate $-x^2 + |x - 10|$ for $x = 2$.

30. Evaluate $3t(t + 2) - (3t^2 + 5t)$ for $t = 19$.

31. Simplify $-(3a - 2b) - 3(-a - b)$.

Solve each equation for *x*. State any restrictions.

32. $2x - 5 = 17$ **33.** $8 - \frac{1}{2}x = 3$ **34.** $3x = 4x - 5$

35. $0.1x + 1.4 = 1.2x - 3$ **36.** $\frac{7 - x}{3} = 5$ **37.** $\frac{x + a}{b} = \frac{1}{a}$

Write an equation to solve each problem.

38. Geometry The lengths of the sides of a rectangle are in the ratio $5 : 3$. The perimeter of the rectangle is 32 cm. Find the length of each side.

39. Two planes left St. Louis for Los Angeles at the same time. After 4 h they were 700 mi apart. The slower plane traveled at 350 mi/h. What was the speed of the faster plane?

40. Geometry The measures of an angle and its supplement differ by 40°. Find the measures of the angles.

Lesson 1-4

- To solve and graph inequalities (p. 26)
- To solve and write compound inequalities (p. 28)

You can solve inequalities using properties that are similar to the properties for equations. An important difference is that multiplying or dividing each side of an inequality by a negative number reverses the inequality symbol. Just as with equations, some inequalities are true for all real numbers, and some have no solutions. If a **compound inequality** uses *and*, the solutions must satisfy both inequalities. If a compound inequality uses *or*, the solutions satisfy either one or both of the inequalities.

Solve each inequality. Graph the solution.

41. $4 - 5z \geq 2$ **42.** $2(5 - 3x) < x - 4(3 - x)$ **43.** $0.3(y - 2) > \frac{1}{2}(6 - y)$

Solve each compound inequality. Graph the solution.

44. $5 \leq 9 - 4x \leq 13$ **45.** $3 \geq 2x$ or $x - 4 > 2$ **46.** $6y > 2$ and $y - 5 \geq -2y$

47. A publisher estimates that the cost of publishing a book is from \$980,000 to \$1,240,000. So far, \$824,150 has been spent. Use a compound inequality to describe the amount A that the publisher can still spend while remaining within the estimate.

Lesson 1-5

- To solve absolute value equations (p. 33)
- To solve absolute value inequalities (p. 35)

 ALG2 1.0

You can rewrite an equation or inequality that involves the absolute value of an **algebraic expression** as a compound sentence. You must consider both cases of the definition of absolute value. Check for **extraneous solutions.**

Solve each equation. Check for extraneous solutions.

48. $|2x + 8| = 3x + 7$ **49.** $|3x - 5| = 4 + 2x$ **50.** $|x - 4| + 3 = 1$

Solve each inequality. Graph the solution.

51. $|3x - 2| + 4 \leq 7$ **52.** $4|y - 9| > 36$ **53.** $\frac{2}{5}|3x - 3| - 4 > 2$

54. The specification for a length x is 43.6 cm with a tolerance of 0.1 cm. Write the specification as an absolute value inequality.

Lesson 1-6

- To find experimental probabilities (p. 39)
- To find theoretical probabilities (p. 41)

The probability of an event can be expressed as a number from 0% (impossible) to 100% (certain).

Experimental probability is the ratio of two numbers. The first is the observed number of times an experiment results in a particular event. The second is the number of trials. **Simulation** uses random numbers or other models to determine an experimental probability.

Theoretical probability in a sample space of equally likely outcomes is also the ratio of two numbers. The first is the number of outcomes corresponding to the particular event. The second is the number of elements in the sample space, which is the set of all possible outcomes. Geometric probability is computed as a ratio of areas.

Suppose you select a number at random from the sample space
$\{-3, -2, -1, 0, 1, 2, 3, 4\}$. **Find each probability.**

55. P(a positive number)   **56.** P(a number less than 2)

57. P(an even number)   **58.** P(a multiple of 3)

59. Games You have won five games of checkers and your opponent has won three. What is the experimental probability of your winning?

60. Tests A five-question multiple-choice quiz has four choices for each answer. Find the experimental probability of getting exactly three correct answers if you guess the answers at random. Define a simulation using the random number table on page 43. Use your simulation to find the experimental probability.

Chapter 1 Test

 1. Writing Describe the relationships among these sets of numbers: natural numbers, whole numbers, integers, rational numbers, irrational numbers, and real numbers.

2. Justifying Steps Justify each step by identifying the property used.

$$
\begin{aligned}
t + 5(t + 1) &= t + (5t + 5) \\
&= (t + 5t) + 5 \\
&= (1t + 5t) + 5 \\
&= (1 + 5)t + 5 \\
&= 6t + 5
\end{aligned}
$$

Evaluate each expression for $x = 5$.

3. $\frac{5}{3}(3x - 6) - (6 - 4x)$

4. $3(x^2 - 4) + 7(x - 2)$

5. $x - 2x + 3x - 4x + 5x$

Simplify each expression.

6. $a^2 + a + a^2$

7. $2x + 3y - 5x + 2y$

8. $5(a - 2b) - 3(a - 2b)$

9. $3[2(x - 3) + 2] + 5(x - 3)$

Solve each equation.

10. $4y - 6 = 2y + 8$

11. $3(2z + 1) = 35$

12. $5(3w - 2) - 7 = 23$

13. $t - 2(3 - 2t) = 2t + 9$

14. $5(s - 12) - 24 = 3(s + 2)$

15. $7(3 - 0.5k) = 3k - 5$

Solve each equation for x. State any restrictions.

16. $ax - bx = 2a$ **17.** $\frac{x}{c} + c = 4c$

18. $\frac{x - 5}{a} + 1 = b$ **19.** $ax + 2 = bx + c$

20. The lateral surface area of a cylinder is given by the formula $S = 2\pi rh$. Solve this equation for r.

Write an equation to solve each problem.

21. Savings Briana and her sister Molly both want to buy the same model bicycle. Briana needs $73 more before she can afford the bike. Molly needs $65 more. If they combine their money, they will have just enough to buy one bicycle that they could share. What is the cost of the bicycle?

22. Musical There is only one freshman in the cast of the high school musical. There are 6 sophomores and 11 juniors. One third of the cast are seniors. How many seniors are in the musical?

Solve each inequality or equation. Graph the solution.

23. $3x + 17 \geq 5$

24. $25 - 2x < 11$

25. $7t > 4t + 3(1 - t)$

26. $\frac{3}{8}x < -6$ or $5x > 2$

27. $2 < 10 - 4d < 6$

28. $4 - x = |2 - 3x|$

29. $|4x + 4| = 8x + 16$

30. $|5 - p| \leq 2$

31. $5|3w + 2| - 3 > 7$

Suppose you select a number at random from the sample space {5, 6, 7, 8, 9, 10, 11, 12, 13, 14}. Find each probability.

32. $P(\text{greater than } 10)$

33. $P(\text{multiple of } 30)$

34. $P(\text{less than } 7 \text{ or greater than } 10)$

35. $P(\text{integer})$

36. Open-Ended Your teacher selects at random two days out of every five days to give a "pop" quiz. Define a simulation to find the experimental probability that you will get a pop quiz on two consecutive days. Then use your simulation to find the probability.

Some problems ask you to use probability to make predictions. Read the question at the right. Then follow the tips to answer it.

A spinner has 16 equal sections. Each section is either red or white. Ed spins the spinner 50 times, and it lands on white 12 times. Which of the following is the most likely number of white sections?

- (A) 2
- (B) 4
- (C) 6
- (D) 8

Tip 1
Try to answer the question before you look at the answer choices.

Think It Through
Experimental probability is

$$\frac{\text{number of favorable outcomes}}{\text{number of trials}}.$$

So, the experimental probability of landing on white is $\frac{12}{50} = 0.24$. Here, the likely number of white sections is $0.24 \times 16 = 3.84 \approx 4$. So the correct answer is B.

Tip 2
Find the experimental probability of white, and use this to estimate the number of white sections.

Vocabulary Review

As you solve problems, you must understand the meanings of mathematical terms. Match each term with its mathematical meaning.

A. inequality

B. sample space

C. extraneous solution

D. compound inequality

E. expression

F. equation

I. a mathematical sentence that contains $>$, $<$, $\geq$, $\leq$, or $\neq$

II. a solution of an equation derived from an original equation that is not a solution of the original equation

III. a pair of inequalities joined by *and* or *or*

IV. set of all possible outcomes

V. a mathematical sentence that contains an equal sign

VI. a mathematical phrase that uses numbers, variables, and operation symbols

Multiple Choice

Read each question. Then write the letter of the correct answer on your paper.

1. Which equation represents the data in the table? **(Lesson 1-5)**

x	−2	−1	1	3	5
y	2	0	0	4	8

- (A) $y = -2x - 2$
- (B) $y = |x| + 2$
- (C) $y = |x| - 1$
- (D) $y = 2|x| - 2$

2. Graph the inequality $|x - 2| - 3 > -2$. **(Lesson 1-5)**

3. A worker is taking boxes of nails on an elevator. Each box weighs 54 pounds, and the worker weighs 170 pounds. The elevator has a weight limit of 2500 pounds. Which inequality describes the number of boxes, b, that he can safely take on each trip? (**Lesson 1-4**)

   (A) $54b - 170 \leq 2500$ (C) $54(b - 170) \leq 2500$

   (B) $54b + 170 \leq 2500$ (D) $54(b + 170) \leq 2500$

4. Which expression is equivalent to $-8(a - 3b) + 2(-a + 4b + 1)$? (**Lesson 1-2**)

   (A) $-10a - 16b + 2$

   (B) $-10a + 32b + 2$

   (C) $-10a + 5b + 2$

   (D) $-10a + b + 1$

5. The figure is a large square divided into five regions. Regions A, B, C, and D are congruent rectangles. Which expression represents the area of region E? (**Lesson 1-2**)

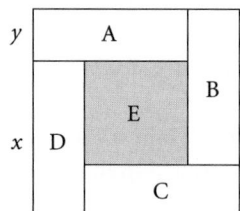

   (A) $x^2 - 2xy + y^2$ (C) $x^2 + xy$

   (B) $x^2 + 2xy + y^2$ (D) $x^2 - y^2$

6. Which value is a solution to $2|3x - 6| \leq 6$? (**Lesson 1-5**)

   (A) -3 (C) 1

   (B) -1 (D) 2

7. A carnival game has a spinner with 20 equal sections. Each section is either red or yellow. The probability of a spin pointing to a red section is 3 times that of pointing to a yellow section. What is the probability of a spin pointing to a red section? (**Lesson 1-6**)

   (A) $\frac{9}{20}$ (C) $\frac{2}{3}$

   (B) $\frac{3}{4}$ (D) $\frac{3}{5}$

8. A meteorologist claims there is a 15% probability of rain. Based on this, what is the probability that there will not be rain? (**Lesson 1-6**)

   (A) 85%   (C) 40%

   (B) 75%   (D) 15%

9. The table shows the amount spent at an office supply store by a random sample of customers.

Office Supply Purchases	
Amount spent	**Number of customers**
Less than $25	34
$25–$50	12
More than $50	4

   Let m represent the total revenue from the customers that spent $25–$50. Which inequality describes this situation? (**Lesson 1-5**)

   (A) $|m - 300| \leq 600$ (C) $|m + 150| \leq 450$

   (B) $|m + 50| \leq 300$ (D) $|m - 450| \leq 150$

10. Mr. Rodriguez invested $2500 and earned 6% simple interest for the one year that he left the money in the account. At the end of the year, he transferred the original $2500 and the interest to an account that paid 8% simple interest. How much interest did he earn from the second account by the end of one year? (**Lesson 1-3**)

   (A) $200   (C) $220

   (B) $212   (D) $225

11. For which value of a does $4 = a + |x - 4|$ have no solution? (**Lesson 1–5**)

   (A) -6 (C) 4

   (B) 0 (D) 6

12. Ms. Allen earned $50,000 in 2002. In 2003, she earned 10% more than her 2002 earnings. In 2004, she earned 20% less than her 2003 earnings. How much did she earn in 2004? (**Skills Handbook, p. 882**)

   (A) $40,000   (C) $45,000

   (B) $44,000   (D) $50,000

13. Which of the following inequalities represents the graph shown below? (**Lesson 1-5**)

   (A) $|x - 4| \leq 8$ (C) $|2x - 4| \geq 12$

   (B) $|x + 12| \leq 4$ (D) $|2x - 4| \leq 12$

14. Two rectangular boxes are each 9 inches tall. Both boxes have square bases. The base edge of the larger box is 1.5 times as long as the base edge of the smaller box. Which statement is true? **(Geometry)**

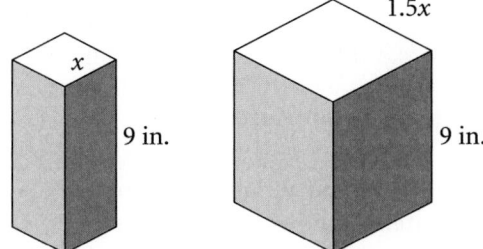

A The larger box holds 10.5 cubic inches more than the smaller box.

B The larger box holds 13.5 cubic inches more than the smaller box.

C The larger box holds 1.5 times as much as the smaller box.

D The larger box holds 2.25 times as much as the smaller box.

15. The two cylinders below have identical bases.

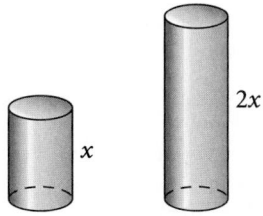

Which statement is true? **(Geometry)**

A The smaller cylinder has one-half the surface area of the larger cylinder for all the values of x.

B The smaller cylinder has the same surface area as the taller cylinder for some values of x.

C The smaller cylinder has one-half the volume of the larger cylinder for all values of x.

D The smaller cylinder has the same volume as the taller cylinder for some values of x.

16. Solve $3(x - 2) + 4 \geq -3x + 1$. **(Lesson 1–4)**

A $x \geq -3$

B $x \geq \frac{1}{2}$

C $x \geq \frac{3}{2}$

D $x \leq 3$

17. Each dimension of a rectangular prism is tripled. How does the surface area of the new rectangular prism compare to the original surface area? **(Geometry)**

A The new surface area is 12 times as great.

B The new surface area is 9 times as great.

C The new surface area is 6 times as great.

D The new surface area is 3 times as great.

18. A rectangular solid has a volume of 81 cubic feet. If the length, width, and height are all changed to $\frac{1}{3}$ of their original size, what will be the volume of the new rectangular solid? **(Geometry)**

A 54 cubic feet   C 9 cubic feet

B 27 cubic feet   D 3 cubic feet

Standards Reference Guide

Algebra 2 Content Standard	Item Number(s)
ALG2 1.0	1, 2, 6, 9, 11, 13, 16

CAHSEE Content Standard	Item Numbers
Alg1 5.0	3
7AF 1.2	4, 5
6SDAP 3.3	7, 8
7NS 1.7	10
7NS 1.6	12
7MG 2.3	14, 15, 17, 18

For additional review and practice, see the *California Standards Review and Practice Workbook* or go online to use the

California Standards Tutorials

Visit: PHSchool.com, **Web Code:** bbq-9045

Functions, Equations, and Graphs

 What You've Learned

California Content Standards

AF 1.4 Students use algebraic terminology (e.g., variable, equation, term, coefficient, inequality, expression, constant) correctly. *Grade 7*

AF 4.1 Students solve two-step linear equations and inequalities in one variable over the rational numbers, interpret the solution or solutions in the context from which they arose, and verify the reasonableness of the results. *Grade 7*

1.0 Students solve equations and inequalities involving absolute value.

 Check Your Readiness **GO** **for Help** to the Lesson in green.

Graphing Numbers on the Number Line (Lesson 1-1)

Graph each group of numbers on a number line.

1. $2, -\frac{7}{4}, -1, \frac{15}{2}$ **2.** $0, \frac{2}{3}, -\sqrt{2}, -3$ **3.** $-\frac{5}{4}, \sqrt{7}, 2.\overline{6}, 4$

Simplifying Expressions (Lesson 1-2)

Simplify by combining like terms.

4. $7s - s$ **5.** $3a + b + a$ **6.** $xy - y + x$

7. $0.5g + g$ **8.** $4t - (t + 3t)$ **9.** $b - 2(1 + c - b)$

10. $5f - (5d - f)$ **11.** $2(h + 2g) - (g - h)$ **12.** $-(3z - 5) + z$

13. $(2 - d)g - 3d(4 + g)$ **14.** $5v - 3(2 - v)$ **15.** $7t - 3s(2 + t) + s$

Solving Absolute-Value Inequalities (Lesson 1-5)

Solve each absolute-value inequality. Graph the solution.

16. $|x - 3| < 5$ **17.** $|2a - 1| \geq 2a + 1$ **18.** $|3x + 4| > -4x - 3$

19. $|3x + 1| + 1 > 12$ **20.** $3|d - 4| \leq 13 - d$ **21.** $-\frac{1}{3}|f + 3| + 2 \geq -5$

Probability (Lesson 1-6)

A bag contains 12 red, 15 green, 10 yellow, 25 purple, and 2 black blocks. Find each theoretical probability for one block selected at random.

22. $P(\text{green})$ **23.** $P(\text{black})$ **24.** $P(\text{red or yellow})$

25. $P(\text{not red})$ **26.** $P(\text{not yellow})$ **27.** $P(\text{black or not red})$

What You'll Learn Next

▲ The Leonardo Bridge is near Oslo, Norway. The thickness of the arch ranges from 65 cm to 4.5 m.

California Content Standards

6.0 Students graph a linear equation and compute the *x*- and *y*- intercepts. *Alg1*

7.0 Students verify that a point lies on a line, given an equation of a line. Students are able to derive linear equations by using the point-slope formula. *Alg1*

16.0 Students understand the concept of a relation and a function, determine whether a given relation defines a function, and give pertinent information about given relations and functions. *Alg1*

New Vocabulary

🔊 **English and Spanish Audio Online**

- **absolute value function** (p. 90)
- **constant of variation** (p. 74)
- **dependent variable** (p. 64)
- **direct variation** (p. 74)
- **domain** (p. 58)
- **function** (p. 59)
- **independent variable** (p. 64)
- **linear equation** (p. 64)
- **linear function** (p. 64)
- **linear inequality** (p. 103)
- **parent function** (p. 95)
- **point-slope form** (p. 67)
- **range** (p. 58)
- **relation** (p. 57)
- **slope** (p. 66)
- **slope-intercept form** (p. 67)
- **standard form** (p. 65)
- **translation** (p. 95)
- **vertical line test** (p. 59)
- ***x*-intercept** (p. 65)
- ***y*-intercept** (p. 65)

The Coordinate Plane

FOR USE WITH LESSON 2-1

There is a one-to-one correspondence between the points in the coordinate plane and the set of ordered pairs (x, y), where x and y are real numbers. The first number is the x-coordinate, or abscissa. The abscissa gives the horizontal position of a point. The second number is the y-coordinate, or ordinate. The ordinate gives the vertical position of a point.

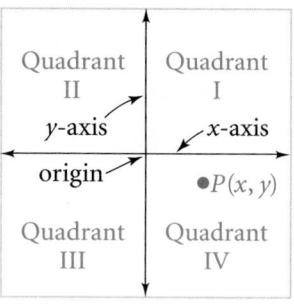

1 EXAMPLE **Graphing Points**

Graph $(4, 3)$ and $(-4, -3)$.

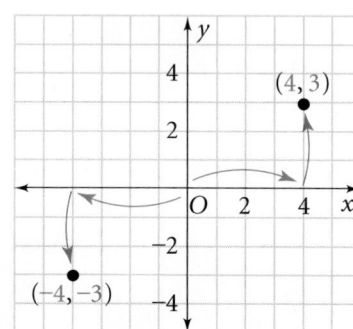

Graph and label each ordered pair.

You can write the coordinates of a point if you are given its graph.

2 EXAMPLE **Writing Coordinates**

Write the coordinates of each point in the graph.

The points are $A(2, 4)$, $B(3, 0)$, $C(-4, 0)$, $D(0, -3)$, $E(-5, 4)$, $F\left(4, \frac{1}{2}\right)$, $G(0, 0)$, and $H\left(-3, -3\frac{1}{2}\right)$.

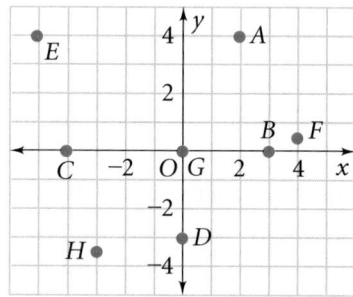

EXERCISES

Graph and label each ordered pair. Name the quadrant or axis where each point lies.

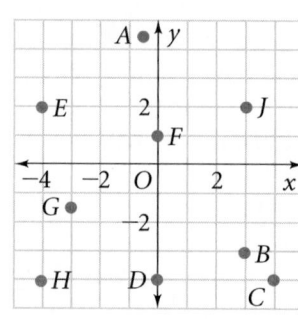

1. $(5, -2)$ **2.** $(-3, 4)$ **3.** $\left(-4, -2\frac{1}{2}\right)$

4. $\left(5\frac{1}{2}, 0\right)$ **5.** $(5, 2)$ **6.** $(0, -3)$

Write the coordinates of each point in the graph at the right.

7. C **8.** G **9.** J **10.** A

2-1 Relations and Functions

What You'll Learn

• To graph relations
• To identify functions

. . . And Why

To write a function for the area of a square, as in Example 6

✓ **Check Skills You'll Need**

GO for Help Page 56 and Lesson 1-2

Graph each ordered pair on the coordinate plane.

1. $(-4, -8)$ **2.** $(3, 6)$ **3.** $(0, 0)$ **4.** $(-1, 3)$ **5.** $(-6, 5)$

Evaluate each expression for $x = -1, 0, 2,$ and 5.

6. $x + 2$ **7.** $-2x + 3$ **8.** $2x^2 + 1$ **9.** $|x - 3|$

🔊 **New Vocabulary**
• relation • domain • range • mapping diagram
• function • vertical-line test • function notation

---

1 Graphing Relations

A camera recorded the egg's height at various times during its fall.

Suppose you use a motion detector to track an egg as it drops from 10 ft above the ground. The motion detector stores input values (times) and output values (heights). A **relation** is a set of pairs of input and output values. You can write a relation as a set of ordered pairs.

input (time in seconds) → {0   0.1   0.2   0.3   0.4}
     ↓   ↓   ↓   ↓   ↓

relation → {(0, 10), (0.1, 9.8), (0.2, 9.4), (0.3, 8.6), (0.4, 7.4)}
     ↑   ↑   ↑   ↑   ↑

output (height in feet) → {10   9.8   9.4   8.6   7.4}

You can graph a relation on a coordinate plane.

1 EXAMPLE   Graphing a Relation

Graph the relation $\{(-2, 4), (3, -2), (-1, 0), (1, 5)\}$.

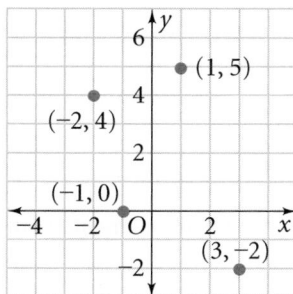

Graph and label each ordered pair.

✓ **CA Standards Check** ❶ Graph each relation.
   a. $\{(0, 4), (-2, 3), (-1, 3), (-2, 2), (1, -3)\}$
   b. $\{(-2, 1), (-1, 0), (0, 1), (1, 2)\}$

The **domain** of a relation is the set of all inputs, or *x*-coordinates of the ordered pairs. The **range** of a relation is the set of all outputs, or *y*-coordinates of the ordered pairs.

You can sometimes find the domain and range of a relation from its graph.

2 EXAMPLE Finding Domain and Range

Write the ordered pairs for the relation shown in the graph. Find the domain and range.

$\{(2, 4), (3, 4.5), (4, 7.5), (5, 7), (6, 5), (6, 7.5)\}$

The domain is $\{2, 3, 4, 5, 6\}$.

The range is $\{4, 4.5, 5, 7, 7.5\}$.

Books & Bookbags

Weight of Bookbag (lb)

Number of Books

✓ CA Standards Check **2** Find the domain and range of each relation.

a.

b.
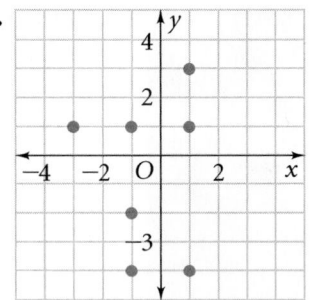

Another way to show a relation is to use a **mapping diagram,** which links elements of the domain with corresponding elements of the range. Write the elements of the domain in one region and the elements of the range in another. Draw arrows to show how each element from the domain is paired with elements from the range.

3 EXAMPLE Making a Mapping Diagram

Make a mapping diagram for the relation $\{(-1, -2), (3, 6), (-5, -10), (3, 2)\}$.

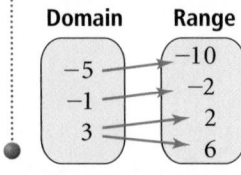

Domain Range

−5
−1
3

−10
−2
2
6

Pair the domain elements with the range elements.

✓ CA Standards Check **3** Make a mapping diagram for each relation.
  a. $\{(0, 2), (1, 3), (2, 4)\}$
  b. $\{(2, 8), (-1, 5), (0, 8), (-1, 3), (-2, 3)\}$

A **function** is a relation in which each element of the domain is paired with exactly one element in the range.

4 **EXAMPLE** **Identifying Functions**

Determine whether each relation is a function.

a. Domain   Range

$$
\begin{array}{cc}
-2 & -1 \\
0 & 3 \\
5 & 4
\end{array}
$$

The element -2 of the domain is paired with both -1 and 3 of the range. The relation is *not* a function.

b. Domain   Range

$$
\begin{array}{cc}
-1 & -1 \\
0 & 3 \\
2 & 5 \\
3 &
\end{array}
$$

Each element of the domain is paired with exactly one element of the range. The relation is a function.

✓ CA Standards Check **4** Determine whether each relation is a function.

a. Domain   Range

$$
\begin{array}{cc}
2 & 5 \\
3 & 6 \\
4 & 8 \\
7 &
\end{array}
$$

b. Domain   Range

$$
\begin{array}{cc}
-1 & -3 \\
0 & 7 \\
1 & 10
\end{array}
$$

Vocabulary Tip

The word <u>discrete</u> means "separate." The word <u>discreet</u> means "careful about what one says or does."

You can identify a function by its domain, its range, and the rule that relates the domain to the range. You can represent a function with a mapping diagram as in Example 4, part (b), or with a graph in the coordinate plane. Sometimes the graph of a function may be *discrete*, a collection of isolated points. Other times the graph may be *continuous*, an uninterrupted line or curve.

You can use the **vertical-line test** on the graph of a relation to tell whether the relation is a function. If a vertical line passes through at least two points on the graph, then one element of the domain is paired with more than one element of the range. The relation is *not* a function.

5 **EXAMPLE** **Using the Vertical-Line Test**

Use the vertical-line test to determine whether each graph represents a function.

For: Exploring Functions Activity
Use: Interactive Textbook, 2-1

Vertical line passes through

← 3 points   1 point →

← Not a function

A function →

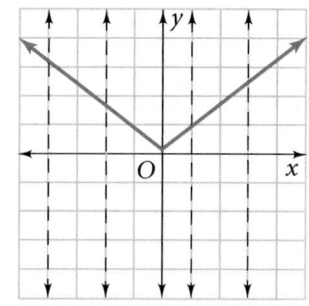

5 Use the vertical-line test to determine whether each graph represents a function.

a.   **b.**   **c.**

Video Tutor Help

Visit: PHSchool.com
Web Code: bbe-0775

A function rule expresses an output value in terms of an input value.

Examples of Function Rules

Input	Input	Input
↓	↓	↓
$y = 2x$	$f(x) = x + 5$	$C = \pi d$
↑	↑	↑
Output	Output	Output

You read the **function notation** $f(x)$ as "f of x" or "a function f of x." Note that $f(x)$ does *not* mean "f times x." When the value of x is 3, $f(3)$, read "f of 3," represents the value of the function at $x = 3$.

Input	Function	Output	Ordered Pair
5 ⟶	Subtract 1 ⟶	4	$(5, 4)$
a ⟶	Add 2 ⟶	$a + 2$	$(a, a + 2)$
3 ⟶	g ⟶	$g(3)$	$(3, g(3))$
x ⟶	f ⟶	$f(x)$	$(x, f(x))$

6 EXAMPLE **Real-World** 🌐 **Connection**

Real-World 🌐 **Connection**

Some tiles are painted with intricate designs.

Art The area of a square tile is a function of the length of a side of the square. Write a function rule for the area of a square. Evaluate the function for a square tile with side length 3.5 in.

Relate area of a square is (side length)^2

Define Let s = the length of one side of the square tile.

Then $A(s)$ = the area of the square tile.

Write $A(s)$ = s^2

$A(3.5) = (3.5)^2$ **Substitute 3.5 for s.**

$= 12.25$ **Simplify.**

● The area of a square tile with side length 3.5 in. is 12.25 in.^{2}.

✓ CA Standards Check **6** Find $f(-3), f(0),$ and $f(5)$ for each function.

a. $f(x) = 3x - 5$ **b.** $f(a) = \frac{3}{4}a - 1$ **c.** $f(y) = -\frac{1}{5}y + \frac{3}{5}$

EXERCISES

For more exercises, see *Extra Skill and Word Problem Practice*.

Standards Practice

A Practice by Example

Example 1
(page 57)

GO for Help

Graph each relation.

1. $\{(-1, 3), (-2, 1), (-3, -3), (-4, -5)\}$ **2.** $\{(0, -2), (2, 0), (3, 1), (5, 3)\}$

3. $\left\{(-1, 0), \left(\frac{1}{2}, -1\right), \left(0, \frac{1}{2}\right), \left(-1, -\frac{1}{2}\right)\right\}$ **4.** $\left\{\left(2\frac{1}{2}, 0\right), \left(-\frac{1}{2}, 0\right), (2, 0), (0, 0)\right\}$

Example 2
(page 58)

Write the ordered pairs for each relation. Find the domain and range.

5.

6.

7.
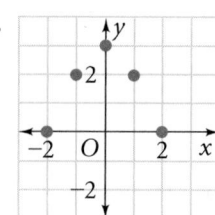

Example 3
(page 58)

Make a mapping diagram for each relation.

8. $\{(0, 0), (-1, -1), (-2, -8), (-3, -27)\}$ **9.** $\{(-2, 8), (-1, 1), (0, 0), (1, 1), (2, 8)\}$

10. $\{(-\frac{1}{2}, 11), (0, 10), (\frac{1}{2}, 5), (1, 12)\}$ **11.** $\{(5, 10), (10, 5), (15, 20), (20, 15)\}$

Example 4
(page 59)

Determine whether each relation is a function.

12. $\{(1, -2), (-2, 0), (-1, 2), (1, 3)\}$ **13.** $\{(1, 1), (2, 2), (3, 5), (4, 10), (5, 15)\}$

14. $\left\{\left(17, \frac{15}{4}\right), \left(\frac{15}{4}, 17\right), \left(15, \frac{17}{4}\right), \left(\frac{17}{4}, 15\right)\right\}$ **15.** $\left\{\left(-3, \frac{2}{5}\right), \left(-2, \frac{3}{5}\right), \left(\frac{3}{2}, -5\right), \left(5, \frac{2}{5}\right)\right\}$

Example 5
(page 59)

Use the vertical-line test to determine whether each graph represents a function.

16.

17.

18.

19.

20.

21.
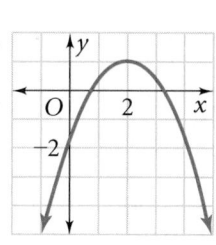

Example 6
(page 60)

For each function, find $f(-5)$, $f(-3)$, $f\left(\frac{1}{2}\right)$, and $f(4)$.

22. $f(a) = 2a + 3$ **23.** $f(y) = -3y - 2$ **24.** $f(z) = z + 9.5$

25. $f(x) = -x - 7$ **26.** $f(d) = 1 - 4d$ **27.** $f(x) = 2x - 3$

28. $f(h) = -6h - \frac{2}{3}$ **29.** $f(x) = \frac{5}{6}x + \frac{1}{3}$ **30.** $f(t) = \frac{1}{2}t - 2$

31. Measurement One meter equals about 39.37 in. Write a function rule for converting inches to meters. Evaluate the function for 59 in.

Graph each relation. Find the domain and range.

32. $\{(2,4),(3,5),(4,6),(5,7)\}$

33. $\{(-1,1),(-2,2),(-3,3),(-4,4)\}$

34. $\left\{\left(-\frac{1}{2},2\right),\left(2,\frac{1}{2}\right),\left(0,-\frac{1}{2}\right),\left(-\frac{1}{2},-2\right)\right\}$ **35.** $\left\{\left(\frac{3}{2},-\frac{1}{2}\right),\left(\frac{5}{2},\frac{1}{2}\right),\left(\frac{1}{2},\frac{1}{2}\right),\left(-\frac{3}{2},\frac{1}{2}\right)\right\}$

Find the domain and range of each relation and determine whether it is a function.

36. $\{(2,4),(4,8),(8,16)\}$

37. $\{(-1,2),(-2,5),(-2,7),(0,2),(9,2)\}$

38.

39.
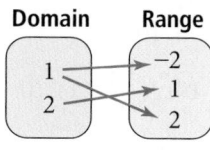

Match each relation with a model.

40. $\{(1,2),(-1,-2),(2,-1)\}$

41. $\{(2,1),(1,2),(1,-2)\}$

42. $\{(-1,2),(-2,1),(-1,-2)\}$

A.

B.

C.
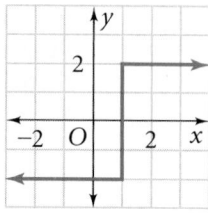

Homework Video Tutor

Visit: PHSchool.com
Web Code: bbe-0201

Determine whether each graph represents *y* as a function of *x*.

43. **44.** **45.**

46. Geometry The volume of a cube is a function of the length of a side of the cube. Write a function for the volume of a cube. Find the volume of a cube with a side 13.5 cm long.

47. Sports The volume of a sphere is a function of the radius of the sphere. Write a function for the volume of a ball. Evaluate the function for a volleyball of radius 10.5 cm.

48. Writing Does the mapping diagram at the left represent a function? Explain.

49. Data Collection Draw a graph to show the relationship between the weight of a letter and the cost of postage. Is it a graph of a function? Explain.

Suppose $f(x) = 2x + 5$ and $g(x) = -\frac{1}{3}x + 2$. **Find each value.** (*Hint:* For $2g(x)$, find $g(x)$ first, and then multiply the result by 2.)

50. $f(-4)$ **51.** $2g(7)$ **52.** $-2f(x+1)$ **53.** $\dfrac{f(1)}{g(3)}$ **54.** $\dfrac{f(-2)}{g(f(-2)+1)}$

 Challenge

For each relation, determine whether *y* is a function of *x*. Explain why or why not.

55. $y = 2x - 3$ **56.** $y^2 = x$ **57.** $x^2 = y - 3$

58. Chemistry The time required for a certain chemical reaction is related to the amount of catalyst present during the reaction. The domain of the relation is the number of grams of catalyst, and the range is the number of seconds required for a fixed amount of the chemical to react. The following relation is the data from several reactions: $\{(2, 180), (2.5, 6), (2.7, 0.05), (2.9, 0.001), (3.0, 6), (3.1, 15), (3.2, 37), (3.3, 176)\}$. Is the relation a function? If the domain and range were interchanged, would the relation be a function? Explain.

Suppose a and b are variables representing integers. Find the domain and range of each relation and determine whether it is a function. Justify your reasoning.

59.

60.

61.

Multiple Choice Practice

For California Standards and CAHSEE Tutorials, visit PHSchool.com. Web Code: bbq-9045

ALG2 1.0

62. Solve $|7 - 4x| < 3$.

    Ⓐ $x < 1$ Ⓑ $1 < x < \frac{5}{2}$ Ⓒ $-\frac{5}{2} < x < 1$ Ⓓ $x < 1$ or $x > \frac{5}{2}$

CAHSEE 7AF 1.1

63. The table shows the sales tax paid on several different items. Which equation best describes the relationship between cost x and sales tax y?

    Ⓐ $y = 0.06x$

    Ⓑ $y = 0.06x^2$

    Ⓒ $y = 0.6x$

    Ⓓ $y = 0.6x^2$

Cost x (dollars)	Sales Tax y (dollars)
20	1.20
25	1.50
35	2.10

CAHSEE Alg1 6.0

64. Find the x-intercept of the line identified by the equation $2x + 3y = 6$.

    Ⓐ -6 Ⓑ -3 Ⓒ 2 Ⓓ 3

Mixed Review

 for Help

Lesson 1-6

Find each probability for choosing a letter at random from the word *mathematics*.

65. $P(e)$ **66.** $P(m)$ **67.** $P(\text{vowel})$ **68.** $P(n)$

69. $P(\text{a letter that occurs more than once})$ **70.** $P(\text{consonant})$ **71.** $P(s \text{ or } t)$

Lesson 1-5

Solve each equation or inequality. Graph the solution on a number line.

72. $|x - 4| = 10$ **73.** $3 + |b| \le 5$ **74.** $|6 - y| > 0$

Skills Handbook

Find each percent of increase or decrease.

75. from 9 m to 10 m   **76.** from 1 gal to 1.5 gal   **77.** from 2 km to 1.5 km

---

Linear Equations

 California Content Standards

Prepares for ALG2 2.0 Students solve systems of linear equations (in two or three variables) by substitution, with graphs, or with matrices.

What You'll Learn

• To graph linear equations

• To write equations of lines

...And Why

To solve a transportation problem, as in Example 2

✓ Check Skills You'll Need

⏩ for Help Lesson 1-2

Evaluate each expression for $x = -2, 0, 1,$ and 4.

1. $\frac{2}{3}x + 7$ **2.** $\frac{3}{5}x - 2$ **3.** $3x + 1$ **4.** $\frac{1}{2}x - 8$

🔊 **New Vocabulary**
- linear function
- linear equation
- dependent variable
- independent variable
- x-intercept
- y-intercept
- standard form of a linear equation
- slope
- point-slope form
- slope-intercept form

---

1   Graphing Linear Equations

A function whose graph is a line is a **linear function** . You can represent a linear function with a **linear equation,** such as $y = 3x + 2$. A solution of a linear equation is any ordered pair (x, y) that makes the equation true.

You can write the solutions of the equation using set notation as $\{(x, y) \mid y = 3x + 2\}$. Read the notation as "the set of ordered pairs x, y such that $y = 3x + 2$." Because the value of y depends on the value of x, y is called the **dependent variable** and x is called the **independent variable.**

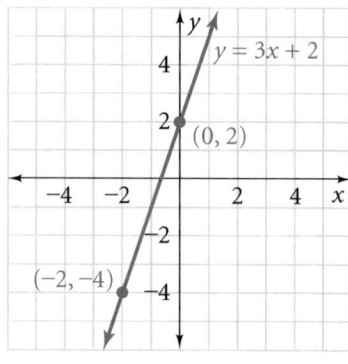

1 EXAMPLE   Graphing a Linear Equation

Graph the equation $y = \frac{2}{3}x + 3$.

Choose two values for x and find the corresponding values of y. Plot the point for each ordered pair and complete the graph by drawing a line through the points.

Problem Solving Hint

Since two points determine a line, you can use two points to graph a line. Check your line by finding a third point.

x	$\frac{2}{3}x + 3$	y	(x, y)
−3	$\frac{2}{3}(-3) + 3$	1	(−3, 1)
3	$\frac{2}{3}(3) + 3$	5	(3, 5)

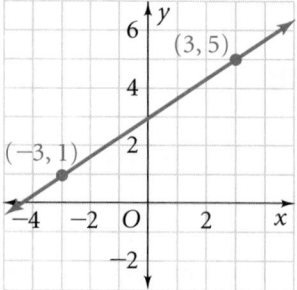

Check Choose a third point on the line and check that its ordered pair satisfies the equation. Since $(0, 3)$ is a point on the line, and $\frac{2}{3}(0) + 3 = 3$, the graph is correct.

1 Graph each equation. Check your work.

a. $y = \frac{3}{4}x$ **b.** $x + y = -2$ **c.** $y = -\frac{1}{2}x + \frac{1}{2}$

The **y-intercept** of a line is the point at which the line crosses the *y*-axis. You can use the same term to identify the *y*-coordinate of this point.

The **x-intercept** of a line is the point at which the line crosses the *x*-axis. You can use the same term to identify the *x*-coordinate of this point.

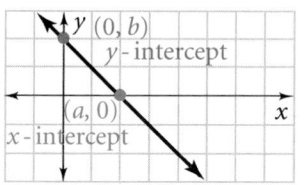

The **standard form of a linear equation** is $Ax + By = C$, where A, B, and C are real numbers, and A and B are not both zero. You can graph a linear equation in standard form by finding the *x*- and *y*-intercepts.

2 **EXAMPLE** **Real-World** 🌐 **Connection**

Transportation The equation $3x + 2y = 120$ models the number of passengers who can sit in a train car, where *x* is the number of adults and *y* is the number of children. Graph the equation. Explain what the *x*- and *y*-intercepts represent. Describe the domain and the range.

Set *x* or *y* equal to zero to find each intercept.

$$3x + 2y = 120 \qquad\qquad 3x + 2y = 120$$
$$3x + 2(0) = 120 \qquad\qquad 3(0) + 2y = 120$$
$$3x = 120 \qquad\qquad\qquad 2y = 120$$
$$x = 40 \qquad\qquad\qquad\quad y = 60$$

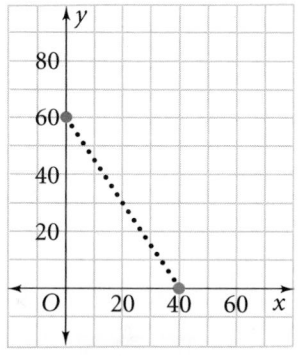

Use the intercepts to graph the equation. The *x*-intercept is $(40, 0)$. When 40 adults are seated, no children can sit. The *y*-intercept is $(0, 60)$. When no adults are seated, 60 children can sit.

The number of passengers is a whole number. The situation is discrete. The domain is limited to the whole numbers 0 to 40; the range to the whole numbers 0 to 60.

2 a. Suppose the train system buys new train cars with molded plastic seats. The model changes to $x + y = 40$. Graph the equation and interpret the *x*- and *y*-intercepts.

    b. Explain how using molded seats changes the number of seated passengers.

Real-World 🌐 **Connection**

In Japan, so many people ride public transportation that they need help getting into the trains.

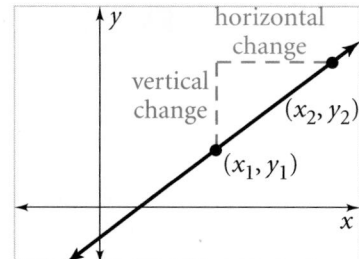

Vocabulary Tip

The <u>slope</u> of a line is also the rate of change between two points on the line.

The **slope** of a nonvertical line is the ratio of the vertical change to a corresponding horizontal change. You can calculate slope by subtracting the corresponding coordinates of two points on the line.

Key Concepts

Definition	Slope Formula

$$\text{slope} = \frac{\text{vertical change (rise)}}{\text{horizontal change (run)}} = \frac{y_2 - y_1}{x_2 - x_1}, \text{where } x_2 - x_1 \neq 0$$

3 EXAMPLE Finding Slope

Find the slope of the line through the points $(3, 2)$ and $(-9, 6)$.

$\text{slope} = \frac{y_2 - y_1}{x_2 - x_1}$ **Use the slope formula.**

$\qquad = \frac{6 - 2}{-9 - 3}$ **Substitute (3, 2) for (x_1, y_1) and (−9, 6) for (x_2, y_2).**

$\qquad = \frac{4}{-12}$ **Subtract.**

$\qquad = -\frac{1}{3}$ **Simplify.**

● The slope of the line is $-\frac{1}{3}$.

✓ CA Standards Check **3** Find the slope of the line through each pair of points.
    a. $(-2, -2)$ and $(4, 2)$ **b.** $(0, -3)$ and $(7, -9)$

2   Writing Equations of Lines

Activity: Point-Slope Form

1. Make a table of values to graph each line.

    a. $y - 1 = -2(x - 2)$ **b.** $y - 2 = \frac{1}{3}(x - 1)$ **c.** $y - 5 = 3(x - 4)$

2. Find the slope of each line. Compare the slope of the line to the red number in the equation of the line. What do you notice?

3. Find the point on the graph of each line with an *x*-coordinate that is equal to the green number in the equation line. Then compare the *y*-coordinate of the point to the blue number in the equation of the line. What do you notice?

4. **Make a Conjecture** All three equations in Question 1 are in the form $y - y_1 = m(x - x_1)$. Make a conjecture about how you can use that form to help you graph an equation.

When you know the slope and a point on a line, you can use the **point-slope form** to write the equation of the line.

 Key Concepts

Definition	**Point-Slope Form**

The line through point (x_1, y_1) with slope m has the equation below.

$$y - y_1 = m(x - x_1)$$

4 EXAMPLE **Writing an Equation Given the Slope and a Point**

Write in standard form an equation of the line with slope $-\frac{1}{2}$ through the point $(8, -1)$.

$y - y_1 = m(x - x_1)$	Use the point-slope equation.
$y - (-1) = -\frac{1}{2}(x - 8)$	Substitute $-\frac{1}{2}$ for m, -1 for y_1, and 8 for x_1.
$y - (-1) = -\frac{1}{2}x - \left(-\frac{1}{2}\right)(8)$	Distributive Property
$y + 1 = -\frac{1}{2}x + 4$	Simplify.
$\frac{1}{2}x + y = 3$	Write in standard form.

 CA Standards Check **4** Write in standard form the equation of each line.

a. slope 2, through $(4, -2)$ **b.** slope $\frac{5}{6}$, through $(5, 6)$

When you know two points on a line, you can write an equation by using the point-slope equation combined with the slope formula.

5 EXAMPLE **Writing an Equation Given Two Points**

Write in point-slope form the equation of the line through $(1, 5)$ and $(4, -1)$.

$y - y_1 = m(x - x_1)$	Write the point-slope equation.
$y - y_1 = \frac{y_2 - y_1}{x_2 - x_1}(x - x_1)$	Substitute the slope formula for m.
$y - 5 = \frac{-1 - 5}{4 - 1}(x - 1)$	Substitute: $x_1 = 1, y_1 = 5, x_2 = 4, y_2 = -1$.
$y - 5 = \frac{-6}{3}(x - 1)$	Simplify.
$y - 5 = -2(x - 1)$	Write in point-slope form.

CA Standards Check **5** Write in point-slope form the equation of the line through each pair of points.
a. $(5, 0)$ and $(-3, 2)$ **b.** $(-2, -1)$ and $(-10, 17)$ **c.** $(5, 1)$ and $(-4, -3)$

Another form of the equation of a line is **slope-intercept form,** which you can use to find slope by examining the equation.

Key Concepts

Definition	**Slope-Intercept Form**

slope⌐   ⌐y-intercept

$$y = mx + b$$

6 **EXAMPLE** **Finding Slope Using Slope-Intercept Form**

Find the slope of $4x + 3y = 7$.

$4x + 3y = 7$

$\quad 3y = -4x + 7$ **Subtract 4x from each side.**

$\quad\quad y = -\frac{4}{3}x + \frac{7}{3}$ **Write in slope-intercept form.**

The slope of the line is $-\frac{4}{3}$.

 CA Standards Check **6** Find the slope of each line.

  a. $3x + 2y = 1$ **b.** $\frac{2}{3}x + \frac{1}{2}y = 1$ **c.** $Ax + By = C$

Key Concepts

Summary	Equations of a Line	
Point-Slope Form	**Standard Form**	**Slope-Intercept Form**
$y - 2 = -3(x + 4)$	$3x + y = -10$	$y = -3x - 10$

The slopes of horizontal, vertical, perpendicular, and parallel lines have special properties.

Horizontal Line

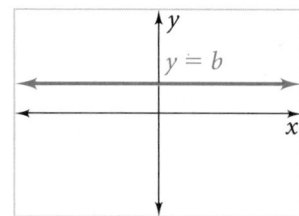

$m = 0$
y is constant.

Vertical Line

m is undefined.
x is constant.

Perpendicular Lines

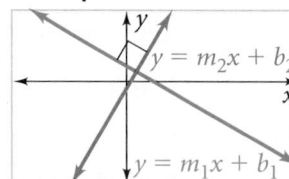

$m_1 \cdot m_2 = -1$
(In other words, m_2 is the negative reciprocal of m_1.)

Parallel Lines

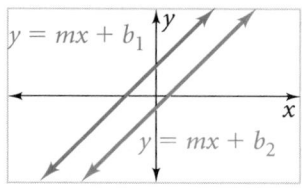

$m = m$
$b_1 \neq b_2$

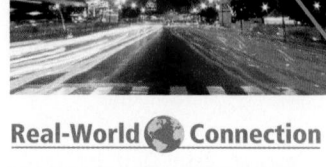

Real-World Connection

The steel girders of the Eiffel Tower model horizontal, vertical, perpendicular, and parallel lines.

Video Tutor Help

Visit: PHSchool.com
Web Code: bbe-0775

7 EXAMPLE Writing an Equation of a Perpendicular Line

Write an equation of the line through each point and perpendicular to $y = \frac{3}{4}x + 2$.
Graph all three lines.

a. $(0, 4)$

$m = -\left(\dfrac{1}{\frac{3}{4}}\right) = -\dfrac{4}{3}$ **Find the negative reciprocal of $\frac{3}{4}$.**

$y = mx + b$ **Use slope-intercept form.**

$y = -\dfrac{4}{3}x + 4$ **Substitute: $m = -\frac{4}{3}$ and $b = 4$.**

b. $(6, 1)$

$y = -\dfrac{4}{3}x + b$ **Slope is $-\frac{4}{3}$.**

$1 = -\dfrac{4}{3}(6) + b$ **Substitute (6, 1) for (x, y).**

$1 = -8 + b$ **Simplify.**

$9 = b$ **Solve for b.**

$y = -\dfrac{4}{3}x + 9$ **Write the equation.**

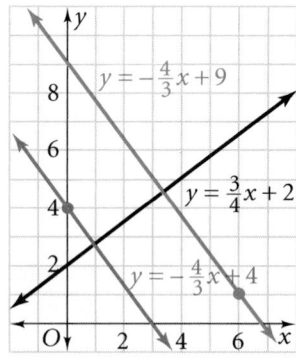

✓ **CA Standards Check** ⑦ Write an equation for each line. Then graph the line.
   a. through $(-1, 3)$ and perpendicular to the line $y = 5x - 3$
   b. through $(2, 1)$ and parallel to the line $y = \frac{2}{3}x + \frac{5}{8}$
   c. vertical and through $(5, -3)$

EXERCISES

For more exercises, see *Extra Skill and Word Problem Practice*.

Standards Practice

A Practice by Example

Example 1
(page 64)

Graph each equation. Check your work.

1. $y = 2x$ **2.** $y = -3x - 1$ **3.** $y = 3x - 2$ **4.** $y = -4x + 5$

5. $5x - 2y = -4$ **6.** $-2x + 5y = -10$ **7.** $y - 3 = -2x$ **8.** $y + 4 = -3x$

Example 2
(page 65)

9. Cost Analysis The equation $y - 0.23x = 0$ relates the cost of operating a car to the number of miles driven, where x is the number of miles driven and y is the cost.
   a. Graph the equation and determine the domain and range.
   b. Explain what the x- and y-intercepts represent.
   c. Explain what 0.23 represents.

10. Fund-Raising The school glee club needs a total of $4500 for a trip to Omaha, Nebraska. To make money, members are selling baseball caps for $4.50 and sweatshirts for $12.50.
   a. Graph the equation $4.5x + 12.5y = 4500$, where x is the number of baseball caps and y is the number of sweatshirts sold.
   b. Explain the meaning of the x- and y-intercepts in terms of the fund-raising.

Example 3
(page 66)

Find the slope of the line through each pair of points.

11. $(1, 6)$ and $(8, -1)$ **12.** $(-3, 9)$ and $(0, 3)$ **13.** $(0, 0)$ and $(2, 6)$

14. $(-4, -3)$ and $(7, 1)$ **15.** $(-2, -1)$ and $(8, -3)$ **16.** $(1, 2)$ and $(2, 3)$

17. $\left(\frac{2}{3}, \frac{4}{7}\right)$ and $\left(\frac{2}{3}, \frac{11}{7}\right)$ **18.** $(-3, 5)$ and $(4, 5)$ **19.** $(-5, -7)$ and $(0, 10)$

Example 4
(page 67)

Write in standard form the equation of each line.

20. slope $= 3; (1, 5)$ **21.** slope $= \frac{5}{6}; (22, 12)$ **22.** slope $= -\frac{3}{5}; (-4, 0)$

23. slope $= 0; (4, -2)$ **24.** slope $= -1; (-3, 5)$ **25.** slope $= 5; (0, 2)$

Example 5
(page 67)

Write in point-slope form the equation of the line through each pair of points.

26. $(-10, 3)$ and $(-2, -5)$ **27.** $(1, 0)$ and $(5, 5)$ **28.** $(-4, 10)$ and $(-6, 15)$

29. $(0, -1)$ and $(3, -5)$ **30.** $(7, 11)$ and $(13, 17)$ **31.** $(1, 9)$ and $(6, 2)$

Example 6
(page 68)

Find the slope of each line.

32. $5x + y = 4$ **33.** $-3x + 2y = 7$ **34.** $-\frac{1}{2}x - y = \frac{3}{4}$

35. $Ax + By = C$ **36.** $Ax - By = C$ **37.** $y = 7$

Example 7
(page 69)

Write an equation for each line. Then graph the line.

38. through $(-2, 1)$ and parallel to $y = -3x + 1$

39. through $(-3, -1)$ and perpendicular to $y = -\frac{2}{5}x - 4$

40. through $(-7, 10)$ and horizontal

41. through $\left(1, -\frac{2}{7}\right)$ and vertical

B **Apply Your Skills**

Graph each equation.

42. $y = -\frac{3}{5}x - \frac{12}{5}$ **43.** $y = -2x + 3$ **44.** $y = -x + 7$

45. $3y - 2x = -12$ **46.** $4x + 5y = 20$ **47.** $4x - 3y = -6$

48. $\frac{2}{3}x + \frac{y}{3} = -\frac{1}{3}$ **49.** $\frac{3}{5}y - \frac{x}{5} = -\frac{6}{5}$ **50.** $\frac{4}{5} = -\frac{1}{3}x - \frac{3}{4}y$

Find the slope of each line.

51.   **52.**   **53.**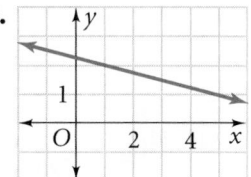

Find the slope and the intercepts of each line.

54. $f(x) = \frac{2}{3}x + 4$ **55.** $y = -x + 1000$ **56.** $y = 0.4 - 0.8x$

57. $g(x) = 54x - 1$ **58.** $x = -3$ **59.** $y = 0$

60. $-\frac{1}{3}x - \frac{2}{3}y = \frac{5}{3}$ **61.** $-Rx + Sy = -T$ **62.** $\frac{A}{D}x + \frac{B}{D}y = \frac{C}{D}$

Find the slope of the line through each pair of points.

63. $\left(\frac{3}{2}, -\frac{1}{2}\right)$ and $\left(-\frac{2}{3}, \frac{1}{3}\right)$ **64.** $\left(-\frac{1}{2}, -\frac{1}{2}\right)$ and $(-3, -4)$ **65.** $\left(0, \frac{1}{2}\right)$ and $\left(\frac{5}{7}, 0\right)$

Write an equation for each line. Each interval is 1 unit.

66.   **67.**   **68.**

Homework Video Tutor

Real-World Connection

You can download data from a motion detector to a computer to produce graphs of distance versus time.

69. Multiple Choice Three students moved away from or toward a motion detector, one at a time. Each graph shows distance from the detector as a function of time.

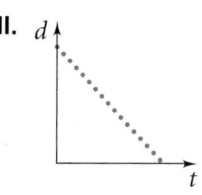

I. 　II. 　III.

Which of the following statements is true?
- Ⓐ Student I was the only student who moved away from the detector.
- Ⓑ Student II was the only student who moved toward the detector.
- Ⓒ Student I was speeding up.
- Ⓓ Student II was slowing down.

70. Critical Thinking Most graphing calculators are designed to graph equations that are solved for y. What lines could not be graphed with this method?

Write an equation for each line. Then graph the line.

71. $m = 0$, through $(5, -1)$ 　　　　**72.** $m = 2$, through $(1, 3)$

73. $m = \frac{5}{6}$, through $(-4, 0)$ 　　　**74.** $m = -\frac{3}{2}$, through $(0, -1)$

Write each equation in standard form.

75. $y = \frac{3}{2}x - 1$ 　　**76.** $x + \frac{1}{3}y = \frac{2}{9}$ 　　**77.** $-\left(\frac{1}{2}x + 2y\right) = \frac{2}{3}$

78. a. Open-Ended Write an equation of a line.
　　b. Write an equation of the line parallel to the line you wrote in part (a) passing through the point $(0.5, 0.6)$.
　　c. Write an equation of the line perpendicular to the line you wrote in part (a) passing through the point $\left(\frac{5}{3}, 2\right)$.
　　d. Write an equation of the line parallel to the line you wrote in part (c) passing through the point $(-3, 1)$.
　　e. Geometry Graph the lines from parts (a), (b), (c), and (d). If they form a polygon, describe it.

Ⓒ Challenge

Points that are on the same line are *collinear*. Use the definition of slope to determine whether the given points are collinear.

79. $(-2, 6), (0, 2), (1, 0)$ 　　　　　　**80.** $(3, -5), (-3, 3), (0, 2)$

Problem Solving Hint

The slopes of parallel lines are equal. The slopes of perpendicular lines are negative reciprocals.

81. Write an equation of a line a through $(-1, 3)$ that is parallel to the line $y = 3x + 1$. Write an equation of a line b through $(-1, 3)$ that is perpendicular to line a. What is the intersection of lines b and $y = 3x + 1$?

82. Geometry Prove that the triangle with vertices $(3, 5), (-2, 6)$, and $(1, 3)$ is a right triangle.

83. Geometry Prove that the quadrilateral with vertices $(2, 5), (4, 8), (7, 6)$, and $(5, 3)$ is a rectangle.

84. Critical Thinking Lines $p, q,$ and r all pass through point $(-3, 4)$. Line p has slope 4 and is perpendicular to line q. Line r passes through Quadrants I and II only. Write an equation for each line. Then graph the three lines on the same coordinate plane.

Multiple Choice Practice

For California Standards and CAHSEE Tutorials, visit PHSchool.com. Web Code: bbq-9045

ALG2 1.0

85. Rosa wants to ride the sea monster at a carnival. She must be at least 4 feet tall, but no more than 5 feet, 8 inches tall. Which of the absolute value inequalities below describes this situation? Let h represent Rosa's height in inches.

  Ⓐ $|h + 58| \le 68$ Ⓒ $|h + 10| \le 48$

  Ⓑ $|h - 58| \le 10$ Ⓓ $|h - 10| \le 58$

CAHSEE
7AF 1.1

86. After driving 40 miles, Ali drives at a constant speed of 55 miles per hour for x hours. Which equation expresses y, the total number of miles he drives?

  Ⓐ $y = 40x + 55$ Ⓒ $y = 40(x + 55)$

  Ⓑ $y = 55x + 40$ Ⓓ $y = 55(x + 40)$

ALG2 1.0

87. The graph of the function $y = |x + 1| + 2$ is shown. What is $f(-1)$?

  Ⓐ -3

  Ⓑ 1

  Ⓒ 2

  Ⓓ 4

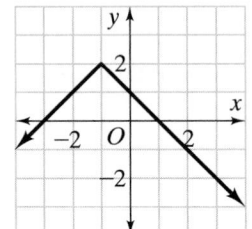

CAHSEE
6SDAP 1.1

88. Livio spent $5.29, $8.35, $3.40, $3.07, and $3.19 on lunches last week. He wants to budget the minimum cost of lunch for the rest of the year. Which measure of central tendency will result in the lowest cost?

  Ⓐ Mean   Ⓒ Mode

  Ⓑ Median   Ⓓ None of these

Mixed Review

Lesson 2-1

Find the domain and range of each relation. Then decide whether it is a function.

89.

90.

91. Domain   Range

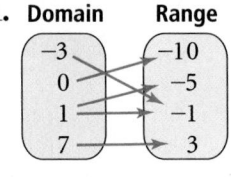

Lesson 1-1

Identify each demonstrated property (or properties) of real numbers.

92. $7.4 - 3.4 + 2.6 = 7.4 + 2.6 - 3.4$ **93.** $\frac{2}{5} + \frac{27}{5} \cdot \frac{5}{27} = \frac{2}{5} + 1$

94. $97(7) = 100(7) - 3(7)$ **95.** $21 + 19.7 - 19.7 = 21$

Skills Handbook

96. Commission A fabric designer earns a 60% commission for works sold in a textile studio. The studio receives the other 40%. How much does the studio receive for selling a length of fabric that costs $15.65? How much does the designer receive?

FOR USE WITH LESSON 2-2

A piecewise function has different rules for different parts of its domain.

1 EXAMPLE Writing a Piecewise Function

Write a piecewise function to represent the graph at the right.

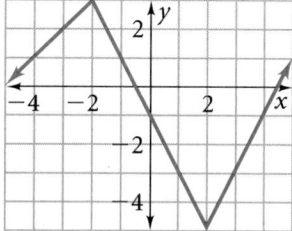

The graph has three distinct sections. The function needs a distinct rule for each of the three corresponding sections of the domain. Since $(-2, 3)$ and $(2, -5)$ both lie on two sections of the graph, arbitrarily assign each point to just one section.

When $x \leq -2$, the rule is $f(x) = x + 5$. When $-2 < x \leq 2$, the rule is $f(x) = -2x - 1$. When $x > 2$, the rule is $f(x) = 2x - 9$.

The piecewise function has three parts. $f(x) = \begin{cases} x + 5, \text{ if } x \leq -2 \\ -2x - 1, \text{ if } -2 < x \leq 2 \\ 2x - 9, \text{ if } x > 2 \end{cases}$

Some piecewise functions are step functions. Their graphs look like the steps of a staircase. One step function is the greatest integer function $f(x) = [x]$, where $[x]$ means the greatest integer less than or equal to x.

2 EXAMPLE Graphing a Piecewise Function

Graph the function $f(x) = [x]$.

Step 1 Choose an interval bounded by two consecutive integers. Make a table of values for the interval $0 \leq x \leq 1$.

x	0	0.25	0.5	0.75	1
f(x)	0	0	0	0	1

Each section of the graph ends at the y-value at which it starts. The left endpoint of each "step" is a closed circle. The right endpoint is an open circle.

Step 2 Graph the function.

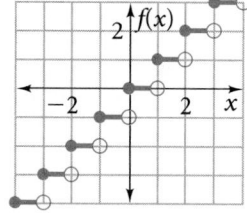

Use closed circles for included endpoints; use open circles for excluded endpoints.

EXERCISES

Graph each piecewise function.

1. $y = [x] + 2$

2. $f(x) = 3[x]$

3. $y = \begin{cases} x + 4, \text{ if } x \leq -2 \\ -x, \text{ if } x > -2 \end{cases}$

4. $f(x) = \begin{cases} -2x + 1, \text{ if } x < 3 \\ x - 8, \text{ if } x \geq 3 \end{cases}$

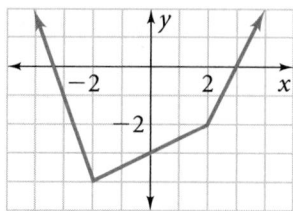

5. Write a piecewise function to represent the graph at the right.

6. Writing Explain how to graph a piecewise function.

Direct Variation

✓ Check Skills You'll Need

 for Help Lesson 1-3 and Skills Handbook page 884

Solve each equation for y.

1. $12y = 3x$ **2.** $12y = 5x$ **3.** $\frac{3}{4}y = 15$ **4.** $0.9y = 27x$ **5.** $5y = 35$

Tell whether each equation is true.

6. $\frac{1}{4} \stackrel{?}{=} \frac{2}{8}$ **7.** $\frac{2}{5} \stackrel{?}{=} \frac{6}{15}$ **8.** $\frac{9}{24} \stackrel{?}{=} \frac{12}{36}$ **9.** $\frac{20}{24} \stackrel{?}{=} \frac{30}{36}$

🔊 **New Vocabulary** • direct variation • constant of variation

---

1   Writing and Interpreting a Direct Variation

A linear function defined by an equation of the form $y = kx$, where $k \neq 0$, represents **direct variation.** As with any line, the slope k is constant.

When x and y are variables, you can write $k = \frac{y}{x}$, so the ratio $y : x$ equals the constant k, the **constant of variation.**

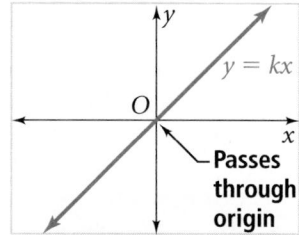

$y = kx$

Passes through origin

1   EXAMPLE   Identifying Direct Variation From a Table

For each function, determine whether y varies directly with x. If so, find the constant of variation and write the equation.

a.

x	y
2	8
3	12
5	20

$\frac{y}{x} = \frac{8}{2} = \frac{12}{3} = \frac{20}{5} = 4$,

so y varies directly with x.
The constant of variation is 4.
The equation is $y = 4x$.

b.

x	y
1	4
2	7
5	16

Since $\frac{4}{1}, \frac{7}{2}$, and $\frac{16}{5}$ are not equal, $\frac{y}{x}$ is not constant.
y does *not* vary directly with x.

✓ CA Standards Check 1

For each function, determine whether y varies directly with x. If so, find the constant of variation and write the equation.

a.

x	y
−6	−2
3	1
12	4

b.

x	y
−1	−2
3	4
6	7

c.

x	y
−9	5
3	$-1\frac{2}{3}$
6	$3\frac{5}{8}$

You can analyze an equation to determine whether it represents direct variation.

2 EXAMPLE **Identifying Direct Variation From an Equation**

For each function, determine whether y varies directly with x. If so, find the constant of variation.

a. $3y = 2x$

$3y = 2x$ is equivalent to $y = \frac{2}{3}x$, so y varies directly with x. The constant of variation is $\frac{2}{3}$.

b. $y = 2x + 3$

Since you cannot write the equation in the form $y = kx$, y does *not* vary directly with x.

✓ **CA Standards Check** **2** For each function, determine whether y varies directly with x. If so, find the constant of variation.

a. $y = \frac{x}{2}$ **b.** $2y - 1 = x$ **c.** $\frac{5}{6}x = \frac{1}{3}y$ **d.** $7x + 4y = 10$

You can write an equation to solve a direct variation problem.

3 EXAMPLE **Real-World 🌐 Connection**

Water Conservation A dripping faucet wastes a cup of water if it drips for three minutes. The amount of water wasted varies directly with the amount of time the faucet drips.

a. Find the constant of variation k and write an equation to model the direct variation.

Relate   water wasted   varies directly   with time

Define Let w = number of cups of water wasted.

Let t = time in minutes the faucet drips.

Write w = k · t

$1 = k(3)$ **Substitute 1 for w and 3 for t.**

$\frac{1}{3} = k$ **Solve for k.**

The constant of variation k is $\frac{1}{3}$. The equation $w = \frac{1}{3}t$ models the direct variation.

b. Find how long the faucet must drip to waste $4\frac{1}{2}$ c of water.

$w = \frac{1}{3}t$ **Use the direct variation.**

$4\frac{1}{2} = \frac{1}{3}t$ **Substitute $4\frac{1}{2}$ for w.**

$\frac{9}{2}(3) = t$ **Solve for t.**

$13\frac{1}{2} = t$ **Simplify.**

The faucet must drip for $13\frac{1}{2}$ min to waste $4\frac{1}{2}$ c of water.

GO 🌐 nline

Video Tutor Help

Visit: PHSchool.com
Web Code: bbe-0775

✓ **CA Standards Check** **3** **Geometry** The circumference of a circle varies directly with the diameter of the circle. The formula $C = \pi d$ relates the circumference to the diameter.
a. What is the constant of variation?
b. Find the diameter of a circle with circumference 105 cm to the nearest tenth.

You can use proportions to solve some direct variation problems. This can save time when the problem does not ask for the constant of variation.

4 EXAMPLE Using a Proportion

Suppose y varies directly with x, and $x = 27$ when $y = -51$. Find x when $y = -17$.

Let $(x_1, y_1) = (27, -51)$ and let $(x_2, y_2) = (x_2, -17)$.

$$\frac{y_1}{x_1} = \frac{y_2}{x_2} \qquad \textbf{Write a proportion.}$$

$$\frac{-51}{27} = \frac{-17}{x_2} \qquad \textbf{Substitute.}$$

$$-51(x_2) = 27(-17) \qquad \textbf{Write the cross products.}$$

$$x_2 = \frac{27(-17)}{-51} \qquad \textbf{Solve for } x_2.$$

$$x_2 = 9 \qquad \textbf{Simplify.}$$

✓ CA Standards Check ④ Find the missing value for each direct variation.
  a. If $y = 4$ when $x = 3$, find y when $x = 6$.
  b. If $y = 7$ when $x = 2$, find y when $x = 8$.
  c. If $y = 10$ when $x = -3$, find x when $y = 2$.
  d. If $y = 1$ when $x = 10$, find y when $x = 2$.

EXERCISES

For more exercises, see *Extra Skill and Word Problem Practice*.

Standards Practice

A Practice by Example

Example 1
(page 74)

For each function, determine whether y varies directly with x. If so, find the constant of variation and write the equation.

1.

x	y
2	4
4	8
16	32

2.

x	y
2	-6
4	-12
5	-15

3.

x	y
11	22
16	32
7	42

4.

x	y
27	9
30	10
60	20

5.

x	y
2	14
3	21
5	35

6.

x	y
3	9
4	13
7	23

7.

x	y
-2	4
-3	6
-5	10

8.

x	y
1	-2
3	-8
5	14

Example 2
(page 75)

Determine whether y varies directly with x. If so, find the constant of variation.

9. $y = 12x$ **10.** $y = 6x$ **11.** $y = -2x$ **12.** $y = 4x + 1$

13. $y = 4x - 3$ **14.** $y = -5x$ **15.** $y - 6x = 0$ **16.** $y + 3 = -3x$

Example 3
(page 75)

For each direct variation, find the constant of variation. Then find the value of y when $x = -5$.

17. $y = 2$ when $x = 7$ **18.** $y = -5$ when $x = 3$

19. $y = -2$ when $x = 2$ **20.** $y = -\frac{2}{3}$ when $x = -\frac{1}{3}$

21. $y = 17$ when $x = -4$ **22.** $y = \frac{1}{2}$ when $x = -2$

23. Environment Suppose you work on a tree farm and you need to find the height of each tree. You know that the length of an object's shadow varies directly with its height. Refer to the diagram.

   a. Find the constant of variation.

   b. Write an equation to calculate the height of the tree.

   c. Find the height of a tree with a shadow 8 ft 4 in. long.

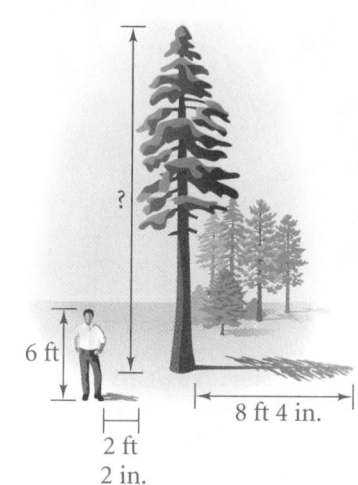

Example 4
(page 76)

For Exercises 24–27, *y* varies directly with *x*.

24. If $y = 4$ when $x = -2$, find x when $y = 6$.

25. If $y = 6$ when $x = 2$, find x when $y = 12$.

26. If $y = 7$ when $x = 2$, find y when $x = 3$.

27. If $y = 5$ when $x = -3$, find y when $x = -1$.

 Apply Your Skills

For each function, determine whether *y* varies directly with *x*. If so, find the constant of variation and write the equation.

28.

x	y
9	6
12	8
15	10

29.

x	y
4	1
6	2
8	3

30.

x	y
23	24
55	56
66	67

31.

x	y
2	2.6
3	3.9
4	5.2

To review proportions, see Skills Handbook, page 884.

32. Multiple Choice A speed of 60 mi/h is equal to a speed of 88 ft/s. Find the speed to the nearest mile per hour of an aircraft travelling 1000 ft/s.

   Ⓐ 528   Ⓑ 682   Ⓒ 972   Ⓓ 1477

Write an equation for a direct variation with a graph that passes through each point.

33. $(1, 2)$ **34.** $(-3, -7)$ **35.** $(2, -9)$ **36.** $(-0.1, 50)$

37. $(-5, -3)$ **38.** $(9, -1)$ **39.** $(7, 2)$ **40.** $(-3, 14)$

In Exercises 41–45, *y* varies directly with *x*.

41. If $y = 7$ when $x = 3$, find x when $y = 21$.

42. If $y = 25$ when $x = 15$, find x when $y = 10$.

43. If $y = 30$ when $x = -3$, find y when $x = -9$.

44. If $y = -20$ when $x = 2$, find y when $x = 14$.

45. If $y = 0.9$ when $x = 4.8$, find y when $x = 6.4$.

Determine whether a line with the given slope through the given point represents a direct variation. Explain.

46. $m = -1.7, (9, -9)$ **47.** $m = -\frac{5}{6}, \left(15, -12\frac{1}{2}\right)$ **48.** $m = \frac{7}{2}, \left(6\frac{1}{2}, 22\frac{3}{4}\right)$

Visit: PHSchool.com
Web Code: bbe-0203

Open-Ended In Exercises 49–51, choose a value of *k* within the given range. Then write and graph a direct variation using your value for *k*.

49. $0 < k < 1$ **50.** $3 < k < 4.5$ **51.** $-1 < k < -\frac{1}{2}$

It takes more effort for an engine to propel a car with underinflated tires. Cars with properly inflated tires get better gas mileage.

52. Gas Mileage Suppose you drive a car 392 mi on one tank of gas. The tank holds 14 gallons. The number of miles traveled varies directly with the number of gallons of gas you use.
  a. Write an equation that relates miles traveled to gallons of gas used.
  b. You only have enough money to buy 3.7 gallons of gas. How far can you drive before refueling?
  c. Last year you drove 11,700 mi. About how many gallons of gas did you use?
  d. Suppose the price of gas averaged $1.57 per gallon last year. Find the cost per mile.

 53. Writing Suppose you use the origin to test whether a linear equation is a direct variation. Does this method work? Support your answer with an example.

54. Error Analysis Find the error in the following computation: If y varies directly with x^2, and $y = 2$ when $x = 4$, then $y = 3$ when $x = 9$.

C Challenge

In Exercises 55–58, y varies directly with x.

55. If x is doubled, what happens to y?

56. If x is halved, what happens to y?

57. If x is divided by 7, what happens to y?

58. If x is multiplied by 10, what happens to y?

59. If z varies directly with the product of x and y ($z = kxy$), then z is said to vary jointly with x and y.
  a. Geometry The area of a triangle varies jointly with its base and height. What is the constant of variation?
  b. Suppose q varies jointly with v and s, and $q = 24$ when $v = 2$ and $s = 3$. Find q when $v = 4$ and $s = 2$.
  c. Critical Thinking Suppose z varies jointly with x and y, and x varies directly with w. Show that z varies jointly with w and y.

 Multiple Choice Practice

For California Standards and CAHSEE Tutorials, visit PHSchool.com. Web Code: bbq-9045

CAHSEE Alg1 8.0

60. Which function best represents the line that contains the point $(-3, 4)$ and is parallel to $y = 5x + 4$?
  Ⓐ $f(x) = 5x - 23$ Ⓒ $f(x) = 5x + 11$
  Ⓑ $f(x) = 5x - 17$ Ⓓ $f(x) = 5x + 19$

CAHSEE Alg1 6.0

61. Ahmad graphed the linear function modeled by the table. What is the y-intercept of Ahmad's graph?
  Ⓐ -3 Ⓒ 1
  Ⓑ -1 Ⓓ 3

x	−2	4	7
y	−7	5	11

CAHSEE 7MR 2.4

62. What is the next term in the sequence?
  $1, 2, 5, 10, 17, 26, \_\_\_\_$
  Ⓐ 35   Ⓑ 37   Ⓒ 39   Ⓓ 41

Lesson 2-2

Use the given information to graph each line.

63. slope $= -\frac{3}{5}$, through $(-2, 5)$ **64.** slope $= -\frac{3}{2}$, through $(1, -4)$

65. slope $= -4$, through $(0, -1)$ **66.** slope $= -2, (-1, 6)$

Lesson 2-1

Graph each relation. Find the domain and range.

67. $\{(0, 1), (1, -3), (-2, -3), (3, -3)\}$ **68.** $\{(4, 0), (7, 0), (4, -1), (7, -1)\}$

69. $\{(1, -2), (2, -1), (4, 1), (5, 2)\}$ **70.** $\{(1, 7), (2, 8), (3, 9), (4, 10)\}$

Skills Handbook

71. Aviation On June 21, 2004, Simon Oliphant-Hope completed a record-setting helicopter trip around the world in 17 d 14 h 2 min 27 s. He spent 196.4 h in flight. What percent of the time was he not in the air?

Checkpoint Quiz 1   **Lessons 2-1 through 2-3**

Find the x- and y-intercepts of each line.

1. $x - 3y = 9$ **2.** $y = 7x + 5$ **3.** $y = 6x$ **4.** $-4x + y = 10$

Write the equation of each line in slope-intercept form.

5. $2x - y = 9$ **6.** $4x = 2 + y$ **7.** $5y = -3x - 10$ **8.** $4x + 6y = 12$

9. a. A group of friends is going to the movies. Each ticket costs \$7.00. Write an equation to model the total cost of the group's tickets.

   b. Graph the equation. Explain what the x- and y-intercepts represent.

   c. Writing Could the domain include fractions? Explain.

10. Which line is perpendicular to $3x + 2y = 6$?

   A. $4x - 6y = 3$ **B.** $y = -\frac{3}{2}x + 4$ **C.** $2x + 3y = 12$ **D.** $y = \frac{3}{2}x + 1$

Algebra at Work

·····················Miniaturist

People who make a career out of designing and creating miniature models of actual objects are called miniaturists. They apply direct variations to reproduce realistic models of items such as houses, stores, or scenes. Common scales used to create miniatures are the following.
- the one-inch scale (1 in. : 1 ft or 1 : 12)
- the half-inch scale (0.5 in. : 1 ft or 1 : 24)
- the quarter-inch scale (0.25 in. : 1 ft or 1 : 48)

Go Online
PHSchool.com   **For:** Information about careers in model design
Web Code: bbb-2031

2-4 Using Linear Models

What You'll Learn

- To write linear equations that model real-world data
- To make predictions from linear models

. . . And Why

To model a burning candle, as in Example 2

✓ **Check Skills You'll Need**

GO for Help Lessons 2-1 and 2-2

Find the change in x and the change in y between each pair of points.

1. $(-0.2, 9)$ and $(3.4, 7.3)$ **2.** $(10, 17)$ and $(11.5, 13.5)$ **3.** $\left(0, \frac{3}{10}\right)$ and $\left(-1, \frac{2}{5}\right)$

Evaluate each function for the given values.

4. $f(x) = \frac{4}{3}x - 2$ for $x = -3, 0, \frac{1}{2}$ **5.** $g(x) = 3(2 - x)$ for $x = 0, \frac{1}{6}, 1$

🔊 **New Vocabulary** • scatter plot • trend line

1 Modeling Real-World Data

You can write linear equations to model real-world problems.

1 EXAMPLE Real-World Connection

Transportation Jacksonville, Florida has an elevation of 12 ft above sea level. A hot-air balloon taking off from Jacksonville rises 50 ft/min. Write an equation to model the balloon's elevation as a function of time. Graph the equation. Interpret the intercept at which the graph intersects the vertical axis.

Relate balloon's elevation = rate · time + starting elevation

Define Let h = the balloon's elevation.

Let t = time (in minutes) since the hot-air balloon lifted off.

Write h = 50 · t + 12

An equation that models the balloon's elevation is $h = 50t + 12$.

Real-World Connection

The elevation of a hot-air balloon is determined by the flow of propane.

The h-intercept is $(0, 12)$.

The t-coordinate, 0, represents the time at the start of the trip.

The h-coordinate, 12, represents the elevation of the balloon at the start of the trip.

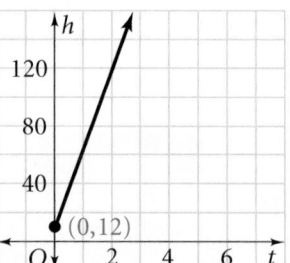

✓ **CA Standards Check** ① Suppose a balloon begins descending at a rate of 20 ft/min from an elevation of 1350 ft.
  a. Write an equation to model the balloon's elevation as a function of time. What is true about the slope of this line?
  b. Graph the equation. Interpret the h-intercept.

You can use two data points from a linear relationship to write a model.

2 EXAMPLE Real-World Connection

Science A candle is 6 in. tall after burning for 1 h. After 3 h, it is $5\frac{1}{2}$ in. tall. Write a linear equation to model the height y of the candle after burning x hours.

Step 1 Identify the data points $(1, 6)$ and $\left(3, \frac{11}{2}\right)$ as (x_1, y_1) and (x_2, y_2).

Step 2 Find the slope of the line.

$$m = \frac{y_2 - y_1}{x_2 - x_1} \quad \text{Use the slope formula.}$$

$$m = \frac{\frac{11}{2} - 6}{3 - 1} \quad \text{Substitute.}$$

$$m = \frac{-\frac{1}{2}}{2} \quad \text{Simplify the numerator and denominator.}$$

$$m = -\frac{1}{4} \quad \text{Simplify.}$$

Step 3 Use one of the points and the point-slope form to write an equation for the line.

$$y - y_1 = m(x - x_1) \quad \text{Use point-slope form.}$$

$$y - 6 = -\frac{1}{4}(x - 1) \quad \text{Substitute.}$$

$$y = -\frac{1}{4}x + 6\frac{1}{4} \quad \text{Solve for } y.$$

● An equation of the line that models the height of the candle is $y = -\frac{1}{4}x + 6\frac{1}{4}$.

✓ CA Standards Check **2** **a. Reasoning** What does the slope $-\frac{1}{4}$ represent?

b. What does the y-intercept $6\frac{1}{4}$ represent?

c. Another candle is 7 in. tall after burning for 1 h and 5 in. tall after burning for 2 h. Write a linear equation to model the height of the candle.

6 in. $5\frac{1}{2}$ in.

after 1 h   after 3 h

---

2 **Predicting With Linear Models**

You can use a linear model to make predictions.

3 EXAMPLE Using a Linear Model

Use the equation from Example 2. In how many hours will the candle be 4 in. tall?

$$y = -\frac{1}{4}x + 6\frac{1}{4} \quad \text{Write the equation.}$$

$$4 = -\frac{1}{4}x + 6\frac{1}{4} \quad \text{Substitute 4 for } y.$$

$$-4\left(4 - 6\frac{1}{4}\right) = x \quad \text{Solve for } x.$$

$$9 = x \quad \text{Simplify.}$$

● The candle will be 4 in. tall after burning for 9 h.

✓ CA Standards Check **3** **a.** How tall will the candle be after burning for 11 h?

b. What was the original height of the candle?

c. When will the candle burn out?

A **scatter plot** is a graph that relates two different sets of data by plotting the data as ordered pairs. You can use a scatter plot to determine a relationship between the data sets.

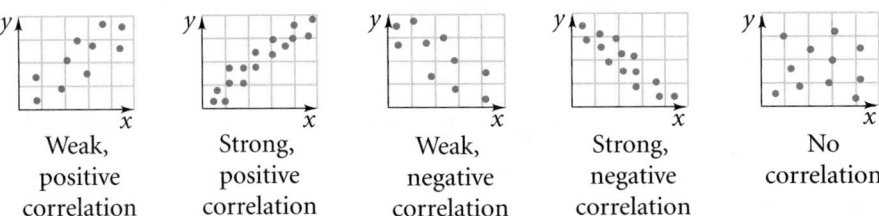

| Weak, positive correlation | Strong, positive correlation | Weak, negative correlation | Strong, negative correlation | No correlation |

A **trend line** is a line that approximates the relationship between the data sets of a scatter plot. You can use a trend line to make predictions.

4 EXAMPLE   Real-World Connection

Automobiles A woman is considering buying the 2001 car shown in the photo. She researches prices for various years of the same model and records the data in a table.

Model Year	2002	2003	2004	2005	2006
Prices	$5784	$6810	$8237	$9660	$10,948
	$5435	$6207	$7751	$9127	$10,455

a. Let x represent the model year. (Use 1 for 2002, 2 for 2003, and so forth.) Let y be the price of the car. Draw a scatter plot. Decide whether a linear model is reasonable.

A linear model seems reasonable, since the points fall close to a line.

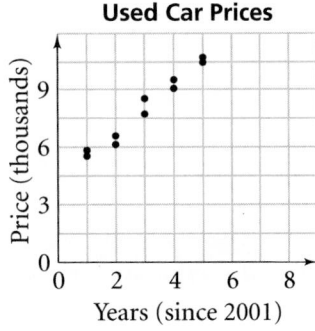

b. Draw a trend line. Write the equation of the line. Determine whether the asking price is reasonable.

Draw a line that has about the same number of data points above and below it. Use the slope and the y-intercept to find the equation of the line. Plot the data point for the asking price.

The equation of the trend line in the graph is $y = 1.3x + 4.1$. A fair price would be the value of y for $x = 0$, or about $4100.

The asking price of $4200 is reasonable.

✓ **CA Standards Check** ❹ Graph each set of data. Decide whether a linear model is reasonable. If so, draw a trend line and write its equation.

a. $\{(-7.5, 19.75), (-2, 9), (0, 6.5), (1.5, 3), (4, -1.5)\}$

b. $\{(0, -3), (0.5, -2.5), (1, -1), (3.5, 21.5), (6, 69), (7, 35)\}$

A Practice by Example

Example 1
(page 80)

1. A car enters an interstate highway 15 mi north of a city. The car travels due north at an average speed of 62.5 mi/h. Write an equation to model the car's distance *d* from the city after traveling for *h* hours. Graph the equation.

2. A pump removes 1000 gal of water from a pool at a constant rate of 50 gal/min.
   a. Write an equation to find the amount of water *y* in the pool after *t* minutes.
   b. Graph the equation and interpret the *t*- and *y*-intercepts.

3. A tree 5 ft tall grows an average of 8 in. each year. Write and graph an equation to model the tree's height *h* after *x* years.

Examples 2 and 3
(page 81)

For each situation, find a linear model and use it to make a prediction.

4. There are 2 leaves along 3 in. of an ivy vine. There are 14 leaves along 15 in. of the same vine. How many leaves are there along 6 in. of the vine?

5. An empty 5-gal water jug weighs 0.75 lb. With 3 c of water inside, the jug weighs 2.25 lb. Predict the weight of the jug with 5 c of water inside.

6. There are 55 blades of grass in 1 in.^{2} of lawn. There are 230 blades of grass in 4 in.^{2} of the same lawn. How many blades of grass are in 3 in.^{2} of lawn?

7. A 2-mi cab ride costs $5.25. A 5-mi cab ride costs $10.50. How much does a 3.8-mi cab ride cost?

Example 4
(page 82)

Graph each set of data. Decide whether a linear model is reasonable. If so, draw a trend line and write its equation.

8. $\{(0, 11), (2, 8), (3, 7), (7, 2), (8, 0)\}$

9. $\{(1.2, 1), (2.5, 6), (2.5, 7.5), (4.1, 11), (7.9, 19)\}$

10. $\left\{\left(-10, 3\frac{1}{2}\right), \left(-5\frac{1}{2}, 1\frac{1}{2}\right), \left(-\frac{1}{10}, -4\right), \left(3\frac{1}{2}, -7\frac{1}{2}\right), (12, -12)\right\}$

11. $\{(-15, 8), (-8, -7), (-3, 0), (0, 5), (7, -3)\}$

B Apply Your Skills

Daily Energy Requirements for Males

Age (years)	Energy Needed (Calories)
1	1100
2	1300
5	1800
8	2200
11	2500
14	2800
17	3000

SOURCE: *Go Figure: The Numbers You Need for Everyday Life*

12. Measurement The numbering system used in Europe for shoe sizes is different from the system used in the United States. Use the data in the table at the right to create a model for converting between systems.
   a. Graph the data. Is a linear model reasonable?
   b. Find the European equivalent of U.S. size 8.
   c. Writing Explain how to use a model to convert European sizes to U.S. sizes.

13. Nutrition The table at the left shows the average daily energy requirements for male children and adolescents.
   a. Graph the data. Model the data with a linear equation.
   b. Estimate the daily energy requirements for a male 16 years old.
   c. Reasoning Do you think your model also applies to adult males? Explain.

Women's Shoe Sizes

U.S. Size	European Size
1	31
3	34
5	36
7	39
9	41
11	44

SOURCE: *Sizes*

14. Sales Suppose you manufacture and sell tarps. The table displays your current sizes and prices.

Tarps

Size	Price	Size	Price
5 × 7 ft	$1.39	18 × 20 ft	$14.39
6 × 8 ft	$1.99	15 × 30 ft	$17.99
8 × 10 ft	$3.19	20 × 30 ft	$23.99
10 × 12 ft	$4.79	20 × 40 ft	$31.99
12 × 16 ft	$7.69	25 × 45 ft	$44.99
10 × 20 ft	$7.99	30 × 50 ft	$59.99
16 × 20 ft	$12.79	30 × 60 ft	$71.99

a. Draw a scatter plot showing the relationship between a tarp's area and its cost. Use area as the independent variable.

b. Use your scatter plot to develop a model relating the area of a tarp to its cost.

c. How good a model do you feel you have? Explain.

d. Is $7.00 a reasonable price for a tarp that measures 10 ft by 15 ft? Explain.

e. Using your model and the prices in the table, determine which tarp size varies the most from your predicted price. How great is the discrepancy between your model and the actual price?

Write an equation for each line.

15. through $(2, 2)$, y-intercept 10

16. x-intercept -2, y-intercept -6

17. y-intercept $-\frac{5}{2}$, x-intercept $-\frac{1}{3}$

18. through $(3.5, -2.3)$, x-intercept 5.1

19. Entertainment Refer to the information below. Suppose you are trying to decide whether to subscribe to cable service or just rent videos.

a. Write an equation to model the cost y of the cable service for 1 month.

b. Write a second equation to model the cost y of renting x movies from the video store. What is the slope? What is the y-intercept?

c. Open-Ended Suppose you currently rent 8 to 12 movies each month. Graph the two equations from parts (a) and (b). Interpret the graph. Use your interpretation to choose between the alternatives. Explain your reasoning.

20. Nutrition The table below shows the relationship between Calories and fat in various fast-food hamburgers.

Hamburger	A	B	C	D	E	F	G	H	I
Calories	720	530	510	500	305	410	440	320	598
Fat (g)	46	30	27	26	13	20	25	13	26

SOURCE: *The Fat Counter*

a. Develop a model for the relationship between Calories and fat.

b. How much fat would you expect a 330–Calorie hamburger to have?

c. Error Analysis A student reports these estimates: 10 g of fat for a 200-Calorie hamburger and 36 g of fat for a 660-Calorie hamburger. Which estimate is *not* reasonable? Explain.

Homework Video Tutor

Visit: PHSchool.com
Web Code: bbe-0204

21. Data Analysis Is the population of a state related to the number of licensed drivers in that state? The table shows population and licensed-driver statistics from a recent year.

a. Which variable should be the independent variable?

b. Draw a scatter plot.

c. Draw a trend line.

d. The population of Michigan was approximately 10 million that year. About how many licensed drivers lived in Michigan that year?

 e. **Writing** Is the correlation between population and number of licensed drivers strong or weak? Explain.

State	Population (millions)	Licensed Drivers (millions)
Arkansas	2.8	1.9
Illinois	12.7	8.1
Kansas	2.7	2.0
Massachusetts	6.4	4.6
California	36.9	22.8
Texas	22.5	14.5

SOURCE: U.S. Census Bureau, National Highway Administration. Go to **www.PHSchool.com** for a data update. Web Code: bbg-9041

22. Multiple Choice At a restaurant, Elena wants to leave a tip that is 15% of the bill B plus $1. Which linear model best describes the total T?

Ⓐ $T = 15B + 1$ Ⓒ $T = 1.15B$

Ⓑ $T = B + 15$ Ⓓ $T = 1.15B + 1$

A linear model for each situation passes through the origin. Find each missing value. Round your answer to the nearest tenth.

23. 47.5 min to jog 5 mi, ■ min to jog 11 mi

24. 8.5 gal of gas to drive 243.1 mi, 3 gal of gas to drive ■ mi

25. $9.45 to buy 7 lb of apples, $17.55 to buy ■ lb

Ⓒ **Challenge**

Vocabulary Tip

Per capita means "for each person." Capita is a form of the Latin word for "head."

26. Social Studies The table at the right shows per capita revenues and expenditures for selected states from a recent year.

a. Show the data on a scatter plot. Draw a trend line.

b. If a state collected revenue of $2000 per capita, how much would you expect it to spend per capita?

c. Ohio spent $3427 per capita during that year. According to your model, how much did it collect in taxes per capita?

State	Per Capita Revenue ($)	Per Capita Expenditure ($)
Arizona	2858	2926
Georgia	3023	3053
Maryland	3535	3573
Mississippi	3608	3710
New Mexico	4780	4587
Nevada	2753	2798
New York	4810	4676
Texas	2835	2723
Utah	3585	3725

SOURCE: U.S. Census Bureau. Go to **www.PHSchool.com** for a data update. Web Code: bbg-9041

d. In that same year, New Jersey collected $3581 per capita in taxes and spent $4039 per capita. Does this information follow the trend? Explain.

27. a. Use the first and last data points to find a linear model for the data in the table at the right.

x	−5	−2	−1	1	3	6
y	22	15	12	8	7	5

b. Use the middle two data points to find a linear model for the data.

c. Which model better represents the data? Can you find a third model that you think best represents the data? Explain.

28. Geometry Write the equation of the perpendicular bisector of the segment with endpoints $(-3, 5)$ and $(7, 1)$.

Multiple Choice Practice

For California Standards and CAHSEE Tutorials, visit PHSchool.com. Web Code: bbq-9045

ALG2 1.0

29. The graph below shows the solutions for which inequality?

$$\xleftarrow{\quad} -5 \; -4 \; -3 \; -2 \; -1 \; 0 \; 1 \; 2 \; 3 \; 4 \; 5 \xrightarrow{\quad}$$

Ⓐ $\left|x - \frac{1}{2}\right| < \frac{5}{2}$ Ⓒ $-2 \le x \le 3$

Ⓑ $\left|x - 2\right| \le 3$ Ⓓ $\left|x + \frac{1}{2}\right| < \frac{3}{2}$

ALG2 1.0

30. Which is NOT a solution of the equation $\left|x + 1\right| - 1 = \left|x\right| - 2$?

Ⓐ -5 Ⓑ -2 Ⓒ -1 Ⓓ 1

CAHSEE
Alg1 8.0

31. What are the slope m and y-intercept b of a line that contains the point $(-4, 3)$ and has the same slope as $x + 2y = 4$?

Ⓐ $m = -\frac{1}{4}; b = 2$ Ⓒ $m = -\frac{1}{2}; b = 1$

Ⓑ $m = -1; b = -1$ Ⓓ $m = -4; b = 2$

CAHSEE
7MG 1.3

32. An equation can be used to find the number of nails per pound. Using the table below, find the equation that best represents y, the total number of nails, as a function of x, the pounds of nails purchased by a carpenter.

Number of pounds of Nails (x)	1.5	4	65
Number of Nails (y)	240	640	10,400

Ⓐ $x = 0.006y$ Ⓑ $y = 0.006x$ Ⓒ $x = 160y$ Ⓓ $y = 160x$

CAHSEE
Alg1 10.0

33. Which expression is equivalent to $(3m - 4)5m - (3m - 4)(2m - 1)$?

Ⓐ $9m^2 - 9m - 4$ Ⓒ $10m^2 - 5m$

Ⓑ $9m^2 - 34m + 4$ Ⓓ $(2m - 1)$

Mixed Review

 for Help

Lesson 2-3

Find each constant of variation. Then find the value of y when $x = -5$.

34. $y = 27$ when $x = -10$ **35.** $y = -36$ when $x = 12$

36. $y = -\frac{2}{5}$ when $x = \frac{1}{3}$ **37.** $y = -\frac{21}{4}$ when $x = -\frac{5}{8}$

Lesson 2-1

Find the range of each function when the domain is $\{-3, -1, 0, 1.5, 4\}$.

38. $f(x) = 2x - 1$ **39.** $y = -(x - 5)$ **40.** $y = x^2 + 3$

41. $g(x) = \frac{x - 4}{2}$ **42.** $y = 100x + 1$ **43.** $y = 9 - 2x$

Skills Handbook

44. Track Svetlana Masterkova of Russia set a record for running the mile, in 4 minutes 12.56 seconds.
  a. Find Svetlana's rate in feet per second. How far did she run in 100 seconds?
  b. Write an equation that relates the distance she ran to time. Use feet per second as the unit.
  c. Calculate Svetlana's speed in miles per hour.

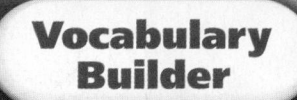

High-Use Academic Words

High-use academic words are words that you often see in textbooks and on tests. These words are not math vocabulary terms, but they are important for you to know to be successful in mathematics.

Words to Learn: Direction Words

Some words tell you what to do in a problem. You need to understand what these words are asking so that you give the correct answer.

Word(s)	Meaning
Explain (after a "yes–no" question)	"Yes" or "no" is only part of the correct answer. You must also write your reasons for your answer.
Determine whether	This is another form of a "yes–no" question. For a correct answer, you must show your process or support your "yes" or "no" response with evidence or reasons.

EXERCISES

1. If the fire alarm sounds, do you know what to do? Explain.

2. Determine whether physical education classes could be held outdoors today.

3. Suppose that a "yes–no" question asks you to "explain."
   a. Does a correct answer with poor reasons have any value? Explain.
   b. Does an incorrect answer with good reasons have any value? Explain.

The library keeps information on overdue-book returns. A five-day record is shown in the table.

4. Determine whether the overdue fines vary directly with the total number of days overdue.

5. Does the total number of days overdue vary directly with the number of overdue books returned? Explain.

6. In general, if x varies directly with y and y varies directly with z, does x vary directly with z? Explain.

7. Explain why the equation $y = 0.15x$ models the amount of fines from overdue books.

8. Word Knowledge Think about the word *model*.
   a. Choose the letter for how well you know the word.
      A. I know its meaning.
      B. I've seen it, but I don't know its meaning.
      C. I don't know it.
   b. Research Look up *model* in a dictionary or online. Write any definition that might apply to its use in mathematics.
   c. Write a sentence involving mathematics that uses the word *model*.

Overdue-Book Returns

Number of Books	Total Days Overdue	Overdue Fines ($)
21	32	4.80
12	20	3.00
30	44	6.60
9	16	2.40
18	28	4.20

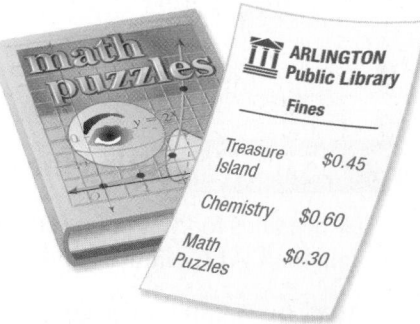

The direct variation $y = 0.15x$ models the total fines y in dollars for x days of overdue books.

Finding a Line of Best Fit

You can use your graphing calculator to display data sets, draw scatter plots, and draw a line to fit the data. The line is the linear regression line—a line of best fit. The LinReg feature on your calculator fits the model $y = ax + b$ to the data.

1 ACTIVITY Finding the LinReg Line of Best Fit

When a honeybee finds a source of food, it returns to the beehive and communicates to other bees the direction and distance of the source. The bee makes a loop, waggles its belly along a line, makes another loop, and then another waggle. The bee repeats its dance several times. The time for each cycle (one loop and waggle) reveals the approximate distance to the food source.

| Distance to Food (km) | 1.35 | 1.5 | 1.5 | 2 | 2.15 | 2.65 | 2.75 | 3.5 | 4 | 5 | 6 |
| Cycle Time (seconds) | 3.5 | 3.8 | 3.9 | 4.4 | 4.3 | 5 | 5.1 | 5.6 | 6 | 7 | 7.6 |

Enter the given data on your calculator. Show a scatter plot of the data. Find the LinReg line of best fit. Then show a graph of the line.

Step 1 Clear any existing lists, and clear any equations from Y= .

Step 2 Enter the data. Press STAT ENTER . Enter the x-values in L1 and the y-values in L2.

Step 3 Find the LinReg line of best fit. Press STAT ▶ 4 ENTER to find LinReg(ax+b) values. Press Y= VARS 5 ▶ ▶ 1 to enter the regression equation as Y1.

Step 4 Draw the graph. Use the STAT PLOT feature and press 1 ENTER to turn on Plot 1.

Use the ▼ key to move down the rows to select a scatter plot using L1 and L2. Press ZOOM 9 to show the scatter plot and the line of best fit.

2 ACTIVITY Using the Line of Best Fit to Predict

A bee finds food 3 km from the hive. Use the Activity 1 line of best fit and the CALC feature to predict the time of a waggle dance cycle.

With the graph shown, select the CALC feature. Press 1, then 3 ENTER to see the y-value for $x = 3$. A waggle dance cycle should take about 5.2 s.

3 ACTIVITY Using the Line of Best Fit to Estimate

A waggle dance cycle is 7.4 s. Use the line of best fit from Activity 1 and the TRACE feature to estimate the distance to the food source.

With the graph shown on the screen, press TRACE ▲ . Then press ▶ or ◀ to get the *y*-value (shown on the screen) as close to 7.4 as possible. You may have to adjust the window dimension Xmax to allow for a large enough trace. The food source is approximately 5.6 km from the beehive.

EXERCISES

In MODE , on the second line, fix the number of decimal places to be 2. Then the slope and *y*-intercept values of the LinReg line will round to the nearest hundredth.

1. Find the LinReg line of best fit for this data set.
   $\{(-5, 6.3), (-4, 5.6), (-3, 4.8), (-2, 3.1), (-1, 2.5), (0, 1.0), (1, -1.4)\}$

2. **Health** Find the LinReg line of best fit for the National Health Expenditures data. Then predict national health expenditures for 2010. (*Hint:* You may have to expand the calculator window to include the year 2010 on the screen.)

Year	1997	1998	1999	2000	2001	2002
National Health Expenditures (billions of dollars)	1093	1150	1223	1309	1421	1553

3. **Congress** Find the LinReg line of best fit for the data below. Then estimate the number of U. S. Representatives for California. California's population for 2000 was 33.9 million.

State	AZ	CO	CT	GA	IL	MO	OH	RI	UT	WA	WI
Population (millions)	5.6	4.6	3.5	8.7	13	5.7	11	1.1	2.4	6.1	5.5
Representatives	8	7	5	13	19	9	18	2	3	9	8

4. There are different ways to find a line of best fit. The line of best fit found by the *least squares* method passes through the point $(\overline{x}, \overline{y})$, where $\overline{x}$ is the mean of the *x*-values of the data points (x, y), and $\overline{y}$ is the mean of the *y*-values.

   a. In MODE , change the number of fixed decimal places to 3. Use the data in the table below. Enter the numbers of teachers in L1. Enter the average salaries in L2. Find the LinReg line of best fit.

   Numbers and Average Salaries of Classroom Teachers

Year	1999	2000	2001	2002
Teachers (millions)	2.81	2.89	2.94	2.98
Average Salary (thousands of dollars)	40.5	41.8	43.4	44.6

   b. Calculate $\overline{x}$ and $\overline{y}$, the means for each data set. (To find $\overline{x}$, for example, press 2nd STAT ▶ ▶ 3 L1 ENTER .)

   c. Graph the LinReg line of best fit. Select the CALC feature. Press 1, enter the value of $\overline{x}$, and then press ENTER . Compare the *y*-value shown to $\overline{y}$.

   d. **Critical Thinking** Does $(\overline{x}, \overline{y})$ lie on the LinReg line of best fit? From this result can you conclude that the LinReg line of best fit and the least squares line of best fit are the same? are different? Explain.

2-5

Absolute Value Functions and Graphs

 California Content Standards

ALG2 1.0 Students solve equations and inequalities involving absolute value. *Develop*

What You'll Learn
- To graph absolute value functions

. . . And Why

To model distance, as in Example 4

✓ **Check Skills You'll Need** **for Help** Lesson 2-2

Graph each equation for the given domain and range.

1. $y = x$ for real numbers x and $y \geq 0$

2. $y = 2x - 4$ for real numbers x and $y \geq 0$

3. $y = -x + 6$ for real numbers x and $y \leq 3$

◀》 **New Vocabulary** • absolute value function • vertex

---

1 ▼ **Graphing Absolute Value Functions**

A function of the form $f(x) = |mx + b| + c$, where $m \neq 0$, is an **absolute value function.** The related equation $y = |mx + b| + c$ is an absolute value equation in two variables. Graphs of absolute value equations in two variables look like angles.

$y = |x|$

$y = |2x - 4|$

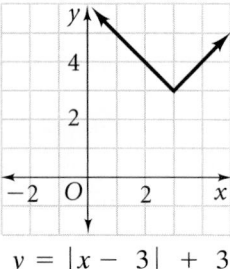

$y = |x - 3| + 3$

Vocabulary Tip

Vertex means "turning point."

The **vertex** of a function is a point where the function reaches a maximum or minimum. In general, the vertex of $y = |mx + b| + c$ is located at $\left(-\frac{b}{m}, c\right)$. In the middle graph above, the x-coordinate of the vertex is $-\left(\frac{-4}{2}\right) = 2$.

1 **EXAMPLE** **Graphing an Absolute Value Function**

Graph $y = |3x + 12|$.

Evaluate the equation for several values of x, beginning with $x = -\frac{b}{m} = -\frac{12}{3} = -4$.

Make a table of values.

x	-6	-4	-3	-2
y	6	0	3	6

Graph the function.

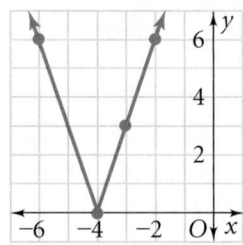

① Graph each equation.

a. $y = |2x - 5|$ **b.** $y = -|x + 1| - 2$

You can use a graphing calculator to graph an absolute value equation.

Graphing Calculator Hint

For a calculator screen that shows *x*- and *y*-intervals of equal width, press ZOOM, and then select ZSquare.

② **EXAMPLE**   **Using a Graphing Calculator**

Graph $y = -|3x + 4| + 6$ on a graphing calculator.

Use the absolute value function.
Graph the equation
$Y1 = -abs(3X + 4) + 6$.

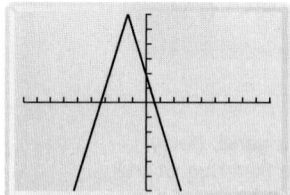

✓ **CA Standards Check** ② Graph each equation on a graphing calculator. Then sketch the graph.

a. $y = -|-x| + 5$ **b.** $y = 3 - \left|\frac{x}{2}\right|$

You can also graph an absolute value equation by first writing it as two linear equations with restricted domains.

③ **EXAMPLE**   **Writing Two Linear Equations**

Graph $y = |x - 3| + 5$.

Step 1   Isolate the absolute value.

$$y = |x - 3| + 5$$
$$y - 5 = |x - 3|$$

Step 2   Use the definition of absolute value. Write one equation for $x - 3 \geq 0$ and a second equation for $x - 3 < 0$.

when $x - 3 \geq 0$	**when $x - 3 < 0$**
$y - 5 = x - 3$	$y - 5 = -(x - 3)$
$y = x + 2$	$y = -x + 8$

Online active math

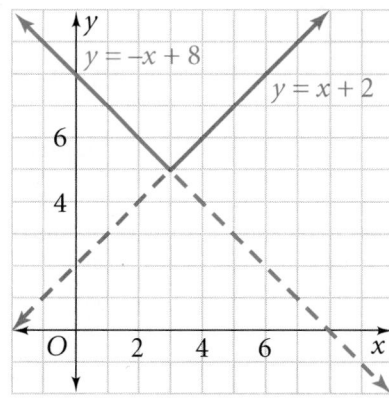

For: Absolute Value Activity
Use: Interactive Textbook, 2-5

Step 3   Graph each equation for the appropriate domain.

When $x - 3 \geq 0$, or $x \geq 3$, $y = x + 2$.

When $x - 3 < 0$, or $x < 3$, $y = -x + 8$.

✓ **CA Standards Check** ③ Graph each equation by writing two equations.

a. $y = \left|\frac{3}{2}x + 4\right| - 3$ **b.** $y = 2 - |x + 1|$

You can use absolute value functions to model time and distance problems. You can consider the time before you arrive at a destination to be negative.

4 EXAMPLE Real-World Connection

Travel Suppose you pass the Betsy Ross House halfway along your trip to school each morning. You walk at a rate of one city block per minute. Sketch a graph of your trip to school based on your distance and time from the Betsy Ross House.

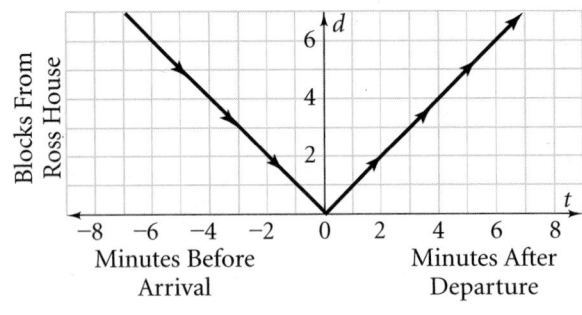

The equation $d = |t|$ models your distance from the Betsy Ross House.

Real-World Connection

According to legend, Betsy Ross made the first flag of the United States in her house in Philadelphia, Pennsylvania.

 CA Standards-Check **4 a. Critical Thinking** Suppose you ride your bicycle to school at a rate of three city blocks per minute. How would the graph of your trip to school change?
b. Sketch a new graph.

 EXERCISES   For more exercises, see *Extra Skill and Word Problem Practice.*

Standards Practice   ALG2 1.0

 A Practice by Example   **Make a table of values for each equation. Then graph the equation.**

Example 1
(page 90)
1. $y = |4x|$ **2.** $y = |4x| - 1$ **3.** $y = |4x - 1|$

 for Help

4. $y = |-3x|$ **5.** $y = |-3x| + 2$ **6.** $y = |-3x + 2|$

7. $y = -|2x|$ **8.** $y = -|2x| + 5$ **9.** $y = -|2x + 5|$

Example 2
(page 91)   **Graph each equation on a graphing calculator. Then sketch the graph.**

10. $y = |x + 2| - 4$ **11.** $y = 4 - |x + 2|$ **12.** $y = 4|x + 2|$

13. $y = \frac{1}{3}|3 - 3x|$ **14.** $y = 3|\frac{1}{3} - \frac{1}{3}x|$ **15.** $y = \frac{3}{2}|x| - \frac{5}{2}$

16. $y = |x| + \frac{1}{2}|x|$ **17.** $y = \frac{1}{2}|x| - |x|$ **18.** $y = \frac{1}{2}|x - \frac{1}{2}|$

Example 3
(page 91)   **Graph each equation by writing two linear equations.**

19. $y = |x + 6|$ **20.** $y = |3x + 6|$ **21.** $y = |3x - 6|$

22. $y = -|x - 5|$ **23.** $y = |2x + 1|$ **24.** $y = \frac{3}{2}|3x - 1|$

25. $y = |x - 2| - 6$ **26.** $y = |\frac{1}{2}x - 4| + 4$ **27.** $y = \frac{1}{2}|\frac{1}{2}x + 2| - 2$

Example 4
(page 92)   **28. Manufacturing** The conveyor belt at a factory operates continuously 24 hours a day, carrying vitamin bottles and moving two feet each minute. Sketch a graph showing the distance in feet from the filling arm of one bottle on the conveyor belt before and after it is filled. Use the *x*-axis for time before and after the bottle is filled and the *y*-axis for distance from the filling arm.

Match each equation with its graph. Each interval is 1 unit.

29. $y = |3x| - 4$ **30.** $y = |3x - 4|$ **31.** $y = 3|x - 4|$ **32.** $y = |3x + 12|$

A.

B.

C.

D.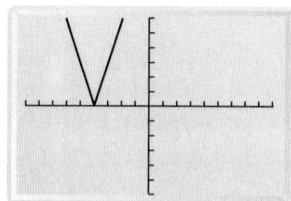

Graph each absolute value equation.

Problem Solving Hint

Before graphing, rewrite each absolute value equation as two linear equations with restricted domains.

33. $y = |4x + 2|$

34. $y = |-3x + 5|$

35. $y = |4 - 2x|$

36. $y = \left|-\frac{1}{4}x - 1\right|$

37. $y = \left|\frac{5}{2}x - 2\right|$

38. $y = \left|\frac{3}{2}x + 2\right|$

39. $y = |3x - 6| + 1$

40. $y = -|x - 3|$

41. $y = |2x + 6|$

42. $y = 2|x + 2| - 3$

43. $y = 6 - |3x|$

44. $y = 6 - |3x + 1|$

45. $y = -|-2x - 1| + 1$

46. $y = 2|x - 3|$

47. $y = -\frac{3}{2}\left|\frac{1}{2}x\right|$

48. $2y = \frac{1}{2}|x + 2|$

49. $\frac{1}{3}y - 3 = -|x + 2|$

50. $-3y = |3x - 6|$

51. Multiple Choice The graph at the right models a car traveling at a constant speed. Which equation best represents the relation shown in the graph?

   Ⓐ $y = |60x|$
   Ⓑ $y = |x + 60|$
   Ⓒ $y = |60 - x|$
   Ⓓ $y = |x| + 60$

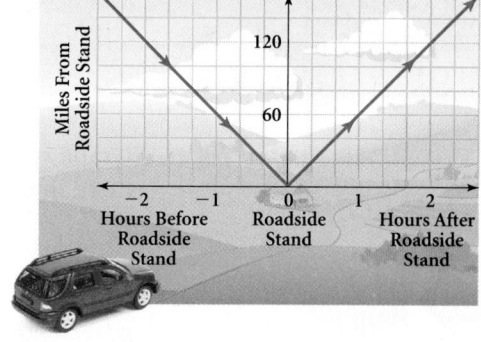

Homework Video Tutor

Visit: PHSchool.com
Web Code: bbe-0205

52. a. Graph the equations $y = \left|\frac{1}{2}x - 6\right| + 3$ and $y = -\left|\frac{1}{2}x + 6\right| - 3$ on the same set of axes.

   b. Writing Describe the similarities and differences in the graphs.

C **Challenge**   **Graph each absolute value equation.**

53. $y = |3x| - x\left|\frac{1}{3}\right|$

54. $y = x - |2x|$

55. $y = |2x| - x$

56. $y = \frac{1}{2}|x - 3| + 5$

57. $y = \frac{1}{2}|x| + 4|x - 1|$

58. $y = |x + 1| + |x|$

59. a. Open-Ended Find two absolute value equations with graphs that share a vertex.

   b. Find two absolute value equations with graphs that share part of a ray.

For California Standards and CAHSEE Tutorials, visit PHSchool.com. Web Code: bbq-9045

ALG2 1.0

60. The table at the right shows values for an absolute value function. What is the equation for this function?

x	y
−3	3
3	1
4	2

Ⓐ $y = |2x| - 3$ Ⓒ $y = |x - 1| - 1$

Ⓑ $y = |x + 1| + 1$ Ⓓ $y = 3|x - 1| - 9$

**CAHSEE
7NS 1.7**

61. Anthony's weekly salary is $400. If he earns a 5% increase each year, what will be his weekly salary, in dollars, two years from now?

Ⓐ $440   Ⓑ $441   Ⓒ $655   Ⓓ $900

**CAHSEE
7MR 1.1**

62. A square is shown below.

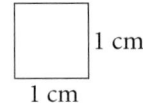

1 cm

1 cm

How many of these squares can fit together without any gaps in order to make a similar figure with a perimeter of 36 centimeters?

Ⓐ 36 squares   Ⓑ 72 squares   Ⓒ 81 squares   Ⓓ 100 squares

ALG2 1.0

63. Solve $|x - 3| = x - 4$.

Ⓐ −1.5   Ⓑ 1   Ⓒ 3.5   Ⓓ no solution

**CAHSEE
7MG 2.4**

64. A map has a scale of 3 cm = 17 km. On the map, Target Rock is 23.1 cm from Lake Montauk. How far is Target Rock from Lake Montauk?

Ⓐ 4.1 km   Ⓑ 78.7 km   Ⓒ 130.9 km   Ⓓ 392.7 km

Mixed Review

Lesson 2-4

Graph each set of data. Decide whether a linear model is reasonable. If so, draw a trend line and write its equation.

65. $\{(0, -5), (5, 25), (7, 44), (9, 70), (11, 90)\}$

66. $\{(-10, 0), (-4, 4), (-1, 6), (2, 8), (5, 10)\}$

67. $\{(-5, 6), (-1, 4), (0, 5), (3, 8), (4, 7)\}$

68. $\{(0, 7), (2, 6), (5, 4.5), (6, 4), (9, 2.5)\}$

Lesson 2-4

Find the slope of each line.

69. $3x + y = 1$ **70.** $5y - 20x = 6$ **71.** $y = \frac{-x}{9}$

72. $12x = 3y - 2$ **73.** $\frac{x}{2} + \frac{y}{3} = 1$ **74.** $0.1y = 0.5x + 0.1$

75. A tutor earns $18 per hour. Write a function to model the tutor's earnings after h hours. What kind of function is this?

Lesson 1-3

Solve each equation.

76. $17x = 187$ **77.** $13c - 26 = 91$ **78.** $2(a - 6) + 11 = 25$

79. $7(b + 3) - 18(1 - b) = 103$ **80.** $6(m + 3) = 3(5 - m) + 66$

2-6 Families of Functions

 California Content Standards

ALG2 1.0 Students solve equations involving absolute value. *Develop*

What You'll Learn

- To analyze translations
- To analyze stretches, shrinks, and reflections

. . . And Why

To analyze a fabric design, as in Example 3

 Check Skills You'll Need

GO for Help Lessons 2-2 and 2-5

Graph each pair of functions on the same coordinate plane.

1. $y = x, y = x + 4$
2. $y = -2x, y = -2x - 3$
3. $y = |x|, y = |x| - 2$
4. $y = -|2x|, y = -|2x| + 1$
5. $y = |x|, y = |x - 1|$
6. $y = -\left|\frac{1}{2}x\right|, y = -\left|\frac{1}{2}x + 2\right|$

🔊 **New Vocabulary**
- parent function
- translation
- stretch
- shrink
- reflection
- transformation
- parameter

---

1 Translations

Vocabulary Tip

<u>Translate</u> is a synonym for <u>transfer</u>.

Technology Activity: A Family of Functions

The four functions in each group are related. Graph each set of functions in the same viewing window. Explain how they are related.

1. $y_1(x) = |x|$ $y_2(x) = |x| + 2$ $y_3(x) = |x| + 4$ $y_4(x) = |x| - 2$

2. $y_1(x) = |x|$ $y_2(x) = |x + 2|$ $y_3(x) = |x + 4|$ $y_4(x) = |x - 2|$

3. $y_1(x) = |x|$ $y_2(x) = 2|x|$ $y_3(x) = 4|x|$ $y_4(x) = \frac{1}{2}|x|$

4. $y_1(x) = |x|$ $y_2(x) = -|x|$ $y_3(x) = 2|x|$ $y_4(x) = -2|x|$

Use the graphs from parts 1–4 to predict the graph of each function below. On graph paper and without plotting points, sketch what you think the graph of *f* should be. Then check your sketch on a graphing calculator.

5. $f(x) = |x + 4| - 2$
6. $f(x) = -2|x| + 4$

7. Sketch what you think the graph of $f(x) = -3|x + 2| - 1$ should be. Then check your sketch on a graphing calculator.

8. Considering all the functions in Exercises 1–7, which function would you call the simplest? Explain.

A family of functions is made up of functions with certain common characteristics.

A **parent function** is the simplest function with these characteristics. The equations of the functions in a family resemble each other. So do the graphs. Offspring of parent functions include translations, stretches, and shrinks.

A **translation** shifts a graph horizontally, vertically, or both. It results in a graph of the same shape and size but possibly in a different position.

The parent absolute value function is $y = |x|$. For a positive number k, $y = |x| \pm k$ is a vertical translation. To graph the function $y = |x| + k$, translate the graph of the parent function up k units. To graph the function $y = |x| - k$, translate the graph of the parent down k units.

1 EXAMPLE — Vertical Translations

a. Describe the translation $y = |x| - 3$ and draw its graph.

$y = |x| - 3$ is a translation of $y = |x|$ by 3 units downward. Each y-value for $y = |x| - 3$ is 3 less than the corresponding y-value for $y = |x|$.

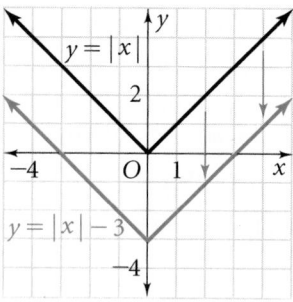

b. Write an equation to translate $y = |x|$ up $\frac{1}{2}$ unit.

An equation that translates $y = |x|$ up $\frac{1}{2}$ unit is $y = |x| + \frac{1}{2}$.

Real-World Connection

Translations of two lines result in the diamond shapes in this window.

✓ **CA Standards Check** **1 a.** Describe the translation $y = |x| + 1$. Then draw the graphs of $y = |x|$ and $y = |x| + 1$ in the same coordinate plane.

b. Write an equation for the translation of $y = |x|$ down $\frac{1}{2}$ unit; Up 3.5 units.

Horizontal translations of the parent function $y = |x|$ share some of the characteristics of vertical translations.

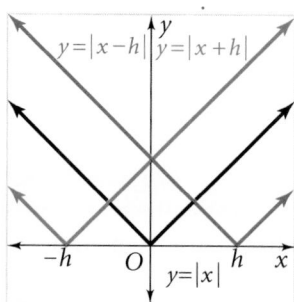

For a positive number h, $y = |x \pm h|$ is a horizontal translation. To graph the function $y = |x - h|$, translate the graph of the parent function right h units. To graph the function $y = |x + h|$, translate the graph left h units.

2 EXAMPLE — Horizontal Translations

a. The blue graph at the right is a translation of $y = |x|$. Write an equation for the graph.

The graph of $y = |x|$ is translated 5 units to the right. An equation for the graph is $y = |x - 5|$.

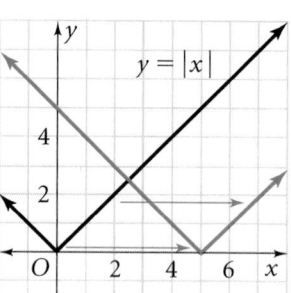

b. Describe the translation $y = |x + 3|$ and draw its graph.

$y = |x + 3|$ is a translation of $y = |x|$ by 3 units to the left.

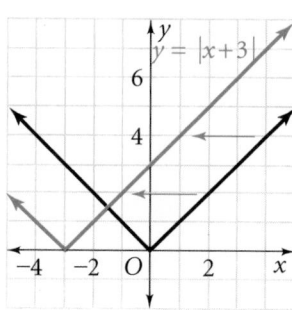

2 a. The graph is a translation of $y = |x|$.
Write an equation for the graph.
b. Describe the translation $y = |x - 1|$. Then draw
the graphs of $y = |x|$ and $y = |x - 1|$ in the same
coordinate plane.

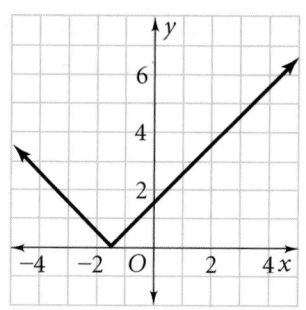

The parent absolute value function is $y = |x|$. For values h and k, $y = |x - h| + k$
is a combined translation of h units horizontally and k units vertically.

 Key Concepts

Summary	**The Family of Absolute Value Functions**

Vertical Translation

Parent function:	$y = |x|$	$y = f(x)$
Translation up k units, $k > 0$:	$y = |x| + k$	$y = f(x) + k$
Translation down k units, $k > 0$:	$y = |x| - k$	$y = f(x) - k$

Horizontal Translation

Parent function:	$y = |x|$	$y = f(x)$
Translation right h units, $h > 0$:	$y = |x - h|$	$y = f(x - h)$
Translation left h units, $h > 0$:	$y = |x + h|$	$y = f(x + h)$

Combined Translation $y = |x - h| + k$ $y = f(x - h) + k$
(right h units, up k units)

3 EXAMPLE   **Real-World** 🌐 **Connection**

Fabric Design   Describe possible translations of Figures A and B
in the Nigerian textile design below.

For: Translating Activity
Use: Interactive Textbook, 2-6

A translation of Figure A   A translation of Figure B
5 units up or 5 units down   about 5 units left and about 3 units up

 ✓ CA Standards Check   **3** Describe a possible translation of Figure C in the textile design.

A vertical **stretch** multiplies all y-values by the same factor greater than 1, thereby stretching a graph vertically. A vertical **shrink** reduces y-values by a factor between 0 and 1, thereby compressing the graph vertically.

More formally, for the parent function $y = |x|$ and a number a, $a > 1$, $y = a|x|$ is a vertical stretch. For $0 < a < 1$, $y = a|x|$ is a vertical shrink.

4   EXAMPLE   Graphing $y = a|x|$

a. Describe and then draw the graph of $y = 2|x|$.

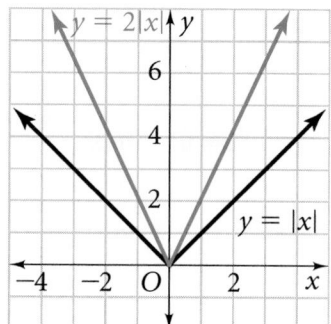

$y = 2|x|$ is a vertical stretch of $y = |x|$ by a factor of 2. Each y-value for $y = 2|x|$ is twice the corresponding y-value for $y = |x|$.

Note that $(2, 2)$ lies on $y = |x|$, whereas $(2, 4)$ lies on $y = 2|x|$.

b. Write an equation for a vertical shrink of $y = |x|$ by a factor of $\frac{1}{2}$.

A vertical shrink of $y = |x|$ by a factor of $\frac{1}{2}$ is $y = \frac{1}{2}|x|$.

✓**CA Standards Check**   **4 a.** Describe the stretch or shrink $y = \frac{1}{3}|x|$. Then draw the graphs of $y = |x|$ and $y = \frac{1}{3}|x|$ in the same coordinate plane.

        b. Write an equation for the vertical stretch of $y = |x|$ by a factor of 3.

A **reflection** across the x-axis changes y-values to their opposites. When you change the y-values of a graph to their opposites, the graph reflects across the x-axis.

For the parent function $y = |x|$, indeed for any function of the form $y = a|x|$, multiplying by –1 gives the reflection $y = -a|x|$, whose graph is a reflection of $y = a|x|$ across the x-axis.

5   EXAMPLE   Graphing $y = -a|x|$

Problem Solving Hint

Learn to recognize the parent function from the shape of the graph.

Multiple Choice Which equation describes the graph?

Ⓐ $y = \frac{1}{2}|x|$

Ⓑ $y = \frac{1}{2}x$

Ⓒ $y = -\frac{1}{2}|x|$

Ⓓ $y = -\frac{1}{2}x$

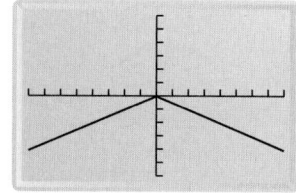

The parent function is $y = |x|$. This is a reflection of $y = \frac{1}{2}|x|$ across the x-axis.
The answer is C.

✓**CA Standards Check**   **5** A function is a vertical stretch of $y = |x|$ by a factor of 5. Write an equation for the reflection of the function across the x-axis.

What you have learned about the absolute value function extends to functions in general.

Each member of a family of functions is a **transformation,** or change, of a parent function. Algebraically, the transformations take the same form using **parameters,** like h, k, and a. Graphically, the results are similar—shifts, stretches, shrinks, and reflections of the parent function.

 Key Concepts

Summary	Families of Functions: Absolute Value Functions

Vertical Stretch or Shrink, and Reflection in *x*-axis

Parent function:	$y = \lvert x \rvert$	$y = f(x)$
Reflection across *x*-axis:	$y = -\lvert x \rvert$	$y = -f(x)$
Stretch $(a > 1)$ Shrink $(0 < a < 1)$ $\}$ by factor a:	$y = a\lvert x \rvert$	$y = af(x)$
Reflection across *x*-axis:	$y = -a\lvert x \rvert$	$y = -af(x)$

Combined Transformation $\quad y = a\lvert x - h \rvert + k \quad y = af(x - h) + k$

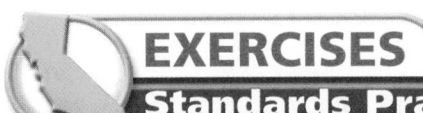 **EXERCISES**

For more exercises, see *Extra Skill and Word Problem Practice.*

Standards Practice ALG2 1.0

 A **Practice by Example**

Example 1
(page 96)

 for Help

For each function, graph the function by translating the parent function.

1. $y = \lvert x \rvert - 3$ **2.** $y = \lvert x \rvert + 4\frac{1}{2}$ **3.** $y = \lvert x \rvert + 2$ **4.** $y = \lvert x \rvert - 6$

Write an equation for each vertical translation of $y = \lvert x \rvert$.

5. $\frac{2}{3}$ unit down   **6.** 4 units up   **7.** 2 units up

Example 2
(page 96)

For each function, identify the translation of the parent function. Then graph the function.

8. $y = \lvert x - 4 \rvert$ **9.** $y = \lvert x + 5 \rvert$ **10.** $y = \lvert x - 1 \rvert$ **11.** $y = \lvert x + 2 \rvert$

Write an equation for each horizontal translation of $y = \lvert x \rvert$.

12.   **13.**   **14.**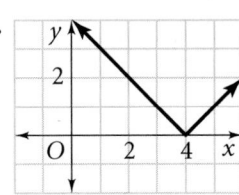

Example 3
(page 97)

Describe a possible translation for each figure.

15. **16.**

Example 4
(page 98)

Graph each function.

17. $y = 4|x|$ **18.** $y = \frac{1}{2}|x|$ **19.** $y = 2|x - 1|$

20. $y = \frac{1}{2}|x| + 2$ **21.** $y = 1.5|x| - 1$ **22.** $y = 0.5|x + 3|$

Write the equation for each graph. Each interval is 1 unit.

23.   **24.**   **25.**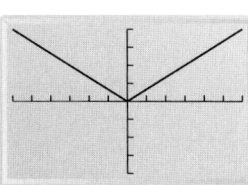

Example 5
(page 98)

26.   **27.**   **28.**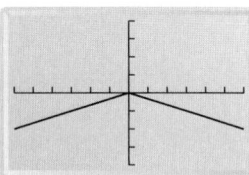

B **Apply Your Skills**

Describe each translation of $f(x) = |x|$ **as** *vertical,* *horizontal,* **or** *combined.* **Then graph each translation.**

29. $f(x) = |x| - 5$ **30.** $f(x) = |x - 5| + 3$ **31.** $f(x) = |x + 1|$

32. $f(x) = \left| x + \frac{1}{2} \right| - 4\frac{1}{2}$ **33.** $f(x) = |x| - 3$ **34.** $f(x) = |x - 3| - 6$

 Write the equation for each graph. Each interval is 1 unit.

35.   **36.**   **37.**

38. Data Analysis Suppose you plot data with years as the independent variable. What type of translation are you making when you start with $x = 0$ rather than a year such as 1998? Explain.

39. Writing Explain why applying a vertical translation and then a horizontal translation produces the same result as applying a horizontal translation and then a vertical translation.

40. a. Graph the parent function $f(x) = x$ and the function $g(x) = 3x$ on a coordinate plane.
  b. Translate the second graph 5 units up. Write an equation for the new line.
  c. Translate the graph from part (b) 2 units right. Write an equation for the new line.
  d. Which equation describes the line you graphed in part (c)?
    A. $y = 3x + 5$ **B.** $y = 3x + 2$ **C.** $y = 3x - 2$
    D. $y = 3(x - 5) + 2$ **E.** $y = 3(x - 2) + 5$
  e. Critical Thinking Write the equation of the translation of $y = mx$ that has a graph passing through point (h, k).

41. Open-Ended Draw a figure in Quadrant I. Use a translation to move your figure into Quadrant III. Describe your translation.

Homework Video Tutor

Visit: PHSchool.com
Web Code: bbe-0206

Each graph shows an absolute value function after a translation 4 units up and 3 units left. Write the equation of the original function.

42.

43.
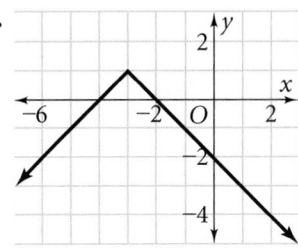

Write an equation for the translation so the graph has the given vertex.

44. $y = -|x|$; vertex $(-5, 0)$

45. $y = 2|x|$; vertex $(-4, 3)$

46. $y = |x|$; vertex (a, b)

47. $y = -|x|$; vertex (p, q)

Graph each pair of functions on the same coordinate plane. Describe the translation that takes the first function to the second function.

48. $y = |x + 1|, y = |x - 5|$

49. $y = |x| + 3, y = |x - 4|$

50. $y = |x - 3|, y = |x| + 1$

51. $y = |x + 1| - 1, y = |x - 2| + 2$

 Challenge

52. Suppose you are playing with a yo-yo, as shown at the right.
  a. Sketch a graph of $h(t)$ to show the height h of the yo-yo above the floor over time t. At $t = 0$, the yo-yo leaves your hand.
  b. Critical Thinking Should your graph be that of a function? Explain.
  c. Suppose you demonstrate your yo-yo ability on an auditorium stage that is 5 ft above the floor. Describe the translation of the graph of $h(t)$ that represents the height of the yo-yo above the auditorium floor.
  d. Choose a function $g(t)$ that represents the height of the yo-yo above the auditorium floor when you are on stage.
  A. $g(t) = h(t + 5)$ **C.** $g(t) = h(t) + 5$
  B. $g(t) = h(t - 5)$ **D.** $g(t) = h(t) - 5$

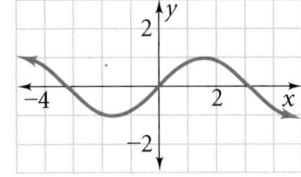

3 ft

53. Use the graph of the function $y = f(x)$ at the right. Sketch the graph of each function.
  a. $f(x + 1)$
  b. $f(x) - 2$
  c. $f(x + 2) + 1$
  d. $-2f(x)$

Multiple Choice Practice

For California Standards and CAHSEE Tutorials, visit PHSchool.com. Web Code: bbq-9045

ALG2 1.0

54. Water freezes at 32 degrees Fahrenheit. Water boils at 212 degrees Fahrenheit. Which inequality best describes the temperatures (in °F) at which water is neither frozen nor boiling?

  Ⓐ $|t - 122| < 90$ Ⓒ $190 < t < 244$
  Ⓑ $|t - 32| < 212$ Ⓓ $|t + 32| < 190$

55. What is the vertex of the absolute value function $y = |2x - 6| + 3$?

  Ⓐ $(3, -3)$ Ⓑ $(-6, 3)$ Ⓒ $(3, 3)$ Ⓓ $(2, 3)$

56. Hal is buying fruit for his store. He plans to spend no more than $50. Peaches cost $2 per pound and apples cost $3 per pound. Which statement best describes all possible quantities Hal might buy, where p represents the number of pounds of peaches and a represents the number of pounds of apples?

  Ⓐ $2p + 3a \le 50$ Ⓒ $2p = 50 - 3a$

  Ⓑ $2p + 3a \ge 50$ Ⓓ $5(p + a) > 50$

Mixed Review

Lesson 2-5

Evaluate each function for five values of x. Then graph each function.

57. $f(x) = |x - 3| + 2$ **58.** $f(x) = |2x + 1| - 3$ **59.** $f(x) = \frac{1}{3}\left|\frac{1}{3}x - 3\right|$

Lesson 1-4

Solve each inequality. Graph each solution on a number line.

60. $x + 7 \le -3$ **61.** $2a + 6 > 15$ **62.** $7.5 - 3b < 12$

Lesson 1-3   **63. Geometry** Keiko, an orca whale who starred in a number of movies, moved into an outdoor pool with a volume of 281,250 cubic feet. The pool's surface is a 150 ft-by-75 ft rectangle. Write and solve an equation to find the depth of the pool.

✓ Checkpoint Quiz 2   Lessons 2-4 through 2-6

Graph each function.

1. $y = x - 5$ **2.** $y = |x + 1| + 4$ **3.** $f(x) = \frac{2}{3}x - 2$

4. $f(x) = |x| - 4$ **5.** $y = |2x - 1| - 2$ **6.** $y = 3x + 3$

Write an equation for each graph.

7.   **8.**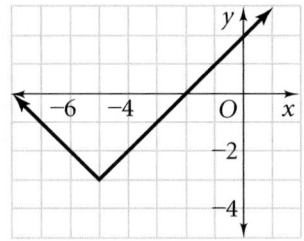

9. a. Use the table below. Model the relation with a scatter plot and a trend line.
  b. Predict the value of y when $x = 10$.

x	1.0	2.0	3.0	4.0	5.0	6.0	7.0
y	-1.5	0.0	1.5	2.0	2.5	3.5	4.0

10. The graph of $y = |x|$ is translated down 5 units and right 4 units. What is the equation of the new graph?

  A. $y = |x + 4| + 5$ **C.** $y = |x - 4| + 5$

  B. $y = |x + 4| - 5$ **D.** $y = |x - 4| - 5$

Two-Variable Inequalities

 California Content Standards

ALG2 1.0 Students solve inequalities involving absolute value. *Master*

What You'll Learn

- To graph linear inequalities
- To graph two-variable absolute value inequalities

... And Why

To solve problems involving combinations, as in Example 2

 Check Skills You'll Need

 for Help Lessons 1-4 and 1-5

Solve each inequality. Graph the solution on a number line.

1. $12p \le 15$ **2.** $4 + t > 17$ **3.** $5 - 2t \ge 11$

Solve and graph each absolute value equation or inequality.

4. $|4c| = 18$ **5.** $|5 - b| = 3$ **6.** $|2h| \ge 7$

 New Vocabulary • linear inequality

---

1 Graphing Linear Inequalities

Activity: Linear Inequalities

1. Graph the line $y = 2x + 3$ on graph paper.

2. a. Plot each point listed below.
$(-2, -3), (-2, -1), (-1, -1), (-1, 5), (0, 4), (0, 5), (1, 6), (2, 3), (2, 7)$
b. Classify each point as *on the line*, *above the line*, or *below the line*.

3. Are all the points that satisfy the inequality $y > 2x + 3$ *above*, *below*, or *on* the line?

Vocabulary Tip

$<$ is less than

$\le$ is less than or equal to

$>$ is greater than

$\ge$ is greater than or equal to

$\ne$ is not equal to

A **linear inequality** is an inequality in two variables whose graph is a region of the coordinate plane that is bounded by a line. To graph a linear inequality, first graph the boundary line. Then decide which side of the line contains solutions to the inequality and whether the boundary line is included.

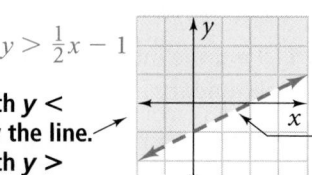

$y > \frac{1}{2}x - 1$

For an inequality with $y <$ or $y \le$, shade below the line.
For an inequality with $y >$ or $y \ge$, shade above the line.

A *dashed* boundary line indicates that the line is not part of the solution.

A *solid* boundary line indicates that the line is part of the solution.

Choose a test point above or below the boundary line. The test point $(0, 0)$ makes the inequality true. Shade the region containing this point.

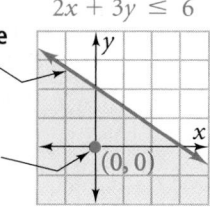

$2x + 3y \le 6$

$(0, 0)$

1 EXAMPLE **Graphing a Linear Inequality**

Graph the inequality $y < \frac{1}{2}x - 3$.

Step 1 Graph the boundary line $y = \frac{1}{2}x - 3$. Since the inequality is *less than*, not *less than or equal to*, use a dashed boundary line.

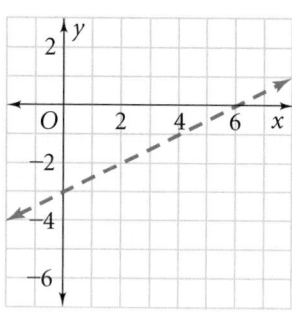

Step 2 Since the inequality is *less than*, y-values must be less than those on the boundary line. Shade the region *below* the boundary line.

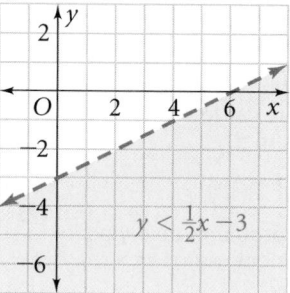

$y < \frac{1}{2}x - 3$

✓ CA Standards Check **1** Graph each inequality.

a. $4x + 2y \leq 4$ **b.** $y \geq 3x$ **c.** $\frac{x}{3} < -y + 2$

You can use linear inequalities to solve problems.

2 EXAMPLE **Real-World 🌐 Connection**

Entertainment At least 35 performers of the Big Tent Circus are in the grand finale. Some pile into cars, while others balance on bicycles. Seven performers are in each car, and five performers are on each bicycle. Draw a graph showing all the combinations of cars and bicycles possible for the finale.

Relate

| the number of performers in cars | plus | the number of performers on bicycles | is greater than or equal to | 35 |

Define Let x = the number of cars.

Let y = the number of bicycles.

Write $7x$ + $5y$ $\geq$ 35

Step 1 Find the intercepts of the boundary line. Use the intercepts to graph the boundary line.

When $y = 0$, $7x + 5(0) = 35$.
$$7x = 35$$
$$x = 5$$

When $x = 0$, $7(0) + 5y = 35$.
$$5y = 35$$
$$y = 7$$

Graph the intercepts $(5, 0)$ and $(0, 7)$. Since the inequality is *greater than or equal to*, use a solid boundary line.

Step 2 Choose a test point not on the boundary line. The test point $(6, 4)$ makes the inequality true. Shade the region containing $(6, 4)$.

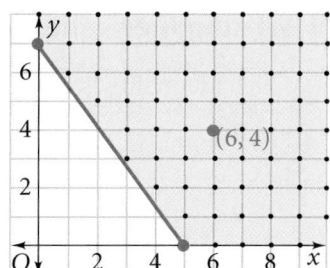

The numbers of cars x and bicycles y are whole numbers. The situation is discrete. In the shaded region, all points with whole number coordinates (shown by dots) represent possible combinations of cars and bicycles for the grand finale.

✓ **CA Standards Check** ② **a.** Find the minimum number of bicycles that will be needed if three cars are available. Then determine three other possible combinations of bicycles and cars.

b. Critical Thinking What inequalities describe the shaded region bounded by the x- and y-axes and the line in the graph above?

---

2 **Graphing Two-Variable Absolute Value Inequalities**

You can graph two-variable absolute value inequalities the same way you graph linear inequalities.

3 **EXAMPLE** **Graphing Absolute Value Inequalities**

Graph each absolute value inequality.

a. $y \leq |x - 4| + 5$

Graph $y = |x - 4| + 5$.
Since the inequality is *less than or equal to,* the boundary is solid and the shaded region is below the boundary.

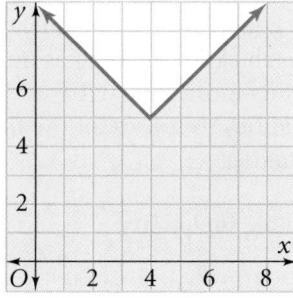

b. $-y + 3 > |x + 1|$

$$-y > |x + 1| - 3$$
$$y < -|x + 1| + 3$$

Graph $y = -|x + 1| + 3$.

Since the inequality is *less than,* the boundary is dashed and the shaded region is below the boundary.

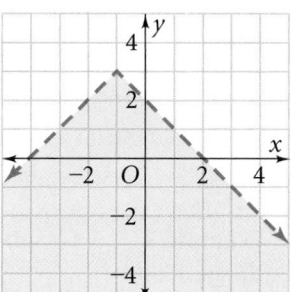

✓ **CA Standards Check** ③ Graph each absolute value inequality.

a. $y > -|x + 2| - 3$ **b.** $2y + 3 \leq -|x - 5|$

You can write an inequality by examining a graph.

4 EXAMPLE **Writing Inequalities**

Multiple Choice Which inequality is represented by the graph?

Ⓐ $y > |x - 3| + 2$

Ⓑ $y < |x - 3| + 2$

Ⓒ $y \geq |x - 3| + 2$

Ⓓ $y \leq |x - 3| + 2$

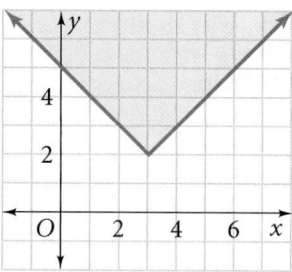

The boundary is $y = |x - 3| + 2$. The boundary is solid. The shaded region is above the boundary. This is the graph of $y \geq |x - 3| + 2$.

● The correct choice is C.

✓ CA Standards Check ④ Write an inequality for each graph.

a.

b.

EXERCISES

Standards Practice

For more exercises, see *Extra Skill and Word Problem Practice.*

ALG2 1.0

Ⓐ Practice by Example

Example 1
(page 104)

Graph each inequality.

1. $y > 2x + 1$ **2.** $y < 3$ **3.** $x \leq 0$

4. $y \leq x - 5$ **5.** $2x + 3y \geq 12$ **6.** $2y \geq 4x - 6$

7. $y > \frac{2}{3}x + \frac{1}{3}$ **8.** $3x - 2y \leq 9$ **9.** $5x > -y + 3$

Example 2
(pages 104–105)

10. Cooking The time needed to roast a chicken depends on its weight. Allow at least 20 min/lb for a chicken weighing as much as 6 lb. Allow at least 15 min/lb for a chicken weighing more than 6 lb.

a. Write two inequalities to represent the time needed to roast a chicken.

b. Graph the inequalities.

Example 3
(page 105)

Graph each absolute value inequality.

11. $y \geq |2x - 1|$ **12.** $y \leq |3x| + 1$ **13.** $y \leq |4 - x|$

14. $y > |-x + 4| + 1$ **15.** $y - 7 > |x + 2|$ **16.** $y + 2 \leq \left|\frac{1}{2}x\right|$

17. $3 - y \geq -|x - 4|$ **18.** $1 - y < |2x - 1|$ **19.** $y + 3 \leq |3x| - 1$

Example 4
(page 106)

Write an inequality for each graph. The equation for the boundary is given.

20. $y = -x - 2$

21. $5x + 3y = 9$

22. $2y = |2x + 6|$

B Apply Your Skills

Graph each inequality on a coordinate plane.

23. $5x - 2y \geq -10$

24. $2x - 5y < -10$

25. $\frac{3}{4}x + \frac{2}{3}y > \frac{5}{2}$

26. $3(x - 2) + 2y \leq 6$

27. $0.5x + 1.2y < 6$

28. $-3x + 4y > -6$

29. $\frac{1}{2}x + \frac{2}{3}y \geq 1$

30. $|x - 1| > y + 7$

31. $y - |2x| \leq 21$

32. $\frac{2}{3}x + 2 \leq \frac{2}{9}y$

33. $0.25y - 1.5x \geq -4$

34. $8x - 4y \geq -3$

35. Open-Ended Write an inequality that has $(10, 15)$, $(-10, 20)$, $(-20, -25)$, and $(25, -10)$ as solutions.

GO for Help

For a guide to solving Exercise 35, see p. 109.

Write an inequality for each graph.

36.

37.

38.

39.

40.

41.

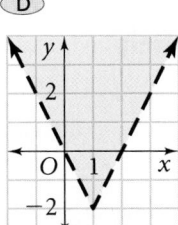

42. Multiple Choice Which graph best represents the solution of the inequality $y \geq 2|x - 1| - 2$?

Ⓐ   Ⓑ   Ⓒ   Ⓓ

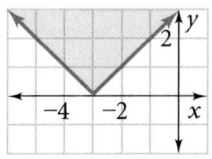

Homework Video Tutor

Visit: PHSchool.com
Web Code: bbe-0207

C Challenge

43. Writing When you graph an inequality, you can often use the point $(0, 0)$ to test which side of the boundary line to shade. Describe a situation in which you could *not* use $(0, 0)$ as a test point.

Graph each inequality on a graphing calculator. Then sketch the graph.

44. $y \leq |x + 1| - |x - 1|$

45. $y > |x| + |x + 3|$

46. $y < |x - 3| - |x + 3|$

47. $y < 7 - |x - 4| + |x|$

Multiple Choice Practice

For California Standards and CAHSEE Tutorials, visit PHSchool.com. Web Code: bbq-9045

ALG2 1.0

48. The graph at the right is the graph for which of the following inequalities?

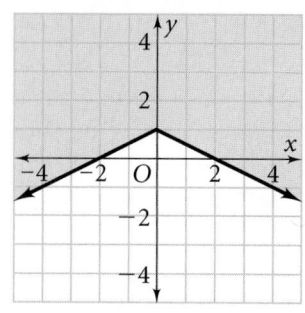

Ⓐ $y \leq \left|\frac{1}{2}x\right| + 1$

Ⓑ $y \leq -\frac{1}{2}|x + 1|$

Ⓒ $y \geq -\frac{1}{2}|x + 1|$

Ⓓ $y \geq \left|\frac{1}{2}x + 1\right|$

CAHSEE Alg1 6.0

49. What are the coordinates of the y-intercept of the line represented by $3x + 2y = -6$?

Ⓐ $(0, -3)$ Ⓑ $(0, -2)$ Ⓒ $(0, 2)$ Ⓓ $(0, 3)$

CAHSEE Alg1 8.0

50. The slopes of two perpendicular lines are negative reciprocals. Suppose one line is represented by the equation $2y - 3x = -7$. What is the slope of the other line?

Ⓐ $\frac{2}{3}$ Ⓑ $-\frac{2}{3}$ Ⓒ $-\frac{3}{2}$ Ⓓ $\frac{3}{7}$

ALG2 1.0

51. Which function has a graph that passes through $(1, 2)$ and $(-1, 4)$?

Ⓐ $y = -|x + 1| + 4$ Ⓒ $y = |2x|$

Ⓑ $y = -|x - 1| + 6$ Ⓓ $y = |x + 1| + 2$

ALG2 1.0

52. A function is described by the equation $f(x) = |x - 2| - 5$. The replacement set for the independent variable is $\{2, 3, 5, 7, 11\}$. Which of the following is contained in the corresponding set for the dependent variable?

Ⓐ -7 Ⓑ -2 Ⓒ 3 Ⓓ 5

Mixed Review

Lesson 2-6

Graph each function by translating its parent function.

53. $y = 2x + 5$ **54.** $y = |x| - 3$ **55.** $f(x) = |x + 6|$

56. $f(x) = x - 2$ **57.** $y = |x + 2|$ **58.** $y = |x - 1| + 5$

Lesson 2-3

Determine whether y varies directly with x. If so, find the constant of variation.

59. $y = x + 1$ **60.** $y = 100x$ **61.** $5x + y = 0$ **62.** $y - 2 = 2x$

63. $x = \frac{y}{3}$ **64.** $-4 = y - x$ **65.** $y = -10x$ **66.** $xy = 1$

67. Commissions The amount of a commission is directly proportional to the amount of a sale. A realtor received a commission of \$13,500 on the sale of a \$225,000 house. How much would the commission be on a \$130,000 house?

Lesson 2-2

Graph each pair of equations on the same coordinate plane.

68. $y = x, y = -x + 5$ **69.** $y = -2x + 1, y = 2x$ **70.** $y = 4x - 1, y = x$

Understanding Math Problems Read the problem below. Then let Carmen's thinking guide you through the solution. Check your understanding with the exercises at the bottom of the page.

Open-Ended Write an inequality that has $(10, 15)$, $(-10, 20)$, $(-20, -25)$, and $(25, -10)$ as solutions.

What Carmen Thinks

These points are not necessarily on the same line. I'll plot the points and see where they lie on the coordinate plane.

The problem asks me to write an inequality with these points as solutions. But the graph of a linear inequality has a boundary line with shading on one side. So, I'll have to choose a boundary line.

There are so many possibilities! I need only two points to draw a line, so I'll use $(-20, -25)$ and $(25, -10)$.

The boundary line is solid since the points lie on it. I can include the other two points in the solution set by shading above the boundary line.

Since I have two points, I can use point-slope form to write the equation of the boundary line.

I can substitute the values of $m, x,$ and y into my equation and simplify.

I need to write an inequality. I shaded above the line toward greater y-values, so the inequality includes "greater than." Since I used a solid boundary line, the inequality is "greater than or equal to."

What Carmen Writes

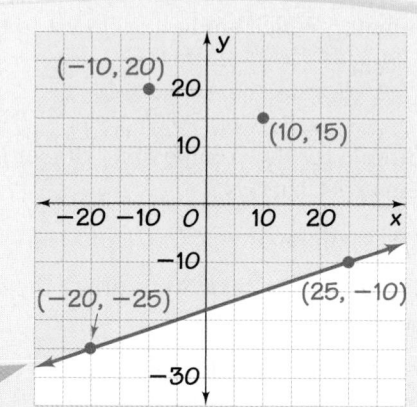

Boundary line through $(-20, -25)$ and $(25, -10)$ has slope $m = \dfrac{-10 - (-25)}{25 - (-20)}$.

$$y - y_1 = m(x - x_1)$$

$$y - (-25) = \frac{-10 - (-25)}{25 - (-20)}(x - (-20))$$

$$y + 25 = \frac{15}{45}(x + 20)$$

$$y = \frac{1}{3}(x + 20) - 25$$

$$y = \frac{1}{3}x - \frac{55}{3} \quad \text{equation of boundary line}$$

$$y \geq \frac{1}{3}x - \frac{55}{3} \quad \text{inequality}$$

EXERCISES

Write a different inequality that has the following ordered pairs as solutions.

1. $(10, 15), (-10, 20), (-20, -25), (25, -10)$ **2.** $(5, 2), (-2, 3), (-4, 5), (4, 9)$

Test-Taking Strategies

Measuring to Solve

To answer some problems, you must first measure with a ruler. Most rulers are labeled with inches on one side and centimeters on the other. You must choose the side that uses the unit of measure given in the problem.

EXAMPLE

Multiple Choice The net of a cylinder is shown at the right. Use a ruler to measure the dimensions of the cylinder to the nearest tenth of a centimeter. Which amount is closest to the volume of the cylinder?

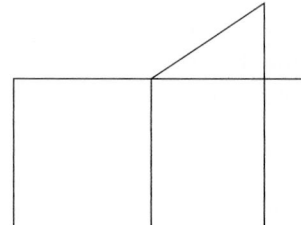

(A) 1.8 cm^3 (C) 2.0 cm^3

(B) 1.9 cm^3 (D) 2.1 cm^3

The formula for the volume of a cylinder (also shown on the Mathematics Chart) is

$$V = Bh, \text{ or } V = \pi r^2 h.$$

Use the centimeter ruler. Measure to the nearest tenth of a centimeter.

$$r = 0.8 \text{ cm}, h = 1.0 \text{ cm}$$

Then, $V = \pi (0.8)^2(1) \approx 2.0 \text{ cm}^3$. The correct answer is C.

EXERCISES

1. The net of a triangular prism is shown at the right. Use a ruler to measure the dimensions to the nearest tenth of a centimeter. Which value best represents the surface area of the prism?

(A) 1.5 cm^2

(B) 4.9 cm^2

(C) 8.9 cm^2

(D) 10.5 cm^2

2. Use a ruler to measure the dimensions of this composite figure to the nearest $\frac{1}{8}$ inch. Which value best represents the area of this composite figure?

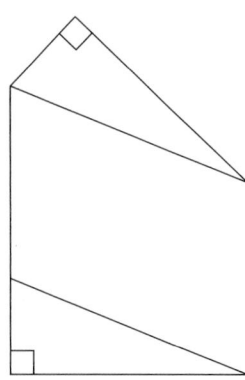

(A) $1\frac{1}{8} \text{ in.}^2$

(B) $1\frac{3}{8} \text{ in.}^2$

(C) $1\frac{5}{8} \text{ in.}^2$

(D) $1\frac{7}{8} \text{ in.}^2$

Chapter 2 Review

Choose the correct term to complete each sentence.

1. In the function $y = f(x)$, y is the (*dependent, independent*) variable.

2. All functions are (*relations, domains*).

3. The graph of a function is (*always, sometimes*) a line.

Go Online
PHSchool.com

For: Vocabulary quiz
Web Code: bbj-0251

4. An equation of the form $y - y_1 = m(x - x_1)$ is in (*point-slope, slope-intercept*) form.

5. The vertex of the graph of an absolute value function is (*always, sometimes*) the lowest point on the graph.

Skills and Concepts

Lesson 2-1

• To graph relations (p. 57)
• To identify functions (p. 59)

A **relation** is a set of ordered pairs that can be represented by points in the coordinate plane or by a **mapping diagram**. The **domain** of a relation is the set of x-coordinates. The **range** is the set of y-coordinates.

When each element of the domain of a relation is paired with exactly one element of the range, the relation is a **function.** You can write a function using the notation $f(x)$, called **function notation.**

Determine whether each relation is a function. Find the domain and range.

6. $\{(5, 0), (8, 1), (1, 3), (5, 2), (3, 8)\}$ 7. $\{(10, 2), (-10, 2), (6, 4), (5, 3), (-6, 7)\}$

8. [graph]

9.

10.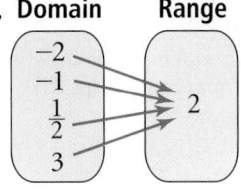

For each function, find $f(-2)$, $f(-0.5)$, and $f(3)$.

11. $f(x) = -x + 4$ 12. $f(x) = \frac{3}{8}x - 3$ 13. $f(x) = -\frac{5}{12}x + 2$

Lesson 2-2

- To graph linear equations (p. 64)
- To write equations of lines (p. 66)

The graph of a **linear function** is a line. You can represent a linear function with a **linear equation.** In a function, the value of y depends on the value of x, so y is the **dependent variable** and x is the **independent variable.**

Given two points on a line, the **slope** of the line is the ratio of the difference of the y-coordinates to the corresponding difference of the x-coordinates. The slope equals the coefficient of x when you write a linear equation in **slope-intercept form.** You can also write a linear equation in **point-slope form** or **standard form.** You can use the slopes of lines to determine whether or not they are parallel, perpendicular, or horizontal. A vertical line has no slope.

Write in standard form an equation for each line.

14. slope $= -3$, through $(4, 0)$

15. through $(2, 3)$ and $(3, 5)$

Find the slope, x-intercept, and y-intercept of each line.

16. $4x - 2y = 3$

17. $Mx = Ny + P$

18. $5 - x = y$

19. a. Write an equation of the line parallel to $x + 2y = 6$ through $(8, 3)$.
  b. Write an equation of the line perpendicular to $x + 2y = 6$ through $(8, 3)$.
  c. Graph the three lines on the same coordinate plane.

Lesson 2-3

- To write and interpret direct variation equations (p. 74)

A linear equation of the form $y = kx$ represents a **direct variation.** The **constant of variation** is k. You can use proportions to solve some direct variation problems.

For each function, determine whether y varies directly with x. If so, find the constant of variation and write the equation.

20.

x	y
−2	3
0	4
2	7

21.

x	y
4	5
6	9
10	17

22.

x	y
0	0
1	1
5	5

Find each constant of variation. Then find the value of y when $x = -0.3$.

23. $y = 2$ when $x = -\frac{1}{2}$

24. $y = \frac{2}{3}$ when $x = 0.2$

25. $y = 7$ when $x = 2$

Lesson 2-4

- To write linear equations that model real-world data (p. 80)
- To make predictions from linear models (p. 81)

You can use mathematical models such as **scatter plots** to show relationships between data sets. You can use the models to make predictions. Sometimes you can draw a **trend line** to model the relation and make predictions.

26. a. Data Analysis Draw a scatter plot of the data below.
  b. Draw a trend line. Write its equation.
  c. Estimate the number of cable TV subscribers in 2010.

Cable TV Subscribers

Year	1980	1985	1990	1995	2000
Millions of Subscribers	17.5	35.4	50.5	60.6	66.3

SOURCE: Television Bureau of Advertising

Draw a scatter plot of each set of data. Decide whether a linear model is reasonable. If so, draw a trend line and write its equation. Then predict the value of *y* when *x* is 15.

27.

x	3	4	5	7	8	9	10
y	5	7	9	10	10	11	13

28.

x	6	7	8	9	10	11	12
y	15.5	14.0	13.0	12.5	12.0	11.5	10.0

Lessons 2-5, 2-6

- To graph absolute value functions (p. 90)
- To analyze translations (p. 95)
- To analyze stretches, shrinks, and reflections (p. 98)

 ALG2 1.0

The **absolute value function** $y = |x|$ has a graph in the shape of a V. It is the **parent function** for the family of functions of the form $y = a|x - h| + k$. The maximum or minimum point of the V is the **vertex** of the graph.

The value of *h* represents a horizontal translation of the parent graph by *h* units left (*h* is positive) or right (*h* is negative). The *k* represents a vertical translation of the graph by *k* units up (*k* is positive) or down (*k* is negative). The *a* represents a vertical stretch for $a > 1$; a vertical shrink for $0 < a < 1$. $y = -a|x|$ is a reflection of $y = a|x|$ across the *x*-axis.

Graph each equation by writing two linear equations.

29. $y = |x - 7|$ **30.** $y = -|x + 10|$ **31.** $y = \frac{1}{3}|2x + 6| + 2$

Write an equation for each translation of the graph of $y = |x|$.

32. 4 units up, 2 units right   **33.** vertex $(-3, 0)$

34. vertex $(5, 2)$ **35.** vertex $(4, 1)$

Graph each function.

36. $f(x) = |x| - 8$ **37.** $f(x) = 2|x - 5|$ **38.** $f(x) = \frac{1}{2}|x - 3| + 3$

39. $y = 3|x + 4|$ **40.** $y = -\frac{1}{4}|x - 2| + \frac{1}{2}$ **41.** $y = -2|x + 1| - 1$

Lesson 2-7

- To graph linear inequalities (p. 103)
- To graph absolute value inequalities (p. 105)

 ALG2 1.0

A **linear inequality** describes a region of the coordinate plane that has a boundary. To graph an inequality involving two variables, first graph the boundary. Then decide which side of the boundary contains solutions. Points on a dashed boundary are not solutions. Points on a solid boundary are solutions.

Graph each inequality.

42. $y \geq -2$ **43.** $y < 3x + 1$ **44.** $y \leq -|x - 5|$ **45.** $y > |2x + 1|$

46. Transportation An air cargo plane can transport as many as 15 regular shipping containers. One super-size container takes up the space of 3 regular containers.
 a. Write an inequality to model the situation.
 b. Describe the domain and range.
 c. Graph the inequality you wrote in part (a).

47. Open-Ended Write an absolute value inequality with a solid boundary that has solutions below the *x*-axis only.

Chapter 2 Test

Find the domain and range. Graph each relation.

1. $\{(0,0),(1,-1),(2,-4),(3,-9),(4,-16)\}$

2. $\{(3,2),(4,3),(5,4),(6,5),(7,6)\}$

Determine whether each relation is a function.

3.

4.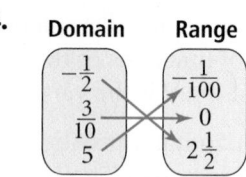

Suppose $f(x) = 2x - 5$ **and** $g(x) = |-3x - 1|$. **Find each value.**

5. $f(3)$

6. $f(1) + g(2)$

7. $g(0)$

8. $g(2) - f(0)$

9. $f(-1) - g(3)$

10. $2g(-4)$

11. Open-Ended Graph a relation that is *not* a function. Find its domain and range.

Find the slope of each line.

12. through $(3,5)$ and $(1,1)$

13. $4x + 3y = 2$

14. through $(-0.5, 0.5)$, perpendicular to $y = -2x - 4$

Write in standard form an equation of the line with the given slope through the given point.

15. slope $= -3, (0,0)$

16. slope $= \frac{2}{5}, (6,7)$

17. slope $= 4, (-2,-5)$

18. slope $= -0.5, (0,6)$

Write in point-slope form an equation of the line through each pair of points.

19. $(0,0)$ and $(-4,7)$

20. $(-1,-6)$ and $(-2,10)$

21. $(3,0)$ and $(-1,-2)$

22. $(9,5)$ and $(8,2)$

23. a. Open-Ended Write an equation of a line with negative slope.
b. Write an equation of the line perpendicular to the line from part (a) passing through $(-6,9)$.
c. Write an equation of the line parallel to the line from part (b) passing through $(12,12)$.
d. Write an equation of the line perpendicular to the line from part (c) passing through $(-1,-4)$.
e. Graph the lines from parts (a), (b), (c), and (d). If they form a polygon, describe it.

For each direct variation, find the constant of variation. Then find the value of y when $x = -0.5$.

24. $y = 4$ when $x = 0.5$

25. $y = 2$ when $x = 3$

26. Transportation The number of minutes a freight train takes to pass an intersection varies directly with the number of cars in the train. A 150-car train passes in 3 min. How long will a 210-car train take to pass?

Graph each function.

27. $y = 3x + 4$

28. $y = |5x - 3| + 1$

29. $y = -|x - 3| + 1$

30. $y = 3 - \frac{2}{5}x$

31. Recreation The table displays the amounts the Jackson family spent on vacations during the years 1996–2006.

Jackson Family Vacation Costs

Year	Cost	Year	Cost
1996	$1000	2002	$2750
1997	$1750	2003	$3200
1998	$1750	2004	$2900
1999	$2000	2005	$3100
2000	$2200	2006	$3300
2001	$2700		

a. Make a scatter plot of the data.
b. Draw a trend line. Write its equation.
c. Estimate the cost to the Jackson family of vacations in 2008.
 d. Writing Explain how to use a trend line with a scatter plot.

Describe each transformation of the parent function $y = |x|$. Then, graph each function.

32. $y = |x| - 4$

33. $y = |x - 1| - 5$

34. $y = -|x + 4| + 3$

35. $y = 2|x + 1|$

36. $y = |x| + 5$

37. $y = -\frac{1}{2}|x + 2| - 3$

Graph each inequality.

38. $y \geq x + 7$

39. $y > |2x + 3| - 3$

40. $4x + 3y < 2$

41. $y \leq -|x + 1| - 2$

Some problems require you to use direct variation to solve a problem.

Tip 1
Some problems give more information than you need. Decide what information you need to answer the question.

A salad dressing recipe calls for $1\frac{1}{3}$ cups of buttermilk, 1 egg, $\frac{1}{2}$ cup of orange juice, and 1 tablespoon of lemon juice. Dan plans to use 2 cups of buttermilk instead. How much orange juice should he use?

Ⓐ $\frac{3}{8}$ cup

Ⓑ $\frac{3}{4}$ cup

Ⓒ $1\frac{1}{6}$ cups

Ⓓ $1\frac{1}{3}$ cups

Tip 2
Use some of the given information to find k, the constant of variation in $y = kx$.

Think It Through
The ratio that shows how the amount of buttermilk changes is

$$k = \frac{2}{1\frac{1}{3}} = 2 \div \frac{4}{3} = \frac{2}{1} \cdot \frac{3}{4} = \frac{3}{2}.$$

A direct variation equation has the form $y = kx$. Let $k = \frac{3}{2}$ and x represent the original amount of orange juice.

$$y = \frac{3}{2}x = \frac{3}{2} \cdot \frac{1}{2} = \frac{3}{4}$$

The correct answer is B.

Vocabulary Review

As you solve problems, you must understand the meanings of mathematical terms. Match each term with its mathematical meaning.

A. linear function

B. direct variation

C. range

D. translation

I. the set of all outputs, or y-coordinates, of a relation

II. shifts a graph horizontally, vertically, or both

III. a function that can be written in the form $y = mx + b$

IV. a function that can be written in the form $y = kx$

Multiple Choice

Read each question. Then write the letter of the correct answer on your paper.

1. Which of the following absolute value inequalities has no solutions in Quadrant IV? **(Lesson 2-7)**

Ⓐ $y + 2 \geq |x - 3|$

Ⓑ $y - 1 > |2x + 6|$

Ⓒ $y > 3 - |5 - x|$

Ⓓ $y \leq |4x| - 7$

2. A meterologist predicts the daily high and low temperatures as 91°F and 69°F. If t represents the temperature, then this situation can be described with the inequality $69 \leq t \leq 91$. Which of the following absolute value inequalities is an equivalent way of expressing this? **(Lesson 1-5)**

Ⓐ $69 \leq |t| \leq 88$

Ⓑ $|t - 69| \leq 88$

Ⓒ $|t - 80| \leq 11$

Ⓓ $|t + 11| \leq 69$

3. For which value of b would the inequality, $3|x - 2| \geq bx - 6$, have infinitely many solutions? **(Lesson 1-5)**

Ⓐ -6

Ⓑ -3

Ⓒ 3

Ⓓ 6

4. Describe the translation of the function $y = |x - 3| + 5$. **(Lesson 2-6)**

Ⓐ $y = |x|$ translated 3 units left and 5 units up

Ⓑ $y = |x|$ translated 3 units right and 5 units up

Ⓒ $y = |x|$ translated 5 units left and 3 units up

Ⓓ $y = |x|$ translated 5 units right and 3 units up

5. Which inequality best describes the graph below? (Lesson 2-7)

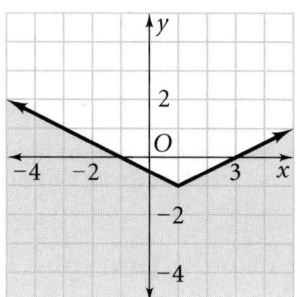

Ⓐ $y < \frac{1}{2}|x + 1| - 1$

Ⓑ $y > \frac{1}{2}|x - 1| - 1$

Ⓒ $y < \frac{1}{2}|x - 1| - 1$

Ⓓ $y > \frac{1}{2}|x + 1| - 1$

6. If a rate of speed r is constant, then distance, rate, and time are related by the direct variation equation $d = rt$, where d represents distance and t represents time. If $r = 30$ miles per hour, which of the following best describes the graph of $d = rt$? (Skills Handbook, p. 884)

Ⓐ A straight line through the point $(0, 0)$

Ⓑ A straight line through the point $(0, 30)$

Ⓒ A parabola through the point $(0, 0)$

Ⓓ A parabola through the point $(0, 30)$

7. Matt drove at a steady speed on the first day of his vacation. The table shows data about the first day.

Time Driving (hours)	Distance (miles)
1.5	87
2.25	130.5
3	174

When Matt stopped for lunch, he had traveled 232 miles. How long did he drive before lunch? (Skills Handbook, p. 884)

Ⓐ 4.25 hours

Ⓑ 4 hours

Ⓒ 3.75 hours

Ⓓ 3.5 hours

8. A recipe for custard sauce calls for 6 egg yolks, $\frac{2}{3}$ cup of sugar, and $1\frac{1}{2}$ cups of hot milk. Chelsea needs more sauce than the recipe yields. She plans to use 1 cup of sugar. How much hot milk should she use? (Lesson 2-3)

Ⓐ $1\frac{5}{6}$ cups

Ⓑ 2 cups

Ⓒ $2\frac{1}{4}$ cups

Ⓓ $2\frac{3}{4}$ cups

9. Which equation is graphed below? (Lesson 2-5)

Ⓐ $y = -3|x + 1| + 3$

Ⓑ $y = 3|x + 1| + 3$

Ⓒ $y = -3|x - 1| + 3$

Ⓓ $y = 3|x + 1| - 3$

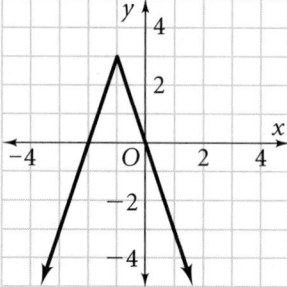

10. Graph the solutions of the inequality $|x - 2| - 3 < 2$. (Lesson 1-5)

Ⓐ

Ⓑ

Ⓒ

Ⓓ

11. Veronica is designing a walkway with 1-foot square tiles. She is considering one of the 4 designs shown below, which all have an area of 6 square feet. Which of the walkway designs has a perimeter of 12 feet? (Skills Handbook, p. 877)

Ⓐ   Ⓒ

Ⓑ   Ⓓ

12. Nina has a rectangular garden in her backyard. She receives some tomato plants from a friend, and decides to double the length of the garden to make room for them. The width of the garden remains the same. Which of the following describes the area of the new garden? **(Skills Handbook, p. 887)**

A It has the same area as the old garden.

B It has twice the area of the old garden.

C It has four times the area of the old garden.

D It has 8 times the area of the old garden.

13. The figure below is a net for a triangular pyramid. What is the surface area of the pyramid? **(Skills Handbook, p. 887)**

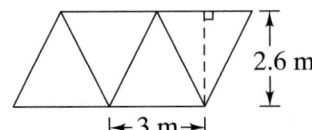

A 7.8 m^2

B 15.6 m^2

C 31.2 m^2

D 78.0 m^2

14. Jesse rents a car for a 3-day weekend. The rental costs $55 per day, plus $0.30 for every mile over 1000 miles that the car is driven. Jesse plans to drive at least 1000 miles. If he drives m miles, which inequality describes the cost C for the car rental? **(Lesson 1-4)**

A $C \geq 3(55) + 0.3(m - 1000)$

B $C > 3(55) + 0.3(1000 - m)$

C $C > 3(55 + 0.3m - 1000)$

D $C \geq 55m + 0.3(m - 1000)$

15. A billboard is mounted in a frame that is $2x + 5$ ft wide and $2x - 5$ ft high. Which expression best represents the perimeter of the billboard? **(Lesson 1-2)**

A $4x$

B $8x$

C $4x^2$

D $4x^2 + 20x - 25$

16. Evaluate the expression, $4x - 2|x - 6| + x^2 - 2$, for $x = -2$. **(Lesson 1-2)**

A -30 C -14

B -22 D 8

17. Which function is graphed below? **(Lesson 2-5)**

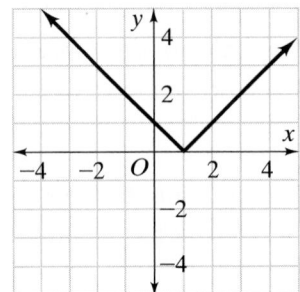

A $y = |x| + 1$

B $y = |x + 1|$

C $y = |x - 1|$

D $y = |x| - 1$

Standards Reference Guide

Algebra 2 Content Standard	Item Number(s)
ALG2 1.0	1–5, 9–10, 16–17

CAHSEE Content Standard	Item Numbers
7AF 4.2	6–8
7MG 2.1	11–13
7AF 4.0	14
7AF 1.1	15

For additional review and practice, see the *California Standards Review and Practice Workbook* or go online to use the

California Standards Tutorials

Visit: PHSchool.com, **Web Code:** bbq-9045

CHAPTER 3

Linear Systems

What You've Learned

California Content Standards

AF 4.1 Students solve two-step linear equations and inequalities in one variable over the rational numbers, interpret the solution, and verify the reasonableness of the results. *Grade 7*

AF 4.2 Students solve multistep problems involving rate, average speed, distance, and time or a direct variation. *Grade 7*

1.0 Students solve equations and inequalities involving absolute value.

Check Your Readiness   **GO for Help** to the Lesson in green.

Combining Like Terms (Lesson 1-2)

Simplify by combining like terms.

1. $3x + (4x - 1)$ **2.** $12 - (p + 7)$ **3.** $(2z + 10) - 8z$ **4.** $(r - 1) - 3$

Solving and Graphing Inequalities (Lesson 1-4)

Solve each inequality. Graph the solutions on a number line.

5. $6a \le 9$ **6.** $8b + 11 > 27$ **7.** $3(24 + 2c) < 0$ **8.** $5(0.2 + d) \le -4$

Graphing Relations (Lesson 2-1)

Graph each relation on a coordinate plane.

9. $\{(0, 4), (-2, 1), (2, 7), (-4, 4), (4, 4)\}$ **10.** $\left\{ \left(0, \frac{1}{2}\right), \left(1, \frac{5}{2}\right), \left(2, \frac{9}{2}\right), \left(3, \frac{13}{2}\right), \left(4, \frac{17}{2}\right) \right\}$

Graphing Equations (Lesson 2-2)

Graph each equation on a coordinate plane.

11. $y = 4x + 1$ **12.** $-6y + x = 3$ **13.** $15x - 3y = 5$ **14.** $x = 2y - 7$

Writing a Linear Model (Lesson 2-4)

15. Each minute, a toll collector serves an average of six motorists. Write an equation to model the average number of motorists this toll collector assists as a function of time. Graph the equation.

Graphing Inequalities (Lesson 2-7)

Graph each inequality on a coordinate plane.

16. $y > 8x + 3$ **17.** $2y + x \le -10$ **18.** $18x - 9y < 2$ **19.** $x \ge 4y - 5$

What You'll Learn Next

▲ Systems of equations can be used to determine the amount of a crop a farmer must harvest to make a profit.

California Content Standards

2.0 Students solve systems of linear equations and inequalities (in two or three variables) by substitution or with graphs.

6.0 Students demonstrate an understanding that linear systems are inconsistent, have exactly one solution, or have infinitely many solutions. *Linear Algebra*

7.0 Students demonstrate an understanding of functions and equations defined parametrically and can graph them. *Mathematical Analysis*

New Vocabulary

◀)) **English and Spanish Audio Online**

- **constraints** (p. 141)
- **coordinate space** (p. 148)
- **dependent system** (p. 122)
- **equivalent systems** (p. 129)
- **feasible region** (p. 142)
- **inconsistent system** (p. 122)
- **independent system** (p. 122)
- **linear programming** (p. 141)
- **linear system** (p. 120)
- **objective function** (p. 141)
- **ordered triples** (p. 148)
- **system of equations** (p. 120)
- **trace** (p. 150)

3-1

Graphing Systems of Equations

 California Content Standards

ALG2 2.0 Students solve systems of linear equations (in two variables) with graphs. *Introduce*
LA 6.0 Students demonstrate an understanding that linear systems are inconsistent, have exactly one solution, or have infinitely many solutions.

What You'll Learn

- To solve a system by graphing

...And Why

To make predictions from data, as in Example 2

✓ **Check Skills You'll Need**

GO for Help Lesson 2-2

Graph each equation.

1. $y = 3x - 2$ **2.** $y = -x$ **3.** $y = -\frac{1}{2}x + 4$

Graph each equation. Use one coordinate plane for all three graphs.

4. $2x - y = 1$ **5.** $2x - y = -1$ **6.** $x + 2y = 2$

🔊 **New Vocabulary**
- system of equations
- independent system
- inconsistent system
- linear system
- dependent system

---

1   Systems of Linear Equations

Technology Activity: Analyzing Graphs

1. Use a graphing calculator to graph each pair of equations.

   a. $y = x + 5$
   $y = -2x + 5$

   b. $y = 3x + 2$
   $y = 3x - 1$

   c. $y = -4x - 2$
   $y = \frac{8x + 4}{-2}$

2. For each pair, answer the following questions.
   a. Do the graphs have any points in common; if so, how many?
   b. Compare the slopes of the graphs. What is the relationship between the slopes and the number of points in common?

3. Copy and complete the table for the graphs of two linear equations.

Description of Lines	How Many Points of Intersection?	Equal Slopes? (yes/no)	Same y-intercepts? (yes/no)
intersecting	■	■	either
parallel	■	■	■
coinciding	■	■	■

 Online
active math

For: Linear Systems Activity
Use: Interactive Textbook, 3-1

A **system of equations** is a set of two or more equations that use the same variables. If the graph of each equation in a system of two variables is a line, then the system is a **linear system**.

A brace is used to keep the equations of a system together. $\begin{cases} y = x + 3 \\ y = -2x + 3 \end{cases}$

A solution of a system of equations is a set of values for the variables that makes all the equations true. You can solve some linear systems by graphing the equations. The points where both (or all) the graphs intersect represent solutions.

1 EXAMPLE Solving by Graphing

Multiple Choice Which ordered pair of numbers is the solution of the system?

$$\begin{cases} x + 2y = -7 \\ 2x - 3y = 0 \end{cases}$$

Ⓐ $(1, -4)$ Ⓑ $(-1, -3)$ Ⓒ $(-6, -4)$ Ⓓ $(-3, -2)$

Graph the equations and find the intersection. The solution appears to be $(-3, -2)$.

Check Show that $(-3, -2)$ makes both equations true.

$x + 2y = -7$	$2x - 3y = 0$
$-3 + 2(-2) \stackrel{?}{=} -7$	$2(-3) - 3(-2) \stackrel{?}{=} 0$
$-3 - 4 \stackrel{?}{=} -7$	$-6 + 6 \stackrel{?}{=} 0$
$-7 = -7$ ✔	$0 = 0$ ✔

● The answer is D.

 CA Standards Check ① Solve $\begin{cases} 2x + y = 5 \\ -x + y = 2 \end{cases}$ by graphing. Check your solution.

2 EXAMPLE Real-World Connection

Sports Winning times for the Olympic 400-m run have been decreasing more rapidly for women than for men. Use the data in the table to find linear models for women's and men's times. Assuming that these trends continue, predict the year in which the women's winning time could equal that of the men.

Winning Times for the Olympic 400-Meter Run (seconds)

Year	1968	1972	1976	1980	1984	1988	1992	1996	2000	2004
Men	43.86	44.66	44.26	44.60	44.27	43.87	43.50	43.49	43.84	44.00
Women	52.03	51.08	49.29	48.88	48.83	48.65	48.83	48.25	49.11	49.41

SOURCE: *The World Almanac*

Step 1 Let $x =$ number of years since 1968.
Let $y =$ winning times in seconds.

Use the **LinReg** feature of a graphing calculator to find linear models.

Men's time: $y \approx -0.01823x + 44.36$
Women's time: $y \approx -0.065x + 50.61$

Step 2 Graph each model. Use the Intersect feature on the graphing calculator. The two lines meet at about $(133.6, 41.9)$.

● If the trends continue, the times for men and women will be equal about 134 years from 1968, in 2102.

Real-World Connection

Cathy Freeman won the 400-m run in the 2000 Olympics.

 CA Standards Check ② **a.** Use the models in Example 2 to predict the winning times for the 400-m run at the Olympics in 2008 and in 2024.

b. Critical Thinking Example 2 assumes that current trends will continue. Explain why that assumption may not be valid.

You can classify a system of two linear equations by the number of solutions. A system that has a unique solution, as in Examples 1 and 2, is an **independent system.** However, not every system has a unique solution.

A **dependent system** has infinitely many solutions. An **inconsistent system** is a system that has no solution.

🔑 **Key Concepts**

Summary	Graphical Solutions of Linear Systems in Two Variables

Intersecting Lines	Coinciding Lines	Parallel Lines
one solution	infinitely many solutions	no solution
Independent	**Dependent**	**Inconsistent**

You can also classify a system of equations without graphing. By comparing the slopes and y-intercepts of the equations, you can find the number of solutions.

3 EXAMPLE Classifying Systems Without Graphing

Classify the system without graphing. $\begin{cases} y = 2x + 3 \\ -2x + y = 1 \end{cases}$

$y = 2x + 3$ ⟵ **Rewrite in slope-intercept form.** → $y = 2x + 1$

$m = 2, b = 3$ ⟵ **Find the slope and y-intercept.** → $m = 2, b = 1$

Since the slopes are the same, the lines could coincide. Compare the y-intercepts. Since the y-intercepts are different, the lines are parallel. There is no solution. The system is an inconsistent system.

✓ **CA Standards Check** ③ Without graphing, classify each system as *independent*, *dependent*, or *inconsistent*.

a. $\begin{cases} 3x + y = 5 \\ 15x + 5y = 2 \end{cases}$ **b.** $\begin{cases} y = 2x + 3 \\ -4x + 2y = 6 \end{cases}$ **c.** $\begin{cases} x - y = 5 \\ y + 3 = 2x \end{cases}$

EXERCISES   For more exercises, see *Extra Skill and Word Problem Practice.*

Standards Practice   ALG2 2.0, LA 6.0

A Practice by Example

Example 1
(page 121)

GO for Help

Solve each system by graphing. Check your answers.

1. $\begin{cases} y = x - 2 \\ y = -2x + 7 \end{cases}$ **2.** $\begin{cases} y = -x + 3 \\ y = \frac{3}{2}x - 2 \end{cases}$ **3.** $\begin{cases} 2x + 4y = 12 \\ x + y = 2 \end{cases}$

4. $\begin{cases} x = -3 \\ y = 5 \end{cases}$ **5.** $\begin{cases} 2x - 2y = 4 \\ y - x = 6 \end{cases}$ **6.** $\begin{cases} 3x + y = 5 \\ x - y = 7 \end{cases}$

7. $\begin{cases} -5x + y = -9 \\ x + 3y = 21 \end{cases}$ **8.** $\begin{cases} y = x \\ y - 5x = 0 \end{cases}$ **9.** $\begin{cases} x = 10 \\ x = y - 10 \end{cases}$

Example 2
(page 121)

For Exercises 10–11, use your graphing calculator. Find linear models for each set of data. Use each model to predict the year in which the quantities will be equal.

10.

Annual U.S. Consumption of Vegetables

Year	Broccoli (lb/person)	Cucumbers (lb/person)
1980	1.5	3.9
1985	2.6	4.4
1990	3.4	4.7
1995	4.3	5.6
1998	5.1	6.5
1999	6.5	6.8
2000	6.1	6.4

SOURCE: *Statistical Abstract of the United States.*
Go to **www.PHSchool.com** for a data update.
Web Code: bbg-9041

11.

U.S. Life Expectancy at Birth

Year	Men (years)	Women (years)
1970	67.1	74.7
1975	68.8	76.6
1980	70.0	77.4
1985	71.1	78.2
1990	71.8	78.8
1995	72.5	78.9
2000	74.3	79.7

SOURCE: U.S. Census Bureau.
Go to **www.PHSchool.com** for a data update.
Web Code: bbg-9041

12. a. Business The spreadsheet shows the monthly revenue and monthly expenses for a new business. Find a linear model for monthly revenue and a linear model for monthly expenses.
   b. Use the models to predict the month in which revenue will equal expenses.

	A	B	C
1	Month	Revenue	Expenses
2	Feb	8000	35000
3	Mar	12000	33000
4	Apr	13000	34000
5	May	18000	32000
6	Jun	20000	31000

Example 3
(page 122)

Without graphing, classify each system as *independent*, *dependent*, or *inconsistent*.

13. $\begin{cases} 7x - y = 6 \\ -7x + y = -6 \end{cases}$

14. $\begin{cases} -3x + y = 4 \\ x - \frac{1}{3}y = 1 \end{cases}$

15. $\begin{cases} 4x + 8y = 12 \\ x + 2y = -3 \end{cases}$

16. $\begin{cases} y = 2x - 1 \\ y = -2x + 5 \end{cases}$

17. $\begin{cases} x = 6 \\ x = -2 \end{cases}$

18. $\begin{cases} 2y = 5x + 6 \\ -10x + 4y = 8 \end{cases}$

19. $\begin{cases} x - 3y = 2 \\ 4x - 12y = 8 \end{cases}$

20. $\begin{cases} x + 4y = 12 \\ 2x - 8y = 4 \end{cases}$

21. $\begin{cases} 4x + 8y = -6 \\ 6x + 12y = -9 \end{cases}$

22. $\begin{cases} 4y - 2x = 6 \\ 8y = 4x - 12 \end{cases}$

23. $\begin{cases} y - x = 0 \\ y = -x \end{cases}$

24. $\begin{cases} 2y - x = 4 \\ \frac{1}{2}x - y = 2 \end{cases}$

B Apply Your Skills

Graph and solve each system. Where necessary, estimate the solution.

25. $\begin{cases} 3 = 4y + x \\ 4y = -x + 3 \end{cases}$

26. $\begin{cases} x - 2y + 1 = 0 \\ x + 4y - 6 = 0 \end{cases}$

27. $\begin{cases} 3x + 6y - 12 = 0 \\ x + 2y = 8 \end{cases}$

28. $\begin{cases} -x + 3y = 6 \\ 2x - y = 8 \end{cases}$

29. $\begin{cases} 3x + y = 3 \\ 2x - y = 7 \end{cases}$

30. $\begin{cases} 2x + 3y = 6 \\ 4x = 6y + 3 \end{cases}$

31. $\begin{cases} 10 - 3x = -3y \\ 2 = 2x + y \end{cases}$

32. $\begin{cases} 3x = -5y + 4 \\ 250 + 150x = 300 \end{cases}$

33. $\begin{cases} x + 3y = 6 \\ 6y + 2x = 12 \end{cases}$

34. $\begin{cases} 2y + x = 8 \\ y - 2x = -6 \end{cases}$

35. $\begin{cases} y = -2x + 6 \\ x - 3y = -6 \end{cases}$

36. $\begin{cases} -x - 2 = -2y \\ 2x - 4y - 4 = 0 \end{cases}$

37. Banking To pay your monthly bills, you can either open a checking account or use an online banking service. A local bank charges $3 per month and $.40 per check, while an online services charges a flat fee of $9 per month.
 a. Write and graph a system of linear equations to model the cost c of each service for b bills that you need to pay monthly.
 b. Find the point of intersection of the two linear models. What does this answer represent?
 c. If you pay about 12 bills per month, which service should you choose? Explain.

Classify each system without graphing.

38. $\begin{cases} 3x - 2y = 8 \\ 4y = 6x - 5 \end{cases}$
39. $\begin{cases} 2x + 8y = 6 \\ x = -4y + 3 \end{cases}$
40. $\begin{cases} 3a + 6b = 14 \\ -a + 2b = 3 \end{cases}$

41. $\begin{cases} 3m = -5n + 4 \\ n - \frac{6}{5} = -\frac{3}{5}m \end{cases}$
42. $\begin{cases} -12x + 4y = 8 \\ y - 4 = 3x \end{cases}$
43. $\begin{cases} -6y + 18 = 12x \\ 3y + 6x = 9 \end{cases}$

44. Fees Suppose you are going on vacation and leaving your dog in a kennel. The Bowowery charges $25 per day, which includes a one-time grooming treatment. The Poochpad charges $20 per day and a one-time fee of $30 for grooming.
 a. Write a system of equations to represent the cost c for d days that your dog will stay at a kennel.
  b. Using a graphing calculator, find the number of days for which the costs are the same.
 c. If your vacation is a week long, which kennel should you choose? Explain.

45. Advertising You and your business partner are mailing advertising flyers to your customers. You address 6 flyers each minute and have already done 80. Your partner addresses 4 flyers each minute and has already done 100. Graph and solve a system of equations to find when the two of you will have addressed equal numbers of flyers.

Open-Ended Write a second equation for each system so that the system will have the indicated number of solutions.

46. one
$\begin{cases} y = -3x + 2 \\ \underline{\quad?\quad} \end{cases}$

47. none
$\begin{cases} y = -4x - 6 \\ \underline{\quad?\quad} \end{cases}$

48. an infinite number
$\begin{cases} 3y = 6x + 7 \\ \underline{\quad?\quad} \end{cases}$

49. Reasoning Is it possible for an inconsistent linear system to consist of two lines with the same y-intercept? Explain.

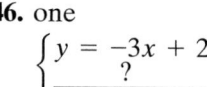 **50. Writing** Summarize the possible relationships for the y-intercepts, slopes, and number of solutions in a system of two linear equations of two variables.

Open-Ended Write a second equation for each system so that the system will have the indicated number of solutions.

51. infinite number of solutions
$\begin{cases} \frac{x}{4} + \frac{y}{3} = 1 \\ \underline{\quad?\quad} \end{cases}$

52. no solutions
$\begin{cases} 5x + 2y = 10 \\ \underline{\quad?\quad} \end{cases}$

53. Write a system of linear equations with the solution set $\{(x, y) \mid y = 5x + 2\}$.

54. Critical Thinking Look back through the exercises on the previous two pages to find several dependent systems. What relationship exists between the equations in each system?

Real-World Connection

Grooming services usually include nail trimming, hair cutting, and tooth brushing.

Homework Video Tutor

Visit: PHSchool.com
Web Code: bbe-0301

Challenge

55. Economics Research shows that in a certain market only 2000 widgets can be sold at \$8 each, but if the price is reduced to \$3, then 10,000 can be sold.

   a. Let p represent price and n represent the number of widgets. Identify the independent variable and the dependent variable.

   b. Use the information above to write a linear *demand* equation.

   c. A shop can make 2000 widgets for \$5 each and 20,000 widgets for \$2 each. Use this information to write a linear *supply* equation.

   d. Find the equilibrium point where supply is equal to demand and profit is a maximum. Explain the meaning of the coordinates of this point within the context of the exercise.

Multiple Choice Practice

For California Standards and CAHSEE Tutorials, visit PHSchool.com. Web Code: bbq-9045

ALG2 2.0

56. Which system of equations is represented by the graph at the right?

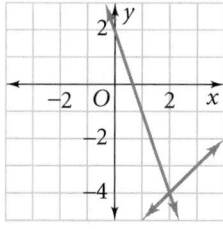

   (A) $y = x;$
       $y = -x + 2$

   (B) $y = x - 5;$
       $y = -2x + 2$

   (C) $y = -x - 6;$
       $y = 3x + 2$

   (D) $y = x - 6;$
       $y = -3x + 2$

CAHSEE 7MR 1.1

57. The figures below show a pattern of dark tiles and white tiles.

   Figure 1   Figure 2   Figure 3

Which rule relates d, the number of dark tiles, to w, the number of white tiles?

   (A) $d = 3w - 2$
   (B) $w = \frac{1}{2}d$
   (C) $d = 2w - 1$
   (D) $w = d - 1$

CAHSEE 7MG 2.1

58. The perimeter of $\triangle ADE$ is 39 units. The perimeter of $\triangle BDC$ is 12 units. If $BC = 5$ units, what is the perimeter of quadrilateral $ABCE$?

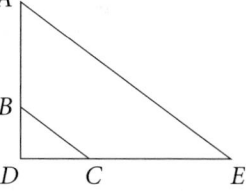

   (A) 22 units
   (C) 46 units

   (B) 37 units
   (D) 56 units

Mixed Review

Lesson 2-7

Graph each inequality on a coordinate plane.

59. $3x - 4y \geq 16$
    60. $-5x > 8y + 4$
    61. $x < -4$

Lesson 2-2

Write an equation for each line.

62. $m = -\frac{2}{3}$; contains $(-9, 4)$
    63. $m = 0$; contains $(3, 4)$

64. $m = 2$; contains $(-2, -3)$
    65. $m = -\frac{1}{2}$; contains $(2, -6)$

Lesson 1-3

Solve each equation and check the solution.

66. $3n = -4(2 + n)$
    67. $-4a + a = 7a - 6$
    68. $\frac{x}{3} + 5 = \frac{1}{6}$

69. $4x - 2 = \frac{1}{2}x$
    70. $\frac{r}{5} + 5 = r - 3$
    71. $2(m - 3) = -4$

Parametric Equations

> **MA 7.0** Students demonstrate an understanding of functions and equations defined parametrically and can graph them.

Parametric equations are equations that express the coordinates x and y as separate functions of a common third variable, called the parameter. You can use parametric equations to determine the position of an object over time.

ACTIVITY

Starting from a birdbath 3 ft above the ground, a bird takes flight. Let t equal time in seconds, x equal horizontal distance in feet, and y equal vertical distance in feet. The equations $x(t) = 5t$ and $y(t) = 8t + 3$ model the bird's distance from the base of the birdbath. Graph the equations. Describe the position of the bird at time $t = 3$.

Step 1 Press **MODE**. Change the function mode to Parametric.

Step 2 Enter the equations.
(When you press **Y=** you will see a list of pairs of equations.)

Step 3 Set the window values as shown.

Step 4 Graph the equations. Press **TRACE** to find $t = 3$.

Three seconds after taking flight, the bird is 15 ft horizontally and 27 ft vertically from the base of the birdbath.

EXERCISES

Graph each pair of parametric equations. Set the window with the t-values at the right. Find the values of x and y at time $t = 3$.

1. $x(t) = t$
$y(t) = -t + 6$

2. $x(t) = -3t$
$y(t) = t - 6$

3. $x(t) = |t - 2|$
$y(t) = t + 2$

```
WINDOW
 Tmin = -10
 Tmax = 10
 Tstep = .1
 Xmin = -10
 Xmax = 10
 Xscl = 1
↓Ymin = -10
```

4. Writing Write a word problem involving the graph of $x(t) = 3t$ and $y(t) = 10t$. Interpret the x- and y-values at times $t = 0$, $t = 5$, and $t = -2$.

Solving Systems Algebraically

 California Content Standards

ALG2 2.0 Students solve systems of linear equations (in two variables) by substitution.
Develop

What You'll Learn

- To solve a system by substitution
- To solve a system by elimination

. . . And Why

To find the cost of joining a health club, as in Example 2

✓ **Check Skills You'll Need**

 for Help Lessons 1-1 and 1-3

Find the additive inverse of each term.

1. 4   **2.** $-x$ **3.** $5x$ **4.** $8y$

Substitute $2y - 1$ **for** x **in each equation. Solve for** y**.**

5. $x + 2y = 3$ **6.** $y - 2x = 8$ **7.** $2y + 3x = -5$

🔊 **New Vocabulary**   • equivalent systems

---

1 **Solving Systems by Substitution**

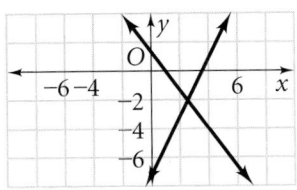

$$\begin{cases} 4x + 3y = 4 \\ 2x - y = 7 \end{cases}$$

Not every system can be solved easily by graphing. Consider the system at the left. Although you can graph each line easily, the exact point of intersection is not obvious. Substitution allows you to find exact solutions without using a graphing calculator.

1 **EXAMPLE**   **Solving by Substitution**

Solve the system by substitution. $\begin{cases} 4x + 3y = 4 \\ 2x - y = 7 \end{cases}$

Step 1 Solve for one of the variables. Solving the second equation for y is easiest.

$$2x - y = 7$$
$$y = 2x - 7$$

Step 2 Substitute the expression for y into the other equation. Solve for x.

$$4x + 3y = 4$$
$$4x + 3(2x - 7) = 4 \quad \textbf{Substitute for } \textbf{\textit{y}}.$$
$$4x + 6x - 21 = 4 \quad \textbf{Distributive Property}$$
$$4x + 6x = 25$$
$$x = 2.5$$

Step 3 Substitute the value of x into either equation. Solve for y.

$$y = 2x - 7$$
$$y = 2(2.5) - 7 \quad \textbf{Substitute for } \textbf{\textit{x}}.$$
$$y = -2$$

● The solution is $(2.5, -2)$.

 CA Standards Check **1** Solve each system by substitution. Check your answers.

a. $\begin{cases} 2x - 3y = 6 \\ x + y = -12 \end{cases}$ **b.** $\begin{cases} 3x - y = 0 \\ 4x + 3y = 26 \end{cases}$

2 EXAMPLE Real-World 🌐 Connection

Fees Refer to the advertisement at the left. The cost of membership in a health club includes a monthly charge and a one-time initiation fee. Find the monthly charge and the initiation fee.

Relate 2 · monthly charge + initiation fee = $100

6 · monthly charge + initiation fee = $200

Define Let m = the monthly charge. Let f = the initiation fee.

Write $\begin{cases} 2m + f = 100 \\ 6m + f = 200 \end{cases}$

$2m + f = 100$ Solve for one of the variables.
$f = -2m + 100$

$6m + (-2m + 100) = 200$ Substitute the expression for f into the other equation. Solve for m.
$m = 25$

$2(25) + f = 100$ Substitute the value of m into one of the equations. Solve for f.
$f = 50$

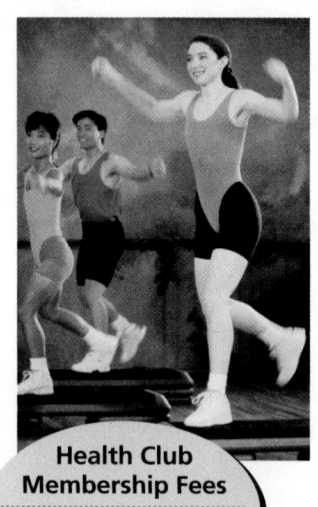

Health Club Membership Fees

2 months: $100
6 months: $200

● The monthly charge is $25, and the initiation fee is $50.

 CA Standards Check ② **Shopping** You can buy CDs at a local store for $15.49 each. You can buy them at an online store for $13.99 each plus $6 for shipping. Solve a system of equations to find the number of CDs that you can buy for the same amount at the two stores.

---

2 Solving Systems by Elimination

You can solve a system of equations using the Addition Property of Equality. If the quantities you add contain a pair of additive inverses, you can eliminate a variable. You can also eliminate a variable by subtracting like terms.

3 EXAMPLE Solving by Elimination

Find the y-value in the solution of $\begin{cases} 4x - 2y = 7 \\ x + 2y = 3 \end{cases}$.

$\begin{aligned} 4x - 2y &= 7 \\ \underline{x + 2y} &= \underline{3} \quad \text{Two terms are additive inverses, so add.} \\ 5x &= 10 \end{aligned}$

$x = 2$ Solve for x.
$x + 2y = 3$ Choose one of the original equations.
$2 + 2y = 3$ Substitute for x.
$y = \frac{1}{2}$ Solve for y.

● The solution is $\left(2, \frac{1}{2}\right)$. The y-value is $\frac{1}{2}$.

 CA Standards Check ③ Solve each system by elimination.

a. $\begin{cases} 3x - 2y = 14 \\ 2x + 2y = 6 \end{cases}$ **b.** $\begin{cases} 4x + 9y = 1 \\ 4x + 6y = -2 \end{cases}$

To make two terms additive inverses, you may need to multiply one or both equations in a system by a nonzero number. In doing so, you create a system equivalent to the original one. **Equivalent systems** are systems that have the same solution(s).

4 EXAMPLE Solving an Equivalent System

Video Tutor Help
Visit: PHSchool.com
Web Code: bbe-0775

Solve the system below by elimination.
$$\begin{cases} 3x + 7y = 15 \\ 5x + 2y = -4 \end{cases}$$

To eliminate the y terms, make them additive inverses by multiplying.

① $3x + 7y = 15$	$6x + 14y = 30$	**Multiply ① by 2.**
② $5x + 2y = -4$	$-35x - 14y = 28$	**Multiply ② by −7.**
	$-29x \quad\quad = 58$	**Add.**
	$x = -2$	**Solve for x.**

$3x + 7y = 15$	**Choose an original equation.**
$3(-2) + 7y = 15$	**Substitute the value of x.**
$-6 + 7y = 15$	**Simplify.**
$7y = 21$	
$y = 3$	**Solve for y.**

● The solution is $(-2, 3)$.

✓ CA Standards Check ④ Explain how to solve the system in Example 4 by eliminating x.

Solving a system algebraically does not always result in a unique solution, as in Examples 3 and 4. You may get an equation that is always true, or one that is never true.

5 EXAMPLE Solving a System Without a Unique Solution

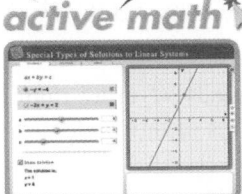

For: Special Solutions Activity
Use: Interactive Textbook, 3-2

Solve each system by elimination.

a. $\begin{cases} 2x - y = 3 \\ -2x + y = -3 \end{cases}$
$\overline{ 0 = 0}$

Elimination gives an equation that is always true. The two equations in the system represent the same line. The system has an infinite number of solutions: $\{(x, y) \mid y = 2x - 3\}$.

b. $\begin{cases} 2x - 3y = 18 \\ -2x + 3y = -6 \end{cases}$
$\overline{ 0 = 12}$

Elimination gives an equation that is always false. The two equations in the system represent parallel lines. The system has no solution.

✓ CA Standards Check ⑤ Solve each system by substitution or elimination.

a. $\begin{cases} -3x + 5y = 7 \\ 6x - 10y = -14 \end{cases}$

b. $\begin{cases} -2x + 4y = 6 \\ -3x + 6y = 8 \end{cases}$

EXERCISES

Standards Practice

For more exercises, see *Extra Skill and Word Problem Practice*.

ALG2 2.0

A Practice by Example

Solve each system by substitution. Check your answers.

Example 1
(page 127)

GO for Help

1. $\begin{cases} 4x + 2y = 7 \\ y = 5x \end{cases}$

2. $\begin{cases} 3c + 2d = 2 \\ d = 4 \end{cases}$

3. $\begin{cases} x + 12y = 68 \\ x = 8y - 12 \end{cases}$

4. $\begin{cases} 4p + 2q = 8 \\ q = 2p + 1 \end{cases}$

5. $\begin{cases} x + 3y = 7 \\ 2x - 4y = 24 \end{cases}$

6. $\begin{cases} x + 6y = 2 \\ 5x + 4y = 36 \end{cases}$

7. $\begin{cases} 3a + b = 3 \\ 2a - 5b = -15 \end{cases}$

8. $\begin{cases} t = 2r + 3 \\ 5r - 4t = 6 \end{cases}$

9. $\begin{cases} y = 2x - 1 \\ 3x - y = -1 \end{cases}$

10. $\begin{cases} 2m + 4n = 10 \\ 3m + 5n = 11 \end{cases}$

11. $\begin{cases} -6 = 3x - 6y \\ 4x = 4 + 5y \end{cases}$

12. $\begin{cases} r + s = -12 \\ 2r - 3s = 6 \end{cases}$

Example 2
(page 128)

13. **Fund-Raising** Suppose you have signed up for a bike-a-thon to raise money for charity. One person is sponsoring you at a rate of $.50 per mile. Each of the other sponsors plans to donate $15 no matter how far you bike.
    a. Write a system of equations to model the donation d for m miles biked.
    b. For how many miles will all sponsors donate the same amount?

14. **Transportation** A youth group with 26 members is going skiing. Each of the five chaperones will drive a van or a sedan. The vans can seat seven people, and the sedans can seat five people. How many of each type of vehicle could transport all 31 people to the ski area in one trip?

15. Suppose you have a part-time job delivering packages. Your employer pays you at a flat rate of $7 per hour. You discover that a competitor pays employees $2 per hour plus $.35 per delivery.
    a. Write a system of equations to model the pay p for d deliveries. Assume a four-hour shift.
    b. How many deliveries would the competitor's employees have to make in four hours to earn the same pay you earn in a four-hour shift?

16. A boat can travel 24 mi in 3 h when traveling with a current. Against the same current, it can travel only 16 mi in 4 h. Find the rate of the current and the rate of the boat in still water.

17. **Geometry** The measure of one acute angle of a right triangle is 30° more than twice the measure of the other acute angle. Find the measures of the angles.

Example 3
(page 128)

Solve each system by elimination.

18. $\begin{cases} x + y = 12 \\ x - y = 2 \end{cases}$

19. $\begin{cases} x + 2y = 10 \\ x + y = 6 \end{cases}$

20. $\begin{cases} 3a + 4b = 9 \\ -3a - 2b = -3 \end{cases}$

21. $\begin{cases} 4x + 2y = 4 \\ 6x + 2y = 8 \end{cases}$

22. $\begin{cases} 2w + 5y = -24 \\ 3w - 5y = 14 \end{cases}$

23. $\begin{cases} 3u + 3v = 15 \\ -2u + 3v = -5 \end{cases}$

24. $\begin{cases} x + 3y = 11 \\ x + 4y = 14 \end{cases}$

25. $\begin{cases} 5x + 3y = 30 \\ 3x + 3y = 18 \end{cases}$

26. $\begin{cases} x - 14 = -y \\ x - y = 2 \end{cases}$

27. $\begin{cases} 3x + 2y = 6 \\ 3x + 3 = y \end{cases}$

28. $\begin{cases} 5x - y = 4 \\ 2x - y = 1 \end{cases}$

29. $\begin{cases} 2r + s = 3 \\ 4r - s = 9 \end{cases}$

Solve each system by elimination.

30. $\begin{cases} 4x - 6y = -26 \\ -2x + 3y = 13 \end{cases}$

31. $\begin{cases} 9a - 3d = 3 \\ -3a + d = -1 \end{cases}$

32. $\begin{cases} 2a + 3b = 12 \\ 5a - b = 13 \end{cases}$

33. $\begin{cases} 2x - 3y = 6 \\ 6x - 9y = 9 \end{cases}$

34. $\begin{cases} 20x + 5y = 120 \\ 10x + 7.5y = 80 \end{cases}$

35. $\begin{cases} 6x - 2y = 11 \\ -9x + 3y = 16 \end{cases}$

36. $\begin{cases} 2x - 3y = -1 \\ 3x + 4y = 8 \end{cases}$

37. $\begin{cases} 5x - 2y = -19 \\ 2x + 3y = 0 \end{cases}$

38. $\begin{cases} r + 3s = 7 \\ 2r - s = 7 \end{cases}$

39. $\begin{cases} y = 4 - x \\ 3x + y = 6 \end{cases}$

40. $\begin{cases} 3x + 2y = 10 \\ 6x + 4y = 15 \end{cases}$

41. $\begin{cases} 3m + 4n = -13 \\ 5m + 6n = -19 \end{cases}$

For a guide to solving
Exercise 42, see p. 133.

42. **Elections** In a mayoral election, the number of votes for the incumbent was 25% more than the number for the opponent. Altogether, the two candidates received 5175 votes. How many votes did the incumbent mayor receive?

43. **Writing** Explain how you decide whether to use substitution or elimination to solve a system.

B **Apply Your Skills**

Solve each system.

44. $\begin{cases} 5x + y = 0 \\ 5x + 2y = 30 \end{cases}$

45. $\begin{cases} 2m = -4n - 4 \\ 3m + 5n = -3 \end{cases}$

46. $\begin{cases} 7x + 2y = -8 \\ 8y = 4x \end{cases}$

47. $\begin{cases} v = 9t + 300 \\ v = 7t + 400 \end{cases}$

48. $\begin{cases} 80x + 60y = 85 \\ 100x - 40y = 20 \end{cases}$

49. $\begin{cases} 2x + 3y = 0 \\ 7x = 3(2y) + 3 \end{cases}$

50. $\begin{cases} \frac{x}{3} + \frac{4y}{3} = 300 \\ 3x - 4y = 300 \end{cases}$

51. $\begin{cases} 0.02a - 1.5b = 4 \\ 0.5b - 0.02a = 1.8 \end{cases}$

52. $\begin{cases} 4y = 2x \\ 2x + y = \frac{x}{2} + 1 \end{cases}$

53. Combined with the equation $3x - 4y = 2$, which equation below forms a system with no solutions?

    Ⓐ $2y = 1.5x - 2$ Ⓒ $3x + 4y = 2$

    Ⓑ $2y = 1.5x - 1$ Ⓓ $4y - 3x = -2$

For each system, choose the method of solving that seems easier to use. Explain why you made each choice.

54. $\begin{cases} 3x - 5y = 26 \\ -2x - 3y = -11 \end{cases}$

55. $\begin{cases} y = \frac{2}{3}x - 3 \\ -x + 3y = 18 \end{cases}$

56. $\begin{cases} 2m + 3n = 12 \\ -5m + n = -13 \end{cases}$

57. $\begin{cases} 3x - y = 5 \\ y = 4x + 2 \end{cases}$

58. $\begin{cases} 2x - 3y = 4 \\ 2x - 5y = -6 \end{cases}$

59. $\begin{cases} 6x - 3y = 3 \\ 5x - 5y = 10 \end{cases}$

60. **Open-Ended** Write a system of equations in which both equations must be multiplied by a nonzero number before using elimination. Solve your system.

61. **Internet Access** The ads at the left show the costs of Internet access for two companies.

    a. Write a system of equations to represent the cost c for t hours of access in one month for each company.

    b. Graph the system from part (a). Label each line.

    c. For how many hours of use will the costs for the companies be the same? How is this information represented on the graph?

    d. If you use the Internet about 20 hours each month, which company should you choose? Explain how you reached an answer.

Homework Video Tutor

Visit: PHSchool.com
Web Code: bbe-0302

62. Break-Even Point A theater production costs $40,000 plus $2800 per performance. A sold-out performance brings in $3675. How many sold-out performances will the production need to break even?

 Challenge

63. Weather The equation $F = \frac{9}{5}C + 32$ relates temperatures on the Celsius and Fahrenheit scales. Does any temperature have the same number reading on both scales? If so, what is the number?

Find the value of a that makes each system a dependent system.

64. $\begin{cases} y = 3x + a \\ 3x - y = 2 \end{cases}$
65. $\begin{cases} 3y = 2x \\ 6y - a - 4x = 0 \end{cases}$
66. $\begin{cases} y = \frac{x}{2} + 4 \\ 2y - x = a \end{cases}$

Multiple Choice Practice

For California Standards and CAHSEE Tutorials, visit PHSchool.com. Web Code: bbq-9045

ALG2 2.0

67. What is the value of x in the solution to the following system?

$$\begin{cases} 5x - 3y = 11 \\ -x + 12y = 3.5 \end{cases}$$

    (A) 0.5   (B) 2   (C) 2.5   (D) 3

ALG2 1.0

68. Which of the following is the solution to $|x - 3| > 3$?

    (A) $x > 6$ (C) $x < 6$

    (B) $x < 0$ or $x > 6$ (D) $x > 0$ and $x < 6$

CAHSEE 7AF 1.1

69. Jan needs to buy grape juice and apple juice for a party. At the store, a bottle of grape juice costs $3.69, and the same size bottle of apple juice costs $2.49. If Jan has $18 to spend, which statement best describes g, the number of bottles of grape juice, and a, the number of bottles of apple juice, that she can buy?

    (A) $6.18(g + a) \le 18$ (C) $3.69g + 2.49a \ge 18$

    (B) $3.69g + 2.49a \le 18$ (D) $18 \ge 3.69g - 2.49a$

Mixed Review

 for Help

Lesson 3-1

Solve each system of equations by graphing.

70. $\begin{cases} y = 3x + 4 \\ 2y = 6x - 2 \end{cases}$
71. $\begin{cases} -3y = 9x + 1 \\ 6y = -18x - 2 \end{cases}$
72. $\begin{cases} 4x - y = -5 \\ -8x + 2y = 15 \end{cases}$

Lesson 2-6

Write an equation for each diagonal translation.

73. $y = x$, 4 units down, 3 units left   **74.** $y = |x|$, $\frac{1}{2}$ unit up, 2 units right

75. $y = 2x - 3$, 1 unit down, 1 unit right   **76.** $y = |x| + 2$, 4 units up, 2 units left

Lesson 1-1

77. What subset(s) of real numbers contain(s) 6?

78. The sum of the first and last of four consecutive odd integers is 48. What are the four integers?

Understanding Word Problems Read the problem below. Then let David's thinking guide you through the solution. Check your understanding with the exercises at the bottom of the page.

Elections In a mayoral election, the number of votes for the incumbent was 25% more than the number for the opponent. Altogether, the two candidates received 5175 votes. How many votes did the incumbent mayor receive?

What David Thinks

I'll restate the important information. In the first sentence, 25% more means the greater number is 1.25 times the lesser number.

The second sentence gives me the total number of votes.

What quantities are being used in the problem? I'll assign variables to the number of votes each candidate received.

Now I can write a system of equations.

Great! The first equation defines the value of n. I'll solve the system by substituting $1.25p$ from the first equation into the second equation.

The problem asks me to find the number of incumbent votes. That's n. I'll use one of the original equations and substitute.

Now I'll write my answer as a sentence.

What David Writes

Incumbent received **25% more votes** than opponent.

$$\text{Incumbent's votes} = 1.25 \left(\text{opponent's votes} \right)$$

5175 votes total for both candidates.

$$\text{Incumbent's votes} + \text{opponent's votes} = 5175$$

n = number of incumbent's votes
p = number of opponent's votes

$$\begin{cases} n = 1.25p \\ n + p = 5175 \end{cases}$$

$$\begin{aligned} n + p &= 5175 \\ 1.25p + p &= 5175 \\ 2.25p &= 5175 \\ p &= 2300 \end{aligned}$$

$$\begin{aligned} n &= 1.25p \\ n &= 1.25(2300) \\ n &= 2875 \end{aligned}$$

The incumbent mayor received **2875** votes.

EXERCISES

1. Two baseball cards together are worth $30. One card is worth 40% more than the other card. How much is the more expensive card worth?

2. A washer and dryer have the same retail price. The store discounts the washer by 10% and the dryer by 20%. The combined sale price for both appliances is $1020. What was the original price of each appliance?

Solving Systems Using Tables

Technology   FOR USE WITH LESSON 3-2

ALG2 2.0 Students solve systems of linear equations (in two variables) by substitution. *Develop*

To solve systems with tables, you compare numbers in the table lists.

ACTIVITY

A magnetic construction set has 38 bars. For a project, Carlos and Colleen need to make 7 regular polygons using the bars. Each polygon must be either a pentagon or a hexagon. Carlos wants to use all the bars. He can write two equations that represent the situation. Then he can solve the system using tables.

1. One equation relates the number of pentagons p and the number of hexagons h. What is that equation?

2. Another equation shows that the total number of bars used by p pentagons and h hexagons is 38. Write that equation.

3. Carlos made two tables side by side. One table lists the numbers of pentagons and hexagons that solve the first equation. The second table lists the numbers that solve the second equation. Build and complete the two tables.

Number of Pentagons	Number of Hexagons
0	7
1	6
2	

Number of Pentagons	Number of Hexagons
0	Not possible
1	

4. Find the rows in the two tables that list the same pairs of numbers.

5. How many polygons of each type do Carlos and Colleen need to make?

EXERCISES

A school track team is going to a track meet. The school has minivans that seat 8 passengers and minibuses that seat 12 passengers, in addition to the drivers in each case. The school wants to fill each vehicle used. There are 4 drivers who can drive any of the vehicles. There are 40 members on the team.

6. Write a system of equations that represents the situation.

7. Use tables to solve the system.

8. Explain what the solution of the system represents.

You can enter two equations as Y1 and Y2 in a graphing calculator. Then you can display a table showing X, Y1, and Y2. Decide how you can use such a table to solve each system of equations below. Then do so. (*Hint:* The screen at the right shows the table for Exercise 9.)

X	Y1	Y2
20.00	14.00	16.00
21.00	15.00	16.50
22.00	16.00	17.00
23.00	17.00	17.50
24.00	18.00	18.00
25.00	19.00	18.50
26.00	20.00	19.00
X=20		

9. $\begin{cases} y = x - 6 \\ y = \frac{1}{2}x + 6 \end{cases}$

10. $\begin{cases} y = 2x - 3 \\ y = -3x + 19.5 \end{cases}$

11. $\begin{cases} y = 1.5x \\ y = -0.75x + 9.75 \end{cases}$

Systems of Inequalities

 California Content Standards

ALG2 1.0 Students solve inequalities involving absolute value. ***Develop, Master***
ALG2 2.0 Students solve systems of linear inequalities (in two variables) with graphs. ***Develop***

What You'll Learn

• To solve systems of linear inequalities

. . . And Why

To model college entrance requirements, as in Example 3

✓ Check Skills You'll Need

GO for Help Lessons 1-4, 2-5, and 2-7

Solve each inequality.

1. $5x - 6 > 27$

2. $-18 - 5y \geq 52$

3. $-5(4x + 1) < 23$

Graph each inequality.

4. $y \leq 4x - 1$

5. $3y \geq 6x + 3$

6. $-5y + 2x > -5$

7. $y \leq |x|$

8. $y \geq |x + 3|$

9. $y < |x - 2| + 4$

---

1 Solving Systems of Inequalities

You can model a situation by writing a system of linear inequalities or a system that combines equations and inequalities.

1 EXAMPLE Solving a System by Using a Table

The California Department of Education measures the ratio of students to computers. In 2003–2004, this ratio was 4.2 for high schools.

Classroom Management A science class has 6 computers for 20 students. Students have the option of using a computer program to investigate frog biology or using a computer and their graphing calculators to investigate the properties of heat transfer. Each frog lab must have 3 students in a group. Each heat lab must have 4 students in a group. In how many ways can you set up the lab groups?

Relate   number of frog lab groups +   number of heat lab groups ≤ 6

3 · number of frog lab groups + 4 · number of heat lab groups = 20

Define Let f = the number of frog lab groups.

Let h = the number of heat lab groups.

Write f + h ≤ 6

3 f + 4 h = 20

The situation is discrete. The replacement values for f and h must be whole numbers.

To solve the system $\begin{cases} f + h \leq 6 \\ 3f + 4h = 20 \end{cases}$ first make a table of values of f and h that solve the inequality.

f	h
0	6, 5, 4, 3, 2, 1, 0
1	5, 4, 3, 2, 1, 0
2	4, 3, 2, 1, 0
3	3, 2, 1, 0
4	2, 1, 0
5	1, 0
6	0

In that table look for values of f and h that solve the equation. Circle any that you find.

The only two whole number solutions of the system are $(0, 5)$ and $(4, 2)$.

There are two possible ways to set up the lab groups. You can assign all students to 5 heat lab groups, or you can assign them to 4 frog lab groups and 2 heat lab groups.

f	h
⓪	6, ⑤, 4, 3, 2, 1, 0
1	5, 4, 3, 2, 1, 0
2	4, 3, 2, 1, 0
3	3, 2, 1, 0
④	②, 1, 0
5	1, 0
6	0

✅ **CA Standards Check** **1** Use tables to solve each system. Assume that replacement values for the variables are whole numbers.

a. $\begin{cases} -x + y = 1 \\ x + 2y \leq 20 \end{cases}$ **b.** $\begin{cases} x - y \geq 1 \\ 2x + 3y \leq 21 \end{cases}$

You can solve a system of linear inequalities by graphing. Recall from Lesson 2-7 that when the variables represent real numbers, the solutions of an inequality include all the points on one side of a boundary line. Thus, for two inequalities, every point in the region of overlap of the two solutions is a solution of the system.

2 **EXAMPLE**   **Solving a System by Graphing**

Solve the system of inequalities. $\begin{cases} x - 2y < 6 \\ y \leq -\frac{3}{2}x + 5 \end{cases}$

Graph each inequality. First graph the boundary lines. Then decide which side of each boundary line contains solutions and whether the boundary line is included.

Problem Solving Hint

After graphing a boundary line, test whether a point not on the line satisfies the inequality. If it does, shade the side of the line containing that point.

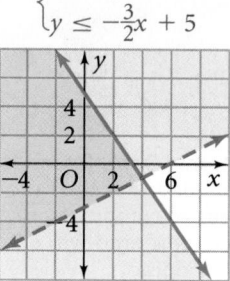

Every point in the red region above the dashed line is a solution of $x - 2y < 6$.

Every point in the blue region or on the solid line is a solution of $y \leq -\frac{3}{2}x + 5$.

Every point in the purple region where the red and blue regions intersect is a solution of the system. For example, $(1, 1)$ is a solution.

Check Check $(1, 1)$ in both inequalities of the system.

$$x - 2y < 6 \qquad\qquad y \leq -\frac{3}{2}x + 5$$
$$1 - 2(1) < 6 \qquad\qquad 1 \leq -\frac{3}{2}(1) + 5$$
$$-1 < 6 \checkmark \qquad\qquad 1 \leq \frac{7}{2} \checkmark$$

✅ **CA Standards Check** **2** Solve each system of inequalities.

a. $\begin{cases} y \leq -2x + 4 \\ x > -3 \end{cases}$ **b.** $\begin{cases} y \leq 3x - 6 \\ y > -4x + 2 \end{cases}$

3 EXAMPLE <u>Real-World</u> **Connection**

College Admissions An entrance exam has two parts, a verbal part and a mathematics part. You can score a maximum total of 1600 points. For admission, the school of your choice requires a math score of at least 600. Write a system of inequalities to model scores that meet the school's requirements. Then solve the system.

Relate verbal score + math score ≤ 1600

math score ≥ 600

Define Let x = the verbal score.

Let y = the mathematics score.

Write $x + y \leq 1600$, or $y \leq 1600 - x$

$y \geq 600$

The system of inequalities is $\begin{cases} y \leq 1600 - x \\ y \geq 600 \end{cases}$.

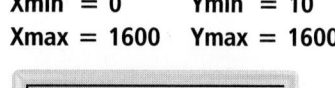

Use a graphing calculator to graph the corresponding equations $y = 1600 - x$ and $y = 600$. Since the first inequality is ≤, shade below the first line. Since the second inequality is ≥, shade above the second line. The region of overlap is a graph of the solution.

✓**CA Standards Check** **③** Another school requires a math score of at least 550 points and a total score of at least 1100 points. You can score up to 800 points on each part. Write and solve a system of inequalities to model scores that meet the school's requirements.

Some systems consist of linear and absolute value inequalities.

4 EXAMPLE **Solving a Linear Absolute Value System**

Solve the system of inequalities. $\begin{cases} y < 4 \\ y \geq |x - 3| \end{cases}$

      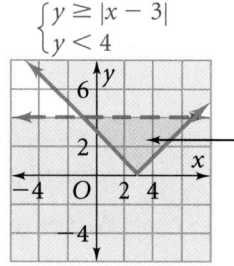

The region of overlap represents the solution.

✓**CA Standards Check** **④** Solve each system of inequalities.

a. $\begin{cases} y \geq x \\ y \leq |x + 5| - 2 \end{cases}$ b. $\begin{cases} y \geq -2x + 4 \\ y \leq |x - 4| \end{cases}$

c. **Critical Thinking** Write a system that includes an absolute value inequality but has no solutions.

EXERCISES
Standards Practice

For more exercises, see *Extra Skill and Word Problem Practice.*

A Practice by Example

Example 1
(page 135)

Find the whole number solutions of each system using tables.

1. $\begin{cases} y + 3x \le 8 \\ y - 3 > 2x \end{cases}$

2. $\begin{cases} x = y + 3 \\ x + y \le 12 \end{cases}$

3. $\begin{cases} x + y < 8 \\ 3x \le y + 6 \end{cases}$

Example 2
(page 136)

Tell whether $(-3, 3)$ is a solution of each system.

4. $\begin{cases} y \ge x + 2 \\ 3y < -6x + 6 \end{cases}$

5. $\begin{cases} y - 2x \le 1 \\ y < -2x - 2 \end{cases}$

6. $\begin{cases} -2y + x \le 4 \\ 3y < -9x + 3 \end{cases}$

Solve each system of inequalities by graphing.

7. $\begin{cases} y \le 2x + 2 \\ y < -x + 1 \end{cases}$

8. $\begin{cases} y > -2 \\ x < 1 \end{cases}$

9. $\begin{cases} y \le 3 \\ y \le \frac{1}{2}x + 1 \end{cases}$

10. $\begin{cases} y \le 3x + 1 \\ -6x + 2y > 5 \end{cases}$

11. $\begin{cases} x + 2y \le 10 \\ x + y \le 3 \end{cases}$

12. $\begin{cases} -x - y \le 2 \\ y - 2x > 1 \end{cases}$

13. $\begin{cases} y > -2x \\ 2x - y \ge 2 \end{cases}$

14. $\begin{cases} c \ge d - 3 \\ c < \frac{1}{2}d + 3 \end{cases}$

15. $\begin{cases} 2x + y < 1 \\ -y + 3x < 1 \end{cases}$

Example 3
(page 137)

16. Fund-Raising You want to bake at least 6 and at most 11 loaves of bread for a bake sale. You want at least twice as many loaves of banana bread as nut bread. Write and graph a system of inequalities to model the situation.

17. Psychology A psychologist needs at least 40 subjects for her experiment. She cannot use more than 30 children. Write and graph a system of inequalities.

Example 4
(page 137)

Solve each system of inequalities by graphing.

18. $\begin{cases} y > 4 \\ y < |x - 1| \end{cases}$

19. $\begin{cases} y < -\frac{1}{3}x + 1 \\ y > |2x - 1| \end{cases}$

20. $\begin{cases} y > x - 2 \\ y \ge |x + 2| \end{cases}$

21. $\begin{cases} y \le -\frac{4}{3}x \\ y \ge -|x| \end{cases}$

22. $\begin{cases} 3y < -x - 1 \\ y \le |x + 1| \end{cases}$

23. $\begin{cases} y > -2 \\ y \le -|x - 3| \end{cases}$

24. $\begin{cases} -2x + y > 3 \\ y \le -|x + 4| \end{cases}$

25. $\begin{cases} 5y \ge 2x - 5 \\ y < |x + 3| \end{cases}$

26. $\begin{cases} y \ge -3x + 3 \\ y > |x + 2| \end{cases}$

27. $\begin{cases} -2y < 4x + 2 \\ y > |2x + 1| \end{cases}$

28. $\begin{cases} -x \ge 4 - y \\ y \ge |3x - 6| \end{cases}$

29. $\begin{cases} y \le x - 4 \\ y > |x - 6| \end{cases}$

B Apply Your Skills

In Exercises 30−39, identify the inequalities A, B, and C for which the given ordered pair is a solution.

A. $x + y \le 2$

B. $y \le \frac{3}{2}x - 1$

C. $y > -\frac{1}{3}x - 2$

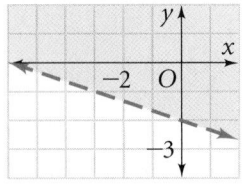

Visit: PHSchool.com
Web Code: bbe-0303

30. $(0, 0)$ **31.** $(-2, -5)$ **32.** $(-2, 0)$ **33.** $(0, -2)$ **34.** $(-15, 15)$

35. $(3, 2)$ **36.** $(2, 0)$ **37.** $(-6, 0)$ **38.** $(4, -1)$ **39.** $(-8, -11)$

138   Chapter 3   Linear Systems

40. Fund-Raising Suppose the Student Council has asked you to form a committee to run a bake sale. The committee needs from 7 to 10 members. The number of seniors should be greater than the number of juniors.
  a. Write a system of inequalities to model the problem.
  b. Graph the system and list the combinations of juniors and seniors that may participate in the committee.
  c. Critical Thinking Explain why your list in part (b) is finite.

41. Open-Ended Write and graph a system of inequalities for which the solution is bounded by a dashed vertical line and a solid horizontal line.

42. Writing Explain how you determine where to shade when solving a system of inequalities.

Solve each system of inequalities by graphing.

43. $\begin{cases} x + y < 8 \\ x \geq 0 \\ y \geq 0 \end{cases}$

44. $\begin{cases} 2y - 4x \leq 0 \\ x \geq 0 \\ y \geq 0 \end{cases}$

45. $\begin{cases} y \geq -2x + 4 \\ x > -3 \\ y \geq 1 \end{cases}$

46. $\begin{cases} y \leq \frac{2}{3}x + 2 \\ y \geq |x| + 2 \end{cases}$

47. $\begin{cases} y < x - 1 \\ y > -|x - 2| + 1 \end{cases}$

48. $\begin{cases} 2x + y \leq 3 \\ y > |x + 3| - 2 \end{cases}$

C Challenge ⬛ **Geometry** **Write a system of inequalities to describe each shaded figure.**

49.

50.

51.

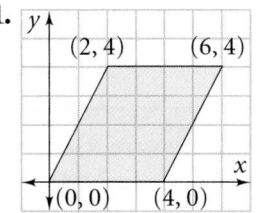

52. a. Graph the "bowtie" inequality, $|y| \leq |x|$.
  b. Write a system of inequalities to describe the graph shown at the right.

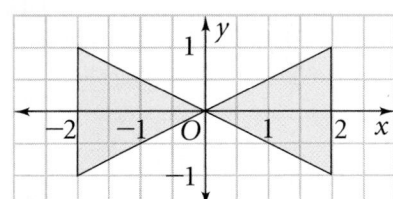

Multiple Choice Practice

For California Standards and CAHSEE Tutorials, visit PHSchool.com. Web Code: bbq-9045

ALG2 2.0   **53.** Solve the system $\begin{cases} x + 2y = -4 \\ 2x - y = -3 \end{cases}$.

  Ⓐ $(2, -3)$ Ⓑ $(-2, -1)$ Ⓒ $(-2, 1)$ Ⓓ $(4, 3)$

CAHSEE   **54.** If the measure of the vertex angle of an isosceles triangle is x, which equation
7AF 1.0   can you use to find y, the measure of one of the congruent base angles?

  Ⓐ $y = \frac{1}{2}(180 - x)$

  Ⓑ $y = 180 - 2x$

  Ⓒ $y = \frac{1}{2}(180 + x)$

  Ⓓ $y = 90 - x$

Lesson 3-2

Solve each system by elimination or substitution.

55. $\begin{cases} y = 3x + 1 \\ 2x - y = 8 \end{cases}$

56. $\begin{cases} 3x + y = 4 \\ 2x - 4y = 7 \end{cases}$

57. $\begin{cases} -x + 5y = 3 \\ 2x - 10y = 4 \end{cases}$

58. $\begin{cases} 2x + 4y = -8 \\ -5x + 4y = 6 \end{cases}$

59. $\begin{cases} y - 3 = x \\ 4x + y = -2 \end{cases}$

60. $\begin{cases} 2 = 4y - 3x \\ 5x = 2y - 3 \end{cases}$

Lesson 2-3

For each function, y varies directly as x.

61. If $y = -6$ when $x = -2$, find y when $x = 3$.

62. If $y = -8$ when $x = 2$, find x when $y = 2$.

63. If $y = 4$ when $x = 7$, find y when $x = -14$.

64. If $y = 9$ when $x = 15$, find x when $y = 6$.

Lesson 6-2

Solve each equation. Check your answers.

65. $|2x + 5| = 6$

66. $|x + 7| = -2$

67. $3|x - 4| + 1 = 13$

68. $-2|x + 1| - 5 = -7$

69. $\frac{1}{2}|3x + 2| - 3 = 4$

70. $-|2x + 5| = -3$

Checkpoint Quiz 1   **Lessons 3-1 through 3-3**

Solve each system of equations.

1. $\begin{cases} 3x + 2y = 6 \\ x - 2y = 10 \end{cases}$

2. $\begin{cases} 4x + 7y = 28 \\ y = 2x - 14 \end{cases}$

3. $\begin{cases} 4x + 5y = -12 \\ 3x - 4y = 22 \end{cases}$

4. $\begin{cases} 3y - 2x = 7 \\ 2y - 2 = 4x \end{cases}$

5. The Village Inn offers two special packages. For two nights and three meals the cost is $158. For two nights and five meals the cost is $181. Write and solve a system of linear equations to find the costs per night and per meal.

6. Smart Shopping An ordinary refrigerator costs $489 and has an estimated annual operating cost of $84. An energy-saving model costs $599, with an estimated annual cost of $61. After how many years will the costs to buy and to operate the two models be equal?

7. Each week you must do a minimum of 18 hours of homework. Participation in sports requires at least 12 hours per week. You have no more than 35 hours per week in total to devote to these activities.
a. Write a system of inequalities to model the situation.
b. Graph and solve the system.

Solve each system of inequalities by graphing.

8. $\begin{cases} y \le -2 \\ y > |x + 1| \end{cases}$

9. $\begin{cases} 8x + 2y > 5 \\ x + 2y \le -3 \end{cases}$

10. $\begin{cases} 4y < 3x - 1 \\ y > 2|x| - 3 \end{cases}$

3-4

Linear Programming

California Content Standards

ALG2 2.0 Students solve systems of linear inequalities (in two variables) with graphs. **Master**

What You'll Learn

- To find maximum and minimum values
- To solve problems with linear programming

. . . And Why

To maximize profit, as in Example 2

 Check Skills You'll Need

GO for Help Lessons 3-2 and 3-3

Solve each system of equations.

1. $\begin{cases} y = -3x + 3 \\ y = 2x - 7 \end{cases}$
2. $\begin{cases} x + 2y = 5 \\ x - y = -1 \end{cases}$
3. $\begin{cases} 4x + 3y = 7 \\ 2x - 5y = -3 \end{cases}$

Solve each system of inequalities by graphing.

4. $\begin{cases} x \geq 5 \\ y > -3x + 6 \end{cases}$
5. $\begin{cases} 3y > 5x + 2 \\ y \leq -x + 7 \end{cases}$
6. $\begin{cases} x + 3y < -6 \\ 2x - 3y \leq 4 \end{cases}$

New Vocabulary • linear programming • objective function • constraints • feasible region

---

 1 Finding Maximum and Minimum Values

Activity: Finding a Minimum Value

Music Suppose you want to buy some tapes and CDs. You can afford as many as 10 tapes or 7 CDs. You want at least 4 CDs and at least 10 hours of recorded music. Each tape holds about 45 minutes of music, and each CD holds about an hour.

1. Write a system of inequalities to model the problem.
   Let *x* represent the number of tapes purchased.
   Let *y* represent the number of CDs purchased.

2. Graph your system of inequalities.

3. Does each ordered pair satisfy the system you have graphed?
   a. (4, 7)   **b.** (12, 7)   **c.** (7, 6)   **d.** (9, 4)   **e.** (10, 4)

Linear programming is a technique that identifies the minimum or maximum value of some quantity. This quantity is modeled with an **objective function.** Limits on the variables in the objective function are **constraints,** written as linear inequalities.

Vocabulary Tip

Constraints are sometimes referred to as restrictions.

The first paragraph of the Activity describes the constraints on buying tapes and CDs. Suppose you buy *x* tapes and *y* CDs. The constraints on *x* and *y* can be modeled with inequalities as follows.

as many as 10 tapes $x \leq 10$ at least 4 CDs $y \geq 4$

as many as 7 CDs $y \leq 7$ at least 10 hours $\frac{3}{4}x + y \geq 10$

Vocabulary Tip

Feasible means "doable" or "suitable."

The constraints form the system of inequalities at the right. The red region in the graph, the **feasible region,** contains all the points that satisfy all the constraints.

$$\begin{cases} x \le 10 \\ y \le 7 \\ y \ge 4 \\ \frac{3}{4}x + y \ge 10 \end{cases}$$

If you buy tapes at $8 each and CDs at $12 each, then the objective function for the total cost C is $C = 8x + 12y$. The blue line is the graph for the total cost $140. The green line is for the total cost $112.

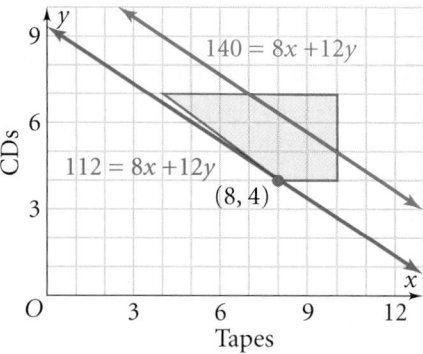

Graphs of the objective function for various values of C are parallel lines. Lines closer to the origin represent lower costs. The graph closest to the origin that intersects the feasible region intersects it at the vertex $(8, 4)$. The graph of the objective function farthest from the origin that intersects the feasible region intersects it at the vertex $(10, 7)$. Graphs of an objective function that represent a maximum or minimum value intersect a feasible region at a vertex.

 Key Concepts

Property	**Vertex Principle of Linear Programming**

If there is a maximum or a minimum value of the linear objective function, it occurs at one or more vertices of the feasible region.

---

1 EXAMPLE **Testing Vertices**

Problem Solving Hint

Remember to check the value of the objective function at each vertex when solving linear programming problems.

Multiple Choice What values of x and y maximize P for the objective function $P = 3x + 2y$?

Constraints $\begin{cases} y \ge \frac{3}{2}x - 3 \\ y \le -x + 7 \\ x \ge 0, y \ge 0 \end{cases}$

Ⓐ $(2, 0)$　　　Ⓒ $(4, 3)$

Ⓑ $(2, 6)$　　　Ⓓ $(4, 4)$

Step 1
Graph the constraints.

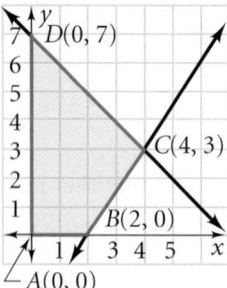

Step 2
Find coordinates for each vertex.

Vertex
$A(0, 0)$
$B(2, 0)$
$C(4, 3)$
$D(0, 7)$

Step 3
Evaluate P at each vertex.

$P = 3x + 2y$
$P = 3(0) + 2(0) = 0$
$P = 3(2) + 2(0) = 6$
$P = 3(4) + 2(3) = 18$
$P = 3(0) + 2(7) = 14$

● When $x = 4$ and $y = 3$, P has its maximum value of 18. The answer is C.

✓ CA Standards Check ① Use the constraints in Example 1 with the objective function $P = 2x + 3y$. Find the values of x and y that maximize and minimize P. Find the value of P at each point.

You can use linear programming to solve many real-world problems.

2 EXAMPLE **Real-World Connection**

Profit Suppose you are selling cases of mixed nuts and roasted peanuts. You can order no more than a total of 500 cans and packages and spend no more than $600. How can you maximize your profit? How much is the maximum profit?

Mixed Nuts
12 cans per case

You pay ...... $24 per case
Sell at .... $3.50 per can

$18 profit per case!

Roasted Peanuts
20 packages per case

You pay ...... $15 per case
Sell at ... $1.50 per package

$15 profit per case!

Define Let x = number of cases of mixed nuts ordered.
Let y = number of cases of roasted peanuts ordered.
Let P = total profit.

Relate Organize the information in a table.

	Mixed Nuts	Roasted Peanuts	Total	
Number of Cases	x	y	$x + y$	
Number of Units	$12x$	$20y$	500	constraint
Cost	$24x$	$15y$	600	constraint
Profit	$18x$	$15y$	$18x + 15y$	objective

Vocabulary Tip

Linear <u>program</u>ming got its name because it provides a plan, or a program, that uses linear equations and inequalities.

Write Write and simplify the constraints. Write the objective function.

$$\begin{cases} 12x + 20y \le 500 \\ 24x + 15y \le 600 \\ x \ge 0, y \ge 0 \end{cases} \Rightarrow \begin{cases} 3x + 5y \le 125 \\ 8x + 5y \le 200 \\ x \ge 0, y \ge 0 \end{cases} \qquad P = 18x + 15y$$

Step 1
Graph the constraints.

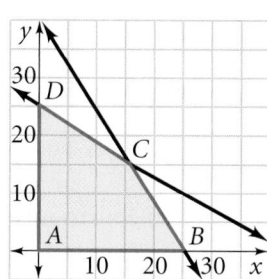

Step 2
Find the coordinates
of each vertex.

Step 3
Evaluate P at
each vertex.

Vertex	$P = 18x + 15y$
$A(0, 0)$	$P = 18(0) + 15(0) = 0$
$B(25, 0)$	$P = 18(25) + 15(0) = 450$
$C(15, 16)$	$P = 18(15) + 15(16) = 510$
$D(0, 25)$	$P = 18(0) + 15(25) = 375$

You can maximize your profit by selling 15 cases of mixed nuts and 16 cases of roasted peanuts. The maximum profit is $510.

 CA Standards Check **2** If you sell mixed nuts for $4.25 per can, what should you order to maximize profit?

A Practice by Example

Example 1
(page 142)

GO for Help

Find the values of *x* and *y* that maximize or minimize the objective function for each graph.

1.
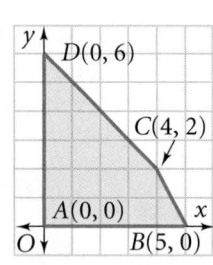
$D(0, 6)$
$C(4, 2)$
$A(0, 0)$
$B(5, 0)$

Maximum for
$P = 3x + 2y$

2.
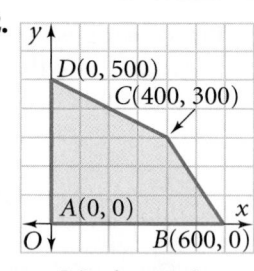
$D(0, 500)$
$C(400, 300)$
$A(0, 0)$
$B(600, 0)$

Maximum for
$P = 7x + 4y$

3.
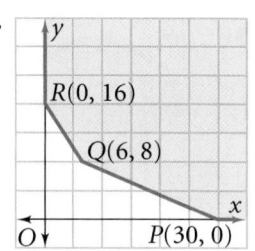
$R(0, 16)$
$Q(6, 8)$
$P(30, 0)$

Minimum for
$C = 2x + 3y$

Graph each system of constraints. Name all vertices. Then find the values of *x* and *y* that maximize or minimize the objective function.

4. $\begin{cases} x \le 5 \\ y \le 4 \\ x \ge 0, y \ge 0 \end{cases}$

Maximum for
$P = 3x + 2y$

5. $\begin{cases} x + y \ge 8 \\ y \ge 5 \\ x \ge 0 \end{cases}$

Minimum for
$P = 3x + 2y$

6. $\begin{cases} x + y \le 8 \\ 2x + y \le 10 \\ x \ge 0, y \ge 0 \end{cases}$

Maximum for
$N = 100x + 40y$

7. $\begin{cases} x + y \ge 6 \\ x \le 8 \\ y \le 5 \end{cases}$

Minimum for
$C = x + 3y$

8. $\begin{cases} x + 2y \ge 8 \\ x \ge 2 \\ y \ge 0 \end{cases}$

Minimum for
$C = x + 3y$

9. $\begin{cases} 2 \le x \le 6 \\ 1 \le y \le 5 \\ x + y \le 8 \end{cases}$

Maximum for
$P = 3x + 2y$

Example 2
(page 143)

10. **Ecology** Teams chosen from 30 forest rangers and 16 trainees are planting trees. An experienced team consisting of two rangers can plant 500 trees per week. A training team consisting of one ranger and two trainees can plant 200 trees per week.

	Experienced Teams	Training Teams	Total
Number of Teams	x	y	$x + y$
Number of Rangers	$2x$	y	30
Number of Trainees	0	$2y$	16
Number of Trees Planted	$500x$	$200y$	$500x + 200y$

a. Write an objective function and constraints for a linear program that models the problem.

b. How many of each type of team should be formed to maximize the number of trees planted? How many trainees are used in this solution? How many trees are planted?

c. Find a solution that uses all the trainees. How many trees will be planted in this case?

11. Air Quality Trees in urban areas help keep air fresh by absorbing carbon dioxide. A city has $2100 to spend on planting spruce and maple trees. The land available for planting is 45,000 ft². How many of each tree should the city plant to maximize carbon dioxide absorption?

Facts for a Single Tree	Spruce	Maple
Planting Cost	$30	$40
Area Required	600 ft²	900 ft²
Carbon Dioxide Absorption	650 lb/yr	300 lb/yr

SOURCES: Auburn University and Anderson & Associates

12. Writing Explain why solving a system of linear equations is a necessary skill for linear programming.

13. Multiple Choice A microbiologist is developing two new strains of bacteria. Each sample of Type I bacteria produces four new viable bacteria, and each sample of Type II produces three new viable bacteria. Altogether, at least 240 new viable bacteria must be produced. At least 30, but not more than 60, of the original samples must be Type I. Not more than 70 of the samples can be Type II. A sample of Type I costs $5 and a sample of Type II costs $7. How many samples of Type II bacteria should be used to minimize cost?

(A) 0   (B) 30   (C) 60   (D) 70

Real-World Connection

A microbiologist studies microorganisms, such as bacteria and viruses, to determine their structure and function.

Graph each system of constraints. Name all vertices. Then find the values of x and y that maximize or minimize the objective function. Find the maximum or minimum value.

14. $\begin{cases} 3x + y \le 7 \\ x + 2y \le 9 \\ x \ge 0, y \ge 0 \end{cases}$

Maximum for
$P = 2x + y$

15. $\begin{cases} 25 \le x \le 75 \\ y \le 110 \\ 8x + 6y \ge 720 \end{cases}$

Minimum for
$C = 8x + 5y$

16. $\begin{cases} x + y \le 11 \\ 2y \ge x \\ x \ge 0, y \ge 0 \end{cases}$

Maximum for
$P = 3x + 2y$

17. $\begin{cases} 2x + y \le 300 \\ x + y \le 200 \\ x \ge 0, y \ge 0 \end{cases}$

Maximum for
$P = x + 2y$

18. $\begin{cases} 5x + y \ge 10 \\ x + y \ge 6 \\ x + 4y \ge 12 \\ x \ge 0, y \ge 0 \end{cases}$

Minimum for
$C = 10,000x + 20,000y$

19. $\begin{cases} 6 \le x + y \le 13 \\ x \ge 3 \\ y \ge 1 \end{cases}$

Maximum for
$P = 4x + 3y$

Homework Video Tutor

Visit: PHSchool.com
Web Code: bbe-0304

20. Cooking Baking a tray of corn muffins takes 4 c milk and 3 c wheat flour. A tray of bran muffins takes 2 c milk and 3 c wheat flour. A baker has 16 c milk and 15 c wheat flour. He makes $3 profit per tray of corn muffins and $2 profit per tray of bran muffins. How many trays of each type of muffin should the baker make to maximize his profit?

C Challenge

21. A vertex of a feasible region does not always have whole-number coordinates. Sometimes you may need to round coordinates to find the solution. Using the objective function and the constraints at the right, find the whole-number values of x and y that minimize C. Then find C for those values of x and y.

$C = 6x + 9y$

$\begin{cases} x + 2y \ge 50 \\ 2x + y \ge 60 \\ x \ge 0, y \ge 0 \end{cases}$

22. Open-Ended Write a system of constraints whose graphs determine a trapezoid. Write an objective function and evaluate it at each vertex.

23. Critical Thinking Sometimes two corners of a graph both yield the maximum profit. In this case, many other points may also yield the maximum profit. Evaluate the profit formula $P = x + 2y$ for the graph shown. Find four points that yield the maximum profit.

For California Standards and CAHSEE Tutorials, visit PHSchool.com. Web Code: bbq-9045

ALG2 2.0

24. Which of the following is the solution for this system of equations?
$$\begin{cases} y = \frac{3}{4}x + 3 \\ -x + 3y = 14 \end{cases}$$

Ⓐ $(4, 6)$ Ⓑ $(4, -6)$ Ⓒ $(6, 4)$ Ⓓ $(6, -4)$

ALG2 2.0

25. At a pizza shop, the cost of one medium pizza and one small pizza is $18.50. The cost of 3 medium pizzas and 2 small pizzas is $71.50. Which pair of equations can be used to determine m, the cost of a medium pizza, and s, the cost of a small pizza?

Ⓐ $m + s = 18.50$
$\quad 3m + 3s = 71.50$

Ⓑ $m + s = 18.50$
$\quad 3m + 2s = 71.50$

Ⓒ $m + s = 18.50$
$\quad 2m + 2s = 71.50$

Ⓓ $m + s = 18.50$
$\quad 2m + 3s = 71.50$

Mixed Review

GO for Help

Lesson 3-3

Solve each system of inequalities by graphing.

26. $\begin{cases} y < -2x + 8 \\ 3y \geq 4x - 6 \end{cases}$

27. $\begin{cases} x - 2y \geq 11 \\ 5x + 4y < 27 \end{cases}$

28. $\begin{cases} 2x + 6y > 12 \\ 3x + 9y \leq 27 \end{cases}$

29. $\begin{cases} 2y + x < 4 \\ y - 2x \geq 4 \end{cases}$

30. $\begin{cases} y + 5 \geq -2x \\ y - x \geq -2 \end{cases}$

31. $\begin{cases} 2y - 4x < 6 \\ 6x < 3y + 12 \end{cases}$

Lesson 2-4

32. Data Analysis Use the data below.

A Survey of Paperback Books: How Long and How Much?

Pages	326	450	246	427	208	339	367	445	404	465	378	265
Price ($)	7.50	7.99	6.99	7.99	6.99	7.95	7.50	7.95	7.95	7.99	7.99	6.99

a. Make a scatter plot of the data.
b. What kind of correlation do you see?
c. Find a linear model.
d. What price would you predict for a paperback containing 100 pages?

Lesson 1-2

Evaluate each expression for $a = 3$ and $b = -5$.

33. $2a + b$

34. $a - b$

35. $-4 + 2ab$

36. $a + \frac{3b}{a}$

37. $3(a - b)$

38. $4a - 2 + 3b$

39. $\frac{a - b}{2a}$

40. $b(2b - a)$

Linear Programming

FOR USE WITH LESSON 3-4

You can solve linear programming problems with your graphing calculator.

ALG2 2.0 Students solve systems of linear inequalities (in two variables) with graphs.
Master

ACTIVITY

Find the values of x and y that will maximize the objective function $P = 13x + 2y$ for the constraints at the right. What is the value of P at this maximum point?

$$\begin{cases} -3x + 2y \le 8 \\ -8x + y \ge -48 \\ x \ge 0, \ y \ge 0 \end{cases}$$

Step 1 Rewrite the first two inequalities to isolate y. Enter the inequalities.

Step 2 Graph, using the window $0 \le x \le 12$, $0 \le y \le 20$.

Step 3 Use the value option of **CALC** to find the upper left vertex. Press 0 **ENTER**.

Step 4 Enter the expression for the objective function on the home screen. Press **ENTER** for the value of P at the vertex.

Step 5 Use the intersect option of **CALC** to find the upper right vertex. Go to the home screen and press **ENTER** for the value of P.

Step 6 Use the zero option of **CALC** to find the lower right vertex. Go to the home screen and press **ENTER** for the value of P.

Compare the values of P for the coordinates of the three vertices you found. The objective function has a value of 0 for the vertex located at the origin. The maximum value 136 occurs when $x = 8$ and $y = 16$.

EXERCISES

Find the values of x and y that maximize or minimize the objective function.

1. $\begin{cases} 4x + 3y \ge 30 \\ x + 3y \ge 21 \\ x \ge 0, y \ge 0 \end{cases}$

Minimum for
$C = 5x + 8y$

2. $\begin{cases} 3x + 5y \le 35 \\ 2x + y \le 14 \\ x \ge 0, y \ge 0 \end{cases}$

Maximum for
$P = 3x + 2y$

3. $\begin{cases} x + y \ge 8 \\ x + 5y \ge 20 \\ x \ge 0, y \ge 2 \end{cases}$

Minimum for
$C = 3x + 4y$

4. $\begin{cases} x + 2y \le 24 \\ 3x + 2y \le 34 \\ 3x + y \le 29 \\ x \ge 0 \end{cases}$

Maximum for
$P = 2x + 3y$

3-5

Graphs in Three Dimensions

California Content Standards

Prepares for **ALG2 2.0** Students solve systems of linear equations (in three variables) by substitution.

What You'll Learn

- To graph points in three dimensions
- To graph equations in three dimensions

. . . And Why

To locate points on a virtual bicycle helmet, as in Example 2

✓ **Check Skills You'll Need**

GO for Help Lesson 2-2

Find the *x*- and *y*-intercepts of the graph of each linear equation.

1. $y = 2x + 6$

2. $2x + 9y = 36$

3. $3x - 8y = -24$

4. $4x - 5y = 40$

Graph each linear equation.

5. $y = 3x$

6. $y = -2x + 4$

7. $4y = 3x - 8$

8. $-3x - 2y = 7$

New Vocabulary • **coordinate space** • **ordered triples** • **trace**

---

1 Graphing Points in Three Dimensions

Suppose you want to describe how to get from point *A* to point *B* along the grid shown at the right. You could say "Move down one unit, forward two units, and left three units," or "Move left three units, forward two units, and down one unit."

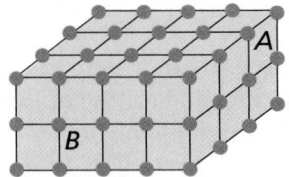

To describe positions in space, you need a three-dimensional coordinate system.

You have learned to graph on an *xy*-coordinate plane using ordered pairs. Adding a third axis, the *z*-axis, to the *xy*-coordinate plane creates **coordinate space.** In coordinate space you graph points using **ordered triples** of the form (x, y, z).

Real-World Connection

The global positioning system locates persons or objects in three dimensions.

Points in a Plane

A two-dimensional coordinate system allows you to graph points in a plane.

Points in Space

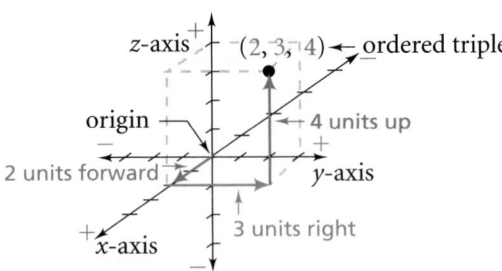

A three-dimensional coordinate system allows you to graph points in space.

In the coordinate plane, point $(2, 3)$ is two units right and three units up from the origin. In coordinate space, point $(2, 3, 4)$ is two units forward, three units right, and four units up.

1 EXAMPLE Graphing in Coordinate Space

Graph each point in coordinate space.

a. $(0, 3, -2)$
Sketch the axes. From the origin, move right 3 units and down 2 units.

b. $(-2, -1, 3)$
Sketch the axes. From the origin, move back 2 units, left 1 unit, and up 3 units.

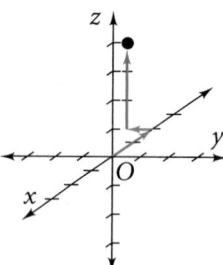

✓ **CA Standards Check** **1** Graph each point in coordinate space.
a. $(0, -4, -2)$ **b.** $(-1, 1, 3)$ **c.** $(3, -5, 2)$ **d.** $(3, 3, -3)$

2 EXAMPLE Real-World 🌐 Connection

Product Design Computers are used to design three-dimensional objects. Programs allow the designer to view the object from different perspectives. Find coordinates for points A, B, and C in the diagram below.

$A(0, 0, 0)$, $B(4, 0, 0)$, $C(3, -2, 1)$

✓ **CA Standards Check** **2 a.** Find coordinates for point D in the diagram.
b. Does the point $(-3, 2, 4)$ lie inside or outside the helmet? Explain.

The graph of an equation is a picture of all the solutions to the equation. In two dimensions, the graph of $3x - 2y = 6$ is a line. In three dimensions, the graph of $3x - 2y + z = 6$ is a plane, as shown at the right.

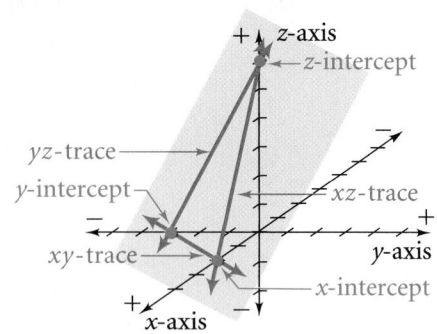

If the graph of a plane intersects one of the coordinate planes in a line, then the line is called a **trace**. For example, the xy-trace is the line in the xy-plane that contains the x- and the y-intercepts. The xz-trace and the yz-trace are defined similarly.

Vocabulary Tip

The x-intercept of a line or plane is the point of intersection with the x-axis.

To sketch a plane, find the x-, y-, and z- intercepts. Then draw the traces and show the plane with shading.

3 EXAMPLE **Sketching a Plane**

Sketch the graph of $2x + 3y + 4z = 12$.

Step 1 Find the intercepts.

$$2x + 3y + 4z = 12$$
$$2x + 3(0) + 4(0) = 12 \quad \textbf{To find the } \textit{x}\textbf{-intercept, substitute 0 for } \textit{y} \textbf{ and } \textit{z}.$$
$$2x = 12$$
$$x = 6 \quad \textbf{The } \textit{x}\textbf{-intercept is 6.}$$
$$2(0) + 3y + 4(0) = 12 \quad \textbf{To find the } \textit{y}\textbf{-intercept, substitute 0 for } \textit{x} \textbf{ and } \textit{z}.$$
$$3y = 12$$
$$y = 4 \quad \textbf{The } \textit{y}\textbf{-intercept is 4.}$$
$$2(0) + 3(0) + 4z = 12 \quad \textbf{To find the } \textit{z}\textbf{-intercept, substitute 0 for } \textit{x} \textbf{ and } \textit{y}.$$
$$4z = 12$$
$$z = 3 \quad \textbf{The } \textit{z}\textbf{-intercept is 3.}$$

Step 2 Graph the intercepts.

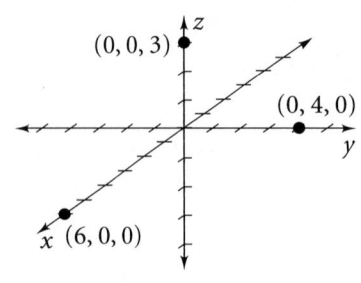

Step 3 Draw the traces. Shade the plane.

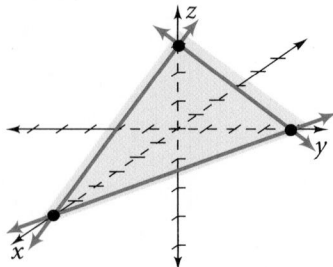

● Each point on the plane represents a solution to $2x + 3y + 4z = 12$.

✓ **CA Standards Check** ③ Sketch the graph of each equation.

a. $x + y + z = 5$ **b.** $2x - y + 3z = 6$ **c.** $x + 2y - z = -4$

A Practice by Example

Example 1
(page 149)

GO for Help

Describe the location of each point in coordinate space.

1. $(-1, 5, 0)$ **2.** $(3, -3, 4)$

3. $(2, 0, 5)$ **4.** $(-4, -7, -1)$

Graph each point in coordinate space.

5. $(5, 0, -2)$ **6.** $(0, 0, 4)$

7. $(10, -2, -5)$ **8.** $(-1, -1, -1)$

9. $(-4, -5, 3)$ **10.** $(25, 40, -30)$

11. $(1, 1, 0)$ **12.** $(0, -2, 2)$

Example 2
(page 149)

Find the coordinates of each point in the diagram.

13. A **14.** B **15.** C

16. D **17.** E **18.** F

Example 3
(page 150)

Sketch the graph of each equation.

19. $x + y + 2z = 4$ **20.** $x + y + z = 2$ **21.** $2x + 6y + z = 6$

22. $x - y - 4z = 8$ **23.** $-x + 3y + z = 6$ **24.** $2x - y - 5z = 10$

B Apply Your Skills

25. Writing While visiting friends in New York, you go to a concert. Explain how the seat information on your ticket at the right represents a point in three-dimensional coordinate space.

26. Multiple Choice Suppose you have $20 to spend on party decorations. Balloons are $.05 each, streamers are $.25 each, and noisemakers are $.40 each. Which equation best models this situation?

Ⓐ $5b + 25s + 40n = 20$

Ⓑ $20(b + s + n) = 0.05 + 0.25 + 0.4$

Ⓒ $0.05b + 0.25s + 0.4n = 20$

Ⓓ $0.05b + 0.25s + 0.4n + 20 = 0$

Sketch the graph of each equation.

27. $7x + 14y - z = 7$ **28.** $-3x + 5y + 10z = 15$

29. $32x + 16y - 8z = 32$ **30.** $-25x + 30y + 50z = 75$

31. $50x + 25y + 100z = 200$ **32.** $14x - 8y + 28z = 28$

Homework Video Tutor

Sketch the graph of each equation and find the equation of each trace.

33. $6x + 6y - 12z = 36$ **34.** $-20x + 10y + 50z = 100$

35. $-12x - 32y - 48z = 96$ **36.** $25x + 125y - 25z = 125$

Visit: PHSchool.com
Web Code: bbe-0305

Online Lesson Quiz Visit: PHSchool.com, **Web Code:** bba-0305

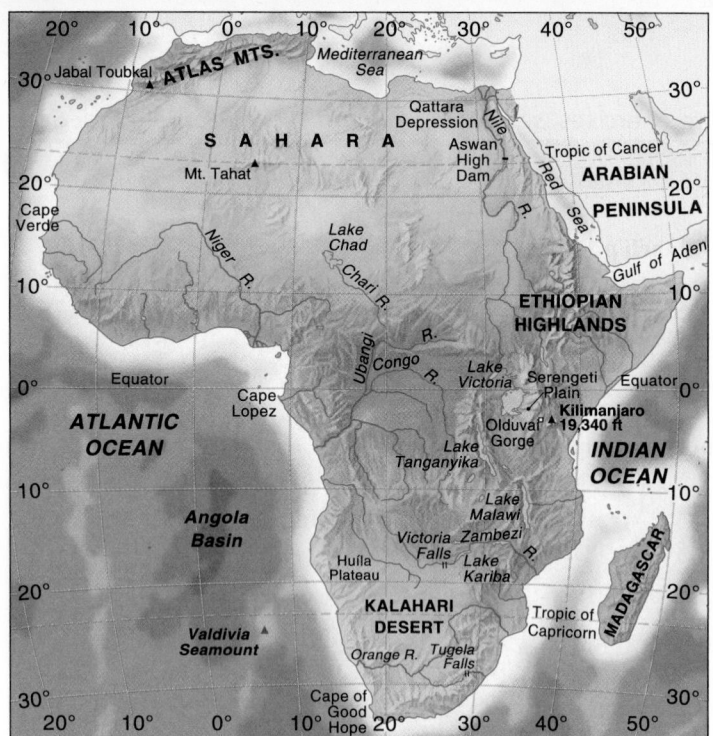

Geography Use the map to identify the geographic feature found at each location.

37. latitude 3° S
longitude 37° E
elevation 19,340 ft

38. latitude 23° N
longitude 5° E
elevation 9,573 ft

39. latitude 25° S
longitude 6° E
elevation −3,072 ft

40. latitude 15° N
longitude 18° W
elevation 0 ft

41. latitude 30° N
longitude 27° E
elevation −440 ft

42. latitude 13° N
longitude 14° E
elevation 919 ft

43. latitude 31° N
longitude 8° W
elevation 49,212 ft

44. latitude 18° S
longitude 25° E
elevation 2,927 ft

45. latitude 22° N
longitude 31° E
elevation 600 ft

46. latitude 1° S
longitude 33° E
elevation 3,720 ft

47. Error Analysis A student claims to find the x-intercept of a plane by substituting 0 for x in the equation of the plane. Explain the student's error.

 Challenge **48. a. Geometry** Use the Pythagorean Theorem to find the distance between $(1, 2, 4)$ and $(3, -2, 7)$. (*Hint:* Recall the Distance Formula.)

b. Make a Conjecture Make a conjecture about how to find the coordinates of the midpoint of a segment in coordinate space.

49. a. Critical Thinking Does every plane have three traces? Explain.

b. Must any two traces of a plane intersect? Explain.

Graph each equation in three-dimensional coordinate space.

50. $x = 3$ **51.** $2x + 3y = 6$ **52.** $y = 0$

Multiple Choice Practice

For California Standards and CAHSEE Tutorials, visit PHSchool.com. Web Code: bbq-9045

ALG2 1.0

53. Points A and B are on a number line. Point B is located at -13. The length of segment AB is 17 units. Solve the equation $|x + 13| = 17$ to find the coordinates of point A.

Ⓐ 4   Ⓑ −30   Ⓒ −4 or 30   Ⓓ −30 or 4

**CAHSEE
7AF 2.2**

54. Which expression best represents the simplification of $(2x^3y^2)(-5x^7y^5)$?

Ⓐ $-10x^4y^3$ Ⓑ $-\dfrac{x^4y^3}{10}$ Ⓒ $-10x^{21}y^{10}$ Ⓓ $-10x^{10}y^7$

**CAHSEE
7MG 3.2**

55. A coordinate grid is placed over a map. City A is located at $(4, -3)$, and City B is located at $(7, 3)$. If City C is at the midpoint between City A and City B, which is closest to the distance in coordinate units from City A to City C?

Ⓐ 3.35   Ⓑ 3.91   Ⓒ 6.71   Ⓓ 9.96

Lesson 3-4

56. Maximize the objective function $P = x + 3y$ under the given constraints. At what vertex does this maximum value occur?
$$\begin{cases} x + y \leq 5 \\ x + 2y \leq 8 \\ x \geq 0, y \geq 0 \end{cases}$$

Lesson 2-7

Graph each inequality.

57. $y \leq x - 3$ **58.** $3y - x > -4$ **59.** $2x - y \geq 0$

Lesson 1-6

60. Probability Your town has a drawing for 50 summer jobs. Including you, 150 students apply.
  a. What is the probability that you will get one of the jobs?
  b. You and a friend apply. What is the probability that you both get jobs?

Checkpoint Quiz 2   **Lessons 3-4 through 3-5**

1. Find the values of x and y that minimize the objective function $C = 2x + 3y$ for the constraints at the right.
$$\begin{cases} y \geq x \\ x + y \leq 32 \\ x \geq 5, y \geq 3 \end{cases}$$

2. Agriculture A farmer has at most 400 acres and $45,000 available to grow corn and soybeans. Use the cost and profit information at the right to decide how many acres of each crop will maximize profit.

Cost and Profit for Corn and Soybeans

	Corn	Soybeans
Number of Acres	x	y
Cost	$100x$	$150y$
Profit	$60x$	$75y$

Graph each equation. Use traces and intercepts.

3. $3x + 2y + z = 6$ **4.** $x - y + z = 4$ **5.** $4x + y + z = 8$

Algebra at Work

·· Radiologist

Radiologists are medical doctors who use X-rays, sound waves, and other means to diagnose diseases. Among the radiologist's most powerful diagnostic devices is the CT (computerized tomography) scan. The patient lies on a table while X-rays are beamed through the patient's body from different angles. Images are recorded and fed into a computer. The computer uses a three-dimensional coordinate system to record information and then to produce images of a cross section of the patient's body.

For: Information about radiology
Web Code: bbb-2031

Systems With Three Variables

 California Content Standards

ALG2 2.0 Students solve systems of linear equations (in three variables) by substitution.
Master

What You'll Learn

- To solve systems in three variables by elimination
- To solve systems in three variables by substitution

. . . And Why

To choose an investment strategy, as in Example 4

✓ Check Skills You'll Need

GO for Help Lessons 3-1 and 3-2

Solve each system.

1. $\begin{cases} 2x - y = 11 \\ x + 2y = -7 \end{cases}$

2. $\begin{cases} -x + 6y = 8 \\ 2x - 12y = -14 \end{cases}$

3. $\begin{cases} 3x + 2y = -5 \\ 4x + 3y = -8 \end{cases}$

Let $y = 4x - 2$. Solve each equation for x.

4. $3x + y = 5$

5. $x - 2y = -3$

6. $4x + 3y = 2$

Determine whether the given ordered pair is a solution of each equation in the system.

7. $(1, 3) \begin{cases} 2x + 5y = 17 \\ -4x + 3y = 5 \end{cases}$

8. $(-4, 2) \begin{cases} x + 2y = 0 \\ 3x - 2y = -16 \end{cases}$

---

1 Solving Three-Variable Systems by Elimination

You can represent systems of equations in three variables as graphs in three dimensions. As you learned in Lesson 3-5, the graph of any equation of the form $Ax + By + Cz = D$, where A, B, and C are not all zero, is a plane. The solutions of a three-variable system can be shown graphically as the intersections of planes.

GO for Help

To review solving systems in two variables by graphing, go to Lesson 3-1.

No solution
No point lies in all three planes.

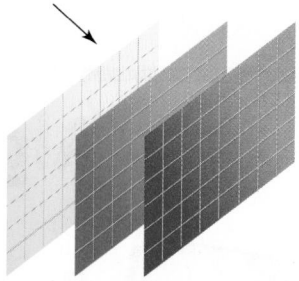

One solution
The planes intersect at one common point.

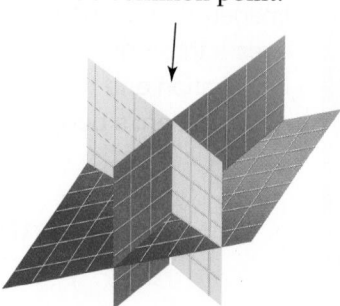

An infinite number of solutions
The planes intersect at all the points along a common line.

When the solution of a system of equations in three variables is represented by one point, you can write it as an ordered triple (x, y, z).

You can solve a system of three equations in three variables by working with the equations in pairs. You will use one of the equations *twice*.

Real-World Connection

You can use a system in three variables to model the amounts of vitamin C, potassium, and beta carotene in this three-fruit salad.

1 EXAMPLE Solving by Elimination

Solve the system by elimination. The equations are numbered to make the procedure easy to follow.

① $\begin{cases} x - 3y + 3z = -4 \\ ② \quad 2x + 3y - z = 15 \\ ③ \quad 4x - 3y - z = 19 \end{cases}$

Step 1 Pair the equations to eliminate y because the y terms are already additive inverses.

① $\begin{cases} x - 3y + 3z = -4 \\ ② \quad 2x + 3y - z = 15 \end{cases}$ **Add.** ② $\begin{cases} 2x + 3y - z = 15 \\ ③ \quad 4x - 3y - z = 19 \end{cases}$

④ $\quad 3x \qquad + 2z = 11$ ⑤ $\quad 6x \qquad - 2z = 34$

Step 2 Write the two new equations as a system. Solve for x and z.

④ $\begin{cases} 3x \qquad + 2z = 11 \\ ⑤ \quad 6x \qquad - 2z = 34 \end{cases}$

$\quad 9x \qquad = 45$

$\quad x = 5$

④ $\quad 3x + 2z = 11$

$3(5) + 2z = 11$ **Substitute the value of x.**

$2z = -4$

$z = -2$

Step 3 Substitute the values for x and z into one of the original equations (①, ②, or ③) and solve for y.

① $\quad x - 3y + 3z = -4$

$5 - 3y + 3(-2) = -4$

$5 - 3y - 6 = -4$

$-3y = -3$

$y = 1$

The solution of the system is $(5, 1, -2)$.

Check Show that $(5, 1, -2)$ makes each equation true.

$x - 3y + 3z = -4$	$2x + 3y - z = 15$	$4x - 3y - z = 19$
$5 - 3(1) + 3(-2) \overset{?}{=} -4$	$2(5) + 3(1) - (-2) \overset{?}{=} 15$	$4(5) - 3(1) - (-2) \overset{?}{=} 19$
$5 - 3 - 6 \overset{?}{=} -4$	$10 + 3 + 2 \overset{?}{=} 15$	$20 - 3 + 2 \overset{?}{=} 19$
$-4 = -4 \checkmark$	$15 = 15 \checkmark$	$19 = 19 \checkmark$

✅ **CA Standards Check** ① Solve each system by elimination. Check your answers.

a. $\begin{cases} 2x + y - z = 5 \\ 3x - y + 2z = -1 \\ x - y - z = 0 \end{cases}$ **b.** $\begin{cases} 2x - y + z = 4 \\ x + 3y - z = 11 \\ 4x + y - z = 14 \end{cases}$

c. Critical Thinking Suppose, in a three-variable system, the coefficient of one of the variables in one of the equations is zero. When pairing the equations to solve the system, would you use that equation twice? Explain.

You can apply the method in Example 1 to any system of three equations in three variables. You may need to multiply one or more of the equations by a nonzero number to form an equivalent system.

2 EXAMPLE **Solving an Equivalent System**

Solve the system by elimination.

① $\begin{cases} 2x + y - z = 5 \\ x + 4y + 2z = 16 \\ 15x + 6y - 2z = 12 \end{cases}$
②
③

Step 1   Pair the equations to eliminate z.

① $\begin{cases} 2x + y - z = 5 \\ x + 4y + 2z = 16 \end{cases}$
②

$\begin{array}{r} 4x + 2y - 2z = 10 \quad \textbf{Multiply by 2.} \\ x + 4y + 2z = 16 \\ \hline ④ \ 5x + 6y \qquad\quad = 26 \end{array}$

② $\begin{cases} x + 4y + 2z = 16 \\ 15x + 6y - 2z = 12 \end{cases}$
③
⑤ $\overline{\quad 16x + 10y \qquad = 28}$

Step 2   Write the two new equations as a system. Solve for x and y.

④ $\begin{cases} 5x + 6y = 26 \\ 16x + 10y = 28 \end{cases}$
⑤

$\begin{array}{r} 25x + 30y = 130 \quad \textbf{Multiply by 5.} \\ -48x - 30y = -84 \quad \textbf{Multiply by } -3. \\ \hline -23x \qquad\quad = 46 \\ x = -2 \end{array}$

④ $\qquad 5x + 6y = 26$

$\qquad 5(-2) + 6y = 26$ **Substitute the value of x.**

$\qquad\qquad\quad y = 6$

Step 3   Substitute the values for x and y into one of the original equations (①, ②, or ③). Solve for z.

① $\qquad 2x + y - z = 5$

$\qquad 2(-2) + 6 - z = 5$

$\qquad\qquad\qquad z = -3$

The solution of the system is $(-2, 6, -3)$.

✓ CA Standards Check   **2** Solve the system by elimination. Check your answers.

$\begin{cases} x + 4y - 5z = -7 \\ 3x + 2y + 3z = 7 \\ 2x + y + 5z = 8 \end{cases}$

The graph illustrates the solution to Example 2. Each equation in the system represents a tilted plane. The graph of ① is red, the graph of ② is blue, and the graph of ③ is green. The three planes intersect at $(-2, 6, -3)$.

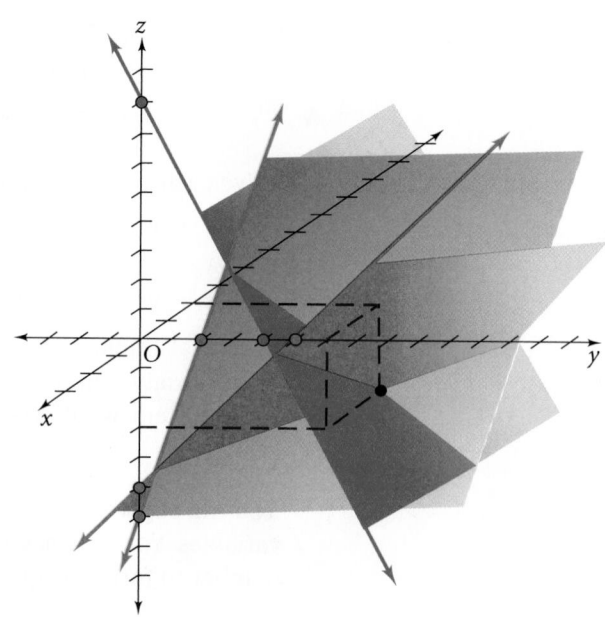

You can also use the substitution method to solve a system of three equations. Substitution is the best method to use when one of the equations can be solved easily for one variable.

3 **EXAMPLE** **Solving by Substitution**

To review the substitution method, go to Lesson 3-2.

Solve the system by substitution.

$$\begin{array}{r} ① \\ ② \\ ③ \end{array} \left\{ \begin{array}{r} x - 2y + z = -4 \\ -4x + y - 2z = 1 \\ 2x + 2y - z = 10 \end{array} \right.$$

Step 1 Choose one equation to solve for one of its variables.

① $x - 2y + z = -4$ **Solve the first equation for x.**

$x - 2y = -z - 4$

$x = 2y - z - 4$

Step 2 Substitute the expression for x into each of the other two equations.

② $-4x + y - 2z = 1$ ③ $2x + 2y - z = 10$

$-4(2y - z - 4) + y - 2z = 1$ **Simplify.** $2(2y - z - 4) + 2y - z = 10$

$-8y + 4z + 16 + y - 2z = 1$ $4y - 2z - 8 + 2y - z = 10$

$-7y + 2z + 16 = 1$ $6y - 3z - 8 = 10$

④ $-7y + 2z = -15$ ⑤ $6y - 3z = 18$

Step 3 Write the two new equations as a system. Solve for y and z.

$$\begin{array}{r} ④ \\ ⑤ \end{array} \left\{ \begin{array}{r} -7y + 2z = -15 \\ 6y - 3z = 18 \end{array} \right.$$

$\begin{array}{r} -21y + 6z = -45 \\ \underline{12y - 6z = 36} \\ -9y = -9 \\ y = 1 \end{array}$ **Multiply by 3.**
Multiply by 2.

④ $-7y + 2z = -15$

$-7(1) + 2z = -15$ **Substitute the value of y.**

$-7 + 2z = -15$

$2z = -8$

$z = -4$

Step 4 Substitute the values for y and z into one of the original equations (①, ②, or ③). Solve for x.

① $x - 2y + z = -4$

$x - 2(1) + (-4) = -4$

$x - 2 - 4 = -4$

$x - 6 = -4$

$x = 2$

● The solution of the system is $(2, 1, -4)$.

 3 Solve each system by substitution. Check your answers.

a. $\left\{ \begin{array}{r} x - 3y + z = 6 \\ 2x - 5y - z = -2 \\ -x + y + 2z = 7 \end{array} \right.$ **b.** $\left\{ \begin{array}{r} 3x + 2y - z = 12 \\ -4x + y - 2z = 4 \\ x - 3y + z = -4 \end{array} \right.$

Investment Options

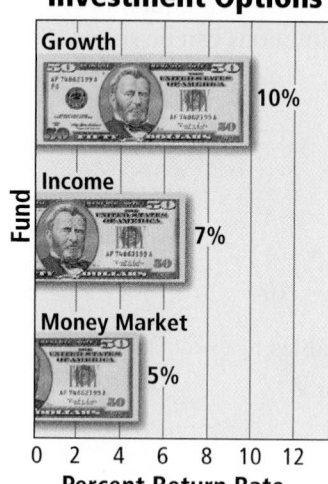

Growth — 10%
Income — 7%
Money Market — 5%

Fund

0 2 4 6 8 10 12
Percent Return Rate

---

4 EXAMPLE   Real-World 🌐 Connection

Money Management Suppose you have saved $3200 from a part-time job and you want to invest your savings in a growth fund, an income fund, and a money market fund. Refer to the graph. To maximize your return, you decide to put twice as much money in the growth fund as in the money market fund. How should you invest the $3200 to get a return of $250 in one year?

Relate   growth fund + income fund + money market fund = 3200

growth fund = 2 times money market fund

10% of growth + 7% of income + 5% of money market = 250

Define   Let g = amount invested in a growth fund.

Let i = amount invested in an income fund.

Let m = amount invested in a money market fund.

Write

① $\begin{cases} g + i + m = 3200 \\ ② \quad g = 2m \\ ③ \quad 0.10g + 0.07i + 0.05m = 250 \end{cases}$

Step 1   Substitute $2m$ for g in equations ① and ③. Simplify.

① $g + i + m = 3200$ ③ $0.10g + 0.07i + 0.05m = 250$

$2m + i + m = 3200$ $0.10(2m) + 0.07i + 0.05m = 250$

④ $3m + i = 3200$ ⑤ $0.25m + 0.07i = 250$

Step 2   Write the two new equations as a system. Solve for m and i.

④ $\begin{cases} 3m + \quad\; i = 3200 \\ ⑤ \quad 0.25m + 0.07i = 250 \end{cases}$

$3m + \quad\quad i = 3200$

$3m + 0.84i = 3000$ **Multiply by 12.**

$0.16i = 200$

$i = 1250$

④ $3m + i = 3200$

$3m + 1250 = 3200$ **Substitute the value of i.**

$3m = 1950$

$m = 650$

Step 3   Substitute the value of m into equation 2 and solve for g.

② $g = 2m$

$g = 2(650)$

$g = 1300$

You should invest $1300 in the growth fund, $1250 in the income fund, and $650 in the money market fund to get a return of $250 in one year.

✓ **CA Standards Check**   ④ Suppose you discover that your growth fund, income fund, and money market fund return rates are better estimated at 12%, 6%, and 3% per year respectively. How should you invest the $3200 to get a return of $255 in one year?

You have learned how to solve systems of equations using the methods of graphing, elimination, and substitution. In Chapter 4, you will learn how to use matrices to solve systems of equations.

A Practice by Example

Examples 1 and 2
(pages 155 and 156)

GO for Help

Solve each system by elimination. Check your answers.

1. $\begin{cases} x - y + z = -1 \\ x + y + 3z = -3 \\ 2x - y + 2z = 0 \end{cases}$ 2. $\begin{cases} x - y - 2z = 4 \\ -x + 2y + z = 1 \\ -x + y - 3z = 11 \end{cases}$ 3. $\begin{cases} 2x - y + z = -2 \\ x + 3y - z = 10 \\ x + 2z = -8 \end{cases}$

4. $\begin{cases} a + b + c = -3 \\ 3b - c = 4 \\ 2a - b - 2c = -5 \end{cases}$ 5. $\begin{cases} 6q - r + 2s = 8 \\ 2q + 3r - s = -9 \\ 4q + 2r + 5s = 1 \end{cases}$ 6. $\begin{cases} x - y + 2z = -7 \\ y + z = 1 \\ x = 2y + 3z \end{cases}$

7. $\begin{cases} x + y + 2z = 3 \\ 2x + y + 3z = 7 \\ -x - 2y + z = 10 \end{cases}$ 8. $\begin{cases} 3x - y + z = 3 \\ x + y + 2z = 4 \\ x + 2y + z = 4 \end{cases}$ 9. $\begin{cases} x - 2y + 3z = 12 \\ 2x - y - 2z = 5 \\ 2x + 2y - z = 4 \end{cases}$

Examples 3 and 4
(pages 157 and 158)

Solve each system by substitution. Check your answers.

10. $\begin{cases} x + 2y + 3z = 6 \\ y + 2z = 0 \\ z = 2 \end{cases}$ 11. $\begin{cases} 3a + b + c = 7 \\ a + 3b - c = 13 \\ b = 2a - 1 \end{cases}$ 12. $\begin{cases} 5r - 4s - 3t = 3 \\ t = s + r \\ r = 3s + 1 \end{cases}$

13. $\begin{cases} 13 = 3x - y \\ 4y - 3x + 2z = -3 \\ z = 2x - 4y \end{cases}$ 14. $\begin{cases} x + 3y - z = -4 \\ 2x - y + 2z = 13 \\ 3x - 2y - z = -9 \end{cases}$ 15. $\begin{cases} x - 4y + z = 6 \\ 2x + 5y - z = 7 \\ 2x - y - z = 1 \end{cases}$

16. $\begin{cases} x - y + 2z = 7 \\ 2x + y + z = 8 \\ x - z = 5 \end{cases}$ 17. $\begin{cases} x + y + z = 2 \\ x + 2z = 5 \\ 2x + y - z = -1 \end{cases}$ 18. $\begin{cases} 5x - y + z = 4 \\ x + 2y - z = 5 \\ 2x + 3y - 3z = 5 \end{cases}$

19. **Finance** A company placed $1,000,000 in three different accounts. It placed part in short-term notes paying 4.5% per year, twice as much in government bonds paying 5%, and the rest in utility bonds paying 4%. The income after one year was $45,500. How much did the company place in each account?

20. **Sports** A stadium has 49,000 seats. Seats sell for $25 in Section A, $20 in Section B, and $15 in Section C. The number of seats in Section A equals the total number of seats in Sections B and C. Suppose the stadium takes in $1,052,000 from each sold-out event. How many seats does each section hold?

21. A change machine contains nickels, dimes, and quarters. There are 75 coins in the machine, and the value of the coins is $7.25. There are 5 times as many nickels as dimes. Find the number of coins of each type in the machine.

B Apply Your Skills

Find the number of solutions of each system.

22.   23.   24.

Solve each system.

25. $\begin{cases} x - 3y + 2z = 11 \\ -x + 4y + 3z = 5 \\ 2x - 2y - 4z = 2 \end{cases}$

26. $\begin{cases} x + 2y + z = 4 \\ 2x - y + 4z = -8 \\ -3x + y - 2z = -1 \end{cases}$

27. $\begin{cases} 4x - y + 2z = -6 \\ -2x + 3y - z = 8 \\ 2y + 3z = -5 \end{cases}$

28. $\begin{cases} 4A + 2U + I = 2 \\ 5A - 3U + 2I = 17 \\ A - 5U = 3 \end{cases}$

29. $\begin{cases} 4x - 2y + 5z = 6 \\ 3x + 3y + 8z = 4 \\ x - 5y - 3z = 5 \end{cases}$

30. $\begin{cases} 2\ell + 2w + h = 72 \\ \ell = 3w \\ h = 2w \end{cases}$

31. $\begin{cases} 3x + 2y - z = 17.8 \\ x - 3y + 2z = 7.9 \\ 2x + y - 3z = 3.9 \end{cases}$

32. $\begin{cases} x + 2y = 2 \\ 2x + 3y - z = -9 \\ 4x + 2y + 5z = 1 \end{cases}$

33. $\begin{cases} 3x + 2y + 2z = -2 \\ 2x + y - z = -2 \\ x - 3y + z = 0 \end{cases}$

34. $\begin{cases} 6x + y - 4z = -8 \\ \dfrac{y}{4} - \dfrac{z}{6} = 0 \\ 2x - z = -2 \end{cases}$

35. $\begin{cases} 4y + 2x = 6 - 3z \\ x + z - 2y = -5 \\ x - 2z = 3y - 7 \end{cases}$

36. $\begin{cases} 5z + 4y = 4 \\ 3x - 2y = 0 \\ x + 3z = -8 \end{cases}$

37. $\begin{cases} x + 6z = 12 \\ -2x + 3y = 6 \\ y - \dfrac{z}{2} = \dfrac{5}{2} \end{cases}$

38. $\begin{cases} 4x - y + z = -5 \\ -x + y - z = 5 \\ 2x - z - 1 = y \end{cases}$

History Exercises 39 and 40 appeared in the book *Algebraical Problems*, published in 1824. Write and solve a system for each problem.

39. Ten apples cost a penny, and 25 pears cost two pennies. Suppose I buy 100 apples and pears for $9\frac{1}{2}$ pennies. How many of each shall I have?

40. A fish was caught whose tail weighed 9 lb. Its head weighed as much as its tail plus half its body. Its body weighed as much as its head and tail. What did the fish weigh?

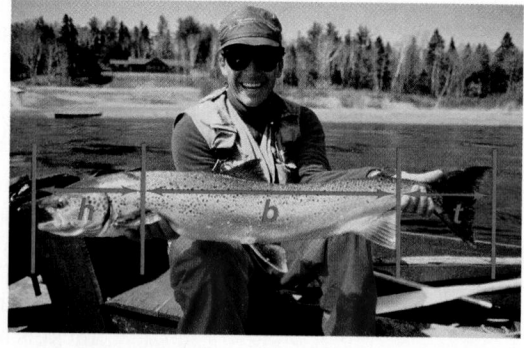

41. **Writing** How do you decide whether substitution is the best method to solve a system in three variables?

42. **Error Analysis** A student says that the system consisting of $x = 0$, $y = 0$, and $z = 0$ has no solutions. Explain the student's error.

43. **Geometry** Refer to the regular five-pointed star at the right. Write and solve a system of three equations to find the measure of each labeled angle.

44. **Open-Ended** Write your own system having three variables. Begin by choosing the solution. Then write three equations that are true for your solution. Use elimination to solve the system.

45. Geometry In the regular polyhedron described below, all faces are congruent polygons. Use a system of three linear equations to find the numbers of vertices, edges, and faces.

Every face has five edges and every edge is shared by two faces. Every face has five vertices and every vertex is shared by three faces. The sum of the number of vertices and faces is two more than the number of edges.

 Multiple Choice Practice

For California Standards and CAHSEE Tutorials, visit PHSchool.com. Web Code: bbq-9045

ALG2 2.0

46. Solve the system $\begin{cases} 2x - y + z = 4 \\ x + 3y - z = 4 \\ 3x + y + z = 8 \end{cases}$.

Ⓐ $(2, 0, 0)$ Ⓑ $(1, 0, 2)$ Ⓒ $(2, 1, 1)$ Ⓓ $(2, 0, -2)$

CAHSEE 7MG 2.3

47. A rectangular solid has a surface area of 94 square feet. If the length, width, and height are all doubled, what will be the surface area, in square feet, of the new rectangular solid?

Ⓐ 94   Ⓑ 188   Ⓒ 376   Ⓓ 564

CAHSEE Alg1 6.0

48. What is the y-intercept of the linear function represented in the table at the right?

x	-3	2	5	8
y	29	9	-3	-15

Ⓐ -4 Ⓒ 17
Ⓑ 4   Ⓓ 19

CAHSEE 7NS 1.6

49. In January, the dog shelter reported that 594 dogs were adopted in Quentin Township last year, which was a 12% decrease from the total number of dogs adopted in the previous year. How many more dogs were adopted in the previous year than last year?

Ⓐ 71   Ⓑ 81   Ⓒ 112   Ⓓ 522

Mixed Review

Lesson 3-5

Graph each equation.

50. $x + y + 4z = 8$ **51.** $2x + 3y - z = 12$ **52.** $-3x + y + 5z = 15$

53. $-2x + 3y - z = 6$ **54.** $6x + 4y - 3z = -12$ **55.** $3x - 6y - 2z = 18$

Graph each equation.

Lesson 2-5

56. $y = |x + 4|$ **57.** $y = |3x - 2|$ **58.** $y = \left|\frac{1}{2}x + 3\right| - 2$

59. $y = |x - 2| + 1$ **60.** $y = |2x + 1|$ **61.** $y = |x + 3| - 2$

Lesson 1-4

Solve each inequality. Graph the solution on a number line.

62. $-4x + 3 \leq 9$ **63.** $-(x + 4) - 3 \geq 11$ **64.** $2(3x - 1) < x - 7$

65. $6 - 2x > 2$ **66.** $3x + 2 < -x + 10$ **67.** $-2(x + 3) \geq x$

Some questions ask you to decide what additional information you need to solve a problem. First, decide how you would solve the problem. Then look at the given information and decide what information you still need.

EXAMPLE

Jen is starting a company that makes DVDs for birthdays, anniversaries, and weddings. She invests $6500 in a digital video camera, lighting equipment, and editing software. She plans on selling the DVDs for $25 each. What other information is needed to determine the break-even point for Jen's company?

- Ⓐ the average playing time of the DVDs
- Ⓑ the average cost of making each DVD
- Ⓒ the number of DVDs Jen sells in her first month of business
- Ⓓ the cost of a digital video camera

To find the break-even point. Jen needs to find her costs, which include the one-time cost of the camera, lighting, and software, plus the cost to make each DVD. Since the cost of each DVD is not given, B is the correct answer.

EXERCISES

1. Kendra's classmate surveyed 23 students in their class and made the graph shown at the right. The shaded region represents the portion of the 23 students who did homework over the weekend. There are 84 students in Kendra's grade. What other information does Kendra need in order to estimate the number of students in her grade who did homework over the weekend?

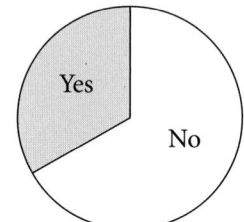

- Ⓐ the measure of the angle that forms the shaded sector
- Ⓑ the area of the circle
- Ⓒ the radius of the circle
- Ⓓ the percentage of students that the whole circle represents

2. Mateo's class voted to donate to a scholarship fund. A local business has promised to match the money that the class donates. The class already has $82 but decides to have a bake sale to raise more money. The average price of the items sold will be $1. What other information is needed to determine the total amount of money Mateo's class and the local business will donate to the scholarship fund?

- Ⓐ the number of students in Mateo's class
- Ⓑ the number of items each classmate buys at the bake sale
- Ⓒ the median price of the items sold at the bake sale
- Ⓓ the number of items sold at the bake sale

Vocabulary Review

🔊 **English and Spanish Audio Online**

constraints (p. 141)
coordinate space (p. 148)
dependent system (p. 122)
equivalent systems (p. 129)
feasible region (p. 142)

inconsistent system (p. 122)
independent system (p. 122)
linear programming (p. 141)
linear system (p. 120)
objective function (p. 141)

ordered triples (p. 148)
system of equations (p. 120)
trace (p. 150)

Match the vocabulary term in Column 1 with the most appropriate phrase in Column 2.

Go Online
PHSchool.com
For: Vocabulary quiz
Web Code: bbj-0351

Column 1

1. dependent linear systems

2. equivalent systems

3. inconsistent linear systems

4. independent linear systems

5. three-variable systems

Column 2

A. have many solutions

B. have no solutions

C. have solutions that can be shown as the intersection of planes

D. have the same solutions

E. have unique solutions

Skills and Concepts

Lesson 3-1

• To solve a system by graphing (p. 120)

 ALG2 2.0, LA 6.0

A **system of equations** is a set of two or more equations that use the same variables. The points where all the graphs intersect represent solutions. You must check the coordinates of the points of intersection in the original equations to be sure you have a solution. A **linear system** consists of linear equations.

An **independent system** has a unique solution while a **dependent system** has infinitely many solutions. An **inconsistent system** has no solutions.

Solve each system by graphing.

6. $\begin{cases} y = 2x + 1 \\ y = 4x + 5 \end{cases}$

7. $\begin{cases} y = 3x - 2 \\ y = -2x + 8 \end{cases}$

8. $\begin{cases} y = 3x - 5 \\ 2y = 6x + 4 \end{cases}$

9. $\begin{cases} 3x + 2y = -6 \\ x - y = -2 \end{cases}$

10. $\begin{cases} 4x - y = 6 \\ -2x + 3y = 12 \end{cases}$

11. $\begin{cases} 12x + 3y = -9 \\ 4x + y = 7 \end{cases}$

Without graphing, classify each system as *independent*, *dependent*, or *inconsistent*.

12. $\begin{cases} 6x + 3y = 12 \\ y = -2x + 4 \end{cases}$

13. $\begin{cases} y = -x + 5 \\ x - y = -3 \end{cases}$

14. $\begin{cases} x + 2y = 2 \\ y = -0.5x - 2 \end{cases}$

15. Banking Suppose a bank charges a monthly rate of $10 for your checking account. You can switch to a different account that charges $6 plus $.20 per check. For what number of checks is the cost of the two accounts the same?

Lesson 3-2

- To solve a system by substitution (p. 127)
- To solve a system by elimination (p. 128)

 ALG2 2.0

If you can easily solve one equation in a system of two equations for one of the variables, you can substitute that expression in the other equation. Then you can find the value of the other variable.

Otherwise, you can multiply one or both equations by a nonzero quantity to create two terms that are additive inverses. This creates an **equivalent system** of equations. Adding the two equations then eliminates one variable. Again, you can solve for the other variable.

In either case, you substitute the value of this second variable into either of the original equations to find the value of the first variable. Recall that some systems have an infinite number of solutions and some have no solutions.

Solve using substitution.

16. $\begin{cases} 3x + 5y = 10 \\ y = -4 \end{cases}$

17. $\begin{cases} 4x + 3y = 12 \\ x = 5y - 20 \end{cases}$

18. $\begin{cases} 8x + y = 17 \\ x + 4y = 37 \end{cases}$

Solve using elimination.

19. $\begin{cases} 2x + y = 13 \\ x - y = -4 \end{cases}$

20. $\begin{cases} 2x + 3y = 4 \\ 4x + 6y = 9 \end{cases}$

21. $\begin{cases} a + b = \frac{1}{3} \\ a - b = \frac{1}{4} \end{cases}$

22. **Nutrition** Roast beef has 25 g of protein and 11 g of calcium per serving. A serving of mashed potatoes has 2 g of protein and 25 g of calcium. How many servings of each are needed to supply exactly 29 g of protein and 61 g of calcium?

Lesson 3-3

- To solve systems of linear inequalities (p. 135)

 ALG2 1.0, 2.0

The solution of a system of inequalities is represented on a graph by the region of overlap of the inequalities. To solve a system by graphing, first graph the boundaries for each inequality. Then shade the regions of the plane containing the solutions for both inequalities.

Solve each system by graphing.

23. $\begin{cases} y < -x + 1 \\ y \geq \frac{3}{4}x - 6 \end{cases}$

24. $\begin{cases} x + y \leq 4 \\ y < 6 \end{cases}$

25. $\begin{cases} y > |x - 4| \\ y < \frac{1}{3}x \end{cases}$

26. For a community breakfast there should be at least three times as much regular coffee as decaffeinated coffee. A total of ten gallons is sufficient for the breakfast. Model this situation with a system of inequalities. Graph to solve the system.

Lesson 3-4

- To find maximum and minimum values (p. 141)
- To solve problems with linear programming (p. 143)

 ALG2 2.0

Linear programming is a technique used to find the maximum or minimum value of an **objective function**. Linear inequalities are **constraints** on the variables of the objective function. The solutions to the system of constraints are contained in the **feasible region**. The maximum or minimum value of the objective function occurs at a vertex of the feasible region.

Graph each system of constraints. Find all vertices. Then find the variable values that maximize or minimize the objective function.

27. $\begin{cases} x \le 8 \\ y \le 5 \\ x \ge 0, y \ge 0 \end{cases}$

Minimum for
$C = x + 5y$

28. $\begin{cases} x \ge 2 \\ y \ge 0 \\ 3x + 2y \ge 12 \end{cases}$

Minimum for
$C = 4x + y$

29. $\begin{cases} 3x + 2y \le 12 \\ x + y \le 5 \\ x \ge 0, y \ge 0 \end{cases}$

Maximum for
$P = 3x + 5y$

30. Profit A lunch stand makes $.75 profit on each chef's salad and $1.20 profit on each Caesar salad. On a typical weekday, it sells between 40 and 60 chef's salads and between 35 and 50 Caesar salads. The total number sold has never exceeded 100 salads. How many of each type should be prepared in order to maximize profit?

Lesson 3-5

• To graph points in three dimensions (p. 148)
• To graph equations in three dimensions (p. 150)

You can plot **ordered triples** in **coordinate space.** To sketch a plane that is the graph of an equation in three variables, find the intercepts. To find the x-intercept, substitute 0 for y and z. Then find the other two intercepts. If the plane does not pass through the origin, connect the resulting intercepts on the three axes. These lines are called the **traces** of the plane.

Graph each point in coordinate space.

31. $(0, 2, 0)$　　**32.** $(1, 0, 0)$　　**33.** $(0, 0, 3)$　　**34.** $(2, 3, 0)$　　**35.** $(1, 0, 4)$

Find the coordinates of each point in the diagram at the right.

36. A

37. B

38. C

39. D

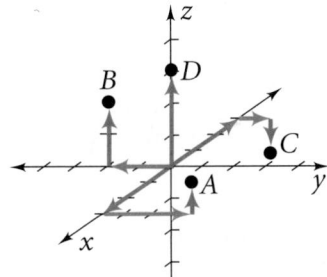

Sketch the graph of each equation.

40. $x - 2y + z = 4$　　**41.** $10x - 4y - 5z = 20$　　**42.** $2x + 6y + 3z = 18$

Lesson 3-6

• To solve systems in three variables by elimination (p. 154)
• To solve systems in three variables by substitution (p. 157)

 ALG2 2.0

You can solve systems of three equations in three variables using the technique of substitution you learned in Lesson 3-2.

Elimination with three equations in three variables involves pairing the equations. Use one equation twice. Then eliminate the same variable in both pairs. The result is a system of two equations in two variables. Proceed using the methods you learned in Lesson 3-2.

Solve each system.

43. $\begin{cases} x + y + z = 10 \\ 2x - y + z = 2 \\ -x + 2y - z = 5 \end{cases}$

44. $\begin{cases} x + 2y + z = 14 \\ y = z + 1 \\ x = -3z + 6 \end{cases}$

45. $\begin{cases} 3x + y - 2z = 22 \\ x + 5y + z = 4 \\ x = -3z \end{cases}$

Chapter 3 Test

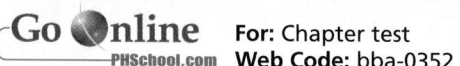

Classify each system without graphing. Then graph each system.

1. $\begin{cases} y = 5x - 2 \\ y = x + 4 \end{cases}$
2. $\begin{cases} 3x + 2y = 9 \\ 3x + 2y = 4 \end{cases}$

Solve using substitution.

3. $\begin{cases} 3x + 2y = 9 \\ x + y = 4 \end{cases}$
4. $\begin{cases} 0.3x - y = 0 \\ y = 2 + 0.25x \end{cases}$

Solve using elimination.

5. $\begin{cases} 3x - y = 1 \\ 2x + y = 14 \end{cases}$
6. $\begin{cases} 4x - 2y = 3 \\ 2y - 4x = \frac{3}{2} \end{cases}$

7. **Writing** Describe how to identify situations in which substitution may be the best method for solving a system of equations.

Graph each system.

8. $\begin{cases} 2x + y < 3 \\ x < y + 3 \end{cases}$
9. $\begin{cases} 3y + 9x < 3 \\ y \geq 2 \end{cases}$

10. $\begin{cases} |x + 3| > y \\ y > 2x - 1 \end{cases}$
11. $\begin{cases} y > -2x + 6 \\ y \leq \frac{1}{4}x - 3 \end{cases}$

Graph each system of constraints. Find all vertices. Evaluate the objective function at each vertex to find the maximum or minimum value.

12. $\begin{cases} x \leq 5 \\ y \leq 4 \\ x \geq 0, y \geq 0 \end{cases}$

Maximum for
$P = 2x + y$

13. $\begin{cases} x + y \leq 8 \\ x + 2y \geq 6 \\ x \geq 0, y \geq 0 \end{cases}$

Minimum for
$C = x + 3y$

14. **Sales** A pizza shop makes $1.50 on each small pizza and $2.15 on each large pizza. On a typical Friday, it sells between 70 and 90 small pizzas and between 100 and 140 large pizzas. The shop can make no more than 210 pizzas in a day. How many of each size of pizza must be sold in order to maximize profit?

15. **Open-Ended** Write a system of constraints whose graph is a parallelogram.

Graph each point in coordinate space.

16. $(0, 5, 0)$
17. $(-1, 0, 0)$
18. $(1, 0, 4)$
19. $(3, 0, -1)$
20. $(1, 4, -1)$
21. $(2, -2, 3)$

Graph each equation. Use intercepts and traces.

22. $x + y + z = 6$
23. $2x - 3y + z = 6$
24. $-2x + y - 5z = 10$
25. $x - y + 2z = 8$

26. You are planning a party. You have $24 to spend on decorations. Balloons cost $.06 each, party favors cost $.48 each, and streamers cost $.08 each. Write and graph an equation for the number of each you can buy if you spend all the money.

Solve each system of equations.

27. $\begin{cases} x - y + z = 0 \\ 3x - 2y + 6z = 9 \\ -x + y - 2z = -2 \end{cases}$
28. $\begin{cases} 2x + y + z = 8 \\ x + 2y - z = -5 \\ z = 2x - y \end{cases}$

Write a system of equations to solve each problem.

29. **Investing** A company invested $50,000 in three funds. After a year it had $54,500. The growth fund had a return rate of 12%, the income fund had a return rate of 8%, and the money market fund had a return rate of 5%. The company invested twice as much in the income fund as in the money market fund. How much did the company invest in each fund?

30. **Earnings** A student can make a weekly salary of $200 plus 15% commission on sales at the Radio Barn or a weekly salary of $300 plus 10% commission on sales at Woofer, Etc. For what amount of sales do these two jobs pay the same?

31. **Purchasing** To help passengers stranded by bad weather one winter, an airport made the purchases detailed below. Find the cost of a cot, a table, and a chair.

	Number of Cots	Number of Tables	Number of Chairs	Total Costs ($)
Nov	10	10	40	1950
Dec	20	0	20	1800
Jan	10	5	20	1350

Tip 2
Write a system:
$x + y + 120 = 180$
$y = x$

Some problems require you to select an appropriate representation (concrete, pictorial, graphical, verbal, or symbolic) to solve problems.

One angle of an isosceles triangle measures 120°. What are the measures of the other two angles?

Ⓐ 120° and 60°

Ⓑ 60° and 60°

Ⓒ 120° and 30°

Ⓓ 30° and 30°

Think It Through
A triangle can have only one obtuse angle, so the vertex angle must measure 120°. Use x and y to represent the congruent base angles of the isosceles base triangle.

$$y = x$$
$$x + x + 120 = 180$$
$$2x + 120 = 180$$
$$2x = 60$$
$$x = 30, y = 30$$

The correct answer is D.

Tip 1
Make a drawing.

120°

Vocabulary Review

As you solve problems, you must understand the meanings of mathematical terms. Match each term with its mathematical meaning.

A. inconsistent system

B. absolute value

C. system of equations

D. linear inequality

I. a number's distance from zero on a number line

II. an inequality in two variables whose graph is a region of the coordinate plane

III. a set of two or more equations that use the same variables

IV. a system that has no solutions

Multiple Choice

Read each question. Then write the letter of the correct answer on your paper.

1. Solve $|2x - 6| > 4$. (Lesson 1-5)

Ⓐ $x < 1$ or $x > 5$

Ⓑ $x > 1$ and $x < 5$

Ⓒ $x > 1$ or $x < 5$

Ⓓ $x > 5$

2. A board must be cut so that its length is 40.50 cm. The tolerance is 0.25 cm. Which inequality describes the allowable lengths for the board? (Lesson 1-5)

Ⓐ $|l - 0.25| \leq 40.50$

Ⓑ $|l + 0.25| \leq 40.50$

Ⓒ $|l - 40.50| \leq 0.25$

Ⓓ $|l - 0.25| \leq 40.75$

3. Solve $|5 - 3x| = x + 1$. (Lesson 1-5)

Ⓐ -5 and 1

Ⓑ 3 and 5

Ⓒ 1 and 3

Ⓓ -1 and $\frac{5}{3}$

4. Which of the following equations has no solution? (Lesson 1-5)

Ⓐ $|x + 1| = 1$

Ⓑ $|-1| = x$

Ⓒ $|x| = -1$

Ⓓ $|-x| = 1$

5. Graph the solution of the inequality $|3x - 12| \geq 3$. (Lesson 1-5)

Cumulative Practice (continued)

6. Graph $y = -|x - 2| + 1$. **(Lesson 2-5)**

A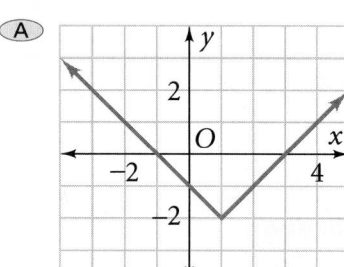

B

C

D

7. Which of the following inequalities best describes the graph? **(Lesson 2-5)**

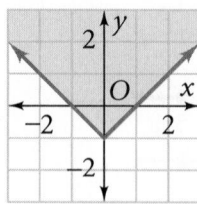

- **A** $y < |x| - 1$
- **B** $y \le |x - 1|$
- **C** $y \ge |x| - 1$
- **D** $y > |x - 1|$

8. Which ordered pair is the solution of the system? **(Lesson 3-2)**

$$\begin{cases} 2x + y = -3 \\ x + 3y = -4 \end{cases}$$

- **A** $(1, -5)$
- **C** $(-1, -1)$
- **B** $(0, -3)$
- **D** $(-3, -4)$

9. Which graph shows the solution to the given system? **(Lesson 3-1)**

$$\begin{cases} \frac{1}{2}x - y = 1 \\ x = 3 \end{cases}$$

A

B

C

D

10. Solve the system of inequalities $\begin{cases} y < |x+1| \\ y \geq -3 \end{cases}$.
(Lesson 3-3)

Ⓐ

Ⓑ

Ⓒ

Ⓓ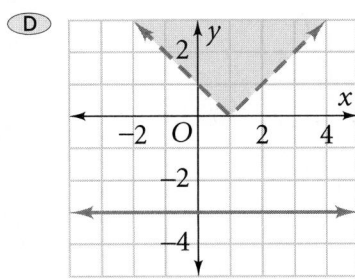

11. Which ordered pair is a solution of the system?
(Lesson 3-3)

$$\begin{cases} x \leq y \\ y > 5 \\ x \leq 8 \end{cases}$$

Ⓐ $(3, 5)$ Ⓒ $(8, 8)$

Ⓑ $(9, 12)$ Ⓓ $(-1, -2)$

12. Which of the following is true about the given system? **(Lesson 3-1)**

$$\begin{cases} -4y = 12 - 8x \\ y = 2x - 3 \end{cases}$$

Ⓐ The system is independent.

Ⓑ The system is dependent.

Ⓒ The system is inconsistent.

Ⓓ The system has no solution.

13. Solve the system $\begin{cases} x - y = -1 \\ x + y = -5 \end{cases}$. **(Lesson 3-2)**

Ⓐ $(-3, -2)$ Ⓒ $(-1, -4)$

Ⓑ $(3, 4)$ Ⓓ $(-1, -5)$

14. Josea wants to solve the system below using substitution. **(Lesson 3-2)**

$$\begin{cases} x = -2y + 4 \\ 2x - 3y = 5 \end{cases}$$

Which of the following is the best way for Josea to proceed?

Ⓐ Solve the first equation for y, then substitute into the second equation.

Ⓑ Solve the second equation for y, then substitute into the first equation.

Ⓒ Substitute $-2y + 4$ for x in the second equation.

Ⓓ Substitute $-2y + 4$ for y in the second equation.

Standards Reference Guide

California Content Standard	Item Number(s)
ALG2 1.0	1–6
ALG2 2.0	7–14

For additional review and practice, see the *California Standards Review and Practice Workbook* or go online to use the

California Standards Tutorials

Visit: PHSchool.com, **Web Code:** bbq-9045

Matrices

 What You've Learned

California Content Standards

2.0 Students solve systems of linear equations and inequalities (in two or three variables) with graphs or by substitution.

6.0 Students demonstrate an understanding that linear systems are inconsistent, have exactly one solution, or have infinitely many solutions. *Linear Algebra*

7.0 Students demonstrate an understanding of functions and equations defined parametrically and can graph them. *Mathematical Analysis*

 Check Your Readiness   **for Help** to the Lesson in green.

Evaluating Expressions (Lesson 1-2)

Evaluate $ad - bc$ for the given values of the variables.

1. $a = -1, b = -2, c = 5, d = 4$

2. $a = \frac{1}{2}, b = -1, c = -\frac{2}{3}, d = 2$

3. $a = 2, b = \frac{1}{2}, c = \frac{1}{4}, d = -\frac{1}{8}$

4. $a = -\frac{1}{3}, b = \frac{1}{2}, c = \frac{1}{4}, d = -\frac{2}{3}$

Solving Equations and Inequalities (Lessons 1-3 and 1-4)

Solve each equation or inequality. Check your answers.

5. $23 - x = 13 + 2x$

6. $\frac{x - 1}{5} = -2$

7. $a + 17 = -3a$

8. $2y - 3 \leq 2y + 5$

9. $11 + 3t > -t$

10. $\frac{3s - 2}{2} < s$

Graphing Equations (Lesson 2-2)

Graph each equation on a coordinate plane.

11. $3x - 2y = 4$

12. $-3x = y$

13. $-7x - 3y = 14$

14. $y = \frac{2}{3}x - 3$

15. $y = 2x - 1$

16. $2x - 3y = -6$

17. $-2x = 3y + 12$

18. $-2y - 4x = 15$

Solving Systems of Equations (Lessons 3-2 and 3-6)

Solve each system.

19. $\begin{cases} -2x + y = -5 \\ 4x + y = -2 \end{cases}$

20. $\begin{cases} 4x - y = -2 \\ -\frac{1}{2}x - y = 1 \end{cases}$

21. $\begin{cases} 3x + y = 5 \\ -x + y = 2 \end{cases}$

22. $\begin{cases} x + y + z = 10 \\ 2x - y = 5 \\ y - z = 15 \end{cases}$

23. $\begin{cases} -x + y + 2z = 16 \\ 2x - 2y - 2z = -16 \\ x + y = 0 \end{cases}$

24. $\begin{cases} -2x + 3y + z = 1 \\ x - 3z = 7 \\ -y + z = -5 \end{cases}$

What You'll Learn Next

California Content Standards

4.0 Students perform addition on matrices. *Linear Algebra*

5.0 Students perform matrix multiplication. *Linear Algebra*

2.0 Students solve systems of linear equations (in two or three variables) with matrices.

▲ An accelerator speeds atomic particles in order to collect data. Matrices can be used to organize the data.

New Vocabulary

- **augmented matrix** (p. 226)
- **determinant** (p. 204)
- **dilation** (p. 196)
- **equal matrices** (p. 181)
- **image** (p. 196)

- **matrix** (p. 172)
- **matrix addition** (p. 178)
- **matrix element** (p. 173)
- **matrix equation** (p. 180)
- **matrix multiplication** (p. 188)

- **preimage** (p. 196)
- **row operations** (p. 227)
- **scalar multiplication** (p. 186)
- **variable matrix** (p. 218)
- **zero matrix** (p. 179)

Organizing Data Into Matrices

What You'll Learn

- To identify matrices and their elements
- To organize data into matrices

. . . And Why

To organize gymnastics data, as in Example 4

✓ **Check Skills You'll Need**

Use the table at the right.

1. How many units were imported to the United States in 1996? In 2000?

2. How many more units were imported in 2000 than in 1996?

3. How many more units were imported than exported in 2000?

4. Compare the percent increase of imports from 1996 to 2004 with the percent increase of exports from 1996 to 2004.

GO for Help Skills Handbook page 882

U.S. Passenger Vehicles and Light Trucks Imports and Exports (millions)

	1996	2000	2004
Imports	4.678	7.028	6.731
Exports	1.295	1.523	1.648

SOURCE: U.S. Department of Commerce.
Go to **www.PHSchool.com** for a data update.
Web code: bbg-9041

🔊 **New Vocabulary** • matrix • matrix element

---

1 Identifying Matrices

Vocabulary Tip

When describing matrices, read × as "by." For example, read 2 × 3 as "two by three."

A **matrix** (plural: matrices) is a rectangular array of numbers written within brackets. You represent a matrix with a capital letter and classify it by its dimensions. The number of horizontal rows and the number of vertical columns determine the dimensions of a matrix.

3 columns
↓ ↓ ↓

$$A = \begin{bmatrix} 2 & 3 & 4 \\ 6 & 7 & 0 \end{bmatrix} \begin{matrix} \leftarrow \\ \leftarrow \end{matrix} \, 2 \text{ rows}$$

Matrix A is a 2 × 3 matrix.

1 EXAMPLE Writing the Dimensions of a Matrix

Write the dimensions of each matrix.

a. $\begin{bmatrix} 4 & 6 & 5 \\ 2 & -3 & -7 \\ 1 & 0 & 9 \end{bmatrix}$

b. $\begin{bmatrix} -4 & \frac{1}{3} & -3 \end{bmatrix}$

c. $\begin{bmatrix} 1 \\ 2 \\ 0 \\ 0.5 \end{bmatrix}$

3 rows × 3 columns

1 row × 3 columns

4 rows × 1 column

This is a 3 × 3 matrix.

This is a 1 × 3 matrix.

This is a 4 × 1 matrix.

✓ **CA Standards Check** ① Write the dimensions of each matrix.

a. $\begin{bmatrix} 4 & 5 & 0 \\ -2 & 0.5 & 17 \end{bmatrix}$

b. $\begin{bmatrix} 8 & -3 & 15 \end{bmatrix}$

c. $\begin{bmatrix} 10 & 0 \\ 1 & -5 \\ -6.2 & 9 \end{bmatrix}$

Each number in a matrix is a **matrix element.** You can identify a matrix element by its position within the matrix. Use a lowercase letter with subscripts. The subscripts represent the element's row number and column number.

2 EXAMPLE **Identifying a Matrix Element**

Identify element a_{13} in matrix A below.

$$A = \begin{bmatrix} 17 & 24 & 3 \\ 10.4 & 12 & 15 \\ 9 & 30 & 15 \end{bmatrix}$$ **a_{13} is the element in the first row and the third column.**

● Element a_{13} is 3.

✓ CA Standards Check **2** Use the matrix from Example 2. Identify each matrix element.
a. a_{33} **b.** a_{11} **c.** a_{21} **d.** a_{12}

2 ▸ Organizing Statistical Data

Successful businesses must track great amounts of data in order to plan the best use of their resources. They use matrices to organize and compare statistical data.

3 EXAMPLE **Real-World** 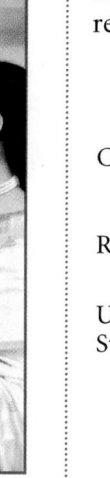 **Connection**

Energy Energy is often measured in British thermal units (Btu). Write a matrix to represent the data below. Estimate the values from the graph.

Annual Energy Production and Consumption

Source: Energy Information Administration, International Energy Database.
Go to **www.PHSchool.com** for a data update.
Web Code: bbg-9041

Real-World **Connection**

One Btu is the amount of heat necessary to raise the temperature of one pound of water by 1°F.

Let each row represent a country and each column represent production or consumption levels.

$$\begin{array}{c}\\ \text{China} \\ \text{Russia} \\ \text{United States} \end{array} \begin{array}{cc} \text{Production} & \text{Consumption} \\ \begin{bmatrix} 42 & 43 \\ 46 & 28 \\ 71 & 98 \end{bmatrix} \end{array}$$

✓ CA Standards Check **3** **a.** Rewrite the matrix as a 2 × 3 matrix. Label the rows and columns.
b. How could you modify your matrix to include data from other countries?
c. **Critical Thinking** Explain the difference between a $c \times d$ matrix and a $d \times c$ matrix.

You can use matrices to show data from a table.

4 EXAMPLE **Real-World Connection**

Gymnastics The table below shows scores from the 2004 Olympics in Athens, Greece.

U.S. Women's Olympic Gymnastics Team Qualifying Scores, 2004

Gymnast	Floor Exercise	Vault	Balance Beam	Uneven Bars
Mohini Bhardwaj	9.525	9.337	9.350	9.487
Courtney Kupets	9.400	9.350	9.550	9.637
Courtney McCool	9.250	9.350	9.112	9.575
Carly Patterson	9.500	9.512	9.725	9.600

SOURCE: Athens 2004 Olympic Games

Real-World Connection

In the vault, as in each of the other gymnastics events, a perfect individual score is 10.

a. Write a matrix W to represent the information. Use a 4×4 matrix.

⌐ **Each column represents a different event.**

$$W = \begin{array}{c} \text{M. Bhardwaj} \\ \text{C. Kupets} \\ \text{C. McCool} \\ \text{C. Patterson} \end{array} \begin{bmatrix} 9.525 & 9.337 & 9.350 & 9.487 \\ 9.400 & 9.350 & 9.550 & 9.637 \\ 9.250 & 9.350 & 9.112 & 9.575 \\ 9.500 & 9.512 & 9.725 & 9.600 \end{bmatrix}$$

with column headers: Floor Exercise, Vault, Balance Beam, Uneven Bars

← **Each row represents a different gymnast.**

b. Which element represents Courtney McCool's score on the vault?

Courtney McCool's scores are in the third row. The vault scores are in the second column. Element w_{32} represents Courtney's score on the vault.

✓ **CA Standards Check** **4 a.** Write a matrix M to represent the information from the table below.
b. Identify element m_{15}. What does this element represent?

Men's Olympic Gymnastics Individual Medal Winners, 2004

Gymnast	Floor Exercise	Pommel Horse	Still Rings	Vault	Parallel Bars	Horizontal Bars
Paul Hamm	9.725	9.700	9.587	9.137	9.837	9.837
Dae Eun Kim	9.650	9.537	9.712	9.412	9.775	9.725
Tae-Young Yang	9.512	9.650	9.725	9.700	9.712	9.475

SOURCE: Athens 2004 Olympic Games

EXERCISES

Standards Practice

A Practice by Example

for Help

Example 1
(page 172)

State the dimensions of each matrix.

1. $\begin{bmatrix} 4 & -2 & 2 \\ 1 & 4 & 1 \\ 0 & 5 & -7 \end{bmatrix}$
2. $\begin{bmatrix} 1 \\ -9 \\ 5 \end{bmatrix}$
3. $\begin{bmatrix} 2 & \sqrt{5} \end{bmatrix}$
4. $\begin{bmatrix} 3 & 2 & 1 \\ 2 & 0 & -3 \end{bmatrix}$
5. $\begin{bmatrix} 2.5 \\ -3 \\ -1.6 \\ 10.0 \end{bmatrix}$

Example 2
(page 173)

Refer to matrices A and B at the right. Identify each matrix element.

$$A = \begin{bmatrix} 0 & -1 \\ 1.5 & 3 \\ 7 & -2 \end{bmatrix} \quad B = \begin{bmatrix} 6 & -3 & \frac{1}{2} \end{bmatrix}$$

6. a_{21} **7.** b_{12} **8.** a_{31}

9. b_{13} **10.** a_{32} **11.** a_{12}

Example 3
(page 173)

Use the graph below for Exercises 12 and 13.

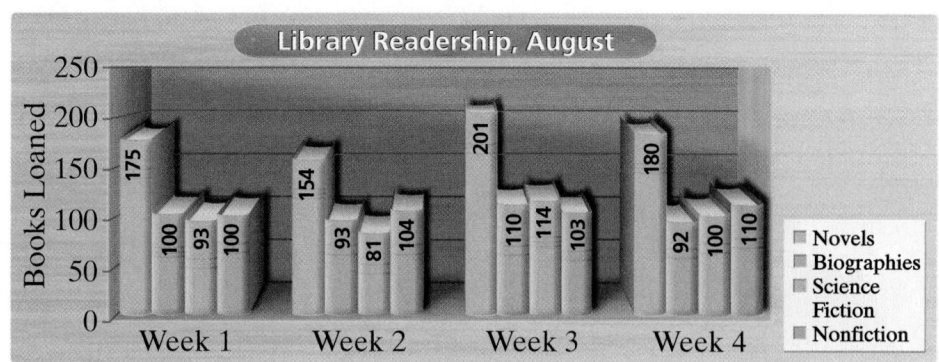

12. Write a matrix to represent the data. Label the rows and columns.

13. Write a different matrix to represent the data. Label the rows and columns.

Example 4
(page 174)

14. a. Write a matrix H to represent the data in the table below.
  b. Find element h_{23}. What does this element represent?

Percent of Public Libraries Offering Programs

Location	Computer Instruction	Book Discussion	Parenting Skills	Employment Guidance
Urban	68	56	28	31
Suburban	59	50	24	18
Rural	49	34	15	12

SOURCE: U.S. National Center for Educational Statistics.
Go to **www.PHSchool.com** for a data update. Web Code: bbg-9041

B **Apply Your Skills**

Use the table below for Exercises 15–17.

15. Display the data in a matrix A with columns representing years. Identify a_{23} and tell what it represents.

Manufacturer's Shipments of Recordings (millions)

Type	1998	1999	2000	2001	2002	2003
CDs	847.0	938.9	942.5	881.9	803.3	745.9
DVDs	0.5	2.5	3.3	7.9	10.7	17.5

SOURCE: Recording Industry Association of America.
Go to **www.PHSchool.com** for a data update. Web Code: bbg-9041

16. Display the data in a matrix A with rows representing years. Identify a_{41} and tell what it represents.

17. State the dimensions of the matrices in Exercises 15 and 16.

18. Error Analysis A student identified element g_{32} from matrix G at the right as -3. What was the student's error?

$$G = \begin{bmatrix} 3 & 2.5 & 4.5 \\ 1.5 & 0 & -3 \\ -3 & 4.5 & 1.5 \end{bmatrix}$$

19. Writing Describe the information necessary to make a matrix containing numerical data meaningful.

Homework Video Tutor

Visit: PHSchool.com
Web Code: bbe-0401

State the dimensions of each matrix. Identify the indicated element.

20. $\begin{bmatrix} 4 & 6 & 5 \\ 2 & -3 & -7 \\ 1 & 0 & 9 \end{bmatrix}, a_{23}$

21. $\begin{bmatrix} -4 & 1 & -3 \\ 2 & 1 & 0 \end{bmatrix}, a_{12}$

22. $\begin{bmatrix} 1 & 1 & 1 \\ 1 & 0 & 0 \\ 1 & 0 & 0 \end{bmatrix}, a_{32}$

23. $[-4 \quad 8 \quad 12], a_{13}$

24. $\begin{bmatrix} -5 \\ 4 \\ 3 \end{bmatrix}, a_{31}$

25. $\begin{bmatrix} -16 & 24 \\ 8 & -2 \end{bmatrix}, a_{21}$

26. **Retail Sales** The graph shows August sales figures at a music store.

Music Store Sales, August

Legend: Rock, R & B, Rap, Classical

a. **Estimation** Record the data in a table.
b. Show the data in a matrix. What do the columns represent? What do the rows represent?

 Challenge

27. **Jobs** The four tables display data from a study conducted by a school principal.
a. Use the information to create four 2 × 2 matrices.
b. How many boys in the school have part-time jobs?
c. How many girls in the school have part-time jobs?
d. What percent of the students with part-time jobs are girls?

Numbers of Students Who Work Part-time

9th Grade	Has Part-time Job	No Part-time Job
Boys	5	95
Girls	15	90

10th Grade	Has Part-time Job	No Part-time Job
Boys	35	65
Girls	30	55

11th Grade	Has Part-time Job	No Part-time Job
Boys	65	35
Girls	75	30

12th Grade	Has Part-time Job	No Part-time Job
Boys	70	25
Girls	65	45

28. **Transportation Costs** A computer accessory company makes computer carrying cases at four plants located in Atlanta, Boston, Chicago, and Denver. Represent the company's shipping costs in a matrix. Label the rows and columns.

Shipping Costs

Atlanta to Boston $19
Atlanta to Chicago $12
Atlanta to Denver $23
Boston to Atlanta $19
Boston to Chicago $10
Boston to Denver $21
Chicago to Atlanta $12
Chicago to Boston $10
Chicago to Denver $15
Denver to Atlanta $23
Denver to Boston $21
Denver to Chicago $15

29. a. Open-Ended Using a 10 × 10 grid, create at least three different letters of
the alphabet with a style similar to the one at the left.
b. Technology The tiny lights that make up a computer screen are called pixels.
To make a letter, the computer tells the screen which pixels to light up.
Represent each letter from part (a) by writing a matrix. Use 1 for a lit pixel
and 0 for an unlit pixel.

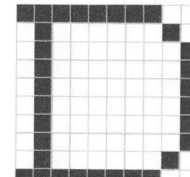

Multiple Choice Practice

For California Standards and CAHSEE Tutorials, visit PHSchool.com. Web Code: bbq-9045

CAHSEE
7MG 3.3

30. The area of right trapezoid $ABCD$ is 80 square
inches. What is the approximate length of $\overline{AD}$?

Ⓐ 10.0 inches

Ⓑ 10.8 inches

Ⓒ 11.0 inches

Ⓓ 11.7 inches

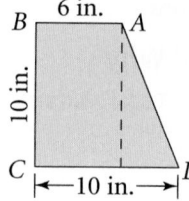

ALG2 1.0

31. Solve $|8x - 3| - 2 > 11$.

Ⓐ $x < -\frac{5}{4}$ or $x > 2$ Ⓒ $x > 2$

Ⓑ $x > -\frac{5}{4}$ or $x < 2$ Ⓓ $x < -\frac{5}{4}$ or $x > \frac{1}{2}$

CAHSEE
7MG 2.1

32. Soup is stored in a cylindrical container with the
dimensions shown in the drawing. Find the
approximate volume of this soup container.

Ⓐ 297 cm^3

Ⓑ 385 cm^3

Ⓒ 747 cm^3

Ⓓ 1539 cm^3

Mixed Review

Lesson 3-6

Solve each system.

33. $\begin{cases} 3x + 2y - 2z = -9 \\ 5x \quad\quad - 3z = -7 \\ x + 4y + 3z = 5 \end{cases}$

34. $\begin{cases} 2x + 3y + 4z = -1 \\ x - 2y + z = 9 \\ x + 4y - 2z = -12 \end{cases}$

Lesson 3-1

Solve each system by graphing.

35. $\begin{cases} 2x + y = 8 \\ x - 3y = -3 \end{cases}$ **36.** $\begin{cases} 2x + y = 7 \\ x + y = -5 \end{cases}$ **37.** $\begin{cases} x + 6y = 7 \\ 2x + 4y = -2 \end{cases}$

Lesson 2-3

Find the constant of variation for a direct variation that includes the given values.

38. $(2, 4)$ **39.** $(-1, 7)$ **40.** $(-4, -10)$ **41.** $(3, 5)$ **42.** $\left(\frac{1}{2}, 9\right)$

In each relation, y varies directly as x. Find y when $x = 9$.

43. $y = 6$ when $x = 4$ **44.** $y = 8$ when $x = 4$

4-2 Adding and Subtracting Matrices

 California Content Standards
LA 4.0 Students perform addition on matrices.

What You'll Learn

- To add and subtract matrices
- To solve certain matrix equations

. . . And Why

To find SAT score totals, as in Example 1

✓ Check Skills You'll Need

GO for Help Skills Handbook page 885

Simplify the elements of each matrix.

1. $\begin{bmatrix} 10 + 4 & 0 + 4 \\ -2 + 4 & -5 + 4 \end{bmatrix}$ 2. $\begin{bmatrix} 5 - 2 & 3 - 2 \\ -1 - 2 & 0 - 2 \end{bmatrix}$ 3. $\begin{bmatrix} -2 + 3 & 0 - 3 \\ 1 - 3 & -5 + 3 \end{bmatrix}$

4. $\begin{bmatrix} 3 + 1 & 4 + 9 \\ -2 + 0 & 5 + 7 \end{bmatrix}$ 5. $\begin{bmatrix} 8 - 4 & -5 - 1 \\ 9 - 1 & 6 - 9 \end{bmatrix}$ 6. $\begin{bmatrix} 2 + 4 & 6 - 8 \\ 4 - 3 & 5 + 2 \end{bmatrix}$

🔊 **New Vocabulary** • matrix addition • zero matrix • matrix equation • equal matrices

---

1 Adding and Subtracting Matrices

Video Tutor Help
Visit: PHSchool.com
Web Code: bbe-0775

Real-World 🌐 Connection

In California, students participate in the STAR (Standardized Testing and Reporting) Program.

Sometimes you want to add or subtract matrices to get new information. You perform **matrix addition** on matrices with equal dimensions by adding the corresponding elements, which are elements in the same position in each matrix.

1 EXAMPLE   Real-World 🌐 Connection

Statistics Use the data in the table.

a. Write two 2 × 4 matrices to represent the mean verbal and math SAT scores.

Verbal

	2000	2001	2002	2003
Male	507	509	507	512
Female	504	502	502	503

Math

	2000	2001	2002	2003
Male	533	533	534	537
Female	498	498	500	503

Mean SAT Scores

	Verbal		Math	
Year	Male	Female	Male	Female
2000	507	504	533	498
2001	509	502	533	498
2002	507	502	534	500
2003	512	503	537	503

SOURCE: College Entrance Examination Board

b. Find the combined mean SAT scores for each year in the table.

$$\begin{bmatrix} 507 & 509 & 507 & 512 \\ 504 & 502 & 502 & 503 \end{bmatrix} + \begin{bmatrix} 533 & 533 & 534 & 537 \\ 498 & 498 & 500 & 503 \end{bmatrix}$$

$$= \begin{bmatrix} 507 + 533 & 509 + 533 & 507 + 534 & 512 + 537 \\ 504 + 498 & 502 + 498 & 502 + 500 & 503 + 503 \end{bmatrix}$$

	2000	2001	2002	2003
Male	1040	1042	1041	1049
Female	1002	1000	1002	1006

a. $\begin{bmatrix} 1 & -2 & 0 \\ 3 & -5 & 7 \end{bmatrix} + \begin{bmatrix} 3 & 9 & -3 \\ -9 & 6 & 12 \end{bmatrix}$

b. $\begin{bmatrix} -12 & 24 \\ -3 & 5 \\ -1 & 10 \end{bmatrix} + \begin{bmatrix} -3 & 1 \\ 2 & -4 \\ -1 & 5 \end{bmatrix}$

 Key Concepts

Definition	**Matrix Addition**

To add matrices A and B with the same dimensions, add corresponding elements.

$$A = \begin{bmatrix} a & b & c \\ d & e & f \end{bmatrix} \qquad B = \begin{bmatrix} r & s & t \\ u & v & w \end{bmatrix}$$

$$A + B = \begin{bmatrix} a & b & c \\ d & e & f \end{bmatrix} + \begin{bmatrix} r & s & t \\ u & v & w \end{bmatrix} = \begin{bmatrix} a+r & b+s & c+t \\ d+u & e+v & f+w \end{bmatrix}$$

Online
active math

For: Matrix Addition Activity
Use: Interactive Textbook, 4-2

The additive identity matrix for the set of all $m \times n$ matrices is the **zero matrix** O, or $O_{m \times n}$, whose elements are all zeros. The opposite, or additive inverse, of an $m \times n$ matrix A is $-A$. $-A$ is the $m \times n$ matrix with elements that are the opposites of the corresponding elements of A.

2 **EXAMPLE** **Using Identity and Inverse Matrices**

Find each sum.

a. $\begin{bmatrix} 1 & 2 \\ 5 & -7 \end{bmatrix} + \begin{bmatrix} 0 & 0 \\ 0 & 0 \end{bmatrix}$

$= \begin{bmatrix} 1+0 & 2+0 \\ 5+0 & -7+0 \end{bmatrix}$

$= \begin{bmatrix} 1 & 2 \\ 5 & -7 \end{bmatrix}$

b. $\begin{bmatrix} 2 & 8 \\ -3 & 0 \end{bmatrix} + \begin{bmatrix} -2 & -8 \\ 3 & 0 \end{bmatrix}$

$= \begin{bmatrix} 2+(-2) & 8+(-8) \\ -3+3 & 0+0 \end{bmatrix}$

$= \begin{bmatrix} 0 & 0 \\ 0 & 0 \end{bmatrix}$

 CA Standards Check **2** Find each sum.

a. $\begin{bmatrix} 14 & 5 \\ 0 & -2 \end{bmatrix} + \begin{bmatrix} -14 & -5 \\ 0 & 2 \end{bmatrix}$

b. $\begin{bmatrix} 0 & 0 & 0 \\ 0 & 0 & 0 \end{bmatrix} + \begin{bmatrix} -1 & 10 & -5 \\ 0 & 2 & -3 \end{bmatrix}$

Some of the properties of real number addition also apply to matrix addition.

 Key Concepts

Properties	**Matrix Addition**

If A, B, and C are $m \times n$ matrices, then

$A + B$ is an $m \times n$ matrix.	Closure Property
$A + B = B + A$	Commutative Property of Addition
$(A + B) + C = A + (B + C)$	Associative Property of Addition
There exists a unique $m \times n$ matrix O such that $O + A = A + O = A$.	Additive Identity Property
For each A, there exists a unique opposite, $-A$. $A + (-A) = O$	Additive Inverse Property

You can define matrix subtraction by using the Additive Inverse Property.

Property	Matrix Subtraction

If two matrices, A and B, have the same dimensions, then $A - B = A + (-B)$.

3 EXAMPLE   Subtracting Matrices

Vocabulary Tip

You can extend the meaning of <u>matrix</u> to describe a rectangular arrangement (rows and columns) of any objects.

$A = \begin{bmatrix} 3 & 2 & 4 \\ -1 & 4 & 0 \end{bmatrix}$ and $B = \begin{bmatrix} 1 & 4 & 3 \\ -2 & 2 & 4 \end{bmatrix}$. Find $A - B$.

Method 1   Use additive inverses.

$A - B = A + (-B) = \begin{bmatrix} 3 & 2 & 4 \\ -1 & 4 & 0 \end{bmatrix} + \begin{bmatrix} -1 & -4 & -3 \\ 2 & -2 & -4 \end{bmatrix}$ **Write the elements of $-B$.**

$= \begin{bmatrix} 3 + (-1) & 2 + (-4) & 4 + (-3) \\ -1 + 2 & 4 + (-2) & 0 + (-4) \end{bmatrix}$ **Add corresponding elements.**

$= \begin{bmatrix} 2 & -2 & 1 \\ 1 & 2 & -4 \end{bmatrix}$ **Simplify.**

Method 2   Use subtraction.

$A - B = \begin{bmatrix} 3 & 2 & 4 \\ -1 & 4 & 0 \end{bmatrix} - \begin{bmatrix} 1 & 4 & 3 \\ -2 & 2 & 4 \end{bmatrix}$

$= \begin{bmatrix} 3 - 1 & 2 - 4 & 4 - 3 \\ -1 - (-2) & 4 - 2 & 0 - 4 \end{bmatrix}$ **Subtract corresponding elements.**

$= \begin{bmatrix} 2 & -2 & 1 \\ 1 & 2 & -4 \end{bmatrix}$ **Simplify.**

✓ **CA Standards Check** ③ Find each difference.

a. $\begin{bmatrix} 6 & -9 & 7 \\ -2 & 1 & 8 \end{bmatrix} - \begin{bmatrix} -4 & 3 & 0 \\ 6 & 5 & 10 \end{bmatrix}$ **b.** $\begin{bmatrix} -3 & 5 \\ -1 & 10 \end{bmatrix} - \begin{bmatrix} -3 & 1 \\ 2 & -4 \end{bmatrix}$

2 Solving Matrix Equations

A **matrix equation** is an equation in which the variable is a matrix. You can use the addition and subtraction properties of equality to solve matrix equations.

4 EXAMPLE   Solving a Matrix Equation

Solve $X - \begin{bmatrix} 1 & 1 \\ 3 & 2 \end{bmatrix} = \begin{bmatrix} 0 & 1 \\ 8 & 9 \end{bmatrix}$ for the matrix X.

$X - \begin{bmatrix} 1 & 1 \\ 3 & 2 \end{bmatrix} = \begin{bmatrix} 0 & 1 \\ 8 & 9 \end{bmatrix}$

$X - \begin{bmatrix} 1 & 1 \\ 3 & 2 \end{bmatrix} + \begin{bmatrix} 1 & 1 \\ 3 & 2 \end{bmatrix} = \begin{bmatrix} 0 & 1 \\ 8 & 9 \end{bmatrix} + \begin{bmatrix} 1 & 1 \\ 3 & 2 \end{bmatrix}$ **Add $\begin{bmatrix} 1 & 1 \\ 3 & 2 \end{bmatrix}$ to each side of the equation.**

$X = \begin{bmatrix} 1 & 2 \\ 11 & 11 \end{bmatrix}$ **Simplify.**

CA Standards Check **4** Solve $X + \begin{bmatrix} -1 & 0 \\ 2 & 5 \end{bmatrix} = \begin{bmatrix} 10 & 7 \\ -4 & 4 \end{bmatrix}$.

Equal matrices are matrices with the same dimensions and equal corresponding elements.

5 EXAMPLE Determining Equal Matrices

Multiple Choice Which matrix is equal to matrix M? $M = \begin{bmatrix} -0.75 & \frac{1}{5} & 0 \\ \frac{1}{2} & -2 & 1.25 \end{bmatrix}$

(A) $\begin{bmatrix} \frac{1}{2} & -2 & 1.25 \\ -0.75 & \frac{1}{5} & 0 \end{bmatrix}$ (C) $\begin{bmatrix} -\frac{3}{4} & 0.2 & 0 \\ 0.5 & \frac{-4}{2} & \frac{5}{4} \end{bmatrix}$

Test-Taking Tip

If you think you can eliminate all but one choice, it is good practice to check that the remaining choice is correct.

(B) $\begin{bmatrix} -\frac{3}{4} & 0.2 \\ 0.5 & -2 \end{bmatrix}$ (D) $\begin{bmatrix} -0.75 & \frac{1}{2} \\ \frac{1}{5} & -2 \\ 0 & 1.25 \end{bmatrix}$

Matrix M is 2×3. Any matrix equal to it must have the same dimensions. Choice B is 2×2. Choice D is 3×2. You can eliminate choices B and D.

Choice A has first-row elements equal to second-row elements in M, but different from first-row elements in M. You can eliminate choice A.

Corresponding elements of M and choice C are equal.

$$-0.75 = -\frac{3}{4}, \quad \frac{1}{5} = 0.2, \quad 0 = 0; \qquad \frac{1}{2} = 0.5, \quad -2 = \frac{-4}{2}, \quad 1.25 = \frac{5}{4}$$

● The answer is choice C.

CA Standards Check **5** Determine whether the two matrices in each pair are equal.

a. $\begin{bmatrix} 4 & 9 \\ 8 & 5 \end{bmatrix}, \begin{bmatrix} \frac{8}{2} & \frac{10}{2} \\ \frac{16}{2} & \frac{18}{2} \end{bmatrix}$ b. $\begin{bmatrix} -2 & 3 \\ 5 & 0 \end{bmatrix}, \begin{bmatrix} -\frac{8}{4} & 6-3 \\ \frac{15}{3} & 4-4 \end{bmatrix}$

6 EXAMPLE Finding Unknown Matrix Elements

Solve the equation $\begin{bmatrix} 2x - 5 & 4 \\ 3 & 3y + 12 \end{bmatrix} = \begin{bmatrix} 25 & 4 \\ 3 & y + 18 \end{bmatrix}$ for x and y.

$\begin{bmatrix} 2x - 5 & 4 \\ 3 & 3y + 12 \end{bmatrix} = \begin{bmatrix} 25 & 4 \\ 3 & y + 18 \end{bmatrix}$

$2x - 5 = 25$ $3y + 12 = y + 18$ **Since the two matrices are equal, their**
$2x = 30$ $2y = 6$ **corresponding elements are equal.**
$x = 15$ $y = 3$

● The solutions are $x = 15$ and $y = 3$.

CA Standards Check **6** Solve each equation for x and y.

a. $\begin{bmatrix} x + 8 & -5 \\ 3 & -y \end{bmatrix} = \begin{bmatrix} 38 & -5 \\ 3 & 4y - 10 \end{bmatrix}$ b. $[3x \quad 4] = [-9 \quad x + y]$

A **Practice by Example**
Example 1
(page 178)

GO for Help

1. Sports The modern pentathlon is a grueling all-day competition. Each member of a team competes in five events: target shooting, fencing, swimming, horseback riding, and cross-country running. Here are scores for the U.S. women at the 2004 Olympic Games.

U.S. Women's Pentathlon Scores, 2004 Olympics

Event	Anita Allen	Mary Beth Iagorashvili
Shooting	952	760
Fencing	720	832
Swimming	1108	1252
Riding	1172	1144
Running	1044	1064

SOURCE: Athens 2004 Olympic Games

a. Write two 5×1 matrices to represent the individual scores for each event.
b. Find the total score for each woman.

Examples 2 and 3
(pages 179 and 180)

Find each sum or difference.

2. $\begin{bmatrix} 2 & -3 & 4 \\ 5 & 6 & -7 \end{bmatrix} + \begin{bmatrix} 0 & 0 & 0 \\ 0 & 0 & 0 \end{bmatrix}$

3. $\begin{bmatrix} 1 & 3 \\ 4 & 0 \end{bmatrix} + \begin{bmatrix} 0 & 5 \\ -1 & 2 \end{bmatrix} + \begin{bmatrix} 0 & -5 \\ 1 & -2 \end{bmatrix}$

4. $\begin{bmatrix} 6.4 & -1.9 \\ -6.4 & 0.8 \end{bmatrix} + \begin{bmatrix} -2.5 & -0.4 \\ 5.8 & 8.3 \end{bmatrix}$

5. $\begin{bmatrix} 6 & -3 \\ -7 & 2 \end{bmatrix} + \begin{bmatrix} -6 & 3 \\ 7 & -2 \end{bmatrix}$

6. $\begin{bmatrix} 5 & 4 & 3 \\ 1 & -2 & 6 \end{bmatrix} - \begin{bmatrix} 1 & 1 & 1 \\ 1 & 1 & 1 \end{bmatrix}$

7. $\begin{bmatrix} 2 & 1 & 2 \\ 1 & 2 & 1 \end{bmatrix} - \begin{bmatrix} 2 & 3 & 2 \\ 3 & 2 & 3 \end{bmatrix}$

8. $\begin{bmatrix} 0.5 & 9.5 \\ -3.5 & 5.5 \end{bmatrix} - \begin{bmatrix} 0.5 & 9.5 \\ -3.5 & 5.5 \end{bmatrix}$

9. $\begin{bmatrix} 1.5 & -1.9 \\ 0 & 4.6 \end{bmatrix} - \begin{bmatrix} 8.3 & -3.2 \\ 2.1 & 5.6 \end{bmatrix}$

Example 4
(page 180)

Solve each matrix equation.

10. $\begin{bmatrix} 1 & 2 \\ 2 & 1 \\ -3 & 4 \end{bmatrix} + X = \begin{bmatrix} 5 & -6 \\ 1 & 0 \\ 8 & 5 \end{bmatrix}$

11. $\begin{bmatrix} 2 & 1 & -1 \\ 0 & 2 & 1 \end{bmatrix} - X = \begin{bmatrix} 11 & 3 & -13 \\ 15 & -9 & 8 \end{bmatrix}$

12. $X - \begin{bmatrix} 1 & 4 \\ -2 & 3 \end{bmatrix} = \begin{bmatrix} 5 & -2 \\ 1 & 0 \end{bmatrix}$

13. $X + \begin{bmatrix} 6 & 1 \\ -2 & 3 \end{bmatrix} = \begin{bmatrix} 2 & 0 \\ -3 & 1 \end{bmatrix}$

Example 5
(page 181)

Determine whether the two matrices in each pair are equal. Justify your reasoning.

14. $\begin{bmatrix} -2 & 3 \\ 5 & 0 \end{bmatrix}, \begin{bmatrix} 2(-1) & 2(1.5) \\ 2(2.5) & 2(0) \end{bmatrix}$

15. $\begin{bmatrix} 4 \\ -6 \\ -8 \end{bmatrix}, \begin{bmatrix} \sqrt{16} & -6 & \sqrt{64} \end{bmatrix}$

Example 6
(page 181)

Find the value of each variable.

16. $\begin{bmatrix} 2 & 2 \\ -1 & 6 \end{bmatrix} - \begin{bmatrix} 4 & -1 \\ 0 & 5 \end{bmatrix} = \begin{bmatrix} x & y \\ -1 & z \end{bmatrix}$

17. $\begin{bmatrix} 2 & 4 \\ 8 & 12 \end{bmatrix} = \begin{bmatrix} 4x - 6 & -10t + 5x \\ 4x & 15t + 1.5x \end{bmatrix}$

Find each matrix sum or difference if possible. If not possible, explain.

$$A = \begin{bmatrix} 3 & 4 \\ 6 & -2 \\ 1 & 0 \end{bmatrix} \qquad B = \begin{bmatrix} -3 & 1 \\ 2 & -4 \\ -1 & 5 \end{bmatrix} \qquad C = \begin{bmatrix} 1 & 2 \\ -3 & 1 \end{bmatrix} \qquad D = \begin{bmatrix} 5 & 1 \\ 0 & 2 \end{bmatrix}$$

18. $A + B$ **19.** $B + D$ **20.** $C + D$ **21.** $B - A$ **22.** $C - D$

23. Multiple Choice You can put the pentathlon scores below into three matrices, one for each athlete. If you add the matrices, what does the sum matrix show?

U.S. Men's Pentathlon Scores, 2000 World Championship

Event	James Gregory	Velizar Iliev	Chad Senior
Shooting	1132	1072	1072
Fencing	760	910	610
Swimming	1173	1177	1285
Riding	1100	1100	1070
Running	1114	1118	1174

SOURCE: U.S. Modern Pentathlon Association

Ⓐ the total team score Ⓒ each athlete's total score
Ⓑ the team score for each event Ⓓ each athlete's score for each event

Solve each matrix equation for X.

24. $\begin{bmatrix} 1 & 2 & -3 \\ 2 & 1 & 3 \end{bmatrix} + X = \begin{bmatrix} 5 & 1 & 8 \\ -6 & 0 & 5 \end{bmatrix}$ **25.** $X - \begin{bmatrix} 4 & 12 \\ 75 & -1 \end{bmatrix} = \begin{bmatrix} 5 & 50 \\ 50 & -10 \end{bmatrix}$

26. Data Analysis Refer to the table.
  a. Find the total number of people participating in each activity.
  b. Find the difference between the numbers of males and females in each activity.
  c. Reasoning In part (b), does the order of the matrices matter? Explain.

U.S. Participation in Selected Leisure Activities (millions)

Activity	Male	Female
Movies	59.2	65.4
Exercise Programs	54.3	59.0
Sports Events	40.5	31.1
Home Improvement	45.4	41.8

SOURCE: U.S. National Endowment for the Arts.
Go to **www.PHSchool.com** for a data update.
Web-Code: bbg-9041

27. Manufacturing The table below shows the number of beach balls produced during one shift at two manufacturing plants. Plant 1 has two shifts per day and Plant 2 has three shifts per day.

Beach Ball Production Per Shift

	1-color Plastic	1-color Rubber	3-color Plastic	3-color Rubber
Plant 1	500	700	1300	1900
Plant 2	400	1200	600	1600

a. Write matrices to represent one day's total output at the two plants.
b. Use your results from part (a). Find the difference between production totals at the plants. Which plant produces more three-color plastic balls? Which plant produces more one-color rubber balls?

Real-World Connection

In the riding portion of the modern pentathlon, athletes ride a 400-m course with 15 obstacles.

Homework Video Tutor

Visit: PHSchool.com
Web Code: bbe-0402

28. Writing Suppose A and B are two matrices with the same dimensions.
    a. Explain how to find $A + B$ and $A - B$.
    b. Explain how to find a matrix C such that $A + C = O$.

Solve each equation for each variable.

29. $\begin{bmatrix} 4b + 2 & -3 & 4d \\ -4a & 2 & 3 \\ 2f - 1 & -14 & 1 \end{bmatrix} = \begin{bmatrix} 11 & 2c - 1 & 0 \\ -8 & 2 & 3 \\ 0 & 3g - 2 & 1 \end{bmatrix}$ **30.** $\begin{bmatrix} x^2 & 4 \\ -2 & y^2 \end{bmatrix} = \begin{bmatrix} 9 & 4 \\ -2 & 5y \end{bmatrix}$

31. $\begin{bmatrix} 4c & 2 - d & 5 \\ -3 & -1 & 2 \\ 0 & -10 & 15 \end{bmatrix} = \begin{bmatrix} 2c + 5 & 4d & g \\ -3 & h & f - g \\ 0 & -4c & 15 \end{bmatrix}$

 Challenge

32. Find the sum of $E = \begin{bmatrix} 3 \\ 4 \\ 7 \end{bmatrix}$ and the additive inverse of $G = \begin{bmatrix} -2 \\ 0 \\ 5 \end{bmatrix}$.

33. Prove that matrix addition is commutative for 2×2 matrices.

34. Prove that matrix addition is associative for 2×2 matrices.

Multiple Choice Practice

For California Standards and CAHSEE Tutorials, visit PHSchool.com. **Web Code: bbq-9045**

CAHSEE
Alg1 5.0

35. Eduardo has an average of 84 on 5 science tests. What average score does he need on the next two tests to raise his overall average to 88?
    (A) 90   (B) 92   (C) 96   (D) 98

ALG2 1.0

36. What is the vertex of the function $y = 2|3 - x| + 1$?
    (A) $(2, 1)$ (B) $(3, 1)$ (C) $(-3, 1)$ (D) $(6, 1)$

ALG2 1.0

37. What is the solution to the equation $|x - 3| = |x - 2|$?
    (A) -2.5 (B) 0 (C) 2.5 (D) no solution

CAHSEE
6SDAP 3.3

38. A coin is tossed and a number cube, numbered 1 to 6, is rolled. What is the probability that the coin shows heads and the number cube shows on even number?
    (A) 0.25   (B) 0.5   (C) 0.67   (D) 0.75

Mixed Review

 GO for Help

Lesson 4-1

39. Open-Ended Write a real-world problem that you can represent with a matrix. Write a matrix for the problem. Label the rows and columns.

Lesson 6-2

40. Business Your friend's mother plans to open a restaurant. The initial investment is $90,000. Weekly expenses will be about $8200. If the weekly income is about $8900, in how many weeks will she get back her investment?

Lesson 2-2

Find the slope and y-intercept of the graph of each function.

41. $y = 2x - 6$ **42.** $3y = 6 + 2x$ **43.** $-x - 2y = 12$ **44.** $y = 5x$

You can use a graphing calculator to work with matrices. First you need to enter the matrix into the calculator.

Go Online
PHSchool.com
For: Graphing calculator procedures
Web Code: bbe-2113

1 EXAMPLE

Enter matrix $A = \begin{bmatrix} -3 & 4 \\ 7 & -5 \\ 0 & -2 \end{bmatrix}$ into your graphing calculator. Select the **EDIT** option of

the **MATRIX** feature to edit matrix [A]. Specify a 3×2 matrix by pressing 3 **ENTER** 2 **ENTER**.

Enter the matrix elements one row at a time, pressing **ENTER** after each element. Then use the **QUIT** feature to return to the main screen.

```
NAMES  MATH  EDIT
1: [A]
2: [B]
3: [C]
4: [D]
5: [E]
```

```
MATRIX [A]  3  ×2
[ 0        0        ]
[ 0        0        ]
[ 0        0        ]


1,1= 0
```

```
MATRIX [A]  3  ×2
[ -3       4        ]
[ 7        -5       ]
[ 0        -2       ]


3,2= -2
```

You can use a graphing calculator to perform matrix operations.

2 EXAMPLE

Perform each operation for matrix $A = \begin{bmatrix} -3 & 4 \\ 7 & -5 \\ 0 & -2 \end{bmatrix}$ and matrix $B = \begin{bmatrix} 10 & -7 \\ 4 & -3 \\ -12 & 11 \end{bmatrix}$.

a. $A + B$

Use the **EDIT** option to select the matrices you want to add. Press **ENTER** to see the sum.

```
[A] + [B]
    [[ 7      -3    ]
     [ 11     -8    ]
     [ -12    9     ]]
```

b. $A - B$

Use the **EDIT** option to select the matrices you want to subtract. Press **ENTER** to see the difference.

```
[A] - [B]
    [[ -13    11    ]
     [ 3      -2    ]
     [ 12     -13   ]]
```

EXERCISES

Find each sum or difference.

1. $\begin{bmatrix} 0 & -3 \\ 5 & -7 \end{bmatrix} - \begin{bmatrix} -5 & 3 \\ 4 & 10 \end{bmatrix}$

2. $\begin{bmatrix} 3 & 5 & -7 \\ 0 & -2 & 0 \end{bmatrix} + \begin{bmatrix} -1 & 6 & 2 \\ -9 & 4 & 0 \end{bmatrix}$

3. $\begin{bmatrix} 3 \\ 5 \end{bmatrix} - \begin{bmatrix} -6 \\ 7 \end{bmatrix}$

4. $[3 \quad 5 \quad -8] + [-6 \quad 4 \quad 1]$

5. $\begin{bmatrix} 17 & 8 & 0 \\ 3 & -5 & 2 \end{bmatrix} - \begin{bmatrix} 4 & 6 & 5 \\ 2 & -2 & 9 \end{bmatrix}$

6. $[-9 \quad 6 \quad 4] + [-3 \quad 8 \quad 4]$

Matrix Multiplication

 California Content Standards

LA 5.0 Students perform matrix multiplication.

What You'll Learn

• To multiply a matrix by a scalar

• To multiply two matrices

. . . And Why

To calculate the gross income, as in Example 5

✓ **Check Skills You'll Need**

GO for Help Lesson 4-2

Find each sum.

1. $\begin{bmatrix} 3 & 5 \\ 2 & 8 \end{bmatrix} + \begin{bmatrix} 3 & 5 \\ 2 & 8 \end{bmatrix} + \begin{bmatrix} 3 & 5 \\ 2 & 8 \end{bmatrix}$

2. $\begin{bmatrix} -4 \\ 7 \end{bmatrix} + \begin{bmatrix} -4 \\ 7 \end{bmatrix} + \begin{bmatrix} -4 \\ 7 \end{bmatrix} + \begin{bmatrix} -4 \\ 7 \end{bmatrix} + \begin{bmatrix} -4 \\ 7 \end{bmatrix}$

3. $\begin{bmatrix} -1 & 3 & 4 \\ 0 & -2 & -5 \end{bmatrix} + \begin{bmatrix} -1 & 3 & 4 \\ 0 & -2 & -5 \end{bmatrix} + \begin{bmatrix} -1 & 3 & 4 \\ 0 & -2 & -5 \end{bmatrix} + \begin{bmatrix} -1 & 3 & 4 \\ 0 & -2 & -5 \end{bmatrix}$

◀)) **New Vocabulary** • scalar • scalar multiplication • matrix multiplication

---

1 Multiplying a Matrix by a Scalar

You can multiply a matrix by a real number.

$$3\begin{bmatrix} 3 & 5 \\ 2 & 8 \end{bmatrix} = \begin{bmatrix} 9 & 15 \\ 6 & 24 \end{bmatrix}$$

The real number factor (such as 3) is called a **scalar.**

 Key Concepts

Definition	**Scalar Multiplication**

Scalar multiplication multiplies a matrix A by a scalar c. To find the resulting matrix cA, multiply each element of A by c.

	SMALL	LARGE
LOWFAT MILK	$.35	$.67
ORANGE JUICE	$.65	$.89
TOMATO JUICE	$.58	$.75

1 **EXAMPLE** **Real-World** Connection

Prices Use the price list. The cafeteria plans to raise the cost of each beverage to one and a half times the current cost. How much will each beverage cost?

$$1.5\begin{bmatrix} 0.35 & 0.67 \\ 0.65 & 0.89 \\ 0.58 & 0.75 \end{bmatrix} = \begin{bmatrix} 1.5(0.35) & 1.5(0.67) \\ 1.5(0.65) & 1.5(0.89) \\ 1.5(0.58) & 1.5(0.75) \end{bmatrix}$$ **Multiply each element by 1.5.**

$$\approx \begin{bmatrix} 0.53 & 1.01 \\ 0.98 & 1.34 \\ 0.87 & 1.13 \end{bmatrix}$$ **Simplify.**

Milk will cost $.53 and $1.01. Orange juice will cost $.98 and $1.34. Tomato juice will cost $.87 and $1.13.

✓ **CA Standards Check** 1 Find $-3\begin{bmatrix} 15 & -12 & 10 & 0 \\ 20 & -10 & 7 & 0 \end{bmatrix}$.

You can find sums and differences of matrices multiplied by scalars.

2 EXAMPLE Using Scalar Products

Find the difference $5A - 3B$ for $A = \begin{bmatrix} 2 & 3 & -7 \\ 1 & 4 & 5 \end{bmatrix}$ and $B = \begin{bmatrix} 3 & 0 & 6 \\ -1 & 8 & 2 \end{bmatrix}$.

$$5A - 3B = 5\begin{bmatrix} 2 & 3 & -7 \\ 1 & 4 & 5 \end{bmatrix} - 3\begin{bmatrix} 3 & 0 & 6 \\ -1 & 8 & 2 \end{bmatrix}$$

$$= \begin{bmatrix} 10 & 15 & -35 \\ 5 & 20 & 25 \end{bmatrix} - \begin{bmatrix} 9 & 0 & 18 \\ -3 & 24 & 6 \end{bmatrix} = \begin{bmatrix} 1 & 15 & -53 \\ 8 & -4 & 19 \end{bmatrix}$$

✓ **CA Standards Check** ② Use matrices A and B from Example 2. Find each sum or difference.
  a. $5B - 4A$ **b.** $A + 6B$

Key Concepts

Properties	**Scalar Multiplication**

If A, B, and O are $m \times n$ matrices and c and d are scalars, then

cA is an $m \times n$ matrix.	Closure Property
$(cd)A = c(dA)$	Associative Property of Multiplication
$c(A + B) = cA + cB$ $(c + d)A = cA + dA$	Distributive Property
$1 \cdot A = A$	Multiplicative Identity Property
$0 \cdot A = O$ and $cO = O$	Multiplicative Property of Zero

Vocabulary Tip

O is the <u>zero</u> <u>matrix</u>—the $m \times n$ matrix with every element zero.

You can use the properties of scalar multiplication to solve matrix equations.

3 EXAMPLE Solving Matrix Equations with Scalars

Solve $4X + 2\begin{bmatrix} 3 & 4 \\ -2 & 1 \end{bmatrix} = \begin{bmatrix} 10 & 0 \\ 4 & 2 \end{bmatrix}$.

$4X + 2\begin{bmatrix} 3 & 4 \\ -2 & 1 \end{bmatrix} = \begin{bmatrix} 10 & 0 \\ 4 & 2 \end{bmatrix}$

$4X + \begin{bmatrix} 6 & 8 \\ -4 & 2 \end{bmatrix} = \begin{bmatrix} 10 & 0 \\ 4 & 2 \end{bmatrix}$ **Scalar multiplication**

$4X = \begin{bmatrix} 10 & 0 \\ 4 & 2 \end{bmatrix} - \begin{bmatrix} 6 & 8 \\ -4 & 2 \end{bmatrix}$ **Subtract** $\begin{bmatrix} 6 & 8 \\ -4 & 2 \end{bmatrix}$ **from each side.**

$4X = \begin{bmatrix} 4 & -8 \\ 8 & 0 \end{bmatrix}$ **Simplify.**

$X = \frac{1}{4}\begin{bmatrix} 4 & -8 \\ 8 & 0 \end{bmatrix} = \begin{bmatrix} 1 & -2 \\ 2 & 0 \end{bmatrix}$ **Multiply each side by $\frac{1}{4}$ and simplify.**

Check $4X + 2\begin{bmatrix} 3 & 4 \\ -2 & 1 \end{bmatrix} = \begin{bmatrix} 10 & 0 \\ 4 & 2 \end{bmatrix}$

$4\begin{bmatrix} 1 & -2 \\ 2 & 0 \end{bmatrix} + 2\begin{bmatrix} 3 & 4 \\ -2 & 1 \end{bmatrix} \stackrel{?}{=} \begin{bmatrix} 10 & 0 \\ 4 & 2 \end{bmatrix}$ **Substitute.**

$\begin{bmatrix} 4 & -8 \\ 8 & 0 \end{bmatrix} + \begin{bmatrix} 6 & 8 \\ -4 & 2 \end{bmatrix} \stackrel{?}{=} \begin{bmatrix} 10 & 0 \\ 4 & 2 \end{bmatrix}$ **Multiply.**

$\begin{bmatrix} 10 & 0 \\ 4 & 2 \end{bmatrix} = \begin{bmatrix} 10 & 0 \\ 4 & 2 \end{bmatrix}$ ✓ **Simplify.**

CA Standards Check ③ Solve each matrix equation. Check your answer.

a. $2X = \begin{bmatrix} 4 & 12 \\ 1 & -4 \end{bmatrix} + \begin{bmatrix} -2 & 0 \\ 3 & 4 \end{bmatrix}$ **b.** $-3X + \begin{bmatrix} 7 & 0 & -1 \\ 2 & -3 & 4 \end{bmatrix} = \begin{bmatrix} 10 & 0 & 8 \\ -19 & -18 & 10 \end{bmatrix}$

2 Multiplying Matrices

Test-Taking Tip

Read questions about tables carefully. Make sure you choose the correct rows, columns, and cells.

Activity: Using Matrices

Use the data in the table.

	Lunch 1	Lunch 2	Lunch 3
Cost per Lunch	$2.50	$1.75	$2.00
Number Sold	50	100	75

1. How much money did the cafeteria collect selling lunch 1? Selling lunch 2? Selling lunch 3?

2. a. How much did the cafeteria collect selling all three lunches?
b. Explain how you used the data in the table to find your answer.

3. a. Write a 1 × 3 matrix to represent the cost of the lunches.
b. Write a 3 × 1 matrix to represent the number of lunches sold.
c. Writing Describe a procedure for using your matrices to find how much money the cafeteria collected from selling all three lunches. Use the words *row*, *column*, and *element*.

Graphing Calculator Hint

You can use the MATRIX feature of a graphing calculator to multiply matrices.

To perform **matrix multiplication,** multiply the elements of each *row* of the first matrix by the elements of each *column* of the second matrix. Add the products.

4 EXAMPLE Multiplying Matrices

Find the product of $\begin{bmatrix} -1 & 0 \\ 3 & -4 \end{bmatrix}$ and $\begin{bmatrix} -3 & 3 \\ 5 & 0 \end{bmatrix}$.

Multiply a_{11} and b_{11}. Then multiply a_{12} and b_{21}. Add the products.

$\begin{bmatrix} -1 & 0 \\ 3 & -4 \end{bmatrix}\begin{bmatrix} -3 & 3 \\ 5 & 0 \end{bmatrix} = \begin{bmatrix} ? & \blacksquare \\ \blacksquare & \blacksquare \end{bmatrix}$ $(-1)(-3) + (0)(5) = 3$

The result is the element in the first row and first column. Repeat with the rest of the rows and columns.

$\begin{bmatrix} -1 & 0 \\ 3 & -4 \end{bmatrix}\begin{bmatrix} -3 & 3 \\ 5 & 0 \end{bmatrix} = \begin{bmatrix} 3 & ? \\ \blacksquare & \blacksquare \end{bmatrix}$ $(-1)(3) + (0)(0) = -3$

$\begin{bmatrix} -1 & 0 \\ 3 & -4 \end{bmatrix}\begin{bmatrix} -3 & 3 \\ 5 & 0 \end{bmatrix} = \begin{bmatrix} 3 & -3 \\ ? & \blacksquare \end{bmatrix}$ $(3)(-3) + (-4)(5) = -29$

$\begin{bmatrix} -1 & 0 \\ 3 & -4 \end{bmatrix}\begin{bmatrix} -3 & 3 \\ 5 & 0 \end{bmatrix} = \begin{bmatrix} 3 & -3 \\ -29 & ? \end{bmatrix}$ $(3)(3) + (-4)(0) = 9$

The product of $\begin{bmatrix} -1 & 0 \\ 3 & -4 \end{bmatrix}$ and $\begin{bmatrix} -3 & 3 \\ 5 & 0 \end{bmatrix}$ is $\begin{bmatrix} 3 & -3 \\ -29 & 9 \end{bmatrix}$.

4 **a.** Find the product of $\begin{bmatrix} -3 & 3 \\ 5 & 0 \end{bmatrix}$ and $\begin{bmatrix} -1 & 0 \\ 3 & -4 \end{bmatrix}$.

b. Critical Thinking Is matrix multiplication commutative? Explain.

 Key Concepts

Definition	Matrix Multiplication

To find element c_{ij} of the product matrix AB, multiply each element in the *i*th row of A by the corresponding element in the *j*th column of B, and then add.

5 **EXAMPLE** Real-World Connection

Real-World Connection

The music on an LP record (a) plays continuously as the stylus travels along the groove. The music on a CD (b) plays in discrete intervals read by a laser.

a   b

A used-record store sells tapes, LP records, and compact discs. The matrices show today's information. Find the store's gross income for the day, in dollars.

Prices

Tapes LPs CDs
$[\$8 \quad \$6 \quad \$13]$

Number of Items Sold

$\begin{matrix} \text{Tapes} \\ \text{LPs} \\ \text{CDs} \end{matrix} \begin{bmatrix} 9 \\ 30 \\ 20 \end{bmatrix}$

Multiply each price by the number of items sold and add the products.

$$[8 \quad 6 \quad 13]\begin{bmatrix} 9 \\ 30 \\ 20 \end{bmatrix} = [8(9) + 6(30) + 13(20)] = [512]$$

● The store's gross income for the day was $512.

 CA Standards Check **5** Find each product if it exists.

a. $[12 \quad 3]\begin{bmatrix} 10 \\ -5 \end{bmatrix}$

b. $\begin{bmatrix} 10 \\ -5 \end{bmatrix}\begin{bmatrix} 12 & 3 \\ 0 & 0 \end{bmatrix}$

The product of two matrices A and B exists only if the number of *columns* of A is equal to the number of *rows* of B.

 Key Concepts

Property	Dimensions of a Product Matrix

If matrix A is an $m \times n$ matrix and matrix B is an $n \times p$ matrix, then the product matrix AB is an $m \times p$ matrix.

Example matrix A • matrix B

The dimensions of product matrix AB are 3×4.

6 EXAMPLE **Determining Whether a Product Matrix Exists**

Use matrices $G = \begin{bmatrix} 2 & 3 \\ -1 & 8 \\ 4 & 0 \end{bmatrix}$ and $H = \begin{bmatrix} 8 & 0 \\ 2 & -5 \end{bmatrix}$. Determine whether products GH and HG are *defined* (exist) or *undefined* (do not exist).

Find the dimensions of each product matrix.

GH	HG
$(3 \times 2)(2 \times 2) \rightarrow 3 \times 2$	$(2 \times 2)(3 \times 2)$
↑ ↑ product	↑ ↑
equal matrix	*not* equal

Product GH is defined and is a 3×2 matrix. Product HG is undefined, because the number of columns of H is not equal to the number of rows of G.

✓ CA Standards Check **6** Let $R = \begin{bmatrix} 4 & -2 \\ 5 & -4 \end{bmatrix}$ and $S = \begin{bmatrix} 8 & 0 & -1 & 0 \\ 2 & -5 & 1 & 8 \end{bmatrix}$.

a. Determine whether products RS and SR are *defined* or *undefined*.
b. Find each defined product.

Matrix multiplication has some of the properties of real number multiplication.

🔑 Key Concepts

Properties	**Matrix Multiplication**

If A, B, and C are $n \times n$ matrices, then

AB is an $n \times n$ matrix.	Closure Property
$(AB)C = A(BC)$	Associative Property of Multiplication
$A(B + C) = AB + AC$ $(B + C)A = BA + CA$	Distributive Property
$OA = AO = O$, where O has the same dimensions as A.	Multiplicative Property of Zero

EXERCISES

For more exercises, see *Extra Skill and Word Problem Practice.*

Standards Practice

LA 5.0

A **Practice by Example**

Examples 1 and 2
(pages 186 and 187)

for Help

Use matrices A, B, C, and D. Find each product, sum, or difference.

$$A = \begin{bmatrix} 3 & 4 \\ 6 & -2 \\ 1 & 0 \end{bmatrix} \qquad B = \begin{bmatrix} -3 & 1 \\ 2 & -4 \\ -1 & 5 \end{bmatrix} \qquad C = \begin{bmatrix} 1 & 2 \\ -3 & 1 \end{bmatrix} \qquad D = \begin{bmatrix} 5 & 1 \\ 0 & 2 \end{bmatrix}$$

1. $3A$ **2.** $4B$ **3.** $-3C$ **4.** $-D$

5. $A - 2B$ **6.** $3A + 2B$ **7.** $4C + 3D$ **8.** $2A - 5B$

Example 3
(page 187)

Solve each matrix equation. Check your answers.

9. $3\begin{bmatrix} 2 & 0 \\ -1 & 5 \end{bmatrix} - 2X = \begin{bmatrix} -10 & 5 \\ 0 & 17 \end{bmatrix}$ **10.** $5X - \begin{bmatrix} 1.5 & -3.6 \\ -0.3 & 2.8 \end{bmatrix} = \begin{bmatrix} 0.2 & 1.3 \\ -5.6 & 1.7 \end{bmatrix}$

Example 4
(page 188)

Find each product.

11. $\begin{bmatrix} -3 & 4 \\ 5 & 2 \end{bmatrix}\begin{bmatrix} 1 & 0 \\ 2 & -3 \end{bmatrix}$

12. $\begin{bmatrix} 1 & 0 \\ 2 & -3 \end{bmatrix}\begin{bmatrix} -3 & 4 \\ 5 & 2 \end{bmatrix}$

13. $\begin{bmatrix} 0 & 2 \\ -4 & 0 \end{bmatrix}\begin{bmatrix} 0 & 2 \\ -4 & 0 \end{bmatrix}$

14. $\begin{bmatrix} -3 & 5 \end{bmatrix}\begin{bmatrix} -3 \\ 5 \end{bmatrix}$

15. $\begin{bmatrix} -3 & 5 \end{bmatrix}\begin{bmatrix} -3 & 0 \\ 5 & 0 \end{bmatrix}$

16. $\begin{bmatrix} -3 & 5 \end{bmatrix}\begin{bmatrix} 0 & -3 \\ 0 & 5 \end{bmatrix}$

17. $\begin{bmatrix} 0 & -3 \\ 0 & 5 \end{bmatrix}\begin{bmatrix} -3 & 0 \\ 5 & 0 \end{bmatrix}$

18. $\begin{bmatrix} 1 & 0 \\ -1 & -5 \\ 0 & 3 \end{bmatrix}\begin{bmatrix} -1 & 0 \\ 0 & -1 \end{bmatrix}$

Example 5
(page 189)

19. **Business** A florist makes three special floral arrangements. One uses three lilies. The second uses three lilies and four carnations. The third uses four daisies and three carnations. Lilies cost $2.15 each, carnations cost $.90 each, and daisies cost $1.30 each.
a. Write a matrix to show the number of each type of flower in each arrangement.
b. Write a matrix to show the cost of each type of flower.
c. Find the matrix showing the cost of each floral arrangement.

Example 6
(page 190)

Determine whether each product is defined or undefined.

$F = \begin{bmatrix} 2 & 3 \\ 6 & 9 \end{bmatrix}$ $G = \begin{bmatrix} -3 & 6 \\ 2 & -4 \end{bmatrix}$ $H = \begin{bmatrix} -5 \\ 6 \end{bmatrix}$ $J = \begin{bmatrix} 0 & 7 \end{bmatrix}$

20. FG 21. GF 22. FH 23. HF 24. GH

25. HG 26. FJ 27. JF 28. HJ 29. JH

B **Apply Your Skills**

Mental Math Find each product.

30. $2\begin{bmatrix} -1 & 4 \\ 2 & 5 \end{bmatrix}$ 31. $-1\begin{bmatrix} 9 & -7 & -4 \\ -8 & -2 & 3 \end{bmatrix}$ 32. $0.5\begin{bmatrix} 3 & 14 \\ 7 & -4 \end{bmatrix}$

33. $\begin{bmatrix} -1 & 0 \\ 0 & -1 \end{bmatrix}\begin{bmatrix} -1 & 0 & 1 \\ 0 & -1 & 1 \end{bmatrix}$ 34. $\begin{bmatrix} 1 & 0 \\ 0 & -1 \end{bmatrix}\begin{bmatrix} -1 & 0 \\ 0 & -1 \end{bmatrix}$

35. **Multiple Choice** Columns in matrix $A = \begin{bmatrix} 3 & 8 \\ 0 & 12 \end{bmatrix}$ show, respectively, the numbers of erasers and pencils sold. The rows show, respectively, the numbers sold on Monday and Tuesday. Matrix $B = \begin{bmatrix} 0.50 \\ 0.25 \end{bmatrix}$ shows the 50¢ cost of one eraser and the quarter cost of one pencil. What does the product AB show?
Ⓐ the total paid for erasers on Monday and Tuesday and the total paid for pencils on Monday and Tuesday
Ⓑ the total paid for erasers and pencils on Monday and the total paid for erasers and pencils on Tuesday
Ⓒ the total paid for pencils and erasers
Ⓓ the cost of 1 pencil and 1 eraser

Homework Video Tutor

Visit: PHSchool.com
Web Code: bbe-0403

Find the dimensions of each product matrix. Then find each product.

36. $\begin{bmatrix} 5 & 7 & 0 \\ -\frac{4}{5} & 3 & 6 \\ 0 & -\frac{2}{3} & 4 \end{bmatrix}\begin{bmatrix} 2 & -1 \\ 1 & 1 \\ 0 & -1 \end{bmatrix}$

37. $\begin{bmatrix} 1 & 0 & 0 \\ 1 & 0 & -2 \\ 0 & 0 & 2 \\ -1 & 0 & 1 \end{bmatrix}\begin{bmatrix} a & 0 & b & 0 \\ 0 & c & 0 & d \\ e & 0 & 0 & f \end{bmatrix}$

For Exercises 38–45, use matrices D, E, and F shown below. Perform the indicated operations if they are defined. If an operation is not defined, label it undefined.

$$D = \begin{bmatrix} 1 & 2 & -1 \\ 0 & 3 & 1 \\ 2 & -1 & -2 \end{bmatrix} \qquad E = \begin{bmatrix} 2 & -5 & 0 \\ 1 & 0 & -2 \\ 3 & 1 & 1 \end{bmatrix} \qquad F = \begin{bmatrix} -3 & 2 \\ -5 & 1 \\ 2 & 4 \end{bmatrix}$$

38. DE

39. $-3F$

40. $(DE)F$

41. $D(EF)$

42. $D - 2E$

43. $(E - D)F$

44. $(DD)E$

45. $(2D)(3F)$

46. Business A hardware store chain displays prices in a 1×3 matrix and daily purchases at its three stores in a 3×3 matrix.

Prices

Hammers Flashlights Lanterns
$$[\$3 \qquad \$5 \qquad \$7]$$

Number of Items Sold

	Store A	Store B	Store C
Hammers	10	9	8
Flashlights	3	14	6
Lanterns	2	5	7

a. Find the product of the two matrices. Explain what the product represents.
b. How would you find the total gross revenue from all three stores?
c. Find the total gross revenue from the flashlights sold at all three stores.

47. Math in the Media Refer to the cartoon. An algorithm is a step-by-step description of a calculation rule. What is the algorithm for matrix multiplication?

48. Open-Ended Find two 2×2 matrices X and Y, with not all elements equal, such that $XY = YX$.

49. Writing Suppose A is a 2×3 matrix and B is a 3×2 matrix. Are AB and BA equal? Explain your reasoning. Include examples.

50. Revenue Write a matrix that represents the daily revenue from the play.

Ticket Prices

Orchestra	Mezzanine	Balcony
$7.00	$6.00	$5.00

Number of Tickets Sold

Location	Thursday	Friday	Saturday
Orchestra	150	130	160
Mezzanine	125	130	175
Balcony	60	52	80

 Challenge

Solve for x and y.

51. $\begin{bmatrix} 2x & 1 \\ 2 & 0 \end{bmatrix} \begin{bmatrix} 1 & 3 \\ 2 & -y \end{bmatrix} = \begin{bmatrix} -4 & -9 \\ 2 & 6 \end{bmatrix}$

52. $\begin{bmatrix} 2x & 1 \\ 2 & 0 \end{bmatrix} \begin{bmatrix} 0 & 3 \\ 2x & -y \end{bmatrix} = \begin{bmatrix} -4 & -9 \\ 0 & 6 \end{bmatrix}$

For Exercises 53–56, use matrices P, Q, R, S, and I. Determine whether the two expressions in each pair are equal.

$$P = \begin{bmatrix} 3 & 4 \\ 1 & 2 \end{bmatrix} \quad Q = \begin{bmatrix} -1 & 0 \\ 3 & -2 \end{bmatrix} \quad R = \begin{bmatrix} 1 & 4 \\ -2 & 1 \end{bmatrix} \quad S = \begin{bmatrix} 0 & 1 \\ 2 & 0 \end{bmatrix} \quad I = \begin{bmatrix} 1 & 0 \\ 0 & 1 \end{bmatrix}$$

53. $(P + Q)R$ and $PR + QR$

54. $(P + Q)I$ and $PI + QI$

55. $(P + Q)(R + S)$ and $(P + Q)R + (P + Q)S$

56. $(P + Q)(R + S)$ and $PR + PS + QR + QS$

Multiple Choice Practice

For California Standards and CAHSEE Tutorials, visit PHSchool.com. Web Code: bbq-9045

ALG2 2.0

57. Tickets to a school play cost $3 for students and $5 for adults. The drama club sold $450 worth of tickets, and 70 more student tickets than adult tickets. Let x represent the number of student tickets sold and y the number of adult tickets sold. Which system describes this situation?

A. $3x + 5y = 450; x = y - 70$

B. $x + y = 450; 3x = 5y + 70$

C. $8(x + y) = 450; x = y + 70$

D. $3x + 5y = 450; x = y + 70$

CAHSEE
7MG 2.3

58. Two similar rectangles have perimeters of 40 feet and 45 feet. The length of the smaller rectangle is 12 feet. What is the length of the larger rectangle?

A. 9 ft   B. 13.5 ft   C. 14.5 ft   D. 17 ft

Mixed Review

Lesson 4-2

Add or subtract.

59. $\begin{bmatrix} -1 & 2 \\ 0 & 17 \end{bmatrix} - \begin{bmatrix} 32 & 14 \\ 6 & -10 \end{bmatrix}$

60. $\begin{bmatrix} 0 & -1 & 5 \\ 6 & 10 & 12 \end{bmatrix} + \begin{bmatrix} 9 & -5 & 7 \\ -4 & 10 & 0 \end{bmatrix}$

Lesson 3-4

Graph each system of constraints. Find all vertices. Then find the values of x and y that maximize or minimize the objective function.

61. $\begin{cases} x + y \le 3 \\ x \ge 0 \\ y \le 2 \end{cases}$
Maximize for
$P = 3x + 4y$.

62. $\begin{cases} x + 2y \le 8 \\ x \ge 2 \\ y \ge 0 \end{cases}$
Minimize for
$C = x + 3y$.

63. $\begin{cases} x + y \le 6 \\ 2x + y \le 10 \\ x \ge 0, y \ge 0 \end{cases}$
Maximize for
$P = 4x + y$.

Lesson 2-7

Graph each inequality.

64. $y < 4x - 1$

65. $y \le -3x + 8$

66. $y \ge |2x + 5| - 3$

Checkpoint Quiz 1 — Lessons 4-1 through 4-3

State the dimensions of each matrix. Identify the indicated element.

1. $\begin{bmatrix} 5 & 2 \\ -8 & 3 \\ 10 & 1 \end{bmatrix}; a_{32}$

2. $\begin{bmatrix} 9 & 1 & 7 \\ 6 & -2 & 4 \end{bmatrix}; a_{22}$

3. $\begin{bmatrix} 8 & 1 & 5 \\ 9 & 4 & 2 \\ 7 & 0 & 3 \end{bmatrix}; a_{13}$

Use matrices A, B, C, and D. Perform each operation.

$$A = \begin{bmatrix} 3 & 1 \\ 5 & 7 \end{bmatrix} \qquad B = \begin{bmatrix} 4 & 6 \\ 1 & 0 \end{bmatrix} \qquad C = \begin{bmatrix} -5 & 3 \\ 1 & 9 \end{bmatrix} \qquad D = \begin{bmatrix} 1.5 & 2 \\ 9 & -6 \end{bmatrix}$$

4. $A + C$ **5.** $B - A$ **6.** $3D$ **7.** BA **8.** $C(DB)$

9. Writing How can you decide whether you can multiply two matrices?

10. Open-Ended Write a matrix equation with solution $\begin{bmatrix} 12 & 7 & -3 & 8 \\ 9 & 0 & -11 & 1 \end{bmatrix}$.

Geometric patterns, such as those formed by geese flying south for the winter or tiles on a plane surface, can be described using geometric transformations. A transformation is a change made to a figure. There are four types.

A translation slides a figure a given distance and direction without changing its size or shape.

preimage

image

A rotation turns a figure through a given angle about a point called the center.

preimage

image

A reflection flips a figure over a given line called its axis of reflection.

preimage

image

A dilation enlarges or reduces a figure by a given scale factor about a point called the center.

image

preimage

EXERCISES

Describe each transformation from the black figure (preimage) to the blue figure (image) as a *translation*, *rotation*, *reflection*, or *dilation*.

1.

2.

3.

4.

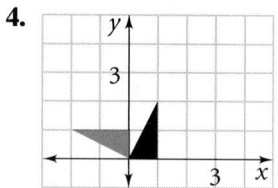

5. a. For Exercise 1, list the coordinates of the preimage vertices. Then list the coordinates of the image vertices.

   b. Make a Conjecture For the type of transformation you found, describe how the coordinates of the image relate to the coordinates of its preimage. Use other examples of that transformation to verify your conjecture.

   c. Make More Conjectures Repeat parts (a) and (b) for Exercises 2–4.

6. Open-Ended In a coordinate plane, draw a rectangle with center not at the origin. Then construct a dilation with center at the origin and scale factor 2.

4-4

Geometric Transformations With Matrices

 California Content Standards
LA 4.0 Students perform addition on matrices.
LA 5.0 Students perform matrix multiplication.

What You'll Learn

- To represent translations and dilations with matrices
- To represent reflections and rotations with matrices

. . . And Why

To transform a photo, as in Example 2

 Check Skills You'll Need

GO for Help Lesson 2-6

Without using graphing technology, graph each function and its translation. Write the new function.

1. $y = x + 2$; left 4 units

2. $f(x) = \frac{1}{2}x + 2$; up 5 units

3. $g(x) = |x|$; right 3 units

4. $y = x$; down 2 units

5. $y = \frac{1}{3}|x - 3|$; down 2 units

6. $f(x) = -2|x|$; right 2 units

New Vocabulary ● image ● preimage ● dilation ● rotation ● center of rotation

---

1 ▸ **Translations and Dilations With Matrices**

Activity: Translating a Geometric Figure

Geometry In Chapter 2 you used vertical and horizontal translations to graph functions. A translation shifts a graph without changing its size or shape.

1. Draw the figure on a coordinate grid as shown.

2. Translate the figure 4 units right and 6 units down. Label the new figure.

3. Identify the coordinates of the vertices of the original figure and the new figure.

4. How does the translation *4 units right and 6 units down* relate the coordinates of the new figure to the coordinates of the original figure?

5. Without graphing, identify the coordinates that result from a translation of the original figure 10 units right and 3 units up.

6. Suppose the original figure is translated so that two vertices have coordinates (0, 0) and (2, 0). Find two possible translations. Write the coordinates for the vertices of each translated figure.

7. **Critical Thinking** What translations of the original figure will result in a tessellation?

8. **Open-Ended** Design another simple figure that will tessellate the plane. Describe the translations needed to fill the plane.

Vocabulary Tip

A <u>tessellation</u> is a repeating pattern of figures that covers a plane, without gaps or overlaps.

You can write the vertices of a figure as a matrix. For example, the matrix below represents the vertices of figure *ABCD*.

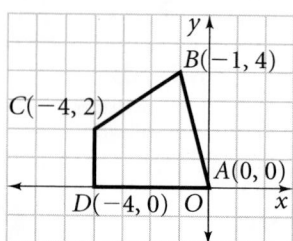

$$\begin{array}{c} \\ x\text{-coordinate} \\ y\text{-coordinate} \end{array} \begin{array}{cccc} A & B & C & D \\ \begin{bmatrix} 0 & -1 & -4 & -4 \\ 0 & 4 & 2 & 0 \end{bmatrix} \end{array}$$

A change made to a figure is a transformation of the figure. The transformed figure is the **image.** The original figure is the **preimage.** A translation (Lesson 2–6) is a transformation that slides a figure without changing the size or shape of the figure. You can use matrix addition to translate all the vertices of a figure in one step.

1 EXAMPLE **Translating a Figure**

Geometry Quadrilateral *ABCD* above has vertices $A(0, 0), B(-1, 4), C(-4, 2),$ and $D(-4, 0)$. Use a matrix to find the coordinates of the vertices of the image translated 6 units right and 2 units down. Then graph *ABCD* and its image $A'B'C'D'$.

<table>
<tr><td>**Vertices of the Quadrilateral**</td><td>**Translation Matrix**</td><td>**Vertices of the Image**</td></tr>
</table>

Add 6 to each *x*-coordinate.

$$\begin{array}{cccc} A & B & C & D \\ \begin{bmatrix} 0 & -1 & -4 & -4 \\ 0 & 4 & 2 & 0 \end{bmatrix} \end{array} + \begin{bmatrix} 6 & 6 & 6 & 6 \\ -2 & -2 & -2 & -2 \end{bmatrix} = \begin{array}{cccc} A' & B' & C' & D' \\ \begin{bmatrix} 6 & 5 & 2 & 2 \\ -2 & 2 & 0 & -2 \end{bmatrix} \end{array}$$

Subtract 2 from each *y*-coordinate.

The vertices of the image are $A'(6, -2), B'(5, 2), C'(2, 0),$ and $D'(2, -2)$.

Graph both quadrilaterals.

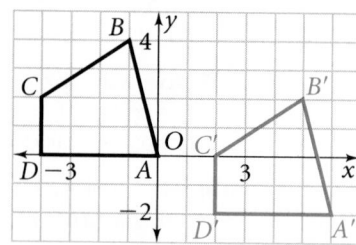

1 a. Critical Thinking Explain how to translate quadrilateral $A'B'C'D'$ from Example 1 so that its image is quadrilateral *ABCD*.

b. What matrix would you use to translate the vertices of a pentagon 3 units left and 2 units up?

c. Use your answer to part (b) to translate the pentagon with vertices $(0, -5),$ $(-1, -1), (-5, 0), (1, 3),$ and $(4, 0)$. Find the coordinates of the vertices of the image. Graph the preimage and the image.

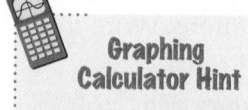
A **dilation** is a transformation that changes the size of a figure. When the center of the dilation is the origin, you can use scalar multiplication to find the coordinates of the vertices of an image. All dilations in this book are centered at the origin.

2 EXAMPLE   Real-World Connection

Graphic Arts An artist sends you a photo electronically. You increase the photo dimensions by a factor of 1.2. Find the coordinates of the enlargement's vertices.

Write a matrix to represent the coordinates of the vertices, which are at $(0, 0)$, $(0, 5.875)$, $(9.75, 5.875)$, and $(9.75, 0)$. Then multiply by the factor 1.2.

$$1.2 \begin{bmatrix} 0 & 0 & 9.75 & 9.75 \\ 0 & 5.875 & 5.875 & 0 \end{bmatrix} = \begin{bmatrix} 0 & 0 & 11.7 & 11.7 \\ 0 & 7.05 & 7.05 & 0 \end{bmatrix}$$

The new coordinates are $(0, 0)$, $(0, 7.05)$, $(11.7, 7.05)$, and $(11.7, 0)$.

 CA Standards Check ❷ The coordinates of the vertices of figure ABC are $A(-5, 0)$, $B(8, -1)$, and $C(4, 5)$. Find the coordinates of each image under the following dilations. Then graph each image and its preimage on the same coordinate plane.

a. 4   **b.** $\frac{1}{5}$ **c.** -1.5

---

2 Reflections and Rotations With Matrices

A reflection, or *flip*, is a transformation that results in symmetry on the coordinate plane. A reflection maps a point in the plane to its mirror image, using a specific line as the mirror. The lines used in this book are the x-axis (see Lesson 2-6), the y-axis, and the lines $y = x$ and $y = -x$.

You can use matrix multiplication to graph reflections in the coordinate plane.

 Key Concepts

Properties	Matrices for Reflections in the Coordinate Plane		
Reflection in the y-axis	Reflection in the x-axis	Reflection in the line $y = x$	Reflection in the line $y = -x$
$\begin{bmatrix} -1 & 0 \\ 0 & 1 \end{bmatrix}$	$\begin{bmatrix} 1 & 0 \\ 0 & -1 \end{bmatrix}$	$\begin{bmatrix} 0 & 1 \\ 1 & 0 \end{bmatrix}$	$\begin{bmatrix} 0 & -1 \\ -1 & 0 \end{bmatrix}$

③ EXAMPLE **Reflecting a Figure**

Reflect the triangle with coordinates $A(0, 0)$, $B(2, 5)$, and $C(-2, 3)$ in each line. Then graph each pair of triangles on the same coordinate plane.

a. y-axis

$$\begin{bmatrix} -1 & 0 \\ 0 & 1 \end{bmatrix} \begin{bmatrix} 0 & 2 & -2 \\ 0 & 5 & 3 \end{bmatrix} = \begin{bmatrix} 0 & -2 & 2 \\ 0 & 5 & 3 \end{bmatrix}$$

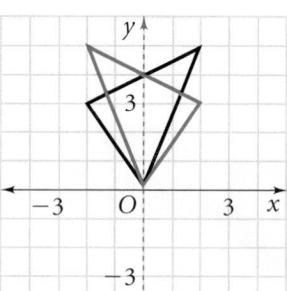

b. x-axis

$$\begin{bmatrix} 1 & 0 \\ 0 & -1 \end{bmatrix} \begin{bmatrix} 0 & 2 & -2 \\ 0 & 5 & 3 \end{bmatrix} = \begin{bmatrix} 0 & 2 & -2 \\ 0 & -5 & -3 \end{bmatrix}$$

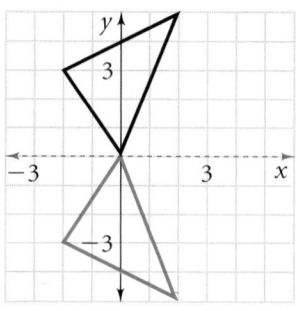

c. $y = x$

$$\begin{bmatrix} 0 & 1 \\ 1 & 0 \end{bmatrix} \begin{bmatrix} 0 & 2 & -2 \\ 0 & 5 & 3 \end{bmatrix} = \begin{bmatrix} 0 & 5 & 3 \\ 0 & 2 & -2 \end{bmatrix}$$

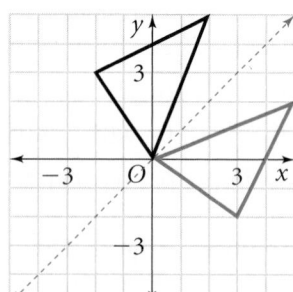

d. $y = -x$

$$\begin{bmatrix} 0 & -1 \\ -1 & 0 \end{bmatrix} \begin{bmatrix} 0 & 2 & -2 \\ 0 & 5 & 3 \end{bmatrix} = \begin{bmatrix} 0 & -5 & -3 \\ 0 & -2 & 2 \end{bmatrix}$$

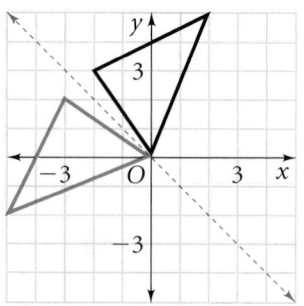

✓ CA Standards Check **③** Reflect the triangle with coordinates $D(-3, 0)$, $E(-4, 4)$, and $F(1, 1)$ in each line. Then graph each pair of triangles on the same coordinate plane.
a. y-axis   **b.** x-axis   **c.** $y = x$ **d.** $y = -x$

A **rotation** is a transformation that turns a figure about a fixed point called the **center of rotation.** You can rotate a figure as much as 360 degrees. In this book, all rotations are counterclockwise about the origin.

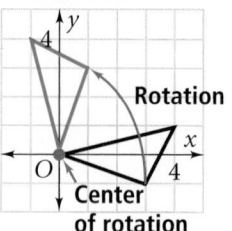

⚷ Key Concepts

Properties	Matrices for Rotations in the Coordinate Plane		
Rotation of 90°	Rotation of 180°	Rotation of 270°	Rotation of 360°
$\begin{bmatrix} 0 & -1 \\ 1 & 0 \end{bmatrix}$	$\begin{bmatrix} -1 & 0 \\ 0 & -1 \end{bmatrix}$	$\begin{bmatrix} 0 & 1 \\ -1 & 0 \end{bmatrix}$	$\begin{bmatrix} 1 & 0 \\ 0 & 1 \end{bmatrix}$

EXAMPLE **Rotating a Figure**

Rotate the triangle with coordinates $A(0,0)$, $B(2,5)$, and $C(-2,3)$. Then graph each pair of triangles on the same coordinate plane.

a. 90°

$$\begin{bmatrix} 0 & -1 \\ 1 & 0 \end{bmatrix}\begin{bmatrix} 0 & 2 & -2 \\ 0 & 5 & 3 \end{bmatrix} = \begin{bmatrix} 0 & -5 & -3 \\ 0 & 2 & -2 \end{bmatrix}$$

b. 180°

$$\begin{bmatrix} -1 & 0 \\ 0 & -1 \end{bmatrix}\begin{bmatrix} 0 & 2 & -2 \\ 0 & 5 & 3 \end{bmatrix} = \begin{bmatrix} 0 & -2 & 2 \\ 0 & -5 & -3 \end{bmatrix}$$

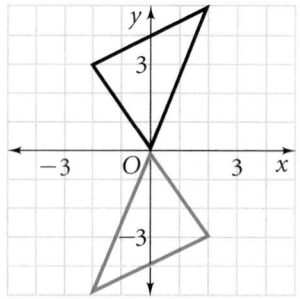

c. 270°

$$\begin{bmatrix} 0 & 1 \\ -1 & 0 \end{bmatrix}\begin{bmatrix} 0 & 2 & -2 \\ 0 & 5 & 3 \end{bmatrix} = \begin{bmatrix} 0 & 5 & 3 \\ 0 & -2 & 2 \end{bmatrix}$$

d. 360°

$$\begin{bmatrix} 1 & 0 \\ 0 & 1 \end{bmatrix}\begin{bmatrix} 0 & 2 & -2 \\ 0 & 5 & 3 \end{bmatrix} = \begin{bmatrix} 0 & 2 & -2 \\ 0 & 5 & 3 \end{bmatrix}$$

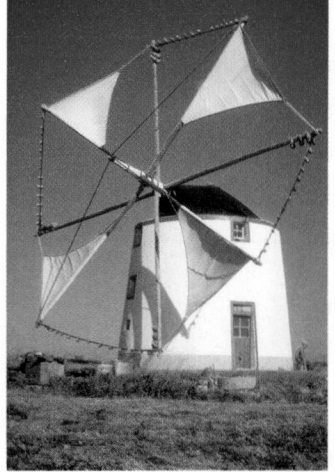

Real-World Connection

The windmill sails form a figure with 90° rotational symmetry.

CA Standards Check ④ Rotate the quadrilateral with coordinates $A(1,1)$, $B(3,1)$, $C(6,4)$, and $D(1,3)$. Then graph each pair of quadrilaterals on the same coordinate plane.
a. 90°   **b.** 180°   **c.** 270°   **d.** 360°

EXERCISES

For more exercises, see *Extra Skill and Word Problem Practice*.

Standards Practice

LA 4.0, 5.0

A Practice by Example

Example 1
(page 196)

Use matrix addition to find the coordinates of each image after a translation of 3 units left and 5 units up. If possible, graph each pair of figures on the same coordinate plane.

1. $A(1, -3)$, $B(1, 1)$, $C(5, 1)$, $D(5, -3)$
2. $G(0, 0)$, $H(4, 4)$, $I(4, -4)$, $J(8, 0)$
3. $J(-10, 2)$, $K(-16, a)$, $L(12, -5)$
4. $R(9, 3)$, $S(3, 6)$, $T(3, 3)$, $U(6, -3)$

Example 2
(page 197)

Graph each figure and its image after the given dilation.

5. $\begin{bmatrix} 0 & 2 & 5 & 8 \\ 0 & 4 & 5 & 1 \end{bmatrix}, 2$

6. $\begin{bmatrix} -7 & -3 & 4 \\ -5 & 4 & 0 \end{bmatrix}, 0.5$

7. $\begin{bmatrix} 0 & -2 & -5 \\ 0 & 0 & 5 \end{bmatrix}, \frac{9}{10}$

8. $\begin{bmatrix} -10 & -5 & 0 & 5 & 10 \\ 8 & 16 & 20 & 16 & 8 \end{bmatrix}, \frac{1}{4}$

9. $\begin{bmatrix} -8 & 2 & 3 & 1 & -2 \\ 6 & 4 & 0 & -4 & 0 \end{bmatrix}, 1.5$

Example 3
(page 198)

Graph each figure and its image after reflection in the given line.

10. $\begin{bmatrix} 0 & -3 & 5 \\ 0 & 1 & 2 \end{bmatrix}; y = x$ **11.** $\begin{bmatrix} -1 & 0 & 5 \\ -1 & 5 & 0 \end{bmatrix}; y\text{-axis}$ **12.** $\begin{bmatrix} -3 & -5 & -10 \\ 4 & 7 & 1 \end{bmatrix}; x\text{-axis}$

Find the coordinates of each image after reflection in the given line.

13. $\begin{bmatrix} 3 & 6 & 3 & 6 \\ -3 & 3 & 3 & -3 \end{bmatrix}; y = -x$ **14.** $\begin{bmatrix} 0 & 4 & 8 & 6 \\ 0 & 4 & 4 & 2 \end{bmatrix}; x\text{-axis}$

15. $\begin{bmatrix} 1 & 2 & 3 & 4 & 2.5 \\ 3 & 2 & 2 & 3 & 5 \end{bmatrix}; y = x$ **16.** $\begin{bmatrix} -1 & -2 & -4 & -6 & -2 \\ -4 & 0 & 0 & -3 & -4 \end{bmatrix}; x\text{-axis}$

Example 4
(page 199)

Graph each figure and its image after the given rotation.

17. $\begin{bmatrix} 0 & -3 & 5 \\ 0 & 1 & 2 \end{bmatrix}; 90°$ **18.** $\begin{bmatrix} -1 & 0 & 5 \\ -1 & 5 & 0 \end{bmatrix}; 180°$ **19.** $\begin{bmatrix} -5 & 6 & 0 \\ -1 & 2 & 4 \end{bmatrix}; 90°$

Find the coordinates of each image after the given rotation.

20. $\begin{bmatrix} 3 & 6 & 3 & 6 \\ -3 & 3 & 3 & -3 \end{bmatrix}; 270°$ **21.** $\begin{bmatrix} 0 & 4 & 8 & 6 \\ 0 & 4 & 4 & 2 \end{bmatrix}; 360°$

22. $\begin{bmatrix} 1 & 2 & 3 & 4 & 2.5 \\ 3 & 2 & 2 & 3 & 5 \end{bmatrix}; 180°$ **23.** $\begin{bmatrix} -1 & -2 & -4 & -6 & -2 \\ -4 & 0 & 0 & -3 & -4 \end{bmatrix}; 270°$

B **Apply Your Skills** **Geometry** **Each matrix represents the vertices of a polygon. Translate each figure 5 units left and 1 unit up. Express your answer as a matrix.**

24. $\begin{bmatrix} -3 & -3 & 2 & 2 \\ -2 & -4 & -2 & -4 \end{bmatrix}$ **25.** $\begin{bmatrix} -3 & 0 & 3 & 0 \\ -9 & -6 & -9 & -12 \end{bmatrix}$ **26.** $\begin{bmatrix} 0 & 1 & -4 \\ 0 & 3 & 5 \end{bmatrix}$

For Exercises 27–34, use $\triangle ABC$. Write the coordinates of each image in matrix form.

27. a dilation four times the original size

28. a translation 2 units left and 3 units down

29. a dilation half the original size

30. a translation 1 unit right and 7 units up

31. a rotation of 90°

32. a reflection in $y = x$

33. a rotation of 180°

34. a reflection in the x-axis

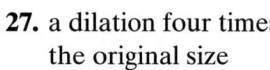

35. Multiple Choice What is true about $\begin{bmatrix} -3 & 0 \\ 0 & -3 \end{bmatrix}\begin{bmatrix} 1 & -2 & 4 \\ 1 & -1 & 2 \end{bmatrix}$ and $-3\begin{bmatrix} 1 & -2 & 4 \\ 1 & -1 & 2 \end{bmatrix}$?

   Ⓐ They are equal matrices.   Ⓒ Both are matrices for reflection.

   Ⓑ They are opposite matrices.   Ⓓ Neither product exists.

36. Writing Graph $\begin{bmatrix} 9 & 10 & 6 \\ 1 & -3 & -2 \end{bmatrix}$ and $2\begin{bmatrix} 9 & 10 & 6 \\ 1 & -3 & -2 \end{bmatrix}$. Compare the graphs. Generalize how a dilation changes a graph.

Vocabulary Tip

A tessellation is a repeating pattern of figures that covers a plane, without gaps or overlap.

37. Geometry Create a tessellation based on the quadrilateral $\begin{bmatrix} 0 & -3 & -5 & 0 \\ 1 & 3 & -1 & -1 \end{bmatrix}$.

Translate the quadrilateral using $\begin{bmatrix} 5 & 5 & 5 & 5 \\ 2 & 2 & 2 & 2 \end{bmatrix}$ and $\begin{bmatrix} 3 & 3 & 3 & 3 \\ -4 & -4 & -4 & -4 \end{bmatrix}$.

38. Writing Explain why you might want to represent a transformation as a matrix.

Use matrices to represent the vertices of graph *f* and graph *g*. Name each transformation.

39.

40.

41.

42.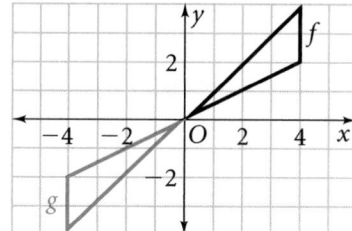

Graph each triangle and its translation on the same coordinate plane.

43. $\begin{bmatrix} 0 & 2 & 3 \\ 0 & 0 & 5 \end{bmatrix}$; 3 units right, 4 units down

44. $\begin{bmatrix} -5 & 3 & 4 \\ 5 & 1 & -4 \end{bmatrix}$; 2 units left, 5 units up

C Challenge

45. Architecture Use the pattern of brown tiles shown at the right.
   a. Copy the graph. Mark scales on the axes so that the dimensions of the square tiles are 1 unit by 1 unit.
   b. Write a matrix for the translation of tile *ABCD* to tile *A'B'C'D'*. What are the coordinates of the vertices of the preimage and the image?
   c. A brown tile is 6 units right and 6 units down from tile *ABCD*. Write a matrix to represent the coordinates of its vertices.
   d. A tile has vertices at $(-6, 9)$, $(-6, 8)$, $(-7, 9)$, and $(-7, 8)$. What translation of tile *ABCD* results in these coordinates?

Geometry Each matrix represents the vertices of a polygon. Write a matrix to represent the vertices of the image after each transformation.

46. $\begin{bmatrix} -3 & 0.5 & -5 \\ 0 & 3 & 3 \end{bmatrix}$; dilation of 2

47. $\begin{bmatrix} 4 & 7 & 10 \\ 0 & 2 & 0 \end{bmatrix}$; rotation of 270°

48. $\begin{bmatrix} 17 & 6 & 6 & 2 \\ 5 & 10 & 2 & 6 \end{bmatrix}$; reflection in $y = x$

49. $\begin{bmatrix} 3 & 4.5 & 5 & 3.5 \\ 3 & 1.5 & 2 & 4 \end{bmatrix}$; rotation of 90°

50. Let the matrix $\begin{bmatrix} x \\ y \end{bmatrix}$ represent points on the graph $y = |x|$.

a. Complete the table. Sketch the graph.

x	−3	−2	−1	0	1	2	3
y							

b. **Critical Thinking** What does the matrix addition $\begin{bmatrix} x \\ y \end{bmatrix} + \begin{bmatrix} -1 \\ 2 \end{bmatrix}$ represent?
Show your answer on your graph from part (a).

Multiple Choice Practice

For California Standards and CAHSEE Tutorials, visit PHSchool.com. Web Code: bbq-9045

ALG2 1.0

51. The graph at the right represents which of the inequalities shown?

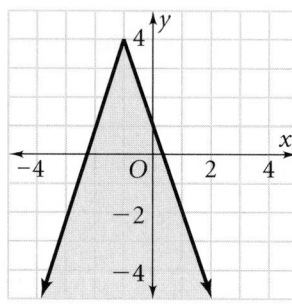

- Ⓐ $y \le -|3x + 1| + 4$
- Ⓑ $y \le -3|x + 1| + 4$
- Ⓒ $y \le -|3x - 1| + 4$
- Ⓓ $y \le -3|x + 1| - 4$

**CAHSEE
7MR 1.1**

52. What is the value of h in the figure at the right?

- Ⓐ $2\sqrt{2}$ cm
- Ⓑ 3 cm
- Ⓒ $2\sqrt{3}$ cm
- Ⓓ $3\sqrt{2}$ cm

Mixed Review

Lesson 4-3

If possible, find the dimensions of each product matrix; then find each product. If the product is not defined, explain why not.

53. $\begin{bmatrix} 1 & 0 & -5 \\ 2 & -1 & 6 \end{bmatrix} \begin{bmatrix} 2 & 4 & -2 \\ 0 & 10 & 4 \\ 0 & 1 & -7 \end{bmatrix}$

54. $\begin{bmatrix} 0 & 7 & k & 5 \\ 0 & 6 & 0 & 5 \end{bmatrix} \begin{bmatrix} 9 & -1 & 3 & 0 \\ 7 & 0 & 7 & 0 \end{bmatrix}$

Lesson 3-5

Graph each equation.

55. $x + y - z = 5$ **56.** $2x - y + 3z = 12$ **57.** $-x + 4y - z = -6$

Lesson 2-1

Make a mapping diagram for each relation. Determine whether it is a function.

58. $\{(-2, 4), (-1, 1), (0, 0), (1, 1), (2, 4)\}$ **59.** $\{(27, -2), (3, -1), (0, 0), (3, 1), (27, 2)\}$

60. $\{(-2, 15), (-1, 1), (0, -3), (1, 3), (2, 15)\}$ **61.** $\{(-3, 8), (-2, 1), (1, -2), (0, -1), (1, 4)\}$

2 × 2 Matrices, Determinants, and Inverses

 California Content Standards

LA 10.0 Students compute the determinants of 2 × 2 matrices.
LA 11.0 Students know that a square matrix is invertible if, and only if, its determinant is nonzero.

What You'll Learn

- To evaluate determinants of 2 × 2 matrices and find inverse matrices
- To use inverse matrices in solving matrix equations

. . . And Why

To predict cell phone ownership, as in Example 5

 Check Skills You'll Need

GO for Help Skills Handbook page 885

Simplify each group of expressions.

1. a. $3(4)$ **b.** $2(6)$ **c.** $3(4) - 2(6)$

2. a. $3(-4)$ **b.** $2(-6)$ **c.** $3(-4) - 2(-6)$

3. a. $-3(-4)$ **b.** $-2(6)$ **c.** $-3(-4) - 2(-6)$

4. a. $-3(4)$ **b.** $-2(-6)$ **c.** $-3(4) - (-2)(-6)$

◀))) **New Vocabulary** • square matrix • multiplicative identity matrix
• multiplicative inverse of a matrix • determinant

---

1   Evaluating Determinants of 2 × 2 Matrices

A **square matrix** is a matrix with the same number of columns as rows.

For any real number a, the number 1 is the multiplicative identity of a, since $a \cdot 1 = 1 \cdot a = a$. Square matrices also have a multiplicative identity.

 Key Concepts

Definition	**Multiplicative Identity Matrix**

For an $n \times n$ square matrix, the **multiplicative identity matrix** is an $n \times n$ square matrix I, or I_n, with 1's along the main diagonal and 0's elsewhere.

$$I_2 = \begin{bmatrix} 1 & 0 \\ 0 & 1 \end{bmatrix}, \qquad I_3 = \begin{bmatrix} 1 & 0 & 0 \\ 0 & 1 & 0 \\ 0 & 0 & 1 \end{bmatrix}, \qquad \text{and so forth}$$

If the product of the real numbers a and b is 1, then a and b are multiplicative inverses. Some, but not all, square matrices have multiplicative inverses.

 Key Concepts

Definition	**Multiplicative Inverse of a Matrix**

If A and X are $n \times n$ matrices, and $AX = XA = I$, then X is the multiplicative inverse of A, written A^{-1}.

$$AA^{-1} = A^{-1}A = I$$

If B is the multiplicative inverse of A, then A is the multiplicative inverse of B. To show that A and B are multiplicative inverses, show that $AB = I$ or that $BA = I$.

Video Tutor Help
Visit: PHSchool.com
Web Code: bbe-0775

1 EXAMPLE **Verifying Inverses**

Show that B is the multiplicative inverse of A.

$$A = \begin{bmatrix} 2 & 3 \\ 1 & 2 \end{bmatrix} \qquad B = \begin{bmatrix} 2 & -3 \\ -1 & 2 \end{bmatrix}$$

$$AB = \begin{bmatrix} 2 & 3 \\ 1 & 2 \end{bmatrix}\begin{bmatrix} 2 & -3 \\ -1 & 2 \end{bmatrix} = \begin{bmatrix} 2(2) + 3(-1) & 2(-3) + 3(2) \\ 1(2) + 2(-1) & 1(-3) + 2(2) \end{bmatrix} = \begin{bmatrix} 1 & 0 \\ 0 & 1 \end{bmatrix}$$

$AB = I$, so B is the multiplicative inverse of A. A is also the multiplicative inverse of B.

Check $BA = \begin{bmatrix} 2 & -3 \\ -1 & 2 \end{bmatrix}\begin{bmatrix} 2 & 3 \\ 1 & 2 \end{bmatrix} = \begin{bmatrix} 2(2) + (-3)(1) & 2(3) + (-3)(2) \\ -1(2) + 2(1) & -1(3) + 2(2) \end{bmatrix} = \begin{bmatrix} 1 & 0 \\ 0 & 1 \end{bmatrix}$ ✓

✓ CA Standards Check **1** Show that the matrices are multiplicative inverses.

a. $\begin{bmatrix} 2 & 1 \\ 2.5 & 1 \end{bmatrix}$ and $\begin{bmatrix} -2 & 2 \\ 5 & -4 \end{bmatrix}$ **b.** $\begin{bmatrix} -2 & -5 \\ -3 & -8 \end{bmatrix}$ and $\begin{bmatrix} -8 & 5 \\ 3 & -2 \end{bmatrix}$

Every square matrix with real-number elements has a real-number determinant. Determinants can help you find inverses.

	Write	Read	Evaluate
	↓	↓	↓

$$A = \begin{bmatrix} a & b \\ c & d \end{bmatrix} \qquad \det A = \begin{vmatrix} a & b \\ c & d \end{vmatrix} \qquad \text{the determinant of } A \qquad \begin{vmatrix} a & b \\ c & d \end{vmatrix} = ad - bc$$

 Key Concepts

Definition   **Determinant of a 2 × 2 Matrix**

The **determinant** of a 2×2 matrix $\begin{bmatrix} a & b \\ c & d \end{bmatrix}$ is $ad - bc$.

Symbols for the determinant of a matrix
↓   ↓

$$\det A \qquad \begin{vmatrix} a & b \\ c & d \end{vmatrix}$$

2 EXAMPLE **Evaluating the Determinant of a 2 × 2 Matrix**

Evaluate each determinant.

a. $\det \begin{bmatrix} -3 & 4 \\ 2 & -5 \end{bmatrix} = \begin{vmatrix} -3 & 4 \\ 2 & -5 \end{vmatrix} = (-3)(-5) - (4)(2) = 15 - 8 = 7$

b. $\det \begin{bmatrix} 2 & -3 \\ 3 & -2 \end{bmatrix} = \begin{vmatrix} 2 & -3 \\ 3 & -2 \end{vmatrix} = (2)(-2) - (-3)(3) = -4 - (-9) = 5$

c. $\det \begin{bmatrix} a & 0 \\ 0 & a \end{bmatrix} = \begin{vmatrix} a & 0 \\ 0 & a \end{vmatrix} = a^2 - 0 = a^2$

✓ CA Standards Check **2** Evaluate the determinant of each matrix.

a. $\begin{bmatrix} 4 & 2 \\ 4 & 2 \end{bmatrix}$ **b.** $\begin{bmatrix} 8 & 7 \\ 2 & 3 \end{bmatrix}$ **c.** $\begin{bmatrix} k & 3 \\ 3 - k & -3 \end{bmatrix}$

The following test will help you determine whether a 2 × 2 matrix has an inverse. The test will also help you find the inverse, if it exists.

 Key Concepts

Property	Inverse of a 2 × 2 Matrix

Let $A = \begin{bmatrix} a & b \\ c & d \end{bmatrix}$. If det $A = 0$, then A has no inverse.

If det $A \neq 0$, then $A^{-1} = \dfrac{1}{\det A}\begin{bmatrix} d & -b \\ -c & a \end{bmatrix} = \dfrac{1}{ad - bc}\begin{bmatrix} d & -b \\ -c & a \end{bmatrix}$.

3 EXAMPLE Finding an Inverse Matrix

Determine whether each matrix has an inverse. If an inverse matrix exists, find it.

a. $M = \begin{bmatrix} -2 & 2 \\ 5 & -4 \end{bmatrix}$ $ad - bc = (-2)(-4) - (2)(5)$ **Find det M.**

$= -2$ **Simplify.**

Since det $M \neq 0$, the inverse of M exists.

Change signs.
$M^{-1} = \begin{bmatrix} -2 & 2 \\ 5 & -4 \end{bmatrix}^{-1}$
Switch positions.

$= \dfrac{1}{\det M}\begin{bmatrix} -4 & -2 \\ -5 & -2 \end{bmatrix}$ **Use the determinant to write the inverse.**

$= \dfrac{1}{-2}\begin{bmatrix} -4 & -2 \\ -5 & -2 \end{bmatrix}$ **Substitute −2 for det M.**

$= \begin{bmatrix} 2 & 1 \\ 2.5 & 1 \end{bmatrix}$ **Multiply.**

b. $N = \begin{bmatrix} 3 & 9 \\ 2 & 6 \end{bmatrix}$ $ad - bc = (3)(6) - (9)(2)$ **Find det N.**

$= 0$ **Simplify.**

Since det $N = 0$, the inverse of N does *not* exist.

✓ CA Standards Check **3** Determine whether each matrix has an inverse. If an inverse matrix exists, find it.

a. $\begin{bmatrix} 2 & 4 \\ 1 & 3 \end{bmatrix}$ **b.** $\begin{bmatrix} 0.5 & 2.3 \\ 3 & 7.2 \end{bmatrix}$

2 Using Inverse Matrices to Solve Equations

If the inverse of matrix A exists, you can use it to solve matrix equations of the form $AX = B$. Multiply each side of the equation by A^{-1} to find X.

$AX = B$

$A^{-1}(AX) = A^{-1}B$ **Multiply each side by A⁻¹.**

$(A^{-1}A)X = A^{-1}B$ **Associative Property of Multiplication**

$IX = A^{-1}B$ **definition of multiplicative inverse**

$X = A^{-1}B$ **definition of multiplicative identity**

Solving a Matrix Equation

Solve $\begin{bmatrix} -2 & -5 \\ 1 & 3 \end{bmatrix} X = \begin{bmatrix} -2 \\ 2 \end{bmatrix}$ for the matrix X.

The matrix equation has the form $AX = B$. First find A^{-1}.

$A^{-1} = \dfrac{1}{ad - bc}\begin{bmatrix} d & -b \\ -c & a \end{bmatrix} = \dfrac{1}{-2(3) - (-5)1}\begin{bmatrix} 3 & 5 \\ -1 & -2 \end{bmatrix}$ **Use the definition of inverse.**

$\qquad\qquad = \begin{bmatrix} -3 & -5 \\ 1 & 2 \end{bmatrix}$ **Simplify.**

Use the equation $X = A^{-1}B$. $\qquad X = \begin{bmatrix} -3 & -5 \\ 1 & 2 \end{bmatrix}\begin{bmatrix} -2 \\ 2 \end{bmatrix}$ **Substitute.**

$\qquad\qquad = \begin{bmatrix} -3(-2) + -5(2) \\ 1(-2) + 2(2) \end{bmatrix} = \begin{bmatrix} -4 \\ 2 \end{bmatrix}$ **Multiply and simplify.**

Check $\qquad \begin{bmatrix} -2 & -5 \\ 1 & 3 \end{bmatrix} X = \begin{bmatrix} -2 \\ 2 \end{bmatrix}$ **Use the original equation.**

$\qquad \begin{bmatrix} -2 & -5 \\ 1 & 3 \end{bmatrix}\begin{bmatrix} -4 \\ 2 \end{bmatrix} \stackrel{?}{=} \begin{bmatrix} -2 \\ 2 \end{bmatrix}$ **Substitute.**

$\qquad \begin{bmatrix} -2(-4) + (-5)(2) \\ 1(-4) + 3(2) \end{bmatrix} \stackrel{?}{=} \begin{bmatrix} -2 \\ 2 \end{bmatrix}$ **Multiply.**

$\qquad\qquad\qquad \begin{bmatrix} -2 \\ 2 \end{bmatrix} = \begin{bmatrix} -2 \\ 2 \end{bmatrix}$ ✓ **Simplify.**

✅ **CA Standards Check** 4 Solve each matrix equation in the form $AX = B$. Use the equation $X = A^{-1}B$.

a. $\begin{bmatrix} 3 & -4 \\ 4 & -5 \end{bmatrix} X = \begin{bmatrix} 0 & -22 \\ 0 & -28 \end{bmatrix}$ **b.** $\begin{bmatrix} 7 & 5 \\ 3 & 2 \end{bmatrix} X = \begin{bmatrix} -9 \\ -4 \end{bmatrix}$

You can use matrices to make predictions about trends.

5 EXAMPLE **Real-World Connection**

Communications The diagram shows the trends in cell phone ownership over four consecutive years.

a. Write a matrix to represent the changes (or transitions) in cell phone use.

$$\begin{array}{cc} & \text{From} \\ & \text{No cell} \quad \text{Cell} \\ \text{To} \begin{array}{c} \text{No cell} \\ \text{Cell} \end{array} & \begin{bmatrix} 0.57 & 0.13 \\ 0.43 & 0.87 \end{bmatrix} \end{array}$$ **Write the percents as decimals.**

b. In a stable population of 16,000 people, 9927 own cell phones, while 6073 do not. Assume the trends continue. Predict the number of people who will own cell phones next year.

$$\begin{array}{c} \text{No cell} \\ \text{Cell} \end{array}\begin{bmatrix} 6073 \\ 9927 \end{bmatrix}$$ **Write the information in a matrix.**

$\begin{bmatrix} 0.57 & 0.13 \\ 0.43 & 0.87 \end{bmatrix}\begin{bmatrix} 6073 \\ 9927 \end{bmatrix} \approx \begin{bmatrix} 4752 \\ 11{,}248 \end{bmatrix}$ **Use the transition matrix from part (a). Multiply.**

Next year, about 11,248 people in the population will own cell phones.

Cell Phone
87%
No Cell Phone
43%
13%
57%

Real-World Connection

Martin Cooper invented the portable cellular radio telephone in 1973.

c. Use the inverse of the matrix from part (a) to find the number of people who owned cell phones last year.

$$\begin{bmatrix} 0.57 & 0.13 \\ 0.43 & 0.87 \end{bmatrix}^{-1} \begin{bmatrix} 6073 \\ 9927 \end{bmatrix} = \begin{bmatrix} 9075 \\ 6925 \end{bmatrix}$$

Last year, 6925 people owned cell phones.

CA Standards Check **5** **a.** **Critical Thinking** Find the percent of the population owning cell phones last year, this year, and next year. Estimate the percent two years from now.

b. Use the answer to Example 5, part (b), and the transition matrix to predict the number of people who will own cell phones two years from now.

c. Use the answer to Example 5, part (c), and the inverse of the transition matrix to estimate the number of people who owned cell phones two years ago.

EXERCISES

For more exercises, see *Extra Skill and Word Problem Practice.*

Standards Practice

LA 10.0, 11.0

A **Practice by Example**

Example 1
(page 204)

Show that the matrices are multiplicative inverses.

1. $\begin{bmatrix} 3 & 2 \\ 4 & 3 \end{bmatrix}, \begin{bmatrix} 3 & -2 \\ -4 & 3 \end{bmatrix}$

2. $\begin{bmatrix} -3 & 7 \\ -2 & 5 \end{bmatrix}, \begin{bmatrix} -5 & 7 \\ -2 & 3 \end{bmatrix}$

3. $\begin{bmatrix} \frac{1}{5} & -\frac{1}{10} \\ 0 & \frac{1}{4} \end{bmatrix}, \begin{bmatrix} 5 & 2 \\ 0 & 4 \end{bmatrix}$

Example 2
(page 204)

Evaluate the determinant of each matrix.

4. $\begin{bmatrix} 7 & 2 \\ 0 & -3 \end{bmatrix}$
5. $\begin{bmatrix} 6 & 2 \\ -6 & -2 \end{bmatrix}$
6. $\begin{bmatrix} 0 & 0.5 \\ 1.5 & 2 \end{bmatrix}$
7. $\begin{bmatrix} \frac{1}{2} & \frac{2}{3} \\ \frac{3}{5} & \frac{1}{4} \end{bmatrix}$
8. $\begin{bmatrix} -1 & 3 \\ 5 & 2 \end{bmatrix}$

9. $\begin{bmatrix} -2 & 0 \\ 2 & -1 \end{bmatrix}$
10. $\begin{bmatrix} 5 & 3 \\ -2 & 1 \end{bmatrix}$
11. $\begin{bmatrix} 5 & 2 \\ 1 & 3 \end{bmatrix}$
12. $\begin{bmatrix} 2 & -1 \\ 5 & -4 \end{bmatrix}$
13. $\begin{bmatrix} -4 & 3 \\ 2 & 0 \end{bmatrix}$

Example 3
(page 205)

Determine whether each matrix has an inverse. If an inverse matrix exists, find it.

14. $\begin{bmatrix} 2 & -1 \\ 1 & 0 \end{bmatrix}$
15. $\begin{bmatrix} 2 & 3 \\ 1 & 1 \end{bmatrix}$
16. $\begin{bmatrix} 2 & 3 \\ 2 & 4 \end{bmatrix}$
17. $\begin{bmatrix} 1 & 3 \\ 2 & 0 \end{bmatrix}$

18. $\begin{bmatrix} 6 & -8 \\ -3 & 4 \end{bmatrix}$
19. $\begin{bmatrix} 4 & 8 \\ -3 & -2 \end{bmatrix}$
20. $\begin{bmatrix} -1.5 & 3 \\ 2.5 & -0.5 \end{bmatrix}$
21. $\begin{bmatrix} 1 & -2 \\ 3 & 0 \end{bmatrix}$

Example 4
(page 206)

Solve each matrix equation. If an equation cannot be solved, explain why.

22. $\begin{bmatrix} 12 & 7 \\ 5 & 3 \end{bmatrix} X = \begin{bmatrix} 2 & -1 \\ 3 & 2 \end{bmatrix}$
23. $\begin{bmatrix} 0 & -4 \\ 0 & -1 \end{bmatrix} X = \begin{bmatrix} 0 \\ 4 \end{bmatrix}$
24. $\begin{bmatrix} 5 & -3 \\ 4 & -2 \end{bmatrix} X = \begin{bmatrix} 5 \\ 10 \end{bmatrix}$

Example 5
(pages 206–207)

25. **Data Analysis** Use the information in the diagram.
a. Write a transition matrix to represent the changes in cable television subscribers.
b. In a stable population of 30,000 people, 20,000 people subscribe to cable television, while 10,000 do not. Predict the number of people who will subscribe to cable television next year.
c. Use the inverse of the matrix from part (a) to find the number of people who subscribed to cable television last year.

Apply Your Skills

Evaluate each determinant.

26. $\begin{vmatrix} 4 & 5 \\ -4 & 4 \end{vmatrix}$ 27. $\begin{vmatrix} -3 & 10 \\ 6 & 20 \end{vmatrix}$ 28. $\begin{vmatrix} -\frac{1}{2} & 2 \\ -2 & 8 \end{vmatrix}$ 29. $\begin{vmatrix} 2 & 0 \\ 0 & 1 \end{vmatrix}$ 30. $\begin{vmatrix} 6 & 9 \\ 3 & 6 \end{vmatrix}$

Determine whether the matrices are multiplicative inverses. If they are not, explain why not.

31. $\begin{bmatrix} 2 & 0.5 \\ 5 & 1 \end{bmatrix}, \begin{bmatrix} -2 & 1 \\ 10 & -4 \end{bmatrix}$ 32. $\begin{bmatrix} -3 & 4 \\ 6 & -8 \end{bmatrix}, \begin{bmatrix} -1 & 0 \\ 5 & 2 \end{bmatrix}$ 33. $\begin{bmatrix} -2 & -5 \\ -2 & -4 \end{bmatrix}, \begin{bmatrix} -2.5 & 2 \\ 1 & -1 \end{bmatrix}$

Homework Video Tutor

Visit: PHSchool.com
Web Code: bbe-0405

Determine whether each matrix has an inverse. If an inverse matrix exists, find it. If it does not exist, explain why not.

34. $\begin{bmatrix} 1 & 4 \\ 1 & 3 \end{bmatrix}$ 35. $\begin{bmatrix} 4 & 7 \\ 3 & 5 \end{bmatrix}$ 36. $\begin{bmatrix} -3 & 11 \\ 2 & -7 \end{bmatrix}$ 37. $\begin{bmatrix} 2 & 0 \\ 0 & 2 \end{bmatrix}$

38. $\begin{bmatrix} 0 & 3 \\ 3 & 0 \end{bmatrix}$ 39. $\begin{bmatrix} -1 & 3 \\ 2 & 0 \end{bmatrix}$ 40. $\begin{bmatrix} 1 & 2 \\ 2 & 1 \end{bmatrix}$ 41. $\begin{bmatrix} 3 & 0 \\ 6 & 0 \end{bmatrix}$

Solve each matrix equation.

42. $\begin{bmatrix} 4 & 7 \\ 1 & 2 \end{bmatrix} X + \begin{bmatrix} 2 & 7 \\ -3 & 4 \end{bmatrix} = \begin{bmatrix} 6 & 2 \\ -2 & 3 \end{bmatrix}$ 43. $\begin{bmatrix} 1 & 9 \\ 6 & -6 \end{bmatrix} = \begin{bmatrix} -7 & -9 \\ 4 & 5 \end{bmatrix} X + \begin{bmatrix} 3 & 4 \\ 4 & -3 \end{bmatrix}$

44. **Writing** Suppose $A = \begin{bmatrix} a & b \\ c & d \end{bmatrix}$ has an inverse. In your own words, describe how to switch or change the elements of A to write A^{-1}.

45. **Entertainment** Use the information in the diagram at the left.
    a. Write a transition matrix to represent the changes in DVD-player ownership.
    b. In a stable population of 30,000 people, 7000 people own DVD players, while 23,000 do not. Predict the number of people in the population who will own DVD players next year.
    c. Use the inverse of the matrix from part (a) to estimate the number of people in the population who owned DVD players last year.
    d. **Error Analysis** A student estimated that the number of people in the population who owned DVD players last year was 8434. What was the student's error?

Challenge

46. **Critical Thinking** Suppose $A = \begin{bmatrix} a & b \\ c & d \end{bmatrix}$. For what values of $a, b, c,$ and d will A be its own inverse? (*Hint:* There is more than one correct answer.)

Solve each matrix equation.

47. $-2 \begin{bmatrix} -2 & 0 \\ 0 & -1 \end{bmatrix} + \begin{bmatrix} 0 & -3 \\ 5 & -4 \end{bmatrix} X + \begin{bmatrix} 0 & -3 \\ 5 & -4 \end{bmatrix} = \begin{bmatrix} 19 & -27 \\ 10 & -24 \end{bmatrix}$

48. $\begin{bmatrix} 0 & -6 \\ 1 & 2 \end{bmatrix} - \begin{bmatrix} 5 & 2 \\ 4 & 3 \end{bmatrix} X - \begin{bmatrix} 2 & -26 \\ 3 & -18 \end{bmatrix} = \begin{bmatrix} 3 & 25 \\ 2 & 24 \end{bmatrix}$

49. **Critical Thinking** Explain why a 2×3 matrix does not have a multiplicative inverse.

50. Let $M = \begin{bmatrix} a & b \\ c & d \end{bmatrix}$ and $N = \begin{bmatrix} e & f \\ g & h \end{bmatrix}$. Prove that the product of the determinants of M and N equals the determinant of the matrix product MN.

(1, 3)   (3, 3)

(−2, −4)

51. a. Coordinate Geometry Find the area of the parallelogram at the left.

b. Evaluate the determinant $\begin{vmatrix} 2 & 0 \\ 1 & 3 \end{vmatrix}$. Compare the value of the determinant to the area from part (a).

c. Make a Conjecture Consider the triangle at the left to be half a parallelogram. Make a conjecture about its area and the value of $\frac{1}{2}\begin{vmatrix} -4 & 0 \\ -2 & -4 \end{vmatrix}$.

d. Open-Ended Graph a different triangle with one vertex at the origin. Find the area of the triangle by writing and evaluating a determinant.

Multiple Choice Practice

For California Standards and CAHSEE Tutorials, visit PHSchool.com. Web Code: bbq-9045

ALG2 2.0

52. Which system of inequalities is best represented by the graph?

Ⓐ $y \leq x - 2, 2x + y > -1$

Ⓑ $2y \leq x - 2, -2x - y > 1$

Ⓒ $y \leq 2x - 2, 2x - y > -1$

Ⓓ $2y \leq x - 2, -2x - y > -1$

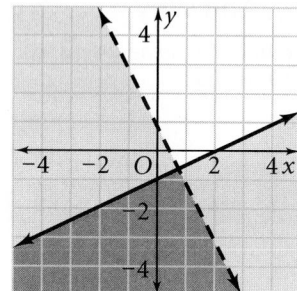

ALG2 1.0

53. Solve $|7m - 24| \leq 39$.

Ⓐ $m \leq 9$

Ⓑ $-\frac{15}{7} \leq m \leq 9$

Ⓒ $-15 \leq m \leq 63$

Ⓓ $m \leq -\frac{15}{7}$ or $m \geq 9$

Mixed Review

GO for Help

Lesson 4-4

Each matrix represents the vertices of a polygon. Write a matrix to represent the vertices of the image after each transformation.

54. $\begin{bmatrix} 0 & 0 & 5 \\ 0 & -4 & 0 \end{bmatrix}$; rotation of 90°   **55.** $\begin{bmatrix} -2 & -5 & 0 \\ 0 & 3 & 5 \end{bmatrix}$; reflection in $y = x$

56. $\begin{bmatrix} 5 & 3 & 2 \\ 7 & 1 & 3 \end{bmatrix}$; 2 units left, 1 unit down   **57.** $\begin{bmatrix} -3 & -2 & -1 \\ 4 & 1 & 5 \end{bmatrix}$; dilation of 2

Lesson 3-6

Solve each system by substitution.

58. $\begin{cases} x = 5 \\ x - y + z = 5 \\ x + y - z = -5 \end{cases}$ **59.** $\begin{cases} x - 3y = 2z \\ x + 2y - z = 0 \\ x + y + z = 10 \end{cases}$ **60.** $\begin{cases} 3x + 3y - z = 9 \\ 2y = x - z \\ x - y + 5z = 9 \end{cases}$

Lesson 2-4

61. a. Exercise Suppose you begin a training program by walking 2 miles every day. During the first week, the walk takes you 40 minutes per day. Each week after that, you reduce your time by one minute. Write a linear model for the number of minutes you take to walk 2 miles in week w.

b. Critical Thinking Can you continue to improve at the same rate? Explain.

4-6

3 × 3 Matrices, Determinants, and Inverses

 California Content Standards

LA 10.0 Students compute the determinants of 3×3 matrices.
LA 11.0 Students know that a square matrix is invertible if, and only if, its determinant is nonzero.

What You'll Learn

• To evaluate determinants of 3 × 3 matrices

• To use inverse matrices in solving matrix equations

. . . And Why

To decode messages, as in Example 5

Check Skills You'll Need

GO for Help Skills Handbook page 885

Find the product of the red elements in each matrix.

1.
$$\begin{bmatrix} 2 & 3 & 0 \\ -1 & 3 & -2 \\ 4 & -3 & -4 \end{bmatrix}$$

2.
$$\begin{bmatrix} 2 & 3 & 0 \\ -1 & 3 & -2 \\ 4 & -3 & -4 \end{bmatrix}$$

3.
$$\begin{bmatrix} 2 & 3 & 0 \\ -1 & 3 & -2 \\ 4 & -3 & -4 \end{bmatrix}$$

4.
$$\begin{bmatrix} 2 & 3 & 0 \\ -1 & 3 & -2 \\ 4 & -3 & -4 \end{bmatrix}$$

5.
$$\begin{bmatrix} 2 & 3 & 0 \\ -1 & 3 & -2 \\ 4 & -3 & -4 \end{bmatrix}$$

6.
$$\begin{bmatrix} 2 & 3 & 0 \\ -1 & 3 & -2 \\ 4 & -3 & -4 \end{bmatrix}$$

1 Evaluating Determinants of 3 × 3 Matrices

As you learned in Lesson 4-5, the determinant of a matrix helps you to find an inverse matrix and solve a matrix equation.

 Key Concepts

Definition **The Determinant of a 3 × 3 Matrix**

The determinant of a 3 × 3 matrix $\begin{bmatrix} a_1 & b_1 & c_1 \\ a_2 & b_2 & c_2 \\ a_3 & b_3 & c_3 \end{bmatrix}$ is

$$\begin{vmatrix} a_1 & b_1 & c_1 \\ a_2 & b_2 & c_2 \\ a_3 & b_3 & c_3 \end{vmatrix} = (a_1b_2c_3 + a_2b_3c_1 + a_3b_1c_2) - (a_1b_3c_2 + a_2b_1c_3 + a_3b_2c_1)$$

Visualize the pattern this way:

$$\begin{matrix} a_1 \, b_1 \, c_1 \\ a_2 \, b_2 \, c_2 \\ a_3 \, b_3 \, c_3 \end{matrix} \quad - \quad \begin{matrix} a_1 \, b_1 \, c_1 \\ a_2 \, b_2 \, c_2 \\ a_3 \, b_3 \, c_3 \end{matrix}$$

 1 EXAMPLE **Evaluating the Determinant of a 3 × 3 Matrix**

Evaluate the determinant of $F = \begin{bmatrix} -1 & 3 & 5 \\ 2 & -4 & 6 \\ 0 & 1 & -1 \end{bmatrix}$.

$$\begin{vmatrix} -1 & 3 & 5 \\ 2 & -4 & 6 \\ 0 & 1 & -1 \end{vmatrix} = [-1(-4)(-1) + 2(1)(5) + 0(3)(6)]$$ **Use the definition.**
$$\qquad\qquad\quad - [-1(1)(6) + 2(3)(-1) + 0(-4)(5)]$$

$$= [-4 + 10 + 0] - [-6 + (-6) + 0]$$ **Multiply.**

$$= 6 - (-12) = 18$$ **Simplify.**

The determinant of F is 18.

a. $\begin{vmatrix} -3 & 4 & 0 \\ 2 & -5 & 1 \\ 0 & 2 & 3 \end{vmatrix}$
b. $\begin{vmatrix} 1 & -1 & 2 \\ 0 & 4 & 2 \\ 3 & -6 & 10 \end{vmatrix}$
c. $\begin{vmatrix} 2 & 0 & -1 \\ 0 & 0 & 0 \\ 1 & -5 & 3 \end{vmatrix}$

You can use a graphing calculator to evaluate the determinant of a 3×3 matrix.

② EXAMPLE   Using a Graphing Calculator

Enter matrix A into your graphing calculator. Use the matrix submenus to evaluate the determinant of A.

$A = \begin{bmatrix} 1 & 7 & 2 \\ -1 & 1 & -2 \\ 1 & 1 & 1 \end{bmatrix}$

```
NAMES MATH EDIT
1:det(
2: T
3:dim(
4:Fill(
5:identity(
6:randM(
7↓augment(
```

```
NAMES MATH EDIT
1: [A]    3×3
2: [B]
3: [C]
4: [D]
5: [E]
```

```
det  ([A]
              -8
■
```

✓ **CA Standards Check** ② Use a graphing calculator to evaluate the determinant of $\begin{bmatrix} 13 & 21 & 11 \\ -2 & 4 & -1 \\ 17 & -2 & 0 \end{bmatrix}$.

---

2 | Using Inverse 3 × 3 Matrices

You can test whether two 3×3 matrices are inverses by finding their product.

③ EXAMPLE   Verifying Inverses

Vocabulary Tip

If A and B are <u>inverse</u> <u>matrices</u>, then $AB = BA = I$. If A has no inverse, then A is <u>singular</u> and det $A = 0$.

A square matrix is <u>invertible</u> (has an inverse) if and only if its determinant is nonzero.

Determine whether the matrices are multiplicative inverses of each other.

a. $A = \begin{bmatrix} 1 & 5 & -1 \\ 1 & 0 & -1 \\ 1 & 0 & 0 \end{bmatrix}$, $B = \begin{bmatrix} 0 & 0 & 1 \\ 0.2 & -0.2 & 0 \\ 0 & -1 & 1 \end{bmatrix}$

$\begin{bmatrix} 1 & 5 & -1 \\ 1 & 0 & -1 \\ 1 & 0 & 0 \end{bmatrix}\begin{bmatrix} 0 & 0 & 1 \\ 0.2 & -0.2 & 0 \\ 0 & -1 & 1 \end{bmatrix} = \begin{bmatrix} 1 & 0 & 0 \\ 0 & 1 & 0 \\ 0 & 0 & 1 \end{bmatrix}$

Since $AB = I$, A and B are multiplicative inverses.

b. $C = \begin{bmatrix} 3 & 4 & 1 \\ -2 & 0 & 2 \\ 1 & 5 & 3 \end{bmatrix}$, $D = \begin{bmatrix} 0 & 1 & 0 \\ 1 & 0 & 1 \\ 0 & 1 & 0 \end{bmatrix}$

$\begin{bmatrix} 3 & 4 & 1 \\ -2 & 0 & 2 \\ 1 & 5 & 3 \end{bmatrix}\begin{bmatrix} 0 & 1 & 0 \\ 1 & 0 & 1 \\ 0 & 1 & 0 \end{bmatrix} = \begin{bmatrix} 4 & 4 & 4 \\ 0 & 0 & 0 \\ 5 & 4 & 5 \end{bmatrix}$

Since $CD \neq I$, C and D are not multiplicative inverses.

✓ **CA Standards Check** ③ a. Verify that A and B are inverses by showing that $BA = I$.
   b. Verify that C and D are not inverses by showing that $DC \neq I$.

You can use 3 × 3 matrices to solve matrix equations.

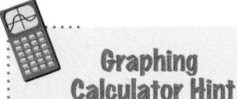
4 EXAMPLE **Solving a Matrix Equation**

Solve the matrix equation $\begin{bmatrix} 0 & 0 & 2 \\ 1 & 3 & -2 \\ 1 & -2 & 1 \end{bmatrix} X = \begin{bmatrix} 6 \\ -11 \\ 8 \end{bmatrix}$.

Let $A = \begin{bmatrix} 0 & 0 & 2 \\ 1 & 3 & -2 \\ 1 & -2 & 1 \end{bmatrix}$. Find A^{-1}.

[A]⁻¹
[[.1   .4   .6   ]
 [.3   .2   -.2   ]
 [.5   0   0   ]]

$X = \begin{bmatrix} 0.1 & 0.4 & 0.6 \\ 0.3 & 0.2 & -0.2 \\ 0.5 & 0 & 0 \end{bmatrix} \begin{bmatrix} 6 \\ -11 \\ 8 \end{bmatrix}$ ← **Use the equation**
X = A⁻¹C.
Multiply. →

[A]⁻¹[C]
[[1]
 [-2]
 [3]]

$X = \begin{bmatrix} 1 \\ -2 \\ 3 \end{bmatrix}$

✓ CA Standards Check 4 a. Verify that A and A^{-1} are inverses.

b. Solve the matrix equation $\begin{bmatrix} 0 & 0 & 2 \\ 1 & 3 & -2 \\ 1 & -2 & 1 \end{bmatrix} X = \begin{bmatrix} 0 \\ -6 \\ 19 \end{bmatrix}$.

You can use 3 × 3 matrices to encode and decode messages.

5 EXAMPLE **Real-World** **Connection**

A	26	N	13
B	25	O	12
C	24	P	11
D	23	Q	10
E	22	R	9
F	21	S	8
G	20	T	7
H	19	U	6
I	18	V	5
J	17	W	4
K	16	X	3
L	15	Y	2
M	14	Z	1

Cryptography Use the alphabet table and the encoding matrix E at the left.

a. Find the decoding matrix E^{-1}.

[E]⁻¹
[[1   -2   2   ]
 [0   4   -2   ]
 [1   -2   0   ]]

Use a graphing calculator.

b. Use the decoding matrix to decode $\begin{bmatrix} 22.5 & 26 & 15.5 \\ 0.25 & 9 & 7.75 \\ -4 & 9 & 3.5 \end{bmatrix}$.

$E = \begin{bmatrix} 0.5 & 0.5 & 0.5 \\ 0.25 & 0.25 & -0.25 \\ 0.5 & 0 & -0.5 \end{bmatrix}$

$\begin{bmatrix} 1 & -2 & 2 \\ 0 & 4 & -2 \\ 1 & -2 & 0 \end{bmatrix} \begin{bmatrix} 22.5 & 26 & 15.5 \\ 0.25 & 9 & 7.75 \\ -4 & 9 & 3.5 \end{bmatrix} = \begin{bmatrix} 14 & 26 & 7 \\ 9 & 18 & 24 \\ 22 & 8 & 0 \end{bmatrix}$ **Use the decoding matrix from part (a). Multiply.**

In the result, 0 is a space-holder.
The numbers 14 26 7 9 18 24 22 8 correspond to the letters MATRICES.

✓ CA Standards Check 5 Literature Use the information from Example 5. Decode the matrix at the right, which gives the title of a Pablo Neruda poem. $\begin{bmatrix} 21 & 10.5 \\ 6 & 4.25 \\ 1 & 5 \end{bmatrix}$

A Practice by Example

Example 1
(page 210)

Evaluate the determinant of each matrix.

1. $\begin{bmatrix} 1 & 2 & 5 \\ 3 & 1 & 0 \\ 1 & 2 & 1 \end{bmatrix}$
2. $\begin{bmatrix} 1 & 4 & 0 \\ 2 & 3 & 5 \\ 0 & 1 & 0 \end{bmatrix}$
3. $\begin{bmatrix} -2 & 4 & 1 \\ 3 & 0 & -1 \\ 1 & 2 & 1 \end{bmatrix}$
4. $\begin{bmatrix} 2 & 3 & 0 \\ 1 & 2 & 5 \\ 7 & 0 & 1 \end{bmatrix}$

Example 2
(page 211)

Use a graphing calculator to evaluate the determinant of each 3 × 3 matrix.

5. $\begin{bmatrix} 1 & 0 & 0 \\ 0 & 1 & 0 \\ 0 & 0 & 1 \end{bmatrix}$
6. $\begin{bmatrix} 0 & -2 & -3 \\ 1 & 2 & 4 \\ -2 & 0 & 1 \end{bmatrix}$
7. $\begin{bmatrix} 12.2 & 13.3 & 9 \\ 1 & -4 & -17 \\ 21.4 & -15 & 0 \end{bmatrix}$

Example 3
(page 211)

Determine whether the matrices are multiplicative inverses.

8. $\begin{bmatrix} 1 & 2 & -1 \\ -1.5 & -3 & 1.75 \\ 0 & -1 & 0.5 \end{bmatrix}, \begin{bmatrix} 1 & 0 & 2 \\ 3 & 2 & -1 \\ 6 & 4 & 0 \end{bmatrix}$
9. $\begin{bmatrix} 2 & 2 & 2 \\ -2 & 2 & -2 \\ -2 & -2 & -2 \end{bmatrix}, \begin{bmatrix} 2 & 2 & 2 \\ -2 & 2 & -2 \\ -2 & -2 & -2 \end{bmatrix}$

Example 4
(page 212)

Solve each matrix equation.

10. $\begin{bmatrix} 5 & 1 & -4 \\ 2 & -3 & -5 \\ 7 & 2 & -6 \end{bmatrix} X = \begin{bmatrix} 5 \\ 2 \\ 5 \end{bmatrix}$
11. $\begin{bmatrix} 6 & 10 & -13 \\ 4 & -2 & 7 \\ 0 & 9 & -8 \end{bmatrix} X = \begin{bmatrix} 84 \\ 18 \\ 56 \end{bmatrix}$

Example 5
(page 212)

Literature Use the information from Example 5. Decode each title.

12. Emily Dickinson, $\begin{bmatrix} 23.5 & 12.5 \\ 4.75 & -0.25 \\ 6 & -3.5 \end{bmatrix}$
13. E. E. Cummings, $\begin{bmatrix} 18 & 14 & 17.5 \\ 0 & 3.5 & 8.75 \\ -3.5 & 2.5 & 4.5 \end{bmatrix}$

B Apply Your Skills

14. **Multiple Choice** If matrix A has an inverse, what must be true?

   I. $AA^{-1} = I$ **II.** $A^{-1}A = I$ **III.** $A^{-1}I = A^{-1}$

   A. I only   B. II only   C. I and II only   D. I, II, and III

15. **Cryptography** Two members of the Hopewell High School math club share messages in code. They use the alphabet table from Example 5.

   a. One of the students has lost her encoding matrix. Luckily, she remembers that the decoding matrix is

   $E^{-1} = \begin{bmatrix} 1 & -1 & 0 \\ 0 & 1 & -1 \\ 0 & 0 & 1 \end{bmatrix}$. Compute E to find the encoding matrix.

   b. Use your answer to part (a) to encode the message MATH IS COOL.

   c. Open-Ended Use the encoding matrix from part (a) to encode a short sentence. Use the decoding matrix to check your work.

Evaluate the determinant of each matrix.

16. $\begin{bmatrix} 0 & 2 & -3 \\ 1 & 2 & 4 \\ -2 & 0 & 1 \end{bmatrix}$
17. $\begin{bmatrix} 5 & 1 & 0 \\ 0 & 2 & -1 \\ -2 & -3 & 1 \end{bmatrix}$
18. $\begin{bmatrix} 4 & 6 & -1 \\ 2 & 3 & 2 \\ 1 & -1 & 1 \end{bmatrix}$
19. $\begin{bmatrix} -3 & 2 & -1 \\ 2 & 5 & 2 \\ 1 & -2 & 0 \end{bmatrix}$

Homework Video Tutor

Visit: PHSchool.com
Web Code: bbe-0406

Find the inverse of each matrix, if it exists.

20. $\begin{bmatrix} -2 & 1 & -1 \\ 2 & 0 & 4 \\ 0 & 2 & 5 \end{bmatrix}$ **21.** $\begin{bmatrix} 2 & 0 & -1 \\ -1 & -1 & 1 \\ 3 & 2 & 0 \end{bmatrix}$ **22.** $\begin{bmatrix} 0 & 0 & 2 \\ 1 & 4 & -2 \\ 3 & -2 & 1 \end{bmatrix}$ **23.** $\begin{bmatrix} 1 & 2 & 6 \\ 1 & -1 & 0 \\ 1 & 0 & 2 \end{bmatrix}$

24. Writing Evaluate the determinant of each matrix. Describe any patterns.

a. $\begin{bmatrix} 1 & 2 & 3 \\ 1 & 2 & 3 \\ 1 & 2 & 3 \end{bmatrix}$ **b.** $\begin{bmatrix} -1 & -2 & -3 \\ -3 & -2 & -1 \\ -1 & -2 & -3 \end{bmatrix}$ **c.** $\begin{bmatrix} 1 & 2 & 3 \\ 2 & 3 & 1 \\ 1 & 2 & 3 \end{bmatrix}$ **d.** $\begin{bmatrix} -1 & 2 & -3 \\ 2 & -3 & -1 \\ -1 & 2 & -3 \end{bmatrix}$

C Challenge

Literature Use the table and decoding matrix from Example 5. Decode each title.

25. Maya Angelou, $\begin{bmatrix} 26.5 & 28 & 15.5 & 16.5 & 13.5 \\ 0.25 & 2 & -3.25 & 8.25 & 6.75 \\ -6 & -6 & -6.5 & 6.5 & 9 \end{bmatrix}$

26. Oliver Wendell Holmes, $\begin{bmatrix} 19 & 24 & 24.5 & 18.5 & 26.5 & 13.5 & 19.5 & 20 \\ 6.5 & 8.5 & 3.25 & 1.75 & 10.25 & 2.75 & 9.75 & 10 \\ 0.5 & 6 & 2 & -7.5 & 9 & 5.5 & 13 & 7 \end{bmatrix}$

Solve each matrix equation.

27. $\begin{bmatrix} 7 & -5 & 3 \\ 0 & 1 & 3 \\ 8 & 4 & -2 \end{bmatrix} X + \begin{bmatrix} 5 \\ -9 \\ 0 \end{bmatrix} = \begin{bmatrix} 54 \\ -12 \\ 96 \end{bmatrix}$

28. $\left(\begin{bmatrix} -1 & 0 & 2 \\ -6 & -5 & 0 \\ 1 & 4 & 1 \end{bmatrix} - \begin{bmatrix} -4 & 0 & 2 \\ 0 & 3 & 6 \\ 0 & 5 & 0 \end{bmatrix} \right) X = \begin{bmatrix} -21 & 10 & 26 \\ -54 & 1 & -15 \\ 1 & 4 & -24 \end{bmatrix}$

Multiple Choice Practice

For California Standards and CAHSEE Tutorials, visit PHSchool.com. Web Code: bbq-9045

ALG2 1.0

29. The table shows property tax rates for a certain town over a five-year period. Which inequality best describes r, the tax rate for this period?

Ⓐ $|r - 1.2| \le 3.9$

Ⓑ $2.7 \le |r + 3.9|$

Ⓒ $|r - 0.6| \le 3.3$

Ⓓ $|r - 3.3| \le 0.6$

Property Tax Rate	
Year	Tax Rate
1	2.7%
2	3.2%
3	3.9%
4	3.2%
5	3.7%

CAHSEE Alg1 5.0

30. Mary made punch composed of 28% cranberry juice. The rest of the punch was apple juice. If Mary drank x ounces of the punch, which equation best represents y, the number of ounces of apple juice she drank?

Ⓐ $y = \frac{7}{18}x$ Ⓑ $y = \frac{18}{7}x$ Ⓒ $y = \frac{7}{25}x$ Ⓓ $y = \frac{18}{25}x$

ALG2 2.0

31. Solve the system $\begin{cases} y = 3x - 2 \\ 2x - y = -1 \end{cases}$.

Ⓐ $(1, 1)$ Ⓑ $(-1, 5)$ Ⓒ $(7, 3)$ Ⓓ $(3, 7)$

GO for Help

Lesson 4-5

Determine whether each matrix has an inverse. If an inverse matrix exists, find it.

32. $\begin{bmatrix} -9 & 3 \\ 4 & 2.5 \end{bmatrix}$ **33.** $\begin{bmatrix} 2 & 3 \\ 8 & 12 \end{bmatrix}$ **34.** $\begin{bmatrix} -3 & 4 \\ 9 & 10 \end{bmatrix}$ **35.** $\begin{bmatrix} 0 & -1 \\ -1 & 0 \end{bmatrix}$

Lesson 3-1

Solve each system of equations.

36. $\begin{cases} 2x + 2y = 10 \\ 3x - y = 4 \end{cases}$

37. $\begin{cases} -x + y + z = 5 \\ 2x + y - z = 2 \\ 3x + 2y + 4z = 0 \end{cases}$

✓ Checkpoint Quiz 2   Lessons 4-4 through 4-6

Use $\triangle ABC$ at the right. Find the coordinates of the image under each transformation.

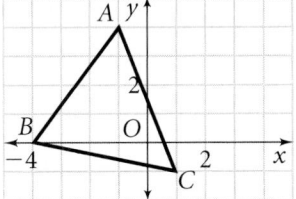

1. a dilation of 2

2. a translation 3 units left and 3 units up

3. a rotation of 270°

4. a reflection in $y = -x$

Solve each matrix equation.

5. $\begin{bmatrix} 0 & 3 \\ 5 & 0 \end{bmatrix} X = \begin{bmatrix} -12 & -15 \\ 10 & 15 \end{bmatrix}$ **6.** $\begin{bmatrix} -1 & 2 & 3 \\ 0 & 3 & 2 \\ 3 & -2 & 0 \end{bmatrix} X = \begin{bmatrix} 17 \\ 18 \\ 11 \end{bmatrix}$ **7.** $\begin{bmatrix} 4 & 5 \\ -1 & 5 \end{bmatrix} X = \begin{bmatrix} 32 \\ 42 \end{bmatrix}$

Evaluate the determinant of each matrix.

8. $\begin{bmatrix} -2 & 3 \\ 0 & 5 \end{bmatrix}$ **9.** $\begin{bmatrix} 0 & 5 & 4 \\ -1 & -1 & 3 \\ 2 & 5 & 0 \end{bmatrix}$ **10.** $\begin{bmatrix} -3 & 2 & 0 \\ 4 & 17 & 10 \\ 1 & -5 & -1 \end{bmatrix}$

········ A P●int in Time

1500   1600   1700   1800   1900   2000

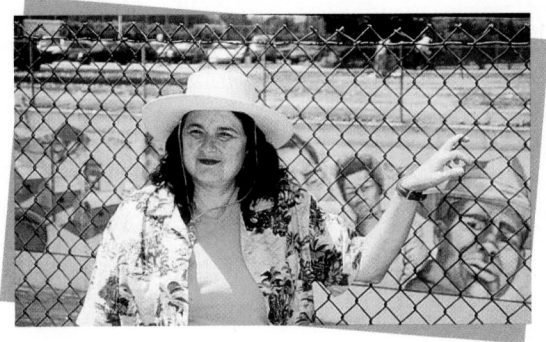

An artist who paints murals creates a sketch and then uses a dilation of the sketch for the actual mural. Judith Francisca Baca is a muralist who serves as the artistic director of the Great Wall of Los Angeles. The 13-ft-by-2400-ft mural, which depicts California's multicultural history, has involved over 400 youths, 100 scholars, and 50 assisting artists.

Go Online
PHSchool.com
For: Information about murals
Web Code: bbe-2032

A finite graph is a set of points, called vertices, connected by curves, or paths.

You can use a matrix to describe a finite graph. A 1 indicates a path between two vertices or one vertex and itself. A 0 indicates that no path exists between two vertices or from one vertex to itself.

1 EXAMPLE

Write a matrix A to represent the finite graph. Explain the significance of element a_{41}.

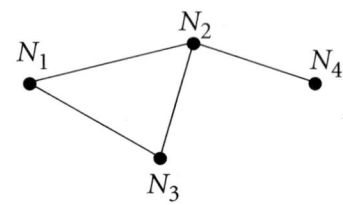

$$A = \begin{array}{c} \\ N_1 \\ N_2 \\ N_3 \\ N_4 \end{array} \begin{array}{cccc} N_1 & N_2 & N_3 & N_4 \\ \begin{bmatrix} 0 & 1 & 1 & 0 \\ 1 & 0 & 1 & 1 \\ 1 & 1 & 0 & 0 \\ 0 & 1 & 0 & 0 \end{bmatrix} \end{array}$$ ⟵ **There is a path from N_2 to N_4.**

Element a_{41} is 0. It indicates that there is no path between N_4 and N_1.

Directed graphs are finite graphs that indicate the direction of a path. The directed graph at the right below represents the information in the map.

You can use a matrix to represent the information in a directed graph.

2 EXAMPLE

Write a matrix B to represent the information from the directed graph. Compare elements b_{12} and b_{21}.

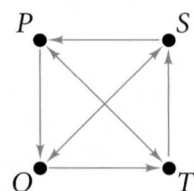

$$B = \begin{array}{c} \textbf{From} \rightarrow \\ \\ \end{array} \begin{array}{c} P \\ Q \\ S \\ T \end{array} \begin{array}{cccc} \textbf{To} \rightarrow P & Q & S & T \\ \begin{bmatrix} 0 & 1 & 0 & 1 \\ 0 & 0 & 1 & 1 \\ 1 & 1 & 0 & 0 \\ 1 & 0 & 1 & 0 \end{bmatrix} \end{array}$$

Element b_{12} is 1, and element b_{21} is 0. The path between P and Q is one way from P to Q.

You can use information in a matrix to draw a directed graph.

3 EXAMPLE

Draw a directed graph to represent the information in the matrix.

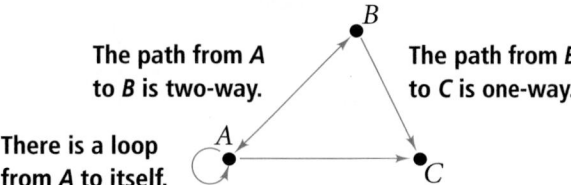

$$\begin{array}{c} \textbf{To} \rightarrow A \ B \ C \\ \begin{array}{c} A \\ \textbf{From} \rightarrow B \\ C \end{array} \left[\begin{array}{ccc} 1 & 1 & 1 \\ 1 & 0 & 1 \\ 0 & 0 & 0 \end{array} \right] \end{array}$$

The path from A to B is two-way.

The path from B to C is one-way.

There is a loop from A to itself.

EXERCISES

Write a matrix to represent each finite or directed graph.

1.

2.

3.

4.

5.

6.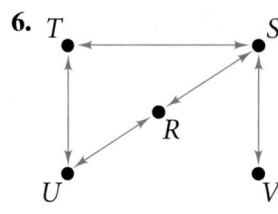

Draw a directed graph to represent the information in each matrix.

7.
$$\begin{array}{c} \ \ \ J \ K \ L \ M \\ \begin{array}{c} J \\ K \\ L \\ M \end{array} \left[\begin{array}{cccc} 0 & 0 & 0 & 1 \\ 0 & 0 & 1 & 1 \\ 0 & 1 & 0 & 1 \\ 1 & 1 & 1 & 0 \end{array} \right] \end{array}$$

8.
$$\begin{array}{c} \ \ \ A \ B \ C \ D \\ \begin{array}{c} A \\ B \\ C \\ D \end{array} \left[\begin{array}{cccc} 0 & 0 & 1 & 1 \\ 1 & 1 & 0 & 0 \\ 0 & 1 & 0 & 1 \\ 1 & 0 & 1 & 0 \end{array} \right] \end{array}$$

9.
$$\begin{array}{c} \ \ \ N_1 \ N_2 \ N_3 \ N_4 \\ \begin{array}{c} N_1 \\ N_2 \\ N_3 \\ N_4 \end{array} \left[\begin{array}{cccc} 1 & 1 & 1 & 1 \\ 0 & 0 & 1 & 1 \\ 1 & 0 & 0 & 0 \\ 0 & 0 & 1 & 0 \end{array} \right] \end{array}$$

10. Travel Alice and Becky live on Parkway East, at the intersections of Owens Bridge and Bay Bridge, respectively. Carl and David live on Parkway West, at the intersections of Bay Bridge and Owens Bridge, respectively. Parkway East is a one-way street running east and Alice lives west of Becky. Parkway West is one way running west. Both bridges are two way.

    a. Draw a directed graph indicating road travel between the houses.

    b. Write a matrix T to represent the information in the directed graph.

    c. Writing Calculate T^2. What does the new matrix model? Explain.

Inverse Matrices and Systems

 California Content Standards

ALG2 2.0 Students solve systems of linear equations (in two or three variables) with matrices. *Introduce, Develop*
LA 9.0 Students demonstrate an understanding of the notion of the inverse to a square matrix and apply that concept to solve systems of linear equations.

What You'll Learn

• To solve systems of equations using inverse matrices

. . . And Why

To calculate business costs, as in Example 4

✓ Check Skills You'll Need

Solve each system.

1. $\begin{cases} 5x + y = 14 \\ 4x + 3y = 20 \end{cases}$

2. $\begin{cases} x - y - z = -9 \\ 3x + y + 2z = 12 \\ x = y - 2z \end{cases}$

3. $\begin{cases} -x + 2y + z = 0 \\ y = -2x + 3 \\ z = 3x \end{cases}$

GO for Help Lesson 3-6

 New Vocabulary • coefficient matrix • variable matrix • constant matrix

---

1 Solving Systems of Equations Using Inverse Matrices

You can represent a system of equations with a matrix equation.

System of equations	Matrix equation
$\begin{cases} x + 2y = 5 \\ 3x + 5y = 14 \end{cases}$	$\begin{bmatrix} 1 & 2 \\ 3 & 5 \end{bmatrix}\begin{bmatrix} x \\ y \end{bmatrix} = \begin{bmatrix} 5 \\ 14 \end{bmatrix}$

Each matrix in an equation of the form $AX = B$ has a name.

GO for Help

To review the definitions of *coefficient* and *variable*, go to Lesson 1-2.

Coefficient matrix A	Variable matrix X	Constant matrix B
$\begin{bmatrix} 1 & 2 \\ 3 & 5 \end{bmatrix}$	$\begin{bmatrix} x \\ y \end{bmatrix}$	$\begin{bmatrix} 5 \\ 14 \end{bmatrix}$

1 EXAMPLE Writing a System as a Matrix Equation

Write the system $\begin{cases} -b + 2c = 4 \\ a + b - c = 0 \\ 2a + 3c = 11 \end{cases}$ as a matrix equation. Then identify the coefficient matrix, the variable matrix, and the constant matrix.

Matrix equation: $\begin{bmatrix} 0 & -1 & 2 \\ 1 & 1 & -1 \\ 2 & 0 & 3 \end{bmatrix}\begin{bmatrix} a \\ b \\ c \end{bmatrix} = \begin{bmatrix} 4 \\ 0 \\ 11 \end{bmatrix}$

Coefficient matrix	Variable matrix	Constant matrix
$\begin{bmatrix} 0 & -1 & 2 \\ 1 & 1 & -1 \\ 2 & 0 & 3 \end{bmatrix}$	$\begin{bmatrix} a \\ b \\ c \end{bmatrix}$	$\begin{bmatrix} 4 \\ 0 \\ 11 \end{bmatrix}$

✓ CA Standards Check **1** Write each system as a matrix equation. Identify the coefficient matrix, the variable matrix, and the constant matrix.

a. $\begin{cases} 3x + 2y = 16 \\ y = 5 \end{cases}$

b. $\begin{cases} x - y + z = 0 \\ x - 2y - z = 5 \\ 2x - y + 2z = 8 \end{cases}$

Sometimes you can find the inverse of the coefficient matrix. Then you can use it to solve systems of equations quickly.

2 EXAMPLE **Solving a System of Two Equations**

GO for Help

To review how to find the inverse of a 2 × 2 matrix, see page 205.

Solve the system $\begin{cases} 2x + 3y = 11 \\ x + 2y = 6 \end{cases}$.

$\begin{bmatrix} 2 & 3 \\ 1 & 2 \end{bmatrix} \begin{bmatrix} x \\ y \end{bmatrix} = \begin{bmatrix} 11 \\ 6 \end{bmatrix}$ **Write the system as a matrix equation.**

$A^{-1} = \begin{bmatrix} 2 & -3 \\ -1 & 2 \end{bmatrix}$ **Find A^{-1}.**

$\begin{bmatrix} x \\ y \end{bmatrix} = A^{-1}B = \begin{bmatrix} 2 & -3 \\ -1 & 2 \end{bmatrix} \begin{bmatrix} 11 \\ 6 \end{bmatrix} = \begin{bmatrix} 4 \\ 1 \end{bmatrix}$ **Solve for the variable matrix.**

The solution of the system is $(4, 1)$.

Check	$2x + 3y = 11$	$x + 2y = 6$	**Use the original equations.**
	$2(4) + 3(1) \stackrel{?}{=} 11$	$4 + 2(1) \stackrel{?}{=} 6$	**Substitute.**
	$8 + 3 = 11 ✓$	$4 + 2 = 6 ✓$	**Simplify.**

✓ CA Standards Check **2** Solve each system. Check your answers.

a. $\begin{cases} 5a + 3b = 7 \\ 3a + 2b = 5 \end{cases}$

b. $\begin{cases} x + 3y = 22 \\ 3x + 2y = 10 \end{cases}$

You can use a graphing calculator to solve a system of three equations.

3 EXAMPLE **Solving a System of Three Equations**

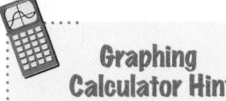

Graphing Calculator Hint

To select A^{-1}, use the MATRIX feature and the [x⁻¹] key.

Solve the system $\begin{cases} 2x + y + 3z = 1 \\ 5x + y - 2z = 8 \\ x - y - 9z = 5 \end{cases}$.

Step 1 Write the system as a matrix equation.

$\begin{bmatrix} 2 & 1 & 3 \\ 5 & 1 & -2 \\ 1 & -1 & -9 \end{bmatrix} \begin{bmatrix} x \\ y \\ z \end{bmatrix} = \begin{bmatrix} 1 \\ 8 \\ 5 \end{bmatrix}$

Step 2 Enter the coefficient matrix as matrix A and the constant matrix as matrix B.

Step 3

The solution is $(4, -10, 1)$.

✓ CA Standards Check **3 a.** Check the solution from Example 3 in each of the original equations.

b. Solve the system $\begin{cases} x + y + z = 2 \\ 2x + y = 5 \\ x + 3y - 3z = 14 \end{cases}$. Check your solution.

There are many business applications for matrices of systems of equations.

4 EXAMPLE **Real-World** **Connection**

Business A bead store has a sale on certain beads. Find the price of each size of bead.

Relate
2 large beads and 3 small beads cost $3.25.
3 large beads and 4 small beads cost $4.75.

Define Let x = the price of one large bead.

Let y = the price of one small bead.

Write $\begin{bmatrix} 2 & 3 \\ 3 & 4 \end{bmatrix} \begin{bmatrix} x \\ y \end{bmatrix} = \begin{bmatrix} 3.25 \\ 4.75 \end{bmatrix}$ **Write the system as a matrix equation.**

```
[A]⁻¹[B]
    [[1.25]
     [.25]]
```

Use a graphing calculator. Store the coefficient matrix as matrix A and the constant matrix as matrix B.

● The price of a large bead is $1.25. The price of a small bead is $.25.

✓ CA Standards Check **4** Suppose the sale is over, and the price of each package increases. The price of a package of two large beads and three small beads increases to $5.55. The price of a package of three large beads and four small beads increases to $8.05. Find the new price of each type of bead.

When the coefficient matrix of a system has an inverse, the system has a unique solution. Similarly, when the coefficient matrix does *not* have an inverse, the system does *not* have a unique solution. In that case, the system either has no solution or has an infinite number of solutions.

5 EXAMPLE **Unique Solutions**

Write the coefficient matrix for each system. Use it to determine whether the system has a unique solution.

Problem Solving Hint

$\det \begin{bmatrix} a & b \\ c & d \end{bmatrix} = ad - bc$

a. $\begin{cases} x + y = 3 \\ x - y = 7 \end{cases}$

$A = \begin{bmatrix} 1 & 1 \\ 1 & -1 \end{bmatrix}$; $\det A = \begin{vmatrix} 1 & 1 \\ 1 & -1 \end{vmatrix} = 1(-1) - 1(1) = -2$

Since $\det A \neq 0$, the matrix has an inverse, so the system has a unique solution.

b. $\begin{cases} x + 2y = 5 \\ 2x + 4y = 8 \end{cases}$

$A = \begin{bmatrix} 1 & 2 \\ 2 & 4 \end{bmatrix}$; $\det A = \begin{vmatrix} 1 & 2 \\ 2 & 4 \end{vmatrix} = 1(4) - 2(2) = 0$

Since $\det A = 0$, the matrix does not have an inverse and the system does *not* have a unique solution.

5 a. Determine whether the system $\begin{cases} 3x + 5y = 1 \\ 2x - y = -8 \end{cases}$ has a unique solution.

b. You can use an inverse matrix to solve a system of equations. What happens when you try to do this with a graphing calculator and the system does not have a unique solution?

EXERCISES

A Practice by Example

Example 1
(page 218)

 GO for Help

Write each system as a matrix equation. Identify the coefficient matrix, the variable matrix, and the constant matrix.

1. $\begin{cases} x + y = 5 \\ x - 2y = -4 \end{cases}$

2. $\begin{cases} y = 3x - 7 \\ x = 2 \end{cases}$

3. $\begin{cases} 3a + 5b = 0 \\ a + b = 2 \end{cases}$

4. $\begin{cases} x + 3y - z = 2 \\ x + 2z = 8 \\ 2y - z = 1 \end{cases}$

5. $\begin{cases} r - s + t = 150 \\ 2r + t = 425 \\ s + 3t = 0 \end{cases}$

6. $\begin{cases} x + 2y = 11 \\ 2x + 3y = 18 \end{cases}$

Examples 2 and 3
(page 219)

Solve each system of equations. Check your answers.

7. $\begin{cases} x + 3y = 5 \\ x + 4y = 6 \end{cases}$

8. $\begin{cases} p - 3q = -1 \\ -5p + 16q = 5 \end{cases}$

9. $\begin{cases} 300x - y = 130 \\ 200x + y = 120 \end{cases}$

10. $\begin{cases} x + 5y = -4 \\ x + 6y = -5 \end{cases}$

11. $\begin{cases} 2x + 3y = 12 \\ x + 2y = 7 \end{cases}$

12. $\begin{cases} 2x + 3y = 5 \\ x + 2y = 6 \end{cases}$

13. $\begin{cases} x + y + z = 4 \\ 4x + 5y = 3 \\ y - 3z = -10 \end{cases}$

14. $\begin{cases} 9y + 2z = 18 \\ 3x + 2y + z = 5 \\ x - y = -1 \end{cases}$

15. $\begin{cases} 9y + 2z = 14 \\ 3x + 2y + z = 5 \\ x - y = -1 \end{cases}$

Example 4
(page 220)

16. Shopping Suppose you want to fill nine 1-lb tins with a holiday snack mix. You plan to buy almonds for $2.45/lb, peanuts for $1.85/lb, and raisins for $.80/lb. You have $15 and want the mix to contain twice as much of the nuts as of the raisins by weight. How much of each ingredient should you buy?

 a. Writing Explain how each equation in the system at the right relates to the problem. What does each variable represent?

b. Solve the system.

$\begin{cases} x + y + z = 9 \\ 2.45x + 1.85y + 0.8z = 15 \\ x + y = 2z \end{cases}$

Example 5
(page 220)

Determine whether each system has a unique solution.

17. $\begin{cases} 20x + 5y = 240 \\ y = 20x \end{cases}$

18. $\begin{cases} 20x + 5y = 145 \\ 30x - 5y = 125 \end{cases}$

19. $\begin{cases} y = 2000 - 65x \\ y = 500 + 55x \end{cases}$

20. $\begin{cases} y = \frac{2}{3}x - 3 \\ y = -x + 7 \end{cases}$

21. $\begin{cases} 3x + 2y = 10 \\ 6x + 4y = 16 \end{cases}$

22. $\begin{cases} x + 2y + z = 4 \\ y = x - 3 \\ z = 2x \end{cases}$

B Apply Your Skills

Solve each matrix equation. If the coefficient matrix has no inverse, write *no unique solution.*

23. $\begin{bmatrix} 1 & 1 \\ 1 & 2 \end{bmatrix}\begin{bmatrix} x \\ y \end{bmatrix} = \begin{bmatrix} 8 \\ 10 \end{bmatrix}$

24. $\begin{bmatrix} 2 & -3 \\ -4 & 6 \end{bmatrix}\begin{bmatrix} a \\ b \end{bmatrix} = \begin{bmatrix} 1 \\ -2 \end{bmatrix}$

25. $\begin{bmatrix} 2 & 1 \\ 4 & 3 \end{bmatrix}\begin{bmatrix} x \\ y \end{bmatrix} = \begin{bmatrix} 10 \\ -2 \end{bmatrix}$

Visit: PHSchool.com
Web Code: bbe-0407

Solve each system.

26. $\begin{cases} -3x + 4y = 2 \\ x - y = -1 \end{cases}$

27. $\begin{cases} x + 2y = 10 \\ 3x + 5y = 26 \end{cases}$

28. $\begin{cases} x - 3y = -1 \\ -6x + 19y = 6 \end{cases}$

29. $\begin{cases} x = 5 - y \\ 3y = z \\ x + z = 7 \end{cases}$

30. $\begin{cases} -x = -4 - z \\ 2y = z - 1 \\ x = 6 - y - z \end{cases}$

31. $\begin{cases} -b + 2c = 4 \\ a + b - c = -10 \\ 2a + 3c = 1 \end{cases}$

32. $\begin{cases} x + y + z = 4 \\ 4x + 5y = 4 \\ y - 3z = -9 \end{cases}$

33. $\begin{cases} x + y + z = 4 \\ 4x + 5y = 3 \\ y - 3z = -10 \end{cases}$

34. $\begin{cases} -2w + x + y = 0 \\ -w + 2x - y + z = 1 \\ -2w + 3x + 3y + 2z = 6 \\ w + x + 2y + z = 5 \end{cases}$

35. $\begin{cases} -2w + x + y = -2 \\ -w + 2x - y + z = -4 \\ -2w + 3x + 3y + 2z = 2 \\ w + x + 2y + z = 6 \end{cases}$

For a guide to solving
Exercise 36, see p. 224.

36. Coordinate Geometry The coordinates (x, y) of a point in a plane are the solution of the system $\begin{cases} 2x + 3y = 13 \\ 5x + 7y = 31 \end{cases}$. Find the coordinates of the point.

37. Geometry A rectangle is twice as long as it is wide. The perimeter is 840 ft. Find the dimensions of the rectangle.

 Challenge

Open-Ended Complete each system for the given number of solutions.

38. infinitely many

$\begin{cases} x + y = 7 \\ 2x + 2y = \blacksquare \end{cases}$

39. one solution

$\begin{cases} x + y + z = 7 \\ y + z = \blacksquare \\ z = \blacksquare \end{cases}$

40. no solution

$\begin{cases} x + y + z = 7 \\ y + z = \blacksquare \\ y + z = \blacksquare \end{cases}$

41. Physics When you mix hot and cold liquids, you can find the temperature of the mixture by using the formula $T = \frac{ah + bc}{a + b}$, where T is the temperature of the mixture, h is the temperature of the hot liquid, c is the temperature of the cold liquid, and a and b represent the amounts of hot and cold liquids. Suppose you mix hot tea and cold milk in a ratio $a : b$ of $9 : 1$, and find that the temperature of the mixture is $117°F$. You then change the tea : milk ratio to $2 : 1$, and the temperature drops to $96°F$. Find the initial temperatures of the tea and the milk.

42. Nutrition A caterer combines ingredients to make a paella, a Spanish fiesta dish. The paella weighs 18 lb, costs $29.50, and supplies 850 g of protein.
a. Write a system of three equations to find the weight of each ingredient.
b. Solve the system. How many pounds of each ingredient did she use?

Paella Nutrition Chart

Food	Cost/lb	Protein/lb
Chicken	$1.50	100 g
Rice	$.40	20 g
Shellfish	$6.00	50 g

Multiple Choice Practice

For California Standards and CAHSEE Tutorials, visit PHSchool.com. Web Code: bbq-9045

ALG2 2.0   **43.** Phil wants to solve the system $\begin{cases} 2x + y = -4 \\ 5x - 3y = 1 \end{cases}$ using matrices. Which of the

following would be used as the coefficient matrix?

A $\begin{bmatrix} 2 & 1 \\ 5 & -3 \end{bmatrix}$ C $\begin{bmatrix} 2 & -4 \\ 5 & 1 \end{bmatrix}$

B $\begin{bmatrix} 2 & 5 \\ 1 & -3 \end{bmatrix}$ D $\begin{bmatrix} 2 & -4 \\ 1 & 1 \end{bmatrix}$

ALG2 2.0   **44.** Use the graph to solve the system $\begin{cases} y = x + 18 \\ 2y = -x + 12 \end{cases}$.

A $(-8, 10)$
B $(0, 6)$
C $(-10, 8)$
D $(12, 18)$

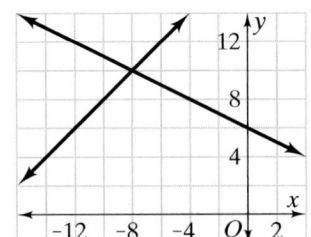

CAHSEE   **45.** Given the function $y = 2.7x + 7.4$, which statement best describes the effect of
Alg1 8.0   decreasing the y-intercept by 6.2?

A   The x-intercept decreases.
B   The y-intercept increases.
C   The new line has a greater slope.
D   The new line is parallel to the original.

ALG2 1.0   **46.** Which equation best describes the graph
at the right?

A $y = |x| - 2$
B $y = -2|x| - 2$
C $y = 2|x| - 2$
D $y = |-2x| - 2$

Mixed Review

 GO for Help

Lesson 4-6   **Evaluate the determinant of each matrix.**

47. $\begin{bmatrix} -1 & 3 & 7 \\ 5 & -4 & -2 \\ 0 & 2 & 10 \end{bmatrix}$ **48.** $\begin{bmatrix} 17 & 0 & 0 \\ 0 & 17 & 0 \\ 0 & 0 & 17 \end{bmatrix}$ **49.** $\begin{bmatrix} -3 & 0 & 5 \\ 5 & -3 & 2 \\ -3 & -5 & -2 \end{bmatrix}$

Lesson 4-2   **Add or subtract.**

50. $\begin{bmatrix} 5 & -3 \\ 4 & 11 \end{bmatrix} + \begin{bmatrix} 4 & 0 \\ -9 & 1 \end{bmatrix}$ **51.** $\begin{bmatrix} -1 & 2 & 0 \\ 10 & -5 & 15 \\ 17 & 3 & -4 \end{bmatrix} - \begin{bmatrix} 0 & 6 & -3 \\ 4 & -7 & 11 \\ -9 & 10 & -1 \end{bmatrix}$

Lesson 2-6   **Describe each translation of $f(x) = |x|$ as *vertical*, *horizontal*, or *combined*.
Then graph the translation.**

52. $f(x) = |x + 4|$ **53.** $f(x) = |x| - 3$ **54.** $f(x) = |x - 5| + 3$

Understanding Math Problems Read the problem below. Then let Jaime's thinking guide you through the solution. Check your understanding with the exercises at the bottom of the page.

Coordinate Geometry The coordinates (x, y) of a point in a plane are the solution of the system $\begin{cases} 2x + 3y = 13 \\ 5x + 7y = 31 \end{cases}$. Find the coordinates of the point.

What Jaime Thinks

The problem tells me that the solution of this system is (x, y). I could graph the lines to see where they intersect, but that's not necessary when I can solve the system with matrices. I'll rewrite the system as a matrix equation.

To solve for the variable matrix that includes x and y, I should multiply each side of the equation by the inverse of the coefficient matrix. I'll use the formula on page 205.

Now that I have the inverse, I can multiply.

Something is wrong. I can't multiply the matrices on the right side of this equation because the dimensions don't match.

Oh!!! I have to multiply the inverse matrix on the left, because matrix multiplication is not commutative!

I'll rewrite the equation correctly. The result will be a 2 × 1 matrix.

This means the x-coordinate is 2 and the y-coordinate is 3. I'll write my answer in a sentence.

What Jaime Writes

$$\begin{cases} 2x + 3y = 13 \\ 5x + 7y = 31 \end{cases} \quad \begin{bmatrix} 2 & 3 \\ 5 & 7 \end{bmatrix}\begin{bmatrix} x \\ y \end{bmatrix} = \begin{bmatrix} 13 \\ 31 \end{bmatrix}$$

Inverse of
$$\begin{bmatrix} 2 & 3 \\ 5 & 7 \end{bmatrix} = \frac{1}{(2)(7) - (5)(3)}\begin{bmatrix} 7 & -3 \\ -5 & 2 \end{bmatrix}$$

$$= -1\begin{bmatrix} 7 & -3 \\ -5 & 2 \end{bmatrix} = \begin{bmatrix} -7 & 3 \\ 5 & -2 \end{bmatrix}$$

$$\begin{bmatrix} -7 & 3 \\ 5 & -2 \end{bmatrix}\begin{bmatrix} 2 & 3 \\ 5 & 7 \end{bmatrix}\begin{bmatrix} x \\ y \end{bmatrix} = \begin{bmatrix} 13 \\ 31 \end{bmatrix}\begin{bmatrix} -7 & 3 \\ 5 & -2 \end{bmatrix}$$
$$\qquad\qquad\qquad\qquad\qquad 2 \times 1 \quad 2 \times 2$$
$$\qquad\qquad\qquad\qquad\quad \text{doesn't work!}$$

$$\begin{bmatrix} -7 & 3 \\ 5 & -2 \end{bmatrix}\begin{bmatrix} 2 & 3 \\ 5 & 7 \end{bmatrix}\begin{bmatrix} x \\ y \end{bmatrix} = \begin{bmatrix} -7 & 3 \\ 5 & -2 \end{bmatrix}\begin{bmatrix} 13 \\ 31 \end{bmatrix}$$

$$\begin{bmatrix} x \\ y \end{bmatrix} = \begin{bmatrix} (-7)(13) + (3)(31) \\ (5)(13) + (-2)(31) \end{bmatrix} = \begin{bmatrix} 2 \\ 3 \end{bmatrix}$$

The coordinates of the point are (2, 3).

EXERCISES

1. The coordinates (x, y) of a point in a plane are the solution of the system $\begin{cases} 12x + 13y = 14 \\ 5x + 7y = 9 \end{cases}$. Find the coordinates of the point.

2. What difficulty would Jaime have with his solution process for a system that has no solutions? Infinitely many solutions?

Augmented Matrices and Systems

 California Content Standards

ALG2 2.0 Students solve systems of linear equations (in two or three variables) with matrices. *Master*

What You'll Learn

- To solve a system of equations using Cramer's Rule
- To solve a system of equations using augmented matrices

. . . And Why

To solve systems of three equations, as in Example 2

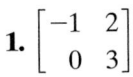 **Check Skills You'll Need**

GO for Help Lessons 4-5 and 4-6

Evaluate the determinant of each matrix.

1. $\begin{bmatrix} -1 & 2 \\ 0 & 3 \end{bmatrix}$

2. $\begin{bmatrix} 0 & 1 \\ -1 & 3 \end{bmatrix}$

3. $\begin{bmatrix} 2 & 1 \\ -1 & 5 \end{bmatrix}$

4. $\begin{bmatrix} 0 & 1 & -3 \\ 4 & 5 & -1 \\ -1 & 0 & 1 \end{bmatrix}$

5. $\begin{bmatrix} 3 & 4 & 5 \\ -1 & 2 & 0 \\ 0 & -1 & 1 \end{bmatrix}$

6. $\begin{bmatrix} 0 & 2 & -1 \\ 3 & 4 & 0 \\ -2 & -1 & 5 \end{bmatrix}$

New Vocabulary • Cramer's Rule • augmented matrix • row operations

---

1 Solving Systems Using Cramer's Rule

You can solve a system of linear equations that has a unique solution by using determinants and a pattern called Cramer's Rule.

 Key Concepts

Definition	Cramer's Rule

| | Use the x- and y-coefficients. | Replace the x-coefficients with the constants. | Replace the y-coefficients with the constants. |

System

$$\begin{cases} ax + by = m \\ cx + dy = n \end{cases}$$

$$D = \begin{vmatrix} a & b \\ c & d \end{vmatrix} \qquad D_x = \begin{vmatrix} m & b \\ n & d \end{vmatrix} \qquad D_y = \begin{vmatrix} a & m \\ c & n \end{vmatrix}$$

The solution of the system is $x = \dfrac{D_x}{D}$ and $y = \dfrac{D_y}{D}$, or $\left(\dfrac{D_x}{D}, \dfrac{D_y}{D} \right)$.

1 EXAMPLE Using Cramer's Rule

Use Cramer's Rule to solve the system $\begin{cases} 3x + 2y = 0 \\ x - y = -5 \end{cases}$.

Evaluate three determinants. Then find x and y.

$$D = \begin{vmatrix} 3 & 2 \\ 1 & -1 \end{vmatrix} = -5 \qquad D_x = \begin{vmatrix} 0 & 2 \\ -5 & -1 \end{vmatrix} = 10 \qquad D_y = \begin{vmatrix} 3 & 0 \\ 1 & -5 \end{vmatrix} = -15$$

$$x = \frac{D_x}{D} = \frac{10}{-5} = -2 \qquad y = \frac{D_y}{D} = \frac{-15}{-5} = 3$$

● The solution of the system is $(-2, 3)$.

CA Standards Check ① Use Cramer's Rule to solve the system $\begin{cases} 3x + y = 5 \\ 2x + 3y = 8 \end{cases}$.

You can also use Cramer's Rule to solve a system of three equations.

2 EXAMPLE Using Cramer's Rule With Three Equations

Multiple Choice What is the value of x in the solution of the system at the right?

$$\begin{cases} \phantom{x + {}} y + 4z = 5 \\ x + y + z = 8 \\ 2x - 5y \phantom{{} + 4z} = 7 \end{cases}$$

  Ⓐ -156 Ⓑ -26 Ⓒ 1 Ⓓ 6

Test-Taking Tip

When solving a system, make sure to match each value you find with the correct variable.

$$D = \begin{vmatrix} 0 & 1 & 4 \\ 1 & 1 & 1 \\ 2 & -5 & 0 \end{vmatrix} = -26 \qquad \textbf{Evaluate the determinant.}$$

$$D_x = \begin{vmatrix} 5 & 1 & 4 \\ 8 & 1 & 1 \\ 7 & -5 & 0 \end{vmatrix} = -156 \qquad \begin{array}{l}\textbf{Replace the } \textit{x}\textbf{-coefficients with the} \\ \textbf{constants and evaluate again.}\end{array}$$

$$x = \frac{D_x}{D} = \frac{-156}{-26} = 6 \qquad \textbf{Find } \textit{x}.$$

● The x-coordinate of the solution is 6. The answer is D.

✓ CA Standards Check **2** **a. Critical Thinking** How would you modify the determinant D to find D_z?
    b. Solve the system for y and z.

---

2   Solving Systems Using Augmented Matrices

Vocabulary Tip

Augmented means "increased in size" or "added to."

You can solve some linear systems by using an augmented matrix. An **augmented matrix** contains the coefficients and the constants from a system of equations. Each row of the matrix represents an equation.

3 EXAMPLE Writing an Augmented Matrix

Write an augmented matrix to represent the system. $\begin{cases} -6x + 2y = 10 \\ 4x \phantom{{}+ 2y} = -20 \end{cases}$

System of equations $\begin{cases} -6x & + & 2y & = & 10 \\ 4x & & & = & -20 \end{cases}$

      x-coefficients ↕   ↕ y-coefficients ↕ constants

Augmented matrix $\begin{bmatrix} -6 & 2 & \vline & 10 \\ 4 & 0 & \vline & -20 \end{bmatrix}$

              ↑— Draw a vertical bar to separate the coefficients from the constants.

● An augmented matrix that represents the system is $\begin{bmatrix} -6 & 2 & \vline & 10 \\ 4 & 0 & \vline & -20 \end{bmatrix}$.

✓ CA Standards Check **3** Write an augmented matrix to represent each system.

  a. $\begin{cases} x - 5y = 15 \\ 3x + 3y = 3 \end{cases}$ **b.** $\begin{cases} x + 2y + 3z = -4 \\ y - 2z = 8 \\ z = -3 \end{cases}$

An augmented matrix contains an entry of zero for any term missing from the system. You can write a system of equations from an augmented matrix.

4 EXAMPLE   Writing a System From an Augmented Matrix

Write a system of equations for the augmented matrix $\begin{bmatrix} 6 & 0 & | & 3 \\ 1 & 1 & | & -5 \end{bmatrix}$.

Augmented matrix $\begin{bmatrix} 6 & 0 & | & 3 \\ 1 & 1 & | & -5 \end{bmatrix}$

x-coefficients $\updownarrow$ $\updownarrow$ y-coefficients $\updownarrow$ constants

System of equations $\begin{cases} 6x + = 3 \\ x + y = -5 \end{cases}$

✓ **CA Standards Check** 4 Write a system of equations for each augmented matrix.

a. $\begin{bmatrix} 5 & 7 & | & -3 \\ 0 & -8 & | & 6 \end{bmatrix}$

b. $\begin{bmatrix} -1 & 0 & 3 & | & -4 \\ 7 & 2 & -1 & | & 0 \\ 0 & 1 & 2 & | & -3 \end{bmatrix}$

In Chapter 3 you learned how to solve systems of equations by using multiples of one or more of the equations to eliminate variables. You can do the same thing to an augmented matrix by using row operations.

Key Concepts

Definition	Row Operations

To solve a system of equations using an augmented matrix, you can use the following **row operations.**

- Switch any two rows.
- Multiply a row by a constant.
- Add one row to another.
- Combine one or more of these steps.

5 EXAMPLE   Using an Augmented Matrix

Use an augmented matrix to solve the system $\begin{cases} x + 2y = -1 \\ 2x + 5y = -4 \end{cases}$.

$\begin{bmatrix} 1 & 2 & | & -1 \\ 2 & 5 & | & -4 \end{bmatrix}$ **Write an augmented matrix.**

$\begin{bmatrix} 1 & 2 & | & -1 \\ 0 & 1 & | & -2 \end{bmatrix}$

$\begin{array}{r} -2(1 \quad 2 \quad -1) \\ 2 \quad 5 \quad -4 \\ \hline 0 \quad 1 \quad -2 \end{array}$ **Multiply Row 1 by −2 and add it to Row 2. Write the new augmented matrix.**

$\begin{bmatrix} 1 & 0 & | & 3 \\ 0 & 1 & | & -2 \end{bmatrix}$

$\begin{array}{r} 1 \quad 2 \quad -1 \\ -2(0 \quad 1 \quad -2) \\ \hline 1 \quad 0 \quad -3 \end{array}$ **Multiply new Row 2 by −2 and add it to Row 1. Write the final augmented matrix.**

The solution to the system is $(3, -2)$.

Check

$x + 2y = -1$	$2x + 5y = -4$	**Use the original equations.**
$3 + 2(-2) \stackrel{?}{=} -1$	$2(3) + 5(-2) \stackrel{?}{=} -4$	**Substitute.**
$3 + (-4) \stackrel{?}{=} -1$	$6 + (-10) \stackrel{?}{=} -4$	**Multiply.**
$-1 = -1$ ✓	$-4 = -4$ ✓	**Simplify.**

✓ **CA Standards Check**   Solve $\begin{cases} x + y = -10 \\ -x + y = 20 \end{cases}$. Check your solution.

Graphing Calculator Hint

In Step 2, rref stands for "reduced row-echelon form." To find rref, use the MATRIX feature, MATH menu. Scroll to item B, then press ENTER .

You can use augmented matrices and row operations to solve systems of three equations. Graphing calculators have a feature that uses row operations to simplify matrices.

6 EXAMPLE Using a Graphing Calculator

Use a graphing calculator to solve the system $\begin{cases} 2x + 3y - z = 11 \\ 3x - 2y + 4z = 10 \\ x + 4y - 2z = 8 \end{cases}$

Step 1 Enter the augmented matrix as matrix A.

```
[A]
[[  2   3   -1   11  ]
 [  3  -2    4   10  ]
 [  1   4   -2    8  ]]
```

Step 2 Use the rref feature of your graphing calculator.

```
rref([A])
[[  1   0   0   4  ]
 [  0   1   0   1  ]
 [  0   0   1   0  ]]
```

The simplified augmented matrix is equivalent to $\begin{cases} x = 4 \\ y = 1 \\ z = 0 \end{cases}$.
The solution is $(4, 1, 0)$.

Partial Check

$$2x + 3y - z = 11 \qquad \text{Use the first equation.}$$
$$2(4) + 3(1) - (0) \stackrel{?}{=} 11 \qquad \text{Substitute.}$$
$$8 + 3 - 0 \stackrel{?}{=} 11 \qquad \text{Multiply.}$$
$$11 = 11 \checkmark \qquad \text{Simplify.}$$

 6 **a.** Check the solution to Example 6 in the remaining two equations.

b. Use a graphing calculator to solve the system $\begin{cases} x + 4y - z = 4 \\ x - 2y + z = -2 \\ 5x - 3y + 8z = 13 \end{cases}$
Check your answer.

EXERCISES

For more exercises, see *Extra Skill and Word Problem Practice.*

Standards Practice

ALG2 2.0

 A **Practice by Example**

Examples 1 and 2
(pages 225 and 226)

GO for Help

Example 3
(page 226)

Use Cramer's Rule to solve each system.

1. $\begin{cases} 2x + y = 4 \\ 3x - y = 6 \end{cases}$

2. $\begin{cases} 2x + y = 7 \\ -2x + 5y = -1 \end{cases}$

3. $\begin{cases} 2x + 4y = 10 \\ 3x + 5y = 14 \end{cases}$

4. $\begin{cases} y + 4z = 5 \\ x + y + z = 8 \\ 2x - 5y = 7 \end{cases}$

5. $\begin{cases} 2x + 3y + z = 5 \\ x + y - 2z = -2 \\ -3x + z = -7 \end{cases}$

Write an augmented matrix for each system.

6. $\begin{cases} 3x - 4y = 17 \\ 8x + y = -3 \end{cases}$

7. $\begin{cases} 3x - 7y + 3z = -3 \\ x + y + 2z = -3 \\ 2x - 3y + 5z = -8 \end{cases}$

8. $\begin{cases} -x + 5y = -1 \\ x - 2y = 1 \end{cases}$

Example 4
(page 227)

Write a system of equations for each augmented matrix.

9. $\begin{bmatrix} 5 & 1 & -3 \\ -2 & 2 & 4 \end{bmatrix}$

10. $\begin{bmatrix} -1 & 2 & -6 \\ 1 & 1 & 7 \end{bmatrix}$

11. $\begin{bmatrix} 2 & 1 & 1 & 1 \\ 1 & 1 & 1 & 2 \\ 1 & -1 & 1 & -2 \end{bmatrix}$

Example 5
(page 227)

Use an augmented matrix to solve each system.

12. $\begin{cases} 2x - 2y = 15 \\ 4x + 4y = 10 \end{cases}$

13. $\begin{cases} 2x - 4y = 20 \\ 4x + 2y = -20 \end{cases}$

14. $\begin{cases} x + 2y = 3 \\ 4x + 2y = -6 \end{cases}$

15. $\begin{cases} x + 5y = -25 \\ 5x + y = 25 \end{cases}$

16. $\begin{cases} -x + 5y = 15 \\ 2x + 3y = 9 \end{cases}$

17. $\begin{cases} 3x + 6y = 2 \\ 2x - y = 3 \end{cases}$

Example 6
(page 228)

Solve each system.

18. $\begin{cases} x + y + z = 2 \\ 2y - 2z = 2 \\ x - 3z = 1 \end{cases}$

19. $\begin{cases} x - y + z = 3 \\ x + 3z = 6 \\ y - 2z = -1 \end{cases}$

20. $\begin{cases} x + y - z = -1 \\ 3x + 4y - z = 8 \\ 6x + 8y - 2z = 16 \end{cases}$

21. $\begin{cases} x + y - z = 1 \\ 3x + 3y + z = 3 \\ 2x + 2y - 2z = 2 \end{cases}$

22. $\begin{cases} x + y = 1 \\ y + z = 2 \\ x - z = -1 \end{cases}$

23. $\begin{cases} x + z = -4 \\ y - z = 1 \\ x + y = -3 \end{cases}$

B Apply Your Skills

Use Cramer's Rule to solve each system.

24. $\begin{cases} 0.5x + 1.5y = 7 \\ 2.5x - 3.5y = -9 \end{cases}$

25. $\begin{cases} -1.2x - 0.3y = 2.1 \\ -0.2x + 0.8y = 4.6 \end{cases}$

26. $\begin{cases} \dfrac{x}{5} - \dfrac{2y}{5} = 4 \\ \dfrac{2x}{5} - \dfrac{3y}{5} = 5 \end{cases}$

27. $\begin{cases} \dfrac{x}{2} + \dfrac{y}{4} = 4 \\ \dfrac{x}{4} - \dfrac{3y}{8} = -2 \end{cases}$

28. $\begin{cases} 2x + 3y + 5z = 12 \\ 4x + 2y + 4z = -2 \\ 5x + 4y + 7z = 7 \end{cases}$

Use an augmented matrix to solve each system.

29. $\begin{cases} x + y + z = 1 \\ y - 3z = 4 \\ x - z = 2 \end{cases}$

30. $\begin{cases} x + y + z = 0 \\ y + 4z = -6 \\ 2x - 2z = 4 \end{cases}$

31. $\begin{cases} 2x + y = 8 \\ x + z = 5 \\ y - z = -1 \end{cases}$

32. Business A manufacturer sells pencils and erasers in packages. The price of a package of five erasers and two pencils is $.23. The price of a package of seven erasers and five pencils is $.41. Find the price of one eraser and one pencil.

33. Multiple Choice Suppose you invested $5000 in three different funds for one year. The funds paid simple interest of 8%, 10%, and 7%, respectively. The total interest at the end of one year was $405. You invested $500 more at 10% than at 8%. How much did you invest in the 10% fund?

    Ⓐ $150   Ⓑ $1000   Ⓒ $1500   Ⓓ $2500

34. Open-Ended Write and solve a system of three equations in three unknowns using Cramer's Rule.

Solve each system.

35. $\begin{cases} 2x - 3y + 2z = 10 \\ x + 3y + 4z = 14 \\ 3x - y + z = 9 \end{cases}$

36. $\begin{cases} 4x - y + z = 3 \\ x + 2y + z = 0 \\ 3x + 7y - 3z = 6 \end{cases}$

37. $\begin{cases} x + 2y + z = 4 \\ 3x + 6y + 3z = 2 \\ x - y + z = 3 \end{cases}$

Homework Video Tutor

Visit: PHSchool.com
Web Code: bbe-0408

38. Colors A hardware store mixes paints in a ratio of two parts red to six parts yellow to make pumpkin orange. A ratio of five parts red to three parts yellow makes red-pepper red. A gallon of pumpkin orange sells for $25, and a gallon of red-pepper red sells for $28.
   a. Write a system of equations to model the situation.
   b. Solve the system.
   c. Find the cost of 1 qt of red paint and the cost of 1 qt of yellow paint.

39. Sales Refer to the signs below. Find the price per pound of each type of nut.

2 lb almonds
3 lb pecans
only $16

1 lb almonds
1 lb pecans
1 lb pistachios
only $12

3 lb pecans
2 lb pistachios
only $24

C **Challenge** Solve using Cramer's Rule. (*Hint:* Start by substituting $m = \frac{1}{x}$ and $n = \frac{1}{y}$.)

40. $\begin{cases} \dfrac{4}{x} + \dfrac{1}{y} = 1 \\ \dfrac{8}{x} + \dfrac{4}{y} = 3 \end{cases}$

41. $\begin{cases} \dfrac{4}{x} - \dfrac{2}{y} = 1 \\ \dfrac{10}{x} + \dfrac{20}{y} = 0 \end{cases}$

Solve each system.

42. $\begin{cases} w + x + y + z = 3 \\ -w + x - 2y + z = -2 \\ 2x - y + z = 1 \\ w + y - z = 2 \end{cases}$

43. $\begin{cases} 2x + 2y + z = 4 \\ w + y - z = -2 \\ w + x + y + z = 3 \\ -4w + z = 2 \end{cases}$

44. Nutrition While stranded on an island, the crew of a sailboat has access to only three sources of food, as shown in the table below. One of the crew members designs a daily diet to supply each person with 120 g of fat, 220 g of carbohydrates, and 80 g of protein.

	A	B	C
Fat	10 g	4 g	12 g
Carbohydrates	11 g	77 g	0 g
Protein	4 g	1 g	16 g

   a. Write a system of three equations in three variables to find the number of portions of each food each person must have to meet the daily diet.
   b. Use an augmented matrix to solve the system of equations from part (a). Round each answer to the nearest tenth.
   c. Writing Suppose food C runs out. How would this change the number of portions of food required each day?

45. Geometry The perimeter of the rectangle at the right is 28 cm. The perimeter of each of the triangles is 24 cm. The diagonal of the rectangle is 2 cm longer than the longer side of the rectangle.

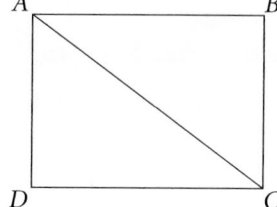

a. Write a system of three equations in three unknowns.
b. Simplify the system to a system of two equations in two unknowns.
c. Write an augmented matrix for the system in part (b).
d. Find the dimensions of the rectangle.
e. Find the length of the diagonal.

Multiple Choice Practice

For California Standards and CAHSEE Tutorials, visit PHSchool.com. Web Code: bbq-9045

ALG2 2.0

46. Fred wants to solve the matrix equation below.

$$\begin{bmatrix} 1 & -2 \\ 3 & 4 \end{bmatrix} \begin{bmatrix} x \\ y \end{bmatrix} = \begin{bmatrix} -5 \\ 5 \end{bmatrix}$$

What is the inverse of the coefficient matrix for this equation?

A $\begin{bmatrix} 0.5 & 0.2 \\ -0.3 & 0.6 \end{bmatrix}$ **C** $\begin{bmatrix} 1 & -5 \\ 3 & 5 \end{bmatrix}$

B $\begin{bmatrix} 0.4 & 0.2 \\ -0.3 & 0.1 \end{bmatrix}$ **D** $\begin{bmatrix} -5 & -2 \\ 5 & 4 \end{bmatrix}$

CAHSEE
7MG 2.1

47. Cups for a certain water cooler are shaped like a cone with the dimensions shown in the diagram. What is the approximate volume of a cup? Use the formula $V = \frac{1}{3}\pi r^2 h$.

A 21π cm^3 **C** 63π cm^3

B 42π cm^3 **D** 84π cm^3

ALG2 1.0

48. Solve the equation $3 - |2 - x| = -2$.

A 3 or 7   **B** -3 or 3   **C** -2 or 5   **D** -3 or 7

Mixed Review

 GO for Help

Lesson 4-7

Solve each system of equations by using the inverse of the coefficient matrix.

49. $\begin{cases} x + 4y + 3z = 3 \\ 2x - 5y - z = 5 \\ 3x + 2y - 2z = -3 \end{cases}$ **50.** $\begin{cases} x + y + z = -1 \\ y + 3z = -5 \\ x + z = -2 \end{cases}$

Lesson 3-3

Solve each system of inequalities by graphing.

51. $\begin{cases} 2x + y < 3 \\ -x - y \geq 1 \end{cases}$ **52.** $\begin{cases} 2x \leq 0 \\ -x + y > -1 \end{cases}$ **53.** $\begin{cases} x < 3 \\ y \geq -4 \\ -x + y < 5 \end{cases}$

Lesson 2-2

Write in point-slope form the equation of the line through each pair of points.

54. $(0, 1)$ and $(2, -5)$ **55.** $(-9, 3)$ and $(-4, -4)$ **56.** $(1, 8)$ and $(7, 2)$

Interpreting Data

A problem may give you a graph and ask you to choose a situation that best interprets the graph. Or it may give you a situation and ask you to choose a graph that best models the situation.

To make the choice, you must break down each situation to find the features that must be present in the graph.

EXAMPLE

In a research study, a rodent population remained stable for some time. It increased rapidly when a predator was removed. Then it declined rapidly as overpopulation caused a food shortage. Which graph best models this situation?

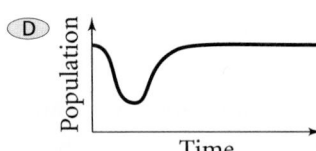

As time increases (from left to right), the correct graph must

• begin with a horizontal part to show a stable population
• rise rapidly to show the predator's absence
• fall rapidly to show the food shortage

Only one graph has all three parts in the correct order. The answer is C.

EXERCISE

1. The graph shows the approximate weights of a male and female dog of a certain breed over the first six months of their lives.

   Based on the data in the graph, which of the following statements is NOT true?

   Ⓐ Both dogs weigh less than 18 kg at age 3 months.

   Ⓑ The difference between the weights decreases as the dogs get older.

   Ⓒ The male dog weighs more than 21 kg at age 5 months.

   Ⓓ The slope of the line that represents the weight of the male dog is greater than the slope of the line that represents the weight of the female dog.

Chapter 4 Review

Choose the correct vocabulary term to complete each sentence.

1. A ___?___ is a rectangular array of numbers.

2. Translations, dilations, reflections, and rotations are all ___?___.

3. Cramer's Rule uses ___?___ to solve a system of equations.

4. If corresponding elements of matrices are equal, the matrices are ___?___.

5. The additive identity of a matrix is the ___?___.

6. A ___?___ consists of a coefficient matrix, a variable matrix, and a constant matrix.

7. An $n \times n$ matrix is called a ___?___.

8. The image of a figure is a transformation of the ___?___.

9. The product of a real number and a matrix is called a ___?___.

10. A matrix is the inverse of another matrix if their product is the ___?___.

Go Online
PHSchool.com
For: Vocabulary quiz
Web Code: bbj-0451

Skills and Concepts

Lesson 4-1

- To identify matrices and their elements (p. 172)
- To organize data into matrices (p. 173)

It is often useful to organize data into matrices. A **matrix** is a rectangular array of numbers classified by its dimensions. An $m \times n$ matrix has m rows and n columns. A **matrix element** a_{ij} is in the ith row and jth column of matrix A.

State the dimensions of each matrix A. Identify the indicated element.

11. $\begin{bmatrix} 5 & 8 & -7 \\ 1 & 11 & 3 \end{bmatrix}; a_{13}$

12. $\begin{bmatrix} 3 & 1 \\ -5 & 0 \\ 7 & 6 \end{bmatrix}; a_{21}$

13. $\begin{bmatrix} 5 & 1 & -2 \\ 4 & -7 & 12 \\ 0 & 78 & 3 \end{bmatrix}; a_{32}$

Use the matrix at the right for Exercises 14–16.

14. How many points has Tamika scored?

15. How many three-point shots has Tran made?

16. What percent of Johanna's points were from one-point shots?

	1-pt Shots	2-pt Shots	3-pt Shots
Tamika	22	30	48
Johanna	21	31	48
Tran	21	29	50

Lessons 4-2, 4-3

- To add and subtract matrices (p. 178)
- To solve certain matrix equations (p. 180)
- To multiply a matrix by a scalar (p. 186)
- To multiply two matrices (p. 188)

LA 4.0, 5.0

To perform **matrix addition** or subtraction, add or subtract the corresponding elements in the matrices. To obtain the product of a matrix and a **scalar,** multiply each matrix element by the scalar. **Matrix multiplication** uses both multiplication and addition. The element in the ith row and jth column of the product of two matrices is the sum of the products of each element of the ith row of the first matrix and the corresponding element of the jth column of the second matrix. The first matrix must have the same number of columns as the second has rows.

Two matrices are **equal matrices** when they have the same dimensions and corresponding elements are equal. This principle is used to solve a **matrix equation.**

Solve each matrix equation for matrix X.

17. $[2 \quad -6 \quad 8] + [-1 \quad -2 \quad 4] = X$

18. $\begin{bmatrix} t \\ 6 \end{bmatrix} - \begin{bmatrix} 1 \\ 3 \end{bmatrix} = X$

19. $\begin{bmatrix} 7 & -1 \\ 0 & 8 \end{bmatrix} + X = \begin{bmatrix} 4 & 9 \\ -3 & 11 \end{bmatrix}$

20. $X - \begin{bmatrix} -7 & 13 & 5 \\ 31 & 0 & -4 \end{bmatrix} = \begin{bmatrix} 9 & -5 & 8 \\ 2 & 0 & -3 \end{bmatrix}$

Solve for each variable.

21. $\begin{bmatrix} x - 5 & 9 \\ 4 & t + 2 \end{bmatrix} = \begin{bmatrix} -7 & w + 1 \\ 8 - r & 1 \end{bmatrix}$

22. $\begin{bmatrix} -4 + t & 2y \\ r & w + 4 \end{bmatrix} = \begin{bmatrix} 2t & 11 \\ -2r + 12 & 9 \end{bmatrix}$

Use matrices A, B, C, and D. Find each scalar product, sum, or difference, if possible. If an operation is not defined, label it _undefined_.

$$A = \begin{bmatrix} 6 & 1 & 0 & 8 \\ -4 & 3 & 7 & 11 \end{bmatrix} \quad B = \begin{bmatrix} 1 & 3 \\ -2 & 4 \end{bmatrix} \quad C = \begin{bmatrix} -2 & 1 \\ 4 & 0 \\ 2 & 2 \\ 1 & 1 \end{bmatrix} \quad D = \begin{bmatrix} 5 & -2 \\ 3 & 6 \end{bmatrix}$$

23. $3A$
24. $B - 2D$
25. AB
26. BA
27. $AC - BD$

Lesson 4-4

- To represent translations and dilations with matrices (p. 195)
- To represent reflections and rotations with matrices (p. 197)

LA 4.0, 5.0

A change made to a figure is a transformation. The original figure is the **preimage,** and the transformed figure is the **image.** A translation slides a figure without changing its size or shape. A **dilation** changes the size of a figure. You can use matrix addition to translate a figure and scalar multiplication to dilate a figure.

You can use multiplication by the appropriate matrix to perform transformations that are specific reflections or **rotations.** For example, to reflect a figure in the y-axis, multiply by $\begin{bmatrix} -1 & 0 \\ 0 & 1 \end{bmatrix}$. To rotate a figure $180°$, multiply by $\begin{bmatrix} -1 & 0 \\ 0 & -1 \end{bmatrix}$.

For Exercises 28–35, use $\triangle ABC$ with vertices $A(3, 1)$, $B(-2, 0)$, and $C(1, 5)$. Write the coordinates of each image in matrix form.

28. a translation 1 unit right and 2 units down

29. a translation 3 units left and 4 units up

30. a reflection in the y-axis

31. a reflection in the line $y = x$

32. a rotation of $270°$

33. a dilation half the original size

34. a dilation twice the original size

35. a rotation of $90°$

A **square matrix** with 1's along its main diagonal and 0's elsewhere is the **multiplicative identity matrix**, I. If A and X are square matrices such that $AX = I$, then X is the **multiplicative inverse matrix** of A, A^{-1}.

You can use formulas to evaluate the determinants of 2 × 2 and 3 × 3 matrices.

$$\begin{vmatrix} a & b \\ c & d \end{vmatrix} = ad - bc \qquad \begin{vmatrix} a_1 & b_1 & c_1 \\ a_2 & b_2 & c_2 \\ a_3 & b_3 & c_3 \end{vmatrix} = a_1b_2c_3 + a_2b_3c_1 + a_3b_1c_2 \\ - a_1b_3c_2 - a_2b_1c_3 - a_3b_2c_1$$

You can use a calculator to find the inverse of a matrix. The inverse of a 2 × 2 matrix can be found by using its determinant. $\begin{bmatrix} a & b \\ c & d \end{bmatrix}^{-1} = \dfrac{1}{ad - bc}\begin{bmatrix} d & -b \\ -c & a \end{bmatrix}$

You can use inverse matrices to solve some matrix equations.

You can also use inverse matrices to solve some systems of equations. When equations in a system are in standard form, the product of the **coefficient matrix** and the **variable matrix** equals the **constant matrix.** You solve the equation by multiplying both sides of the equation by the inverse of the coefficient matrix. If that inverse does not exist, the system does not have a unique solution.

Evaluate the determinant of each matrix, and find the inverse, if possible.

36. $\begin{bmatrix} 6 & 1 \\ 0 & 4 \end{bmatrix}$ **37.** $\begin{bmatrix} 5 & -2 \\ 10 & -4 \end{bmatrix}$ **38.** $\begin{bmatrix} 10 & 1 \\ 8 & 5 \end{bmatrix}$ **39.** $\begin{bmatrix} 1 & 0 & 2 \\ -1 & 0 & 1 \\ -1 & -2 & 0 \end{bmatrix}$

Use an inverse matrix to solve each equation or system.

40. $\begin{bmatrix} 3 & 5 \\ 6 & 2 \end{bmatrix}X = \begin{bmatrix} -2 & 6 \\ 4 & 12 \end{bmatrix}$ **41.** $\begin{cases} x - y = 3 \\ 2x - y = -1 \end{cases}$ **42.** $\begin{bmatrix} 4 & 1 \\ 2 & 1 \end{bmatrix}\begin{bmatrix} x \\ y \end{bmatrix} = \begin{bmatrix} 10 \\ 6 \end{bmatrix}$

43. $\begin{bmatrix} -6 & 0 \\ 7 & 1 \end{bmatrix}X = \begin{bmatrix} -12 & -6 \\ 17 & 9 \end{bmatrix}$ **44.** $\begin{cases} x + 2y = 15 \\ 2x + 4y = 30 \end{cases}$ **45.** $\begin{cases} a + 2b + c = 14 \\ b = c + 1 \\ a = -3c + 6 \end{cases}$

46. Physical Fitness A club of 17 students is going on a canoe trip. The group of people on the trip includes 5 chaperones, one for each canoe. Some canoes hold 5 people, while some hold 4 people. How many of each kind of canoe should the group rent?

Cramer's Rule for solving systems of equations uses determinants to solve for each variable. D is the determinant of the coefficient matrix. D_y is the determinant formed by replacing the coefficients of y in D with the constant terms.

You can also use **row operations** on an augmented matrix to solve a system.

Solve each system using Cramer's Rule. Check your answers by solving each system using an augmented matrix.

47. $\begin{cases} 2x - y = 15 \\ x + 3y = -17 \end{cases}$ **48.** $\begin{cases} 3r + s - 2t = 22 \\ r + 5s + t = 4 \\ r = -3t \end{cases}$

Chapter 4 Test

History Use the table below for Exercises 1–3.

President	Years	Vetoes	Overrides
Kennedy	3	21	9
Johnson	5	30	0
Nixon	5.5	43	7
Ford	2.5	66	12
Carter	4	31	2
Reagan	8	78	9
G.H.W. Bush	4	46	1
Clinton	8	38	2

SOURCE: Congressional Research Service.
Go to **www.PHSchool.com** for a data update.
Web Code: bbg-2041

1. Display the data in a matrix in which each row represents a president.

2. State the dimensions of the matrix.

3. Find and identify a_{32}.

Find each sum or difference.

4. $\begin{bmatrix} 4 & 7 \\ -2 & 1 \end{bmatrix} - \begin{bmatrix} -9 & 3 \\ 6 & 0 \end{bmatrix}$

5. $\begin{bmatrix} 4 & -5 & 1 \\ 10 & 7 & 4 \\ 21 & -9 & -6 \end{bmatrix} + \begin{bmatrix} -7 & -10 & 4 \\ 17 & 0 & 3 \\ -2 & -6 & 1 \end{bmatrix}$

Find each product.

6. $\begin{bmatrix} 2 & 6 \\ 1 & 0 \end{bmatrix}\begin{bmatrix} -1 & 5 \\ 3 & 1 \end{bmatrix}$

7. $2\begin{bmatrix} -8 & 5 & -1 \\ 0 & 9 & 7 \end{bmatrix}$

8. $\begin{bmatrix} 0 & 3 \\ -4 & 9 \end{bmatrix}\begin{bmatrix} -4 & 6 & 1 & 3 \\ 9 & -8 & 10 & 7 \end{bmatrix}$

Parallelogram $ABCD$ has coordinates $A(2, -1)$, $B(4, 3)$, $C(1, 5)$, and $D(-1, 1)$. Write a matrix for the vertices of its image after each transformation.

9. a dilation of size $\frac{2}{3}$

10. a translation right 2 units and down 4 units

11. a reflection in $y = x$ **12.** a rotation of 270°

13. Graph parallelogram $ABCD$ and its image from Question 11 on the same coordinate plane.

14. Open-Ended Write a matrix that has no inverse.

15. Writing Explain how to determine whether two matrices can be multiplied and what the dimensions of the product matrix will be.

16. Find the value of each variable.
$\begin{bmatrix} x & 1 & y \\ 2 & 0 & 1 \end{bmatrix} = \begin{bmatrix} 1-x & z & 2 \\ 2+w & 4-t & 1 \end{bmatrix}$

Find the determinant of each matrix.

17. $\begin{bmatrix} 1 & 0 & 0 \\ 0 & 1 & 0 \\ 0 & 0 & 1 \end{bmatrix}$ **18.** $\begin{bmatrix} 2 & 3 & 0 \\ -1 & 1 & 0 \\ 4 & 2 & 1 \end{bmatrix}$ **19.** $\begin{bmatrix} 8 & -3 \\ 2 & 9 \end{bmatrix}$

20. $\begin{bmatrix} 0 & 3 \\ x & t \end{bmatrix}$ **21.** $\begin{bmatrix} \frac{1}{2} & -1 \\ 3 & 0 \end{bmatrix}$

Find the inverse of each matrix, if it exists.

22. $\begin{bmatrix} 3 & 8 \\ -7 & 10 \end{bmatrix}$ **23.** $\begin{bmatrix} 0 & -5 \\ 9 & 6 \end{bmatrix}$ **24.** $\begin{bmatrix} \frac{1}{2} & -1 \\ 0 & 4 \end{bmatrix}$

25. $\begin{bmatrix} -8 & 4 & -11 \\ 5 & 2 & 9 \\ -5 & 6 & 2 \end{bmatrix}$ **26.** $\begin{bmatrix} 1 & 1 & 2 \\ 2 & 1 & 3 \\ 2 & 1 & 1 \end{bmatrix}$

Solve each matrix equation.

27. $\begin{bmatrix} 3 & -8 \\ 10 & 5 \end{bmatrix} - X = \begin{bmatrix} 2 & 8 \\ -1 & 12 \end{bmatrix}$

28. $\begin{bmatrix} 3 & 2 \\ -1 & 5 \end{bmatrix} X = \begin{bmatrix} -10 & -11 \\ 26 & -36 \end{bmatrix}$

29. $2X - \begin{bmatrix} -2 & 0 \\ 1 & 4 \end{bmatrix} = \begin{bmatrix} 5 & 10 \\ -15 & 9 \end{bmatrix}$

Solve each system using inverse matrices.

30. $\begin{cases} 2x - y = 5 \\ x + 4y = 7 \end{cases}$ **31.** $\begin{cases} x + 2y + z = -1 \\ 4x - y - z = -1 \\ 2z = -3y \end{cases}$

32. Solve $\begin{cases} -2x + 7y = 19 \\ x + 3y = 10 \end{cases}$ using Cramer's Rule.

33. Solve the system using an augmented matrix.
$\begin{cases} x + y + z = 9 \\ 4x + 3y - z = -6 \\ -x - y + 2z = 21 \end{cases}$

Some problems require you to find the equations of lines.

Which system is represented by the graph below?

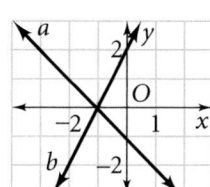

Tip 1
Use the equation $y = mx + b$, where m represents the slope and b is the y-intercept.

Ⓐ $\begin{cases} y = x - 1 \\ y = 2x + 2 \end{cases}$ Ⓒ $\begin{cases} y = -x - 1 \\ y = 2x + 2 \end{cases}$

Ⓑ $\begin{cases} y = -x - 1 \\ y = x + 2 \end{cases}$ Ⓓ $\begin{cases} y = -x - 2 \\ y = 2x - 1 \end{cases}$

Tip 2
Remember that slope $= \frac{\text{rise}}{\text{run}}$.

Think It Through
Slope of line a:

$$m = \frac{(y_2 - y_1)}{(x_2 - x_1)} = \frac{(1 - -1)}{(-2 - 0)} = \frac{2}{-2} = -1$$

The y-intercept of line a is $(0, -1)$.
The equation of line a is $y = -x - 1$.

Slope of line b:

$$m = \frac{(y_2 - y_1)}{(x_2 - x_1)} = \frac{(-2 - 2)}{(-2 - 0)} = \frac{-4}{-2} = 2$$

The y-intercept of line b is $(0, 2)$.
The equation of line b is $y = 2x + 2$.

The correct choice is C.

Vocabulary Review

As you solve problems, you must understand the meanings of mathematical terms. Match each term with its mathematical meaning.

A. domain of a function

B. range of a function

C. matrix

D. determinant

E. square matrix

I. a matrix with the same number of rows and columns

II. set of all outputs, or y-coordinates of the ordered pairs

III. set of all inputs, or x-coordinates of the ordered pairs

IV. a real number that can be computed from the elements of a square matrix

V. a rectangular array of numbers written within brackets

Multiple Choice

Read each question. Then write the letter of the correct answer on your paper.

1. Find the sum of the solutions of $|13 - 3x| = |x + 1|$. **(Lesson 1-5)**

Ⓐ -4 Ⓒ 10

Ⓑ 3 Ⓓ 12

2. The graph of $y = |x - 1|$ is translated up 4 units and to the right 3 units. Which equation represents the translated graph? **(Lesson 2-6)**

Ⓐ $y = |x - 3| + 4$

Ⓑ $y = |x - 4| + 4$

Ⓒ $y = |x - 4| - 3$

Ⓓ $y = |x + 2| + 4$

3. Which inequality is described by the graph at the right? **(Lesson 2-7)**

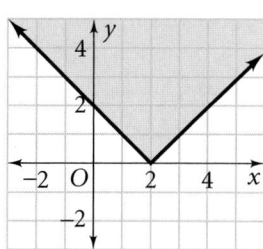

Ⓐ $y < |x - 2|$

Ⓑ $y > |x + 2|$

Ⓒ $y > |x - 2|$

Ⓓ $y > |x| + 2$

4. Which of the following absolute value equations has exactly one solution? **(Lesson 1-5)**

Ⓐ $|x - 4| = |x|$ Ⓒ $|x - 1| = x - 1$

Ⓑ $|3x| = 15$ Ⓓ $|x - 4| = |3x - 1|$

5. The domain of the function below is $-3 \leq x \leq 3$. This can also be written as the absolute value inequality $|x| \leq 3$.

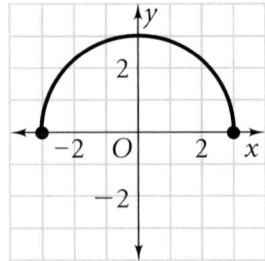

Which of the following decribes the range of the function? **(Lesson 1-5)**

Ⓐ $|y| \leq 3$

Ⓑ $|y - 3| \leq 1.5$

Ⓒ $|y - 1.5| \leq 1.5$

Ⓓ $|y - 1.5| \leq 3$

6. Solve $|2w - 3| > 3$. **(Lesson 1-5)**

Ⓐ $w > 0$ or $w < -3$

Ⓑ $0 < w < 3$

Ⓒ $w < 0$ or $w > 12$

Ⓓ $w < 0$ or $w > 3$

7. A 60-acre plot of land was purchased for $900,000. Some of the land was swampland, which cost $12,000 per acre. The rest of the land was irrigable land which cost $30,000 per acre. How much of the purchased land was irrigable? **(Lesson 3-2)**

Ⓐ 10 acres Ⓒ 45 acres

Ⓑ 30 acres Ⓓ 50 acres

8. Solve the system $\begin{cases} -3x + 2y = 9 \\ x = 1 - 2y \end{cases}$. **(Lesson 3-2)**

Ⓐ $(-3, 0)$ Ⓒ $(-2, 1.5)$

Ⓑ $(1, 6)$ Ⓓ $(2, -0.5)$

9. Which of the following systems is an inconsistent system? **(Lesson 3-1)**

Ⓐ $\begin{cases} x + 5y = 1 \\ x - 5y = 1 \end{cases}$ Ⓒ $\begin{cases} x = 7 \\ y = 2x \end{cases}$

Ⓑ $\begin{cases} 4x + 2y = 6 \\ 3 - 2x = y \end{cases}$ Ⓓ $\begin{cases} 2y = 8x + 3 \\ -4x = 1 - y \end{cases}$

10. Which system is represented by the graph below? **(Lesson 3-3)**

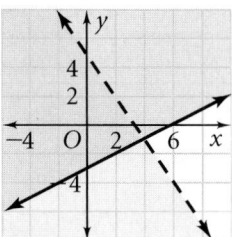

Ⓐ $\begin{cases} 2y + 6 \geq x \\ y < -\frac{3}{2}x + 5 \end{cases}$ Ⓒ $\begin{cases} 2y - 6 \geq x \\ y < -\frac{3}{2}x + 5 \end{cases}$

Ⓑ $\begin{cases} 2y + 6 \geq x \\ y > -\frac{3}{2}x + 5 \end{cases}$ Ⓓ $\begin{cases} 2y + 6 \geq x \\ -y < \frac{3}{2}x + 5 \end{cases}$

11. For which system is $(0, 3)$ NOT a solution? **(Lesson 3-3)**

Ⓐ $\begin{cases} x + y \geq 3 \\ y < -x + 5 \end{cases}$

Ⓑ $\begin{cases} y \geq 3 \\ y < -2x + 3 \end{cases}$

Ⓒ $\begin{cases} y \geq x \\ 2x + 3y > 8 \end{cases}$

Ⓓ $\begin{cases} 2 \geq x - y \\ x < y - 1 \end{cases}$

12. Lucinda scored 16 points in a basketball game. She scored by making F free throws (worth 1 point each) and R regular baskets (worth 2 points each). She made 3 times as many regular baskets as free throws. Which system best represents this situation? **(Lesson 3-2)**

Ⓐ $\begin{cases} F + R = 16 \\ R = 3F \end{cases}$

Ⓑ $\begin{cases} F + R = 16 \\ F = 3R \end{cases}$

Ⓒ $\begin{cases} F + 2R = 16 \\ R = 3F \end{cases}$

Ⓓ $\begin{cases} F + 2R = 16 \\ F = 3R \end{cases}$

13. Which system has a solution of $(3, -5)$?
(Lesson 4-7)

(A) $\begin{bmatrix} 3 & -5 \\ -4 & 6 \end{bmatrix} \begin{bmatrix} x \\ y \end{bmatrix} = \begin{bmatrix} 1 \\ -4 \end{bmatrix}$

(B) $\begin{bmatrix} 2 & 4 \\ 3 & -5 \end{bmatrix} \begin{bmatrix} x \\ y \end{bmatrix} = \begin{bmatrix} 2 \\ 7 \end{bmatrix}$

(C) $\begin{bmatrix} 3 & 0 \\ 6 & -3 \end{bmatrix} \begin{bmatrix} x \\ y \end{bmatrix} = \begin{bmatrix} 3 \\ -5 \end{bmatrix}$

(D) $\begin{bmatrix} 2 & 3 \\ 4 & 2 \end{bmatrix} \begin{bmatrix} x \\ y \end{bmatrix} = \begin{bmatrix} -9 \\ 2 \end{bmatrix}$

14. What is the solution to the matrix equation
$\begin{bmatrix} 0 & 4 & -1 \\ 4 & -2 & 3 \\ 9 & 0 & 2 \end{bmatrix} \begin{bmatrix} a \\ b \\ c \end{bmatrix} = \begin{bmatrix} 7 \\ 5 \\ 1 \end{bmatrix}$? (Lesson 4-7)

(A) $(-1, 3, 5)$

(B) $(1, -3, 5)$

(C) $(1, 3, -5)$

(D) $(1, -3, -5)$

15. Which system is described by the graph below?
(Lesson 3-1)

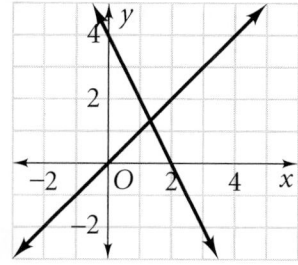

(A) $\begin{cases} x = y \\ 2x - y = 4 \end{cases}$

(B) $\begin{cases} x = 1 \\ 2x + y = 4 \end{cases}$

(C) $\begin{cases} x = y \\ 2x + y = 4 \end{cases}$

(D) $\begin{cases} x = y \\ x + 2y = 4 \end{cases}$

16. Solve $\begin{bmatrix} 5 & -3 \\ 2 & -1 \end{bmatrix} \begin{bmatrix} x \\ y \end{bmatrix} = \begin{bmatrix} 2 \\ 1 \end{bmatrix}$. (Lesson 4-7)

(A) $(1, 1)$ (C) $(2, 3)$

(B) $(-2, -4)$ (D) $(-2, 1)$

17. A vending machine contains 340 coins whose sum is $61.50. They are all nickels, quarters, and dimes. There are 4 times as many quarters as nickels. Which system best represents this situation?
(Lesson 3-6)

(A) $\begin{cases} N + D + Q = 61.50 \\ 0.05N + 0.1D + 0.25Q = 340 \\ Q = 4N \end{cases}$

(B) $\begin{cases} N + D + Q = 340 \\ 0.05N + 0.1D + 0.25Q = 61.50 \\ Q = 4N \end{cases}$

(C) $\begin{cases} N + D + Q = 340 \\ 5N + 10D + 25Q = 61.50 \\ N = 4Q \end{cases}$

(D) $\begin{cases} N + D + Q = 340 \\ 5N + 10D + 25Q = 61.50 \\ N = 4Q \end{cases}$

Standards Reference Guide

California Content Standard	Item Number(s)
ALG2 1.0	1–6
ALG2 2.0	7–17

For additional review and practice, see the *California Standards Review and Practice Workbook* or go online to use the

California Standards Tutorials

Visit: PHSchool.com, **Web Code:** bbq-9045

Quadratic Equation and Functions

 What You've Learned

California Content Standards

1.0 Students solve equations and inequalities involving absolute value.

2.0 Students solve systems of linear equations (in two or three variables) with matrices.

7.0 Students demonstrate an understanding of functions and equations defined parametrically and can graph them. *Mathematical Analysis*

 Check Your Readiness   **for Help** to the Lesson in green.

Simplifying Expressions (Lesson 1-2)

Simplify each expression.

1. $x^2 + 3x^2 - 5x$

2. $\dfrac{x^2}{2} - \dfrac{x^2}{3} + \dfrac{x^2}{5}$

3. $-6x(x + 2) - x(x + 1)$

Solving Linear Equations (Lesson 1-3)

Solve each equation. Check your answers.

4. $4 - 2x = x + 2$

5. $6x + 2.5 = 4x - 1.1$

6. $3(x - 1) = 8(2x - 2)$

Graphing Linear Functions (Lesson 2-2)

Graph each function.

7. $y = -5x - 1$

8. $y = 3x + 12$

9. $y = -6x + 6$

10. $2x - 3y = -4$

11. $-3x + 9y = -12$

12. $y - 1 = -4x$

Using Linear Models (Lesson 2-4)

Graph each set of ordered pairs. Decide whether a linear model is reasonable. If so, draw a trend line and write its equation.

13. $\{(0, 12), (2, 17), (4, 25), (6, 29), (8, 36)\}$

14. $\{(5.5, 16), (6.8, 18.4), (7.5, 19.3), (8, 20), (8.5, 20.8)\}$

15. Each second, a car that begins with a speed of 40 ft/s increases its speed by 6 ft/s. Write and graph an equation to model the car's speed at s seconds.

Graphing Translations (Lesson 2-6)

16. Identify the parent function of $y = |x - 5|$. Graph $y = |x - 5|$ by translating its parent function.

What You'll Learn Next

▲ Many styles of art incorporate parabolas and other functions for their smooth curves.

California Content Standards

4.0 Students factor polynomials representing the difference of squares.

6.0 Students add, subtract, multiply, and divide complex numbers.

8.0 Students solve and graph quadratic equations by factoring. Students apply this technique in solving word problems.

10.0 Students graph quadratic functions and determine the maxima, minima, and zeros of the function.

New Vocabulary

◀)) **English and Spanish Audio Online**

- **axis of symmetry** (p. 243)
- **completing the square** (p. 286)
- **complex number** (p. 279)
- **complex number plane** (p. 279)
- **difference of two squares** (p. 267)
- **discriminant** (p. 295)

- **factoring** (p. 263)
- **imaginary number** (p. 278)
- **parabola** (p. 243)
- **perfect square trinomial** (p. 266)
- **Quadratic Formula** (p. 293)
- **quadratic function** (p. 242)

- **standard form of a quadratic function** (p. 242)
- **vertex form of a quadratic function** (p. 256)
- **zero of a function** (p. 272)
- **Zero Product Property** (p. 271)

Modeling Data With Quadratic Functions

 California Content Standards

ALG2 10.0 Students graph quadratic functions and determine the maxima, minima, and zeros of the function. *Introduce*

ALG2 9.0 Students demonstrate and explain the effect that changing a coefficient has on the graph of quadratic functions. *Introduce*

What You'll Learn

- To identify quadratic functions and graphs
- To model data with quadratic functions

... And Why

To model the flow of water from a container, as in Example 4

✓ **Check Skills You'll Need**

GO for Help Lessons 1-2 and 2-2

Evaluate each function for $x = -3, -1, 0, 1,$ and 3.

1. $f(x) = x$ **2.** $f(x) = x^2$

3. $f(x) = -x$ **4.** $f(x) = -x^2$

5. $f(x) = \frac{1}{3}x^2$ **6.** $f(x) = -\frac{1}{3}x^2$

Write each equation in slope-intercept form.

7. $3x + 4y = 8$ **8.** $2x - y = -7$ **9.** $\frac{1}{2}x + 3y = 9$

🔊 **New Vocabulary** • quadratic function • standard form of a quadratic function • parabola • axis of symmetry • vertex of a parabola

---

1   Quadratic Functions and Their Graphs

A **quadratic function** is a function that can be written in the standard form $f(x) = ax^2 + bx + c$, where $a \neq 0$. The domain of a quadratic function is all real numbers.

 Key Concepts

Definition	**Standard Form of a Quadratic Function**
	$f(x) = \underset{\text{quadratic term}}{ax^2} + \underset{\text{linear term}}{bx} + \underset{\text{constant term}}{c}$

The condition $a \neq 0$ gives every quadratic function a quadratic term, but not necessarily a linear term or a constant term. If $a = 0$, then the function has no quadratic term, and it is not a quadratic function.

Vocabulary Tip

You can use the FOIL acronym to remember how to multiply.

$$y = (2x + 3)(x - 4)$$

First — Last
Inner
Outer

1 EXAMPLE   Classifying Functions

Determine whether each function is linear or quadratic. Identify the quadratic, linear, and constant terms.

a. $y = (2x + 3)(x - 4)$

$= 2x^2 - 8x + 3x - 12$ **Multiply.**

$= 2x^2 - 5x - 12$ **Write in standard form.**

This is a quadratic function.
Quadratic term: $2x^2$
Linear term: $-5x$
Constant term: -12

b. $f(x) = 3(x^2 - 2x) - 3(x^2 - 2)$

$= 3x^2 - 6x - 3x^2 + 6$

$= -6x + 6$

This is a linear function.
Quadratic term: none
Linear term: $-6x$
Constant term: 6

---

1 Determine whether each function is linear or quadratic. Identify the quadratic, linear, and constant terms.
a. $f(x) = (x^2 + 5x) - x^2$ **b.** $f(x) = (x - 5)(3x - 1)$ **c.** $f(x) = x(x + 3)$

The graph of a quadratic function is a **parabola.** The **axis of symmetry** is the line that divides a parabola into two parts that are mirror images. The **vertex of a parabola** is the point at which the parabola intersects the axis of symmetry. The y-value of the vertex of a parabola represents the maximum or minimum value of the function.

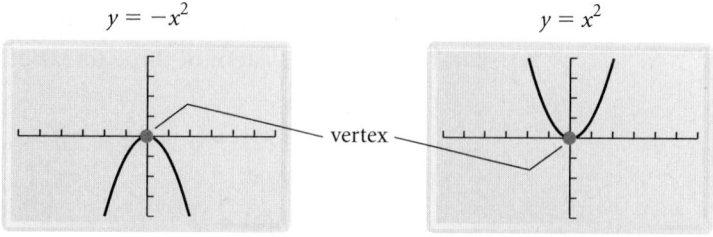

Maximum Value   Minimum Value

The axis of symmetry of the graph of a quadratic function is always a vertical line defined by the x-coordinate of the vertex. In each graph above, the axis of symmetry is the y-axis, $x = 0$.

Real-World Connection

Objects tossed into the air follow parabolic paths.

Each point of the parabola has a corresponding point on its mirror image. Two corresponding points are the same distance from the axis of symmetry. In general the domain of a quadratic function is all real numbers.

2 EXAMPLE **Points on a Parabola**

Below is the graph of $f(x) = 2x^2 - 8x + 8$. Identify the vertex, axis of symmetry, points P' and Q' corresponding to P and Q, and the range of $f(x)$.

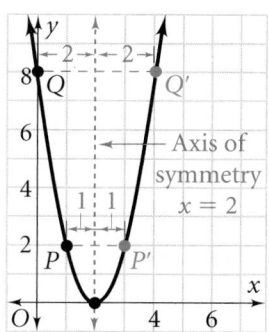

The vertex is $(2, 0)$.

The axis of symmetry is $x = 2$, the vertical line passing through the vertex.

$P(1, 2)$ is one unit to the left of the axis of symmetry. Corresponding point $P'(3, 2)$ is one unit to the right of the axis of symmetry.

$Q(0, 8)$ is two units to the left of the axis of symmetry. Corresponding point $Q'(4, 8)$ is two units to the right of the axis of symmetry.

● The range of this function is all nonnegative real numbers.

2 Identify the vertex and the axis of symmetry of each parabola. Identify points corresponding to P and Q.

a.

b.

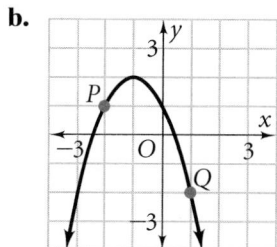

Given three noncollinear points, you can find a quadratic function whose graph passes through those points.

3 **EXAMPLE** Fitting a Quadratic Function to 3 Points

Find a quadratic function that includes the values in the table.

x	y
2	3
3	13
4	29

Substitute the values of x and y into $y = ax^2 + bx + c$.
The result is a system of three linear equations.

$y = ax^2 + bx + c$

$3 = a(2)^2 + b(2) + c = 4a + 2b + c$ **Use (2, 3).**

$13 = a(3)^2 + b(3) + c = 9a + 3b + c$ **Use (3, 13).**

$29 = a(4)^2 + b(4) + c = 16a + 4b + c$ **Use (4, 29).**

Using one of the methods of Chapter 3, solve the system.
$\begin{cases} 4a + 2b + c = 3 \\ 9a + 3b + c = 13 \\ 16a + 4b + c = 29 \end{cases}$

The solution is $a = 3, b = -5, c = 1$. Substitute these values into standard form.

$y = (3)x^2 + (-5)x + (1)$

● The quadratic function is $y = 3x^2 - 5x + 1$.

✓ **CA Standards Check** **3** Find a quadratic function with a graph that includes $(1, 0), (2, -3)$, and $(3, -10)$.

You can use the quadratic regression feature of a graphing calculator to model data with a quadratic function.

4 **EXAMPLE** Real-World Connection

Hydraulics The table at the left shows the height of a column of water as it drains from its container. Model the data with a quadratic function. Graph the data and the function. Use the model to estimate the water level at 35 seconds.

Elapsed Time	Water Level
0 s	120 mm
10 s	100 mm
20 s	83 mm
30 s	66 mm
40 s	50 mm
50 s	37 mm
60 s	28 mm

Step 1 Enter the data. Use **QuadReg**.

```
QuadReg
y = ax² + bx + c
a = .0091666667
b = -2.103571429
c = 120.3333333
■
```

Step 2 Graph the data and the function.

Step 3 Use the table feature to find $f(35)$.

X	Y₁
29	67.039
30	65.476
31	63.932
32	62.406
33	60.898
34	59.409
35	57.937

$Y_1 = 57.9375$

An approximate model of the quadratic function is $y = 0.009167x^2 - 2.10x + 120$.
● At 35 seconds the water level is approximately 58 mm.

✓ **CA Standards Check** **4** **a.** Use the quadratic model to estimate the water level at 25 seconds.
b. Use the quadratic model to predict the water level at 3 minutes.
c. **Critical Thinking** Is your prediction in part (b) reasonable? Explain.

A **Practice by Example**

Example 1
(page 242)

GO for Help

Determine whether each function is linear or quadratic. Identify the quadratic, linear, and constant terms.

1. $y = x + 4$
2. $y = 2x^2 - (3x - 5)$
3. $y = 3x(x - 2)$

4. $f(x) = x^2 - 7$
5. $y = (x - 2)(x + 5)$
6. $g(x) = -7(x - 4)$

7. $h(x) = (3x)(2x) + 6$
8. $y = x(1 - x) - (1 - x^2)$ **9.** $f(x) = -x(2x + 8)$

Example 2
(page 243)

Identify the vertex and the axis of symmetry of each parabola.

10.

11.

12.
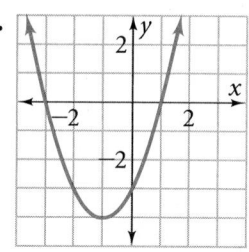

For each parabola, identify points corresponding to *P* and *Q*.

13.

14.

15.
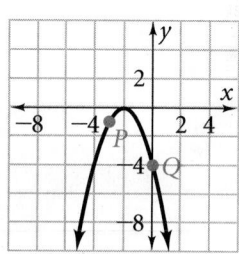

Example 3
(page 244)

Find a quadratic function that includes each set of values.

16. $(1, -2), (2, -2), (3, -4)$ **17.** $(1, -2), (2, -4), (3, -4)$ **18.** $(-1, 6), (1, 4), (2, 9)$

19.

x	−1	1	2
f(x)	−1	3	8

20.

x	−1	1	2
f(x)	17	17	8

Example 4
(page 244)

21. Physics A man throws a ball off the top of a building. The table shows the height of the ball at different times.
a. Find a quadratic model for the data.
b. Use the model to estimate the height of the ball at 2.5 seconds.

Height of a Ball

Time	Height
0 s	46 ft
1 s	63 ft
2 s	48 ft
3 s	1 ft

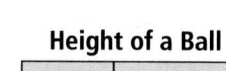

22. Communications The table shows the percent of U.S. houses with cable TV.
a. Find a quadratic model using 1960 as year 0, 1970 as year 10, and so on.
b. Use the model to estimate the percent of households with cable TV in 1995.

Television Cable Access

Year	1960	1970	1980	1990	2000
% of Households	0	7	20	56	68

Source: *Time Almanac*

Determine whether a quadratic model exists for each set of values. If so, write the model.

23. $f(-2) = 16, f(0) = 0, f(1) = 4$ **24.** $f(0) = 5, f(2) = 3, f(-1) = 0$

25. $f(-1) = -4, f(1) = -2, f(2) = -1$ **26.** $f(-2) = 7, f(0) = 1, f(2) = 0$

Identify the vertex and the axis of symmetry for each function.

27.   **28.**   **29.**

 30. a. Geometry Copy and complete the table. It shows the total number of segments that can be drawn among x points, no three of which are collinear.

Number of points, x	2	3	▨	▨
Number of segments, y	1	3	▨	▨

  b. Write a quadratic model for the data.
  c. Predict the number of segments that can be drawn among ten points.

 31. a. Postal Rates Find a quadratic model for the data. Use 1978 as year 0.

Price of First-Class Stamp

Year	1978	1981	1983	1988	1995	2001	2002	2006
Price (cents)	15	18	20	25	32	34	37	39

  b. Describe a reasonable domain and range for your model. (*Hint:* This is a discrete, real situation.)
  c. Estimation Estimate when first-class postage was 29¢.
  d. Use your model to predict when first-class postage will be 50¢. Explain why your prediction may not be valid.

The graph of each function contains the given point. Find the value of c.

32. $y = x^2 + c; (0, 3)$ **33.** $y = x^2 - c; (4, 8)$

34. $y = -5x^2 + c; (2, -14)$ **35.** $y = 2x^2 + c; \left(-\frac{3}{4}, -\frac{1}{4}\right)$

36. $y = -\frac{3}{4}x^2 + c; \left(3, -\frac{1}{2}\right)$ **37.** $y = (x + c)^2; (10, 0)$

 38. Road Safety The table below gives the stopping distance for an automobile under certain road conditions.

Speed (mi/h)	20	30	40	50	55
Stopping Distance (ft)	17	38	67	105	127

  a. Find a linear model for the data.
  b. Find a quadratic model for the data.
  c. Writing Compare the models. Which is better? Explain.

39. Open-Ended Write three different quadratic functions, each with a graph that includes $(0, 0)$ and $(5, -1)$.

Challenge

40. Critical Thinking What is the minimum number of data points you need to find a quadratic model for a data set? Explain.

41. How are the graphs of $y = x^2$ and $y = |x|$ similar? How are they different?

42. A parabola contains the points $(0, -4)$, $(2, 4)$, and $(4, 4)$. Find the vertex.

43. A model for the height of an arrow shot into the air is $h(t) = -16t^2 + 72t + 5$, where t is time and h is height. Without graphing, consider the function's graph.
  a. What can you learn by finding the graph's intercept with the h-axis?
  b. What can you learn by finding the graph's intercept(s) with the t-axis?

 Multiple Choice Practice

For California Standards and CAHSEE Tutorials, visit PHSchool.com. Web Code: bbq-9045

ALG2 10.0
44. What is the maximum value of the function $y = 12 - 3x^2$?
  Ⓐ -3 Ⓑ 2 Ⓒ 12 Ⓓ 24

ALG2 2.0
45. Solve the system $\begin{cases} 3y = 2x + 7 \\ x = y - 3 \end{cases}$.
  Ⓐ $(1, 3)$ Ⓒ $(0, 3)$
  Ⓑ $(-2, 1)$ Ⓓ $(-1, 2)$

ALG2 10.0
46. Which function has a minimum value of -7?
  Ⓐ $y = 4x^2 - 7x$
  Ⓑ $y = 2x^2 - 8x + 1$
  Ⓒ $y = 3x^2 - 2x - 2$
  Ⓓ $y = 5x^2 + 2$

Mixed Review

Lesson 4-8

 for Help

Write the augmented matrix for each system. Then solve the system.

47. $\begin{cases} 3x - y = 7 \\ 2x + 2y = 10 \end{cases}$
        48. $\begin{cases} 3x + y - 2z = -3 \\ x - 3y - z = -2 \\ 2x + 2y + 3z = 11 \end{cases}$

Lesson 4-3

Find each product.

49. $\begin{bmatrix} 2 & -3 \end{bmatrix} \begin{bmatrix} 3 & -2 & 4 & 1 \\ 2 & 0 & -3 & 2 \end{bmatrix}$
        50. $\begin{bmatrix} 3 & 10 \\ 1 & 5 \end{bmatrix} \begin{bmatrix} -7 & 2 \\ 8 & 4 \end{bmatrix}$

Lesson 3-2

Solve each system by elimination.

51. $\begin{cases} x + y = 7 \\ 5x - y = 5 \end{cases}$
  52. $\begin{cases} 2x - 3y = -14 \\ 3x - y = 7 \end{cases}$
  53. $\begin{cases} x - 3y = 2 \\ x - 2y = 1 \end{cases}$

Lesson 2-3

For each direct variation, find the value of y when $x = 2$.

54. $y = 2$ when $x = 5$ **55.** $y = 1$ when $x = 4$ **56.** $y = -2$ when $x = 4$

Modeling Using Residuals

You can use more than one model for a set of data. You can determine which is a better model by analyzing the differences between the y-values of the data and the y-values of each model. These differences are called residuals. The better model will have residuals that are closer to zero.

ACTIVITY

The calculator screen shows the graphs of a linear model and a quadratic model for the data below. Which model better fits the data?

Participation in Backpacking or Wilderness Camp Activities

Year (1990 = 0)	1995	1997	1999	2001	2003
Millions of Participants	10.2	12.0	15.3	14.5	13.7

SOURCE: National Sporting Goods Association

Step 1 Press STAT ENTER to enter the data in L_1 and L_2. Then use the LinReg and QuadReg features to find linear and quadratic models.

Step 2 Enter the linear model as Y_1 and the quadratic model as Y_2.

Step 3 To find the residuals of the linear model and store the differences in L_3, enter L_2 − VARS ▶ 1 1 (L_1) STO▶ L_3 ENTER .

Step 4 Find the residuals of the quadratic model. Store the differences in L_4.

Step 5 Compare the residuals in L_3 and L_4. The values in L_4 are closer to zero, so the quadratic model is the better fit.

L2	L3	L4	2
10.2	−1.04	.28857	
12	−.19	−.8543	
15.3	2.16	.83143	
14.5	.41	−.2543	
13.7	−1.34	−.0114	
------	------	------.	

L2(6) =

EXERCISES

For each set of data, find a linear model and a quadratic model. Which model is the better fit? Justify your reasoning.

1. **Money Spent in the U.S. on Personal Technology**

Year (0 = 1970)	0	10	20	22	24	26
Billions of Dollars	8.8	17.6	53.8	61.2	78.5	89.7

2. **Fishing Licenses Sold**

Year (0 = 1970)	0	5	10	15	20	25	30
Millions Sold	31.1	34.7	35.2	35.7	36.9	37.9	37.6

3. For each of Exercises 1 and 2, state whether the situation is discrete and describe a reasonable domain and range. Explain your responses.

Properties of Parabolas

 California Content Standards

ALG2 10.0 Students graph quadratic functions and determine the maxima, minima, and zeros of the function. *Develop, Master*

ALG2 9.0 Students demonstrate and explain the effect that changing a coefficient has on the graph of quadratic functions. *Develop*

What You'll Learn

- To graph quadratic functions
- To find maximum and minimum values of quadratic functions

. . . And Why

To maximize a company's revenue

 Check Skills You'll Need

GO for Help Lessons 2-2 and 2-5

Find the *y*-intercept of the graph of each function.

1. $y = 3x + 3$ **2.** $y = -2x - 1$ **3.** $4x - 3y = 12$

Find the vertex of the graph of each function.

4. $y = |-2x|$ **5.** $y = \left|-\frac{2}{3}x - 1\right|$ **6.** $y = |3x + 7|$

Graph each equation.

7. $y = -4x - 3$ **8.** $\frac{1}{2}x + y = -2$ **9.** $y = |5x - 5|$

1   Graphing Parabolas

Vocabulary Tip

The word <u>symmetry</u> comes from a prefix meaning "same" and a root meaning "measure."

The standard form of a quadratic function is $y = ax^2 + bx + c$ with $a \neq 0$. When $b = 0$, the function simplifies to $y = ax^2 + c$.

The graph of $y = ax^2 + c$ is a parabola with an axis of symmetry $x = 0$, the *y*-axis. The vertex of the graph is the *y*-intercept $(0, c)$.

1 EXAMPLE   **Graphing a Function of the Form $y = ax^2 + c$**

Graph $y = -\frac{1}{2}x^2 + 2$.

Step 1 Graph the vertex, which is the *y*-intercept $(0, 2)$.

Step 2 Make a table of values to find some points on one side of the axis of symmetry $x = 0$. Graph the points.

x	1	2	3	4
y	$1\frac{1}{2}$	0	$-2\frac{1}{2}$	-6

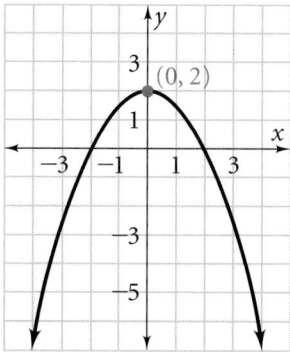

Step 4 Graph corresponding points on the other side of the axis of symmetry.

Step 5 Sketch the curve.

 CA Standards Check   **1 a.** Graph $y = 2x^2 - 4$.

b. Graph $y = -5 + 3x^2$.

c. Reasoning What are the coordinates of the vertex of the graph of a function in the form $y = ax^2$?

When $b \neq 0$ in the standard form of a quadratic function, $y = ax^2 + bx + c$, the values of both a and b affect the position of the axis of symmetry.

You can use the values of a, b, and c to find characteristics of the graph of a quadratic function.

Key Concepts

| Properties | Graph of a Quadratic Function in Standard Form |

The graph of $f(x) = ax^2 + bx + c$ is a parabola when $a \neq 0$.

- When $a > 0$, the parabola opens up. When $a < 0$, the parabola opens down.
- The axis of symmetry is the line $x = -\dfrac{b}{2a}$.
- The x-coordinate of the vertex is $-\dfrac{b}{2a}$. The y-coordinate of the vertex is the y value of the function when $x = -\dfrac{b}{2a}$, or $y = f\left(-\dfrac{b}{2a}\right)$.
- The y-intercept is $(0, c)$.

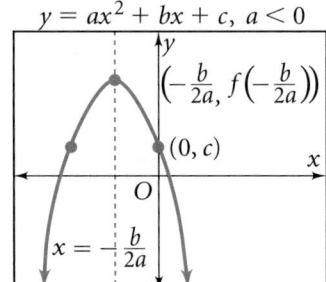

Vocabulary Tip

The _y-intercept_ is the point at which a line crosses the y-axis or the y-coordinate of that point.

---

2 EXAMPLE Graphing a Function of the Form $y = ax^2 + bx + c$

Graph $y = x^2 - 2x - 3$. Label the vertex and the axis of symmetry.

Step 1 Find and graph the axis of symmetry.
$$x = -\frac{b}{2a} = -\frac{(-2)}{2(1)} = 1$$

Step 2 Find and graph the vertex. The x-coordinate of the vertex is $-\frac{b}{2a}$, or 1.

The y-coordinate is $y = (1)^2 - 2(1) - 3 = -4$. So the vertex is $(1, -4)$.

Step 3 Find and graph the y-intercept and its reflection. Since $c = -3$, the y-intercept is $(0, -3)$ and its reflection is $(2, -3)$.

Step 4 Evaluate the function for another value of x, such as $y = (3)^2 - 2(3) - 3 = 0$. Graph $(3, 0)$ and its reflection $(-1, 0)$.

Step 5 Sketch the curve.

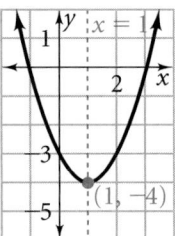

Since $a > 0$, the graph opens up.

 CA Standards Check ❷ Graph each function. Label the vertex and the axis of symmetry.
a. $y = -x^2 + 4x + 2$
b. $y = -\frac{1}{3}x^2 - 2x - 3$

The *y*-coordinate of the vertex of a parabola represents the maximum or minimum value of a quadratic function.

Online
active math

For: Quadratic Activity
Use: Interactive Textbook, 5-2

3 **EXAMPLE** **Finding a Minimum Value**

Graph $y = 3x^2 + 12x + 8$. What is the minimum value of the function?

Since $a > 0$, the graph of the function opens up, and the vertex represents the minimum value. Find the coordinates of the vertex.

$x = -\dfrac{b}{2a} = -\dfrac{12}{2(3)} = -2$ **Find the *x*-coordinate of the vertex.**

$y = 3(-2)^2 + 12(-2) + 8 = -4$ **Find the *y*-coordinate of the vertex.**

Graph the vertex and the axis of symmetry $x = -2$.
Graph two points on one side of the axis of symmetry, such as $(0, 8)$ and $(-1, -1)$. Then graph corresponding points $(-4, 8)$ and $(-3, -1)$.

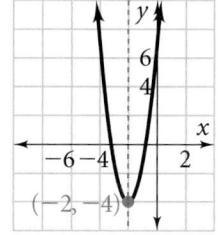

● The minimum value of the function is -4.

✓ CA Standards Check **3** **a.** Graph $y = 2x^2 + 8x - 1$. Find the minimum value of the function.
    b. Critical Thinking What is the maximum value of the function?

You can find a maximum or minimum value without graphing the function.

4 **EXAMPLE** **Real-World** 🌐 **Connection**

Economics A company knows that $-2.5p + 500$ models the number it sells per month of a certain make of unicycle, where the price p can be set as low as \$70 or as high as \$120. Revenue from sales is the product of the price and the number sold. What price will maximize the revenue? What is the maximum revenue?

Relate revenue equals price times number of unicycles sold

Define Let R = revenue. Let p = price of a unicycle.

Let $-2.5p + 500$ = number of unicycles sold.

Write $R = p \, (-2.5p + 500)$

$= -2.5p^2 + 500p$ **Write in standard form.**

Find the maximum value of the function. Since $a < 0$, the graph of the function opens down, and the vertex represents a maximum value.

$p = -\dfrac{b}{2a} = -\dfrac{500}{2(-2.5)} = 100$ **Find *p* at the vertex.**

$R = -2.5(100)^2 + 500(100)$ **Evaluate *R* for *p* = 100.**

$= 25{,}000$ **Simplify.**

● A price of \$100 will maximize revenue. The maximum revenue is \$25,000.

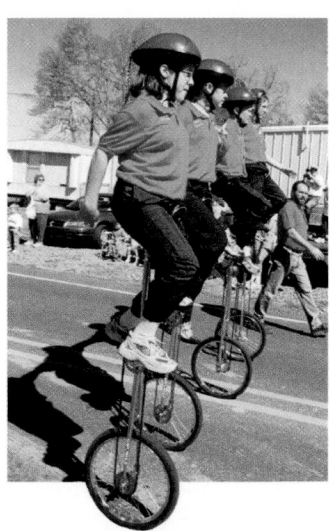

Real-World 🌐 **Connection**

The number of unicycles a company sells can be modeled by $-2.5p + 500$.

✓ CA Standards Check **4** The number of widgets the Woodget Company sells can be modeled by $-5p + 100$, where p is the price of a widget. What price will maximize revenue? What is the maximum revenue?

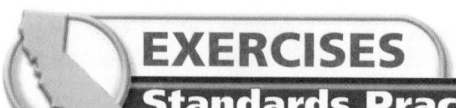
A Practice by Example

Example 1
(page 249)

GO for Help

Graph each function.

1. $y = -x^2 + 1$

2. $y = -x^2 - 1$

3. $y = 2x^2 + 4$

4. $y = 3x^2 - 6$

5. $y = -\frac{1}{3}x^2 - 1$

6. $y = -5x^2 + 12$

7. $y = \frac{1}{2}x^2 + 3$

8. $y = \frac{1}{4}x^2 - 3$

9. $y = -2x^2 + \frac{3}{4}$

Example 2
(page 250)

Graph each function. Label the vertex and the axis of symmetry.

10. $y = x^2 + 2x + 1$

11. $y = -x^2 + 2x + 1$

12. $y = x^2 + 4x + 1$

13. $y = x^2 + 6x + 9$

14. $y = -x^2 - 3x + 6$

15. $y = 2x^2 + 4x$

16. $y = 4x^2 - 12x + 9$

17. $y = -6x^2 - 12x - 1$

18. $y = -\frac{3}{4}x^2 + 6x + 6$

19. $y = 3x^2 - 12x + 10$

20. $y = \frac{1}{2}x^2 + 2x - 8$

21. $y = -4x^2 - 24x - 36$

Example 3
(page 251)

Graph each function. If $a > 0$ find the minimum value. If $a < 0$ find the maximum value.

22. $y = -x^2 + 2x + 5$

23. $y = 3x^2 - 4x - 2$

24. $y = -2x^2 - 3x + 4$

25. $y = \frac{1}{3}x^2 + 2x + 5$

26. $y = -x^2 - x + 6$

27. $y = 2x^2 + 5$

Example 4
(page 251)

28. Revenue A model for a company's revenue is $R = -15p^2 + 300p + 12{,}000$, where p is the price in dollars of the company's product. What price will maximize revenue? Find the maximum revenue.

29. Physics The equation for the motion of a projectile fired straight up at an initial velocity of 64 ft/s is $h = 64t - 16t^2$, where h is the height in feet and t is the time in seconds. Find the time the projectile needs to reach its highest point. How high it will go?

30. Manufacturing The equation for the cost in dollars of producing automobile tires is $C = 0.000015x^2 - 0.03x + 35$, where x is the number of tires produced. Find the number of tires that minimizes the cost. What is the cost for that number of tires?

B Apply Your Skills

Sketch each parabola using the given information.

31. vertex $(3, 6)$, y-intercept 2

32. vertex $(-1, -4)$, y-intercept 3

33. vertex $(0, 5)$, point $(1, -2)$

34. vertex $(2, 3)$, point $(6, 9)$

35. Find a pair of numbers with a sum of 26 and a product that is a maximum. Find the maximum product.

36. Find two numbers with a difference of 10 and a product that is a minimum. Find the minimum product.

Match each function with its graph.

37. $y = x^2 + 4x + 1$ **38.** $y = -x^2 - 4x + 1$ **39.** $y = -\frac{1}{2}x^2 - 2x + 1$

A.   **B.**   **C.**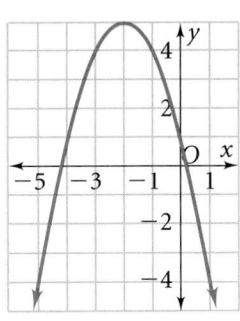

40. Open-Ended Write the equation of a parabola symmetric about $x = -10$.

41. Woodworking Suppose you want to frame a collage of pictures. You have a 9-ft strip of wood for the frame. What dimensions of the frame give you the maximum area for the collage? What is the maximum area?

42. Physics Suppose you throw a ball over a 10-ft fence. Barely clearing the fence, the ball reaches its highest point directly above the fence and lands 10 ft from the fence. Using the fence as the axis of symmetry, write a quadratic function that models the ball's height.

43. Packaging The bottom of a box is to be a rectangle with a perimeter of 36 cm. The box must be 4 cm high. What dimensions give the maximum volume?

For each function, the vertex of the function's graph is given. Find c.

44. $y = x^2 - 6x + c; (3, -4)$ **45.** $y = -3x^2 + 6x + c; (1, 0)$

46. $y = x^2 + 10x + c; (-5, -27)$ **47.** $y = c - x^2 - 2x; (-1, 3)$

Find the quadratic function $y = ax^2 + c$ with a graph that has the given points.

48. $(0, 2), (3, 5)$ **49.** $(0, -3), (1, -7)$ **50.** $\left(2, \frac{5}{2}\right), \left(0, -\frac{1}{2}\right)$

51. $(-3, 89), (2, 39)$ **52.** $(-2, -10), (4, -40)$ **53.** $(-1, 14), (4, 104)$

54. A rock club's profit from booking local bands depends on the ticket price. Using past receipts, the owners find that the profit p can be modeled by the function $p = -15t^2 + 600t + 50$, where t represents the ticket price in dollars.
 a. What price yields the maximum profit?
 b. What is the maximum profit?
 c. Open-Ended What price would you pay to see your favorite local band? How much profit would the club owner make using that ticket price?

55. Multiple Choice A landscape architect is planning a playground. She wants to fence a rectangular space using an existing wall. What is the greatest area she can fence in using 100 ft of donated fencing?
 Ⓐ 1000 ft^2 Ⓒ 2500 ft^2
 Ⓑ 1250 ft^2 Ⓓ $10,000$ ft^2

56. **History** Around 2500 B.C. in the Indus Valley of South Asia, the Harappan
people built one of the first cities. The Harappans built rectangular houses that
had open central courtyards surrounded by solid brick walls.
   a. Suppose you build a model of a Harappan house. For the outer walls you
   plan to use 2400 bricks. The walls of the model are 10 bricks high and 1 brick
   thick. Draw several possible floor plans.
   b. Find the dimensions of the floor plan that give the model of maximum area.

**Each point lies on a parabola that has its vertex at (0, 1). Write the equation of the
parabola. Indicate whether the graph opens up or down.**

57. $(-3, 10)$ 58. $(-1, 6)$ 59. $(2, -1)$ 60. $(4, -7)$

61. $(3, 4)$ 62. $(5, -4)$ 63. $(8, -15)$ 64. $(-6, -2)$

65. **Construction** A construction worker places his toolbox on a board that rests on
two cement posts 10 ft apart. The toolbox is halfway between the posts. Under
the weight of the toolbox, the board sags by one quarter inch. Model the shape
of the board in three different ways by writing a function whose graph satisfies
each condition below.
   a. The origin of the graph corresponds to the position of the toolbox.
   b. The origin of the graph corresponds to the position of the post on the left.
   c. The origin of the graph corresponds to the position of the post on the right.

├──── 10 ft ────┤

66. A student says that the graph of $y = ax^2 + bx + c$ gets wider as a increases.
   a. **Error Analysis** Use examples to show that the student is wrong.
   b. **Writing** Summarize the relationship between $|a|$ and the width of the graph
   of $y = ax^2 + bx + c$.

C **Challenge**

For each function, the vertex of the function's graph is given. Find a and b.

67. $y = ax^2 + bx - 27; (2, -3)$ 68. $y = ax^2 + bx + 5; (-1, 4)$

69. $y = ax^2 + bx + 8; (2, -4)$ 70. $y = ax^2 + bx; (-3, 2)$

**The formula for the area enclosed by a parabola and the x-axis from x-intercepts
x_1 to x_2 is $A = \frac{2}{3}h(x_2 - x_1)$, where h is the height. Find the enclosed area for
each parabola.**

71.   72.   73.

Multiple Choice Practice

For California Standards and CAHSEE Tutorials, visit PHSchool.com. Web Code: bbq-9045

ALG2 10.0

74. Which quadratic function represents the parabola shown at the right?

Ⓐ $y = x^2 - x - 3$

Ⓑ $y = 3x^2 - 1$

Ⓒ $y = x^2 - 3x - 1$

Ⓓ $y = -x^2 + 3x + 1$

**CAHSEE
7MG 2.1**

75. Which equation best represents the area A of the rectangle at the right?

Ⓐ $A = 2r(r + s)$

Ⓑ $A = r(r + s)$

Ⓒ $A = 2r + 2(r + s)$

Ⓓ $A = r^2 + (r + s)^2$

Mixed Review

Lesson 5-1

76. Find a quadratic model for the values in the table.

x	0	5	10	15	20
y	17	39	54	61	61

Lesson 4-2

Solve each matrix equation.

77. $X + \begin{bmatrix} 0 & 4 \\ -2 & 1 \end{bmatrix} = \begin{bmatrix} 3 & 0 \\ 1 & 1 \end{bmatrix}$

78. $X - \begin{bmatrix} 3 & 3 \\ -2 & -1 \end{bmatrix} = \begin{bmatrix} 1 & 0 \\ 0 & 1 \end{bmatrix}$

Lesson 3-3

79. Manufacturing A new factory will require at least 40,000 ft² of storage space. No more than 25,000 ft² of the space will be covered with a roof. Write a system of inequalities to represent the constraints. Solve the system by graphing.

Algebra at Work

········· **Landscape Architect**

Landscape architects create outdoor environments for parks, office buildings, and homes. They plan walls, staircases, pools, walkways, and plantings. Landscape architects blend ideas from art, science, nature, and math in their work. They need training in all four areas before they begin their careers. For example, when planning a decorative fountain, an architect needs to predict the parabolic path of the spray. The height and distance of the spray depend on the speed of the water and the angle at which it exits a pipe. Basic principles of physics often help architects. By making adjustments to a model, they can plan the effect they want.

 For: Information about landscape architecture
PHSchool.com **Web Code:** bbb-2031

Transforming Parabolas

 California Content Standards

ALG2 9.0 Students demonstrate and explain the effect that changing a coefficient has on the graph of quadratic functions; that is, students can determine how the graph of a parabola changes as *a, b,* and *c* vary in the equation $y = a(x - b)^2 + c$. **Master**

What You'll Learn

• To use the vertex form of a quadratic function

. . . And Why

To model a suspension bridge, as in Example 3

✓ **Check Skills You'll Need**

 for Help Lesson 2-6

Identify the parent function of each function. Then graph the function by transforming the graph of the parent function.

1. $y = x + 2$　　　　**2.** $y = 3|x| + 2$　　　　**3.** $y = -|x + 1| - 1$

Write an equation for each translation.

4. $y = x$, 2 units down　　　　**5.** $y = |x|$, 4 units up, 1 unit right

🔊 **New Vocabulary** • vertex form of a quadratic function

---

1 Using Vertex Form

Activity: Vertex Form

1. Each function in the first column is written in standard form. In the second column, each function has been rewritten in vertex form. Use multiplication to verify that the functions in each row are equivalent.

Standard Form $y = ax^2 + bx + c$	$-\dfrac{b}{2a}$	Vertex Form $y = a(x - h)^2 + k$	h
$y = x^2 - 4x + 4$	▪	$y = (x - 2)^2$	▪
$y = x^2 + 6x + 8$	▪	$y = (x + 3)^2 - 1$	▪
$y = -3x^2 - 12x - 8$	▪	$y = -3(x + 2)^2 + 4$	▪
$y = 2x^2 + 12x + 19$	▪	$y = 2(x + 3)^2 + 1$	▪

2. **a. Patterns** Copy and complete the table.
   b. Compare the values of $-\dfrac{b}{2a}$ and h in each row. Write a formula to show the relationship between $-\dfrac{b}{2a}$ and h.

In Chapter 2, you learned to graph absolute value functions as transformations of their parent function $y = |x|$. Similarly, you can graph a quadratic function as a transformation of the parent function $y = x^2$.

To transform the graph of a quadratic function, you can use the **vertex form of a quadratic function,** $y = a(x - h)^2 + k$.

Key Concepts

Summary	The Family of Quadratic Functions

Vertical Stretch or Shrink, and/or Reflection in *x*-axis

Parent function:	$y = x^2$
Reflection in *x*-axis:	$y = -x^2$
Stretch ($a > 1$) or shrink ($0 < a < 1$) by factor *a*:	$y = ax^2$
Reflection in *x*-axis:	$y = -ax^2$

Vertex Form $y = a(x - h)^2 + k$

The graph (and vertex) of $y = ax^2$ shifts
h units horizontally and *k* units vertically.

For $h > 0$, the graph shifts right.
For $h < 0$, the graph shifts left.
For $k > 0$, the graph shifts up.
For $k < 0$, the graph shifts down.

The vertex is (h, k), and the axis of symmetry is the line $x = h$.

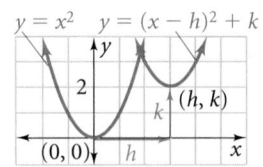

Vocabulary Tip

<u>Vertex</u> means "turning point."

---

1 EXAMPLE **Using Vertex Form to Graph a Parabola**

Graph $y = -\frac{1}{2}(x - 2)^2 + 3$.

The vertex of $y = -\frac{1}{2}(x - 2)^2 + 3$ is 2 units right and 3 units up from the origin.
The axis of symmetry is $x = 2$.

Step 1 Graph the vertex $(2, 3)$. Draw the axis of symmetry $x = 2$.

Step 2 Find another point. When $x = 0$,
$y = -\frac{1}{2}(0 - 2)^2 + 3 = 1$. Graph $(0, 1)$.

Step 3 Graph the point $(4, 1)$. It is 2 units to the right of the axis of symmetry at $(4, 1)$.

Step 4 Sketch the curve.

✓ **CA Standards Check** **1 a.** Graph $y = 2(x + 1)^2 - 4$.
b. In graphing the function in part (a), which method did you choose—stretching the parent function to graph $y = 2x^2$ and then translating the graph of $y = 2x^2$, or graphing the vertex and axis of symmetry? Explain your choice.

You can use the vertex form to write the equation of a parabola.

---

2 EXAMPLE **Writing the Equation of a Parabola**

Write the equation of the parabola at the right.

$y = a(x - h)^2 + k$	**Use the vertex form.**
$y = a(x - 3)^2 + 4$	**Substitute $h = 3$ and $k = 4$.**
$-4 = a(5 - 3)^2 + 4$	**Substitute $(5, -4)$.**
$-8 = 4a$	**Simplify.**
$-2 = a$	**Solve for *a*.**

The equation of the parabola is $y = -2(x - 3)^2 + 4$.

Online active math

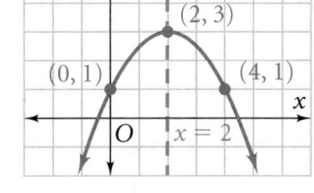

For: Vertex Form Activity
Use: Interactive Textbook, 5-3

② Use vertex form to write the equation of the parabola below.

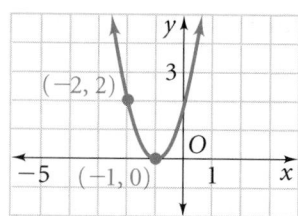

You can use vertex form to model real-world problems.

3 EXAMPLE   **Real-World** **Connection**

Civil Engineering The photo shows the Verrazano–Narrows Bridge in New York, which has the longest span of any suspension bridge in the United States. A suspension cable of the bridge forms a curve that resembles a parabola. The curve can be modeled with the function $y = 0.0001432(x - 2130)^2$, where x and y are measured in feet.

The origin of the function's graph is at the base of one of the two towers that support the cable. How far apart are the towers? How high are they?

Start by drawing a diagram.

The function is in vertex form. Since $h = 2130$ and $k = 0$, the vertex is at $(2130, 0)$. The vertex is halfway between the towers, so the distance between the towers is $2(2130 \text{ ft}) = 4260$ ft.

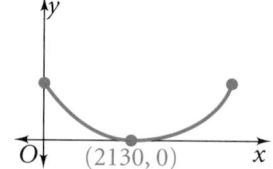

To find the tower's height, find y for $x = 0$.

$$y = 0.0001432(0 - 2130)^2$$
$$y = 0.0001432(-2130)^2$$
$$\approx 650$$

● The towers are 4260 ft apart and about 650 ft high.

✓ **CA Standards Check** ② Suppose the towers in Example 3 are 4000 ft apart and 600 ft high. Write a function that could model the curve of the suspension cable.

Both the vertex form and the standard form give useful information about a parabola. The standard form makes it easy to identify the y-intercept. The vertex form makes it easy to identify the vertex and the axis of symmetry, and to graph the parabola as a transformation of the parent function. The graph shows the relationship between the two forms.

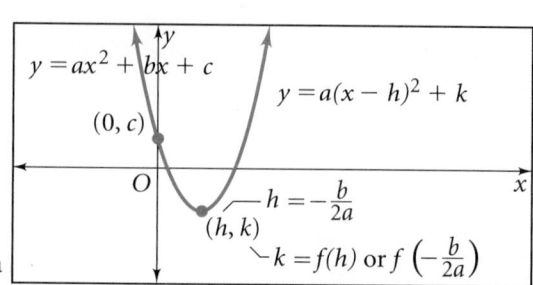

You can convert a function from standard form to vertex form.

4 EXAMPLE **Converting to Vertex Form**

Write $y = 2x^2 + 10x + 7$ in vertex form.

$x = -\dfrac{b}{2a}$ **Find the *x*-coordinate of the vertex.**

$= -\dfrac{10}{2(2)}$ **Substitute for *a* and *b*.**

$= -2.5$

$y = 2(-2.5)^2 + 10(-2.5) + 7$ **Find the *y*-coordinate of the vertex.**

$= -5.5$

The vertex is at $(-2.5, -5.5)$.

$y = a(x - h)^2 + k$ **Write the vertex form.**

$= 2(x - (-2.5))^2 - 5.5$ **Substitute for *a*, *h*, and *k*.**

$= 2(x + 2.5)^2 - 5.5$ **Simplify.**

● The vertex form of the function is $y = 2(x + 2.5)^2 - 5.5$.

✓ **CA Standards Check** ④ Write $y = -3x^2 + 12x + 5$ in vertex form.

EXERCISES

For more exercises, see *Extra Skill and Word Problem Practice.*

Standards Practice

ALG2 9.0

A Practice by Example

Example 1
(page 257)

Graph each function. Identify the axis of symmetry.

1. $y = (x - 1)^2 + 2$ **2.** $y = (x + 3)^2 - 4$

3. $y = 2(x - 2)^2 + 5$ **4.** $y = 2(x + 1)^2$

5. $y = -3(x + 7)^2 - 8$ **6.** $y = -\dfrac{1}{2}(x - 2)^2 + 1$

7. $y = (x - 5)^2 - 3$ **8.** $y = (x + 2)^2 - 3$

9. $y = -(x - 1)^2 + 4$ **10.** $y = 3(x + 5)^2 - 8$

11. $y = -(x - 7)^2 + 10$ **12.** $y = -4(x + 8)^2 - 6$

Example 2
(page 257)

Write the equation of each parabola in vertex form.

13.

14.

15.

16.
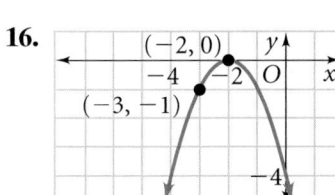

Write the equation of each parabola in vertex form.

17.

18.

19.

20.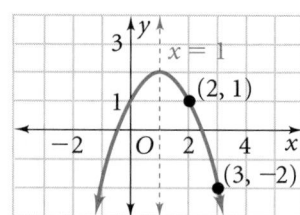

Example 3
(page 258)

Identify the vertex and the y-intercept of the graph of each function.

21. $y = -1.5(x + 20)^2$

22. $y = 0.1(x - 3.2)^2$

23. $y = 24(x + 5.5)^2$

24. $y = 0.0035(x + 1)^2 - 1$

25. $y = -(x - 4)^2 - 25$

26. $y = (x - 125)^2 + 125$

Example 4
(page 259)

Write each function in vertex form.

27. $y = x^2 - 4x + 6$

28. $y = x^2 + 2x + 5$

29. $y = 6x^2 - 10$

30. $y = -5x^2 + 12$

31. $y = 4x^2 + 7x$

32. $y = 2x^2 + x$

33. $y = 2x^2 - 5x + 12$

34. $y = -2x^2 + 8x + 3$

35. $y = \frac{9}{4}x^2 + 3x - 1$

B **Apply Your Skills**

Sketch each parabola. Identify the axis of symmetry.

36. $y = 2(x + 2)^2 - 3$

37. $y = -3(x - 2)^2$

38. $y = 5(x + 0.3)^2 - 10$

39. $y = -0.5(x - 2)^2 - 5$

Begin with the parent $y = x^2$ graph. Show how to transform it to graph each function below. Draw the final graph in a different color.

40. $y = -2(x + 1)^2 + 1$

41. $y = 0.2(x - 12)^2 - 3$

42. Business The Big Brick Bakery sells more bagels when it reduces its prices, but then its profit changes. The function $y = -1000(x - 0.55)^2 + 300$ models the bakery's daily profit in dollars, from selling bagels, where x is the price of a bagel in dollars. The bakery wants to maximize the profit.
a. What is the domain of the function? Can x be negative? Explain.
b. Find the daily profit for selling bagels for $.40 each; for $.85 each.
c. What price should the bakery charge to maximize its profit from bagels?
d. What is the maximum profit?

Write the equation of each parabola in vertex form.

43. vertex $(1, 2)$, point $(2, -5)$

44. vertex $(3, 6)$, y-intercept 2

45. vertex $(-3, 6)$, point $(1, -2)$

46. vertex $(-2, 6)$, y-intercept 12

47. vertex $(-1, -4)$, y-intercept 3

48. vertex $(0, 5)$, point $(1, -2)$

49. vertex $\left(\frac{1}{10}, -\frac{9}{10}\right)$, y-intercept -1

50. vertex $\left(\frac{1}{4}, -\frac{3}{2}\right)$, point $(1, 3)$

Write each function in standard form.

51. $y = (5x + 6)^2 - 9$ **52.** $y = -(3x - 4)^2 + 6$ **53.** $y = 2x(x + 7) + 8x$

54. $y = \frac{1}{2}(x - 5)^2 + 5$ **55.** $y = -0.1(10x + 20)^2$ **56.** $y = (1 - 4x)^2 + 1$

57. a. Technology Determine the axis of symmetry for each parabola defined by the spreadsheet values at the right.
  b. How could you use the spreadsheet columns to verify that the axes of symmetry are correct?
  c. Write functions in vertex form that model the data. Check that the axes of symmetry are correct.

	A	B			A	B
1	X1	Y1		1	X2	Y2
2	1	−35		2	1	10
3	2	−15		3	2	2
4	3	−3		4	3	2
5	4	1		5	4	10
6	5	−3		6	5	26

58. Writing Describe the family of quadratic functions whose members each have $(3, 4)$ as its vertex.

Determine whether each function is written in vertex form. If a function is not in vertex form, rewrite the function.

59. $y = -2x^2 + 35$ **60.** $y = -8x^2$ **61.** $y = -3x^2 - 2x + 1$

62. $y = -2(x + 1)^2 - 1$ **63.** $y = x^2 + 2x + 8$ **64.** $y = \frac{3}{10}x^2 - 1$

65. $y = -4x^2 + 6x + 3$ **66.** $y = 0.5x^2 + 10$ **67.** $y = 100x^2 - 40x + 10$

Determine a and k so both points are on the graph of the function.

68. $(0, 1), (2, 1); y = a(x - 1)^2 + k$ **69.** $(-3, 2), (0, 11); y = a(x + 2)^2 + k$

70. $(1, 11), (2, -19); y = a(x + 1)^2 + k$ **71.** $(-2, 6), (3, 1); y = a(x - 3)^2 + k$

72. $(-2, 10), (1, -34); y = 2a(x + 1)^2 + k$ **73.** $(4, 26), (5, -25); y = a(x - 30)^2 + k$

Homework Video Tutor

Visit: PHSchool.com
Web Code: bbe-0503

74. Multiple Choice One parabola shown has equation $y = (x - 4)^2 + 2$. What is an equation for the other?
  Ⓐ $y = -(x - 4)^2 + 2$ Ⓒ $y = (-x - 4)^2 + 2$
  Ⓑ $y = (x + 4)^2 - 2$ Ⓓ $y = -(x + 4)^2 - 2$

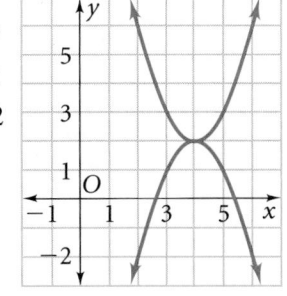

75. Open-Ended Write a quadratic function in vertex form for which the graph has a vertex at $(-2, 5)$. Rewrite the function in standard form.

76. Determine whether the function $f(x) = 0.25(2x - 15)^2 + 150$ has a maximum or a minimum value. Then find the value.

77. Critical Thinking Describe the differences between the graphs of $y = (x + 6)^2$ and $y = (x - 6)^2 + 7$.

Ⓒ Challenge

78. a. In the function $y = ax^2 + bx + c, c$ represents the y-intercept. Find the value of the y-intercept in the function $y = a(x - h)^2 + k$.
  b. Under what conditions does k represent the y-intercept?

Find a quadratic function $y = a(x - h)^2$ for which the graph includes the given points.

79. $(-2, 1), (2, 1)$ **80.** $(-5, 2), (-1, 2)$ **81.** $(-1, -4), (7, -4)$

82. $(2, -1), (4, 0)$ **83.** $(-2, 18), (1, 0)$ **84.** $(1, -64), (-3, 0)$

GO ●nline Lesson Quiz Visit: PHSchool.com, **Web Code:** bba-0503

261

For California Standards and CAHSEE Tutorials, visit PHSchool.com. Web Code: bbq-9045

ALG2 9.0

85. What is the equation of the function $y = x^2$ translated 3 units up and 4 units left?

   Ⓐ $y = (x - 3)^2 - 4$ Ⓒ $y = (x + 4)^2 + 3$

   Ⓑ $y = (x - 4)^2 + 3$ Ⓓ $y = (x + 3)^2 - 4$

ALG2 10.0

86. What is the minimum value of the function $y = x^2 - 2x - 3$?

   Ⓐ -4 Ⓑ -3 Ⓒ -2 Ⓓ 2

ALG2 2.0

87. Which of the following ordered pairs is a solution to the system of equations given by $x + y = 5$ and $3x - 2y = 0$?

   Ⓐ $(1, 4)$ Ⓑ $(2, 3)$ Ⓒ $(3, 2)$ Ⓓ $(5, 0)$

ALG2 10.0

88. What is the zero of $f(x) = 3(x - 2)^2$?

   Ⓐ -3 Ⓑ -2 Ⓒ 2 Ⓓ 3

Mixed Review

Lesson 5-2

Graph each function.

89. $y = x^2 - 5$ **90.** $y = x^2 - 4x + 8$ **91.** $y = 3x^2 + 6x + 5$

Lesson 4-5

Solve each matrix equation.

92. $\begin{bmatrix} 0 & 1 \\ -1 & 2 \end{bmatrix} X = \begin{bmatrix} 20 \\ 10 \end{bmatrix}$ **93.** $\begin{bmatrix} -1 & 3 \\ 1 & -2 \end{bmatrix} X = \begin{bmatrix} 4 \\ -4 \end{bmatrix}$

Lesson 3-4

94. Find the maximum and minimum values of the objective function $P = 2x + y$, under the constraints at the right.

$\begin{cases} y \geq 2x - 2 & x \geq 0 \\ y \leq -x + 4 & y \geq 0 \end{cases}$

✓ Checkpoint Quiz 1   Lessons 5-1 through 5-3

Find a quadratic model in standard form for each set of values.

1. $(0, 3), (1, 10), (2, 19)$ **2.** $(-2, -15), (0, 1), (2, 1)$ **3.** $(0, 0), (1, -5), (2, 0)$

Graph each function.

4. $y = 4x^2 + 16x + 7$ **5.** $y = (x + 8)^2 - 3$ **6.** $y = -(x + 2)^2 - 7$

Determine whether each function has a maximum or minimum value. Then find the value.

7. $y = -x^2 + 6x + 5$ **8.** $y = \frac{1}{2}(x - 6)^2 + 7$

9. Rewrite the equation $y = -3x^2 - 6x - 8$ in vertex form. Identify the vertex and the axis of symmetry.

10. Open-Ended Write the equation of a parabola with a vertex at $(3, 2)$. Write the axis of symmetry and the coordinates of two other points on the graph.

Factoring Quadratic Expressions

 California Content Standards

ALG2 4.0 Students factor polynomials representing the difference of squares and perfect square trinomials. *Introduce, Develop*

What You'll Learn

- To find common and binomial factors of quadratic expressions
- To factor special quadratic expressions

...And Why

To model the cross section of a pipe, as in Example 8

 Check Skills You'll Need

GO for Help Lessons 1-2 and 5-1

Simplify each expression.

1. $x^2 + x + 4x - 1$ **2.** $6x^2 - 4(3)x + 2x - 3$ **3.** $4x^2 - 2(5 - x) - 3x$

Multiply.

4. $2x(5 - x)$ **5.** $(2x - 7)(2x - 7)$ **6.** $(4x + 3)(4x - 3)$

◄)) New Vocabulary
- factoring • greatest common factor (GCF) of an expression
- perfect square trinomial • difference of two squares

---

1   Finding Common and Binomial Factors

> **Activity: Factoring**
>
> **1.** Since $6 \cdot 3 = 18$, 6 and 3 make up a factor pair for 18.
>   **a.** Find the other factor pairs for 18, including negative integers.
>   **b.** Find the sum of the integers in each factor pair for 18.
>
> **2. a.** Does 12 have a factor pair with a sum of -8? A sum of -9?
>   **b.** Using all the factor pairs of 12, how many sums are possible?
>   **c.** How many sums are possible for the factor pairs of -12?

Vocabulary Tip

One number is a <u>factor</u> of another if the first divides into the second with no remainder.

Factoring is rewriting an expression as the product of its factors. The **greatest common factor (GCF) of an expression** is a common factor of the terms of the expression. It's the common factor with the greatest coefficient and the greatest exponent. You can factor any expression that has a GCF not equal to 1.

1 EXAMPLE   Finding Common Factors

Factor each expression.
a. $4x^2 + 20x - 12$

$\quad 4x^2 + 20x - 12 = 4x^2 + 4(5x) - 4(3)$ **Factor out the GCF, 4.**

$\quad\quad\quad\quad\quad\quad\quad\quad = 4(x^2 + 5x - 3)$ **Rewrite using the Distributive Property.**

b. $9n^2 - 24n$

$\quad 9n^2 - 24n = 3n(3n) - 3n(8)$ **Factor out the GCF, 3n.**

$\quad\quad\quad\quad\quad\quad = 3n(3n - 8)$ **Rewrite using the Distributive Property.**

 1 Factor each expression.

    a. $9x^2 + 3x - 18$ **b.** $7p^2 + 21$ **c.** $4w^2 + 2w$

A quadratic trinomial is an expression in the form $ax^2 + bx + c$. You can factor many quadratic trinomials into two binomial factors. First find two factors with a product ac and a sum b. Then find common factors.

If ac and b are positive, then the factors of ac are both positive.

2 EXAMPLE **Factoring When $ac > 0$ and $b > 0$**

Factor $x^2 + 8x + 7$.

Step 1 Find factors with product ac and sum b.

Since $ac = 7$ and $b = 8$, find positive factors with product 7 and sum 8.

Factors of 7	1, 7
Sum of factors	8

These are the only positive factors of 7.

Step 2 Rewrite the term bx using the factors you found. Group the remaining terms and find the common factors for each group. After removing common factors from each group, you should find two identical binomials.

You can use models to factor the expression in Example 2.

$x^2 + 8x + 7$

$x^2 + x + 7x + 7$ **Rewrite bx: $8x = x + 7x$.**

$x(x + 1) + 7(x + 1)$ **Find common factors.**

Step 3 Rewrite the expression as the product of two binomials.

$x(x + 1) + 7(x + 1)$

$(x + 1)(x + 7)$ **Rewrite using the Distributive Property.**

Check $(x + 1)(x + 7) = x^2 + 7x + x + 7$

$= x^2 + 8x + 7$ ✓

✓ CA Standards Check **2** Factor each expression. Check your answers.

a. $x^2 + 6x + 8$ **b.** $x^2 + 12x + 32$ **c.** $x^2 + 14x + 40$

If ac is positive and b is negative, then the factors of ac are both negative.

3 EXAMPLE **Factoring When $ac > 0$ and $b < 0$**

Factor $x^2 - 17x + 72$.

Step 1 Find factors with product ac and sum b.

Since $ac = 72$ and $b = -17$, find negative factors with product 72 and sum -17.

Factors of 72	-1, -72	-2, -36	-3, -24	-4, -18	-6, -12	-8, -9
Sum of factors	-73	-38	-27	-22	-18	-17

Step 2 Rewrite the term bx using the factors you found. Then find common factors and rewrite the expression as the product of two binomials.

$x^2 - 17x + 72$

$x^2 - 8x - 9x + 72$ **Rewrite bx.**

$x(x - 8) - 9(x - 8)$ **Find common factors.**

$(x - 9)(x - 8)$ **Rewrite using the Distributive Property.**

③ Factor each expression.

    a. $x^2 - 6x + 8$ **b.** $x^2 - 7x + 12$ **c.** $x^2 - 11x + 24$

Note in Example 3 that the factors of c, -9 and -8, appear in the binomials of the factored form, $(x - 9)(x - 8)$. That is also the case for the factors in Example 2, and it is the case whenever $a = 1$. So when $a = 1$, you can skip a few steps in factoring. See Example 4.

If ac is negative, then the factors of ac have different signs.

④ EXAMPLE   **Factoring When $ac < 0$**

Factor $x^2 - x - 12$.

Step 1   Find factors with product ac and sum b.

Since $ac = -12$ and $b = -1$, find factors with product -12 and sum -1.

Factors of −12	1, −12	−1, 12	2, −6	−2, 6	3, −4	−3, 4
Sum of factors	−11	11	−4	4	−1	1

Step 2   Since $a = 1$, you can write binomials using the factors you found.
$x^2 - x - 12$
● $(x - 4)(x + 3)$ **Use the factors you found.**

✓ **CA Standards Check** ④ Factor each expression.

    a. $x^2 - 14x - 32$ **b.** $x^2 + 3x - 10$ **c.** $x^2 + 4x - 5$

If ac is positive, as in Examples 2 and 3, then the factors of ac have the same sign. This is true even when $a \neq 1$.

⑤ EXAMPLE   **Factoring When $a \neq 1$ and $ac > 0$**

Factor $3x^2 - 16x + 5$.

Step 1   Find factors with product ac and sum b.

Since $ac = 15$ and $b = -16$, find negative factors with product 15 and sum -16.

Factors of 15	−1, −15	−3, −5
Sum of factors	−16	−8

Step 2   Rewrite the term bx using the factors you found. Then find common factors and rewrite the expression as the product of two binomials.

$3x^2 - 16x + 5$
$3x^2 - x - 15x + 5$ **Rewrite bx.**
$x(3x - 1) - 5(3x - 1)$ **Find common factors.**
● $(x - 5)(3x - 1)$ **Rewrite using the Distributive Property.**

✓ **CA Standards Check** ⑤ Factor each expression. Check your answers.

    a. $2x^2 + 11x + 12$ **b.** $4x^2 + 7x + 3$ **c.** $2x^2 - 7x + 6$

Again, if ac is negative, then the factors of ac have different signs.

6 EXAMPLE Factoring When $a \neq 1$ and $ac < 0$

Factor $4x^2 - 4x - 15$.

Step 1 Find factors with product ac and sum b.

Since $ac = -60$ and $b = -4$, find factors with product -60 and sum -4.

Factors of −60	1, −60	−1, 60	2, −30	−2, 30	3, −20	−3, 20
Sum of factors	−59	59	−28	28	−17	17
Factors of −60	4, −15	−4, 15	5, −12	−5, 12	6, −10	−6, 10
Sum of factors	−11	11	−7	7	−4	4

Step 2 Rewrite the term bx using the factors you found. Then find common factors and rewrite the expression as the product of two binomials.

$4x^2 - 4x - 15$
$4x^2 + 6x - 10x - 15$ **Rewrite bx.**

$2x(2x + 3) - 5(2x + 3)$ **Find common factors.**
$(2x - 5)(2x + 3)$ **Rewrite using the Distributive Property.**

✓ **CA Standards Check** **6** Factor each expression.
a. $2x^2 + 7x - 9$ **b.** $3x^2 - 16x - 12$ **c.** $4x^2 + 5x - 6$

Factoring Special Expressions

A **perfect square trinomial** is the product you obtain when you square a binomial. An example is $x^2 + 10x + 25$, which can be written as $(x + 5)^2$. The first term and the third term of the trinomial are always positive, as they represent the squares of the two terms of the binomial. The middle term of the trinomial is two times the product of the terms of the binomial.

Key Concepts

Property	Factoring Perfect Square Trinomials
$a^2 + 2ab + b^2 = (a + b)^2$	$a^2 - 2ab + b^2 = (a - b)^2$

7 EXAMPLE Factoring a Perfect Square Trinomial

Factor $9x^2 - 42x + 49$.

$9x^2 - 42x + 49 = (3x)^2 - 42x + 7^2$ **Rewrite the first and third terms as squares.**

$= (3x)^2 - 2(3x)(7) + 7^2$ **Rewrite the middle term to verify the perfect square trinomial pattern.**

$= (3x - 7)^2$ $a^2 - 2ab + b^2 = (a - b)^2$

✓ **CA Standards Check** **7** Factor each expression.
a. $4x^2 + 12x + 9$ **b.** $64x^2 - 16x + 1$ **c.** $25x^2 + 90x + 81$

An expression of the form $a^2 - b^2$ is defined as the **difference of two squares**. It also follows a pattern that makes it easy to factor.

 Key Concepts

Property	Factoring a Difference of Two Squares
	$a^2 - b^2 = (a + b)(a - b)$

8 EXAMPLE **Real-World** 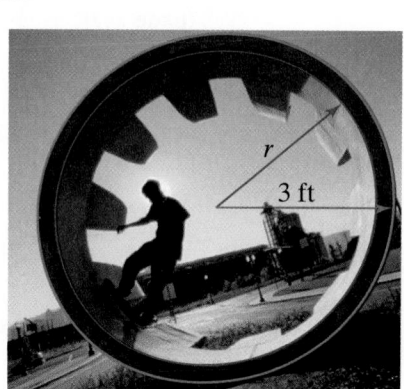 **Connection**

Multiple Choice The photo shows the thin ring that is the cross-section of the pipe. Which expression gives the area of the cross-section in completely factored form?

- **A** $\pi(3 + r)(3 - r)$
- **C** $\pi(9 - r^2)$
- **B** $\pi(3 - r)(3 - r)$
- **D** $9 - \pi r^2$

Relate | pipe's area | equals | the outer area |

| minus | the inner area |

Define Let $r =$ inner radius in feet.

Write | area | $=$ | $\pi(3)^2$ | $-$ | πr^2 |

$$\text{area} = \pi(3)^2 - \pi r^2$$
$$= \pi(3^2 - r^2)$$
$$= \pi(3 + r)(3 - r)$$

The cross-sectional area is $\pi(3 + r)(3 - r)$ ft^2. The correct choice is A.

Test-Taking Tip

A correct solution to the problem may not be the correct answer to the question asked.

✓ CA Standards Check **8** Factor each expression: **a.** $x^2 - 64$ **b.** $4a^2 - 49$

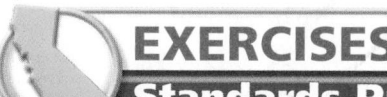 **EXERCISES**

Standards Practice

For more exercises, see *Extra Skill and Word Problem Practice*.

ALG2 4.0

 A **Practice by Example**

 GO for **Help**

Example 1 (page 263)

Find the GCF of each expression. Then factor the expression.

1. $3a^2 + 9$ 2. $25b^2 - 35$ 3. $x^2 - 2x$

4. $5t^2 + 7t$ 5. $14y^2 + 7y$ 6. $27p^2 - 9p$

Factor each expression.

Example 2 (page 264)

7. $x^2 + 3x + 2$ 8. $x^2 + 5x + 6$ 9. $x^2 + 7x + 10$

10. $x^2 + 10x + 16$ 11. $y^2 + 15y + 36$ 12. $x^2 + 22x + 40$

Example 3 (page 264)

13. $x^2 - 3x + 2$ 14. $x^2 - 13x + 12$ 15. $r^2 - 11r + 18$

16. $x^2 - 10x + 24$ 17. $d^2 - 12d + 27$ 18. $x^2 - 13x + 36$

Example 4 (page 265)

19. $x^2 - 5x - 14$ 20. $x^2 + x - 20$ 21. $x^2 - 3x - 40$

22. $c^2 + 2c - 63$ 23. $x^2 + 10x - 75$ 24. $t^2 - 7t - 44$

Example 5 (page 265)

25. $3x^2 + 31x + 36$ 26. $2x^2 - 19x + 24$ 27. $5r^2 + 23r + 26$

28. $2m^2 - 11m + 15$ 29. $5t^2 + 28t + 32$ 30. $2x^2 - 27x + 36$

Example 6
(page 266)

Factor each expression.

31. $3x^2 + 7x - 20$ **32.** $5y^2 + 12y - 32$ **33.** $7x^2 - 8x - 12$

34. $2z^2 + z - 28$ **35.** $3x^2 + 8x - 16$ **36.** $28k^2 + 13k - 6$

Example 7
(page 266)

37. $x^2 + 2x + 1$ **38.** $t^2 - 14t + 49$ **39.** $x^2 - 18x + 81$

40. $4n^2 - 20n + 25$ **41.** $9x^2 + 48x + 64$ **42.** $81z^2 + 36z + 4$

43. $x^2 - 4$ **44.** $c^2 - 64$ **45.** $9x^2 - 1$

Example 8
(page 267)

46. Manufacturing Refer to the diagram at the right. A machine will cut a small square of plastic from a larger square. Write an expression for the remaining area. Factor the expression.

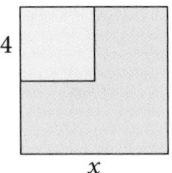

47. The area in square centimeters of a square mat is $25x^2 - 10x + 1$. Find the dimensions of the mat in terms of x.

B Apply Your Skills

48. The area of a rectangular cloth is $(6x^2 - 19x - 85)$ cm². The length is $(2x + 5)$ cm. Find the width.

49. Refer to the diagram at the right. Suppose you cut a small square from a square sheet of cardboard. Write an expression for the remaining area. Factor the expression.

50. Interior Design Refer to the photo at the left. The area of the rug is $(x^2 - 11x + 28)$ ft². What is the width?

Factor each expression completely.

51. $9x^2 - 36$ **52.** $18z^2 - 8$ **53.** $12y^2 - 75$

54. $64t^2 - 16$ **55.** $12x^2 + 36x + 27$ **56.** $16x^2 - 80x + 100$

57. $2a^2 - 16a + 32$ **58.** $3x^2 - 24x - 27$ **59.** $18b^2 + 24b - 10$

60. $4n^2 - 20n + 24$ **61.** $3y^2 + 24y + 45$ **62.** $-x^2 + 5x - 4$

63. $4x^2 - 22x + 10$ **64.** $\frac{1}{2}x^2 - \frac{1}{2}$ **65.** $-6z^2 - 600$

66. Geometry Express the volume of the shaded pipe at the right in completely factored form.

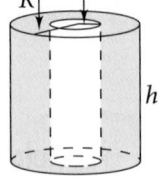

67. Agriculture The area in square feet of a rectangular field is $x^2 - 120x + 3500$. The width in feet is $x - 50$. Find the length.

68. Writing Explain how to factor $3x^2 + 6x - 72$ completely.

69. Open-Ended Write a quadratic trinomial that can be factored, where $a \neq 1$, $ac > 0$, and $b < 0$. Factor the expression.

70. Error Analysis Find the error below. Then factor the expression correctly.

$2x^2 - 7x + 5$

$2x^2 - 5x - 2x + 5$

$x(2x - 5) + (2x - 5)$

$(x + 1)(2x - 5)$

(x – 4) ft

Homework Video Tutor

Visit: PHSchool.com
Web Code: bbe-0504

Challenge

71. Critical Thinking Explain how to factor $4x^4 + 24x^3 + 32x^2$.

Factor each expression completely.

72. $0.25t^2 - 0.16$

73. $8100x^2 - 10,000$

74. $3600z^2 - 4900$

75. $(x + 3)^2 + 3(x + 3) - 54$

76. $(x - 2)^2 - 15(x - 2) + 56$

77. $6(x + 5)^2 - 5(x + 5) + 1$

78. $3(2a - 3)^2 + 17(2a - 3) + 10$

Multiple Choice Practice

For California Standards and CAHSEE Tutorials, visit PHSchool.com. Web Code: bbq-9045

ALG2 4.0

79. What is the factored form of $9a^2 - 25b^2$?

    Ⓐ $(3a + 5b)(3a + 5b)$ Ⓒ $(3a - 5b)(3a - 5b)$

    Ⓑ $(3a + 5b)(3a - 5b)$ Ⓓ $(3a - 5b)(a + b)$

ALG2 1.0

80. Solve $|2y + 7| \geq -3$.

    Ⓐ $y \geq -5$ Ⓒ no solution

    Ⓑ $y \leq -5$ or $y \geq -2$ Ⓓ all real numbers

ALG2 2.0

81. Solve the system $\begin{cases} 4x - y = -6 \\ 3y = -x - 5 \end{cases}$.

    Ⓐ $(1, 10)$ Ⓒ $(-1, 2)$

    Ⓑ $(2, -1)$ Ⓓ $(-1, -2)$

ALG2 2.0

82. Which system of inequalities is best represented by the graph?

    Ⓐ $x + y \leq 2, 2x - y \leq 5$

    Ⓑ $y \leq x - 2, 2x + y \leq 5$

    Ⓒ $y \leq x + 2, 2x - y \leq -5$

    Ⓓ $y \leq x + 2, 2x + y \leq -5$

Mixed Review

Lesson 5-3

Write each function in vertex form.

83. $y = x^2 - 2x + 1$ **84.** $y = -2x^2 + 2x + 5$ **85.** $y = 5x^2 - 1$

Lesson 4-6

Evaluate each determinant.

86. $\begin{vmatrix} 2 & -1 & 0 \\ 1 & 0 & 3 \\ 4 & -2 & 1 \end{vmatrix}$ **87.** $\begin{vmatrix} 1 & 5 & 0 \\ 3 & 3 & 5 \\ 0 & 1 & 2 \end{vmatrix}$ **88.** $\begin{vmatrix} 0 & 4 & 1 \\ 1 & 0 & 1 \\ 1 & 2 & 1 \end{vmatrix}$

Lesson 3-6

89. Coins The combined mass of a penny and a nickel and a dime is 9.8 g. Ten nickels and three pennies have the same mass as 25 dimes. Fifty dimes have the same mass as 18 nickels and 10 pennies. Write and solve a system of equations to find the mass of each type of coin.

Square Roots and Radicals

FOR USE WITH LESSON 5-5

A radical symbol $\sqrt{}$ indicates a square root. The expression $\sqrt{16}$ means the principal, or positive, square root of 16. The expression $-\sqrt{16}$ means the negative square root of 16. In general, $\sqrt{x^2} = |x|$ for all real numbers x.

Properties	Square Roots

Multiplication Property of Square Roots

For any numbers $a \geq 0$ and $b \geq 0$, $\sqrt{ab} = \sqrt{a} \cdot \sqrt{b}$.

Division Property of Square Roots

For any numbers $a \geq 0$ and $b > 0$, $\sqrt{\dfrac{a}{b}} = \dfrac{\sqrt{a}}{\sqrt{b}}$.

You can use the properties of square roots to simplify radical expressions.

1 EXAMPLE Radical Expressions Containing Perfect Squares

Simplify $\sqrt{48}$.

$\sqrt{48} = \sqrt{16} \cdot \sqrt{3}$ **Multiplication Property of Square Roots**

$\phantom{\sqrt{48}} = 4\sqrt{3}$ **Simplify.**

2 EXAMPLE Denominators Containing Radical Expressions

Simplify $-\sqrt{\dfrac{5}{7}}$.

$-\sqrt{\dfrac{5}{7}} = -\dfrac{\sqrt{5}}{\sqrt{7}}$ **Division Property of Square Roots**

$\phantom{-\sqrt{\dfrac{5}{7}}} = -\dfrac{\sqrt{5}}{\sqrt{7}} \cdot \dfrac{\sqrt{7}}{\sqrt{7}}$ **Multiply both the numerator and the denominator by $\sqrt{7}$.**

$\phantom{-\sqrt{\dfrac{5}{7}}} = -\dfrac{\sqrt{35}}{\sqrt{49}}$ **Multiplication Property of Square Roots**

$\phantom{-\sqrt{\dfrac{5}{7}}} = -\dfrac{\sqrt{35}}{7}$ **Simplify.**

EXERCISES

Simplify each radical expression.

1. $\sqrt{18}$ **2.** $\sqrt{75}$ **3.** $-\sqrt{32}$ **4.** $\sqrt{\dfrac{3}{5}}$

5. $-\sqrt{\dfrac{7}{12}}$ **6.** $\sqrt{\dfrac{3}{8}}$ **7.** $-\sqrt{200}$ **8.** $5\sqrt{320}$

9. $(2\sqrt{27})^2$ **10.** $-\sqrt{10^4}$ **11.** $\sqrt{x^2 y^2}$ **12.** $\sqrt{\dfrac{8}{x^2}}$

5-5

Quadratic Equations

 California Content Standards

ALG2 8.0 Students solve and graph quadratic equations by factoring. Students apply this technique in solving word problems. *Introduce, Develop*
ALG2 10.0 Students graph quadratic functions and determine zeros of the function. *Master*

What You'll Learn

- To solve quadratic equations by factoring and by finding square roots
- To solve quadratic equations by graphing

. . . And Why

To solve equations involving art, as in Example 5

✓ Check Skills You'll Need

GO for Help Lessons 5-2 and 5-4

Factor each expression.

1. $x^2 + 5x - 14$
2. $4x^2 - 12x$
3. $9x^2 - 16$

Graph each function.

4. $y = x^2 - 2x - 5$
5. $y = x^2 - 4x + 4$
6. $y = x^2 - 4x$

🔊 New Vocabulary • standard form of a quadratic equation
• Zero-Product Property • zero of a function

---

1 Solving by Factoring and Finding Square Roots

The **standard form of a quadratic equation** is $ax^2 + bx + c = 0$, where $a \neq 0$. You can solve some quadratic equations in standard form by factoring the quadratic expression and then using the Zero-Product Property.

 Key Concepts

Property	Zero-Product Property
If $ab = 0$, then $a = 0$ or $b = 0$.	
Example If $(x + 3)(x - 7) = 0$, then $(x + 3) = 0$ or $(x - 7) = 0$.	

1 EXAMPLE Solving by Factoring

Solve $2x^2 - 11x = -15$.

$2x^2 - 11x + 15 = 0$ **Write in standard form.**

$(x - 3)(2x - 5) = 0$ **Factor the quadratic expression.**

$x - 3 = 0$ or $2x - 5 = 0$ **Use the Zero-Product Property.**

$x = 3$ or $x = \frac{5}{2}$ **Solve for x.**

The solutions are 3 and $\frac{5}{2}$.

Check $\qquad 2x^2 - 11x = -15 \qquad\qquad\qquad 2x^2 - 11x = -15$

$2(3)^2 - 11(3) \stackrel{?}{=} -15 \qquad\qquad 2\left(\frac{5}{2}\right)^2 - 11\left(\frac{5}{2}\right) \stackrel{?}{=} -15$

$18 - 33 \stackrel{?}{=} -15 \qquad\qquad\qquad \frac{25}{2} - \frac{55}{2} \stackrel{?}{=} -15$

$-15 = -15 \checkmark \qquad\qquad\qquad\qquad -15 = -15 \checkmark$

 CA Standards Check **1** Solve each equation by factoring. Check your answers.

a. $x^2 + 7x = 18$
b. $2x^2 + 4x = 6$
c. $16x^2 = 8x$

You can solve an equation in the form $ax^2 = c$ by finding square roots.

2 EXAMPLE **Solving by Finding Square Roots**

Solve $5x^2 - 180 = 0$.

$5x^2 - 180 = 0$

$\quad\quad 5x^2 = 180$ **Rewrite in the form $ax^2 = c$.**

$\quad\quad \frac{5x^2}{5} = \frac{180}{5}$ **Isolate x^2.**

$\quad\quad\quad x^2 = 36$ **Simplify.**

$\quad\quad\quad\quad x = \pm 6$ **Find square roots.**

 CA Standards Check **2** Solve each equation by finding square roots.

a. $4x^2 - 25 = 0$ **b.** $3x^2 = 24$ **c.** $x^2 - \frac{1}{4} = 0$

3 EXAMPLE **Real-World** **Connection**

Firefighting Smoke jumpers are in free fall from the time they jump out of a plane until they open their parachutes. The function $y = -16t^2 + 1600$ models a jumper's height y in feet at t seconds for a jump from 1600 ft. How long is a jumper in free fall if the parachute opens at 1000 ft?

$\quad\quad y = -16t^2 + 1600$

$\quad 1000 = -16t^2 + 1600$ **Substitute 1000 for y.**

$\quad -600 = -16t^2$ **Isolate t^2.**

$\quad 37.5 = t^2$

$\quad \pm 6.1 \approx t$ **Find square roots.**

The jumper is in free fall for about 6.1 seconds.

Check Is the answer reasonable? The negative number -6.1 is also a solution to the equation. However, since a negative value for time has no meaning in this case, only the positive solution is reasonable.

Real-World **Connection**

Smoke jumpers are firefighters who parachute into areas near forest fires.

 CA Standards Check **3** **a.** A smoke jumper jumps from 1400 ft. The function describing the height is $y = -16t^2 + 1400$. Using square roots, find the time during which the jumper is in free fall if the parachute opens at 1000 ft.

b. Solve the equation in part (a) by factoring. Which method do you prefer—using square roots or factoring? Explain.

2 **Solving by Tables and Graphing**

Not every quadratic equation can be solved by factoring or by finding square roots. You can solve $ax^2 + bx + c = 0$ by graphing $y_1 = ax^2 + bx + c$—its related quadratic function. The value of y_1 is 0 where the graph intersects the x-axis. Each x-intercept is a **zero of the function** and a root of the equation.

You can also solve $ax^2 + bx + c = 0$ by displaying values of $y_1 = ax^2 + bx + c$ in a table. Scroll through the table to find where y_1 changes sign, effectively where the graph crosses the x-axis. Then "zoom-in" on the y_1 values by adjusting TblStart and Δ Tbl.

4 EXAMPLE **Solving by Tables**

Solve $x^2 - 5x + 2 = 0$.

Enter $y_1 = x^2 - 5x + 2$ in your graphing calculator. Use the TABLE window to see where y_1 changes sign. Change Δ Tbl to 0.01 and look again for the sign change. Continue this tabular zoom-in and find one solution to be $x \approx 0.44$.

X	Y₁
0	2
1	-2
2	-4
3	-4
4	-2
5	2
6	8

Y₁ =X²−5X+2

X	Y₁
.4	.16
.41	.1181
.42	.0764
.43	.0349
.44	−.0064
.45	−.0475
.46	−.0884

Y₁ =X²−5X+2

✓ **CA Standards Check** **4** In the first window above, the second sign change occurs between $x = 4$ and $x = 5$. Use tabular zoom-in to find the other solution to two decimal places.

5 EXAMPLE **Solving by Graphing**

Art Artists often use a golden rectangle in their work because forms based on it are visually pleasing. You can divide a golden rectangle into a square of side length one and a smaller rectangle that is similar to the original one. The ratio of the longer side to the shorter side of a golden rectangle is the golden ratio. Use the figure at the right to find the golden ratio.

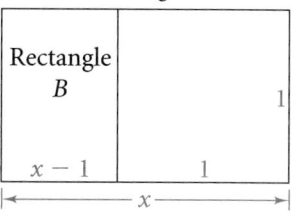

Rectangle A

Rectangle B

$x - 1$ 1

x

Vocabulary Tip

Two rectangles are similar if their corresponding sides are in proportion.

Relate $\dfrac{\text{longer side of } A}{\text{shorter side of } A} = \dfrac{\text{longer side of } B}{\text{shorter side of } B}$

Define Let x = longer side of rectangle A. Then $x - 1$ = shorter side of rectangle B.

Write $\dfrac{x}{1} = \dfrac{1}{x - 1}$

$x^2 - x = 1$ **Find cross-products.**

$x^2 - x - 1 = 0$ **Write in standard form.**

Graph the function $y_1 = x^2 - x - 1$. Use "zero" in the CALC feature to find the positive solution.

Zero
X= 1.618034 Y= 0

The ratio is about $1.62 : 1$.

✓ **CA Standards Check** **5** Solve each equation. When necessary, round to the nearest hundredth.
a. $x^2 - 2x = 4$ **b.** $x^2 + \frac{1}{2}x - \frac{1}{4} = 0$

Real-World **Connection**

Francisco José de Goya y Lucientes (1746–1828) was a Spanish painter. In *Portrait of a Man,* Goya placed the most significant elements of the painting within golden rectangles.

EXERCISES

For more exercises, see *Extra Skill and Word Problem Practice*.

Standards Practice

ALG2 8.0, 10.0

A Practice by Example

Example 1
(page 271)

GO for Help

Solve each equation by factoring. Check your answers.

1. $x^2 + 6x + 8 = 0$ **2.** $x^2 + 18 = 9x$ **3.** $2x^2 - x = 3$

4. $x^2 - 10x + 25 = 0$ **5.** $2x^2 + 6x = -4$ **6.** $3x^2 = 16x + 12$

Example 2
(page 272)

Solve each equation by finding square roots.

7. $5x^2 = 80$ **8.** $x^2 - 4 = 0$ **9.** $2x^2 = 32$

10. $9x^2 = 25$ **11.** $3x^2 - 15 = 0$ **12.** $5x^2 - 40 = 0$

Example 3
(page 272)

Solve each equation by factoring or by taking square roots.

13. $x^2 - 4x = 0$ **14.** $6x^2 + 4x = 0$ **15.** $12x^2 - 147 = 0$

16. $3x^2 = 48$ **17.** $2x^2 = 8x$ **18.** $4x^2 - 80 = 0$

19. Firefighters A smoke jumper jumps from a plane that is 1700 ft above the ground. The function $y = -16t^2 + 1700$ gives the jumper's height y in feet at t seconds.
    a. How long is the jumper in free fall if the parachute opens at 1000 ft?
    b. How long is the jumper in free fall if the parachute opens at 940 ft?

Example 4
(page 273)

Solve each equation using tables. Give each answer to at most two decimal places.

20. $x^2 + 5x + 3 = 0$ **21.** $x^2 - 7x = 11$ **22.** $2x^2 - x = 2$

Example 5
(page 273)

Solve each equation by graphing. Give each answer to at most two decimal places.

23. $6x^2 = -19x - 15$ **24.** $3x^2 - 5x - 4 = 0$ **25.** $5x^2 - 7x - 3 = 8$

26. $6x^2 + 31x = 12$ **27.** $1 = 4x^2 + 3x$ **28.** $\frac{1}{2}x^2 - x = 8$

29. $x^2 = 4x + 8$ **30.** $x^2 + 4x = 6$ **31.** $2x^2 - 2x - 5 = 0$

B Apply Your Skills

32. a. Art Verify that the Chinese painting at the right is a golden rectangle.
    b. What element in the painting divides it into a square and another golden rectangle?

33. Multiple Choice The period of a pendulum is the time the pendulum takes to swing back and forth. The function $\ell = 0.81t^2$ relates the length ℓ in feet of a pendulum to the time t in seconds that it takes to swing back and forth. The convention center in Portland, Oregon, has the longest pendulum in the United States. The pendulum's length is 90 ft. Find the period.

Ⓐ 8.5 seconds   Ⓑ 10.5 seconds   Ⓒ 90 seconds   Ⓓ 111 seconds

34. Open-Ended Write an equation in standard form that you can solve by factoring and an equation that you cannot solve by factoring.

Homework Video Tutor

Visit: PHSchool.com
Web Code: bbe-0505

35. Gardening Suppose you want to expand the garden shown at the right by planting a border of flowers. The border will be of the same width around the entire garden. The flowers you bought will fill an area of 276 ft². How wide should the border be?

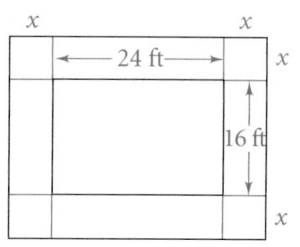

Solve each equation by factoring, by taking square roots, or by graphing. If necessary, round your answer to the nearest hundredth.

36. $x^2 + 6x + 5 = 45$ **37.** $x^2 - 11x + 24 = 0$ **38.** $3x^2 = 27$

39. $2x^2 - 5x - 3 = 0$ **40.** $x^2 + 2x = 6 - 6x$ **41.** $6x^2 + 13x + 6 = 0$

42. $2x^2 + 8x = 5x + 20$ **43.** $7x^2 - 243 = 0$ **44.** $3x^2 + 7x = 9$

45. $12x^2 - 154 = 0$ **46.** $x^2 + 4x = 0$ **47.** $x^2 = 8x - 7$

48. $x^2 + 2x = 15$ **49.** $x^2 + 11x + 10 = 0$ **50.** $4x^2 + 4x = 3$

51. $(x + 3)^2 = 9$ **52.** $2x^2 - 6x = 8$ **53.** $2x^2 + x - 28 = 0$

Critical Thinking **The graphs of each pair of functions intersect. Find their points of intersection without using a calculator. (*Hint:* Solve as a system using substitution.)**

54. $y = x^2$
$y = -\frac{1}{2}x^2 + \frac{3}{2}x + 3$

55. $y = x^2 - 2$
$y = 3x^2 - 4x - 2$

56. $y = -x^2 + x + 4$
$y = 2x^2 - 6$

 57. Writing Explain how you found the intersections in Exercises 54–56.

Open-Ended **Write a quadratic equation with the given solutions.**

58. 3 and 5 **59.** -3 and 2 **60.** -1 and -6 **61.** $\frac{1}{2}$ and $\frac{2}{3}$

C Challenge

62. Matrices Find the possible values of x and y. (A matrix with exponent 2 means that you multiply the matrix by itself.)

$$\begin{bmatrix} x & 2 \\ 3 & y \end{bmatrix}^2 = \begin{bmatrix} 22 & 10 \\ 15 & \blacksquare \end{bmatrix}$$

63. Using tables, how might you recognize that a quadratic equation likely has exactly one solution? no solutions?

64. The equation $x^2 - 10x + 24 = 0$ can be written in factored form as $(x - 4)(x - 6) = 0$. How can you use this fact to find the vertex of the graph of $y = x^2 - 10x + 24$?

65. Physics Suppose you throw a ball straight up from the ground with a velocity of 80 ft/s. As the ball moves upward, gravity slows it. Eventually the ball begins to fall back to the ground. The height h of the ball after t seconds in the air is given by the quadratic function $h(t) = -16t^2 + 80t$.
a. How high does the ball go?
b. For how many seconds is the ball in the air before it hits the ground?

66. a. Let $a > 0$. Use algebraic or arithmetic ideas to explain why the lowest point on the graph of $y = a(x - h)^2 + k$ must occur when $x = h$.
b. Suppose that the function in part (a) is $y = a(x - h)^3 + k$. Is your reasoning still valid? Explain.

Multiple Choice Practice

For California Standards and CAHSEE Tutorials, visit PHSchool.com. Web Code: bbq-9045

ALG2 10.0

67. A 3-pound object is thrown from the top of a building. The table shows the distance from the ground of the object as a function of time. Which function below best represents this situation?

Ⓐ $d = 20t^2 + 36$

Ⓑ $d = -16t^2 + 36t + 36$

Ⓒ $d = -16t^2 - 36t + 36$

Ⓓ $d = -16t^2 + 32t + 44$

Distance from Ground of a Three-Pound Object

Time (s)	Distance (ft)
0	36
1	56
2	44

CAHSEE 7MR 1.1

68. Sue saved 12% of her 2004 net income. The graph at the right shows how she spent and saved her 2005 net income. Sue stated that she saved more money in 2005 than in 2004. Which conclusion is valid based on the information given?

Ⓐ Sue's statement is accurate because 15% is more than 12%.

Ⓑ Sue's statement is accurate because net income does not include taxes and deductions.

Ⓒ The accuracy of Sue's statement cannot be determined because her net incomes for 2004 and 2005 are not given.

Ⓓ The accuracy of Sue's statement cannot be determined because there is no circle graph showing how she spent and saved her 2004 net income.

Sue's 2005 Budget

Other 15%

Mortgage 30%

Savings 15%

Food 20%

Clothing 20%

ALG2 4.0

69. The expression $25n^2 + 30n + 9$ is a perfect square trinomial. Which of the following is the factored form of this trinomial?

Ⓐ $(5n^2 + 3)^2$

Ⓑ $(5n + 9)(5n + 9)$

Ⓒ $(5n + 3)(5n + 3)$

Ⓓ $5n(5n + 6) + 9$

Mixed Review

GO for Help

Lesson 5-4

Factor each expression.

70. $3x^2 - 4x + 1$ **71.** $25z^2 - 9$ **72.** $6s^2 + 9s$

Lesson 4-1

State the dimensions of each matrix. Identify the indicated element.

73. $\begin{bmatrix} 4 & 6 & 5 \\ 1 & -3 & 0 \\ 1 & 1 & 9 \end{bmatrix}; a_{13}$ **74.** $\begin{bmatrix} 4 & -1 & 6 \\ 2 & 0 & 0 \end{bmatrix}; a_{21}$ **75.** $\begin{bmatrix} -9 & 1 & -1 \\ 0 & 6 & 0 \\ 1 & 0 & -2 \end{bmatrix}; a_{32}$

Lesson 1-1

Name the property of real numbers illustrated by each equation.

76. $3(2x + y) = 6x + 3y$ **77.** $3x^2 + 7y = 7y + 3x^2$

78. $4(3x) = (4 \cdot 3)x$ **79.** $3 + (-3) = 0$

Writing Equations From Roots

FOR USE WITH LESSON 5-5

ALG2 8.0 Students solve and graph quadratic equations by factoring. *Master*

ALG2 10.0 Students graph quadratic functions and determine the zeros of the function. *Master*

You can use the Zero-Product Property to write a quadratic function from its zeros or a quadratic equation from its roots.

1 ACTIVITY

1. a. Write a nonzero linear function $f(x)$ that has a zero at $x = 3$.
   b. Write a nonzero linear function $g(x)$ that has a zero at $x = 2$.

2. a. For f and g from Part 1, write the product function $h(x) = f(x) \cdot g(x)$.
   b. What kind of function is $h(x)$?   **c.** Solve the equation $h(x) = 0$.

Mental Math Write a quadratic function with zeros at each pair of values.

3. 3 and 4   **4.** 2 and 2.5   **5.** -1 and $\frac{3}{2}$ **6.** 1 and -1 **7.** -6 and -6

Mental Math Write a quadratic equation with each pair of values as roots.

8. 2 and 1   **9.** 1.5 and 3   **10.** -2 and 2   **11.** 6 and 12   **12.** $\frac{1}{2}$ and -4

You can also use zeros or roots to write quadratic expressions in standard form.

2 ACTIVITY

13. a. Copy and complete the table. Write the product $(x - a)(x - b)$ in standard form for each pair a and b.
   b. Is there a pattern in the table? Explain.

14. a. If you know the roots, you can write a quadratic function or equation with a quadratic expression in standard form. Explain how.
   b. Demonstrate your method for each pair of values in Exercises 3–12.

a	b	a + b	ab	(x − a)(x − b)
2	3	5	6	$x^2 - 5x + 6$
−2	3	1	−6	■
2	−3	■	■	■
−2	−3	■	■	■
−5	−6	■	■	■
7	−12	■	■	■

EXERCISES

15. Explain how to write a quadratic equation that has 2 as its only root.

16. Write the equation $q(x) = 0$ suggested by each graph. Each tick mark is 1 unit.

a.

b.

c.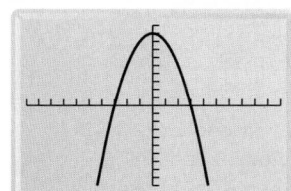

17. Describe the family of quadratic functions that have zeros at r and s. Sketch several members of the family in the coordinate plane.

18. True or False? The x-value of the vertex of a quadratic function with two zeros is the average of the zeros. Give a convincing argument.

Complex Numbers

 California Content Standards

ALG2 5.0 Students can plot complex numbers as points in the plane. *Introduce, Develop*
ALG2 6.0 Students add, subtract, multiply, and divide complex numbers. *Introduce, Develop*

What You'll Learn

- To identify and graph complex numbers
- To add, subtract, multiply, and divide complex numbers

. . . And Why

To explore fractals, as in Example 8

✓ Check Skills You'll Need   **for Help**   Skills Handbook page 881

Simplify each expression. Assume variables are nonnegative.

1. $\sqrt{3^2 + 4^2}$ **2.** $\sqrt{(-2)^2 + 8^2}$ **3.** $\sqrt{5^2 + (-12)^2}$

4. $\sqrt{6^2 + 10^2}$ **5.** $\sqrt{x^2 + x^2}$ **6.** $\sqrt{(3x)^2 + (4x)^2}$

◀))) New Vocabulary   • i • imaginary number   • complex numbers   • complex number plane   • absolute value of a complex number   • complex conjugate

---

1   Identifying Complex Numbers

When you learned to count, you used the natural numbers 1, 2, 3, and so on. Your number system has grown to include other types of numbers. You have used real numbers, which include both rational numbers such as $\frac{1}{2}$ and irrational numbers such as $\sqrt{2}$. Now your number system will expand to include numbers such as $\sqrt{-2}$.

The imaginary number **i** is defined as the number whose square is -1. So $i^2 = -1$ and $i = \sqrt{-1}$. An **imaginary number** is any number of the form $a + bi$, where a and b are real numbers, and $b \neq 0$.

 Key Concepts

Property	**Square Root of a Negative Real Number**

For any positive real number a, $\sqrt{-a} = i\sqrt{a}$.

Example $\sqrt{-4} = i\sqrt{4} = i \cdot 2 = 2i$
Note that $\left(\sqrt{-4}\right)^2 = \left(i\sqrt{4}\right)^2 = i^2\sqrt{4}^2 = -1 \cdot 4 = -4$ (not 4).

GO **Online**

Video Tutor Help
Visit: PHSchool.com
Web Code: bbe-0775

1 EXAMPLE   **Simplifying Numbers Using i**

Simplify $\sqrt{-8}$ by using the imaginary number i.

$\sqrt{-8} = i \cdot \sqrt{8}$ Use the Square Root Property of Negative Numbers.
$= i \cdot 2\sqrt{2}$ Simplify $\sqrt{8}$.
$= 2i\sqrt{2}$ Use the Commutative Property.

 CA Standards Check   **①** Simplify each number by using the imaginary number i.

    a. $\sqrt{-2}$ **b.** $\sqrt{-12}$ **c.** $\sqrt{-36}$

    d. Now that $\sqrt{a}$ is defined for $a < 0$, explain why $\sqrt{a^2} \neq \left(\sqrt{a}\right)^2$.

Imaginary numbers and real numbers together make up the set of **complex numbers.**

Key Concepts

Definition	Complex Numbers

A complex number can be written in the form $a + bi$, where a and b are real numbers, including 0.

$$a + bi$$

Real part → Imaginary part

---

2 EXAMPLE **Simplifying Imaginary Numbers**

Write the complex number $\sqrt{-9} + 6$ in the form $a + bi$.

$\sqrt{-9} + 6 = 3i + 6$ **Simplify the radical expression.**

$\quad\quad\quad = 6 + 3i$ **Write in the form $a + bi$.**

✓ **CA Standards Check** **2** Write the complex number $\sqrt{-18} + 7$ in the form $a + bi$.

The diagram below shows the sets of numbers that are part of the complex number system, and examples of each set.

Complex Numbers

Real Numbers: $-5,\ -\sqrt{3},\ 0,\ \sqrt{5},\ \frac{8}{3},\ 9$

Rational Numbers: $-5,\ 0,\ \frac{8}{3},\ 9$

Integers: $-5,\ 0,\ 9$

Whole Numbers: $0,\ 9$

Natural Numbers: 9

Irrational Numbers:

$-\sqrt{3}$

$\sqrt{5}$

Imaginary Numbers:

$-4i$

$3 + 2i$

$2i\sqrt{2}$

You can use the **complex number plane** to represent a complex number geometrically. Locate the real part of the number on the horizontal axis and the imaginary part on the vertical axis. You graph $3 - 4i$ in the same way you would graph $(3, -4)$ on the coordinate plane.

Vocabulary Tip

Pythagorean Theorem:
$c^2 = a^2 + b^2$ and
$c = \sqrt{a^2 + b^2}$

The **absolute value of a complex number** is its distance from the origin on the complex number plane. You can find the absolute value by using the Pythagorean Theorem. In general, $|a + bi| = \sqrt{a^2 + b^2}$.

---

3 EXAMPLE **Finding Absolute Value**

a. Find $|5i|$.

$5i$ is 5 units from the origin on the imaginary axis. So $|5i| = 5$.

b. Find $|3 - 4i|$.

$|3 - 4i| = \sqrt{3^2 + (-4)^2}$

$\quad\quad\quad = \sqrt{9 + 16} = 5$

✓ **CA Standards Check** **3** Find the absolute value of each complex number.

a. $|6 - 4i|$ **b.** $|-2 + 5i|$ **c.** $|4i|$

To add or subtract complex numbers, combine the real parts and the imaginary parts separately.

4 EXAMPLE Adding Complex Numbers

Simplify the expression $(5 + 7i) + (-2 + 6i)$.

$(5 + 7i) + (-2 + 6i) = 5 + (-2) + 7i + 6i$	**Use commutative and associative properties.**
$= 3 + 13i$	**Simplify.**

✓ **CA Standards Check** ④ Simplify each expression.
a. $(8 + 3i) - (2 + 4i)$ **b.** $7 - (3 + 2i)$ **c.** $(4 - 6i) + 3i$

For two imaginary numbers bi and ci, $(bi)(ci) = bc(i)^2 = bc(-1) = -bc$. For two complex numbers of the form $a + bi$, use the procedure for multiplying binomials.

5 EXAMPLE Multiplying Complex Numbers

a. Find $(5i)(-4i)$.

$(5i)(-4i) = -20i^2$	**Multiply the real numbers.**
$= -20(-1)$	**Substitute −1 for i^2.**
$= 20$	**Multiply.**

b. Find $(2 + 3i)(-3 + 5i)$.

$(2 + 3i)(-3 + 5i) = -6 + 10i - 9i + 15i^2$	**Multiply the binomials.**
$= -6 + 10i - 9i + 15(-1)$	**Substitute −1 for i^2.**
$= -21 + i$	**Simplify.**

✓ **CA Standards Check** ⑤ Simplify each expression.
a. $(12i)(7i)$ **b.** $(6 - 5i)(4 - 3i)$ **c.** $(4 - 9i)(4 + 3i)$

The **complex conjugate** of the complex number $a + bi$ is $a - bi$. To divide by a complex number, you must multiply the numerator and denominator by the complex conjugate of the divisor.

6 EXAMPLE Dividing by a Complex Number

a. Find $\dfrac{5}{2i}$.   **b.** Find $\dfrac{3 + 2i}{1 - 5i}$.

$$\frac{5}{2i} = \frac{5}{2i} \cdot \frac{-2i}{-2i}$$ ← Multiply by the complex conjugate. → $$\frac{3 + 2i}{1 - 5i} = \frac{3 + 2i}{1 - 5i} \cdot \frac{1 + 5i}{1 + 5i}$$

$$= \frac{-10i}{-4i^2}$$ ← **Multiply.** → $$= \frac{3 + 15i + 2i + 10i^2}{1 + 5i - 5i - 25i^2}$$

$$= \frac{5i}{2(-1)}$$ ← **Substitute −1 for i^2.** → $$= \frac{3 + 15i + 2i + 10(-1)}{1 + 5i - 5i - 25(-1)}$$

$$= -\frac{5i}{2}$$ ← **Simplify.** → $$= \frac{17i - 7}{26}$$

⑥ Simplify each expression.

a. $-\dfrac{8}{i}$ **b.** $\dfrac{1-4i}{3+i}$ **c.** $\dfrac{5i}{2+2i}$

Some quadratic equations have solutions that are complex numbers.

7 EXAMPLE Finding Complex Solutions

Solve $4x^2 + 100 = 0$.

$4x^2 + 100 = 0$

$$4x^2 = -100 \qquad \textbf{Isolate } x^2.$$
$$x^2 = -25$$
$$x = \pm\sqrt{-25} \qquad \textbf{Find square roots.}$$
$$= \pm 5i \qquad \textbf{Simplify.}$$

Check

$4x^2 + 100 = 0$ 　　　　　 $4x^2 + 100 = 0$

$4(5i)^2 + 100 \overset{?}{=} 0$ 　　 $4(-5i)^2 + 100 \overset{?}{=} 0$

$4(25i^2) \overset{?}{=} -100$ 　　 $4(25i^2) \overset{?}{=} -100$

$4(-25) \overset{?}{=} -100$ 　　 $4(-25) = -100$

$-100 = -100 \ ✓$ 　　 $-100 = -100 \ ✓$

⑦ Solve each equation. Check your answers.

a. $3x^2 + 48 = 0$ **b.** $-5x^2 - 150 = 0$ **c.** $8x^2 + 2 = 0$

Functions of the form $f(z) = z^2 + c$ where c is a complex number generate fractal graphs on the complex plane like the one at the left. To test if z belongs to the graph, use 0 as the first input value and repeatedly use each output as the next input. If the output values do not become infinitely large, then z is on the graph.

8 EXAMPLE Real-World 🌐 Connection

Fractals Find the first three output values for $f(z) = z^2 + i$.

$f(z) = z^2 + i$

$f(0) = 0^2 + i \qquad \textbf{Use } z = 0 \textbf{ as the first input value.}$

$\quad = i$

$f(i) = i^2 + i \qquad \textbf{First output becomes second input. Evaluate for } z = i.$

$\quad = -1 + i$

$f(-1 + i) = (-1 + i)^2 + i \qquad \textbf{Second output becomes third input.}$
$\textbf{Evaluate for } z = -1 + i.$

$\quad = [(-1)^2 + (-1)(i) + (-1)(i) + (i)^2] + i$

$\quad = (1 - 2i - 1) + i$

$\quad = -i \qquad \textbf{Third output would be next input.}$

The first three output values are i, $-1 + i$, and $-i$.

⑧ Find the first three output values for $f(z) = z^2 - 1 + i$.

A Practice by Example

Example 1
(page 278)

Simplify each number by using the imaginary number *i*.

1. $\sqrt{-4}$ **2.** $\sqrt{-7}$ **3.** $\sqrt{-15}$ **4.** $\sqrt{-81}$ **5.** $\sqrt{-50}$

6. $\sqrt{-16}$ **7.** $\sqrt{-32}$ **8.** $3\sqrt{-9}$ **9.** $-\sqrt{-100}$ **10.** $\sqrt{-72}$

Example 2
(page 279)

Write each number in the form $a + bi$.

11. $2 + \sqrt{-3}$ **12.** $\sqrt{-8} + 8$ **13.** $6 - \sqrt{-28}$ **14.** $\sqrt{-4} + 3$

15. $7 - \sqrt{-25}$ **16.** $\sqrt{-1} + 2$ **17.** $-\sqrt{-50} - 2$ **18.** $\sqrt{-72} + 4$

Example 3
(page 279)

Find the absolute value of each complex number.

19. $|2i|$ **20.** $|5 + 12i|$ **21.** $|2 - 2i|$ **22.** $|1 - 4i|$ **23.** $|3 - 6i|$

Example 4
(page 280)

Simplify each expression.

24. $(2 + 4i) + (4 - i)$ **25.** $(-3 - 5i) + (4 - 2i)$ **26.** $(7 + 9i) + (-5i)$

27. $6 - (8 + 3i)$ **28.** $(12 + 5i) - (2 - i)$ **29.** $(-6 - 7i) - (1 + 3i)$

Example 5
(page 280)

30. $(-2i)(5i)$ **31.** $(4 - 3i)(5 + 2i)$ **32.** $(8 + i)(2 + 7i)$

33. $(-6 - 5i)(1 + 3i)$ **34.** $(-6i)^2$ **35.** $(9 + 4i)^2$

Example 6
(page 280)

36. $\dfrac{4 - 3i}{3 - 2i}$ **37.** $-\dfrac{12}{7i}$ **38.** $\dfrac{i}{2 + 5i}$

Example 7
(page 281)

Solve each equation. Check your answers.

39. $x^2 + 25 = 0$ **40.** $2x^2 + 1 = 0$ **41.** $3s^2 + 2 = -62$

42. $x^2 = -7$ **43.** $x^2 + 36 = 0$ **44.** $-5x^2 - 3 = 0$

Example 8
(page 281)

Find the first three output values of each fractal-generating function. Use $z = 0$ as the first input value.

45. $z^2 - i$ **46.** $f(z) = z^2 - 2i$ **47.** $f(z) = z^2 + 1 - i$

B Apply Your Skills

Solve each equation.

48. $x^2 + 16 = -49$ **49.** $x^2 - 30 = -79$ **50.** $3x^2 + 1 = x^2 - 1$

51. Writing In reality, is it possible for Mr. Milde's average to be an imaginary number? Explain.

ROBOTMAN by Jim Meddick

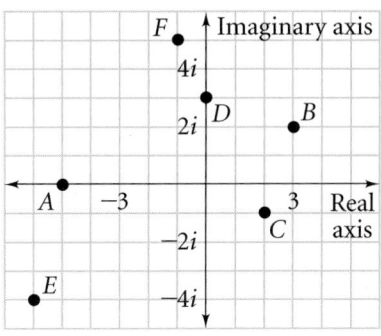

52. a. Name the complex number represented by each point on the graph at the right.
  b. Find the additive inverse of each number.

53. Multiple Choice In a complex number plane, what geometric figure describes the complex numbers with absolute value 10?

  Ⓐ square   Ⓒ line
  Ⓑ circle   Ⓓ two points

54. Solve $(x + 3i)(x - 3i) = 34$.

Simplify each expression.

55. $(8i)(4i)(-9i)$

56. $(2 + \sqrt{-1}) + (-3 + \sqrt{-16})$

57. $(4 + \sqrt{-9}) + (6 - \sqrt{-49})$

58. $(10 + \sqrt{-9}) - (2 + \sqrt{-25})$

59. $(-2 + \sqrt{-9})(6 + \sqrt{-25})$

60. $(1 - \sqrt{-4})(-3 - \sqrt{-25})$

61. $\dfrac{-3 + \sqrt{-16}}{5 - \sqrt{-1}}$

62. $\dfrac{2 - i(1 - i)}{-3i + 2}$

63. $\dfrac{5 + i}{2(i - 2)}$

64. a. Copy and complete the table.
  b. The number pairs p and q in the table are complex conjugates. Describe at least three patterns you see in complex conjugate pairs.

Values of p and q	$p + q$	$p \cdot q$	$\lvert p \rvert$	$\lvert q \rvert$
$p = 1 + 2i, q = 1 - 2i$	▓	▓	▓	▓
$p = 3 - i, q = 3 + i$	▓	▓	▓	▓
$p = -6 + 8i, q = -6 - 8i$	▓	▓	▓	▓

  c. Plot each pair of conjugates. How are the points of each pair related?
  d. True or false: The conjugate of an additive inverse is equal to the additive inverse of the conjugate. Explain your answer.

Two complex numbers $a + bi$ and $c + di$ are equal when $a = c$ and $b = d$. Solve each equation for x and y. Assume x and y are real.

65. $2x + 3yi = -14 + 9i$ **66.** $3x + 19i = 16 - 8yi$ **67.** $-14 - 3i = 2x + yi$

68. Show that the product of a nonzero complex number $a + bi$ and its conjugate (as described in Exercise 67) is a real number.

69. Fractals The fractal at the left can be described by the function $f(z) = z^2 + c$. If $c = 0.383 + 0.11i$, find the first two output values of the function. Use $z = 0$ as the first input value.

70. For what real values of x and y is $(x + yi)^2$ an imaginary number?

71. Complex numbers can be used to generate interesting patterns. Here is a pattern generated by powers of $1 + 3i$.

$(1 + 3i)^1 = 1 + 3i$ and $1^2 + 3^2 = 10$
$(1 + 3i)^2 = -8 + 6i$ and $(-8)^2 + 6^2 = 10^2$
$(1 + 3i)^3 = -26 - 18i$ and $(-26)^2 + (-18)^2 = 10^3$
$(1 + 3i)^4 = 28 - 96i$ and $28^2 + (-96)^2 = 10^4$

Find the powers of $3 + 4i$ through $(3 + 4i)^5$. Generate and verify a similar pattern.

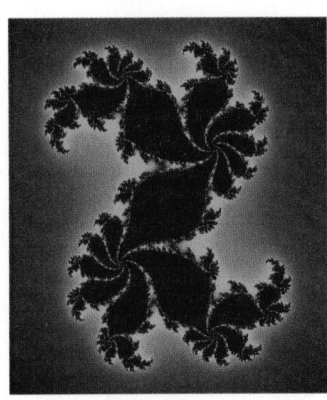

Exercise 72

72. Critical Thinking Graph $1 + 3i$ and $6 + 2i$. Also graph their sum. Draw the quadrilateral that has these three points and the origin as vertices. Repeat with other complex numbers. What do you notice?

Multiple Choice Practice

For California Standards and CAHSEE Tutorials, visit PHSchool.com. Web Code: bbq-9045

ALG2 6.0

73. Simplify $(3 - 4i)(-5 + 2i)$.

- Ⓐ $-23 + 14i$
- Ⓒ $-23 + 14i$
- Ⓑ $-7 + 26i$
- Ⓓ $-15 + 26i$

ALG2 10.0

74. Which of the following statements is false for the function graphed?

- Ⓐ The minimum value of the function is zero.
- Ⓑ The vertex of the function is $(0, 0)$.
- Ⓒ The function is symmetric about the x-axis.
- Ⓓ The function is a quadratic function.

Mixed Review

Lesson 5-5

Solve each equation using a graphing calculator.

75. $2x^2 + 3x - 4 = 0$ **76.** $4x^2 + x = 1$ **77.** $x^2 = -7x - 8$

Lesson 5-2

Graph each function.

78. $y = -2(x + 1)^2 - 3$ **79.** $y = \frac{1}{2}(x - 4)^2 + 1$ **80.** $y = 3(x - 1)^2 - 5$

Lesson 3-5

Graph each point in coordinate space.

81. $(2, 0, -4)$ **82.** $(0, -3, 5)$ **83.** $(9, -1, 0)$

Checkpoint Quiz 2   Lessons 5-4 through 5-6

Factor each quadratic expression.

1. $2x^2 + x - 6$ **2.** $5x^2 - 45$ **3.** $4x^2 - 36x + 81$

Solve each equation.

4. $(3x - 3)(2x + 8) = 0$ **5.** $x^2 - 2x + 1 = 0$ **6.** $x^2 + 121 = 0$

Find the absolute value of each number.

7. $5 - 2i$ **8.** $9 - i$ **9.** $7 + 4i$

10. Can you solve the equation $x^2 + 7x + 14 = 0$ by graphing the related function $y = x^2 + 7x + 14$? Explain.

Activity Lab

Completing the Square

Hands-On   FOR USE WITH LESSON 5-7

Prepares for ALG2 8.0 Students solve and graph quadratic equations by completing the square.

Copy the model shown.

1. a. Add unit tiles until you have a complete square. How many tiles did you add?
   b. Write an expression to represent the sum of the areas of the tiles.
   c. Write an expression to represent the length times the width of the completed square.
   d. How do the six x-tiles in the model relate to the length of the sides of the completed square? To the number of unit tiles used?

2. Suppose the expression $x^2 + 8x + \blacksquare$ can also be modeled by a complete square of tiles.
   a. Draw a diagram or use models to find the missing value.
   b. What is the coefficient of x in the expression?
   c. Critical Thinking How can you use the coefficient of x to find the length of the completed square?

3. Suppose $x^2 - 4x + \blacksquare$ can be modeled by a complete square of tiles. Using red to represent negative values, draw a diagram or use models to find the missing value.

$x^2 + 6x + \blacksquare$

EXERCISES

Complete each square. Then write an expression that represents the sum of the areas of the tiles and an expression that represents the length times the width of the completed square.

1.   **2.**   **3.**

Assume that each expression can be modeled by a complete square of tiles. Find the missing value.

4. $x^2 + 14x + \blacksquare$ **5.** $x^2 + 20x + \blacksquare$

6. $x^2 + 10x + \blacksquare$ **7.** $x^2 + 100x + \blacksquare$

8. $x^2 + 32x + \blacksquare$ **9.** $x^2 - 8x + \blacksquare$

10. Make a Conjecture In Lesson 5-5, you solved quadratic equations by taking square roots. How could you use that method together with completing the square to solve $x^2 + 6x + 6 = 0$?

Completing the Square

 California Content Standards

ALG2 8.0 Students solve quadratic equations by completing the square. Students apply this technique in solving word problems. *Introduce, Develop*

What You'll Learn

- To solve equations by completing the square
- To rewrite functions by completing the square

. . . And Why

To find a price to maximize profit, as in Example 7

✓ Check Skills You'll Need

Simplify each expression.

1. $(x - 3)(x - 3)$

2. $(2x - 1)(2x - 1)$

3. $(x + 4)(x + 4) - 3$

4. $\pm\sqrt{25}$

5. $\pm\sqrt{48}$

6. $\pm\sqrt{-4}$

7. $\pm\sqrt{\dfrac{9}{16}}$

GO for Help Lesson 5-1 and page 270

◀)) **New Vocabulary** • completing the square

---

1 Solving Equations by Completing the Square

You can solve an equation in which one side is a perfect square trinomial by finding square roots.

1 EXAMPLE Solving a Perfect Square Trinomial Equation

Solve $x^2 + 10x + 25 = 36$.

$$x^2 + 10x + 25 = 36$$
$$(x + 5)^2 = 36 \qquad \text{Factor the trinomial.}$$
$$x + 5 = \pm 6 \qquad \text{Find square roots.}$$
$$x + 5 = 6 \quad \text{or} \quad x + 5 = -6 \qquad \text{Solve for } x.$$
$$x = 1 \quad \text{or} \qquad x = -11$$

Vocabulary Tip

Quadratic comes from the Latin word for "square."

✓ **CA Standards Check** ❶ Solve $x^2 - 14x + 49 = 81$.

If one side of an equation is not a perfect square trinomial, you can rewrite the constant term to get a perfect square trinomial. The process of finding the last term of a perfect square trinomial is called **completing the square.** Use the following relationship to find the term that will complete the square.

$$x^2 + bx + \left(\frac{b}{2}\right)^2 = \left(x + \frac{b}{2}\right)^2$$

Video Tutor Help

Visit: PHSchool.com
Web Code: bbe-0775

2 EXAMPLE Completing the Square

Find the missing value to complete the square: $x^2 - 8x + \blacksquare$.

$$\left(\frac{b}{2}\right)^2 = \left(\frac{-8}{2}\right)^2 = 16 \qquad \text{Find } \left(\frac{b}{2}\right)^2. \text{ Substitute } -8 \text{ for } b.$$
$$x^2 - 8x + 16 \qquad \text{Complete the square.}$$

  ❷ Find the missing value to complete the square: $x^2 + 7x + \blacksquare$.

You can solve any quadratic equation by completing the square.

3 EXAMPLE Solving by Completing the Square

Solve $x^2 - 12x + 5 = 0$.

$$\left(\frac{-12}{2}\right)^2 = 36 \qquad \text{Find } \left(\frac{b}{2}\right)^2.$$

$$x^2 - 12x = -5 \qquad \text{Rewrite so all terms containing } x \text{ are on one side.}$$

$$x^2 - 12x + 36 = -5 + 36 \qquad \text{Complete the square by adding 36 to each side.}$$

$$(x - 6)^2 = 31 \qquad \text{Factor the perfect square trinomial.}$$

$$x - 6 = \pm\sqrt{31} \qquad \text{Find square roots.}$$

$$x = 6 \pm \sqrt{31} \qquad \text{Solve for } x.$$

Check $\qquad\qquad\qquad\qquad x^2 - 12x + 5 \stackrel{?}{=} 0$

$$(6 + \sqrt{31})^2 - 12(6 + \sqrt{31}) + 5 \stackrel{?}{=} 0$$

$$6^2 + 2(6\sqrt{31}) + (\sqrt{31})^2 - 72 - 12\sqrt{31} + 5 \stackrel{?}{=} 0$$

$$36 + 12\sqrt{31} + 31 - 72 - 12\sqrt{31} + 5 \stackrel{?}{=} 0$$

$$(36 + 31 - 72 + 5) + (12\sqrt{31} - 12\sqrt{31}) \stackrel{?}{=} 0$$

$$0 = 0 \checkmark$$

$$x^2 - 12x + 5 \stackrel{?}{=} 0$$

$$(6 - \sqrt{31})^2 - 12(6 - \sqrt{31}) + 5 \stackrel{?}{=} 0$$

$$6^2 - 2(6\sqrt{31}) + (\sqrt{31})^2 - 72 + 12\sqrt{31} + 5 \stackrel{?}{=} 0$$

$$36 - 12\sqrt{31} + 31 - 72 + 12\sqrt{31} + 5 \stackrel{?}{=} 0$$

$$(36 + 31 - 72 + 5) - (12\sqrt{31} - 12\sqrt{31}) \stackrel{?}{=} 0$$

$$0 = 0 \checkmark$$

This stamp commemorates the 1200th birthday of al-Khwarizmi (780–850), who showed how to solve equations by completing the square. His book *Al-jabr w'al muqabala* gave algebra its name.

✓ **CA Standards Check** ③ Solve each equation. Check your solution.
a. $x^2 + 4x - 4 = 0$ \qquad\qquad **b.** $x^2 - 2x - 1 = 0$

By completing the square, you can solve equations that cannot be solved by factoring, finding square roots, or graphing.

4 EXAMPLE Finding Complex Solutions

Solve $x^2 - 8x + 36 = 0$.

$$\left(\frac{-8}{2}\right)^2 = 16 \qquad \text{Find } \left(\frac{b}{2}\right)^2.$$

$$x^2 - 8x = -36 \qquad \text{Rewrite so all terms containing } x \text{ are on one side.}$$

$$x^2 - 8x + 16 = -36 + 16 \qquad \text{Complete the square by adding 16 to each side.}$$

$$(x - 4)^2 = -20 \qquad \text{Factor the perfect square trinomial.}$$

$$x - 4 = \pm\sqrt{-20} \qquad \text{Find square roots.}$$

$$x = 4 \pm 2i\sqrt{5} \qquad \text{Solve for } x \text{ and simplify.}$$

✓ **CA Standards Check** ④ **a.** Check the solution to Example 4.
b. Try solving the same equation with a graphing calculator. Explain your results.
c. Solve $x^2 + 6x = -34$.

When the quadratic term has a coefficient that is not 1, you can still solve by completing the square. First divide each side of the equation by the coefficient.

5 EXAMPLE Solving When $a \neq 1$

Solve $5x^2 = 6x + 8$.

$$5x^2 = 6x + 8$$

$$x^2 = \tfrac{6}{5}x + \tfrac{8}{5} \qquad \text{Divide each side by 5.}$$

$$x^2 - \tfrac{6}{5}x = \tfrac{8}{5} \qquad \text{Rewrite so all terms containing } x \text{ are on one side.}$$

$$\left(\frac{-\tfrac{6}{5}}{2}\right)^2 = \left(-\tfrac{3}{5}\right)^2 = \tfrac{9}{25} \qquad \text{Find } \left(\tfrac{b}{2}\right)^2.$$

$$x^2 - \tfrac{6}{5}x + \tfrac{9}{25} = \tfrac{8}{5} + \tfrac{9}{25} \qquad \text{Complete the square by adding } \tfrac{9}{25} \text{ to each side.}$$

$$\left(x - \tfrac{3}{5}\right)^2 = \tfrac{49}{25} \qquad \text{Factor the perfect square trinomial.}$$

$$x - \tfrac{3}{5} = \pm\sqrt{\tfrac{49}{25}} \qquad \text{Find square roots.}$$

$$x = \tfrac{3}{5} \pm \tfrac{7}{5} \qquad \text{Solve for } x.$$

$$x = 2, -\tfrac{4}{5} \qquad \text{Simplify.}$$

 CA Standards Check ⑤ Solve each quadratic equation by completing the square.

    a. $2x^2 + x = 6$ **b.** $2x^2 = 3x - 4$

2 Rewriting a Function by Completing the Square

In Lesson 5-3 you converted quadratic functions into vertex form by using $x = -\tfrac{b}{2a}$ to find the x-coordinate of the parabola's vertex. Then, by substituting for x, you found the y-coordinate of the vertex. Another way of rewriting a function is to complete the square.

Vocabulary Tip

Vertex form of a quadratic function:
$y = a(x - h)^2 + k$

When completing the square, you can work with just one side of the function equation. For example, $y = x^2 + 6x + 2$ is equivalent to $y = x^2 + 6x + 9 + 2 - 9$. When you add 9 to the right side of the equation, you must remember to subtract 9 to keep the equations equivalent.

6 EXAMPLE Rewriting in Vertex Form

Write $y = x^2 + 6x + 2$ in vertex form.

$$y = x^2 + 6x + 2$$

$$= x^2 + 6x + 3^2 + 2 - 3^2 \qquad \text{Complete the square. Add and subtract } 3^2 \text{ on the right side.}$$

$$= (x + 3)^2 + 2 - 9 \qquad \text{Factor the perfect square trinomial.}$$

$$= (x + 3)^2 - 7 \qquad \text{Simplify.}$$

The vertex form is $y = (x + 3)^2 - 7$.

 CA Standards Check ⑥ Write each equation in vertex form.

    a. $y = x^2 - 10x - 2$ **b.** $y = x^2 + 5x + 3$

When the coefficient of the quadratic term is not 1, factor out the coefficient from the quadratic and linear terms. Remember that the factored coefficient is distributed to all terms within the parentheses.

7 EXAMPLE **Real-World Connection**

The profit P from handmade sweaters depends on the price s at which each sweater is sold. The function $P = -s^2 + 120s - 2000$ models the monthly profit from sweaters for one custom tailor. What is the maximum monthly profit, in dollars, determined by this model?

$P = -s^2 + 120s - 2000$

$\quad = -(s^2 - 120s) - 2000$ **Factor out -1.**

$\quad = -[s^2 - 120s + (-60)^2] - 2000 + (-60)^2$

                                   Complete the square.

$\quad = -(s - 60)^2 - 2000 + 3600$ **Factor.**

$\quad = -(s - 60)^2 + 1600$ **Simplify.**

The quadratic function is in vertex form. The vertex is $(60, 1600)$. A price of $60 per sweater gives a maximum monthly profit of $1600.

CA Standards Check **7** **a.** Use vertex form to find the vertex of $P = -\frac{1}{2}s^2 + 280s - 1200$.

         b. How do you know the vertex represents a maximum point?

EXERCISES

For more exercises, see *Extra Skill and Word Problem Practice.*

Standards Practice
                                                ALG2 8.0

A **Practice by Example**

Example 1
(page 286)

Solve each equation.

1. $x^2 + 6x + 9 = 1$ **2.** $x^2 - 4x + 4 = 100$ **3.** $x^2 - 2x + 1 = 4$

4. $x^2 + 8x + 16 = \frac{16}{9}$ **5.** $4x^2 + 4x + 1 = 49$ **6.** $x^2 - 12x + 36 = 25$

Example 2
(page 286)

Complete the square.

7. $x^2 + 18x + $ ▪   **8.** $x^2 - x + $ ▪   **9.** $x^2 - 24x + $ ▪

10. $x^2 + 20x + $ ▪   **11.** $m^2 - 3m + $ ▪   **12.** $x^2 + 4x + $ ▪

Examples 3 and 4
(page 287)

Solve each quadratic equation by completing the square.

13. $x^2 - 3x = 28$ **14.** $x^2 - 3x = 4$ **15.** $x^2 + 6x + 41 = 0$

16. $x^2 - 2x = -2$ **17.** $w^2 - 8w - 9 = 0$ **18.** $x^2 + 6x = -22$

19. $x^2 + 4 = 0$ **20.** $-x^2 - 2x = 5$ **21.** $6x - 3x^2 = -12$

Example 5
(page 288)

22. $2p^2 = 6p - 20$ **23.** $3x^2 - 12x + 7 = 0$ **24.** $4c^2 + 10c = -7$

25. $2x^2 + x - 28 = 0$ **26.** $9x^2 - 12x + 5 = 0$ **27.** $4x^2 + 4x = 3$

Example 6
(page 288)

Rewrite each equation in vertex form.

28. $y = x^2 + 4x - 7$ **29.** $y = -x^2 + 4x - 1$ **30.** $y = -2x^2 + 6x + 1$

31. $y = x^2 + 4x + 1$ **32.** $y = 2x^2 - 8x + 1$ **33.** $y = -x^2 - 2x + 3$

Example 7
(page 289)

Rewrite each equation in vertex form. Then find the vertex of the graph.

34. $y = -4x^2 - 5x + 3$ **35.** $y = \frac{1}{2}x^2 - 5x + 12$ **36.** $y = -\frac{1}{5}x^2 + \frac{4}{5}x + \frac{11}{5}$

37. Manufacturing An electronics company has a new line of portable radios with CD players. Their research suggests that the daily sales s for the new product can be modeled by $s = -p^2 + 120p + 1400$, where p is the price of each unit.
   a. Find the vertex of the graph of the function by completing the square.
   b. Describe a reasonable domain and range for the sales function. Explain.
   c. What price gives maximum daily sales? What are the maximum daily sales?

38. Writing Explain the process of rewriting $x^2 + 8x + 11 = 0$ as $(x + 4)^2 = 5$.

39. Sports The height of a punted football can be modeled with the quadratic function $h = -0.01x^2 + 1.18x + 2$. The horizontal distance in feet from the point of impact with the kicker's foot is x, and h is the height of the ball in feet.

 GO for Help

For a guide to solving Exercise 39, parts (a)–(c), see page 292.

   a. Find the vertex of the graph of the function by completing the square.
   b. What is the maximum height of the punt?
   c. The nearest defensive player is 5 ft horizontally from the point of impact. How high must the player reach to block the punt?
   d. Suppose the ball was not blocked but continued on its path. How far down field would the ball go before it hit the ground?
   e. Critical Thinking The linear equation $h = 1.13x + 2$ could model the path of the football shown in the graph. Why is this not a good model?

B Apply Your Skills

Find the value of k that would make the left side of each equation a perfect square trinomial.

40. $x^2 + kx + 25 = 0$ **41.** $x^2 - kx + 100 = 0$ **42.** $x^2 - kx + 121 = 0$

43. $x^2 + kx + 64 = 0$ **44.** $x^2 - kx + 81 = 0$ **45.** $25x^2 - kx + 1 = 0$

46. $x^2 + kx + \frac{1}{4} = 0$ **47.** $9x^2 - kx + 4 = 0$ **48.** $36x^2 - kx + 1 = 0$

49. Geometry The table shows some possible dimensions of rectangles with a perimeter of 100 units. Complete the table.

Width	1	2	3	4	5	6	7	8	9	10
Length	49	48								
Area	49									

Homework Video Tutor

Visit: PHSchool.com
Web Code: bbe-0507

   a. Plot the points (width, area). Find a model for the data set.
   b. Find another point in the data set and use it to verify your model.
   c. What is a reasonable domain for this function? Explain.
   d. Find the maximum possible area. Find its dimensions.
   e. Find an equation for area in terms of width without using the table. Do you get the same equation as in part (a)? Explain.

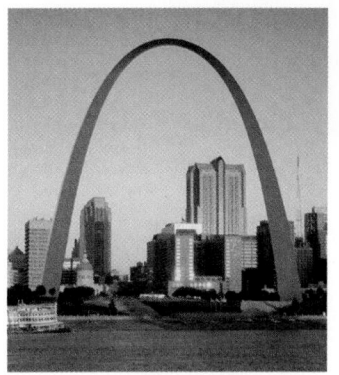

Gateway Arch in St. Louis

50. Architecture The shape of the Gateway Arch in St. Louis, Missouri, is a catenary curve, which closely resembles a parabola. The function $y = -\frac{2}{315}x^2 + 4x$ models the shape of the arch, where y is the height in feet and x is the horizontal distance from the base of the left side of the arch in feet.
a. Graph the function and find its vertex.
b. Describe a reasonable domain and range for the function. Explain.
c. According to the model, what is the maximum height of the arch?
d. What is the width of the arch at the base?

Solve each quadratic equation by completing the square.

51. $\frac{1}{3}x^2 + 8x - 3 = 0$ **52.** $\frac{1}{2}x^2 + 4x = 2$ **53.** $x^2 - \frac{1}{2}x = \frac{1}{3}$

54. $3x^2 + x = \frac{2}{3}$ **55.** $2x^2 - \frac{1}{2}x = \frac{1}{8}$ **56.** $x^2 + \frac{3}{4}x = \frac{1}{2}$

C Challenge   **Solve for x in terms of a.**

57. $2x^2 - ax = 6a^2$ **58.** $3x^2 + ax = a^2$ **59.** $2a^2x^2 - 8ax = -6$

60. $4a^2x^2 + 8ax + 3 = 0$ **61.** $3x^2 + ax^2 = 9x + 9a$ **62.** $6a^2x^2 - 11ax = 10$

63. Solve $x^2 = \left(6\sqrt{2}\right)x + 7$ by completing the square.

Multiple Choice Practice

For California Standards and CAHSEE Tutorials, visit PHSchool.com. Web Code: bbq-9045

ALG2 8.0   **64.** Gina wants to solve the equation $x^2 - 8x = 3$ by completing the square. What value should she add to each side of the equation so that the right hand side is a perfect square trinomial?

    Ⓐ -3 Ⓑ 4 Ⓒ 8 Ⓓ 16

ALG2 2.0   **65.** Which point is a solution of the system $\begin{cases} x + y \geq 2 \\ y \leq -1 + 3x \end{cases}$?

    Ⓐ $(-6, 4)$ Ⓑ $(-4, 4)$ Ⓒ $(5, -3)$ Ⓓ $(4, -4)$

ALG2 2.0   **66.** Solve $\begin{bmatrix} 3 & -5 \\ -1 & 2 \end{bmatrix} \begin{bmatrix} x \\ y \end{bmatrix} = \begin{bmatrix} 6 \\ -3 \end{bmatrix}$.

    Ⓐ $(2, 0)$ Ⓑ $(6, -3)$ Ⓒ $(-3, -3)$ Ⓓ $(3, -5)$

Mixed Review

GO for Help

Lesson 5-6   **Simplify each expression.**

67. $(2 - 3i) + (-4 + 5i)$ **68.** $(7 + 3i) - (2 + i)$ **69.** $(4 - 9i)(3 + 8i)$

Lesson 5-1   **Find a quadratic model for each set of data.**

70. $(-4, 3), (-3, 3), (-2, 4)$ **71.** $\left(-1, \frac{1}{2}\right), (0, 2), (2, 2)$ **72.** $(0, 2), (1, 0), (2, 4)$

Lesson 4-8   **Use Cramer's Rule to solve each system.**

73. $\begin{cases} 2x + y = 4 \\ 3x - y = 6 \end{cases}$ **74.** $\begin{cases} 2x + y = 7 \\ -2x + 5y = -1 \end{cases}$ **75.** $\begin{cases} 2x + 4y = 10 \\ 3x + 5y = 14 \end{cases}$

Understanding Word Problems Read the problem below. Let the explanation guide you in using the formula. Check your understanding with the Exercises.

Sports The height of a punted football can be modeled with the quadratic function $h = -0.01x^2 + 1.18x + 2$. The horizontal distance in feet from the point of impact with the kicker's foot is x, and h is the height of the ball in feet.

    a. Find the vertex of the graph of the function by completing the square.

    b. What is the maximum height of the punt?

    c. The nearest defensive player is 5 ft horizontally from the point of impact. How high must the player reach to block the punt?

To understand a formula, identify the formula and its parts.

From the problem, the formula is
$h = -0.01x^2 + 1.18x + 2$.
The graph gives you other information.

height of the ball   horizontal distance from the kicker's foot

$$h = -0.01x^2 + 1.18x + 2$$

height at time of kick

Part (a) of the problem asks you to find the vertex of the graph. By completing the square, you can get an equation in vertex form.

$$h = -0.01(x - 59)^2 + 36.81 \quad \textbf{vertex form}$$

    x-coordinate   *y*-coordinate

Since the *y*-coordinate of the vertex is 36.81, you know that the maximum height of the football is 36.81 ft. That answers part (b).

To block the punt, the defensive player must touch the football along its path. To answer part (c), find the height of the ball (and the height of the defensive player's hand) when it is horizontally 5 ft from the kicker, or when $x = 5$.

$$h(5) = -0.01x^2 + 1.18x + 2 \qquad \textbf{Use the formula.}$$
$$= -0.01(5)^2 + 1.18(5) + 2 \quad \textbf{Substitute.}$$
$$= 7.65 \qquad\qquad\qquad \textbf{Simplify.}$$

The defensive player must reach 7.65 ft above the ground to block the punt.

EXERCISES

1. What is the ball's height when it has traveled 20 yd (60 ft) downfield?

2. How far downfield has the ball traveled when it reaches its maximum height?

3. a. How far downfield has the ball traveled when it reaches a height of 6 ft?

    b. Reasoning Explain why part (a) has more than one answer.

5-8

The Quadratic Formula

 California Content Standards

ALG2 8.0 Students solve quadratic equations by using the quadratic formula. They also solve quadratic equations in the complex number system. *Introduce, Develop*

What You'll Learn

- To solve quadratic equations by using the Quadratic Formula
- To determine types of solutions by using the discriminant

. . . And Why

To investigate the motion of a field hockey ball, as in Example 5

✓ Check Skills You'll Need

 for Help Lessons 1-2 and 5-1

Write each quadratic equation in standard form.

1. $y = 8 - 10x^2$

2. $y = (x + 2)^2 - 1$

3. $y = -2x(x - 1) + (x + 1)^2$

4. $y = (3x)^2 - (x - 1)^2$

Evaluate the expression $b^2 - 4ac$ for the given values of a, b, and c.

5. $a = 1, b = 6, c = 3$

6. $a = -5, b = 2, c = 4$

7. $a = 3, b = -6, c = 7$

8. $a = 2, b = 3, c = -10$

New Vocabulary • Quadratic Formula • discriminant

---

1 Using the Quadratic Formula

You can derive a formula for solving quadratic equations by completing the square. Below is the equation $2x^2 + 6x + 1 = 0$. Next to it is the general form of a quadratic equation, $ax^2 + bx + c = 0$. Each equation is solved for x.

$$2x^2 + 6x + 1 = 0 \qquad\qquad ax^2 + bx + c = 0$$

$$x^2 + 3x + \frac{1}{2} = 0 \qquad\qquad x^2 + \frac{b}{a}x + \frac{c}{a} = 0$$

$$x^2 + 3x = -\frac{1}{2} \qquad\qquad x^2 + \frac{b}{a}x = -\frac{c}{a}$$

$$x^2 + 2\left(\frac{3}{2}\right)x + \left(\frac{3}{2}\right)^2 = \left(\frac{3}{2}\right)^2 - \frac{1}{2} \qquad x^2 + 2\left(\frac{b}{2a}\right)x + \left(\frac{b}{2a}\right)^2 = \left(\frac{b}{2a}\right)^2 - \frac{c}{a}$$

$$\left(x + \frac{3}{2}\right)^2 = \frac{9}{4} - \frac{2}{4} \qquad\qquad \left(x + \frac{b}{2a}\right)^2 = \frac{b^2}{4a^2} - \frac{c}{a}$$

$$\left(x + \frac{3}{2}\right)^2 = \frac{7}{4} \qquad\qquad \left(x + \frac{b}{2a}\right)^2 = \frac{b^2 - 4ac}{4a^2}$$

$$x + \frac{3}{2} = \pm\sqrt{\frac{7}{4}} \qquad\qquad x + \frac{b}{2a} = \pm\sqrt{\frac{b^2 - 4ac}{4a^2}}$$

$$x = -\frac{3}{2} \pm \frac{\sqrt{7}}{2} \qquad\qquad x = -\frac{b}{2a} \pm \frac{\sqrt{b^2 - 4ac}}{2a}$$

$$x = \frac{-3 \pm \sqrt{7}}{2} \qquad\qquad x = \frac{-b \pm \sqrt{b^2 - 4ac}}{2a}$$

 Key Concepts

Theorem	**Quadratic Formula**

A quadratic equation written in standard form $ax^2 + bx + c = 0$ can be solved with the Quadratic Formula.

$$x = \frac{-b \pm \sqrt{b^2 - 4ac}}{2a}$$

Video Tutor Help

Visit: PHSchool.com
Web Code: bbe-0775

1 EXAMPLE **Using the Quadratic Formula**

Use the Quadratic Formula to solve $3x^2 - 5x = 2$.

$$3x^2 - 5x - 2 = 0$$ Write in standard form.

$$a = 3, b = -5, c = -2$$ Find the values of a, b, and c.

$$x = \frac{-b \pm \sqrt{b^2 - 4ac}}{2a}$$ Write the Quadratic Formula.

$$= \frac{-(-5) \pm \sqrt{(-5)^2 - 4(3)(-2)}}{2(3)}$$ Substitute.

$$= \frac{5 \pm \sqrt{25 - (-24)}}{6}$$ Simplify.

$$= \frac{5 \pm \sqrt{49}}{6}$$

$$= \frac{5 \pm 7}{6}$$

$$= \frac{12}{6} \text{ or } \frac{-2}{6}$$

$$= 2 \text{ or } -\frac{1}{3}$$

Check

$$3x^2 - 5x = 2 \qquad\qquad 3x^2 - 5x = 2$$

$$3(2)^2 - 5(2) \stackrel{?}{=} 2 \qquad 3\left(-\frac{1}{3}\right)^2 - 5\left(-\frac{1}{3}\right) \stackrel{?}{=} 2$$

$$12 - 10 \stackrel{?}{=} 2 \qquad\qquad \frac{1}{3} + \frac{5}{3} \stackrel{?}{=} 2$$

$$2 = 2 \checkmark \qquad\qquad 2 = 2 \checkmark$$

 1 Use the Quadratic Formula to solve $3x^2 - x = 4$. Check your solutions.

The Quadratic Formula will give you complex solutions that you cannot find by graphing or factoring.

2 EXAMPLE **Finding Complex Solutions**

Solve $2x^2 = -6x - 7$.

$$2x^2 + 6x + 7 = 0$$ Write in standard form.

$$a = 2, b = 6, c = 7$$ Find the values of a, b, and c.

$$x = \frac{-(6) \pm \sqrt{(6)^2 - 4(2)(7)}}{2(2)}$$ Substitute.

$$= \frac{-6 \pm \sqrt{36 - 56}}{4}$$ Simplify.

$$= \frac{-6 \pm \sqrt{-20}}{4}$$

$$= \frac{-6 \pm 2i\sqrt{5}}{4}$$

$$= -\frac{3}{2} \pm \frac{i\sqrt{5}}{2}$$

CA Standards Check **2** **a.** Use the Quadratic Formula to solve $-2x^2 = 4x + 3$.
b. Graph the related quadratic function $y = 2x^2 + 4x + 3$. Explain why you cannot use the graph to find the solution.

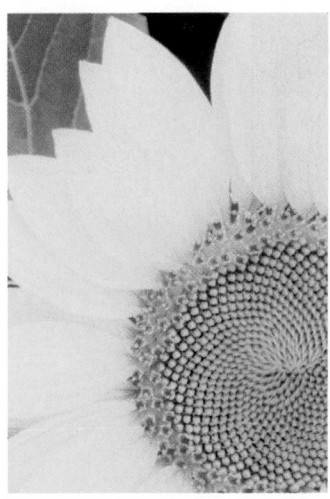

In Lesson 5-5, you found an approximate value for the golden ratio by graphing the related function for the equation $x^2 - x - 1 = 0$. Now you can use the Quadratic Formula to find an exact value for the golden ratio.

3 EXAMPLE   Real-World Connection

Art The golden ratio is the ratio of the longer side to the shorter side of a golden rectangle. Solve $x^2 - x - 1 = 0$ for x to find the exact value of the golden ratio.

$$x^2 - x - 1 = 0$$

$a = 1, b = -1, c = -1$ **Find the values of a, b, and c.**

$$x = \frac{-b \pm \sqrt{b^2 - 4ac}}{2a}$$ **Use the Quadratic Formula.**

$$= \frac{-(-1) \pm \sqrt{(-1)^2 - 4(1)(-1)}}{2(1)}$$ **Substitute for a, b, and c.**

$$= \frac{1 \pm \sqrt{5}}{2}$$ **Simplify.**

The golden ratio is $\frac{1 + \sqrt{5}}{2} : 1$, or simply $\frac{1 + \sqrt{5}}{2}$.

Check   Is the answer reasonable? Since $\frac{1 - \sqrt{5}}{2}$ is a negative number, and a ratio of actual lengths cannot be negative, that answer is not reasonable. Since $\frac{1 + \sqrt{5}}{2} \approx 1.62$, which is the approximate value for the golden ratio found in Lesson 5-5, that answer is reasonable.

Real-World Connection

In sunflowers, the ratio of the number of clockwise spirals to the number of counterclockwise spirals approximates the golden ratio.

✔ **CA Standards Check** ❸ Use the Quadratic Formula to solve each equation. Find the exact solutions. Then approximate any radical solutions. Round to the nearest hundredth.

    a. $4x^2 = 8x - 3$ **b.** $x^2 + 4x = 41$

❷ Using the Discriminant

Quadratic equations can have real or complex solutions. You can determine the type and number of solutions by finding the discriminant.

  Key Concepts

Definition	Discriminant of a Quadratic Equation

The **discriminant** of a quadratic equation in the form $ax^2 + bx + c = 0$ is the value of the expression $b^2 - 4ac$.

$$x = \frac{-b \pm \sqrt{b^2 - 4ac}}{2a} \quad \leftarrow \text{discriminant}$$

The table on the next page shows the relationships among the value of the discriminant, the solutions of a quadratic equation, and the graph of the related function. These relationships are true for real number values of a, b, and c.

Value of the Discriminant	Type and Number of Solutions for $ax^2 + bx + c = 0$	Examples of Graphs of Related Functions $y = ax^2 + bx + c$
$b^2 - 4ac > 0$	two real solutions	two x-intercepts
$b^2 - 4ac = 0$	one real solution	one x-intercept
$b^2 - 4ac < 0$	no real solution; two imaginary solutions	no x-intercept

4 EXAMPLE Using the Discriminant

Determine the type and number of solutions of $x^2 + 6x + 8 = 0$.

$a = 1, b = 6, c = 8$ **Find the values of a, b, and c.**

$b^2 - 4ac = (6)^2 - 4(1)(8)$ **Evaluate the discriminant.**

$\qquad\qquad = 4$ **Simplify.**

● Since the discriminant is positive, $x^2 + 6x + 8 = 0$ has two real solutions.

✓ CA Standards Check ④ Determine the type and number of solutions of each equation.
    a. $x^2 + 6x + 9 = 0$ **b.** $x^2 + 6x + 10 = 0$

5 EXAMPLE Real-World Connection

Multiple Choice Suppose a scoop releases a field hockey ball with an upward velocity of 34 ft/s. The function $h = -16t^2 + 34t$ models the height h in feet of the ball at time t in seconds. When will the ball reach a height of 20 ft?

  Ⓐ in 2 seconds   Ⓑ in 6 seconds   Ⓒ in 11 seconds   Ⓓ never

Real-World Connection

A scoop is a field hockey pass that propels the ball from the ground into the air.

$\qquad h = -16t^2 + 34t$

$\quad 20 = -16t^2 + 34t$ **Substitute 20 for h.**

$\qquad 0 = -16t^2 + 34t - 20$ **Write the equation in standard form.**

$a = -16, b = 34, c = -20$ **Find the values of a, b, and c.**

$b^2 - 4ac = (34)^2 - 4(-16)(-20)$ **Evaluate the discriminant.**

$\qquad\qquad = 1156 - 1280$ **Simplify.**

$\qquad\qquad = -124$

Since the discriminant is negative, the equation $20 = -16t^2 + 34t$ has no real
● solutions. The ball will not reach a height of 20 ft. The answer is choice D.

✓ CA Standards Check ⑤ Will the ball in Example 5 ever reach a height of 15 ft? Explain.

You are now familiar with six methods of solving quadratic equations: finding square roots, factoring, using tables, graphing, completing the square, and using the Quadratic Formula. For $ax^2 = c$, finding square roots works best. The discriminant can help you decide how to solve equations that have an x-term.

 Key Concepts

Summary	Methods for Solving Quadratic Equations
Discriminant	**Methods**
positive square number	• factoring, tables, graphing, Quadratic Formula, or completing the square
positive nonsquare number	• for approximate solutions: tables, graphing, Quadratic Formula, or completing the square • for exact solutions: Quadratic Formula or completing the square
zero	• factoring, graphing, Quadratic Formula, or completing the square
negative	• Quadratic Formula or completing the square

Test-Taking Tip

Learn to use a tool like the discriminant. It may not answer a test item but it could help you find an answer quickly.

 EXERCISES

Standards Practice

For more exercises, see *Extra Skill and Word Problem Practice.*

ALG2 8.0

 Practice by Example

Example 1
(page 294)

 for Help

Example 2
(page 294)

Solve each equation using the Quadratic Formula.

1. $x^2 - 4x + 3 = 0$
2. $x^2 + 8x + 12 = 0$
3. $2x^2 + 5x - 7 = 0$

4. $3x^2 + 2x - 1 = 0$
5. $x^2 + 10x = -25$
6. $2x^2 + 3x - 5 = 0$

7. $x^2 = 3x - 1$
8. $x^2 + 6x - 5 = 0$
9. $3x^2 - 4x - 2 = 0$

10. $8x^2 - 2x - 3 = 0$
11. $x(x - 5) = -4$
12. $9x^2 + 12x - 5 = 0$

13. $x^2 - 6x + 11 = 0$
14. $x^2 = 2x - 5$
15. $x^2 + 3x + 5 = 0$

16. $2x^2 + 8x + 12 = 0$
17. $x^2 - 2x + 3 = 0$
18. $3x^2 + 4x + 10 = 0$

19. $-x^2 + 5x - 7 = 0$
20. $2x^2 = 7x - 8$
21. $15x^2 + 2x + 1 = 0$

Example 3
(page 295)

Solve each equation using the Quadratic Formula. Find the exact solutions. Then approximate any radical solutions. Round to the nearest hundredth.

22. $2x^2 - 5x - 3 = 0$
23. $3x^2 - 10x + 5 = 0$
24. $3x^2 + 4x - 3 = 0$

25. $6x^2 - 5x - 1 = 0$
26. $7x^2 - x - 12 = 0$
27. $5x^2 + 8x - 11 = 0$

28. $4x^2 + 4x = 22$
29. $2x^2 - 1 = 5x$
30. $2x^2 + x = \frac{1}{2}$

Examples 4 and 5
(page 296)

Evaluate the discriminant of each equation. Tell how many solutions each equation has and whether the solutions are real or imaginary.

31. $x^2 + 4x + 5 = 0$
32. $x^2 - 4x - 5 = 0$
33. $4x^2 + 20x + 25 = 0$

34. $2x^2 + x + 28 = 0$
35. $2x^2 + 7x - 15 = 0$
36. $6x^2 - 2x + 5 = 0$

37. $2x^2 + 7x = -6$
38. $x^2 - 12x + 36 = 0$
39. $x^2 = 8x - 16$

40. Business The weekly revenue for a company is $R = -3p^2 + 60p + 1060$, where p is the price of the company's product. Use the discriminant to find whether there is a price for which the weekly revenue would be $1500.

Apply Your Skills

Solve each equation using any method. When necessary, round real solutions to the nearest hundredth. For imaginary solutions, write exact solutions.

41. $x^2 = 11x - 10$

42. $5x^2 = 210x$

43. $4x^2 + 4x = 3$

44. $2x^2 + 4x = 10$

45. $x^2 - 2x + 2 = 0$

46. $x^2 - 3x - 8 = 0$

47. $-3x^2 + 147 = 0$

48. $x^2 + 8x = 4$

49. $x^2 = 6x - 11$

50. $4x^2 - 4x - 3 = 0$

51. $\frac{x-3}{2} = \frac{6}{x-2}$

52. $\frac{x+2}{5} = \frac{3}{x+1}$

53. a. The area of a rectangle is 36 in.^{2}. The perimeter of the rectangle is 36 in. Write an equation using one variable to find the dimensions of the rectangle.
 b. Find the dimensions of the rectangle to the nearest hundredth of an inch.

54. Matrices Find the value of n in the determinant at the right.

55. Writing Summarize how to use the discriminant to analyze the types of solutions of a quadratic equation.

$$\begin{vmatrix} 2 & n & 4 \\ n & 2 & -1 \\ 4 & n & 7 \end{vmatrix} = -37$$

56. Air Pollution The function $y = 0.0721x^2 - 2.8867x + 117.061$ models the emissions of carbon monoxide in the United States since 1985. In the function, y represents the amount of carbon monoxide released in a year in millions of tons, and $x = 0$ represents the year 1985.
 a. How can you use a graph to estimate the year in which less than 100 million tons of carbon monoxide were released into the air?
 b. How can you use the Quadratic Formula to estimate the year in which less than 100 million tons of carbon monoxide were released into the air?
 c. Which method do you prefer? Explain why.

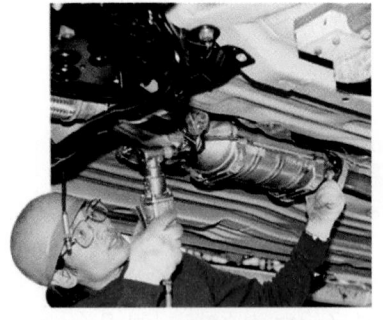

Without graphing, tell how many x-intercepts each function has.

57. $y = -2x^2 + 3x - 1$

58. $y = 0.25x^2 + 2x + 4$

59. $y = x^2 + 3x + 5$

60. $y = -x^2 + 3x + 10$

61. $y = 3x^2 - 10x + 6$

62. $y = 10x^2 + 13x - 3$

63. Critical Thinking Determine the value(s) of k for which $3x^2 + kx + 12 = 0$ has each type of solution.
 a. exactly one real solution **b.** two imaginary solutions **c.** two real solutions

64. Open-Ended Find a value of k for which $x^2 + kx + 9 = 0$ has the given type of solution.
 a. two imaginary solutions **b.** two real solutions   **c.** one real solution

65. Error Analysis After analyzing a quadratic equation with real coefficients, a student says that the equation has exactly one imaginary solution. Explain how you know that the student is wrong.

66. Use the discriminant to match each function with its graph.
 a. $f(x) = x^2 - 4x + 2$ **b.** $f(x) = x^2 - 4x + 4$ **c.** $f(x) = x^2 - 4x + 6$

I.

II.

III.

Homework Video Tutor

Visit: PHSchool.com
Web Code: bbe-0508

67. a. Geometry Write an equation to find the dimensions of a square that has the same area as the circle at the left.

b. Find the length of a side of the square, to the nearest hundredth centimeter.

68. Physics The equation $h = 80t - 16t^2$ models the height h feet reached in t seconds by an object propelled straight up from the ground.

a. Will the object ever reach a height of 90 ft?

b. Verify your answer to part (a) with a graph.

c. For what values of t will the object be in the air?

C Challenge

Write a quadratic equation with the given solutions.

69. $\dfrac{3 + \sqrt{5}}{2}, \dfrac{3 - \sqrt{5}}{2}$ **70.** $\dfrac{-5 + \sqrt{13}}{2}, \dfrac{-5 - \sqrt{13}}{2}$ **71.** $\dfrac{5 + i\sqrt{3}}{2}, \dfrac{5 - i\sqrt{3}}{2}$

Use the Quadratic Formula to solve each equation for x in terms of a.

72. $2a^2x^2 - 6ax = -5$ **73.** $5a^2x^2 - 10ax = 12$ **74.** $x^2 + 2ax = 25a^2$

75. Use the Quadratic Formula to prove each statement.

a. The sum of the solutions of the quadratic equation $ax^2 + bx + c = 0$ is $-\dfrac{b}{a}$.

b. The product of the solutions of the quadratic equation $ax^2 + bx + c = 0$ is $\dfrac{c}{a}$.

Multiple Choice Practice

For California Standards and CAHSEE Tutorials, visit PHSchool.com. Web Code: bbq-9045

ALG2 8.0

76. Which equation has $-3 \pm 5i$ as its solutions?

Ⓐ $x^2 + 6x = -34$ Ⓒ $x^2 + 3x = 4$

Ⓑ $x^2 + 6x = -14$ Ⓓ $x^2 + 3x = 2$

ALG2 9.0

77. Which description of the graph of $y = ax^2 + bx + c$ is NOT possible?

Ⓐ There are two x-intercepts, the vertex is below the x-axis, and $a > 0$.

Ⓑ There is one x-intercept and the vertex is on the x-axis.

Ⓒ There are two x-intercepts, the vertex is below the x-axis, and $a < 0$.

Ⓓ There are no x-intercepts, the vertex is above the x-axis, and $a > 0$.

Mixed Review

Lesson 5-7

Solve by completing the square.

78. $x^2 - 8x - 20 = 0$ **79.** $2y^2 = 4y - 1$ **80.** $x^2 - 3x - 8 = 0$

Lesson 4-4

Each matrix represents vertices of a polygon. Translate each figure 3 units right and 2 units down. Express your answer as a matrix.

81. $\begin{bmatrix} 2 & 3 & -1 \\ -5 & 1 & 0 \end{bmatrix}$ **82.** $\begin{bmatrix} 0 & -3 & 1 & -5 \\ 2 & -1 & 4 & -2 \end{bmatrix}$

Lesson 4-3

Multiply.

83. $\begin{bmatrix} 0 & -3 \\ -3 & 1 \end{bmatrix}\begin{bmatrix} 4 & 0 \\ -9 & 1 \end{bmatrix}$ **84.** $\begin{bmatrix} 3 & 10 \\ 1 & 5 \end{bmatrix}\begin{bmatrix} -2 & 4 \\ -1 & 4 \end{bmatrix}$

You can solve quadratic inequalities using graphs, tables, and algebraic methods. Indeed, the most effective way may be a combination of methods.

1 ACTIVITY

To find which of $x^2 - 12$ or $3x + 6$ is greater, enter the two functions as Y_1 and Y_2 in your graphing calculator, you could use the TABLE option to compare the two functions for various values of x, as shown below.

```
Plot1 Plot2 Plot3
\Y1 ▪ X² – 12
\Y2 ▪ 3X + 6
\Y3 =
\Y4 =
\Y5 =
\Y6 =
\Y7 =
```

```
TABLE SETUP
 TblStart=–10
 Tbl=5
 Indpnt: AUTO ASK
 Depend: AUTO ASK
```

X	Y1	Y2
–10	88	–24
–5	13	–9
0	–12	6
5	13	21
10	88	36
15	213	51
20	388	66
X=–10		

1. For which values of x in the table is $x^2 - 12 > 3x + 6$?

2. For which values of x in the table is $x^2 - 12 < 3x + 6$?

3. Does this table tell you all values of x for which $x^2 - 12 < 3x + 6$? Explain.

4. In the TBLSET (TABLE SETUP) menu, change TblStart to -9 and ΔTbl to 3. Display the table again. Does the table with this setup give you more information? Why?

You can compare functions more efficiently by making one side of the inequality 0.

5. Show that $x^2 - 12 < 3x + 6$ is equivalent to $x^2 - 3x - 18 < 0$.

6. Enter $x^2 - 3x - 18$ as Y_3 in your graphing calculator. Place the cursor on the = sign after Y_1 and press ENTER . This operation turns off the display of the equation Y_1. Turn off Y_2 as well, and then display the table. You will see the screen shown at the right. For which values of x in the table is $x^2 - 3x - 18 < 0$?

X	Y3	
–9	90	
–6	36	
–3	0	
0	–18	
3	–18	
6	0	
9	36	
X=9		

2 ACTIVITY

For a visual model, look at the same inequalities graphically. Turn off Y_3 and turn on Y_1 and Y_2. Begin by graphing the two functions in the original inequality as shown in the screens below.

```
Plot1 Plot2 Plot3
\Y1 ▪ X² – 12
\Y2 ▪ 3X + 6
\Y3 = X² – 3X – 18
\Y4 =
\Y5 =
\Y6 =
\Y7 =
```

```
WINDOW
Xmin=–10
Xmax= 10
X s c l = 1
Ymin=–20
Ymax= 30
Y s c l = 5
X r e s = 1
```

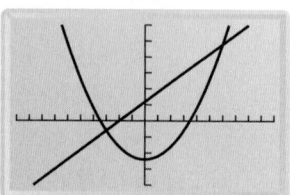

7. Which graph represents the function $f(x) = x^2 - 12$? Which graph represents $f(x) = 3x + 6$? How can you tell?

8. Use your calculator to find the values of x for which $x^2 - 12 < 3x + 6$ in this window.

9. Do you think there are values of x outside this window for which $x^2 - 12 < 3x + 6$? Explain.

Now turn off Y_1 and Y_2 and turn on Y_3. Graph Y_3 in the same window as above.

10. Use your calculator to find the values of x for which $x^2 - 3x - 18 < 0$. Are these the same values of x you found in Exercise 8?

11. Compare the strategy in Exercise 8 with the strategy in Exercise 10 for solving the inequality $x^2 - 12 < 3x + 6$ graphically. Is one easier than the other? Explain.

3 ACTIVITY

As an added tool, you can incorporate some algebra into the solution.

12. Factor the quadratic to find the two values of x for which $x^2 - 3x - 18 = 0$.

13. Shown at the left below is the graph of $y_3 = x^2 - 3x - 18$. What happens in this graph at the two x-values you found in Exercise 12?

 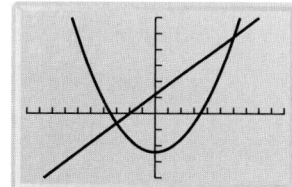

14. Shown at the right above is the graph of the functions $y_1 = x^2 - 12$ and $y_2 = 3x + 6$. What happens with these graphs at the two x-values you found in Exercise 12?

15. Tell how you can combine the algebra of Exercise 12 with the geometry of one of the graphs in Exercises 13 or 14 to give a complete solution of the inequality $x^2 - 12 < 3x + 6$.

EXERCISES

16. It is compelling to graph $Y_1, Y_2,$ and Y_3 in the same window. When you do (see right), there is no relationship immediately apparent. However, based on your work above, what can you say is true about the graphs of $Y_1, Y_2,$ and Y_3?

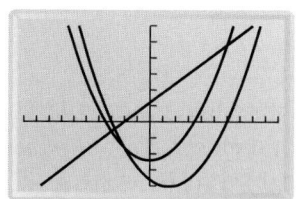

Here are some special quadratic inequalities to solve. You can use what you know about the family of quadratic functions to help solve some of them.

17. a. $x^2 - 2 < -x - 3$ **b.** $x^2 - 2 > -x - 3$ **18. a.** $x^2 < 2x^2$ **b.** $x^2 < \frac{1}{2}x^2$

19. a. $2(x - 2)(x + 3) < (x - 2)(x + 3)$ **20. a.** $-3x(x - 2) < (x - 2)(x - 4)$

     b. $-2(x - 2)(x + 3) < (x - 2)(x + 3)$ **b.** $-\frac{1}{3}x(x - 2) < (x - 2)(x - 4)$

                                                   c. $-x(x - 2) < (x - 2)(x - 4)$

21. Let $y_1 = f(x)$ and $y_2 = g(x)$.
     a. Describe how you could use graphs to solve the inequality $f(x) < g(x)$.
     b. How are the solutions of $f(x) < g(x)$ and $f(x) > g(x)$ related?

22. Assume that f and g are discrete functions whose domains are whole numbers. Describe how you could use a table to solve the inequality $f(x) < g(x)$.

Using a Variable

You can solve many problems by using a variable to represent an unknown quantity. In fact, some questions require that you use a variable in an equation or inequality to show how you would model a given situation.

EXAMPLE

Each year, Sylvia's club sells used videos at a street fair to raise funds. It costs $150 to rent a booth at the fair. The club will spend $2 for each video and sell each video for $5. Which equation can be used to find the number of videos v that the club must sell so that its income equals its expenses for the v videos?

- (A) $5v = 150 + 2v$
- (B) $2v = 150 + 5v$
- (C) $5v = 150 - 2v$
- (D) $150 = 5v + 2v$

You are given the variable v to use. Find the key relationship.

Relate: Income (sales)   must equal   expenses (booth and videos)

Write: $5v$ $=$ $150 + 2v$

● The correct answer is A.

EXERCISES

For each exercise below, use one or more variables and find a key relationship. Then give the correct answer.

1. Galeno is making a poster with an area of 50 square inches. He wants the length to be 3 inches greater than the height. To the nearest tenth of an inch, what will the length of the poster be?
   - (A) 6.2 in.
   - (B) 6.8 in.
   - (C) 7.8 in.
   - (D) 8.7 in.

2. In the right triangle ABC, $\overline{BC}$ and $\overline{DE}$ are parallel. If $AB = 10$, what is the area of triangle ADE?
   - (A) 37.5 units^2
   - (B) 15 units^2
   - (C) 12 units^2
   - (D) 6 units^2

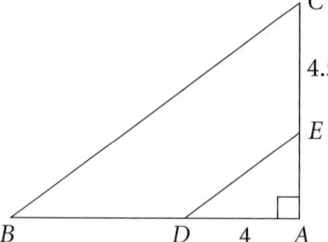

3. Gina swims 30 laps in a pool to train for her next swim meet. She has already swum l laps. If she swims more than 1.5 laps/min, which inequality best represents the amount of time in minutes m that it takes her to finish the swim?
   - (A) $m \geq \frac{1.5}{30 - l}$
   - (B) $m \leq \frac{1.5}{30 - l}$
   - (C) $m < \frac{30 - l}{1.5}$
   - (D) $m > \frac{30 - l}{1.5}$

Chapter 5 Review

Vocabulary Review

absolute value of a complex number (p. 279)	factoring (p. 263)	standard form of a quadratic equation (p. 271)
axis of symmetry (p. 243)	greatest common factor (GCF) of an expression (p. 263)	standard form of a quadratic function (p. 242)
completing the square (p. 286)	*i* (p. 278)	vertex form of a quadratic function (p. 256)
complex number (p. 279)	imaginary number (p. 278)	vertex of a parabola (p. 243)
complex number plane (p. 279)	parabola (p. 243)	zero of a function (p. 272)
complex conjugate (p. 280)	perfect square trinomial (p. 266)	Zero Product Property (p. 271)
difference of two squares (p. 267)	Quadratic Formula (p. 293)	
discriminant (p. 295)	quadratic function (p. 242)	

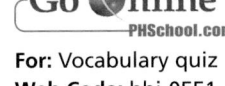

Go Online
PHSchool.com
For: Vocabulary quiz
Web Code: bbj-0551

Choose the correct vocabulary term to complete each sentence.

1. The square of a binomial is a(n) _?_ .

2. Every quadratic equation can be solved with the _?_ .

3. The _?_ reveals a translation of a parent quadratic function.

4. A(n) _?_ is also an *x*-intercept of the graph of the function.

5. The _?_ completely determines the types of roots of a quadratic function.

Skills and Concepts

Lesson 5-1

- To identify quadratic functions and graphs (p. 242)
- To model data with quadratic functions (p. 244)

ALG2 9.0, 10.0

The **standard form of a quadratic function** is $f(x) = ax^2 + bx + c$, where $a \neq 0$. The quadratic term is ax^2. The graph of a **quadratic function** is a **parabola**.

The **axis of symmetry** is a line that divides a parabola into two mirror images. The **vertex of a parabola** is the point at the intersection of the parabola and its axis of symmetry. Corresponding points on the parabola are the same distance from the axis of symmetry.

You can find a quadratic model for a set of data by solving a system of three equations for *a*, *b*, and *c*, or by using the quadratic regression feature of a graphing calculator.

Determine whether each function is linear or quadratic. Identify the quadratic, linear, and constant terms.

6. $y = (3 - x)(2x + 1)$ **7.** $y = x - x^2 + 3$ **8.** $y = 3 - 4x$

Identify the vertex, the axis of symmetry, and the points corresponding to P and Q.

9.   **10.**   **11.**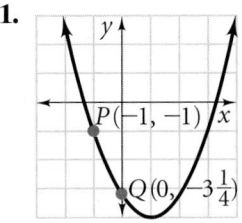

12. a. Sports Find a quadratic model for the attendance at women's college basketball games from 1995–1997 by solving three equations in a, b, and c.
  b. Predict the year attendance will reach 12,000,000.
  c. Use the quadratic regression feature of your calculator to find a model for all the data.
  d. What does this regression model predict as the first year attendance will reach 12,000,000?
  e. Find the maximum likely attendance.

Year	Attendance (thousands)
1995	4962
1996	5234
1997	6734
1998	7387
1999	8010
2000	8698

SOURCE: National Collegiate Athletic Association

Lessons 5-2, 5-3

• To graph quadratic functions (p. 249)
• To find maximum and minimum values of quadratic functions (p. 251)
• To use the vertex form of a quadratic function (p. 256)

ALG2 9.0, 10.0

The parent function for the family of quadratic functions is $f(x) = x^2$. The constants a, b, and c characterize the graph of $y = ax^2 + bx + c$. The axis of symmetry is $x = -\frac{b}{2a}$, the vertex is at $\left(-\frac{b}{2a}, f\left(-\frac{b}{2a}\right)\right)$, and $f\left(-\frac{b}{2a}\right)$ is the maximum or minimum value. The **vertex form of a quadratic function** is $y = a(x - h)^2 + k$. The vertex is (h, k), the maximum or minimum value is k, and the axis of symmetry is the line $x = h$. If $a > 0$, the parabola opens up. If $a < 0$, it opens down.

Graph each function. Identify the vertex, y-intercept, and axis of symmetry.

13. $y = 2(x + 1)^2 - 4$

14. $y = (x - 5)^2$

15. $y = -(x - 2)^2 + 1$

16. $y = -x^2 + 7$

Write each function in vertex form. Find its maximum or minimum value.

17. $y = x^2 + x - 12$

18. $y = -x^2 + 2x + 2$

19. $y = 2x^2 + 8x - 3$

20. $y = -0.5x^2 + 5$

21.

22.

23.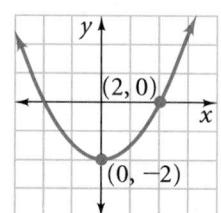

Lessons 5-4, 5-5

• To find common and binomial factors of quadratic expressions (p. 263)
• To factor special quadratic expressions (p. 266)
• To solve quadratic equations by factoring and by finding square roots (p. 271)
• To solve quadratic equations by graphing (p. 272)

ALG2 4.0, 8.0, 10.0

You can solve some quadratic equations by finding square roots of both sides or by finding the zeros of the related function. You can solve some quadratic equations in the **standard form of a quadratic equation** $ax^2 + bx + c = 0$ by **factoring** and using the **Zero Product Property**. For a **perfect square trinomial**, $ax^2 \pm 2abx + b^2 = (a \pm b)^2$. For the **difference of two squares**, $a^2 - b^2 = (a + b)(a - b)$. In all cases, first factor out the **greatest common factor (GCF) of the expression.**

Solve by factoring, taking square roots, or, if necessary, by graphing. Give exact radical answers. For answers found by graphing, round to the nearest hundredth.

24. $x^2 - 7x = 0$

25. $x^2 + 2x - 8 = 0$

26. $(x + 3)^2 = 9$

27. $4(x - 2)^2 = 32$

28. $2x^2 - 6x - 8 = 0$

29. $x^2 - 5x - 5 = 0$

30. $3x^2 - 14x + 8 = 0$

31. $x^2 - 3x - 4 = 0$

32. $x^2 + 8x + 16 = 0$

33. $x^2 - 6x + 9 = 0$

34. $4x^2 - 12x + 9 = 0$

35. $x^2 - 9 = 0$

36. $6x^2 - 13x - 5 = 0$

37. $4x^2 + 3 = -8x$

38. $3x^2 + 4x - 10 = 0$

Lesson 5-6

- To identify and graph complex numbers (p. 278)
- To add, subtract, multiply, and divide complex numbers (p. 280)

 ALG2 5.0, 6.0

An **imaginary number** has the form $a + bi$, where $b \neq 0$. The imaginary number i is defined as $i^2 = -1$. A **complex number** has the form $a + bi$, where a and b are any real numbers. The **absolute value of a complex number** is its distance from the origin in the **complex number plane.** You graph $a + bi$ in the complex plane just as you graphed (a, b) in the coordinate plane. Complex numbers follow rules of operation like those of real numbers. Some quadratic equations have imaginary numbers as roots. Functions of complex numbers may be used to generate fractals.

Simplify each expression.

39. $\sqrt{-25}$ **40.** $\sqrt{-2} - 1$ **41.** $-4 - \sqrt{-1}$ **42.** $\sqrt{-27}$

43. $2\sqrt{-32} + 4$ **44.** $|3 - i|$ **45.** $|-2 + 3i|$ **46.** $|4i|$

47. $(3 + 4i) - (7 - 2i)$ **48.** $(5 - i)(9 + 6i)$

49. $(3 + 8i) + (5 - 2i)$ **50.** $(4 + 6i)(2 + i)$

Find the additive inverse of each number. Graph the number and its inverse.

51. $2 - i$ **52.** $-4 + 3i$ **53.** $-7 - 4i$ **54.** $-2i$

Solve each equation.

55. $x^2 + 2 = 0$ **56.** $x^2 = -5$

57. $3x^2 + 12 = 0$ **58.** $6x^2 + 4 = 0$

Find the first three outputs of each fractal-generating function. Begin with $z = 0$.

59. $f(z) = z^2 - i$ **60.** $f(z) = i - z^2$

Lessons 5-7, 5-8

- To solve equations by completing the square (p. 286)
- To rewrite functions in vertex form by completing the square (p. 288)
- To solve quadratic equations by using the Quadratic Formula (p. 293)
- To determine types of solutions by using the discriminant (p. 295)

 ALG2 8.0

Completing the square is based on the relationship $x^2 + bx + \left(\frac{b}{2}\right)^2 = \left(x + \frac{b}{2}\right)^2$. You can use it to write a quadratic function in vertex form. If the coefficient of the quadratic term is not 1, you must factor out the coefficient from the variable terms.

You can solve any quadratic equation by using the Quadratic Formula.

If $ax^2 + bx + c = 0$, then $x = \frac{-b \pm \sqrt{b^2 - 4ac}}{2a}$.

The discriminant $b^2 - 4ac$ determines the number and type of solutions of the equation. If $b^2 - 4ac > 0$, the equation has two real solutions. If $b^2 - 4ac = 0$, the equation has one real solution. If $b^2 - 4ac < 0$, the equation has no real solutions and two imaginary solutions.

Solve each equation by completing the square.

61. $9x^2 + 6x + 1 = 4$ **62.** $x^2 + 3x = -25$ **63.** $x^2 - 2x + 4 = 0$

64. $-x^2 + x - 7 = 0$ **65.** $2x^2 + 3x = 8$ **66.** $4x^2 - x - 3 = 0$

Rewrite the equation in vertex form by completing the square. Find the vertex.

67. $y = x^2 + 3x - 1$ **68.** $y = 2x^2 - x - 1$ **69.** $y = x^2 + x + 2$

Determine the number and type of solutions. Solve using the Quadratic Formula.

70. $x^2 - 6x + 2 = 0$ **71.** $-2x^2 + 7x = 10$ **72.** $x^2 + 4 = 6x$

Go Online
PHSchool.com
For: Chapter test
Web Code: bba-0552

1. Write the equation of the parabola in standard form. Find the coordinates of the points corresponding to P, Q, and R.

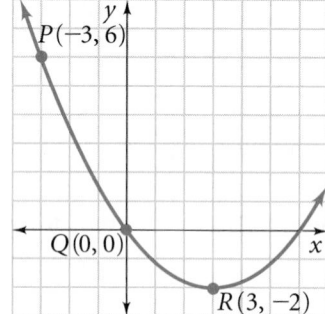

Sketch a graph of the parabola with the given vertex through the given point.

2. vertex $(0, 0)$, point $(-3, 3)$

3. vertex $(1, 5)$, point $(2, 11)$

Graph each quadratic function. Identify the axis of symmetry and the coordinates of the vertex.

4. $y = x^2 - 7$

5. $y = x^2 + 2x + 6$

6. $y = -x^2 + 5x - 3$

7. $y = -\frac{1}{2}x^2 - 8$

Simplify each expression.

8. $\sqrt{-16}$

9. $4\sqrt{-9} - 2$

10. $(4 - i) + (5 - 9i)$

11. $(2 + 3i)(8 - 5i)$

12. $(-3 + 2i) - (6 + i)$

13. $\dfrac{2 - 5i}{1 - i}$

14. **Physics** For a model rocket, the altitude h, in meters, as a function of time t, in seconds, is given by $h = 68t - 4.9t^2$. Find the maximum height of the rocket. How long does it take to reach the maximum height?

Find the additive inverse of each number.

15. $3 - 7i$

16. $-2 + i$

Graph each number on the complex plane. Then find its absolute value.

17. $7 - 2i$

18. $8i$

19. $4 + 8i$

20. 5

21. $6 - 4i$

22. $-2 + 3i$

23. **Writing** Compare graphing a number on the complex plane to graphing a point on the coordinate plane. How are they similar? How are they different?

Solve each quadratic equation.

24. $x^2 - 25 = 0$

25. $x^2 + 5x - 24 = 0$

26. $x^2 + 8x - 9 = 0$

27. $3x^2 - 21x + 3 = 0$

28. $6x^2 = 9x$

29. $4x^2 + 4x + 4 = 0$

30. $5x^2 + x + 2 = 0$

31. $-3x^2 - 2x + 7 = 0$

32. $2x^2 + 6x + 12 = 0$

Write each function in vertex form. Sketch the graph of the function and label its vertex.

33. $y = x^2 - 6x + 5$

34. $y = -x^2 + 8x - 10$

35. $y = 2x^2 - 3x - 1$

36. $y = -\frac{1}{2}x^2 + 4x - 9$

Evaluate the discriminant of each equation. How many real and imaginary solutions does each have?

37. $x^2 + 6x - 7 = 0$

38. $3x^2 - x + 3 = 0$

39. $-2x^2 - 4x + 1 = 0$

40. $-x^2 + 6x - 9 = 0$

41. **Open-Ended** Sketch the graph of a quadratic function $f(x) = ax^2 + bx + c$ whose related quadratic equation $ax^2 + bx + c = 0$ has no real solutions.

Some questions require you to solve quadratic equations.

The equation $h = -16t^2 + 8t + 3$ gives the height of a ball h, in feet above ground, at t seconds after it is thrown upward. In how many seconds after it is thrown will the ball hit the ground?

Ⓐ $\frac{1}{4}$ second

Ⓑ $\frac{3}{4}$ second

Ⓒ $2\frac{2}{3}$ seconds

Ⓓ 3 seconds

Tip 1
When the ball hits the ground, $h = 0$.
Solve $0 = -16t^2 + 8t + 3$.

Tip 2
Use the quadratic formula.
If $at^2 + bt + c = 0$,
then $t = \frac{-bt \pm \sqrt{b^2 - 4ac}}{2a}$.

Think It Through

$$t = \frac{-8 \pm \sqrt{8^2 - 4(-16)(3)}}{2(-16)}$$

$$t = \frac{-8 \pm \sqrt{256}}{-32} = \frac{-8 \pm 16}{-32}$$

$$t = \frac{3}{4} \text{ or } -\frac{1}{4}$$

For this situation, time must be positive, so $t = \frac{3}{4}$.
The correct answer is B.

Vocabulary Review

As you solve problems, you must understand the meanings of mathematical terms. Match each term with its mathematical meaning.

A. parabola

B. axis of symmetry

C. zero of a function

D. imaginary number

E. factoring

I. the x-intercept of the graph of the function

II. the line that divides a parabola into two parts that are mirror images

III. any number in the form $a + bi$ where a and b are real numbers and b does not equal 0

IV. the graph of a quadratic function

V. rewriting an expression as the product of its factorrs

Multiple Choice

Read each question. Then write the letter of the correct answer on your paper.

1. Which list of functions is ordered from widest to narrowest graph? **(Lesson 5-3)**

   Ⓐ $y = 4x^2, y = -\frac{1}{9}x^2, y = \frac{2}{3}x^2$

   Ⓑ $y = -\frac{1}{9}x^2, y = 4x^2, y = \frac{2}{3}x^2$

   Ⓒ $y = -\frac{1}{9}x^2, y = \frac{2}{3}x^2, y = 4x^2$

   Ⓓ $y = 4x^2, y = \frac{2}{3}x^2, y = -\frac{1}{9}x^2$

2. Which statement describes what happens to the graph of $y = ax^2$ when the value of a changes from 1 to $\frac{1}{3}$? **(Lesson 5-3)**

   Ⓐ The graph translates $\frac{1}{3}$ unit down.

   Ⓑ The graph translates $\frac{1}{3}$ unit right.

   Ⓒ The graph narrows.

   Ⓓ The graph widens.

3. Which statement describes what happens to the graph of $y = ax^2$ when the value of a changes from 1 to -1? **(Lesson 5-3)**

   Ⓐ The graph translates 2 units down.

   Ⓑ The graph translates 2 units left.

   Ⓒ The graph reflects across the x-axis.

   Ⓓ The graph reflects across the y-axis.

4. When graphed, which function would be translated 3 units up from the graph of $f(x) = x^2 + 2$? **(Lesson 5-3)**

- Ⓐ $g(x) = x^2 + 3$
- Ⓑ $g(x) = x^2 - 3$
- Ⓒ $g(x) = x^2 + 5$
- Ⓓ $g(x) = x^2 - 1$

5. How does the graph of $y = x^2 - 3$ differ from the graph of $y = x^2 + 4$? **(Lesson 5-3)**

- Ⓐ The graph of $y = x^2 - 3$ is 7 units to the right of the graph of $y = x^2 + 4$.
- Ⓑ The graph of $y = x^2 - 3$ is 7 units to the left of the graph of $y = x^2 + 4$.
- Ⓒ The graph of $y = x^2 - 3$ is 7 units below the graph of $y = x^2 + 4$.
- Ⓓ The graph of $y = x^2 - 3$ is 7 units above the graph of $y = x^2 + 4$.

6. What are the x-intercepts of the graph of $y = 3x^2 - 6x - 45$? **(Lesson 5-2)**

- Ⓐ 3 and 5
- Ⓑ -3 and 5
- Ⓒ -3 and -5
- Ⓓ 3 and -5

7. What are the solutions to the equation $2x^2 - 66 = -16x$? **(Lesson 5-5)**

- Ⓐ $x = 11, x = 3$
- Ⓑ $x = -11, x = -3$
- Ⓒ $x = -3, x = 11$
- Ⓓ $x = -11, x = 3$

8. What are the solutions to the equation $9x^2 - 5 = -29$? **(Lesson 5-8)**

- Ⓐ $x = \frac{2i + \sqrt{6}}{3}; x = \frac{2i - \sqrt{6}}{3}$
- Ⓑ $x = \frac{2i\sqrt{6}}{3}; x = -\frac{2i\sqrt{6}}{3}$
- Ⓒ $x = 2i\sqrt{6}; x = -2i\sqrt{6}$
- Ⓓ $x = \frac{4i\sqrt{6}}{9}; x = -\frac{4i\sqrt{6}}{9}$

9. Which of the following graphs best represents the equation $y = 2(x - 1)^2 + x - 1$? **(Lesson 5-2)**

Ⓐ

Ⓑ

Ⓒ

Ⓓ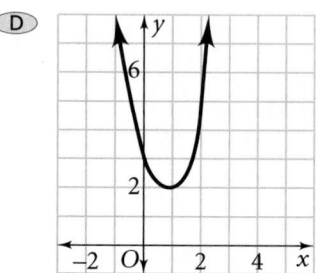

10. What are the solutions of the equation below?
$$x^3 + 4x^2 + x - 6 = 0$$
(Lesson 5-5)

- Ⓐ $-1, -2, 3$
- Ⓑ $1, -2, -3$
- Ⓒ $-1, 2, -3$
- Ⓓ $-1, 2, 3$

11. What are the solutions to the equation $3x^2 - 7x + 5 = 0$? (Lesson 5-8)

  Ⓐ $x = \frac{7 + \sqrt{11}}{6}; x = \frac{7 - \sqrt{11}}{6}$

  Ⓑ $x = 7 + i\sqrt{11}; x = 7 - i\sqrt{11}$

  Ⓒ $x = \frac{7 + \sqrt{11}}{2}; x = \frac{7 - \sqrt{11}}{2}$

  Ⓓ $x = \frac{7 + i\sqrt{11}}{6}; x = \frac{7 - i\sqrt{11}}{6}$

12. If $i = \sqrt{-1}$, what is the value of i^6? (Lesson 5-6)

  Ⓐ i

  Ⓑ $-i$

  Ⓒ 1

  Ⓓ -1

13. What is the product of the complex numbers $(7 - 2i)(5 + 3i)$? (Lesson 5-6)

  Ⓐ $11i + 41$

  Ⓑ $35 - 6i$

  Ⓒ 55

  Ⓓ $35 + 17i$

14. What is an equivalent form of $\frac{6 + 3i}{5 - 2i}$? (Lesson 5-6)

  Ⓐ $\frac{51}{29i}$

  Ⓑ $\frac{24 - 27i}{29}$

  Ⓒ $\frac{24 + 27i}{29}$

  Ⓓ $\frac{51i}{29}$

15. If $i = \sqrt{-1}$, then $7i(12i) =$ (Lesson 5-6)

  Ⓐ 84

  Ⓑ -84

  Ⓒ $19i$

  Ⓓ $84i$

16. The total area of a rectangle is $9a^6 - 25b^{10}$. Which factors could represent the length times width? (Lesson 5-4)

  Ⓐ $(3a^3 - 5b^5)(3a^3 - 5b^5)$

  Ⓑ $(3a^3 - 5b^5)(3a^3 + 5b^5)$

  Ⓒ $(3a - 5b)(3a - 5b)$

  Ⓓ $(3a^2 - 5b^2)(3a^2 + 5b^2)$

17. What can you tell about the roots of $3x^2 + 4x - 1 = 0$ from the discriminant? (Lesson 5-8)

  Ⓐ There are two real roots.

  Ⓑ There are two imaginary roots.

  Ⓒ There is one real and one imaginary root.

  Ⓓ There are no roots.

18. For which function is 5 a zero? (Lesson 5-5)

  Ⓐ $y = (x - 5)^2$

  Ⓑ $y = (x + 5)^2$

  Ⓒ $y = (x - 1)^2 + 5$

  Ⓓ $y = (x + 1)^2 - 5$

Standards Reference Guide

California Content Standard	Item Number(s)
ALG2 9.0	1–5
ALG2 10.0	6, 9, 18
ALG2 8.0	7, 8, 10–11, 17
ALG2 5.0	12
ALG2 6.0	13–15
ALG2 4.0	16

For additional review and practice, see the *California Standards Review and Practice Workbook* or go online to use the

California Standards Tutorials

Visit: PHSchool.com, **Web Code:** bbq-9045

Polynomials and Polynomial Functions

What You've Learned

California Content Standards

8.0 Students solve and graph quadratic equations by factoring, completing the square, or using the quadratic formula.

9.0 Students demonstrate and explain the effect that changing a coefficient has on the graph of quadratic functions.

10.0 Students graph quadratic functions and determine the maxima, minima, and zeros.

 Check Your Readiness

GO for Help to the Lesson in green.

Finding models (Lesson 5-1)

Find a quadratic model for each set of values.

1. $(-1, 3), (0, 1), (2, 9)$ **2.** $(0, -1), (2, -2), (4, -5)$ **3.** $(-4, 75), (0, 3), (11, 300)$

Graphing functions (Lessons 2-2 and 5-2)

Graph each function.

4. $6x - 4y = -10$ **5.** $y = 3x^2 - 10x + 2$ **6.** $y = \frac{3}{4}(x^2 + 12) + 1$

Solving systems by graphing (Lesson 5-5)

 Solve each equation by graphing. Round to the nearest hundredth.

7. $1 = 4x^2 - 3x$ **8.** $\frac{1}{2}x^2 + x - 14 = 0$ **9.** $5x^2 + 30x = 12$

Solving equations algebraically (Lessons 5-5 and 5-8)

Solve each equation algebraically.

10. $x^2 - 5x - 36 = 0$ **11.** $2x^2 - 13x + 21 = 0$ **12.** $3x^2 - 4x = 3$

Finding the number and type of solutions (Lesson 5-8)

Evaluate the discriminant of each equation. Tell how many solutions each equation has and whether the solutions are real or imaginary.

13. $x^2 - 12x + 30 = 0$ **14.** $-4x^2 + 20x - 25 = 0$ **15.** $2x^2 = 8x - 8$

Finding probability (Lesson 1-6)

16. Suppose you select an integer from 100 to 200 at random. What is $P(\text{odd})$?

What You'll Learn Next

California Content Standards

3.0 Students are adept at operations on polynomials.

4.0 Students factor polynomials representing the sum and difference of two cubes.

20.0 Students know the binomial theorem and use it to expand binomial expressions that are raised to positive integer powers.

▲ A polynomial function can be used to model the path of a soccer ball.

Polynomial Functions

 California Content Standards
ALG2 3.0 Students are adept at operations on polynomials. *Introduce*

What You'll Learn

- To classify polynomials
- To model data using polynomial functions

. . . And Why

To model the world's gold production, as in Example 3

 Check Skills You'll Need

GO for Help Lesson 1-2

Simplify each expression by combining like terms.

1. $3x + 5x - 7x$ **2.** $-8xy^2 - 2x^2y + 5x^2y$ **3.** $-4x + 7x^2 + x$

Find the number of terms in each expression.

4. $\frac{1}{2}bh$ **5.** $1 - x$ **6.** $4x^3 - x^2 - 9$

 New Vocabulary   • polynomial   • polynomial function   • degree
                 • standard form of a polynomial   • degree of a polynomial

1   Exploring Polynomial Functions

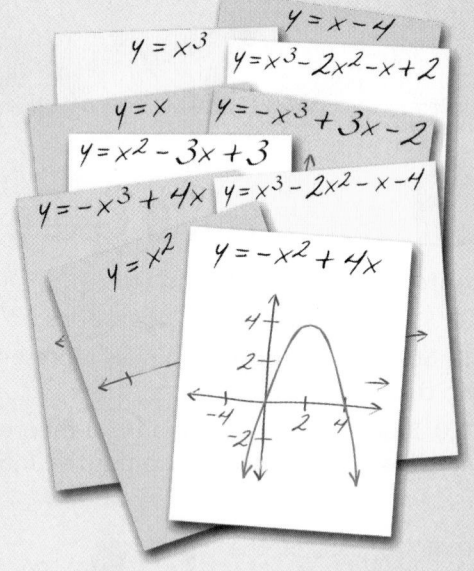

Technology Activity: Graphs of Polynomial Functions

- Use a graphing calculator to graph each equation listed at the right.

- Sketch each graph on a separate index card or sheet of paper. Label the graph with its equation.

- Sort the graphs into groups based on their shapes.

1. How are the graphs of the linear equations alike?

2. How are the graphs of the quadratic equations alike?

3. How are the graphs of the remaining equations alike? How are they different?

4. a. Estimate the *x*-intercept(s) of each graph. Write them on each card.

     b. Make a Conjecture Compare the number of *x*-intercepts of each graph and the greatest exponent found in its equation. What is the relationship?

(graphs on cards:)
$y = x^3$
$y = x - 4$
$y = x^3 - 2x^2 - x + 2$
$y = x$
$y = -x^3 + 3x - 2$
$y = x^2 - 3x + 3$
$y = -x^3 + 4x$
$y = x^3 - 2x^2 - x - 4$
$y = x^2$
$y = -x^2 + 4x$

A monomial is an expression that is either a real number, a variable, or a product of real numbers and variables with whole-number exponents. A **polynomial** is a monomial or the sum of monomials. For any polynomial, you can write the corresponding polynomial function, as shown below.

Definition	Polynomial Function
$P(x) = a_n x^n + a_{n-1} x^{n-1} + \cdots + a_1 x + a_0$	where n is a nonnegative integer and the coefficients $a_n, \ldots, a_0$ are real numbers.

Vocabulary Tip

The prefix <u>poly</u> means "many."

The exponent of the variable in a term determines the **degree** of that term. The terms in the polynomial shown below are in *descending order* by degree. This order demonstrates the **standard form of a polynomial.** A one-variable polynomial in standard form has no two terms with the same degree, since all like terms have been combined.

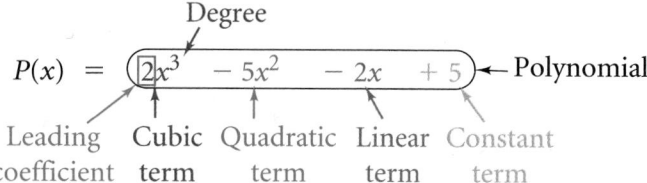

You can classify a polynomial by the number of terms it contains. A polynomial of more than three terms does not usually have a special name. You can also classify a polynomial by its degree. The **degree of a polynomial** is the greatest degree of any term of the polynomial. The name assigned to each degree is listed below.

Degree	Name Using Degree	Polynomial Example	Number of Terms	Name Using Number of Terms
0	constant	6	1	monomial
1	linear	$x + 3$	2	binomial
2	quadratic	$3x^2$	1	monomial
3	cubic	$2x^3 - 5x^2 - 2x$	3	trinomial
4	quartic	$x^4 + 3x^2$	2	binomial
5	quintic	$-2x^5 + 3x^2 - x + 4$	4	polynomial of 4 terms

1 **EXAMPLE** **Classifying Polynomials**

Write each polynomial in standard form. Then classify it by degree and by number of terms.

a. $-7x + 5x^4$

$5x^4 - 7x$
The term with the largest degree is $5x^4$, so the polynomial is degree 4. It has two terms. The polynomial is a quartic binomial.

b. $x^2 - 4x + 3x^3 + 2x$

$3x^3 + x^2 - 2x$
The term with the largest degree is $3x^3$, so the polynomial is degree 3. It has three terms. The polynomial is a cubic trinomial.

CA Standards Check **1** Write each polynomial in standard form. Then classify it by degree and by number of terms.

a. $4x - 6x + 5$ **b.** $3x^3 + x^2 - 4x + 2x^3$ **c.** $6 - 2x^5$

You have already used lines and parabolas to model data. Sometimes you can fit data more closely by using a polynomial model of degree three or greater.

2 EXAMPLE Comparing Models

Using a graphing calculator, determine whether a linear model, a quadratic model, or a cubic model best fits the values in the table.

x	0	5	10	15	20
y	10.1	2.8	8.1	16.0	17.8

Enter the data. Use the LinReg, QuadReg, and CubicReg options of a graphing calculator to find the best-fitting model for each polynomial classification.

Graph each model and compare.

Linear model	**Quadratic model**	**Cubic model**

The cubic model appears to best fit the given values.

CA Standards Check 2 Can you use the model in Example 2 to predict the value of y for x = 25? Explain.

Finding a close fit helps you estimate values between known data points.

3 EXAMPLE Real-World Connection

Gold The table below shows world gold production for several years. Find a quartic function to model the data. Use it to estimate production in 1988.

World Gold Production (millions of troy ounces)

Year	1975	1980	1985	1990	1995	2000	2005
Production	38.5	39.2	49.3	70.2	71.8	82.6	81.0

SOURCES: *The World Almanac* and *World Gold*

Enter the data. Let 0 represent 1975. To find a quartic model, use the QuarticReg option of a graphing calculator. Graph the model.

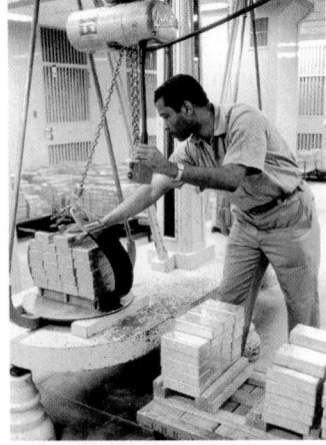

Real-World Connection

The Federal Reserve stores gold in bars that weigh 400 troy ounces each.

```
QuarticReg
  y=ax^4+bx^3+...+e
  a=2.9212121E-4
  b=-.0227272727
  c=.5362727273
  d=-2.089480519
↓e=38.49372294
```

X	Y₁
7	43.051
8	45.659
9	48.475
10	51.42
11	54.425
12	57.428
13	60.372

X=13

The function $f(x) = 0.0002921x^4 - 0.02273x^3 + 0.536x^2 - 2.089x + 38.49$ is an approximate model for a quartic function.

To estimate gold production in 1988, you can use the Table option of a graphing calculator to find that $f(13) \approx 60.322$. According to the model, about 60 million troy ounces of gold were produced in 1988.

✓ CA Standards Check **3** Use the quartic model in Example 3 to estimate gold production in 1997.

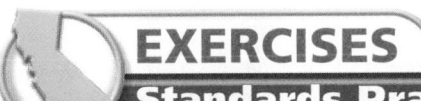

For more exercises, see *Extra Skill and Word Problem Practice*.

Standards Practice ALG2 3.0

A Practice by Example

Example 1
(page 313)

Write each polynomial in standard form. Then classify it by degree and by number of terms.

1. $7x + 3x + 5$

2. $5 - 3x$

3. $2m^2 - 3 + 7m$

4. $-x^3 + x^4 + x$

5. $-4p + 3p + 2p^2$

6. $5a^2 + 3a^3 + 1$

7. $(-x^5$

8. $3 + 12x^4$

9. $6x^3 - x^3$

10. $7x^3 - 10x^3 + x^3$

11. $4x + 5x^2 + 8$

12. $x^2 - x^4 + 2x^2$

Example 2
(page 314)

Find a cubic model for each set of values.

13. $(-2, -7), (-1, 0), (0, 1), (1, 2), (2, 9)$

14. $(0, -12), (1, 10), (2, 4), (3, 42)$

15. $(-1, 2.5), (0, 1), (1, 1.5), (2, 13)$

16. $(-3, 91), (-2, 84), (-1, 93), (0, 100)$

17. Vital Statistics The data at the right indicate that the life expectancy for residents of the United States has been increasing.
  a. Find quadratic models for the data set.
  b. Find cubic models for the data set.
  c. Graph each model. Compare the quadratic and cubic models to determine whether one is a better fit.

Life Expectancy (years)

Year of Birth	Males	Females
1960	66.6	73.1
1970	67.1	74.7
1980	70.0	77.4
1990	71.8	78.8
2000	74.1	79.5

SOURCE: National Center for Health Statistics. Go to **www.PHSchool.com** for a data update. Web Code: bbg-9041

Example 3
(pages 314–315)

Find a cubic model for each function. Then use your model to estimate the value of y when $x = 17$.

18. $(-1, -3), (0, 0), (1, -1), (2, 0)$

19. $(10, 0), (11, 121), (12, 288), (13, 507)$

20. $(10, 500), (14, 588), (16, 512), (20, 0)$

21. $(1, 91), (10, 95), (20, 260), (30, 365)$

22.

x	0	3	5	6	9	11	12	14	16	18	20
y	42	31	26	21	17	15	19	22	28	30	29

23.

x	0	2	3	6	8	10	12	14	16	18	20
y	4.1	6	15.7	21.1	23.6	23.1	24.7	24.9	23.9	25.2	29.5

B Apply Your Skills

24. Open-Ended Write a third-degree polynomial function. Make a table of values and a graph. Find the x- and y-intercepts.

Write each polynomial in standard form. Then classify it by degree and by number of terms.

25. $8x - 4x + x^3$ **26.** $a^2 + a^3 - 4a^4$ **27.** 7

28. $2x(3x)$ **29.** $x^3(2 + x)$ **30.** $\dfrac{3x^5 + 4x}{6}$

31. Packaging Design The diagram at the right shows a cologne bottle that consists of a cylindrical base and a hemispherical top.
    a. Write an expression for the cylinder's volume.
    b. Write an expression for the volume of the hemispherical top.
    c. Write a polynomial to represent the total volume.

$h = 10$ cm

r

32. Writing Explain why cubic functions are useful for interpolating between known data points. Why are they often not reliable for extrapolating data?

Vocabulary Tip

To <u>interpolate</u> means to estimate a value inside the range of known values. To <u>extrapolate</u> means to estimate a value outside the range of known values.

Simplify. Classify each result by number of terms.

33. $(2c^2 + 9) - (3c^2 - 7)$ **34.** $(-8d^3 - 7) + (-d^3 - 6)$

35. $(7x^2 + 8x - 5) + (9x^2 - 9x)$ **36.** $(5x^3 - 6x + 8) - (3x^3 - 9)$

37. $(3a - 2b) + (6b - 2a)$ **38.** $(4x - 5y) - (4x + 7y)$

39. $(3x^2 - 6y - 1) + (5x^2 + 1)$ **40.** $(-a^2 - 3) - (3a - a^2 - 5)$

41. $(7x^3 + 9x^2 - 8x + 11) - (5x^3 - 13x - 16)$

42. $(-12x^3 + 5x - 23) - (4x^4 + 31 - 9x^3)$

43. $(30x^3 - 49x^2 + 7x) + (50x^3 - 75 - 60x^2)$

44. $(-3x^3 + 7x^2 - 8) - (-5x^3 + 9x^2 - 8x + 19)$

45. $(3a^2 - ab - 7) + (5a^2 + ab + 8) - (-2a^2 + 3ab - 9)$

Find each product. Classify the result by number of terms.

46. $x(2x)(4x + 1)$ **47.** $5x^2(6x - 2)$ **48.** $(2a - 5)(a^2 - 1)$

49. $b(b - 3)^2$ **50.** $(x - 2)^3$ **51.** $(x^2 + 1)^2$

52. $(2x + 5)^3 + 1$ **53.** $(a - b)^2(a + b)$ **54.** $(a - 1)^4$

55. $(s + 3)(4s - 1)(3s + 7)$ **56.** $(x + 1)(x - 1)(x + 2)$

57. $(2c - 3)(2c + 4)(2c - 1)$ **58.** $(s + t)(s - t)(s + t)(s - t)$

59. The table shows U.S. energy production for a number of years.
    a. Find a linear model, a cubic model, and a quartic model for the data set. Let 0 represent 1960.
    b. Graph each model. Compare the three models to determine which fits best.
    c. Use your answer to part (b) to estimate U.S. energy production in 1997.

Homework Video Tutor

Visit: PHSchool.com
Web Code: bbe-0601

U.S. Energy Production

Year	1960	1965	1970	1975	1980	1985	1990	1995	2000
Production ($\times 10^{15}$ Btu)	41.5	49.3	62.1	59.9	64.8	64.9	70.8	71.0	71.2

SOURCE: Energy Information Administration. Go to **www.PHSchool.com** for a data update.
Web Code: bbg-9041

Challenge **60. Geometry** Use the formula $V = \frac{\pi h}{3}(r^2 + rs + s^2)$ to find the volume of the truncated cone. Express your answer in scientific notation with the appropriate number of significant digits.

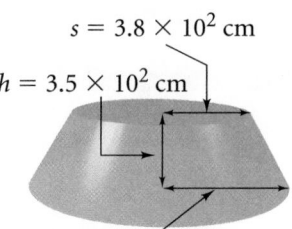

$s = 3.8 \times 10^2$ cm

$h = 3.5 \times 10^2$ cm

$r = 5.6 \times 10^2$ cm

61. Critical Thinking Recall that each family of functions has a simplest function called the parent function.

    a. Compare the graphs of $y = x^3$ and $y = x^3 + 4$. Describe how the graph of $y = x^3 + 4$ relates to the graph of $y = x^3$.

    b. Compare the graphs of $y = x^3$ and $y = 4x^3$. Describe how the graph of $y = 4x^3$ relates to the graph of $y = x^3$.

    c. Identify the parent function among the functions in parts (a) and (b).

Multiple Choice Practice

For California Standards and CAHSEE Tutorials, visit PHSchool.com. Web Code: bbq-9045

ALG2 3.0

62. Which expression is equal to $x^2(3x^2 - 2x) - 3x^4$?

    Ⓐ $-2x^2$ Ⓑ $-2x^3$ Ⓒ $2x^3$ Ⓓ $3x^3$

ALG2 2.0

63. What is the solution to the system of equations shown at the right?

$$\begin{cases} 3x - 2y - 5z = -7 \\ -x + y + 4z = 1 \\ 7x + 4y - 2z = 0 \end{cases}$$

    Ⓐ $(-1, -2, -3)$

    Ⓑ $(2, 1, 3)$

    Ⓒ $(-2, 3, -1)$

    Ⓓ no solution

ALG2 4.0

64. Which factors could represent $36a^{10} - 121b^{26}$?

    Ⓐ $(4a^2 + 11b^2)(9a^5 - 11b^{13})$ Ⓒ $(4a^2 - 11b^2)(9a^5 - 11b^{13})$

    Ⓑ $(6a^5 + 11b^{13})(6a^5 + 11b^{13})$ Ⓓ $(6a^5 - 11b^{13})(6a^5 + 11b^{13})$

ALG2 8.0

65. There are two numbers with the following properties:

    1) The first number is 4 more than the second.

    2) The product of the two numbers is 3 more than 3 times their sum.

    Which of the following represents possible values of these two numbers?

    Ⓐ $5, -3$ Ⓑ $5, 9$ Ⓒ $-5, -9$ Ⓓ $-5, 3$

Mixed Review

 for Help

Lesson 5-8

Use the discriminant to find the number of real solutions.

66. $3x^2 + x - 6 = 0$ **67.** $5x^2 - 9 = 0$ **68.** $-x^2 + 2x - 8 = 0$

Lesson 5-3

69. Graph $f(x) = 3x^2 - 1$. Translate the graph right five units and down two units. What is the vertex of the new graph?

Lesson 4-4

Each matrix represents the vertices of a polygon. Translate each figure 3 units left and 2 units down. Express your answer as a matrix.

70. $\begin{bmatrix} 4 & 0 & 4 & 8 \\ -6 & -1 & 2 & -1 \end{bmatrix}$ **71.** $\begin{bmatrix} 5 & 0 & -3 \\ 7 & 0 & 2 \end{bmatrix}$ **72.** $\begin{bmatrix} 1 & 2 & 1 & 2 \\ -1 & -1 & -2 & -2 \end{bmatrix}$

Extension | **End Behavior**

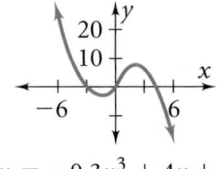

FOR USE WITH LESSON 6-1

The end behavior of a graph describes the far left and the far right portions of the graph. The graphs of polynomial functions show four types of end behavior— *up and up, down and down, down and up,* and *up and down.*

Up and Up	Down and Down	Down and Up	Up and Down
$(\nwarrow, \nearrow)$	$(\swarrow, \searrow)$	$(\swarrow, \nearrow)$	$(\nwarrow, \searrow)$
Example	Example	Example	Example

$y = x^4 - 3x^3 + 5x$ $y = -x^2 + 6x$ $y = x^3$ $y = -0.3x^3 + 4x + 2$

You can determine *by inspection* the end behavior of the graph of a polynomial function in standard form. Look at the coefficient and degree of the leading term.

Right   If the leading coefficient is positive, then the graph rises to the right. If the leading coefficient is negative, then the graph falls to the right.

Left   If the degree of the polynomial is even, then the left behavior is the same as the right behavior. If the degree of the polynomial is odd, then the left behavior is the opposite of the right behavior.

EXAMPLE   **Describing End Behavior**

Determine by inspection the end behavior of the graph of each polynomial.

a. $y = 4x^3 - 3x$

The leading coefficient 4 is positive, so the graph rises to the right. The degree of the polynomial is 3, which is odd. The left behavior is opposite the right behavior, so the graph falls to the left. The end behavior is $(\swarrow, \nearrow)$.

b. $f(x) = -2x^4 + 8x^3 - 8x^2$

The leading coefficient –2 is negative, so the graph falls to the right. The degree of the polynomial is 4, which is even. The left behavior is the same as the right behavior, so the graph falls to the left. The end behavior is $(\swarrow, \searrow)$.

EXERCISES

Determine by inspection the end behavior of the graph of each function.

1. $y = 3x + 2$

2. $y = 4x^3$

3. $g(t) = -t^2 + t$

4. $f(x) = 2x + x^5$

5. $g(x) = x^6$

6. $y = 3x^5 - 4x^4$

7. $y = -7x^8$

8. $f(x) = \frac{1}{2}x^4 - 2$

9. $y = -\frac{1}{2}x^3 + 4x^2 + x - 1$

10. $g(x) = x - x^3 + 5$

6-2

Polynomials and Linear Factors

 California Content Standards

ALG2 10.0 Students graph quadratic functions and determine the maxima, minima, and zeros of the function. *Master*

What You'll Learn

- To analyze the factored form of a polynomial
- To write a polynomial function from its zeros

. . . And Why

To find the dimensions of carry-on luggage, as in Example 3

 Check Skills You'll Need

Factor each quadratic expression.

1. $x^2 + 7x + 12$ 2. $x^2 + 8x - 20$ 3. $x^2 - 14x + 24$

Find each product.

4. $x(x + 4)$ 5. $(x + 1)^2$ 6. $(x - 3)^2(x + 2)$

 for Help Lessons 5-1 and 5-4

New Vocabulary • relative maximum • relative minimum • Factor Theorem • multiple zero • multiplicity

---

1 The Factored Form of a Polynomial

Just as you can rewrite a whole number as a product of its prime factors, you can write a polynomial as a product of its linear factors. Compare the factor trees for the whole number 6 and the quadratic expression $x^2 + 4x - 12$.

$$6 \qquad\qquad x^2 + 4x - 12$$

Prime factors → 2   3 $(x + 6)\,(x - 2)$ ← Linear factors

In the factor tree for the whole number 6, each branch ends with a prime number. Likewise, in the factor tree for the polynomial $x^2 + 4x - 12$, each branch ends with a "prime" linear factor. A linear factor is similar to a prime number in that it cannot be factored any further. Once a polynomial has been factored completely to its linear factors, it is in factored form.

1 EXAMPLE Writing a Polynomial in Standard Form

Write the expression $(x + 1)(x + 2)(x + 3)$ as a polynomial in standard form.

$(x + 1)(x + 2)(x + 3) = (x + 1)(x^2 + 3x + 2x + 6)$ **Multiply $(x + 2)$ and $(x + 3)$.**

$= (x + 1)(x^2 + 5x + 6)$ **Simplify.**

$= x(x^2 + 5x + 6) + 1(x^2 + 5x + 6)$ **Distributive Property**

$= x^3 + 5x^2 + 6x + x^2 + 5x + 6$ **Multiply.**

$= x^3 + 6x^2 + 11x + 6$ **Simplify.**

The expression $(x + 1)(x + 2)(x + 3)$ is the factored form of $x^3 + 6x^2 + 11x + 6$.

 CA Standards Check **1** Write the expression $(x + 1)(x + 1)(x + 2)$ as a polynomial in standard form.

You can sometimes use the GCF of the terms to help you factor a polynomial.

2 EXAMPLE **Writing a Polynomial in Factored Form**

Write $2x^3 + 10x^2 + 12x$ in factored form.

$2x^3 + 10x^2 + 12x = 2x(x^2 + 5x + 6)$ **Factor out the GCF, 2x.**

$= 2x(x + 2)(x + 3)$ **Factor $x^2 + 5x + 6$.**

Check $2x(x + 2)(x + 3) = 2x(x^2 + 5x + 6)$ **Multiply $(x + 2) (x + 3)$.**

$= 2x^3 + 10x^2 + 12x$ ✓   **Distributive Property**

✓ **CA Standards Check** ② Write $6x^3 - 15x^2 - 36x$ in factored form. Check by multiplication.

You can use polynomial functions to solve real-world problems. Consider the formula for volume: $V = $ depth · length · width. Each dimension can represent a linear factor of a polynomial function.

3 EXAMPLE **Real-World 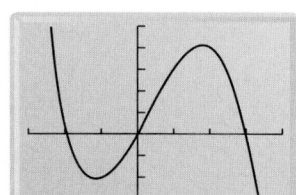 Connection**

Travel Several popular models of carry-on luggage have a length 10 in. greater than their depth. To comply with airline regulations, the sum of the length, width, and depth may not exceed 40 in.

a. Assume that the sum of the length, width, and depth is 40 in. Graph the function relating volume V to depth x. Find the x-intercepts. What do they represent?

Relate   Volume $=$ depth · length · width

Define   Let $x =$ depth. Then $x + 10 =$ length, and

$40 - (\text{depth} + \text{length}) =$ width.

Write $V(x) = x \,(x + 10)\, (40 - (x + x + 10))$

$= x(x + 10)(30 - 2x)$

Graph the function for volume. The x-intercepts of the function are $x = 0, x = -10$, and $x = 15$. These values of x produce a volume of zero.

Xmin=−15
Xmax=20
Xscl=5
Ymin=−1500
Ymax=2500
Yscl=500

b. Describe a realistic domain.

The function has values over the set of all real numbers x. Since x represents the depth of the luggage, $x > 0$. Since the volume must be positive, $x < 15$. A realistic domain is $0 < x < 15$.

c. What is the maximum possible volume of a piece of luggage? What are the corresponding dimensions of the luggage?

Look for the greatest value of y that occurs within the domain $0 < x < 15$. Use the Maximum feature of a graphing calculator to find the maximum volume. A volume of approximately 2052 in.^{3} occurs for a depth of about 8.9 in. Then the length is about 18.9 in. and the width is about 12.2 in.

✓ **CA Standards Check** ③ Suppose an airline raises the allowable sum of the luggage dimensions to 45 in. Find the maximum possible volume and the corresponding dimensions.

 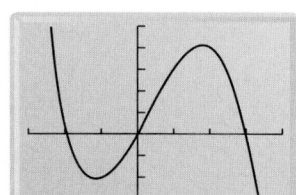

The maximum value in Example 3 is the greatest value of the points in a region of the graph. It is called a **relative maximum.** Similarly, a **relative minimum** is the least *y*-value among nearby points on a graph.

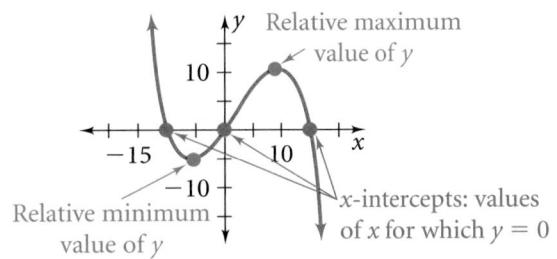

Recall that the *x*-intercepts of the graph of a function are called zeros because the value of the function is zero at each *x*-intercept.

2 Factors and Zeros of a Polynomial Function

If a polynomial is in factored form, you can use the Zero Product Property to find values that will make the polynomial equal zero.

4 EXAMPLE **Finding Zeros of a Polynomial Function**

Find the zeros of $y = (x - 2)(x + 1)(x + 3)$. Then graph the function.

Using the Zero Product Property, find a zero for each linear factor.

$$x - 2 = 0 \quad \text{or} \quad x + 1 = 0 \quad \text{or} \quad x + 3 = 0$$
$$x = 2 \qquad\qquad x = -1 \qquad\qquad x = -3$$

The zeros of the function are $2, -1,$ and -3. Now graph the function.

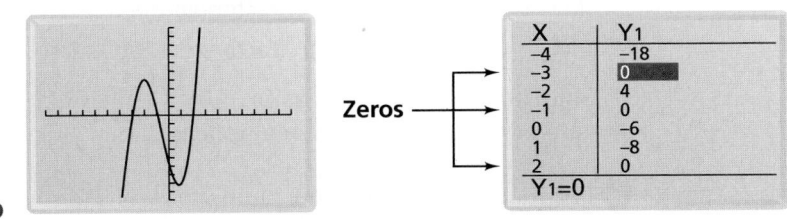

CA Standards Check **4** **a.** Find the zeros of the function $y = (x - 7)(x - 5)(x - 3)$.
b. Graph the function and label the zeros.

You can reverse the process and write linear factors when you know the zeros. The relationship between the linear factors of a polynomial and the zeros of a polynomial is described by the Factor Theorem.

 Key Concepts

Theorem	**Factor Theorem**

The expression $x - a$ is a linear factor of a polynomial if and only if the value a is a zero of the related polynomial function.

5 EXAMPLE **Writing a Polynomial Function From its Zeros**

Write a polynomial function in standard form with zeros at $-2, 3$, and 3.

$$
\begin{array}{ccc}
-2 & 3 & 3 \\
\downarrow & \downarrow & \downarrow
\end{array} \qquad \text{zeros}
$$

$$
\begin{aligned}
f(x) &= (x + 2)(x - 3)(x - 3) & \text{Write a linear factor for each zero.} \\
&= (x + 2)(x^2 - 6x + 9) & \text{Multiply } (x - 3) \text{ and } (x - 3). \\
&= x(x^2 - 6x + 9) + 2(x^2 - 6x + 9) & \text{Distributive Property} \\
&= x^3 - 6x^2 + 9x + 2x^2 - 12x + 18 & \text{Distributive Property} \\
&= x^3 - 4x^2 - 3x + 18 & \text{Simplify.}
\end{aligned}
$$

● The function $f(x) = x^3 - 4x^2 - 3x + 18$ has zeros at $-2, 3$, and 3.

✓ **CA Standards Check** **5** **a.** Write a polynomial function in standard form with zeros at $-4, -2$, and 1.
b. Write a polynomial function in standard form with zeros at $-4, -2$, and 0.
c. Critical Thinking Explain why the zero at 0 produces more than one possible answer to part (b).

Vocabulary Tip

Distinct means "separate and different."

While the polynomial function in Example 5 has three zeros, it has only two distinct zeros: -2 and 3. If a linear factor of a polynomial is repeated, then the zero is repeated. A repeated zero is called a **multiple zero.** A multiple zero has a **multiplicity** equal to the number of times the zero occurs. In Example 5, the zero 3 has multiplicity 2.

6 EXAMPLE **Finding the Multiplicity of a Zero**

Find any multiple zeros of $f(x) = x^4 + 6x^3 + 8x^2$ and state the multiplicity.

$$
\begin{aligned}
f(x) &= x^4 + 6x^3 + 8x^2 \\
f(x) &= x^2(x^2 + 6x + 8) & \text{Factor out the GCF, } x^2. \\
f(x) &= x^2(x + 4)(x + 2) & \text{Factor } x^2 + 6x + 8.
\end{aligned}
$$

Since you can rewrite x^2 as $(x - 0)(x - 0)$, or $(x - 0)^2$, the number 0 is a multiple zero of the function, with multiplicity 2.

✓ **CA Standards Check** **6** For each function, find any multiple zeros and state the multiplicity.
a. $f(x) = (x - 2)(x + 1)(x + 1)^2$ **b.** $y = x^3 - 4x^2 + 4x$

The Factor Theorem helps relate four key facts about a polynomial. These facts are equivalent—that is, if you know one of them, you know them all.

Key Concepts

Summary	**Equivalent Statements about Polynomials**

① -4 is a solution of $x^2 + 3x - 4 = 0$.
② -4 is an x-intercept of the graph of $y = x^2 + 3x - 4$.
③ -4 is a zero of $y = x^2 + 3x - 4$.
④ $x + 4$ is a factor of $x^2 + 3x - 4$.

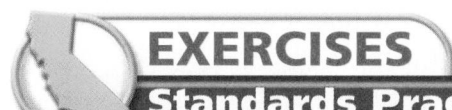
A **Practice by Example**

Example 1
(page 319)

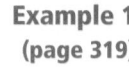

Write each expression as a polynomial in standard form.

1. $(x + 3)(x - 2)$ **2.** $(x + 3)(x + 4)(x + 5)$ **3.** $(x - 3)^2 (x - 1)$

4. $x(x + 2)^2$ **5.** $x(x + 5)^2$ **6.** $x(x - 1)(x + 1)$

Example 2
(page 320)

Write each polynomial in factored form. Check by multiplication.

7. $x^3 - 36x$ **8.** $9x^3 + 6x^2 - 3x$ **9.** $10x^3 - 10x^2 + 15x$

10. $x^3 + 7x^2 + 10x$ **11.** $x^3 + 8x^2 + 16x$ **12.** $x^3 - 7x^2 - 18x$

Example 3
(page 320)

Find the relative maximum, relative minimum, and zeros of each function.

13. $f(x) = x^3 + 4x^2 - 5x$ **14.** $f(x) = -x^3 + 16x^2 - 76x + 96$

15. Metalwork A metalworker wants to make an open box from a sheet of metal, by cutting equal squares from each corner as shown.
a. Write an expression for the length, width, and height of the open box.
b. Use your answer from part (a) to write a function for volume. (*Hint:* Use factored form.)
c. Graph the function. Find the maximum volume that can be contained by the box and the size of the square cut that produces this volume.

Example 4
(page 321)

Find the zeros of each function. Then graph the function.

16. $y = (x - 1)(x + 2)$ **17.** $y = (x - 2)(x + 9)$ **18.** $y = x(x + 5)(x - 8)$

19. $y = (x + 1)(x - 2)(x - 3)$ **20.** $y = (x + 1)(x - 1)(x - 2)$

Example 5
(page 322)

Write a polynomial function in standard form with the given zeros.

21. $x = 5, 6, 7$ **22.** $x = -2, 0, 1$ **23.** $x = -5, -5, 1$ **24.** $x = 3, 3, 3$

25. $x = 1, -1, -2$ **26.** $x = -1, -2, -3$ **27.** $x = 0, 0, 2$ **28.** $x = -\frac{1}{2}, 0, 4$

Example 6
(page 322)

Find the zeros of each function. State the multiplicity of multiple zeros.

29. $y = (x + 3)^3$ **30.** $y = x(x - 1)^3$ **31.** $y = 2x^3 + x^2 - x$

32. $y = 3x^3 - 3x$ **33.** $y = (x - 4)^2$ **34.** $y = (x - 2)^2(x - 1)$

35. $y = (2x + 3)(x - 1)^2$ **36.** $y = (x + 1)^2(x - 1)(x - 2)$

B **Apply Your Skills** **37. Geometry** A box has length $2x + 1$ units, width $x + 4$ units, and height $x + 3$ units. To build the box using x^3, x^2, x, and unit (1) blocks, how many of each will you need?

1   x x^2 x^3

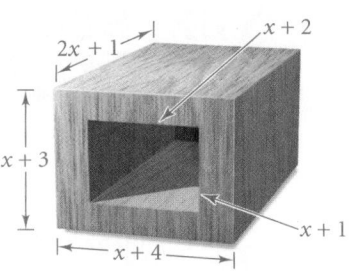

38. Carpentry A carpenter hollowed out
the interior of a block of wood as shown at
the right.
  a. Express the volume of the original block
  and the volume of the wood removed as
  polynomials in standard form.
  b. Write a polynomial for the volume
  of the wood remaining.

39. Geometry A rectangular box is $2x + 3$ units long, $2x - 3$ units wide, and
$3x$ units high. Express its volume as a polynomial.

40. Measurement The volume in cubic feet of a CD holder can be expressed
as $V(x) = -x^3 - x^2 + 6x$, or, when factored, as the product of its three
dimensions. The depth is expressed as $2 - x$. Assume that the height is greater
than the width.
  a. Factor the polynomial to find linear expressions for the height and the width.
  b. Graph the function. Find the x-intercepts. What do they represent?
  c. Describe a realistic domain for the function.
  d. Find the maximum volume of the CD holder.

Write each function in standard form.

41. $y = (x + 1)(x - 4)(3 - 2x)$ **42.** $y = (x + 7)(5x + 2)(x - 6)^2$

Write each function in factored form. Check by multiplication.

43. $y = 3x^3 - 27x^2 + 24x$ **44.** $y = -2x^3 - 2x^2 + 40x$

45. $y = x^4 + 3x^3 - 4x^2$ **46.** $y = \frac{1}{2}x^3 - \frac{1}{8}x$

 Find the relative maximum, relative minimum, and zeros of each function.

47. $y = 2x^3 - 23x^2 + 78x - 72$ **48.** $y = x^4 + 3x^3 - x^2 - 3x$

49. $y = 8x^3 - 10x^2 - x - 3$ **50.** $y = (x + 1)^4 - 1$

Write a polynomial function in standard form with the given zeros.

51. $5, -2, 0$ **52.** 7 multiplicity 3   **53.** $-2, -1, 3, 4$

For each function, determine the zeros. State the multiplicity of any multiple zeros.

54. $y = (x + 4)(x - 5)^3$ **55.** $f(x) = x^4 + 2x^3 + x^2$ **56.** $f(x) = x^3 - 36x$

57. Critical Thinking How can you find where the graph of a polynomial function
crosses the y-axis?

58. A storage company needs to design a new storage box that has twice the
volume of its largest box. Its largest box is 5 ft long, 4 ft wide, and 3 ft high.
The new box must be formed by increasing each dimension by the same
amount. Find the increase in each dimension.

59. Open-Ended Write a polynomial function with the following features: it has
three distinct zeros; one of the zeros is 1; another zero has a multiplicity of 2.

60. Writing Explain how the graph of a polynomial function can help you factor
the polynomial.

61. Critical Thinking A polynomial function has a zero at $x = -2a$. Find one
of its factors.

Challenge **62. Coordinate Geometry** The diagram at the right shows a rectangular region with one corner on the graph of $y = -x^2 + 2x + 4$.
  a. Write a polynomial in standard form for the area A of the rectangular region.
  b. Find the area of the rectangular region for $x = 2\frac{1}{2}$.

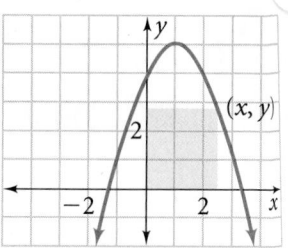

63. Find a fourth-degree polynomial function with zeros $1, -1, i,$ and $-i$. Write the function in both factored form and standard form.

64. a. Compare the graphs of $y = (x + 1)(x + 2)(x + 3)$ and $y = (x - 1)(x - 2)(x - 3)$. What transformation could you use to describe the change from one graph to the other?
  b. Compare the graphs of $y = (x + 1)(x + 3)(x + 7)$ and $y = (x - 1)(x - 3)(x - 7)$. Does the transformation that you chose in part (a) still hold true? Explain.
  c. Make a Conjecture What transformation could you use to describe the effect of changing the signs of the zeros of a polynomial function?

Multiple Choice Practice

For California Standards and CAHSEE Tutorials, visit PHSchool.com. Web Code: bbq-9045

ALG2 10.0   **65.** Samantha studied the parabola at the right. Which is an accurate conclusion that she could draw about this parabola?
  Ⓐ The vertex is at $(2, 0)$.
  Ⓑ The maximum value is at $(0, 4)$.
  Ⓒ The minimum value is at $(-2, 0)$.
  Ⓓ The axis of symmetry is the x-axis.

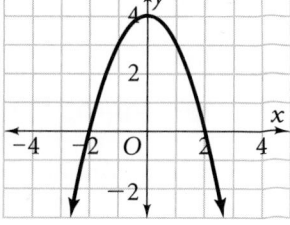

ALG2 6.0   **66.** What is an equivalent form of $\dfrac{5}{8 - i}$?
  Ⓐ $\dfrac{8 - i}{13}$ Ⓒ $\dfrac{8 + i}{7}$
  Ⓑ $\dfrac{8 + i}{13}$ Ⓓ $\dfrac{40 + i}{13}$

Mixed Review

Lesson 6-1   **Write each polynomial in standard form. Then classify it by degree and by number of terms.**

67. $x^2 - 1 - 3x^5 + 2x^2$ **68.** $-2x^3 - 7x^4 + x^3$ **69.** $6x + x^3 - 6x - 2$

Lesson 5-4   **Factor each expression.**

70. $x^2 + 5x + 4$ **71.** $x^2 - 2x - 15$ **72.** $x^2 - 12x + 36$

Lesson 4-5   **Evaluate the determinant of each matrix.**

73. $A = \begin{bmatrix} 1 & -4 \\ 2 & 0 \end{bmatrix}$ **74.** $B = \begin{bmatrix} 5 & 3 \\ 2 & -1 \end{bmatrix}$ **75.** $C = \begin{bmatrix} 3 & -2 \\ 3 & -2 \end{bmatrix}$

6-3

Dividing Polynomials

 California Content Standards

ALG2 3.0 Students are adept at operations on polynomials, including long division. *Develop, Master*

What You'll Learn

• To divide polynomials using long division

• To divide polynomials using synthetic division

. . . And Why

To find the dimensions of a sarcophagus, as in Example 4

✓ Check Skills You'll Need

Simplify each expression.

1. $(x + 3)(x - 4) + 2$

2. $(2x + 1)(x - 3)$

3. $(x + 2)(x + 1) - 11$

4. $-3(2 - x)(x + 5)$

Write each polynomial in standard form. Then list the coefficients.

5. $5x - 2x^2 + 9 + 4x^3$

6. $10 + 5x^3 - 9x^2$

7. $3x + x^2 - x + 7 - 2x^2$

8. $-4x^4 - 7x^2 + x^3 + x^4$

GO for Help Lessons 5-1 and 6-1

◀))) New Vocabulary • synthetic division • Remainder Theorem

1 Using Long Division

You can use polynomial division to help find all the zeros of a polynomial function. Division of polynomials is similar to numerical division.

Recall that when a numerical division has a remainder of zero, as shown below, the divisor and quotient are both factors of the dividend.

Vocabulary Tip

$$\begin{array}{r} 4 \leftarrow \text{Quotient} \\ 6\overline{)24} \leftarrow \text{Dividend} \\ \uparrow \\ \text{Divisor} \end{array}$$

$$\begin{array}{r} 7 \\ 8\overline{)56} \\ \underline{56} \\ 0 \end{array} \quad \text{7 and 8 are factors of 56.}$$

If numerical division leaves a nonzero remainder, as shown below, then neither the divisor nor the quotient is a factor of the dividend.

$$\begin{array}{r} 8 \\ 5\overline{)42} \\ \underline{40} \\ 2 \end{array} \quad \text{Neither 5 nor 8 is a factor of 42.}$$

Division serves as a test of whether one number is a factor of another.

The same is true for polynomial division. If you divide a polynomial by one of its factors, then you get another factor. When a polynomial division leaves a zero remainder, as shown below with monomials, you have factored the polynomial.

$$\begin{array}{r} 2x \\ x\overline{)2x^2} \\ \underline{2x^2} \\ 0 \end{array} \quad x \text{ and } 2x \text{ are factors of } 2x^2.$$

To divide polynomials other than monomials, follow the same procedure you use to divide whole numbers.

Video Tutor Help

Visit: PHSchool.com
Web Code: bbe-0775

1 EXAMPLE **Polynomial Long Division**

Divide $x^2 + 3x - 12$ by $x - 3$.

$$
\begin{array}{r}
x \\
x - 3 \overline{)x^2 + 3x - 12} \\
\underline{x^2 - 3x} \\
6x - 12
\end{array}
$$

Divide: $\frac{x^2}{x} = x.$

Multiply: $x(x - 3) = x^2 - 3x.$

Subtract: $x^2 + 3x - (x^2 - 3x) = 6x.$ Bring down -12.

Repeat the process of dividing, multiplying, and subtracting.

$$
\begin{array}{r}
x + 6 \\
x - 3 \overline{)x^2 + 3x - 12} \\
\underline{x^2 - 3x} \\
6x - 12 \\
\underline{6x - 18} \\
6
\end{array}
$$

Divide: $\frac{6x}{x} = 6.$

Multiply: $6(x - 3) = 6x - 18.$

Subtract: $6x - 12 - (6x - 18) = 6.$

The quotient is $x + 6$ with a remainder of 6, or simply $x + 6$, R 6.

Check Show that (divisor)(quotient) + remainder = dividend.

$$(x - 3)(x + 6) + 6 = (x^2 + 6x - 3x - 18) + 6 \quad \textbf{Multiply } (x - 3)(x + 6).$$
$$= x^2 + 3x - 12 \quad \textbf{Simplify.}$$

 CA Standards Check **1** Divide $x^2 - 3x + 1$ by $x - 4$. Check your answer.

You can use polynomial long division to find the factors of a polynomial.

2 EXAMPLE **Checking Factors**

Determine whether $x + 4$ is a factor of each polynomial.

a. $x^2 + 6x + 8$

$$
\begin{array}{r}
x + 2 \\
x + 4 \overline{)x^2 + 6x + 8} \\
\underline{x^2 + 4x} \\
2x + 8 \\
\underline{2x + 8} \\
0
\end{array}
$$

Since the remainder is zero,
$x + 4$ is a factor of $x^2 + 6x + 8$.

b. $x^3 + 3x^2 - 6x - 7$

$$
\begin{array}{r}
x^2 - x - 2 \\
x + 4 \overline{)x^3 + 3x^2 - 6x - 7} \\
\underline{x^3 + 4x^2} \\
-x^2 - 6x \\
\underline{-x^2 - 4x} \\
-2x - 7 \\
\underline{-2x - 8} \\
1
\end{array}
$$

Since the remainder $\neq 0$, $x + 4$ is
not a factor of $x^3 + 3x^2 - 6x - 7$.

 CA Standards Check **2** Determine whether each divisor is a factor of each dividend.

a. $(2x^2 - 19x + 24) \div (x - 8)$ **b.** $(x^3 - 4x^2 + 3x + 2) \div (x + 2)$

---

2 **Using Synthetic Division**

To divide by a linear factor, you can use a simplified process that is known as **synthetic division.** In synthetic division, you omit all variables and exponents. By reversing the sign in the divisor, you can add throughout the process instead of subtracting.

Using Synthetic Division

Use synthetic division to divide $3x^3 - 4x^2 + 2x - 1$ by $x + 1$.

Step 1 Reverse the sign of the constant term in the divisor. Write the coefficients of the polynomial in standard form.

Write $\quad x + 1\overline{)3x^3 - 4x^2 + 2x - 1}$

as $\quad \underline{-1}\,|\; 3 \quad -4 \quad\;\; 2 \quad -1$

Step 2 Bring down the first coefficient.

$$
\begin{array}{r|rrrr}
-1 & 3 & -4 & 2 & -1 \\
  &   & \blacksquare & \blacksquare & \blacksquare \\
\hline
  & 3 & \blacksquare & \blacksquare & \blacksquare
\end{array}
$$

Bring down the 3. This begins the quotient.

Step 3 Multiply the first coefficient by the new divisor. Write the result under the next coefficient. Add.

$$
\begin{array}{r|rrrr}
-1 & 3 & -4 & 2 & -1 \\
\times & & -3 & \blacksquare & \blacksquare \\
\hline
 & 3 & -7 & \blacksquare & \blacksquare
\end{array}
$$

Multiply 3 by −1. Write the result under −4.

Add −4 and −3.

Step 4 Repeat the steps of multiplying and adding until the remainder is found.

$$
\begin{array}{r|rrrr}
-1 & 3 & -4 & 2 & -1 \\
 & & -3 & 7 & -9 \\
\hline
 & 3 & -7 & 9 & -10
\end{array}
$$

$\qquad\;\; 3x^2 \;-\; 7x \;+\; 9 \quad$ Remainder

● The quotient is $3x^2 - 7x + 9$, R −10.

 CA Standards Check **3** Use synthetic division to divide $x^3 + 4x^2 + x - 6$ by $x + 1$.

4 EXAMPLE **Real-World Connection**

The volume in cubic feet of a sarcophagus (excluding the cover) can be expressed as the product of its three dimensions: $V(x) = x^3 - 13x + 12$. The length is $x + 4$.

a. Find linear expressions with integer coefficients for the other dimensions. Assume that the width is greater than the height.

$$
\begin{array}{r|rrrr}
-4 & 1 & 0 & -13 & 12 \\
 & & -4 & 16 & -12 \\
\hline
 & 1 & -4 & 3 & 0
\end{array}
$$

$\;\; x^2 \;\; -4x \;+\; 3 \quad$ Remainder

Divide. Use 0 as a place holder for any missing term.

$x^2 - 4x + 3 = (x - 1)(x - 3)$ **Factor the quotient.**

The width and the height are $x - 1$ and $x - 3$, respectively.

b. If the length of the sarcophagus is 10 ft, what are the other two dimensions?

$x + 4 = 10$ **The length, $x + 4$, is 10.**

$\quad x = 6$ **Find x.**

Since the width equals $x - 1$ and the height equals $x - 3$, the width is 5 ft and the height is 3 ft.

 CA Standards Check **4** **a.** Use synthetic division to divide $x^3 - 2x^2 - 5x + 6$ by $x + 2$.
b. Use your answer from part (a) to completely factor $x^3 - 2x^2 - 5x + 6$.

For: Synthetic Division Activity
Use: Interactive Textbook, 6-3

In Example 1, you saw that $x - 3$ is not a factor of $x^2 + 3x - 12$ because their quotient has a remainder of 6. If $x - 3$ were a factor of $x^2 + 3x - 12$, then 3 would be a zero of $P(x) = x^2 + 3x - 12$, and $P(3)$ would equal zero. You know that $P(3)$ does not equal zero, but what *does* it equal?

You can find $P(3)$ by substituting 3 for x.

$$P(x) = x^2 + 3x - 12$$
$$P(3) = (3)^2 + 3(3) - 12$$
$$\quad = 6$$

$P(3)$ equals the remainder in Example 1, because

dividend = divisor × quotient + remainder.

$$P(x) = (x - 3)(x + 6) + 6$$
$$P(3) = (3 - 3)(3 + 6) + 6$$
$$\quad = 0(3 + 6) + 6$$
$$\quad = 6$$

This relationship is defined by the **Remainder Theorem.**

Key Concepts

Theorem	**Remainder Theorem**

If a polynomial $P(x)$ of degree $n \geq 1$ is divided by $(x - a)$, where a is a constant, then the remainder is $P(a)$.

You can use the Remainder Theorem to find values of $P(x)$.

5 **EXAMPLE** **Evaluating a Polynomial by Synthetic Division**

Find $P(-4)$ for $P(x) = x^4 - 5x^2 + 4x + 12$.

By the Remainder Theorem, $P(-4)$ equals the remainder when $P(x)$ is divided by $x - (-4)$.

$$\begin{array}{r|rrrrr} -4 & 1 & 0 & -5 & 4 & 12 \\ & & -4 & 16 & -44 & 160 \\ \hline & 1 & -4 & 11 & -40 & 172 \end{array}$$

The remainder is 172, so $P(-4) = 172$.

Test-Taking Tip
If you know two ways to solve a problem, the second way is an excellent check that your answer is correct (if you have the time).

 CA Standards Check **5** Use synthetic division to find $P(-1)$ for $P(x) = 2x^4 + 6x^3 - 5x^2 - 60$.

A Practice by Example

Example 1
(page 327)

for Help

Divide using long division. Check your answers.

1. $(x^2 - 3x - 40) \div (x + 5)$
2. $(3x^2 + 7x - 20) \div (x + 4)$

3. $(x^3 + 3x^2 - x + 2) \div (x - 1)$
4. $(2x^3 - 3x^2 - 18x - 8) \div (x - 4)$

5. $(9x^3 - 18x^2 - x + 2) \div (3x + 1)$
6. $(9x^2 - 21x - 20) \div (x - 1)$

7. $(x^2 - 7x + 10) \div (x + 3)$
8. $(x^3 - 13x - 12) \div (x - 4)$

Example 2
(page 327)

Determine whether each binomial is a factor of $x^3 + 4x^2 + x - 6$.

9. $x + 1$
10. $x + 2$
11. $x + 3$
12. $x - 3$

Example 3
(page 328)

Divide using synthetic division.

13. $(x^3 + 3x^2 - x - 3) \div (x - 1)$
14. $(x^3 - 4x^2 + 6x - 4) \div (x - 2)$

15. $(x^3 - 7x^2 - 7x + 20) \div (x + 4)$
16. $(x^3 - 3x^2 - 5x - 25) \div (x - 5)$

17. $(x^3 - 2x^2 - 5x + 6) \div (x - 1)$
18. $(-2x^3 + 5x^2 - x + 2) \div (x + 2)$

19. $(x^2 + 3) \div (x - 1)$
20. $(3x^3 + 17x^2 + 21x - 9) \div (x + 3)$

21. $(x^3 + 27) \div (x + 3)$
22. $(6x^2 - 8x - 2) \div (x - 1)$

Example 4
(pages 328–329)

Use synthetic division and the given factor to completely factor each polynomial function.

23. $y = x^3 + 2x^2 - 5x - 6; (x + 1)$
24. $y = x^3 - 4x^2 - 9x + 36; (x + 3)$

25. Geometry Refer to the diagram. The volume in cubic inches of the decorative box can be expressed as the product of the lengths of its sides as $V(x) = x^3 + x^2 - 6x$. Write linear expressions with integer coefficients for the locker's length and height.

width = $x - 2$

Example 5
(page 329)

Use synthetic division and the Remainder Theorem to find $P(a)$.

26. $P(x) = x^3 + 4x^2 - 8x - 6; a = -2$
27. $P(x) = x^3 + 4x^2 + 4x; a = -2$

28. $P(x) = x^3 - 7x^2 + 15x - 9; a = 3$
29. $P(x) = x^3 + 7x^2 + 4x; a = -2$

30. $P(x) = 6x^3 - x^2 + 4x + 3; a = 3$
31. $P(x) = 2x^3 - x^2 + 10x + 5; a = \frac{1}{2}$

32. $P(x) = 2x^3 + 4x^2 - 10x - 9; a = 3$
33. $P(x) = 2x^4 + 6x^3 + 5x^2 - 45; a = -3$

B Apply Your Skills

34. Reasoning A polynomial $P(x)$ is divided by a binomial $x - a$. The remainder is zero. What conclusion can you draw? Explain.

35. Error Analysis A student represented the product of three linear factors as $x^3 - x^2 - 2x$. She used $x - 1$ as one of the factors. Use division to prove that the student made an error.

36. Open-Ended Write a polynomial division that has a quotient of $x + 3$ and a remainder of 2.

Divide.

37. $(2x^3 + 9x^2 + 14x + 5) \div (2x + 1)$ **38.** $(x^4 + 3x^2 + x + 4) \div (x + 3)$

39. $(x^5 + 1) \div (x + 1)$ **40.** $(x^4 + 4x^3 - x - 4) \div (x^3 - 1)$

41. $(3x^4 - 5x^3 + 2x^2 + 3x - 2) \div (3x - 2)$

Determine whether each binomial is a factor of $x^3 + x^2 - 16x - 16$.

42. $x + 2$ **43.** $x - 4$ **44.** $x + 1$

45. $x - 1$ **46.** $x - 2$ **47.** $x + 4$

Homework Video Tutor

Visit: PHSchool.com
Web Code: bbe-0603

Use synthetic division to determine whether each binomial is a factor of $3x^3 + 10x^2 - x - 12$.

48. $x + 3$ **49.** $x - 1$ **50.** $x + 2$ **51.** $x - 4$

Divide using synthetic division.

52. $(x^4 - 2x^3 + x^2 + x - 1) \div (x - 1)$ **53.** $(x^4 - 6x^2 - 27) \div (x + 2)$

54. $(x^4 - 5x^2 + 4x + 12) \div (x + 2)$ **55.** $\left(x^4 - \frac{9}{2}x^3 + 3x^2 - \frac{1}{2}x\right) \div \left(x - \frac{1}{2}\right)$

 Challenge

56. Reasoning Divide. Look for patterns in your answers.
   a. $(x^2 - 1) \div (x - 1)$ **b.** $(x^3 - 1) \div (x - 1)$ **c.** $(x^4 - 1) \div (x - 1)$
   d. Using the patterns, factor $x^5 - 1$.

57. Divide. Look for patterns in your answers.
   a. $(x^3 + 1) \div (x + 1)$ **b.** $(x^5 + 1) \div (x + 1)$ **c.** $(x^7 + 1) \div (x + 1)$
   d. Using the patterns, factor $x^9 + 1$.

58. Critical Thinking Explain why a polynomial of degree n, divided by a polynomial of degree 1, yields a quotient of degree $n - 1$ and a remainder that is a constant.

59. Use synthetic division to find $(x^2 + 4) \div (x - 2i)$.

 60. Writing Suppose 3, -1, and 4 are zeros of a cubic polynomial function. Sketch a graph of the function. Could there be more than one graph? Explain.

Multiple Choice Practice

For California Standards and CAHSEE Tutorials, visit PHSchool.com. **Web Code:** bbq-9045

ALG2 3.0

61. The volume of a shoebox can be expressed as $x^3 - 13x - 12$. The height of the box is $x + 1$. Which of the following expressions could represent the width and length of the box?
   Ⓐ $(x + 3)(x + 4)$ Ⓒ $(x - 3)(x + 4)$
   Ⓑ $(x - 4)(x + 3)$ Ⓓ $(x - 3)(x - 4)$

ALG2 2.0

62. Isabella has 18 coins in her pocket; they are all quarters or dimes. She has a total of $3.45. How many quarters and dimes does she have?
   Ⓐ 6 quarters, 12 dimes   Ⓒ 11 quarters, 7 dimes
   Ⓑ 7 quarters, 11 dimes   Ⓓ 13 quarters, 5 dimes

Lesson 6-2 **Write a polynomial function in standard form with the given zeros.**

63. $3, -5$ **64.** $0, 1, 8$ **65.** $-1, 2, 5$ **66.** 1, multiplicity 4

Lesson 5-6 **Simplify each expression.**

67. $(-4i)(6i)$ **68.** $(2 + i)(2 - i)$ **69.** $(4 - 3i)(5 + i)$

Lesson 4-6 **Find the inverse of each matrix, if it exists.**

70. $\begin{bmatrix} 1 & 0 & 3 \\ 1 & 1 & 0 \\ -1 & 0 & -1 \end{bmatrix}$
71. $\begin{bmatrix} 1 & 2 & 0 \\ 0 & 2 & -2 \\ 1 & 0 & 2 \end{bmatrix}$
72. $\begin{bmatrix} 2 & 1 & 0 \\ -1 & 1 & -2 \\ 3 & -2 & 4 \end{bmatrix}$

✓ Checkpoint Quiz 1   Lessons 6-1 through 6-3

1. Write a polynomial function with at least three zeros that are negative, one of which has multiplicity 2.

Write each polynomial in standard form. Then classify it by degree and by number of terms.

2. $-2x^3 + 6 - x^3 + 5x$ **3.** $\frac{1}{2}x + x^4 - 3x^2 + 2x$ **4.** $3(x - 1)(x + 4)$

For each function, determine the zeros and their multiplicity.

5. $y = (x - 2)^2(x - 1)$ **6.** $y = (2x + 1)(x - 4)$ **7.** $y = x^3(x - 3)(x + 1)^2$

Divide.

8. $(x^3 + 3x^2 + 3x + 1) \div (x + 1)$ **9.** $(2x^3 - 7x^2 + 7x - 2) \div (x - 2)$

10. Use synthetic division to find $P(4)$ for $P(x) = 2x^4 - 3x^2 + 4x - 1$.

Algebra at Work

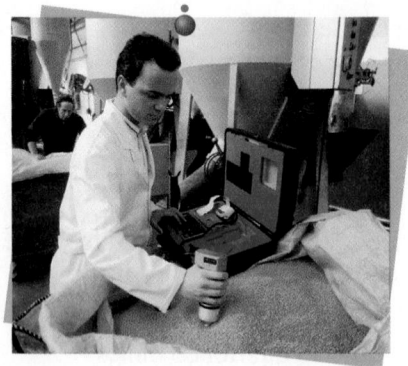

·············· Quality Control Engineer

Quality control engineers establish procedures for assuring that products meet minimum standards of quality such as length or purity. Each product is sampled regularly. Data relating to each standard are collected and analyzed. All samples must fall within certain limiting parameters. Quality is further controlled by requiring that a significant portion of the samples fall within even stricter limiting parameters.

Go Online
PHSchool.com
For: Information about quality control
Web Code: bbb-2031

6-4 Solving Polynomial Equations

 California Content Standards

ALG2 4.0 Students factor polynomials representing the sum and difference of two cubes. *Master*

What You'll Learn

- To solve polynomial equations by graphing
- To solve polynomial equations by factoring

. . . And Why

To calculate the dimensions of a portable kennel, as in Example 2

✓ Check Skills You'll Need

GO for Help Lessons 3-1 and 5-4

Graph each system. Find any points of intersection.

1. $\begin{cases} y = 3x + 1 \\ y = -2x + 6 \end{cases}$
2. $\begin{cases} -2x + 3y = 0 \\ x + 3y = 3 \end{cases}$
3. $\begin{cases} 2y = -x + 8 \\ x + 2y = -6 \end{cases}$

Factor each expression.

4. $x^2 - 2x - 15$
5. $x^2 - 9x + 14$
6. $x^2 + 6x + 5$

🔊 New Vocabulary
- sum of cubes
- difference of cubes

---

1 Solving Equations by Graphing

You can solve a polynomial equation by graphing each side of the equation separately and finding the x values at the point(s) of intersection.

1 EXAMPLE Solving by Graphing

Solve $x^3 + 3x^2 = x + 3$ by graphing.

Step 1 Graph $y_1 = x^3 + 3x^2$ and $y_2 = x + 3$ on a graphing calculator.

Graphing Calculator Hint

You can also solve the equation in Example 1 by graphing the related function $y = x^3 + 3x^2 - x - 3$ and finding its zeros.

Step 2 Use the Intersect feature to find the x values at the points of intersection.

The solutions are $-3, -1$, and 1.

Check Show that each solution makes the original equation a true statement.

$x^3 + 3x^2 = x + 3$ $x^3 + 3x^2 = x + 3$ $x^3 + 3x^2 = x + 3$

$(-3)^3 + 3(-3)^2 \stackrel{?}{=} -3 + 3$ $(-1)^3 + 3(-1)^2 \stackrel{?}{=} -1 + 3$ $(1)^3 + 3(1)^2 \stackrel{?}{=} 1 + 3$

$-27 + 27 \stackrel{?}{=} -3 + 3$ $-1 + 3 \stackrel{?}{=} -1 + 3$ $1 + 3 \stackrel{?}{=} 1 + 3$

$0 = 0 ✓$ $2 = 2 ✓$ $4 = 4 ✓$

✓ **CA Standards Check** 1 Graph and solve $x^3 - 2x^2 = -3$. Check your answers.

You can write and solve a polynomial equation that models a real-world situation.

2 EXAMPLE **Real-World Connection**

Pet Transportation The dimensions in inches of a portable kennel can be expressed as width x, length $x + 7$, and height $x - 1$. The volume is 5.9 ft^3. Find the portable kennel's dimensions.

$5.9 \text{ ft}^3 \cdot \dfrac{12^3 \text{ in.}^3}{\text{ft}^3} = 10{,}195.2 \text{ in.}^3$ **Convert the volume to cubic inches.**

$V = \ell \cdot w \cdot h$ **Write the formula for volume.**

$10{,}195.2 = (x + 7)x(x - 1)$ **Substitute.**

Graph $y_1 = 10{,}195.2$ and $y_2 = (x + 7)x(x - 1)$. Use the Intersect feature of the calculator. When $y = 10{,}195.2$, $x \approx 20$. So $x + 7 \approx 27$ and $x - 1 \approx 19$.

The dimensions of the portable kennel are about 27 in. by 20 in. by 19 in.

Intersection
X=19.954686 Y=10195.2

 CA Standards Check **2** Find the dimensions of a carrier with volume 7 ft^3, width x inches, length $(x + 3)$ inches, and height $(x - 2)$ inches.

Real-World Connection

International regulations specify the allowable dimensions of pet transportation carriers.

---

2 **Solving Equations by Factoring**

Recall that a quadratic *difference of squares* has a special factoring pattern. A cubic **sum of cubes** and **difference of cubes** also have special factoring patterns.

Key Concepts

Properties	Sum and Difference of Cubes
	$a^3 + b^3 = (a + b)(a^2 - ab + b^2)$
	$a^3 - b^3 = (a - b)(a^2 + ab + b^2)$

You can verify the patterns by multiplying. Here are steps for the sum of cubes:

$(a + b)(a^2 - ab + b^2) = a(a^2 - ab + b^2) + b(a^2 - ab + b^2)$

$= a^3 - a^2b + ab^2 + a^2b - ab^2 + b^3$

$= a^3 + b^3$

3 EXAMPLE **Factoring a Sum or Difference of Cubes**

Multiple Choice If you factor $x^3 - 8$ in the form $(x - A)(x^2 + Bx + C)$, what is the value of A?

  Ⓐ 2   Ⓑ −2   Ⓒ 4   Ⓓ −4

$x^3 - 8 = (x)^3 - (2)^3$ **Rewrite the expression as the difference of cubes.**

$= (x - 2)(x^2 + 2x + (2)^2)$ **Factor.**

$= (x - 2)(x^2 + 2x + 4)$ **Simplify.**

The answer is choice A.

 Test-Taking Tip

Remembering patterns may help you find answers more quickly.

 CA Standards Check **3** Factor $8x^3 - 1$.

In Chapter 5, you found the complex roots of quadratic equations. You can do the same with polynomial equations of higher degree.

4 EXAMPLE Solving a Polynomial Equation

Solve $27x^3 + 1 = 0$. Find all complex roots.

$$27x^3 + 1 = (3x)^3 + (1)^3 \qquad \text{\textbf{Rewrite the cubic expression as the sum of cubes.}}$$
$$= (3x + 1)((3x)^2 - 3x + 1) \quad \text{\textbf{Factor.}}$$
$$= (3x + 1)(9x^2 - 3x + 1) \quad \text{\textbf{Simplify.}}$$

Since $3x + 1$ is a factor, $x = -\frac{1}{3}$ is a root.

The quadratic expression $9x^2 - 3x + 1$ cannot be factored, so use the Quadratic Formula to solve the related quadratic equation $9x^2 - 3x + 1 = 0$.

Vocabulary Tip

$\sqrt{-1} = i$

$$x = \frac{-b \pm \sqrt{b^2 - 4ac}}{2a} \qquad \text{\textbf{Quadratic Formula}}$$

$$= \frac{-(-3) \pm \sqrt{(-3)^2 - 4(9)(1)}}{2(9)} \qquad \text{\textbf{Substitute 9 for } a, -3 \text{ for } b, \text{ and 1 for } c.}$$

$$= \frac{3 \pm \sqrt{-27}}{18} \qquad \text{\textbf{Use the Order of Operations.}}$$

$$= \frac{3 \pm 3i\sqrt{3}}{18} \qquad \text{\textbf{Simplify.}}$$

$$= \frac{1 \pm i\sqrt{3}}{6}$$

● The roots are $-\frac{1}{3}$ and $\frac{1 \pm i\sqrt{3}}{6}$.

✔ CA Standards Check ❹ Solve each equation.

    a. $x^3 + 8 = 0$ **b.** $27x^3 - 1 = 0$

You can sometimes factor a polynomial of higher degree by using the techniques you have used in solving polynomials of lower degree.

5 EXAMPLE Factoring by Using a Quadratic Pattern

Factor $x^4 - 2x^2 - 8$.

Step 1   You can write $x^4 - 2x^2 - 8$ in the pattern of a quadratic expression, so you can factor it like one. Make a temporary substitution of variables.

$$x^4 - 2x^2 - 8 = (x^2)^2 - 2(x^2) - 8 \quad \text{\textbf{Rewrite in the pattern of a quadratic expression.}}$$

$$= a^2 - 2a - 8 \qquad \text{\textbf{Substitute } a \text{ for } x^2.}$$

Step 2   Factor $a^2 - 2a - 8$.

$$a^2 - 2a - 8 = (a - 4)(a + 2)$$

Step 3   Substitute back to the original variable.

$$(a - 4)(a + 2) = (x^2 - 4)(x^2 + 2) \qquad \text{\textbf{Substitute } x^2 \text{ for } a.}$$

$$= (x + 2)(x - 2)(x^2 + 2) \quad \text{\textbf{Factor completely.}}$$

● The factored form of $x^4 - 2x^2 - 8$ is $(x + 2)(x - 2)(x^2 + 2)$.

✔ CA Standards Check ❺ Factor each expression.

    a. $x^4 + 7x^2 + 6$ **b.** $x^4 - 3x^2 - 10$

6 **EXAMPLE** Solving a Higher-Degree Polynomial Equation

Solve $x^4 - x^2 = 12$.

$$x^4 - x^2 = 12$$

$$x^4 - x^2 - 12 = 0$$ **Rewrite so one side of the equation is equal to zero.**

$$(x^2)^2 - (x^2) - 12 = 0$$ **Write in the form of a quadratic expression. Think of the expression as $a^2 - a - 12$, which factors as $(a - 4)(a + 3)$.**

$$(x^2 - 4)(x^2 + 3) = 0$$

$$(x - 2)(x + 2)(x^2 + 3) = 0$$

$x = 2$ or $x = -2$ or $x^2 = -3$ **Use the Factor Theorem.**

$\quad\quad x = \pm 2$ or $\quad x = \pm\sqrt{-3}$ **Solve for x.**

$\quad\quad x = \pm 2$ or $\quad x = \pm i\sqrt{3}$ **Simplify.**

The solutions are $2, -2, i\sqrt{3}$, and $-i\sqrt{3}$.

✓ **CA Standards Check** **6** Solve $x^4 + 11x^2 + 18 = 0$.

EXERCISES

For more exercises, see *Extra Skill and Word Problem Practice.*

Standards Practice

ALG2 4.0

A **Practice by Example**

Examples 1 and 2
(pages 333 and 334)

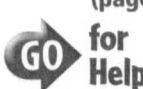
GO for Help

Solve each equation by graphing. Check your answers.

1. $x^3 - 4x^2 - 7x = -10$ **2.** $3x^3 - 6x^2 - 9x = 0$ **3.** $4x^3 - 8x^2 + 4x = 0$

4. $6x^2 = 48x$ **5.** $x^3 + 3x^2 + 2x = 0$ **6.** $2x^3 + 5x^2 = 7x$

7. $4x^3 = 4x^2 + 3x$ **8.** $2x^4 - 5x^3 - 3x^2 = 0$ **9.** $x^2 - 8x + 7 = 0$

10. Savings The polynomial $1600x^3 + 1200x^2 + 800x$ represents your savings, with interest, from a summer job after three years. The annual interest rate equals $x - 1$. Find the interest rate needed so that you will have $4000 at the end of three years.

11. Geometry The volume V of a container is modeled by the function $V(x) = x^3 - 3x^2 - 4x$. Let $x, x + 1$, and $x - 4$ represent the width, the length, and the height respectively. The container has a volume of 70 ft^3. Find the container's dimensions.

Example 3
(page 334)

Factor each expression.

12. $x^3 + 64$ **13.** $x^3 - 1000$ **14.** $125x^3 - 27$

Example 4
(page 335)

Solve each equation.

15. $x^3 - 27 = 0$ **16.** $x^3 + 64 = 0$ **17.** $x^3 - 125 = 0$

18. $2x^3 + 2 = 0$ **19.** $8x^3 - 1 = 0$ **20.** $64x^3 + 8 = 0$

Example 5
(page 335)

Factor each expression.

21. $x^4 - 8x^2 + 7$ **22.** $x^4 + 8x^2 - 20$ **23.** $x^4 - 7x^2 + 12$

24. $x^4 - 5x^2 + 4$ **25.** $x^4 - 1$ **26.** $4x^4 - 6x^2 + 2$

Example 6
(page 336)

Solve each equation.

27. $x^4 - 10x^2 + 9 = 0$ **28.** $x^4 - 8x^2 + 16 = 0$ **29.** $x^4 - 12x^2 - 64 = 0$

30. $x^4 + 7x^2 - 18 = 0$ **31.** $x^4 + 4x^2 - 12 = 0$ **32.** $x^4 + 8x^2 + 15 = 0$

B **Apply Your Skills**

Solve each equation by graphing. Where necessary, round to the nearest hundredth.

33. $x^3 - x^2 - 6x - 4 = 0$ **34.** $2x^4 + 18x^3 = 0$

35. $x^4 + 2x^3 - 7x^2 - 8x = -12$ **36.** $x^4 + x^3 = 4x^2 + 4x - 5$

37. $x^3 + 13x = 10x^2$ **38.** $x^3 - 6x^2 + 6x = 0$ **39.** $12x^3 = 60x^2 + 75x$

40. The product of three consecutive integers $n - 1, n$, and $n + 1$ is 210. Write and solve an equation to find the numbers.

41. Multiple Choice The chamber in the vacuum bottle below consists of a cylinder on top of a hemisphere. The chamber holds 500 cm^3. What is the radius of the chamber, to the nearest hundredth of a centimeter?

Ⓐ 2.75 cm   Ⓑ 3.12 cm   Ⓒ 3.32 cm   Ⓓ 3.58 cm

Real-World Connection

The vacuum bottle, or Dewar flask, was invented by the chemist James Dewar for storing liquefied gases.

Solve each equation.

42. $125x^3 + 216 = 0$ **43.** $81x^3 - 192 = 0$ **44.** $x^4 - 64 = 0$

45. $-2x^4 + 46x^2 = -100$ **46.** $27 = -x^4 - 12x^2$ **47.** $x^5 - 5x^3 + 4x = 0$

48. $x^4 - 100 = 0$ **49.** $5x^3 = 5x^2 + 12x$ **50.** $64 - x^3 = 0$

51. $x^3 - 6x^2 + 6x = 0$ **52.** $2x^3 = 5x^2 + 12x$ **53.** $3x^4 + 12x^2 - 15 = 0$

54. $x^3 + 3x^2 - 4x - 12 = 0$ **55.** $x^3 - 5x^2 + 3x + 9 = 0$

56. $4x^3 - 16x^2 + 12x = 0$ **57.** $2x^4 - 14x^3 + 12x^2 = 0$

58. $4x^4 - 2x^2 - 4 = 2$ **59.** $9x^4 - 9x^2 + 2 = 20$

60. Open-Ended To solve a polynomial equation, you can use any combination of graphing, factoring, and the Quadratic Formula. Write and solve an equation to illustrate each method.

For Exercises 61 and 62, write a polynomial function to describe each volume. Then graph your function to solve each problem.

For a guide to solving Exercise 61, see p. 339.

61. Geometry Suppose a 2-in. slice is cut from one face of the cheese block as shown. The remaining solid has a volume of 224 in.^{3}. Find the dimensions of the original block.

62. Geometry The width of a box is 2 m less than the length. The height is 1 m less than the length. The volume is 60 m^3. Find the length of the box.

Homework Video Tutor

Visit: PHSchool.com
Web Code: bbe-0604

Graph each function to find the zeros. Rewrite the function with the polynomial in factored form.

63. $y = 2x^2 + 3x - 5$ **64.** $y = x^4 - 10x^2 + 9$ **65.** $y = x^3 - 3x^2 + 4$

66. $y = x^3 - 2x^2 - 5x + 6$ **67.** $y = x^3 + 2x^2 - 11x - 12$

68. Error Analysis A student claims that 1, 2, 3, and 4 are the zeros of a cubic polynomial function. Explain why the student is mistaken.

 Challenge

69. a. Open-Ended Write and solve a fourth-degree polynomial equation that includes the difference of squares.
  b. Critical Thinking Are all the roots real numbers? Justify your answer.

70. Writing From a large cube with edges *a* units long, you cut a smaller cube with edges three units long. Explain how the diagram at the right illustrates that $a^3 - 27 = (a - 3)(a^2 + 3a + 9)$.

71. a. The sum of two positive numbers is 4 and the sum of their cubes is 28. What is the sum of their squares?
  b. The product of two positive numbers is 96 and the sum of their squares is 208. What are the two numbers?

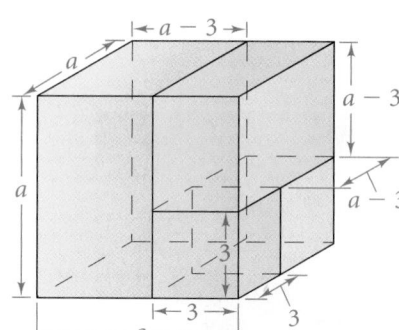

Multiple Choice Practice

For California Standards and CAHSEE Tutorials, visit PHSchool.com. Web Code: bbq-9045

ALG2 4.0

72. Evan receives a paycheck from his part-time job. The amount the paycheck is worth can be represented by $a^3 - 64$. Which of the following expressions could represent the total number of hours he worked multiplied by his hourly wage?
  Ⓐ $(a - 8)(a^2 + 8)$
  Ⓒ $(a + 4)(a^2 + 4a + 16)$
  Ⓑ $(a - 4)(a^2 + 4a + 16)$
  Ⓓ $(a^2 - 4)(a^2 + 16)$

ALG2 8.0

73. What are the *x*-intercepts of the graph of the equation $y = x^2 + x - 30$?
  Ⓐ $x = 6, x = 5$
  Ⓒ $x = -6, x = -5$
  Ⓑ $x = -6, x = 5$
  Ⓓ $x = 6, x = -5$

Mixed Review

Lesson 6-3

Divide.

74. $(x^3 - 2x^2 - 13x - 10) \div (x + 1)$ **75.** $(2x^3 - 7x^2 - 7x + 14) \div (x - 4)$

Lesson 5-5

Solve each equation by factoring or by taking square roots.

76. $n^2 - 4n = 12$ **77.** $n^2 + 1 = 37$ **78.** $2n^2 - 5n - 3 = 0$

Lesson 4-7

Solve each matrix equation. If the coefficient matrix has no inverse, write *no unique solution*.

79. $\begin{bmatrix} 2 & -1 \\ -3 & 2 \end{bmatrix}\begin{bmatrix} x \\ y \end{bmatrix} = \begin{bmatrix} 5 \\ -10 \end{bmatrix}$ **80.** $\begin{bmatrix} 1 & 4 \\ -2 & -8 \end{bmatrix}\begin{bmatrix} x \\ y \end{bmatrix} = \begin{bmatrix} 2 \\ -4 \end{bmatrix}$

GPS — Guided Problem Solving

FOR USE WITH PAGE 337, EXERCISE 61

Understanding Word Problems Read the problem below. Then let Ian's thinking guide you through the solution. Check your understanding with the exercises at the bottom of the page.

Geometry Suppose a 2-in. slice is cut from one face of the cheese block as shown. The remaining solid has a volume of 224 in.^{3}. Find the dimensions of the original block.

What Ian Thinks

From the diagram, it looks like the widths and heights of the two blocks are equal. I can subtract the amount cut off from the total length to find the length left.

The problem tells me that the volume of the leftover block is 224 in.^{3}. I can write a relationship, substitute, and simplify.

The polynomial equation is a cubic, and the problem asks me to solve by graphing. I'll graph two equations and find their intersection.

I'll enter the equations as Y_1 and Y_2, and I'll change my window values to accommodate a y-value of 224.

Next, I'll use the INTERSECT feature. When $y = 224, x = 4$. OK! Now I know x.

I can use x to find the dimensions of the original block.

What Ian Writes

$$\text{length of leftover block} = 4x - \text{length of cut block}$$

$$= 4x - 2$$

$$\text{volume of leftover block} = \ell wh = 224$$

$$V = (4x - 2)(x)(x) = 224$$

$$(4x - 2)(x^2) = 224$$

$$4x^3 - 2x^2 = 224$$

$$Y1 = 4x^3 - 2x^2$$
$$Y2 = 224$$

Xmin=−10
Xmax=10
Xscl=1
Ymin=−100
Ymax=300
Yscl=50

Intersection
X=4   Y=224

Width = Height = x = 4
Length = $4x$ = 4(4) = 16

The block of cheese measured
16 in. × 4 in. × 4 in.

EXERCISES

1. Slices of wood $\frac{1}{4}$-in. thick are cut from opposite sides of a cube of wood. The remaining solid has a volume of 151.25 in.^{3}. Find the dimensions of the original block of wood.

2. The water level in a fish tank is 4 in. from the top. The depth of the water is the same as the width of the tank, which is half of its length. The volume of the water in the tank is 4394 in.^{3}. What is the capacity of the fish tank?

Continuous and *discrete* are two rather sophisticated mathematics words that you can use in everyday conversations. Their mathematical and everyday meanings are compatible:

Continuous means unbroken.

Discrete means separate and distinct.

1 EXAMPLE

On a number line,

- real numbers are continuous,

- but integers are discrete.

2 EXAMPLE

At the gas pump,

- the gas pumped and its value are continuous;

- the amount you pay is discrete.

EXERCISES

Is the quantity *continuous* or *discrete*? Explain.

1. number of airplanes at an airport

2. altitude of an airplane

3. height of a growing flower

4. number of flowers in a garden

5. length of lead in a pencil

6. number of beans in a beanbag

You can use different quantities to describe different aspects of a situation. Name one continuous quantity and one discrete quantity for each situation.

7. a train ride between two cities

8. a soccer game

9. plowing a field

10. the weather today

Sometimes a situation itself can be described as *continuous* or *discrete*. Which word would you use to describe each situation below? Explain.

11. milk pouring into a glass

12. walking to school

13. bacteria living in a culture

14. Earth-to-sun distance

Is the mathematical object *continuous* or *discrete*? Explain.

15. the graph of a linear function

16. the graph of an absolute value function

17. a scatter plot of 100 data points

18. the zeros of a third-degree polynomial function

19. Motion Pictures Film editors watch for *continuity* from one scene to the next (both of which may have needed several "takes"). They want to avoid having a tennis racket suddenly switch from a left hand to a right hand or, worse yet, disappear entirely. Research and describe a continuity error found in a movie.

Theorems About Roots of Polynomial Equations

 California Content Standards

ALG2 5.0 Students demonstrate knowledge of how real and complex numbers are related arithmetically. *Master*
ALG2 6.0 Students add, subtract, multiply, and divide complex numbers. *Master*
ALG2 8.0 Students solve and graph quadratic equations by factoring. *Master*

What You'll Learn

- To solve equations using the Rational Root Theorem
- To use the Irrational Root Theorem and the Imaginary Root Theorem

. . . And Why

To find all the roots of a polynomial equation, as in Example 2

✓ **Check Skills You'll Need**

 for Help Lessons 1-1, 5-1, and 5-6

List all the integer factors of each number.

1. 12   **2.** 24   **3.** 36   **4.** 48

Multiply.

5. $(x - 5)(x^2 + 7)$ **6.** $(x + 2)(x + \sqrt{3})(x - \sqrt{3})$

Define each set of numbers.

7. rational   **8.** irrational   **9.** imaginary

◀》 **New Vocabulary**
- Rational Root Theorem
- conjugates
- Irrational Root Theorem
- Imaginary Root Theorem

---

1   The Rational Root Theorem

Vocabulary Tip

A polynomial equation has <u>roots</u>. A polynomial function has <u>zeros</u>.

You have learned several methods for finding the roots of a polynomial equation. Another method involves analyzing one or more integer coefficients of the polynomial in the equation.

Consider the equivalent equations $x^3 - 5x^2 - 2x + 24 = 0$ and $(x + 2)(x - 3)(x - 4) = 0$, which have $-2, 3$, and 4 as roots. The product of $2, 3$, and 4 is 24. Notice that all the roots are factors of the constant term, 24. In general, if the coefficients (including the constant term) in a polynomial equation are integers, then any integer root of the equation is a factor of the constant term.

A similar pattern applies to rational roots. Consider the equivalent equations $24x^3 - 22x^2 - 5x + 6 = 0$ and $\left(x + \frac{1}{2}\right)\left(x - \frac{2}{3}\right)\left(x - \frac{3}{4}\right) = 0$, which have $-\frac{1}{2}, \frac{2}{3}$, and $\frac{3}{4}$ as roots. The numerators $1, 2$, and 3 all are factors of the constant term, 6. The denominators $2, 3$, and 4 are factors of the leading coefficient, 24.

Both the constant term and the leading coefficient of a polynomial can play a key role in identifying the rational roots of the related polynomial equation. This role is expressed in the Rational Root Theorem.

 Key Concepts

Theorem	**Rational Root Theorem**

If $\frac{p}{q}$ is in simplest form and is a rational root of the polynomial equation $a_n x^n + a_{n-1} x^{n-1} + \cdots + a_1 x + a_0 = 0$ with integer coefficients, then p must be a factor of a_0 and q must be a factor of a_n.

You can use the Rational Root Theorem to find any rational roots of a polynomial equation with integer coefficients.

1 EXAMPLE Finding Rational Roots

Find the rational roots of $x^3 + x^2 - 3x - 3 = 0$.

Step 1 List the possible rational roots.

The leading coefficient is 1. The constant term is -3. By the Rational Root Theorem, the only possible rational roots of the equation have the form $\frac{\text{factor of } -3}{\text{factor of } 1}$.

The factors of -3 are ± 1 and ± 3. The factors of 1 are ± 1. The only possible rational roots are ± 1 and ± 3.

Step 2 Test each possible rational root.

Test 1: $x^3 + x^2 - 3x - 3 = (1)^3 + (1)^2 - 3(1) - 3$

$= -4 \neq 0$

Test 3: $x^3 + x^2 - 3x - 3 = (3)^3 + (3)^2 - 3(3) - 3$

$= 24 \neq 0$

Test -1: $x^3 + x^2 - 3x - 3 = (-1)^3 + (-1)^2 - 3(-1) - 3$

$= 0$ **So -1 is a root.**

Test -3: $x^3 + x^2 - 3x - 3 = (-3)^3 + (-3)^2 - 3(-3) - 3$

$= -12 \neq 0$

● The only rational root of $x^3 + x^2 - 3x - 3 = 0$ is -1.

✔ **CA Standards Check** ❶ Find the rational roots of $x^3 - 4x^2 - 2x + 8 = 0$.

You can often use the Rational Root Theorem to find all the roots of a polynomial equation.

2 EXAMPLE Using the Rational Root Theorem

Find the roots of $2x^3 - x^2 + 2x - 1 = 0$.

Step 1 List the possible rational roots.

The leading coefficient is 2. The constant term is -1. By the Rational Root Theorem, the only possible rational roots of the equation have the form $\frac{\text{factor of } -1}{\text{factor of } 2}$.

The factors of -1 are ± 1. The factors of 2 are ± 1 and ± 2. So the only possible rational roots are ± 1 and $\pm \frac{1}{2}$.

Step 2 Test each possible rational root until you find a root.

Test 1: $2x^3 - x^2 + 2x - 1 = 2(1)^3 - (1)^2 + 2(1) - 1$

$= 2 \neq 0$

Test $\frac{1}{2}$: $2x^3 - x^2 + 2x - 1 = 2\left(\frac{1}{2}\right)^3 - \left(\frac{1}{2}\right)^2 + 2\left(\frac{1}{2}\right) - 1$

$= 0$ **So $\frac{1}{2}$ is a root.**

Step 3 Use synthetic division with the root you found in Step 2 to find the quotient.

$$\begin{array}{r|rrrr} \tfrac{1}{2} & 2 & -1 & 2 & -1 \\ & & 1 & 0 & 1 \\ \hline & 2 & 0 & 2 & 0 \end{array}$$

$$\underset{2x^2}{\downarrow} \quad \underset{}{\downarrow} \quad \underset{+2}{\downarrow} \quad \underset{\text{Remainder}}{\downarrow}$$

Step 4 Find the roots of $2x^2 + 2 = 0$.

$$2x^2 + 2 = 0$$
$$2(x^2 + 1) = 0 \quad \textbf{Factor out the GCF, 2.}$$
$$x^2 + 1 = 0$$
$$x^2 = -1$$
$$x = \pm i$$

● The roots of $2x^3 - x^2 + 2x - 1 = 0$ are $\tfrac{1}{2}, i,$ and $-i$.

✔ **CA Standards Check** ② Find the roots of each equation.

a. $x^3 - 2x^2 - 5x + 10 = 0$ **b.** $3x^3 + x^2 - x + 1 = 0$

---

2   Irrational Root Theorem and Imaginary Root Theorem

In Chapter 5 you learned to find irrational solutions to quadratic equations. For example, by the Quadratic Formula, the solutions of $x^2 - 4x - 1 = 0$ are $2 + \sqrt{5}$ and $2 - \sqrt{5}$. Number pairs of the form $a + \sqrt{b}$ and $a - \sqrt{b}$ are called **conjugates.**

You can often use conjugates to find the irrational roots of a polynomial equation.

🔑 **Key Concepts**

Theorem	**Irrational Root Theorem**

Let a and b be rational numbers and let $\sqrt{b}$ be an irrational number. If $a + \sqrt{b}$ is a root of a polynomial equation with rational coefficients, then the conjugate $a - \sqrt{b}$ also is a root.

3 EXAMPLE   **Finding Irrational Roots**

A polynomial equation with integer coefficients has the roots $1 + \sqrt{3}$ and $-\sqrt{11}$. Find two additional roots.

By the Irrational Root Theorem, if $1 + \sqrt{3}$ is a root, then its conjugate $1 - \sqrt{3}$ is also a root. If $-\sqrt{11}$ is a root, then its conjugate $\sqrt{11}$ also is a root.

● The additional roots are $1 - \sqrt{3}$ and $\sqrt{11}$.

✔ **CA Standards Check** ③ **a.** A polynomial equation with rational coefficients has the roots $2 - \sqrt{7}$ and $\sqrt{5}$. Find two additional roots.

     b. Critical Thinking One of the roots of a polynomial equation is $4 - \sqrt{2}$. Can you be certain that $4 + \sqrt{2}$ also is a root of the equation? Explain.

Number pairs of the form $a + bi$ and $a - bi$ are complex conjugates. You can use complex conjugates to find an equation's imaginary roots.

Key Concepts

Theorem	Imaginary Root Theorem

If the imaginary number $a + bi$ is a root of a polynomial equation with real coefficients, then the conjugate $a - bi$ also is a root.

4 EXAMPLE **Finding Imaginary Roots**

A polynomial equation with integer coefficients has the roots $3 - i$ and $2i$. Find two additional roots.

By the Imaginary Root Theorem, if $3 - i$ is a root, then its complex conjugate $3 + i$ also is a root. If $2i$ is a root, then its complex conjugate $-2i$ also is a root.

● The additional roots are $3 + i$ and $2i$.

CA Standards Check ④ **a.** If a polynomial equation with real coefficients has $3i$ and $-2 + i$ among its roots, then what two other roots must it have?
b. Critical Thinking Describe the degree of the equation.

You can often use the Irrational Root Theorem and the Imaginary Root Theorem to write a polynomial equation if you know some of its roots.

5 EXAMPLE **Writing a Polynomial Equation from Its Roots**

Find a third-degree polynomial equation with rational coefficients that has roots 3 and $1 + i$.

Step 1 Find the other root using the Imaginary Root Theorem.

Since $1 + i$ is a root, then its complex conjugate $1 - i$ also is a root.

Step 2 Write the factored form of the polynomial using the Factor Theorem.

$(x - 3)(x - (1 + i))(x - (1 - i))$

Step 3 Multiply the factors.

$(x - 3)[x^2 - x(1 - i) - x(1 + i) + (1 + i)(1 - i)]$ **Multiply $(x - (1 + i))$ $(x - (1 - i))$.**

$(x - 3)(x^2 - x + ix - x - ix + 1 - i^2)$ **Simplify.**

$(x - 3)(x^2 - x - x + 1 + 1)$

$(x - 3)(x^2 - 2x + 2)$ **Multiply.**

$x^3 - 5x^2 + 8x - 6$

A third-degree polynomial equation with rational coefficients and roots 3
● and $1 + i$ is $x^3 - 5x^2 + 8x - 6 = 0$.

CA Standards Check ⑤ **a.** Find a third-degree polynomial equation with rational coefficients that has roots -1 and $2 - i$.
b. Find a fourth-degree polynomial equation with rational coefficients that has roots i and $2i$.

EXERCISES

Standards Practice

For more exercises, see *Extra Skill and Word Problem Practice*.

ALG2 5.0, 6.0, 8.0

A Practice by Example

Example 1
(page 342)

GO for Help

Use the Rational Root Theorem to list all possible rational roots for each polynomial equation. Then find any actual rational roots.

1. $x^3 - x^2 + 2x - 2 = 0$

2. $x^3 + 4x^2 + x - 6 = 0$

3. $x^3 + x^2 + 4x + 4 = 0$

4. $2x^3 - 9x^2 - 11x + 8 = 0$

5. $x^3 + 2x^2 - 8x - 16 = 0$

6. $x^4 + 2x^2 - 15 = 0$

Example 2
(pages 342–343)

Find the roots of each polynomial equation.

7. $x^3 - 2x^2 + 5x - 10 = 0$

8. $x^3 - 5x^2 + 7x - 35 = 0$

9. $2x^4 - 5x^3 - 17x^2 + 41x - 21 = 0$

10. $4x^3 + 16x^2 - 22x - 10 = 0$

11. $4x^4 - 37x^2 + 9 = 0$

12. $9x^4 + 3x^3 - 30x^2 + 6x + 12 = 0$

Examples 3 and 4
(pages 343 and 344)

A polynomial equation with rational coefficients has the given roots. Find two additional roots.

13. $\sqrt{5}$ and $-\sqrt{13}$

14. $4 - \sqrt{6}$ and $\sqrt{3}$

15. $1 - \sqrt{10}$ and $2 + \sqrt{2}$

16. $1 + i$ and $-5i$

17. $2 + 3i$ and $6i$

18. $4 - i$ and $3 + 7i$

Example 5
(page 344)

Find a third-degree polynomial equation with rational coefficients that has the given numbers as roots.

19. 1 and $3i$

20. -5 and $1 - i$

21. 2 and $-4i$

22. $3 + i$ and -3

23. $-2i$ and 6

24. -1 and $i + 1$

B Apply Your Skills

Use the Rational Root Theorem to list all possible rational roots for each polynomial equation. Then find any actual rational roots.

25. $12x^3 - 32x^2 + 25x - 6 = 0$

26. $10x^3 - 49x^2 + 68x - 20 = 0$

27. $6x^4 - 5x^3 - 65x^2 + 85x - 21 = 0$

28. $8x^3 - 28x^2 + 14x + 15 = 0$

Find a fourth-degree polynomial equation with integer coefficients that has the given numbers as roots.

29. $3 + i$ and $-2i$

30. $\sqrt{3}$ and $1 - i$

31. $3 + \sqrt{2}$ and $\sqrt{5}$

In each equation, *r*, *s*, and *t* represent integers. Indicate whether the statement is *sometimes*, *always*, or *never* true. Explain your answer.

32. A root of the equation $3x^3 + rx^2 + sx + 8 = 0$ is 5.

33. A root of the equation $3x^3 + rx^2 + sx + 8 = 0$ is -2.

34. If a is a root of $x^3 + rx^2 + sx + t = 0$, then a is a factor of t.

35. $\sqrt{5}$ and $-\sqrt{5}$ are roots of $x^3 + rx^2 + sx + t = 0$.

36. $2 + i$ and $-2 - i$ are roots of $x^3 + rx^2 + sx + t = 0$.

37. Multiple Choice A fourth-degree polynomial with integer coefficients has zeros at 1 and $3 + \sqrt{5}$. Which number CANNOT also be a zero of this polynomial?

   Ⓐ 1   Ⓑ -3 Ⓒ $3 - \sqrt{5}$ Ⓓ $3 + \sqrt{2}$

Homework Video Tutor

Visit: PHSchool.com
Web Code: bbe-0605

38. Error Analysis A student claims that $2i$ is the only imaginary root of a polynomial equation that has real coefficients. Explain the student's mistake.

39. Open-Ended Write a fourth-degree polynomial equation with integer coefficients that has two irrational roots and two imaginary roots.

 Challenge

40. a. Using *real* and *imaginary* as types of roots, list all possible combinations of root type for a fourth-degree polynomial equation.
 b. Repeat the process for a fifth-degree polynomial equation.
 c. Make a Conjecture Make a conjecture about the number of real roots of an odd-degree polynomial equation.

41. Writing A student states that $2 + \sqrt{3}$ is a root of $x^2 - 2x - (3 + 2\sqrt{3}) = 0$. The student claims that $2 - \sqrt{3}$ is another root of the equation by the Irrational Root Theorem. Explain how you would respond to the student.

42. What polynomial equation with complex coefficients and no multiple roots has $-4i$ and $2 + 3i$ as its only roots?

43. a. Find a polynomial equation in which $1 + \sqrt{2}$ is the only root.
 b. Find a polynomial equation with root $1 + \sqrt{2}$ of multiplicity 2.
 c. Find c such that $1 + \sqrt{2}$ is a solution of $x^2 - 2x + c = 0$.

Multiple Choice Practice

For California Standards and CAHSEE Tutorials, visit PHSchool.com. Web Code: bbq-9045

ALG2 8.0

44. From the roof of a 30-foot-high building, Gunther threw a ball upward with an initial velocity of 40 feet per second. The table shows the relationship between the time elapsed and the ball's height above the ground. If the height of the ball is a quadratic function of time, between what times did the ball reach a height of 50 feet?

Time (seconds)	Height (feet)
0.0	30
0.5	46
1.0	54
1.5	54
2.0	46
2.5	30

 (A) Between 0 seconds and 0.5 second

 (B) Between 1 second and 1.5 seconds

 (C) Between 0.5 second and 1 second and between 1.5 seconds and 2 seconds

 (D) Between 1 second and 1.5 seconds and between 1.5 seconds and 2 seconds

Mixed Review

Lesson 6-4 Solve each equation.

45. $8x^3 + 27 = 0$ **46.** $x^4 - x^2 - 20 = 0$ **47.** $2x^4 - 50 = 0$

Lesson 5-7 Solve each equation by completing the square.

48. $x^2 - 6x - 7 = 0$ **49.** $p^2 + 4p = -8$ **50.** $4x^2 - 11 = 12x$

Lesson 4-8 Use Cramer's Rule to solve each system.

51. $\begin{cases} -3x + y = -7 \\ 5x + 2y = -3 \end{cases}$ **52.** $\begin{cases} x - 3y = -12 \\ 2x + 7y = 2 \end{cases}$ **53.** $\begin{cases} 2x - 8y = 10 \\ -3x + y = -15 \end{cases}$

6-6

The Fundamental Theorem of Algebra

 California Content Standards

MA 4.0 Students know the statement of, and can apply, the fundamental theorem of algebra.

What You'll Learn

• To use the Fundamental Theorem of Algebra in solving polynomial equations with complex roots

. . . And Why

To find all the zeros of a polynomial function, as in Example 2

✓ Check Skills You'll Need **GO for Help** Lessons 5-8 and 6-1

Find the degree of each polynomial.

1. $3x^2 - x + 5$ **2.** $-x + 3 - x^3$ **3.** $-4x^5 + 1$

Solve each equation using the quadratic formula.

4. $x^2 + 16 = 0$ **5.** $x^2 - 2x + 3 = 0$ **6.** $2x^2 + 5x + 4 = 0$

New Vocabulary • Fundamental Theorem of Algebra

---

1 The Fundamental Theorem of Algebra

> ### Activity: Counting Zeros
>
> In this activity you will find the solutions to polynomial equations, identify the types of solutions, and then count the number of solutions.
>
> **1. a.** Find the solutions of $x^4 - 5x^2 + 4 = 0$.
>   **b.** Identify each solution as *real* or *imaginary*.
>   **c.** How many solutions are there?
>
> **2. a.** Find the solutions of $x^4 + 7x^2 + 12 = 0$.
>   **b.** Identify each solution as *real* or *imaginary*.
>   **c.** How many solutions are there?
>
> **3.** Make a conjecture about the number of zeros of a fourth-degree polynomial function, regardless of the types of zeros.

Real-World Connection

Germany issued this stamp in honor of the bicentennial of the birth of Gauss.

You have solved polynomial equations and found that their roots are included in the set of complex numbers. That is, the roots have been integers, rational numbers, irrational numbers, and imaginary numbers. But can all polynomial equations be solved using complex numbers?

In 1799, the German mathematician Carl Friedrich Gauss (1777–1855) proved that the answer to this question is yes. The roots of every polynomial equation, even those with imaginary coefficients, are complex numbers. The answer is so important that his theorem is called the **Fundamental Theorem of Algebra.**

A corollary to the Fundamental Theorem of Algebra describes the relationship between the degree of a polynomial and the number of zeros of the related polynomial function.

Theorem   **Fundamental Theorem of Algebra**

If $P(x)$ is a polynomial of degree $n \geq 1$ with complex coefficients, then $P(x) = 0$ has at least one complex root.

Corollary

Including complex roots and multiple roots, an nth degree polynomial equation has exactly n roots; the related polynomial function has exactly n zeros.

Vocabulary Tip

A <u>corollary</u> of a theorem is itself a theorem. It may be easily and immediately deduced from the original theorem.

In other words, the corollary says that you can factor a polynomial of degree n into n linear factors. The number n includes multiple roots. For example, the equation $x^3 = 0$ should have three roots by the corollary to the Fundamental Theorem of Algebra. Since $x^3 = 0$ can be rewritten as $x \cdot x \cdot x = 0$ or $(x - 0)(x - 0)(x - 0) = 0$, the equation has three linear factors and three roots, all of which are zero.

1 EXAMPLE   **Using the Fundamental Theorem of Algebra**

For the equation $x^3 + 2x^2 - 4x - 6 = 0$, find the number of complex roots, the possible number of real roots, and the possible rational roots.

By the corollary to the Fundamental Theorem of Algebra, $x^3 + 2x^2 - 4x - 6 = 0$ has three complex roots.

By the Imaginary Root Theorem, the equation has either no imaginary roots or two imaginary roots (one conjugate pair). So the equation has either three real roots or one real root.

By the Rational Root Theorem, the possible rational roots of the equation are $\pm 1, \pm 2, \pm 3,$ and ± 6.

✓ CA Standards Check **1** For the equation $x^4 - 3x^3 + x^2 - x + 3 = 0$, find the number of complex roots, the possible number of real roots, and the possible rational roots.

You can often find all the zeros of a polynomial function by using some combination of graphing, the Factor Theorem, polynomial division, the Remainder Theorem, and the Quadratic Formula.

2 EXAMPLE   **Finding All Zeros of a Polynomial Function**

Find the number of complex zeros of $f(x) = x^3 + x^2 - x + 2$. Find all the zeros.

By the corollary to the Fundamental Theorem of Algebra, there are three complex zeros. You can use synthetic division to find a rational zero.

Step 1 Find a rational root from the possible roots of ± 1 and ± 2. Use synthetic division to test each possible root until you get a remainder of zero.

$$
\begin{array}{r|rrrr}
-2 & 1 & 1 & -1 & 2 \\
   &   & -2 & 2 & -2 \\
\hline
   & 1 & -1 & 1 & 0 \\
   & \downarrow & \downarrow & \downarrow & \\
   & 1x^2 & -1x & +1 &
\end{array}
$$

So -2 is one of the roots.

Step 2 Since the expression $x^2 - x + 1$ cannot be factored, use the Quadratic Formula to solve the related quadratic equation $x^2 - x + 1 = 0$.

$$x = \frac{-b \pm \sqrt{b^2 - 4ac}}{2a}$$

$$x = \frac{-(-1) \pm \sqrt{(-1)^2 - 4(1)(1)}}{2(1)}$$

$$x = \frac{1 \pm \sqrt{-3}}{2}$$

$$x = \frac{1 \pm i\sqrt{3}}{2}$$

The polynomial function $f(x) = x^3 + x^2 - x + 2$ has one real zero of $x = -2$, and two complex zeros of $x = \frac{1 + i\sqrt{3}}{2}$ and $x = \frac{1 - i\sqrt{3}}{2}$.

✓ **CA Standards Check** **2** **a.** Find all zeros of $y = x^3 - 2x^2 + 4x - 8$.
b. Which zeros can you verify on a graphing calculator? Explain.

EXERCISES
Standards Practice

For more exercises, see *Extra Skill and Word Problem Practice*.

MA 4.0

A **Practice by Example**

Example 1
(page 348)

For each equation, state the number of complex roots, the possible number of real roots, and the possible rational roots.

1. $x^3 + 4x^2 + 5x - 1 = 0$ **2.** $3x^2 - 7 = 0$

3. $-x^4 = 0$ **4.** $2x^5 - 4x^4 - 4x^2 + 5 = 0$

5. $x^7 - x^3 - 2x - 3 = 0$ **6.** $4x + 8 = 0$

7. $-2x^6 - x^2 + x - 7 = 0$ **8.** $x^{10} + x^8 - x^4 + 3x^2 - x + 1 = 0$

Example 2
(pages 348–349)

Find all the zeros of each function.

9. $y = 2x^3 + x^2 + 1$ **10.** $f(x) = x^3 - 3x^2 + x - 3$

11. $g(x) = x^3 - 5x^2 + 5x - 4$ **12.** $y = x^3 - 2x^2 - 3x + 6$

13. $y = x^4 - 6x^2 + 8$ **14.** $f(x) = x^4 - 3x^2 - 4$

15. $y = x^3 - 3x^2 - 9x$ **16.** $y = x^3 + 6x^2 + x + 6$

B **Apply Your Skills**

For each equation, state the number of complex roots, the possible number of real roots, and the possible rational roots.

17. $2x^4 - x^3 + 2x^2 + 5x - 26 = 0$ **18.** $x^5 - x^3 - 11x^2 + 9x + 18 = 0$

19. $-12 + x + 10x^2 + 3x^3 = 0$ **20.** $4x^6 - x^5 - 24 = 0$

Find all the zeros of each function.

21. $y = x^3 - 4x^2 + 9x - 36$ **22.** $f(x) = x^3 + 2x^2 - 5x - 10$

23. $y = 2x^3 + 14x^2 + 13x + 6$ **24.** $y = 4x^3 + 9x^2 + 22x + 5$

25. $g(x) = x^3 - \frac{1}{2}x^2 + 20x - 10$ **26.** $y = 15x^3 - x^2 + 3x - 2$

27. Open-Ended Write a polynomial function that has four possible rational zeros but no actual rational zeros.

Homework Video Tutor

Visit: PHSchool.com
Web Code: bbe-0606

Challenge   **Graph each function. Approximate the real zeros to the nearest hundredth.**

28. $f(x) = x^4 + 3x^2 - 2$ **29.** $f(x) = x^4 + 2x^3 - 2x^2 + 4x - 8$

30. Writing Using the Rational Root Theorem, explain why the following statement is false: If a polynomial has no constant term, then the corresponding polynomial equation has only the number 0 as a possible rational root.

31. Critical Thinking Consider a polynomial with integer coefficients in which the leading coefficient is not equal to 1. Can the related polynomial equation have a rational root that is an integer? Explain.

Multiple Choice Practice

For California Standards and CAHSEE Tutorials, visit PHSchool.com. Web Code: bbq-9045

ALG2 5.0   **32.** If $i = \sqrt{-1}$, which point shows the location of $4 - 3i$ on the plane?

    Ⓐ point A Ⓒ point C

    Ⓑ point B Ⓓ point D

ALG2 3.0   **33.** The length of a rectangular backyard can be represented by the expression, $2x^2 - 5x + 3$. The width of the yard is $3x^2 + 4x - 6$. Which of the following expressions best represents the perimeter of the yard?

    Ⓐ $10x^2 - 2x - 6$

    Ⓑ $5x^2 - x - 3$

    Ⓒ $6x^4 - 20x^2 - 18$

    Ⓓ $10x^2 + 2x + 6$

Mixed Review

Lesson 6-5   **34.** Find a fourth-degree polynomial equation with integer coefficients that has $2i$ and $-3 + i$ as roots.

Lesson 5-8   **Solve each equation using the Quadratic Formula.**

35. $x^2 - 6x + 9 = 0$ **36.** $2x^2 + 5x = -9$ **37.** $2(x^2 + 2) = 3x$

Lesson 5-1   **Find a quadratic model for each function.**

38. $f(-1) = 0, f(2) = 3, f(1) = 4$ **39.** $f(-4) = 11, f(-5) = 5, f(-6) = 3$

Permutations and Combinations

 California Content Standards

ALG2 18.0 Students use fundamental counting principles to compute combinations and permutations. *Introduce, Develop*
ALG2 19.0 Students use combinations and permutations to compute probabilities. *Introduce, Develop*

What You'll Learn

- To count permutations
- To count combinations

. . . And Why

To find the number of ways you can vote for candidates as in Example 5

✓ **Check Skills You'll Need**

GO for Help Lesson 1-2

Simplify each expression.

1. $10 \cdot 9 \cdot 8 \cdot 7 \cdot 6$　　　　**2.** $\frac{4 \cdot 3 \cdot 2}{6 \cdot 5}$　　　　**3.** $\frac{7 \cdot 6 \cdot 5 \cdot 4 \cdot 3 \cdot 2 \cdot 1}{4 \cdot 3 \cdot 2 \cdot 1}$

Let $a * b = 2a(a + b)$. Evaluate each expression.

4. $3 * 4$　　　**5.** $2 * 7$　　　**6.** $5 * 1$　　　**7.** $6 * 10$

🔊 **New Vocabulary** • permutation • *n* factorial • combination

---

1 Permutations

A **permutation** is an arrangement of items in a particular order. You can often find the number of permutations of some sets of items by using the Multiplication Counting Principle.

You can use the Multiplication Counting Principle when you plan to choose all of the items of a particular set. Suppose you want to find the number of permutations for three items. There are three ways to choose the first item, two ways to choose the second item, and only one way to choose the third item. By the Multiplication Counting Principle, there are $3 \cdot 2 \cdot 1$ permutations.

Using factorial notation, you can write $3 \cdot 2 \cdot 1$ as 3!, read "three factorial."

🔑 **Key Concepts**

Definition	**n Factorial**

For any positive integer $n, n! = n(n - 1) \cdot \cdots \cdot 3 \cdot 2 \cdot 1$.
For $n = 0, n! = 1$.

Graphing Calculator Hint

To calculate factorials, press MATH and then choose the PRB menu and the ! option.

1 EXAMPLE Finding Permutations

In how many different orders can ten dogs line up to be groomed?

Since all ten dogs are being groomed, you are using all the items from the original set. You can use the Multiplication Counting Principle or factorial notation.

There are ten ways to select the first dog in line, nine ways to select the next dog, and so on. The total number of permutations is $10 \cdot 9 \cdot \cdots \cdot 2 \cdot 1 = 10!$.

$10! = 3,628,800$

● The ten dogs can line up in 3,628,800 different orders.

 1 In how many ways can you arrange six trophies on a shelf?

Some permutations do not use all the items available in a set. You can still use the Multiplication Counting Principle or factorial notation. The relationship between permutations and factorials can be summarized with a formula.

 Key Concepts

Definition   **Number of Permutations**

The number of permutations of n items of a set arranged r items at a time is $_nP_r$.

$$_nP_r = \frac{n!}{(n-r)!} \text{ for } 0 \le r \le n$$

Example $_{10}P_4 = \frac{10!}{(10-4)!} = \frac{10!}{6!} = 5040$

2 EXAMPLE   Real-World Connection

Boating Seven yachts enter a race. First, second, and third places will be given to the three fastest yachts. How many arrangements of first, second, and third places are possible with seven yachts?

Method 1 Use the Multiplication Counting Principle.
$7 \cdot 6 \cdot 5 = 210$

Method 2 Use the permutation formula. Since there are seven yachts arranged three at a time, $n = 7$ and $r = 3$.

$$_7P_3 = \frac{7!}{(7-3)!} = \frac{7!}{4!} = 210$$

● There are 210 possible arrangements of first, second, and third places.

✓ CA Standards Check   **2** How many arrangements of first, second, and third places are possible with ten yachts?

---

2 Combinations

In Example 2, you found the number of ways in which three of seven yachts can finish first, second, and third in a race. Each yacht would have a unique place. Consider a situation in which the three fastest yachts win the race with equal status, that is, without first, second, and third places. In that case, the *order* in which the three winning yachts cross the finish line does not matter. A selection in which order does not matter is a **combination.**

As with permutations, you can calculate the number of combinations of n items chosen r at a time by using a formula.

 Key Concepts

Definition   **Number of Combinations**

The number of combinations of n items of a set chosen r items at a time is $_nC_r$.

$$_nC_r = \frac{n!}{r!(n-r)!} \text{ for } 0 \le r \le n$$

Example $_5C_3 = \frac{5!}{3!(5-3)!} = \frac{5!}{3! \cdot 2!} = \frac{120}{6 \cdot 2} = 10$

CA Standards Check

3 **EXAMPLE** **Finding Combinations**

Evaluate $_{12}C_3$.

$$_{12}C_3 = \frac{12!}{3!(12-3)!}$$ Use the formula $_nC_r = \frac{n!}{r!(n-r)!}$.

$$= \frac{12!}{3! \cdot 9!}$$ Simplify.

$$= \frac{12 \cdot 11 \cdot 10 \cdot 9 \cdot 8 \cdot 7 \cdot 6 \cdot 5 \cdot 4 \cdot 3 \cdot 2 \cdot 1}{3 \cdot 2 \cdot 1 \cdot 9 \cdot 8 \cdot 7 \cdot 6 \cdot 5 \cdot 4 \cdot 3 \cdot 2 \cdot 1}$$ Simplify each factorial.

$$= \frac{12 \cdot 11 \cdot 10}{3 \cdot 2 \cdot 1}$$

$$= 220$$

3 Evaluate each expression.
    a. $_{10}C_5$ **b.** $_8C_2$ **c.** $_{25}C_7$

You can use a graphing calculator to find combinations.

4 **EXAMPLE** **Real-World** **Connection**

Literature A reading list for a course in world literature has 20 books on it. In how many ways can you choose four books to read?

Relate   20 books   chosen   4 books at a time

Define   Let n = total number of books.

         Let r = number of books chosen at a time.

Write $_nC_r = {}_{20}C_4$

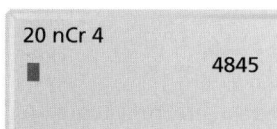

Use the $_nC_r$ feature of your calculator.

You can choose four books in 4845 different ways.

 CA Standards Check   **4** Of the 20 books, in how many ways can you choose seven books? Twelve books?

5 **EXAMPLE** **Real-World** **Connection**

Multiple Choice Ten candidates are running for three seats in the student government. Tom, Ana, and Julio are three of the candidates. What is the probability that Tom, Ana and Julio all win?

   Ⓐ $\frac{1}{6}$ Ⓑ $\frac{1}{120}$ Ⓒ $\frac{1}{176}$ Ⓓ $\frac{1}{216}$

$$_{10}C_3 = \frac{10!}{3!(10-3)!}$$ Use the formula $_nC_r = \frac{n!}{r!(n-r)!}$.

$$= \frac{10!}{3!7!}$$ Simplify.

$$= 120$$

There are 120 possible combinations and only one of them can include Tom, Ana, and Julio. The probability is $\frac{1}{120}$. The correct choice is B.

5 What is the probability that Tom, Ana, and Julio will all win if there are four candidates chosen for four seats?

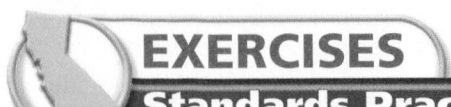

For more exercises, see *Extra Skill and Word Problem Practice*.

Standards Practice   ALG2 18.0, 19.0

A Practice by Example

Example 1
(page 351)

Evaluate each expression.

1. $5!$ **2.** $10!$ **3.** $13!$ **4.** $5!3!$

5. $\dfrac{12!}{6!}$ **6.** $5(4!)$ **7.** $\dfrac{10!}{7!3!}$ **8.** $\dfrac{15!}{10!5!}$

9. Automobiles You should rotate tires on a car at regular intervals.
  a. In how many ways can four tires be arranged on a car?
  b. If the spare tire is included, how many arrangements are possible?

Example 2
(page 352)

Evaluate each expression.

10. $_8P_1$ **11.** $_8P_2$ **12.** $_8P_3$ **13.** $_8P_4$

14. $_3P_2$ **15.** $_5P_4$ **16.** $_9P_6$ **17.** $_5P_3$

18. Fifteen students ask to visit a college admissions counselor. Each visit includes one student. In how many ways can ten time slots be assigned?

19. How many different nine-player batting orders can be chosen from a baseball squad of 16?

20. The prom committee has four sites available for the banquet and three sites for the dance. How many arrangements are possible for the banquet and dance?

Examples 3 and 4
(page 353)

Evaluate each expression.

21. $_6C_2$ **22.** $_8C_5$ **23.** $_4C_4$ **24.** $_4C_3$

25. $_7C_3$ **26.** $3(_5C_4)$ **27.** $_6C_2 + {_6C_3}$ **28.** $\dfrac{_7C_4}{_9C_4}$

29. Sports How many different teams of 11 players can be chosen from a soccer squad of 16?

30. Suppose you find seven articles related to the topic of your research paper. In how many ways can you choose five articles to read?

Example 5
(page 353)

31. You attend band camp with two friends. If roommates are randomly assigned and there are 22 other campers, what is the probability that you and your two friends will room together?

B Apply Your Skills

Assume *a* and *b* are positive integers. Decide whether each statement is *true* or *false*. If it is true, explain why. If it is not true, give a counterexample.

32. $a! + b! = b! + a!$ **33.** $a!(b!c!) = (a!b!)c!$ **34.** $(a + b)! = a! + b!$

35. $(ab)! = a!b!$ **36.** $(a!)! = (a!)^2$ **37.** $(a!)^b = a^{(b!)}$

38. Multiple Choice A car door lock has a five-button keypad. Each button has two numerals. How many different five-button patterns are possible? You can use a button more than once.

The entry code 21914 uses the same button sequence as the code 11023.

  Ⓐ 120   Ⓑ 720   Ⓒ 3125   Ⓓ 5555

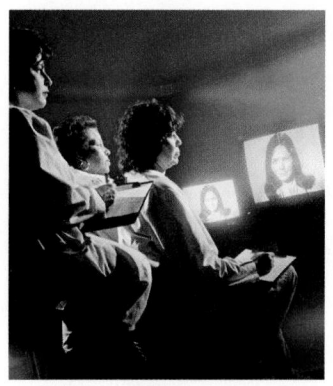

Real-World Connection

Consumer researchers use formulas to compare and rate products.

39. Consumer Issues A consumer magazine rates televisions by identifying two levels of price, five levels of repair frequency, three levels of features, and two levels of picture quality. How many different ratings are possible?

40. Writing In how many ways is it possible to arrange the two numbers a and b in an ordered pair? Explain why such a pair is called an *ordered* pair.

Evaluate each expression.

41. $\dfrac{_{50}C_5}{_{50}C_{10}}$ **42.** $\dfrac{1}{3}(_{10}C_5)$ **43.** $\dfrac{_{25}C_2}{_{50}C_2}$ **44.** $\dfrac{_6C_2}{3}$

Indicate whether each situation involves a combination or a permutation.

45. 5 runners crossing the finish line   **46.** 12 books arranged on a shelf

47. 4 books pulled at random from a shelf

48. 3 flavors of juice selected from a variety pack

How many combinations of four can you make from each set?

49. 300 people in a club   **50.** $\{0, 1, 2, 3, 4, 5, 6, 7, 8, 9\}$

51. 25 baseball cards   **52.** a rose, a daisy, a peony, a daffodil, and a tulip

53. Each line in the MODE screen of a graphing calculator shows two or more choices. In how many different ways can you set the mode of this calculator?

54. a. Geometry Eight points lie on a circle. How many triangles can you make using three of the points as vertices?
  b. How many pentagons can you make using five points as vertices?
  c. Reasoning Explain why your answers to parts (a) and (b) should be the same.

How many four-letter permutations can you form from the letters of each word?

55. MODEL   **56.** EQUATIONS   **57.** LINEAR   **58.** REAL

59. MATRICES   **60.** FORMULA   **61.** CONJUGATES   **62.** SUM

Open-Ended **Write a problem that can be solved using each technique.**

63. the Multiplication Counting Principle   **64.** a single factorial

65. the permutation formula   **66.** the combination formula

67. a. Refer to the cartoon below. How many different sets of answers are possible if the test includes eleven true-or-false questions?
  b. Do you agree with the statement in the last frame? Justify your answer.

68. a. The graph at the right shows the function $y = {}_xC_2$. Use it to graph the function $y = {}_xC_{x-2}$.
   b. Critical Thinking Explain why the graph consists of discrete points rather than a continuous curve.

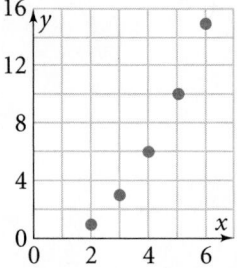

69. a. In how many ways can you choose three flags from a collection of seven different flags?
   b. Once you choose three flags, in how many different orders can you arrange them?
   c. Writing You want to arrange three flags from a group of seven. Explain why ${}_7C_3 \cdot 3!$ is equivalent to the permutation formula.

70. In the sequence $1!, 2!, 3!, 4!, 5!, 6!, \ldots$, the first term that ends with a zero is $5!$.
   a. Explain why $5!$ and all the terms following $5!$ end with a zero.
   b. Find the number of zeros with which $100!$ ends.

71. Find a number n for which entering $n!$ in your calculator causes overflow error.

72. Data Analysis The bar graph at the right shows the results of 40 responses to a survey.
   a. How many people said they squeeze the toothpaste from the middle of the tube?
   b. Use your answer to part (a). Find the number of possible combinations of five people who said they squeeze the toothpaste from the middle of the tube.
   c. Suppose five people are chosen at random from all the people who responded to the survey. How many combinations of five people are possible?
   d. Probability What is the probability that the five people selected at random all squeeze toothpaste from the middle of the tube?

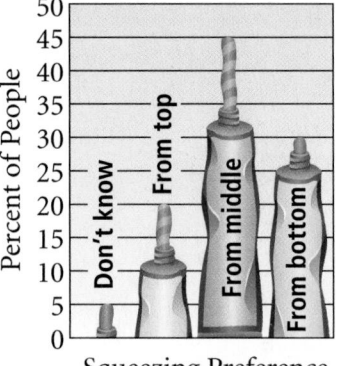

Toothpaste Survey Results

Squeezing Preference

 Multiple Choice Practice

For California Standards and CAHSEE Tutorials, visit PHSchool.com. Web Code: bbq-9045

ALG2 18.0

73. There are 24 students in a science class. They must all give a presentation. The teacher will determine the order of presenters. How many different ways can she assign 5 students to give their presentations on the first day?

   (A) 24   (B) 120   (C) 42,504   (D) 5,100,480

ALG2 10.0

74. Which of the following equations represents the graph shown at the right?

   (A) $y = 2(x + 1)^2 - 1$
   (B) $y = 2(x - 1)^2 - 1$
   (C) $y = 2(x - 1)^2 + 1$
   (D) $y = 2(x + 1)^2 + 1$

Lesson 6-6

75. For the equation $12x^3 - 17x^2 + 3x + 2 = 0$, find the number of complex roots, the possible number of real roots, and the possible rational roots.

76. Find all the zeros of the function $f(x) = x^3 - 2x^2 + 6x - 12$.

Lesson 6-1

Write each polynomial in standard form. Then classify it by degree and by number of terms.

77. $-3x^2 + 6 - x^3$ **78.** $2(x - 1)^2 + 6$ **79.** $t^2 - 3t + 4t^2$

80. $-100 + x^4$ **81.** $x(x + 2)(x - 2)$ **82.** $(t^2 - t)^2$

Lesson 5-4

Factor each expression completely.

83. $4x^2 - 8x + 4$ **84.** $-x^2 - 6x - 9$ **85.** $3x^2 - 75$

Lesson 5-2

Determine whether the function has a maximum or minimum value. Then find the value.

86. $y = x^2 + 4x - 8$ **87.** $y = -2x^2 + 5x + 1$ **88.** $y = 4x^2 - 7$

✓ Checkpoint Quiz 2   Lessons 6-4 through 6-7

Solve each equation.

1. $x^3 - 2x^2 = 5x - 6$ **2.** $27x^3 - 1 = 0$ **3.** $x^4 - 4x^2 - 45 = 0$

Use the Rational Root Theorem to find all the roots of each equation.

4. $2x^3 + x^2 + x - 1 = 0$ **5.** $3x^3 + 4x^2 - 12x - 16 = 0$

6. Two roots of a polynomial equation with real coefficients are $3 - 5i$ and $\sqrt{2}$.
  a. Find two additional roots.
  b. Describe the degree of the polynomial.

7. How many roots does a fifth-degree polynomial equation have? Explain.

8. Evaluate each expression.
  a. $_4\mathrm{P}_3 + {}_6\mathrm{P}_5$ **b.** $_4\mathrm{C}_3 + {}_6\mathrm{C}_5$

9. **Food Preparation** The students at a culinary arts school are learning to prepare seven different items. In how many ways can you choose each number of items?
  a. two items   **b.** three items   **c.** four items   **d.** five items

10. **Advertising** Use the ad and the telephone keypad shown below. Find the last seven digits of this phone number. How many seven-number arrangements can be made with these digits?

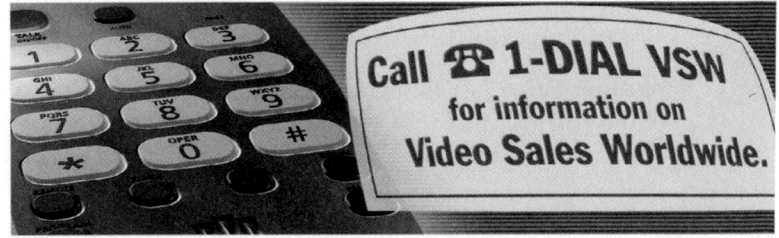

Pascal's Triangle

Activity Lab

ALG2 20.0 Students know the binomial theorem and use it to expand binomial expressions that are raised to positive integer powers. *Introduce*

Suppose you are standing at the corner of the grid shown below (point A1). You are allowed to travel down or to the right only.

The only way you can get to point A2 is by traveling down one unit. You can get to point B1 by traveling to the right one unit. The numbers of ways you can get to points A2, B1, and B2 are written next to these points.

1. The number 2 is written next to point B2. What are the two different ways you can get from point A1 to point B2?

2. Copy the grid. Travel only down or to the right. In how many ways can you get from point A1 to point A3?

3. Use your copy of the grid from Exercise 2. In how many ways can you get from point A1 to point C2?

4. In how many ways can you get to the fountain at point E6 from your starting point at A1?

5. Mark the number of ways you can get to each point from point A1.

6. **Reasoning** Describe any patterns you see in the numbers on the grid.

7. **a.** Make a copy of your completed grid. Color the numbers that are multiples of 2. (You may need to extend the grid to see a pattern.)
   b. The pattern you see in part (a) is called the Sierpinski triangle. Find another way to describe how to obtain this pattern.

8. **Writing** The completed grid is called Pascal's Triangle. Rotate your copy of the grid 45° clockwise so that point A1 is at the top. Explain why the grid is called a triangle.

The Binomial Theorem

 California Content Standards

ALG2 20.0 Students know the binomial theorem and use it to expand binomial expressions that are raised to positive integer powers. *Develop, Master*

What You'll Learn

- To use Pascal's Triangle
- To use the Binomial Theorem

. . . And Why

To find probabilities associated with basketball, as in Example 4

 Check Skills You'll Need

GO for Help Lessons 5-1 and 6-7

Multiply.

1. $(x + 2)^2$ **2.** $(2x + 3)^2$ **3.** $(x - 3)^3$ **4.** $(a + b)^4$

Evaluate.

5. $_5C_0$ **6.** $_5C_1$ **7.** $_5C_2$ **8.** $_5C_3$ **9.** $_5C_4$

🔊 **New Vocabulary** • **expand** • **Pascal's Triangle** • **Binomial Theorem**

---

1   Binomial Expansion and Pascal's Triangle

You have learned to multiply binomials using the FOIL method and the Distributive Property. If you are raising a *single* binomial to a power, you have another option for finding the product.

Consider the expansion of several binomials. To **expand** a binomial being raised to a power, first multiply; then write the result as a polynomial in standard form.

$$(a + b)^2 = (a + b)(a + b) = a^2 + 2ab + b^2$$

$$(a + b)^3 = (a + b)(a + b)(a + b) = a^3 + 3a^2b + 3ab^2 + b^3$$

In the first case, the coefficients of the product are 1, 2, 1. In the second case, they are 1, 3, 3, 1. Notice that each set of coefficients matches a row of **Pascal's Triangle** below. Pascal's Triangle is a triangular array of numbers formed by first lining the border with 1's, and then placing the sum of two adjacent numbers within a row between and underneath the two original numbers.

Coefficients of an Expansion (Pascal's Triangle)

$(a + b)^0$					1				
$(a + b)^1$				1		1			
$(a + b)^2$			1		2		1		
$(a + b)^3$		1		3		3		1	
$(a + b)^4$	1		4		6		4		1
$(a + b)^5$	1	5		10		10		5	1

Real-World Connection

In addition to his famous triangle, Pascal made many contributions to math, physics, and philosophy. In 1642 he built the first mechanical digital calculating machine.

The earliest known version of Pascal's Triangle was developed between 300 and 200 B.C. by the Indian mathematician Halayudha. Although other cultures were aware of the triangle, it has been named for Blaise Pascal (1623–1662), a French mathematician.

Each row of Pascal's Triangle contains coefficients for the expansion of $(a + b)^n$. For example, when $n = 6$, you can find the coefficients for the expansion of $(a + b)^6$ in the row that begins 1, 6, 15, . . .

Pascal's Triangle

```
           1
          1  1
         1  2  1
        1  3  3  1
       1  4  6  4  1
      1  5 10 10  5  1
     1  6 15 20 15  6  1
    1  7 21 35 35 21  7  1
   1  8 28 56 70 56 28  8  1
```

1 EXAMPLE Using Pascal's Triangle

Use Pascal's Triangle to expand $(a + b)^6$.

Use the row that has 6 as its second number.

The exponents for a begin with 6 and decrease to 0.

$$1a^6b^0 + 6a^5b^1 + 15a^4b^2 + 20a^3b^3 + 15a^2b^4 + 6a^1b^5 + 1a^0b^6$$

The exponents for b begin with 0 and increase to 6.

In simplest form, the expansion is
$a^6 + 6a^5b + 15a^4b^2 + 20a^3b^3 + 15a^2b^4 + 6ab^5 + b^6$.

CA Standards Check ① Use Pascal's Triangle to expand $(a + b)^8$.

Sometimes the terms of the binomial have coefficients other than 1. You can still base the expansion to standard form on the pattern for $(a + b)^n$.

2 EXAMPLE Expanding a Binomial

Use Pascal's Triangle to expand $(x - 2)^3$.

First write the pattern for raising a binomial to the third power.

$$\begin{array}{cccc} 1 & 3 & 3 & 1 \end{array} \quad \textbf{coefficients from Pascal's Triangle}$$

$$(a + b)^3 = a^3 + 3a^2b + 3ab^2 + b^3$$

Since $(x - 2)^3 = (x + (-2))^3$, substitute x for a and -2 for b.

$$(x + (-2))^3 = x^3 + 3x^2(-2) + 3x(-2)^2 + (-2)^3$$
$$= x^3 - 6x^2 + 12x - 8$$

The expansion of $(x - 2)^3$ is $x^3 - 6x^2 + 12x - 8$.

CA Standards Check ② Use Pascal's Triangle to expand $(x - 2)^4$.

2 The Binomial Theorem

You can also use combinations to help find the terms of a binomial expansion. For example, if you evaluate the combinations $_4C_0, _4C_1, _4C_2, _4C_3$, and $_4C_4$, you can see a pattern. The results, $1, 4, 6, 4$, and 1 match the row of Pascal's Triangle that you would use to expand $(a + b)^4$. You can use the **Binomial Theorem** as a general formula for expanding a binomial.

Key Concepts

Theorem	Binomial Theorem

For every positive integer n, $(a + b)^n =$
$$_nC_0a^n + _nC_1a^{n-1}b + _nC_2a^{n-2}b^2 + \cdots + _nC_{n-1}ab^{n-1} + _nC_nb^n .$$

Notice that the sequence of exponents decreases for a while it increases for b.

3 EXAMPLE Using the Binomial Theorem

Graphing Calculator Hint

To evaluate a combination, use the MATH feature, the PRB menu, and the $_nC_r$ option.

Use the Binomial Theorem to expand $(g + h)^4$.

Write the pattern for raising a binomial to the fourth power.

$(a + b)^4 = {_4}C_0 a^4 + {_4}C_1 a^3 b + {_4}C_2 a^2 b^2 + {_4}C_3 ab^3 + {_4}C_4 b^4$

Substitute g for a and h for b. Evaluate each combination.

$(g + h)^4 = {_4}C_0 g^4 + {_4}C_1 g^3 h + {_4}C_2 g^2 h^2 + {_4}C_3 gh^3 + {_4}C_4 h^4$
$\qquad = g^4 + 4g^3 h + 6g^2 h^2 + 4gh^3 + h^4$

- The expansion of $(g + h)^4$ is $g^4 + 4g^3 h + 6g^2 h^2 + 4gh^3 + h^4$.

✓ CA Standards Check ③ Use the Binomial Theorem to expand each binomial.
a. $(v + w)^9$ **b.** $(c - 2)^5$

You can use the Binomial Theorem to solve probability problems. Suppose an event has a probability of success p and a probability of failure q. Each term in the expansion of $(p + q)^n$ represents a probability. For example, $_{10}C_2 p^8 q^2$ represents the probability of exactly eight successes in ten trials.

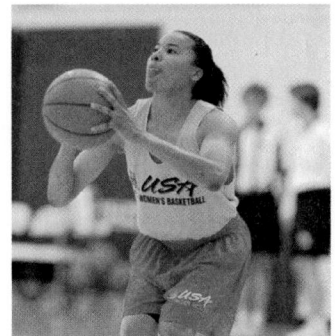

Real-World Connection

WNBA star Dawn Staley made about 90% of the free throws she attempted.

4 EXAMPLE Real-World Connection

Sports Refer to the photo. Assume that Dawn's probability of success on any single shot is the same as her cumulative record. Find the probability that she will make exactly 6 out of 10 consecutive free throws.

Since you want 6 successes (and 4 failures), use the term containing $p^6 q^4$. This term has the coefficient $_{10}C_4$.

Probability (6 out of 10) $= {_{10}}C_4 p^6 q^4$
$\qquad = \dfrac{10!}{4! \cdot 6!} \cdot (0.9)^6 (0.1)^4$ **The probability p of success = 90%, or 0.9.**
$\qquad = 0.011160261$ **Simplify.**

Dawn Staley has about a 1% chance of making exactly 6 out of 10 consecutive free throws.

✓ CA Standards Check ④ **a.** Find the probability that Dawn Staley will make exactly 9 out of 10 consecutive free throw attempts.
b. Find the probability that she will make exactly 10 out of 10 attempts.

EXERCISES

For more exercises, see *Extra Skill and Word Problem Practice*.

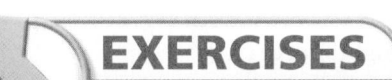

Standards Practice

ALG2 20.0

A Practice by Example

Examples 1 and 2
(page 360)

GO for Help

Use Pascal's Triangle to expand each binomial.

1. $(a + b)^3$ **2.** $(x - y)^2$ **3.** $(a + b)^4$

4. $(x - y)^5$ **5.** $(a - b)^6$ **6.** $(x - y)^7$

7. $(x + y)^8$ **8.** $(d + 1)^9$ **9.** $(x - 3)^3$

10. $(a + 3b)^4$ **11.** $(x - 2)^6$ **12.** $(x - 4)^8$

Example 3
(page 361)

Use the Binomial Theorem to expand each binomial.

13. $(x + y)^4$ **14.** $(w + 1)^5$ **15.** $(s - t)^2$ **16.** $(x - 1)^6$

17. $(x - y)^4$ **18.** $(p + q)^7$ **19.** $(x - 3)^5$ **20.** $(4 - x)^3$

Example 4
(page 361)

21. Probability A coin is tossed ten times. The probability of heads on each toss is 0.5. Evaluate each probability.
  a. exactly 5 heads   **b.** exactly 6 heads   **c.** exactly 7 heads

22. A calculator contains four batteries. With normal use, each battery has a 90% chance of lasting for one year. Find the probability that all four batteries will last a year.

B Apply Your Skills

Expand each binomial.

23. $(x + y)^7$ **24.** $(x - 5y)^8$ **25.** $(3x - y)^4$ **26.** $(x - 4y)^5$

27. $(7 - 2x)^6$ **28.** $(2x + 3y)^3$ **29.** $(x^2 + y^2)^2$ **30.** $(x^2 - 2y)^3$

31. $(x + 1)^6$ **32.** $(x - 1)^6$ **33.** $(x + 2)^5$ **34.** $(x - 2)^5$

35. $(2x + 3y)^4$ **36.** $(3x + 5y)^3$ **37.** $(2x - 2y)^6$ **38.** $(3x + 2y)^4$

39. $(2x + y)^5$ **40.** $(3x + y)^7$ **41.** $(x - 3y)^6$ **42.** $(x + 5y)^3$

43. Genetics A family has five children. Assume that the probability of having a boy is 0.5. Write the term in the expansion of $(b + g)^5$ for each outcome described. Then evaluate each probability.
  a. exactly 3 boys   **b.** exactly 4 boys   **c.** exactly 4 girls

44. In the expansion of $(m + n)^9$, one of the terms contains m^3.
  a. What is the exponent of n in this term?
  b. What is the coefficient of this term?

45. Suppose ${}_8C_3 x^5 y^3$ is a term of a binomial expansion. Write the next term.

46. The term $126c^4d^5$ appears in the expansion of $(c + d)^n$. Find n.

47. The coefficient of the second term in the expansion of $(r + s)^n$ is 7. Find the value of n, and write the complete term.

Find the specified term of each binomial expansion.

48. Third term of $(x + 3)^{12}$ **49.** Fourth term of $(x + 2)^5$

50. Second term of $(x + 3)^9$ **51.** Third term of $(x - 2)^{12}$

52. Twelfth term of $(2 + x)^{11}$ **53.** Seventh term of $(x - 2y)^6$

54. Eighth term of $(x - 2y)^{15}$ **55.** Third term of $(3x - 2)^9$

56. Seventh term of $(x^2 - 2y)^{11}$ **57.** Eighth term of $(x^2 + y^2)^{13}$

58. Writing Explain why the terms of $(a - 4)^6$ have alternating positive and negative signs.

59. Geometry A cube has sides of length s. Suppose each of the dimensions of the cube is increased by 0.5.
  a. Write a binomial expression for the volume of the new cube.
  b. Expand the binomial.

60. Error Analysis A student claims that ${}_7C_5 p^2 q^4$ is a term in a binomial expansion. Explain the student's error.

Real-World **Connection**

Worldwide, about 51.4% of babies born are male.

Homework Video Tutor

State the number of terms in each expansion and give the first two terms.

61. $(d + e)^{12}$ **62.** $(x - y)^{15}$ **63.** $(2a + b)^5$ **64.** $(x - 3y)^7$

 Challenge

65. a. Expand $(1 + i)^4$.
     b. Verify that $1 - i$ is a fourth root of -4 by repeating the process in part (a) for $(1 - i)^4$.

66. Verify that $-1 + \sqrt{3}i$ is a cube root of 8 by expanding $(-1 + \sqrt{3}i)^3$.

67. Open-Ended Write a probability problem for which $_5C_3(0.5)^2(0.5)^3$ is the solution.

68. a. Show that $(k + 1)! = (k + 1) \cdot k!$.
     b. Show that $_nC_k + {_nC_{k + 1}} = {_{n + 1}C_{k + 1}}$.
     c. Suppose $n = 4$ and $k = 2$. What entries in Pascal's Triangle are represented by $_nC_k$, $_nC_{k + 1}$, and $_{n + 1}C_{k + 1}$? Verify that the equation in part (b) is true for these entries.

 Multiple Choice Practice

For California Standards and CAHSEE Tutorials, visit PHSchool.com. Web Code: bbq-9045

ALG2 20.0

69. A cube has sides of length $a - 3$. Which of the following expressions best represents the volume of the cube?
     Ⓐ $a^3 + 9a^2 + 27a - 27$ Ⓒ $a^3 + 9a^2 + 27a + 27$
     Ⓑ $a^3 - 9a^2 + 27a + 27$ Ⓓ $a^3 - 9a^2 + 27a - 27$

ALG2 9.0

70. The equation of the parabola at the right is $y = x^2$. How would the parabola change if the equation became $y = (x - 4)^2$?
     Ⓐ The parabola would shift 4 units to the left.
     Ⓑ The parabola would shift 4 units to the right.
     Ⓒ The parabola would shift 4 units up.
     Ⓓ The parabola would shift 4 units down.

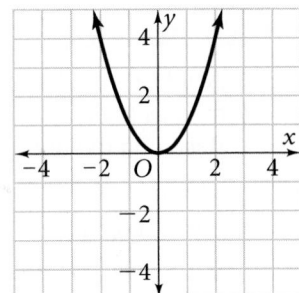

Mixed Review

GO for Help

Lesson 6-7

Simplify each expression.

71. $_5P_2$ **72.** $4!$ **73.** $_7C_3$

74. $11!$ **75.** $\dfrac{7!}{3!(7 - 3)!}$ **76.** $_5C_2 + {_5C_3}$

Lesson 6-2

Find the relative maximum, relative minimum, and zeros of each function.

77. $f(x) = x^3 - 2x^2 - 11x + 12$ **78.** $f(x) = -x^3 - x^2 + 25x + 25$

Lesson 5-3

Write each function in vertex form.

79. $y = x^2 - 6x + 2$ **80.** $y = x^2 + 7x - 1$ **81.** $y = -4x^2 + 9$

A picture or a graph can help you solve a problem. If a problem does not already have a diagram, you can draw one.

1 EXAMPLE

How does the graph of $y = \frac{1}{2}x^2 + 4$ differ from the graph $y = \frac{1}{2}x^2 - 3$?

- Ⓐ The graph of $y = \frac{1}{2}x^2 + 4$ is 7 units to the left of the graph of $y = \frac{1}{2}x^2 - 3$.
- Ⓑ The graph of $y = \frac{1}{2}x^2 + 4$ is 7 units to the right of the graph of $y = \frac{1}{2}x^2 - 3$.
- Ⓒ The graph of $y = \frac{1}{2}x^2 + 4$ is 7 units below the graph of $y = \frac{1}{2}x^2 - 3$.
- Ⓓ The graph of $y = \frac{1}{2}x^2 + 4$ is 7 units above the graph of $y = \frac{1}{2}x^2 - 3$.

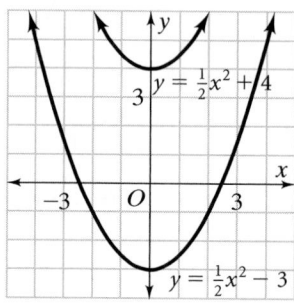

You can use what you know about the family of quadratic functions, or you can graph both functions on the same coordinate grid, as shown at the right. The graph of $y = \frac{1}{2}x^2 + 4$ is 7 units above the graph of $y = \frac{1}{2}x^2 - 3$. The correct answer is D.

2 EXAMPLE

Ariel tosses a ball into the air. The function $h = -16t^2 + 18t + 3$ models the height of a ball h, in feet, in terms of time t, in seconds. Based on the model, which of the following is true?

- Ⓐ The ball will be in the air for more than 2 seconds.
- Ⓑ The ball will not reach a height of 15 feet.
- Ⓒ The ball will reach its greatest height after 1 second.
- Ⓓ The ball will reach a height of 25 feet.

Graph the function. The ball reaches a maximum height of about 8 feet after about 0.5 second. The ball lands before 1.5 seconds, so B is the correct answer.

EXERCISES

Use a diagram to answer each question.

1. What are the slope m and y-intercept b of a line that contains the point $(-3, 3)$ and has the same y-intercept as the line $2x + 5y = 10$?

- Ⓐ $m = 3$
  $b = -2$
- Ⓑ $m = \frac{1}{3}$
  $b = 2$
- Ⓒ $m = -\frac{1}{3}$
  $b = 2$
- Ⓓ $m = -3$
  $b = 2$

2. The rectangle $PQRS$ has coordinates $P(3, 5)$, $Q(7, 5)$, $R(7, -2)$, and $S(3, -2)$. If $PQRS$ is rotated $90°$ clockwise around Q to form rectangle $P'Q'R'S'$, what are the coordinates of R'?

- Ⓐ $(7, 9)$
- Ⓑ $(0, 9)$
- Ⓒ $(14, 5)$
- Ⓓ $(0, 5)$

Chapter 6 Review

Vocabulary Review

◀)) **English and Spanish Audio Online**

Binomial Theorem (p. 360)
combination (p. 352)
conjugates (p. 343)
degree (p. 313)
degree of a polynomial (p. 313)
difference of cubes (p. 334)
expand (p. 359)
Factor Theorem (p. 321)

Fundamental Theorem of Algebra
(p. 347)
Imaginary Root Theorem (p. 344)
Irrational Root Theorem (p. 343)
multiple zero (p. 322)
multiplicity (p. 322)
n factorial (p. 351)
Pascal's Triangle (p. 359)
permutation (p. 351)

polynomial (p. 313)
polynomial function (p. 313)
Rational Root Theorem (p. 341)
relative maximum (p. 321)
relative minimum (p. 321)
Remainder Theorem (p. 329)
standard form of a polynomial (p. 313)
sum of cubes (p. 334)
synthetic division (p. 327)

Choose the correct vocabulary word or phrase to complete each sentence.

1. The exponent of the variable in a term determines its __?__.

2. The __?__ has terms written in descending order by degree.

3. The number of appearances of a zero of a polynomial function describes the __?__ of that zero.

4. The numbers $a + bi$ and $a - bi$ are called __?__.

5. Order is not important when counting __?__.

For: Vocabulary quiz
Web Code: bbj-0651

Skills and Concepts

Lesson 6-1

• To classify polynomials (p. 312)
• To model data using polynomial functions (p. 314)

 ALG2 3.0

A **polynomial** is a monomial or a sum of monomials with whole-number exponents. The exponent of the variable in a term is the **degree** of that term. The **degree of a polynomial** is the greatest degree of any term of the polynomial. When the terms of a polynomial are in descending order by degree, the polynomial is in standard form. You can classify a polynomial by the number of terms it contains or by its degree. A **polynomial function** in one variable can be written in the form $P(x) = a_n x^n + a_{n-1} x^{n-1} + \ldots + a_1 x + a_0$, where $n \geq 0$ and the coefficients $a_n, \ldots, a_0$ are complex numbers.

You can use a calculator to find cubic or quartic polynomial functions to model data, just as you have done with linear and quadratic polynomial functions.

Write each polynomial in standard form. Then classify it by degree and by number of terms.

6. $p^3 - 2p + 2p^3$ **7.** $3 - 5x^9$ **8.** $x - x^3 - x^5$

9. $3x + 2x^2 - x + 4x^3$ **10.** $5 + x + x^4 - x^2 + x^7$ **11.** s

12. Find both a cubic and a quartic model for the set of values. Graph each model. Compare the two models to determine which is a better fit.

x	1.2	1.4	1.6	1.8	2.0	2.2
y	3.1	−4.2	4.1	7.5	−8.9	10

Lessons 6-2 and 6-3

- To analyze the factored form of a polynomial (p. 319)
- To write a polynomial function from its zeros (p. 321)
- To divide polynomials using long division (p. 326)
- To divide polynomials using synthetic division (p. 327)

 ALG2 10.0, 3.0

A polynomial can be factored into linear factors. The **Factor Theorem** states that the expression $x - a$ is a linear factor of a polynomial if and only if a is a zero of the related polynomial function. Then a is an x-intercept of the polynomial function and is a solution of the related polynomial equation.

If the zeros of a polynomial function are known, a polynomial function can be determined by finding the product of the corresponding linear factors. If $x - a$ is repeated as a factor k times, then a is a **multiple zero** of the polynomial—a zero of **multiplicity** k.

When you consider only neighboring points on a graph, the greatest y-value occurs at a **relative maximum** and the least y-value occurs at a **relative minimum.**

You can divide a polynomial by one of its factors to find another factor. When you divide by a linear factor, you can simplify this division by writing only the coefficients of each term. This process is called **synthetic division**. The **Remainder Theorem** guarantees that $P(a)$ is the remainder when $P(x)$ is divided by $x - a$.

Write each polynomial function in factored form. List the zeros of the function, and their multiplicity. Find any relative maximum or relative minimum values. Round to the nearest hundredth if necessary.

13. $f(x) = x^3 - x^2 - 12x$ **14.** $g(x) = 4 - x^2$ **15.** $y = x^3(x + 2)^4$

Write a polynomial function in standard form with the given zeros.

16. $-3, -2, 0, 2$ **17.** $1, 1, 2$ **18.** $-3, 0, 0, 1$ **19.** $-2, -2, -2$

Divide. Use both long division and synthetic division. Show your work.

20. $(x^3 + 3x^2 - 2x - 4) \div (x - 2)$ **21.** $(x^4 - x + 2) \div (x + 1)$

Use synthetic division and the given factor to completely factor each polynomial.

22. $x^3 - 3x^2 - x + 3; x + 1$ **23.** $x^3 - 4x^2 - 3x + 18; x - 3$

Use synthetic division and the Remainder Theorem to find $P(a)$.

24. $P(x) = x^4 + x^3 - x^2 - 2x; a = 3$ **25.** $P(x) = 4 - x - x^5; a = 2$

26. $P(x) = 5x^4 - x^2 + 1; a = -2$ **27.** $P(x) = x^3 - 8x^2 + 5x - 7; a = 1$

Lesson 6-4

- To solve polynomial equations by graphing (p. 333)
- To solve polynomial equations by factoring (p. 334)

 ALG2 4.0

You can solve polynomial equations by graphing or by factoring. The **sum of cubes** and the **difference of cubes** have factor formulas. Sometimes you can factor polynomial expressions of higher degree by rewriting the expression in the standard form of a quadratic equation.

Solve each equation by graphing. If necessary, round to the nearest hundredth.

28. $x^3 - 4x^2 + 5 = 0$ **29.** $x - 3 = 4 - x^2 + x^3$ **30.** $x^3 + x = 3x^2 - 3x^3$

31. $x^3 + x + 5 = 0$ **32.** $-5 = 2 - x^2 + x^3$ **33.** $x^3 + 4 = x^3 - 3x^2$

Factor the expression on the left side of each equation. Then solve each equation.

34. $x^3 - 8 = 0$ **35.** $4t^6 - t^4 = 0$ **36.** $8x^3 + 1 = 0$

37. $x^3 - 5x^2 + 4x = 0$ **38.** $x^3 - 2x^2 - 5x = 0$ **39.** $x^6 + 16x^3 + 64 = 0$

Lessons 6-5 and 6-6

- To solve equations using the Rational Root Theorem (p. 341)
- To use the Irrational Root Theorem and the Imaginary Root Theorem (p. 343)
- To use the Fundamental Theorem of Algebra in solving polynomial equations with complex roots (p. 347)

 ALG2 5.0, 6.0, 8.0, MA 4.0

The **Rational Root Theorem** identifies all possible rational roots of a polynomial equation with integer coefficients. A rational root of a polynomial equation is the quotient of a factor of the constant term and a factor of the leading coefficient.

Number pairs of the form $a + \sqrt{b}$ and $a - \sqrt{b}$ are called **conjugates,** while those of the form $a + bi$ and $a - bi$ are called **complex conjugates.** The **Irrational Root Theorem** states that irrational roots of a polynomial equation with rational coefficients occur in conjugate pairs. Similarly, the **Imaginary Root Theorem** states that imaginary roots of a polynomial equation with real coefficients occur in complex conjugate pairs.

The **Fundamental Theorem of Algebra** and its corollary assert that an nth degree polynomial equation, where $n \geq 1$, has exactly n complex roots.

For each equation, state the number of complex roots, the possible number of real roots, and the possible rational roots. Then find all the roots.

40. $x^3 - 6x^2 + 11x - 6 = 0$

41. $10x^4 - 13x^3 - 21x^2 + 10x + 8 = 0$

42. $x^4 - 6x^2 + 7 = 0$

43. $x^4 + 6x^3 + 13x^2 + 12x + 4 = 0$

44. $x^3 - 3x^2 + x + 5 = 0$

45. $x^4 - 2x^3 - 7x^2 + 18x - 18 = 0$

Write a polynomial equation of least possible degree, with integer coefficients, that has the given numbers as roots.

46. $2, i, -i$

47. $4 + \sqrt{2}, 4 - \sqrt{3}$

48. $3 + i, 2 - i$

49. $0, -2i, 3 + \sqrt{2}$

50. $1 + 2i, 3 - \sqrt{3}$

51. $\sqrt{5}, -\sqrt{7}$

Lessons 6-7 and 6-8

- To count permutations (p. 351)
- To count combinations (p. 352)
- To use Pascal's Triangle (p. 359)
- To use the Binomial Theorem (p. 360)

 ALG2 18.0, 19.0, 20.0

The notation $n!$, read **"n factorial,"** means $n(n - 1)(n - 2) \cdot \ldots \cdot 3 \cdot 2 \cdot 1$, and $0! = 1$.

A **permutation** is an arrangement of items in a particular order. You can count permutations using the Multiplication Counting Principle or factorial notation. To compute the number of permutations of n objects chosen r at a time, you can also use the formula $_nP_r = \frac{n!}{(n - r)!}$, for $0 \leq r \leq n$.

A selection in which order does not matter is a **combination.** The number of combinations of n objects chosen r at a time is $_nC_r = \frac{n!}{r!(n - r)!}$, for $0 \leq r \leq n$.

Use the **Binomial Theorem** to **expand** a binomial raised to a power. For $n \geq 0$, $(a + b)^n = {_nC_0}a^n + {_nC_1}a^{n - 1}b + {_nC_2}a^{n - 2}b^2 + \ldots + {_nC_{n - 1}}ab^{n - 1} + {_nC_n}b^n$. The coefficients in the expansion of $(a + b)^n$ are found in **Pascal's Triangle.** You can also use the Binomial Theorem to find probabilities when an event has only two possible outcomes.

Evaluate each expression.

52. $3(4!)$ **53.** $_4P_3$ **54.** $_7C_4$ **55.** $_5P_2 + {_5C_3}$ **56.** $\frac{_6C_3}{_5C_3}$

57. In how many ways can you arrange 5 different canisters in a row on a shelf?

58. Find the fourth term in the binomial expansion of $(2x + 3y)^6$.

59. A coin is tossed seven times. Find the probability of getting exactly four heads.

Chapter 6 Test

Go Online PHSchool.com For: Chapter test Web Code: bba-0652

Write each polynomial in standard form. Then classify it by degree and by number of terms.

1. $3x^2 - 7x^4 + 9 - x^4$

2. $11x^2 + \frac{3}{8}x - 3x^2$

3. $2x(x - 3)(x + 2)$

4. $(t - 2)(t + 1)(t + 1)$

Graph each function. Approximate the real zeros to the nearest hundredth.

5. $P(x) = -x^3 - x^2 + x$

6. $P(x) = (x + 1)(x + 2)(x^2 + 4x - 5)$

7. $f(x) = x^4 + 3x^3 - 1$

8. $g(x) = -x^6 - x^3 + 2$

9. $f(x) = x^3 - 3x^2 + 2$

Write a polynomial function with rational coefficients in standard form with the given zeros.

10. $x = 1, 2, \frac{3}{5}$

11. $x = -2, 0, \sqrt{3}$

12. $x = -4, -4, -4$

13. $x = -1, 1, 1$

14. $x = \sqrt{2}, -i$

15. $x = 3 + i, 1 - \sqrt{5}$

16. Open-Ended Write a polynomial function with real coefficients that has an imaginary zero and an irrational zero.

Solve each equation.

17. $(2x - 3)(3x + 2)(x + 2)(x + 2)\left(x - \frac{7}{8}\right) = 0$

18. $(x^2 - 3)(x^2 + 3x - 4) = 0$

19. $\left(x + \frac{2}{3}\right)(x^2 + 5x + 1) = 0$

20. $x^3 - 2x^2 + x = 0$

21. $x^3 + 3x^2 - 5x - 4 = 0$

Divide using long division.

22. $(x^2 + 3x - 4) \div (x - 1)$

23. $(x^3 + 7x^2 - 5x - 6) \div (x + 2)$

Divide using synthetic division.

24. $(3x^2 - 3x + 4) \div (x + 1)$

25. $(x^3 + x^2 + x - 14) \div (x + 2)$

Use synthetic division and the Remainder Theorem to find $P(a)$.

26. $P(x) = 6x^4 + 19x^3 - 2x^2 - 44x - 24; a = \frac{-2}{3}$

27. $P(x) = -x^3 - x^2 + x; a = 0$

28. $P(x) = 2x^3 - 2x^2 - 12x; a = 3$

29. $P(x) = x^4 + 3x^3 - 7x^2 - 9x + 12; a = 3$

30. $P(x) = x^3 + 3x^2 - 5x - 4; a = -1$

Evaluate each expression.

31. $6!$

32. $\frac{6!}{4!2!}$

33. $_7C_3$

34. $_5P_2$

35. $_{11}P_9$

36. $_9C_8$

37. $2(_5C_4) - _3C_2$

Indicate whether each situation involves a combination or a permutation. Then solve.

38. How many ways are there to select five actors from a troupe of nine to improvise a scene?

39. How many different three-student study groups can be formed from a class of 15?

40. You are looking for a new apartment. There are five apartments available. In how many ways can you inspect the apartments?

Use the Binomial Theorem to expand each binomial.

41. $(x + z)^5$

42. $(1 - 2t)^2$

43. A weighted coin has $P(\text{heads}) = \frac{2}{5}$. The coin is tossed seven times. Find the probability of getting exactly six heads.

44. Writing Describe how to use combinations to produce row n of Pascal's Triangle.

45. Geometry The volume V of a prism is modeled by $V = 2\ell^3 - 2\ell$, where ℓ is the length of the prism. The width of the prism equals $\ell - 1$. Find the height of the prism.

Standards Mastery

Cumulative Practice

Some problems require you to simplify expressions with imaginary numbers.

Which is equivalent to $(3 - 4i)(2 + i)$?

- Ⓐ $2 - 5i$
- Ⓑ $2 + 5i$
- Ⓒ $10 - 5i$
- Ⓓ $10 + 5i$

Tip 2
Recall that $i^2 = -1$.

Think It Through

$(3 - 4i)(2 + i) =$

$3(2) + 3i - 8i - 4i^2 =$

$6 - 5i - 4(-1) =$

$10 - 5i$

The correct answer is C.

Tip 1
When multiplying binomials, you should use FOIL.

Vocabulary Review

As you solve problems, you must understand the meanings of mathematical terms. Match each term with its mathematical meaning.

A. conjugates

B. synthetic division

C. complex conjugates

D. permutation

E. relative maximum

F. polynomial

I. the process of dividing a polynomial by a linear factor by omitting all variables and exponents and using addition

II. number pairs of the form $a + bi$ and $a - bi$

III. a monomial or the sum of monomials

IV. the greatest value of the points in a region of the graph

V. number pairs of the form $a + \sqrt{b}$ and $a - \sqrt{b}$

VI. an arrangement of items in a particular order

Multiple Choice

Read each question. Then write the letter of the correct answer on your paper.

1. All 385 tickets for the Jefferson High School spring play sold in 10 days. The ticket receipts totaled $1960. If the cost of an adult ticket was $6 and the cost of a child's ticket was $4, how many adult tickets were sold? **(Lesson 3-2)**

   - Ⓐ 175
   - Ⓑ 210
   - Ⓒ 350
   - Ⓓ 385

2. Carson had 22 coins in dimes and quarters. Their total value was $4.15. He wrote a system of equations to represent this situation, letting x represent the number of dimes and y represent the number of quarters. Then he solved the system by graphing. What is the solution? **(Lesson 3-1)**

   - Ⓐ $(8, 14)$
   - Ⓑ $(9, 13)$
   - Ⓒ $(14, 8)$
   - Ⓓ $(13, 9)$

3. Which statement is true about this system of linear equations? $\begin{cases} 3x - 4y = 12 \\ 6x - 8y = 12 \end{cases}$ **(Lesson 3-1)**

   - Ⓐ The solution is $(0, -1)$.
   - Ⓑ The solution is $(8, 4)$.
   - Ⓒ There is no solution because the lines are parallel.
   - Ⓓ There are infinitely many solutions because the lines are the same.

4. Tia deposited x dollars in a bank account that paid 4% simple interest. She also deposited y dollars in a bank account that paid 8% simple interest. The system $\begin{cases} 0.04x + 0.08y = 240 \\ 0.04x = 0.08y \end{cases}$ represents one year's interest on Tia's deposits. Based on the solution of the system of equations, which of the following can be concluded? **(Lesson 3-2)**

- Ⓐ Tia deposited $3000 in each account, and the amounts of interest earned were $240 and $120.
- Ⓑ Tia deposited $3000 in each account, and the interest earned in each account was $120.
- Ⓒ The deposit amounts were $3000 and $1500, and the amounts of interest earned were $240 and $120.
- Ⓓ The deposit amounts were $3000 and $1500, and the amount of interest earned in each account was $120.

5. Which point corresponds to a zero of the function $f = x^2 + 2x - 15$? **(Lesson 5-2)**

- Ⓐ $(0, -15)$
- Ⓒ $(-5, 0)$
- Ⓑ $(0, -13)$
- Ⓓ $(-3, 0)$

6. Which is true about the graph of $y = x^2 + 4x + 4$? **(Lesson 5-2)**

- Ⓐ The only x-intercept is -2.
- Ⓑ The only x-intercept is 2.
- Ⓒ The x-intercepts are 2 and -2.
- Ⓓ There are no x-intercepts.

7. Which is true about the graph of $y = x^2 + 2x + 8$? **(Lesson 5-2)**

- Ⓐ The only x-intercept is 2.
- Ⓑ The only x-intercept is 4.
- Ⓒ The x-intercepts are 2 and 4.
- Ⓓ There are no x-intercepts.

8. The total area of the parallelogram below is $4x^4 + 3x^3 - 14x^2 + 33x - 35$. Which of the following expressions best represents the length of the parallelogram? **(Lesson 6-3)**

- Ⓐ $x^3 + 2x^2 - x + 7$
- Ⓑ $x^3 - 2x^2 + x - 7$
- Ⓒ $4x^4 + 3x^3 - 14x^2 + 33x - 7$
- Ⓓ $x^3 + 5x^2 - x + 5$

9. The length of a photo is $2x^2 - x + 5$ and the width is $3x + 3$. Which polynomial represents the area? **(Lesson 6-2)**

- Ⓐ $6x^3 - 3x^2 + 15x$
- Ⓑ $6x^3 - 3x^2 - 12x - 15$
- Ⓒ $6x^2 - 3x + 15$
- Ⓓ $6x^3 + 3x^2 + 12x + 15$

10. The balance in Mario's bank account can be represented by $4x^4 - 3x^2 + 5x + 9$. If he makes a withdrawal of $2x^4 - 7x^3 + 6x^2 + x - 11$, which polynomial represents his new balance? **(Lesson 6-1)**

- Ⓐ $6x^4 - 7x^3 + 3x^2 + 6x - 20$
- Ⓑ $2x^4 + 7x^3 - 9x^2 + 4x + 20$
- Ⓒ $2x^4 - 7x^3 - 9x^2 + 4x - 20$
- Ⓓ $6x^4 + 7x^3 - 3x^2 + 6x + 20$

11. Katheryn wants to create several different passwords for her computer. She wants to use arrangements of the letters of her name. How many different 5-letter passwords can she create? **(Lesson 6-7)**

- Ⓐ 40
- Ⓑ 56
- Ⓒ 6,720
- Ⓓ 40,320

12. Manuel owns 8 baseball hats and 10 sweatshirts. He's packing for a trip and wants to bring 3 hats and 4 sweatshirts. How many ways can he choose what to pack ? **(Lesson 6-7)**

- Ⓐ 12
- Ⓑ 80
- Ⓒ 5,040
- Ⓓ 11,760

13. What are the factors of $8w^3 + 27z^3$? **(Lesson 6-4)**

- Ⓐ $(2w + 3z)(2w + 3z)(2w + 3z)$
- Ⓑ $(2w - 3z)(4w^2 + 8wz + 9z^2)$
- Ⓒ $(2w - 3z)(4w^2 + 6wz + 9z^2)$
- Ⓓ $(2w + 3z)(4w^2 - 6wz + 9z^2)$

14. The total cost of $x + 2$ pens is $x^3 + 5x^2 + 2x - 8$. What is the cost of each pen? **(Lesson 6-4)**

- Ⓐ $x^2 + 3x - 4$
- Ⓑ $x^2 - 3x + 4$
- Ⓒ $x^2 - 3x - 4$
- Ⓓ $x^2 + 5x + 2$

15. What are the factors of $2x^3 + 5x^2 - 22x + 15$? (Lesson 6-4)

  A) $(2x - 3)(x + 5)(x - 1)$

  B) $(2x + 3)(x + 5)(x - 1)$

  C) $(2x + 3)(x + 5)(x + 1)$

  D) $(2x - 3)(x - 5)(x - 1)$

16. What is the product of the complex numbers $(6 + 2i)$ and $(5 - i)$? (Lesson 5-6)

  A) 30

  B) $32 + 4i$

  C) $30 - 2i$

  D) $11 + i$

17. What is an equivalent form of $\dfrac{5}{2 + 2i}$? (Lesson 5-6)

  A) $\dfrac{5}{4i}$

  B) $\dfrac{10 - 10i}{4 - 4i}$

  C) $\dfrac{5 + 5i}{4}$

  D) $\dfrac{5 - 5i}{4}$

18. If $i = \sqrt{-1}$, then what is the product of $6i$ and $(3 + i)$? (Lesson 5-6)

  A) $12i$

  B) $24i$

  C) $18i - 6$

  D) $18i + 6$

19. What are the solutions to the equation $6 - \dfrac{2}{x^2} = \dfrac{4}{x}$? (Lesson 5-8)

  A) $x = 1, x = -\dfrac{1}{3}$

  B) $x = 1, x = -1$

  C) $x = -1, x = \dfrac{1}{3}$

  D) $x = \dfrac{1}{3}, x = -\dfrac{1}{3}$

20. What are the solutions to the equation $x^2 - 6x + 12 = 0$? (Lesson 5-7)

  A) $x = 4i\sqrt{3}, x = 2i\sqrt{3}$

  B) $x = 3 + i\sqrt{3}, x = 3 - i\sqrt{3}$

  C) $x = i, x = -i$

  D) $x = 3 + 2i\sqrt{3}, x = 3 - 2i\sqrt{3}$

21. Soledad found that one root of the quadratic equation $0 = x^2 - 3x - 108$ is -9. What is the other root of the equation? (Lesson 5-7)

  A) -3

  B) 3

  C) -12

  D) 12

Standards Reference Guide

California Content Standard	Item Number(s)
ALG2 2.0	1–4
ALG2 10.0	5–7
ALG2 3.0	8–10
ALG2 18.0	11–12
ALG2 4.0	13–15
ALG2 6.0	16–18
ALG2 8.0	19–21

For additional review and practice, see the *California Standards Review and Practice Workbook* or go online to use the

California Standards Tutorials

Visit: PHschool.com, **Web Code:** bbq-9045

CHAPTER 7

Radical Functions and Rational Exponents

 ## What You've Learned

California Content Standards

3.0 Students are adept at operations on polynomials, including long division.

4.0 Students factor polynomials representing the difference of squares, perfect square trinomials, and the sum and difference of two cubes.

6.0 Students add, subtract, multiply, and divide complex numbers.

✓ Check Your Readiness

GO▷ for Help to the Lesson in green.

Multiplying Binomials (Lesson 6-2)

Multiply.

1. $(3y - 2)(y - 4)$ **2.** $(7a + 10)(7a - 10)$ **3.** $(x - 3)(x + 6)(x + 1)$

Simplifying Exponential Expressions (Skills Handbook p. 892)

Simplify each expression. Use only positive integer exponents.

4. $(3x^3)^2$ **5.** $(2b^{-2})(4b^5)$ **6.** $(xy^{-3})^2$ **7.** $\dfrac{18a^2}{3a^{-4}}$ **8.** $\dfrac{4ab^{-3}}{6a^2b^3}$

Solving by Factoring (Lessons 5-5 and 6-4)

Solve each equation by factoring.

9. $x^2 - 5x - 14 = 0$ **10.** $2x^2 - 11x + 15 = 0$ **11.** $3x^2 + 10x - 8 = 0$

12. $12x^2 - 12x + 3 = 0$ **13.** $8x^2 - 98 = 0$ **14.** $x^4 - 14x^2 + 49 = 0$

Finding the Domain and Range of Functions (Lesson 2-1)

Find the domain and range of each function.

15. $\{(1, 2), (2, 3), (3, 4), (4, 5)\}$ **16.** $\{(1, 2), (2, 2), (3, 2), (4, 2)\}$

17. $f(x) = -x - 1$ **18.** $f(x) = 2x^2 + 3$

Graphing Quadratic Functions (Lesson 5-3)

Graph each function.

19. $y = 2x^2 - 4$ **20.** $y = -3(x^2 + 1)$ **21.** $y = \frac{1}{2}(x - 3)^2 + 1$

22. $y = -(x + 4)^2 - 5$ **23.** $y = \frac{1}{4}(x + 2)^2 - 1$ **24.** $y = 7 - (5 - x)^2$

What You'll Learn Next

California Content Standards

12.0 Students know the laws of fractional exponents.

15.0 Students determine whether a specific algebraic statement involving radical expressions is sometimes true, always true, or never true.

24.0 Students solve problems involving functional concepts, such as composition, defining the inverse function and performing arithmetic operations on functions.

▲ Gravity simulators can prevent bone loss in astronauts, as explained in Lesson 7-4.

New Vocabulary

🔊 **English and Spanish Audio Online**

- **composite function** (p. 405)
- **index** (p. 376)
- **inverse functions** (p. 415)
- **inverse relation** (p. 413)
- **like radicals** (p. 386)

- **nth root** (p. 375)
- **principal root** (p. 376)
- **radical equation** (p. 397)
- **radical function** (p. 421)
- **radicand** (p. 376)

- **rational exponent** (p. 391)
- **rationalize the denominator** (p. 382)
- **square root equation** (p. 397)
- **square root function** (p. 421)

Properties of Exponents

> **ALG2 11.2** Students judge the validity of an argument according to whether the properties of real numbers and exponents have been applied correctly at each step. *Introduce*

Exponents are used to indicate powers. Their properties are listed below. Assume throughout your work that no denominator is equal to zero and that m and n are integers.

- $a^0 = 1, a \neq 0$
- $a^m \cdot a^n = a^{m+n}$
- $(ab)^n = a^n b^n$
- $(a^m)^n = a^{mn}$

- $a^{-n} = \dfrac{1}{a^n}$
- $\dfrac{a^m}{a^n} = a^{m-n}$
- $\left(\dfrac{a}{b}\right)^n = \dfrac{a^n}{b^n}$

EXAMPLE

Simplify and rewrite each expression using only positive exponents.

a. $(7a^2)(-2a^{-5})$

$(7a^2)(-2a^{-5})$

$= 7(-2)a^{2+(-5)}$

$= -14a^{-3}$

$= \dfrac{-14}{a^3}$, or $-\dfrac{14}{a^3}$

b. $(-2x^{-1}y^2)^3$

$(-2x^{-1}y^2)^3$

$= (-2)^3(x^{-1})^3(y^2)^3$

$= -8x^{-3}y^6$

$= \dfrac{-8y^6}{x^3}$, or $-\dfrac{8y^6}{x^3}$

c. $\dfrac{2ab^5c^2}{a^3bc^2}$

$\dfrac{2ab^5c^2}{a^3bc^2}$

$= 2a^{1-3}b^{5-1}c^{2-2}$

$= 2a^{-2}b^4c^0$

$= \dfrac{2b^4}{a^2}$

EXERCISES

Simplify each expression. Use only positive exponents.

1. $(3a^2)(4a^6)$

2. $(-4x^2)(-2x^{-2})$

3. $(4x^3y^5)^2$

4. $(2x^{-5}y^4)^3$

5. $\dfrac{8a^5}{2a^2}$

6. $\dfrac{6x^7y^5}{3x^{-1}}$

7. $\dfrac{(4x^2)^0}{2xy^5}$

8. $\left(\dfrac{3x^2}{2}\right)^2$

9. $(-6m^2n^2)(3mn)$

10. $(3x^4y^5)^{-3}$

11. $\dfrac{(2r^{-1}s^2t^0)^{-2}}{2rs}$

12. $x^5(2x)^3$

13. $\dfrac{x^4x^{-2}}{x^{-5}}$

14. $\dfrac{(12x^2y^6)^2}{8x^4y^7}$

15. $(4p^2q)(p^2q^3)$

16. $\dfrac{4x^3}{2x}$

17. $(p^2)^{-2}$

18. $\dfrac{-15x^4}{3x}$

19. $\dfrac{r^2s^3t^4}{r^2s^4t^{-4}}$

20. $\dfrac{xy^2}{2} \cdot \dfrac{6x}{y^2}$

21. $(s^2t)^3(st)$

22. $(3x^{-3}y^{-2})^{-2}$

23. $(h^4k^5)^0$

24. $\dfrac{s^2t^3}{r} \cdot \dfrac{sr^3}{t}$

 25. Your friend tells you that $(k^3)^{-2} = -k^6$. Judge the validity of her argument according to whether the properties of exponents have been applied correctly.

Roots and Radical Expressions

 California Content Standards

ALG2 15.0 Students determine whether a specific algebraic statement involving radical expressions is sometimes true, always true, or never true. *Introduce*

What You'll Learn

• To simplify *n*th roots

. . . And Why

To solve a packaging problem, as in Example 4

✓ Check Skills You'll Need

GO for Help Lesson 5-4

Write each number as a square of a number.

1. 25   **2.** 0.09   **3.** $\frac{4}{49}$

Write each expression as a square of an expression.

4. x^{10} **5.** $x^4 y^2$ **6.** $169 x^6 y^{12}$

◄)) New Vocabulary • *n*th root • radicand • index • principal root

---

1 Roots and Radical Expressions

Since $5^2 = 25$, 5 is a square root of 25.

Since $5^3 = 125$, 5 is a cube root of 125.

Since $5^4 = 625$, 5 is a fourth root of 625.

Since $5^5 = 3125$, 5 is a fifth root of 3125.

This pattern leads to the definition of *n*th root.

 Key Concepts

Definition	**nth Root**

For any real numbers a and b, and any positive integer n, if $a^n = b$, then a is an **nth root** of b.

Vocabulary Tip

The term <u>root</u> is used in more than one way in mathematics:
  root of an equation
  root of a number.

The roots of the equation $y^4 = 16$ are the fourth roots of 16.

Since $2^4 = 16$ and $(-2)^4 = 16$, both 2 and -2 are fourth roots of 16.

Since there is no real number x such that $x^4 = -16$, -16 has no real fourth root.

Since -5 is the only real number whose cube is -125, -5 is the only real cube root of -125.

Some roots, such as the square roots of 10, are irrational numbers. Nevertheless, there is a positive square root and a negative square root of 10.

Here is a summary of the number of possible real roots of a real number.

Type of Number	Number of Real *n*th Roots When *n* Is Even	Number of Real *n*th Roots When *n* Is Odd
positive	2	1
0	1	1
negative	none	1

EXAMPLE Finding All Real Roots

Find all the real roots.

a. the cube roots of 0.008, -1000, and $\frac{1}{27}$

Since $(0.2)^3 = 0.008$, 0.2 is the cube root of 0.008.
Since $(-10)^3 = -1000$, -10 is the cube root of -1000.
Since $\left(\frac{1}{3}\right)^3 = \frac{1}{27}$, $\frac{1}{3}$ is the cube root of $\frac{1}{27}$.

b. the fourth roots of 1, -0.0001, and $\frac{16}{81}$

Since $1^4 = 1$ and $(-1)^4 = 1$, 1 and -1 are fourth roots of 1.
There is no real number with a fourth power of -0.0001.
Since $\left(\frac{2}{3}\right)^4 = \frac{16}{81}$ and $\left(-\frac{2}{3}\right)^4 = \frac{16}{81}$, $\frac{2}{3}$ and $-\frac{2}{3}$ are fourth roots of $\frac{16}{81}$.

✅ **CA Standards Check** ① **a.** Find all the real fifth roots of 0, -1, and 32.
b. Find all the real square roots of 0.0001, -1, and $\frac{36}{121}$.

Like the word *radish*, radical comes from the Latin word for root.

A radical sign is used to indicate a root. The number under the radical sign is the **radicand.** The **index** gives the degree of the root.

When a number has two real roots, the positive root is called the **principal root** and the radical sign indicates the principal root. The principal fourth root of 16 is written as $\sqrt[4]{16}$.

index   radical sign

radicand

The principal fourth root of 16 is 2 because $\sqrt[4]{16}$ equals $\sqrt[4]{2^4}$. The other fourth root of 16 is written as $-\sqrt[4]{16}$, which equals -2.

EXAMPLE Finding Roots

Find each real-number root.

a. $\sqrt[3]{-8}$
$\sqrt[3]{-8} = \sqrt[3]{(-2)^3}$ **Rewrite −8 as the third power of a number.**
$\quad\quad\quad = -2$ **Simplify.**

b. $\sqrt{-100}$

There is no real number whose square is -100.

✅ **CA Standards Check** ② Find each real-number root.
a. $\sqrt[3]{-27}$ **b.** $\sqrt[4]{81}$ **c.** $\sqrt{49}$

Notice that when $x = 5$, $\sqrt{x^2} = \sqrt{5^2} = \sqrt{25} = 5 = x$, and when $x = -5$, $\sqrt{x^2} = \sqrt{(-5)^2} = \sqrt{25} = 5 \neq x$.

 Key Concepts

Property	***n*th Root of a^n, $a < 0$**

For any negative real number a,
$$\sqrt[n]{a^n} = |a| \text{ when } n \text{ is even.}$$

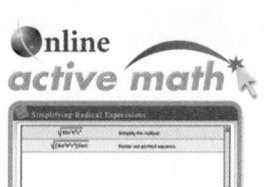
3 EXAMPLE **Simplifying Radical Expressions**

Simplify each radical expression.

a. $\sqrt{4x^6}$

$$\sqrt{4x^6} = \sqrt{2^2(x^3)^2} = \sqrt{(2x^3)^2} = 2|x^3|$$

Absolute value symbols ensure that the root is positive when x is negative.

b. $\sqrt[3]{a^3b^6}$

$$\sqrt[3]{a^3b^6} = \sqrt[3]{a^3(b^2)^3} = \sqrt[3]{(ab^2)^3} = ab^2$$

Absolute value symbols must not be used here. If a is negative, then the radicand is negative and the root must also be negative.

c. $\sqrt[4]{x^4y^8}$

$$\sqrt[4]{x^4y^8} = \sqrt[4]{x^4(y^2)^4} = \sqrt[4]{(xy^2)^4} = |x|y^2$$

Absolute value symbols ensure that the root is positive when x is negative. They are not needed for y because y^2 is never negative.

✓ **CA Standards Check** ③ Simplify each radical expression. Use absolute value symbols when needed.

a. $\sqrt{4x^2y^4}$ **b.** $\sqrt[3]{-27c^6}$ **c.** $\sqrt[4]{x^8y^{12}}$

4 EXAMPLE **Real-World** 🌐 **Connection**

Packaging A citrus grower wants to ship a select grade of oranges that weigh from 8 to 9 ounces in gift cartons. Each carton will hold three dozen oranges, in 3 layers of 3 oranges by 4 oranges.

The weight of an orange is related to its diameter by the formula $w = \frac{d^3}{4}$, where d is the diameter in inches and w is the weight in ounces. Cartons can be ordered in whole-inch dimensions. What size cartons should the grower order?

Find the diameters of the oranges.

Graphing Calculator Hint

Use the $\sqrt[3]{}$ feature in the MATH menu to find cube roots. For other roots, type the index first and then select the $\sqrt[x]{}$ feature.

$8 \le w \le 9$	**Write an inequality.**
$8 \le \frac{d^3}{4} \le 9$	**Substitute for w in terms of d.**
$32 \le d^3 \le 36$	**Multiply by 4.**
$\sqrt[3]{32} \le \sqrt[3]{d^3} \le \sqrt[3]{36}$	**Take cube roots.**
$3.17 \le d \le 3.30$	**The diameters range from 3.17 in. to 3.30 in.**

The length of a row of 4 of the largest oranges is 4(3.30 in.) = 13.2 in. The length of a row of 3 of the largest oranges is 3(3.30 in.) = 9.90 in. The grower should order cartons that are 14 in. long by 10 in. wide by 10 in. high to accommodate three dozen of the largest oranges.

✓ **CA Standards Check** ④ Use the formula in Example 4 to find the diameter of each orange.

a. 3 oz **b.** 5.5 oz **c.** 6.25 oz

A Practice by Example

Example 1
(page 376)

for Help

Find all the real square roots of each number.

1. 225　　　**2.** 0.0049　　　**3.** $-\frac{1}{121}$　　　**4.** $\frac{64}{169}$

Find all the real cube roots of each number.

5. -64　　　**6.** 0.125　　　**7.** $-\frac{27}{216}$　　　**8.** 0.000343

Find all the real fourth roots of each number.

9. 16　　　**10.** -16　　　**11.** 0.0081　　　**12.** $\frac{10,000}{81}$

Example 2
(page 376)

Find each real-number root.

13. $\sqrt{36}$　　　**14.** $-\sqrt{36}$　　　**15.** $\sqrt{-36}$　　　**16.** $\sqrt{0.36}$

17. $-\sqrt[3]{64}$　　　**18.** $\sqrt[3]{-64}$　　　**19.** $-\sqrt[4]{81}$　　　**20.** $\sqrt[4]{-81}$

Example 3
(page 377)

Simplify each radical expression. Use absolute value symbols when needed.

21. $\sqrt{16x^2}$　　　**22.** $\sqrt{0.25x^6}$　　　**23.** $\sqrt{x^8y^{18}}$　　　**24.** $\sqrt{64b^{48}}$

25. $\sqrt[3]{-64a^3}$　　　**26.** $\sqrt[3]{27y^6}$　　　**27.** $\sqrt[4]{x^8y^{12}}$　　　**28.** $\sqrt[5]{32y^{10}}$

Example 4
(page 377)

Geometry The formula for the volume of a sphere is $V = \frac{4}{3}\pi r^3$. Find the radius to the nearest hundredth of a sphere with each volume.

29. 10 in.^{3}　　　**30.** 20 ft^3　　　**31.** 0.45 cm^3　　　**32.** 0.002 mm^3

B Apply Your Skills

Find the two real-number solutions of each equation.

33. $x^2 = 100$　　　**34.** $x^4 = 1$　　　**35.** $x^2 = 0.25$　　　**36.** $x^4 = \frac{16}{81}$

37. Arrange the numbers $\sqrt[3]{-64}$, $-\sqrt[3]{-64}$, $\sqrt{64}$, and $\sqrt[6]{64}$ in order from least to greatest.

38. Boat Building Boat builders share an old rule of thumb for sailboats. The maximum speed K in knots is 1.35 times the square root of the length L in feet of the boat's waterline.
　a. A customer is planning to order a sailboat with a maximum speed of 8 knots. How long should the waterline be?
　b. How much longer would the waterline have to be to achieve a maximum speed of 10 knots?

Simplify each radical expression. Use absolute value symbols when needed.

39. $\sqrt[3]{0.125}$　　　**40.** $\sqrt[3]{\frac{8}{216}}$　　　**41.** $\sqrt[4]{0.0016}$　　　**42.** $\sqrt[4]{\frac{1}{256}}$

43. $\sqrt[4]{16c^4}$　　　**44.** $\sqrt[3]{81x^3y^6}$　　　**45.** $\sqrt{144x^3y^4z^5}$　　　**46.** $\sqrt[5]{y^{20}}$

47. $\sqrt[5]{-y^{20}}$　　　**48.** $\sqrt[5]{k^{15}}$　　　**49.** $\sqrt[5]{-k^{15}}$　　　**50.** $\sqrt{(x+3)^2}$

51. $\sqrt{(x+1)^4}$　　　**52.** $\sqrt[2n]{x^{2n}}$　　　**53.** $\sqrt[2n]{x^{4n}}$　　　**54.** $\sqrt[2n]{x^{6n}}$

Real-World 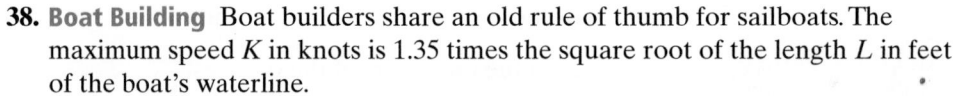 **Connection**

The waterline of a boat is the intersection of the boat with the surface of the water when the boat is at rest.

55. Open-Ended Find three radical expressions that simplify to $-2x^2$.

56. Critical Thinking For what positive integers n is each of the statements true?
   a. If $x^n = b$, then x is an nth root of b.   **b.** If $x^n = b$, then $x = \sqrt[n]{b}$.

57. Writing Is 10 a first root of 10? Explain.

Tell whether each equation is true for *all*, *some*, or *no values* of the variable. Explain your answers.

58. $\sqrt{x^4} = x^2$ **59.** $\sqrt{x^6} = x^3$ **60.** $\sqrt[3]{x^8} = x^2$ **61.** $\sqrt[3]{x^3} = |x|$

 Challenge

Simplify each radical expression. n is an even number.

62. $\sqrt[n]{m^n}$ **63.** $\sqrt[n]{m^{2n}}$ **64.** $\sqrt[n]{m^{3n}}$ **65.** $\sqrt[n]{m^{4n}}$

Simplify each radical expression. n is an odd number.

66. $\sqrt[n]{m^n}$ **67.** $\sqrt[n]{m^{2n}}$ **68.** $\sqrt[n]{m^{3n}}$ **69.** $\sqrt[n]{m^{4n}}$

Multiple Choice Practice

For California Standards and CAHSEE Tutorials, visit PHSchool.com. Web Code: bbq-9045

ALG2 15.0   **70.** If x is a real number, for what values of x is the equation $\sqrt[4]{x^{12}} = x^3$ always true?

   Ⓐ all values of x Ⓒ no values of x
   Ⓑ some values of x Ⓓ impossible to determine

ALG2 5.0   **71.** If $i = \sqrt{-1}$, which of the following complex numbers is represented by point A in the graph at the right?

   Ⓐ $6 + 5i$ Ⓒ $5 - 6i$
   Ⓑ $6 - 5i$ Ⓓ i

ALG2 3.0   **72.** The length of a rectangular pool is $x + 1$ feet, the width is $x - 2$ feet, and the depth is $x - 5$ feet. Which polynomial best represents the volume of the pool?

   Ⓐ $x^3 - 6x^2 + 3x + 6$ Ⓒ $x^3 + 6x^2 + 3x + 10$
   Ⓑ $x^3 - 6x^2 - 3x - 10$ Ⓓ $x^3 - 6x^2 + 3x + 10$

Mixed Review

Lesson 6-8   **Expand each binomial.**

73. $(x + y)^5$ **74.** $(2 - 3y)^4$ **75.** $(3x - 5)^6$ **76.** $(2a - b)^7$

Lesson 6-2   **Write each function in factored form. Check by multiplying.**

77. $y = 4x^3 - 49x$ **78.** $y = 81x^2 + 36x + 4$

79. $y = 4x^3 + 8x^2 + 4x$ **80.** $y = 12x^3 + 14x^2 + 2x$

Lesson 5-3   **Rewrite each equation in vertex form.**

81. $y = 3x^2 - 7$ **82.** $y = -2x^2 + x - 10$ **83.** $y = \frac{x^2}{4} + 2x - 1$

7-2

Multiplying and Dividing Radical Expressions

What You'll Learn

- To multiply radical expressions
- To divide radical expressions

...And Why

To transform a famous formula, as in Example 6

✓ **Check Skills You'll Need**

Find each missing factor.

1. $150 = 5^2(\blacksquare)$
2. $54 = (\blacksquare)^3(2)$
3. $48 = 4^2(\blacksquare)$
4. $x^5 = (\blacksquare)^2(x)$
5. $3a^3b^4 = (\blacksquare)^3(3b)$
6. $75a^7b^8 = (\blacksquare)^2(3a)$

GO for Help page 374

🔊 **New Vocabulary**   • rationalize the denominator

---

1 Multiplying Radical Expressions

To multiply radicals consider the following.

$\sqrt{16} \cdot \sqrt{9} = 4 \cdot 3 = 12$ and $\sqrt{16 \cdot 9} = \sqrt{144} = 12$.
So $\sqrt{16} \cdot \sqrt{9} = \sqrt{16 \cdot 9}$.

$\sqrt[3]{-8} \cdot \sqrt[3]{27} = -2 \cdot 3 = -6$ and $\sqrt[3]{-8 \cdot 27} = \sqrt[3]{-216} = -6$.
So $\sqrt[3]{-8} \cdot \sqrt[3]{27} = \sqrt[3]{-8 \cdot 27}$.

In general, the product of the principal nth roots of two numbers equals the principal nth root of their product.

 Key Concepts

Property   **Multiplying Radical Expressions**
If $\sqrt[n]{a}$ and $\sqrt[n]{b}$ are real numbers, then $\sqrt[n]{a} \cdot \sqrt[n]{b} = \sqrt[n]{ab}$.

1 EXAMPLE **Multiplying Radicals**

Multiply. Simplify if possible.

a. $\sqrt{2} \cdot \sqrt{8}$

$\sqrt{2} \cdot \sqrt{8} = \sqrt{2 \cdot 8} = \sqrt{16} = 4$

b. $\sqrt[3]{-5} \cdot \sqrt[3]{25}$

$\sqrt[3]{-5} \cdot \sqrt[3]{25} = \sqrt[3]{-125} = \sqrt[3]{(-5)^3} = -5$

c. $\sqrt{-2} \cdot \sqrt{8}$

The property for multiplying radicals does *not* apply. $\sqrt{-2}$ is not a real number.

 CA Standards Check **1** Multiply. Simplify if possible.

a. $\sqrt{3} \cdot \sqrt{12}$ **b.** $\sqrt[3]{3} \cdot \sqrt[3]{-9}$ **c.** $\sqrt[4]{4} \cdot \sqrt[4]{-4}$

$2\sqrt[3]{3}$ is considered to be a simplified form of $\sqrt[3]{24}$. You can use the property for multiplying radical expressions to simplify some radical expressions.

2 EXAMPLE   Simplifying Radical Expressions

Simplify each expression. Assume that all variables are positive. Then absolute value symbols are never needed in the simplified expression.

a. $\sqrt{72x^3}$

$$\sqrt{72x^3} = \sqrt{6^2 \cdot 2 \cdot x^2 \cdot x} \qquad \text{Factor into perfect squares.}$$
$$= \sqrt{6^2 x^2} \cdot \sqrt{2x} \qquad \sqrt[n]{a} \cdot \sqrt[n]{b} = \sqrt[n]{ab}$$
$$= 6x\sqrt{2x} \qquad \text{Simplify.}$$

b. $\sqrt[3]{80n^5}$

$$\sqrt[3]{80n^5} = \sqrt[3]{2^3 \cdot 10 \cdot n^3 \cdot n^2} \qquad \text{Factor into perfect cubes.}$$
$$= \sqrt[3]{2^3 n^3} \cdot \sqrt[3]{10n^2} \qquad \sqrt[n]{a} \cdot \sqrt[n]{b} = \sqrt[n]{ab}$$
$$= 2n\sqrt[3]{10n^2} \qquad \text{Simplify.}$$

✓**CA Standards Check** ❷ Simplify $\sqrt{50x^4}$ and $\sqrt[3]{18x^4}$. Assume that x is positive.

Simplify the products of radicals as much as possible.

3 EXAMPLE   Multiplying Radical Expressions

Multiply and simplify $\sqrt[3]{54x^2y^3} \cdot \sqrt[3]{5x^3y^4}$. Assume that all variables are positive.

$$\sqrt[3]{54x^2y^3} \cdot \sqrt[3]{5x^3y^4} = \sqrt[3]{54x^2y^3 \cdot 5x^3y^4} \qquad \sqrt[n]{a} \cdot \sqrt[n]{b} = \sqrt[n]{ab}$$
$$= \sqrt[3]{3^3 x^3 (y^2)^3 \cdot 10x^2y} \qquad \text{Factor into perfect cubes.}$$
$$= \sqrt[3]{3^3 x^3 (y^2)^3} \cdot \sqrt[3]{10x^2y} \qquad \sqrt[n]{a} \cdot \sqrt[n]{b} = \sqrt[n]{ab}$$
$$= 3xy^2\sqrt[3]{10x^2y} \qquad \text{Simplify.}$$

✓**CA Standards Check** ❸ Multiply and simplify $3\sqrt{7x^3} \cdot 2\sqrt{21x^3y^2}$. Assume that all variables are positive.

2   Dividing Radical Expressions

To divide radicals, consider the following.

$$\frac{\sqrt{36}}{\sqrt{25}} = \frac{6}{5} \text{ and } \sqrt{\frac{36}{25}} = \sqrt{\left(\frac{6}{5}\right)^2} = \frac{6}{5}. \text{ So } \frac{\sqrt{36}}{\sqrt{25}} = \sqrt{\frac{36}{25}}.$$

In general, the quotient of the principal nth roots of two numbers equals the principal nth root of their quotient.

🔑 **Key Concepts**

Property	Dividing Radical Expressions
If $\sqrt[n]{a}$ and $\sqrt[n]{b}$ are real numbers and $b \neq 0$, then $\dfrac{\sqrt[n]{a}}{\sqrt[n]{b}} = \sqrt[n]{\dfrac{a}{b}}$.	

4 EXAMPLE Dividing Radicals

Divide and simplify. Assume that all variables are positive.

a. $\dfrac{\sqrt[3]{32}}{\sqrt[3]{-4}}$

$$\dfrac{\sqrt[3]{32}}{\sqrt[3]{-4}} = \sqrt[3]{\dfrac{32}{-4}} = \sqrt[3]{-8} = -2$$

b. $\dfrac{\sqrt[3]{162x^5}}{\sqrt[3]{3x^2}}$

$$\dfrac{\sqrt[3]{162x^5}}{\sqrt[3]{3x^2}} = \sqrt[3]{\dfrac{162x^5}{3x^2}} = \sqrt[3]{54x^3} = \sqrt[3]{3^3x^3 \cdot 2} = \sqrt[3]{3^3x^3} \cdot \sqrt[3]{2} = 3x\sqrt[3]{2}$$

✓ **CA Standards Check** **4** Divide and simplify. Assume that all variables are positive.

a. $\dfrac{\sqrt{243}}{\sqrt{27}}$ 　　　　 **b.** $\dfrac{\sqrt{12x^4}}{\sqrt{3x}}$ 　　　　 **c.** $\dfrac{\sqrt[4]{1024x^{15}}}{\sqrt[4]{4x}}$

To **rationalize the denominator** of an expression, rewrite it so there are no radicals in any denominator and no denominators in any radical.

Rationalizing the denominator of a numerical expression makes it easier to calculate its decimal approximation. For example, $\dfrac{1}{\sqrt{2}} = \dfrac{\sqrt{2}}{2}$ and it is easier to divide by 2 than by $\sqrt{2}$.

5 EXAMPLE Rationalizing the Denominator

Rationalize the denominator of each expression. Assume that all variables are positive.

a. $\dfrac{\sqrt{2}}{\sqrt{3}}$

Method 1

$$\dfrac{\sqrt{2}}{\sqrt{3}} = \sqrt{\dfrac{2}{3}} = \sqrt{\dfrac{2 \cdot 3}{3 \cdot 3}} = \sqrt{\dfrac{6}{3^2}} = \dfrac{\sqrt{6}}{\sqrt{3^2}} = \dfrac{\sqrt{6}}{3}$$

Rewrite as a square root of a fraction. Then make the denominator a perfect square.

Method 2

$$\dfrac{\sqrt{2}}{\sqrt{3}} = \dfrac{\sqrt{2} \cdot \sqrt{3}}{\sqrt{3} \cdot \sqrt{3}} = \dfrac{\sqrt{6}}{3}$$

Multiply the numerator and denominator by $\sqrt{3}$ so the denominator becomes a whole number.

b. $\dfrac{\sqrt{x^3}}{\sqrt{5xy}}$

$$\dfrac{\sqrt{x^3}}{\sqrt{5xy}} = \dfrac{\sqrt{x^3} \cdot \sqrt{5xy}}{\sqrt{5xy} \cdot \sqrt{5xy}} = \dfrac{\sqrt{5x^4y}}{5xy} = \dfrac{x^2\sqrt{5y}}{5xy} = \dfrac{x\sqrt{5y}}{5y}$$

c. $\sqrt[3]{\dfrac{2}{3x}}$

$$\sqrt[3]{\dfrac{2}{3x}} = \sqrt[3]{\dfrac{2 \cdot 3^2x^2}{3x \cdot 3^2x^2}} = \sqrt[3]{\dfrac{18x^2}{3^3x^3}} = \dfrac{\sqrt[3]{18x^2}}{3x}$$

Rewrite the fraction so the denominator is a perfect cube.

✓ **CA Standards Check** **5** Rationalize the denominator of each expression. Assume that the variables are positive.

a. $\sqrt{\dfrac{7}{5}}$ 　　　　 **b.** $\dfrac{\sqrt{2x^3}}{\sqrt{10xy}}$ 　　　　 **c.** $\dfrac{\sqrt[3]{4}}{\sqrt[3]{6x}}$

Einstein's famous formula $E = mc^2$ relates energy E, mass m, and the speed of light c. Express c in terms of E and m and rationalize the denominator.

$$E = mc^2$$

$$c^2 = \frac{E}{m}$$

$$c = \sqrt{\frac{E}{m}} = \sqrt{\frac{Em}{m^2}} = \frac{\sqrt{Em}}{\sqrt{m^2}} = \frac{\sqrt{Em}}{m}$$

✓ **CA Standards Check** **6** The formula $a = \frac{d}{t^2}$ relates the acceleration a of a moving object to the distance d it moves in the time t. Solve the formula for t and rationalize the denominator.

EXERCISES

For more exercises, see *Extra Skill and Word Problem Practice*.

Standards Practice

A Practice by Example

Example 1
(page 380)

GO for Help

Multiply, if possible. Then simplify.

1. $\sqrt{8} \cdot \sqrt{32}$
2. $\sqrt[3]{4} \cdot \sqrt[3]{16}$
3. $\sqrt[3]{9} \cdot \sqrt[3]{-81}$
4. $\sqrt[4]{8} \cdot \sqrt[4]{32}$
5. $\sqrt{-5} \cdot \sqrt{5}$
6. $\sqrt[3]{-5} \cdot \sqrt[3]{-25}$
7. $\sqrt[3]{9} \cdot \sqrt[3]{-24}$
8. $\sqrt[3]{-12} \cdot \sqrt[3]{-18}$

Example 2
(page 381)

Simplify. Assume that all variables are positive.

9. $\sqrt{20x^3}$
10. $\sqrt[3]{81x^2}$
11. $\sqrt{50x^5}$
12. $\sqrt[3]{32a^5}$
13. $\sqrt[3]{54y^{10}}$
14. $\sqrt{200a^6b^7}$
15. $\sqrt[3]{-250x^6y^5}$
16. $\sqrt[4]{64x^3y^6}$

Example 3
(page 381)

Multiply and simplify. Assume that all variables are positive.

17. $\sqrt[3]{6} \cdot \sqrt[3]{16}$
18. $\sqrt{8y^5} \cdot \sqrt{40y^2}$
19. $\sqrt{7x^5} \cdot \sqrt{42xy^9}$
20. $4\sqrt{2x} \cdot 5\sqrt{6xy^2}$
21. $3\sqrt[3]{5y^3} \cdot 2\sqrt[3]{50y^4}$
22. $-\sqrt[3]{2x^2y^2} \cdot 2\sqrt[3]{15x^5y}$

Example 4
(page 382)

Divide and simplify. Assume that all variables are positive.

23. $\frac{\sqrt{500}}{\sqrt{5}}$
24. $\frac{\sqrt{48x^3}}{\sqrt{3xy^2}}$
25. $\frac{\sqrt{56x^5y^5}}{\sqrt{7xy}}$
26. $\frac{\sqrt[3]{250x^7y^3}}{\sqrt[3]{2x^2y}}$

Example 5
(page 382)

Rationalize the denominator of each expression. Assume that all variables are positive.

27. $\frac{\sqrt{x}}{\sqrt{2}}$
28. $\frac{\sqrt{5}}{\sqrt{8x}}$
29. $\frac{\sqrt[3]{x}}{\sqrt[3]{2}}$
30. $\sqrt[3]{\frac{5}{3x}}$
31. $\frac{\sqrt[4]{2}}{\sqrt[4]{5}}$
32. $\frac{15\sqrt{60x^5}}{3\sqrt{12x}}$
33. $\frac{\sqrt{3xy^2}}{\sqrt{5xy^3}}$
34. $\frac{\sqrt{5x^4y}}{\sqrt{2x^2y^3}}$

Example 6
(page 383)

35. Physics The formula $F = \frac{Gm_1m_2}{r^2}$ relates the gravitational force F between an object of mass m_1 and an object of mass m_2 separated by distance r. G is a constant known as the constant of gravitation. Solve the formula for r. Rationalize the denominator.

36. a. Simplify $\dfrac{\sqrt{2} + \sqrt{3}}{\sqrt{75}}$ by multiplying the numerator and denominator by $\sqrt{75}$.

   b. Simplify the expression in (a) by multiplying by $\sqrt{3}$ instead of $\sqrt{75}$.

   c. Explain how you would simplify $\dfrac{\sqrt{2} + \sqrt{3}}{\sqrt{98}}$.

Simplify each expression. Rationalize all denominators. Assume that all variables are positive.

37. $\sqrt{5} \cdot \sqrt{40}$

38. $\sqrt[3]{4} \cdot \sqrt[3]{80}$

39. $\sqrt{x^5 y^5} \cdot 3\sqrt{2x^7 y^6}$

40. $5\sqrt{2xy^6} \cdot 2\sqrt{2x^3 y}$

41. $\sqrt{2}(\sqrt{50} + 7)$

42. $3(5 + \sqrt{21})$

43. $\sqrt{5}(\sqrt{5} + \sqrt{15})$

44. $\sqrt[3]{2x} \cdot \sqrt[3]{4} \cdot \sqrt[3]{2x^2}$

45. $\sqrt[3]{3x^2} \cdot \sqrt[3]{x^2} \cdot \sqrt[3]{9x^3}$

46. $\dfrac{\sqrt{5x^4}}{\sqrt{2x^2 y^3}}$

47. $\dfrac{5\sqrt{2}}{3\sqrt{7x}}$

48. $\dfrac{1}{\sqrt[3]{9x}}$

49. $\dfrac{10}{\sqrt[3]{5x^2}}$

50. $\dfrac{\sqrt[3]{14}}{\sqrt[3]{7x^2 y}}$

51. $\dfrac{3\sqrt{11x^3 y}}{-2\sqrt{12x^4 y}}$

52. $-2\left(\sqrt[3]{32} + \sqrt[3]{54}\right)$

53. $\dfrac{3 + \sqrt{5}}{\sqrt{5}}$

54. $\dfrac{\sqrt{3} - \sqrt{2}}{\sqrt{8}}$

55. Satellites The circular velocity v, in miles per hour, of a satellite orbiting Earth is given by the formula $v = \sqrt{\dfrac{1.24 \times 10^{12}}{r}}$, where r is the distance in miles from the satellite to the center of Earth. How much greater is the velocity of a satellite orbiting at an altitude of 100 mi than one orbiting at an altitude of 200 mi? (The radius of Earth is 3950 mi.)

56. Geometry A rectangular shelf is $\sqrt{440}$ cm by $\sqrt{20}$ cm. Find its area.

57. Error Analysis Explain the error in this simplification of radical expressions.
$$\sqrt{-2} \cdot \sqrt{-8} = \sqrt{-2(-8)} = \sqrt{16} = 4$$

58. Physics A freely falling object hit the ground in $\sqrt{18a^5}$ seconds. It fell h feet. Use the formula $h = 16t^2$ to find h in terms of a.

59. Writing Does $\sqrt{x^3} = \sqrt[3]{x^2}$ for all, some, or no values of x? Explain.

60. Open-Ended Of the equivalent expressions $\sqrt{\frac{2}{3}}$, $\frac{\sqrt{2}}{\sqrt{3}}$, and $\frac{\sqrt{6}}{3}$, which do you prefer to use for finding a decimal approximation with a calculator? Justify your reasoning.

Simplify each expression. Rationalize all denominators. Assume that all variables are positive.

61. $\sqrt{\sqrt{16x^4 y^4}}$

62. $\sqrt[3]{\sqrt{64x^6 y^{12}}}$

63. $\sqrt{\sqrt[3]{8000}}$

64. $\sqrt[3]{x^{-1} y^{-2}}$

65. $\sqrt[5]{x^{-4} y}$

66. $\sqrt[6]{\dfrac{y^{-3}}{x^{-4}}}$

67. Critical Thinking When $\sqrt{x^a y^b}$ is simplified, the result is $\dfrac{1}{x^c y^{3d}}$, where c and d are positive integers. Express a in terms of c, and b in terms of d.

68. Critical Thinking In Example 3 you saw that $\sqrt[3]{54x^2 y^3} \cdot \sqrt[3]{5x^3 y^4}$ simplifies to $3xy^2 \sqrt[3]{10x^2 y}$, if you assume that all the variables are positive. Now assume that the variables represent any real numbers. What changes must be made in the answer? Explain.

Multiple Choice Practice

For California Standards and CAHSEE Tutorials, visit PHSchool.com. Web Code: bbq-9045

ALG2 20.0

69. Which term in the expansion of $(2a - 3b)^6$ has the coefficient 2160?

   Ⓐ second term   Ⓒ fourth term

   Ⓑ third term   Ⓓ fifth term

ALG2 9.0

70. How many units must you shift the graph of $y = 3(x + 3)^2$ to get the graph of $y = 3(x + 3)^2 - 2$?

   Ⓐ 2 units down   Ⓒ 2 units left

   Ⓑ 2 units up   Ⓓ 2 units right

ALG2 2.0

71. Which system is represented by the graph at the right?

   Ⓐ Line 1: $y = 2x$
        Line 2: $y = -3x + 3$

   Ⓑ Line 1: $3x + 5y = 15$
        Line 2: $y = x$

   Ⓒ Line 1: $y = x$
        Line 2: $3x + 5y = 15$

   Ⓓ Line 1: $y = -x$
        Line 2: $3x - 5y = 15$

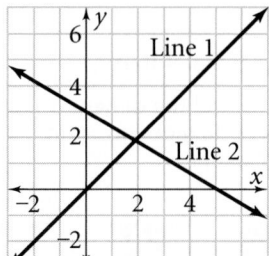

ALG2 8.0

72. What are the roots of $0 = x^2 + 3x - 28$?

   Ⓐ -4 and 7 Ⓒ -4 and -7

   Ⓑ 4 and -7 Ⓓ 4 and 7

Mixed Review

Lesson 7-1

Simplify each radical expression. Use absolute value symbols as needed.

73. $\sqrt{121a^{90}}$ **74.** $-\sqrt{81c^{48}d^{64}}$

75. $\sqrt[3]{-64a^{81}}$ **76.** $\sqrt[5]{32y^{25}}$

77. $\sqrt{0.25x^6}$ **78.** $\sqrt[7]{x^{14}y^{35}}$

79. $\sqrt[4]{16x^{36}y^{96}}$ **80.** $\sqrt{0.0064x^{40}}$

Lesson 6-3

Divide. Tell whether each divisor is a factor of the dividend.

81. $(y^3 - 64) \div (y + 4)$ **82.** $(x^3 + 27) \div (x + 3)$

83. $(6a^3 + a^2 - a + 4) \div (2a + 1)$ **84.** $(2x^4 - 3x^3 - 4x + 10) \div (x - 2)$

Lesson 5-7

Complete the square.

85. $x^2 + 10x + \blacksquare$ **86.** $x^2 - 10x + \blacksquare$

87. $x^2 + 11x + \blacksquare$ **88.** $x^2 - 11x + \blacksquare$

89. $x^2 - \frac{x}{3} + \blacksquare$ **90.** $x^2 + 0.3x + \blacksquare$

91. $x^2 - \frac{3}{4}x + \blacksquare$ **92.** $x^2 + \frac{3}{5}x + \blacksquare$

Binomial Radical Expressions

 California Content Standards

ALG2 15.0 Students determine whether a specific algebraic statement involving radical expressions is sometimes true, always true, or never true. *Develop*

What You'll Learn

• To add and subtract radical expressions

• To multiply and divide binomial radical expressions

. . . And Why

To find the dimensions of a window design, as in Example 2

✓ Check Skills You'll Need

Multiply.

1. $(5x + 4)(3x - 2)$

2. $(-8x + 5)(3x - 7)$

3. $(x + 4)(x - 4)$

4. $(4x + 5)(4x - 5)$

5. $(x + 5)^2$

6. $(2x - 9)^2$

GO for Help Lesson 5-1 or Skills Handbook page 893

◀)) New Vocabulary • like radicals

---

1 Adding and Subtracting Radical Expressions

Like radicals are radical expressions that have the same index and the same radicand. To add or subtract like radicals, use the Distributive Property.

1 EXAMPLE Adding and Subtracting Radical Expressions

Add or subtract if possible.

a. $5\sqrt[3]{x} - 3\sqrt[3]{x}$

$5\sqrt[3]{x} - 3\sqrt[3]{x} = (5 - 3)\sqrt[3]{x}$ **Distributive Property with like radicals**

$= 2\sqrt[3]{x}$ **Simplify.**

b. $4\sqrt{2} + 5\sqrt{3}$

The radicals are not like radicals. They cannot be combined.

✓ CA Standards Check **1** Add or subtract if possible.

a. $2\sqrt{7} + 3\sqrt{7}$ **b.** $7\sqrt[4]{5} - 2\sqrt[3]{5}$ **c.** $4\sqrt{xy} + 5\sqrt{xy}$

2 EXAMPLE Real-World ⊕ Connection

In the stained-glass window design at the left, the side of each small square is 5 in. Find the perimeter of the window to the nearest tenth of an inch.

The diagonal of a square with side s is $s\sqrt{2}$. So the window's height is $2(5\sqrt{2})$ in., or $10\sqrt{2}$ in. The length is $3(5\sqrt{2})$ in., or $15\sqrt{2}$ in. The perimeter is $2(10\sqrt{2} + 15\sqrt{2})$ in., or $50\sqrt{2}$ in. To the nearest tenth of an inch, the perimeter is 70.7 in.

✓ CA Standards Check **2** Find the perimeter of the window if each small square is 6 in. on a side.

Simplify radicals before adding or subtracting so you can find all the like radicals.

Test-Taking Tip

Read directions carefully to determine if an answer that contains a radical should be exact or an approximation.

3 EXAMPLE **Simplifying Before Adding or Subtracting**

Simplify $6\sqrt{18} + 4\sqrt{8} - 3\sqrt{72}$.

$$6\sqrt{18} + 4\sqrt{8} - 3\sqrt{72} = 6\sqrt{3^2 \cdot 2} + 4\sqrt{2^2 \cdot 2} - 3\sqrt{6^2 \cdot 2} \quad \text{Factor each radicand.}$$
$$= 6 \cdot 3\sqrt{2} + 4 \cdot 2\sqrt{2} - 3 \cdot 6\sqrt{2} \quad \text{Simplify each radical.}$$
$$= 18\sqrt{2} + 8\sqrt{2} - 18\sqrt{2} \quad \text{Multiply.}$$
$$= (18 + 8 - 18)\sqrt{2} \quad \text{Distributive Property}$$
$$= 8\sqrt{2}$$

 CA Standards Check **3** Simplify $\sqrt{50} + 3\sqrt{32} - 5\sqrt{18}$.

---

2 **Multiplying and Dividing Binomial Radical Expressions**

GO **Online**

Video Tutor Help

Visit: PHSchool.com
Web Code: bbe-0775

Multiply radical expressions that are in the form of binomials by using FOIL.

4 EXAMPLE **Multiplying Binomial Radical Expressions**

Multiply $(3 + 2\sqrt{5})(2 + 4\sqrt{5})$.

$$(3 + 2\sqrt{5})(2 + 4\sqrt{5}) = 3 \cdot 2 + 3 \cdot 4\sqrt{5} + 2 \cdot 2\sqrt{5} + 2\sqrt{5} \cdot 4\sqrt{5} \quad \text{Use FOIL.}$$
$$= 6 + 12\sqrt{5} + 4\sqrt{5} + 40 \quad \text{Multiply.}$$
$$= 6 + (12 + 4)\sqrt{5} + 40 \quad \text{Combine like radicals.}$$
$$= 46 + 16\sqrt{5}$$

 CA Standards Check **4** Multiply $(\sqrt{2} - \sqrt{3})^2$.

GO **for Help**

To review conjugates, go to Lesson 6-5.

Conjugates are expressions, such as $\sqrt{a} + \sqrt{b}$ and $\sqrt{a} - \sqrt{b}$, that differ only in the sign of the second terms. If a and b are rational numbers, then the product of these conjugates is a rational number.

Let a and b represent rational numbers.
$$(\sqrt{a} + \sqrt{b})(\sqrt{a} - \sqrt{b}) = (\sqrt{a})^2 - (\sqrt{b})^2 \quad \text{The product is the difference of squares.}$$
$$= a - b \quad \text{Simplify.}$$
The difference of the rational numbers a and b is a rational number. So the product of the conjugates is a rational number.

5 EXAMPLE **Multiplying Conjugates**

Multiply $(2 + \sqrt{3})(2 - \sqrt{3})$.

$$(2 + \sqrt{3})(2 - \sqrt{3}) = 2^2 - (\sqrt{3})^2 \quad (a + b)(a - b) = a^2 - b^2$$
$$= 4 - 3$$
$$= 1$$

 CA Standards Check **5** Multiply $(\sqrt{5} + \sqrt{2})(\sqrt{5} - \sqrt{2})$.

Sometimes you need to rationalize the denominator of a fraction when the denominator is a binomial radical expression. Multiply the numerator and denominator of the fraction by the conjugate of the denominator.

6 EXAMPLE **Rationalizing Binomial Radical Denominators**

Rationalize the denominator of $\dfrac{3 + \sqrt{5}}{1 - \sqrt{5}}$.

$\dfrac{3 + \sqrt{5}}{1 - \sqrt{5}} = \dfrac{3 + \sqrt{5}}{1 - \sqrt{5}} \cdot \dfrac{1 + \sqrt{5}}{1 + \sqrt{5}}$ **$1 + \sqrt{5}$ is the conjugate of $1 - \sqrt{5}$.**

$= \dfrac{(3 + \sqrt{5})(1 + \sqrt{5})}{(1 - \sqrt{5})(1 + \sqrt{5})}$ **Multiply.**

$= \dfrac{3 + 3\sqrt{5} + \sqrt{5} + (\sqrt{5})^2}{1^2 - (\sqrt{5})^2}$ **Simplify.**

$= \dfrac{8 + 4\sqrt{5}}{-4}$

$= \dfrac{8}{-4} + \dfrac{4\sqrt{5}}{-4}$

$= -2 - \sqrt{5}$

✓ **CA Standards Check** **6** Rationalize the denominator of $\dfrac{6 + \sqrt{15}}{4 - \sqrt{15}}$.

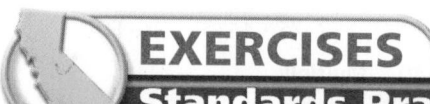

EXERCISES

For more exercises, see *Extra Skill and Word Problem Practice.*

Standards Practice

ALG2 15.0

A Practice by Example

Examples 1 and 2
(page 386)

GO for Help

Add or subtract if possible.

1. $5\sqrt{6} + \sqrt{6}$ **2.** $6\sqrt[3]{3} - 2\sqrt[3]{3}$ **3.** $4\sqrt{3} + 4\sqrt[3]{3}$

4. $3\sqrt{x} - 5\sqrt{x}$ **5.** $14\sqrt{x} + 3\sqrt{y}$ **6.** $7\sqrt[3]{x^2} - 2\sqrt[3]{x^2}$

Example 3
(page 387)

Simplify.

7. $6\sqrt{18} + 3\sqrt{50}$ **8.** $14\sqrt{20} - 3\sqrt{125}$ **9.** $\sqrt{18} + \sqrt{32}$

10. $\sqrt[3]{54} + \sqrt[3]{16}$ **11.** $3\sqrt[3]{81} - 2\sqrt[3]{54}$ **12.** $\sqrt[4]{32} + \sqrt[4]{48}$

Example 4
(page 387)

Multiply.

13. $(3 + \sqrt{5})(1 + \sqrt{5})$ **14.** $(2 + \sqrt{7})(1 + 3\sqrt{7})$

15. $(3 - 4\sqrt{2})(5 - 6\sqrt{2})$ **16.** $(\sqrt{3} + \sqrt{5})^2$

17. $(\sqrt{13} + 6)^2$ **18.** $(2\sqrt{5} + 3\sqrt{2})^2$

Example 5
(page 387)

Multiply each pair of conjugates.

19. $(5 - \sqrt{11})(5 + \sqrt{11})$ **20.** $(4 - 2\sqrt{3})(4 + 2\sqrt{3})$

21. $(2\sqrt{6} + 8)(2\sqrt{6} - 8)$ **22.** $(\sqrt{3} + \sqrt{5})(\sqrt{3} - \sqrt{5})$

Example 6
(page 388)

Rationalize each denominator. Simplify the answer.

23. $\dfrac{4}{1 + \sqrt{3}}$ **24.** $\dfrac{4}{3\sqrt{3} - 2}$ **25.** $\dfrac{5 + \sqrt{3}}{2 - \sqrt{3}}$ **26.** $\dfrac{3 + \sqrt{8}}{2 - 2\sqrt{8}}$

Simplify. Rationalize all denominators. Assume that all the variables are positive.

27. $\sqrt{72} + \sqrt{32} + \sqrt{18}$

28. $\sqrt{75} + 2\sqrt{48} - 5\sqrt{3}$

29. $5\sqrt{32x} + 4\sqrt{98x}$

30. $\sqrt{75} - 4\sqrt{18} + 2\sqrt{32}$

Visit: PHSchool.com
Web Code: bbe-0703

31. $4\sqrt{216y^2} + 3\sqrt{54y^2}$

32. $3\sqrt[3]{16} - 4\sqrt[3]{54} + \sqrt[3]{128}$

33. $(\sqrt{3} - \sqrt{7})(\sqrt{3} + 2\sqrt{7})$

34. $(2\sqrt{5} + 3\sqrt{2})(5\sqrt{5} - 7\sqrt{2})$

35. $(1 + \sqrt{72})(5 + \sqrt{2})$

36. $(2 - \sqrt{98})(3 + \sqrt{18})$

37. $(\sqrt{x} + \sqrt{3})(\sqrt{x} + 2\sqrt{3})$

38. $(2\sqrt{y} - 3\sqrt{2})(4\sqrt{y} - 5\sqrt{2})$

39. $\dfrac{4 + \sqrt{27}}{2 - 3\sqrt{27}}$

40. $\dfrac{4 + \sqrt{6}}{\sqrt{2} + \sqrt{3}}$

Real-World Connection

The golden ratio is found in the growth patterns of many plants. $\dfrac{AC}{CD} = \dfrac{BC}{BD} = \dfrac{1 + \sqrt{5}}{2}$

41. $\dfrac{5 - \sqrt{21}}{\sqrt{3} - \sqrt{7}}$

42. $\dfrac{3 + \sqrt[3]{2}}{\sqrt[3]{2}}$

43. $\dfrac{5 + \sqrt[4]{x}}{\sqrt[4]{x}}$

44. $\dfrac{4 - 2\sqrt[3]{6}}{\sqrt[3]{4}}$

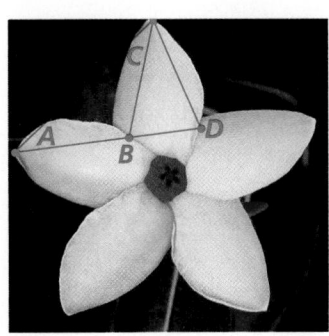

45. The golden ratio is $\dfrac{1 + \sqrt{5}}{2}$. Find the difference between the golden ratio and its reciprocal.

46. Critical Thinking Describe the possible values of a such that $\sqrt{72} + \sqrt{a}$ can be simplified to a single term.

47. Writing Discuss the advantages and disadvantages of first simplifying $\sqrt{72} + \sqrt{32} + \sqrt{18}$ in order to estimate its decimal value.

48. Physics An object is moving at a speed of $(3 + \sqrt{2})$ ft/s. How long will it take the object to travel 20 ft?

49. Open-Ended Find two pairs of conjugates with a product of 3.

50. Multiple Choice The length of a rectangle is $(3 + \sqrt{5})x$. The height is $(1 + 2\sqrt{5})y$. Which expression best describes the area of a rectangle?

   Ⓐ $(4 + 3\sqrt{5})(x + y)$ Ⓒ $(6 + 2\sqrt{5})x + (2 + 4\sqrt{5})y$

   Ⓑ $13xy$ Ⓓ $(13 + 7\sqrt{5})xy$

Ⓒ Challenge

Add or subtract.

51. $\dfrac{1}{1 - \sqrt{5}} + \dfrac{1}{1 + \sqrt{5}}$

52. $\dfrac{4}{\sqrt{5} - \sqrt{3}} - \dfrac{4}{\sqrt{5} + \sqrt{3}}$

53. For what values of a and b does $\sqrt{a} + \sqrt{b} = \sqrt{a + b}$?

54. Error Analysis A student used the steps shown below to simplify an expression. Find the student's error and explain why the step is incorrect.

$$\dfrac{1}{(1 - \sqrt{2})^2} = (1 - \sqrt{2})^{-2}$$

$$= 1^{-2} - (\sqrt{2})^{-2}$$

$$= \dfrac{1}{1^2} - \dfrac{1}{(\sqrt{2^2})} = \dfrac{1}{1} - \dfrac{1}{2} = \dfrac{1}{2}$$

55. In the expression $\sqrt[n]{x^m}$, m and n are positive integers and x is a real number. The expression can be simplified.
   a. If $x > 0$, what are the possible values for m and n?
   b. If $x < 0$, what are the possible values for m and n?
   c. If $x < 0$ and an absolute value symbol is needed in the simplified expression, what are the possible values of m and n?

For California Standards and CAHSEE Tutorials, visit PHSchool.com. Web Code: bbq-9045

ALG2 15.0

56. If x is a real number, for what values of x is the equation $\sqrt[4]{x^4} = |x|$ true?

   (A) all values of x

   (B) non-negative values of x

   (C) negative values of x

   (D) no values of x

ALG2 6.0

57. How can you rewrite the expression $(8 - 5i)^2$ in the form $a + bi$?

   (A) $39 + 80i$ (C) $69 + 80i$

   (B) $39 - 80i$ (D) $69 - 80i$

ALG2 4.0

58. What is the factored form of $4x^2 + 15x - 4$?

   (A) $(2x + 2)(2x - 2)$ (C) $(2x - 4)(2x + 1)$

   (B) $(4x + 1)(x - 4)$ (D) $(4x - 1)(x + 4)$

ALG2 10.0

59. The vertex of the graph of $y = -x^2 - 16x - 62$ lies in which quadrant?

   (A) IV   (B) III   (C) II   (D) I

Mixed Review

Lesson 7-2

GO for Help

Simplify each expression. Rationalize all denominators. Assume that all variables are positive.

60. $\sqrt[3]{3} \cdot \sqrt[3]{18}$ **61.** $\sqrt{3x} \cdot \sqrt{5x}$ **62.** $\dfrac{\sqrt{32}}{\sqrt{2}}$ **63.** $\dfrac{\sqrt{62}}{\sqrt{6}}$

64. $\sqrt[3]{2x^2} \cdot \sqrt[3]{4x}$ **65.** $\sqrt{7x} \cdot \sqrt{14x^3}$ **66.** $\dfrac{\sqrt{6m}}{\sqrt{2mn}}$ **67.** $\sqrt[3]{\dfrac{4}{5x}}$

Lesson 6-4

Solve each equation.

68. $2x^3 - 16 = 0$ **69.** $x^3 + 1000 = 0$ **70.** $125x^3 - 1 = 0$

71. $x^4 - 14x^2 + 49 = 0$ **72.** $25x^4 - 40x^2 + 16 = 0$ **73.** $81x^4 - 1 = 0$

✓ Checkpoint Quiz 1   **Lessons 7-1 through 7-3**

Simplify each radical expression. Use absolute value symbols when needed.

1. $\sqrt[4]{b^4 c^8}$ **2.** $\sqrt[5]{x^5 y^{10}}$ **3.** $\sqrt[3]{-a^3}$ **4.** $\sqrt[5]{-y^{10}}$

Simplify each expression. Rationalize all denominators. Assume that all variables are positive.

5. $\sqrt{8}(\sqrt{24} + 3\sqrt{8})$ **6.** $2\sqrt{5x^3} \cdot 3\sqrt{28x^3 y^2}$

7. $4\sqrt[3]{81} - 3\sqrt[3]{54}$ **8.** $\dfrac{4\sqrt{2xy}}{9\sqrt{5x^2 y}}$

9. $(\sqrt{5} + 2\sqrt{3})(\sqrt{5} - 2\sqrt{3})$ **10.** $\dfrac{5}{4\sqrt{7} + 5}$

7-4 **Rational Exponents**

 California Content Standards
ALG2 12.0 Students know the laws of fractional exponents. *Introduce, Develop*

What You'll Learn

• To simplify expressions with rational exponents

... And Why

To model simulated gravity in a spacecraft, as in Example 3

✓ **Check Skills You'll Need**

Simplify.

1. 2^{-4}

2. $(3x)^{-2}$

3. $(5x^2y)^{-3}$

4. $2^{-2} + 4^{-1}$

5. $(2a^{-2}b^3)^4$

6. $(4a^3b^{-1})^{-2}$

GO for Help page 374

🔊 **New Vocabulary** • rational exponent

---

1 **Simplifying Expressions With Rational Exponents**

Another way to write a radical expression is to use a **rational exponent.** See the examples at the right.

Like the radical form, the exponent form always indicates the principal root.

Radical form		Exponent form
$\sqrt{25}$	=	$25^{\frac{1}{2}}$
$\sqrt[3]{27}$	=	$27^{\frac{1}{3}}$
$\sqrt[4]{16}$	=	$16^{\frac{1}{4}}$

Vocabulary Tip

Exponent comes from the Latin word meaning "place outside."

1 EXAMPLE **Simplifying Expressions With Rational Exponents**

Simplify each expression.

a. $125^{\frac{1}{3}}$

$125^{\frac{1}{3}} = \sqrt[3]{125}$ **Rewrite as a radical.**

$= \sqrt[3]{5^3}$ **Rewrite 125 as a cube.**

$= 5$ **Simplify.**

b. $5^{\frac{1}{2}} \cdot 5^{\frac{1}{2}}$

$5^{\frac{1}{2}} \cdot 5^{\frac{1}{2}} = \sqrt{5} \cdot \sqrt{5}$ **Rewrite as radicals.**

$= 5$ **By definition, $\sqrt{5}$ is the number whose square is 5.**

c. $10^{\frac{1}{3}} \cdot 100^{\frac{1}{3}}$

$10^{\frac{1}{3}} \cdot 100^{\frac{1}{3}} = \sqrt[3]{10} \cdot \sqrt[3]{100}$ **Rewrite as radicals.**

$= \sqrt[3]{10 \cdot 100}$ **Property for multiplying radical expressions**

$= \sqrt[3]{10^3}$ **Rewrite the radicand as a cube.**

$= 10$ **Simplify.**

 ✓ **CA Standards Check** **1** Simplify each expression.

a. $16^{\frac{1}{4}}$ **b.** $2^{\frac{1}{2}} \cdot 2^{\frac{1}{2}}$ **c.** $2^{\frac{1}{2}} \cdot 8^{\frac{1}{2}}$

A rational exponent may have a numerator other than 1. The property $(a^m)^n = a^{mn}$ shows how to rewrite an expression with an exponent that is an improper fraction.

$$25^{\frac{3}{2}} = 25^{(3 \cdot \frac{1}{2})} = (25^3)^{\frac{1}{2}} = \sqrt{25^3} \quad \text{or} \quad 25^{\frac{3}{2}} = 25^{(\frac{1}{2} \cdot 3)} = (25^{\frac{1}{2}})^3 = (\sqrt{25})^3$$

 Key Concepts

Definition	Rational Exponents

If the *n*th root of *a* is a real number and *m* is an integer, then

$$a^{\frac{1}{n}} = \sqrt[n]{a} \quad \text{and} \quad a^{\frac{m}{n}} = \sqrt[n]{a^m} = (\sqrt[n]{a})^m. \qquad \text{If } m \text{ is negative, } a \neq 0.$$

2 EXAMPLE **Converting to and From Radical Form**

a. Write the exponential expressions $x^{\frac{3}{5}}$ and $y^{-2.5}$ in radical form.

$$x^{\frac{3}{5}} = \sqrt[5]{x^3} \text{ or } (\sqrt[5]{x})^3 \qquad\qquad y^{-2.5} = y^{-\frac{5}{2}} = \frac{1}{\sqrt{y^5}} \text{ or } \frac{1}{(\sqrt{y})^5}$$

b. Write the radical expressions $\sqrt{a^3}$ and $(\sqrt[5]{b})^2$ in exponential form.

$$\sqrt{a^3} = a^{\frac{3}{2}} \qquad\qquad\qquad (\sqrt[5]{b})^2 = b^{\frac{2}{5}}$$

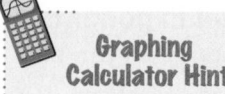 **CA Standards Check** **2 a.** Write the expressions $y^{-\frac{3}{8}}$ and $z^{0.4}$ in radical form.

b. Write the expressions $\sqrt[3]{x^2}$ and $(\sqrt{y})^3$ in exponential form.

c. **Critical Thinking** Refer to the definition of rational exponents. Explain the need for the following restriction: If *m* is negative, $a \neq 0$.

3 EXAMPLE **Real-World Connection**

Graphing Calculator Hint

Use the ∧ key to enter an exponent. If the exponent is a fraction, enclose it in parentheses. For example, $729^{\frac{2}{3}}$ is entered as 729 ∧ (2 ÷ 3).

Space Travel Bone loss for astronauts on lengthy space voyages may be prevented with a bedlike apparatus that rotates to simulate the effect of gravity. In the formula $N = \dfrac{a^{0.5}}{2\pi r^{0.5}}$, *N* is the rate of rotation in revolutions per second, *a* is the simulated acceleration in m/s², and *r* is the radius of the apparatus in meters. How fast would an apparatus with a radius of 1.7 m have to rotate to simulate the acceleration of 9.8 m/s² that is due to Earth's gravity?

$N = \dfrac{a^{0.5}}{2\pi r^{0.5}}$ **Write the formula.**

$= \dfrac{9.8^{0.5}}{2\pi (1.7)^{0.5}}$ **Substitute for *a* and *r*.**

≈ 0.382 **Use a calculator.**

The apparatus would have to rotate about 0.382 revolutions per second, or about 23 revolutions per minute.

 CA Standards Check **3** Calculate the rate of rotation needed for the apparatus in Example 3 to simulate a gravitational acceleration half as strong as Earth's.

All of the properties of integer exponents also apply to rational exponents. Here is a summary.

 Key Concepts

GO for Help

Refer to the properties of integer exponents on p. 374.

| **Summary** | **Properties of Rational Exponents** |

Let m and n represent rational numbers. Assume that no denominator equals 0.

Property	**Example**
$a^m \cdot a^n = a^{m+n}$	$8^{\frac{1}{3}} \cdot 8^{\frac{2}{3}} = 8^{\frac{1}{3}+\frac{2}{3}} = 8^1 = 8$
$(a^m)^n = a^{mn}$	$\left(5^{\frac{1}{2}}\right)^4 = 5^{\frac{1}{2}\cdot 4} = 5^2 = 25$
$(ab)^m = a^m b^m$	$(4 \cdot 5)^{\frac{1}{2}} = 4^{\frac{1}{2}} \cdot 5^{\frac{1}{2}} = 2 \cdot 5^{\frac{1}{2}}$
$a^{-m} = \frac{1}{a^m}$	$9^{-\frac{1}{2}} = \frac{1}{9^{\frac{1}{2}}} = \frac{1}{3}$
$\frac{a^m}{a^n} = a^{m-n}$	$\frac{\pi^{\frac{3}{2}}}{\pi^{\frac{1}{2}}} = \pi^{\frac{3}{2}-\frac{1}{2}} = \pi^1 = \pi$
$\left(\frac{a}{b}\right)^m = \frac{a^m}{b^m}$	$\left(\frac{5}{27}\right)^{\frac{1}{3}} = \frac{5^{\frac{1}{3}}}{27^{\frac{1}{3}}} = \frac{5^{\frac{1}{3}}}{3}$

You can simplify a number with a rational exponent by using the properties of exponents or by converting the expression to a radical expression.

4 EXAMPLE **Simplifying Numbers With Rational Exponents**

GO Online

Video Tutor Help

Visit: PHSchool.com
Web Code: bbe-0775

Simplify each number.

a. $(-32)^{\frac{3}{5}}$

Method 1
$$(-32)^{\frac{3}{5}} = \left((-2)^5\right)^{\frac{3}{5}}$$
$$= (-2)^{5 \cdot \frac{3}{5}}$$
$$= (-2)^3$$
$$= -8$$

Method 2
$$(-32)^{\frac{3}{5}} = \left(\sqrt[5]{-32}\right)^3$$
$$= \left(\sqrt[5]{(-2)^5}\right)^3$$
$$= (-2)^3$$
$$= -8$$

b. $4^{-3.5}$

Method 1
$$4^{-3.5} = 4^{-\frac{7}{2}}$$
$$= (2^2)^{-\frac{7}{2}}$$
$$= 2^{2 \cdot -\frac{7}{2}}$$
$$= 2^{-7}$$
$$= \frac{1}{2^7}$$
$$= \frac{1}{128}$$

Method 2
$$4^{-3.5} = 4^{-\frac{7}{2}}$$
$$= \frac{1}{4^{\frac{7}{2}}}$$
$$= \frac{1}{(\sqrt{4})^7}$$
$$= \frac{1}{2^7}$$
$$= \frac{1}{128}$$

✓ CA Standards Check **4** Simplify each number.

a. $25^{-\frac{3}{2}}$ **b.** $32^{\frac{3}{5}}$ **c.** $(-32)^{\frac{4}{5}}$

To write an expression with rational exponents in simplest form, write every exponent as a positive number.

5 EXAMPLE **Writing Expressions in Simplest Form**

Write $\left(16y^{-8}\right)^{-\frac{3}{4}}$ in simplest form.

$$\left(16y^{-8}\right)^{-\frac{3}{4}} = \left(2^4 y^{-8}\right)^{-\frac{3}{4}}$$

$$= 2^{4 \cdot \left(-\frac{3}{4}\right)} \cdot y^{-8 \cdot \left(-\frac{3}{4}\right)}$$

$$= 2^{-3} y^6$$

$$= \frac{y^6}{2^3}$$

$$= \frac{y^6}{8}$$

✓ **CA Standards Check** **5** Write $\left(8x^{15}\right)^{-\frac{1}{3}}$ in simplest form.

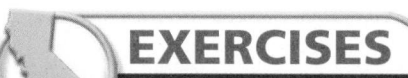

EXERCISES

For more exercises, see *Extra Skill and Word Problem Practice*.

Standards Practice

ALG2 12.0

A **Practice by Example**

Example 1
(page 391)

Simplify each expression.

1. $36^{\frac{1}{2}}$ **2.** $27^{\frac{1}{3}}$ **3.** $49^{\frac{1}{2}}$

4. $10^{\frac{1}{2}} \cdot 10^{\frac{1}{2}}$ **5.** $(-3)^{\frac{1}{3}} \cdot (-3)^{\frac{1}{3}} \cdot (-3)^{\frac{1}{3}}$ **6.** $3^{\frac{1}{2}} \cdot 12^{\frac{1}{2}}$

7. $2^{\frac{1}{2}} \cdot 32^{\frac{1}{2}}$ **8.** $3^{\frac{1}{3}} \cdot 9^{\frac{1}{3}}$ **9.** $3^{\frac{1}{4}} \cdot 27^{\frac{1}{4}}$

Example 2
(page 392)

Write each expression in radical form.

10. $x^{\frac{1}{6}}$ **11.** $x^{\frac{1}{5}}$ **12.** $x^{\frac{2}{7}}$ **13.** $y^{\frac{2}{5}}$

14. $y^{-\frac{9}{8}}$ **15.** $t^{-\frac{3}{4}}$ **16.** $x^{1.5}$ **17.** $y^{1.2}$

Write each expression in exponential form.

18. $\sqrt{-10}$ **19.** $\sqrt{7x^3}$ **20.** $\sqrt{(7x)^3}$ **21.** $\left(\sqrt{7x}\right)^3$

22. $\sqrt[3]{a^2}$ **23.** $\left(\sqrt[3]{a}\right)^2$ **24.** $\sqrt[4]{c^2}$ **25.** $\sqrt[3]{(5xy)^6}$

Example 3
(page 392)

The optimal height h of the letters of a message printed on pavement is given by the formula $h = \frac{0.00252d^{2.27}}{e}$. Here d is the distance of the driver from the letters and e is the height of the driver's eye above the pavement. All of the distances are in meters. Find h for the given values of d and e.

26. $d = 100$ m, $e = 1.2$ m   **27.** $d = 50$ m, $e = 1.2$ m

28. $d = 50$ m, $e = 2.3$ m   **29.** $d = 25$ m, $e = 2.3$ m

Example 4
(page 393)

Simplify each number.

30. $8^{\frac{2}{3}}$ **31.** $64^{\frac{2}{3}}$ **32.** $(-8)^{\frac{2}{3}}$ **33.** $(-32)^{\frac{6}{5}}$

34. $(32)^{-\frac{4}{5}}$ **35.** $4^{1.5}$ **36.** $16^{1.5}$ **37.** $10{,}000^{0.75}$

Example 5
(page 394)

Write each expression in simplest form. Assume that all variables are positive.

38. $\left(x^{\frac{2}{3}}\right)^{-3}$ **39.** $\left(x^{-\frac{4}{7}}\right)^{7}$ **40.** $\left(3x^{\frac{2}{3}}\right)^{-1}$ **41.** $5\left(x^{\frac{2}{3}}\right)^{-1}$

42. $\left(-27x^{-9}\right)^{\frac{1}{3}}$ **43.** $\left(-32y^{15}\right)^{\frac{1}{5}}$ **44.** $\left(\dfrac{x^3}{x^{-1}}\right)^{-\frac{1}{4}}$ **45.** $\left(\dfrac{x^2}{x^{-11}}\right)^{\frac{1}{3}}$

46. $\left(x^{\frac{1}{2}}y^{-\frac{2}{3}}\right)^{-6}$ **47.** $\left(x^{\frac{2}{3}}y^{-\frac{1}{6}}\right)^{-12}$ **48.** $\left(\dfrac{x^{\frac{1}{4}}}{y^{-\frac{3}{4}}}\right)^{12}$ **49.** $\left(\dfrac{x^{-\frac{2}{3}}}{y^{-\frac{1}{3}}}\right)^{15}$

 Apply Your Skills

Simplify each number.

50. $(-343)^{\frac{1}{3}}$ **51.** $(-243)^{\frac{1}{5}}$ **52.** $32^{1.2}$ **53.** $243^{1.2}$

54. $64^{3.5}$ **55.** $100^{4.5}$ **56.** $32^{-0.4}$ **57.** $64^{-0.5}$

58. $(-216)^{-\frac{2}{3}}$ **59.** $2(16)^{\frac{3}{4}}$ **60.** $-(-27)^{-\frac{4}{3}}$ **61.** $\dfrac{1000^{\frac{4}{3}}}{100^{\frac{3}{2}}}$

62. Archaeology The ratio R of radioactive carbon to nonradioactive carbon left in a sample of an organism that died T years ago can be approximated by the formula $R = A(2.7)^{-\frac{T}{8033}}$. Here A is the ratio of radioactive carbon to nonradioactive carbon in the living organism. What percent of A is left after 2000 years? After 4000 years? After 8000 years?

63. Multiple Choice The expression $0.036m^{\frac{3}{4}}$ is used in the study of fluids. Which best represents the value of the expression for $m = 46 \times 10^4$?

    Ⓐ 636   Ⓑ 1460   Ⓒ 1660   Ⓓ 16,600

64. Physics In the expression $PV^{\frac{7}{5}}$, P represents the pressure and V represents the volume of a sample of a gas. Evaluate the expression for $P = 6$ and $V = 32$.

Real-World Connection

Archaeologists estimate the ages of artifacts and fossils by using exponential functions.

Simplify each expression. Assume that all variables are positive.

65. $x^{\frac{2}{7}} \cdot x^{\frac{3}{14}}$ **66.** $y^{\frac{1}{2}} \cdot y^{\frac{3}{10}}$ **67.** $x^{\frac{3}{5}} \div x^{\frac{1}{10}}$ **68.** $y^{\frac{5}{7}} \div y^{\frac{3}{14}}$

69. $\dfrac{x^{\frac{2}{3}}y^{-\frac{1}{4}}}{x^{\frac{1}{2}}y^{-\frac{1}{2}}}$ **70.** $\dfrac{x^{\frac{1}{2}}y^{-\frac{1}{3}}}{x^{\frac{3}{4}}y^{\frac{1}{2}}}$ **71.** $\left(\dfrac{16x^{14}}{81y^{18}}\right)^{\frac{1}{2}}$ **72.** $\left(\dfrac{81y^{16}}{16x^{12}}\right)^{\frac{1}{2}}$

73. $\left(x^{\frac{1}{2}} \cdot x^{\frac{5}{12}}\right)^{\frac{1}{3}} \div x^{\frac{2}{3}}$ **74.** $\left(x^{\frac{3}{4}} \div x^{\frac{7}{8}}\right) \cdot x^{-\frac{1}{6}}$ **75.** $\left[\left(x^{-\frac{1}{2}}\right)^2\right]^{\frac{1}{3}}$ **76.** $\left[\left(\sqrt{x^3y^3}\right)^{\frac{1}{3}}\right]^{-1}$

77. Writing Explain why $(-64)^{\frac{1}{3}} = -64^{\frac{1}{3}}$ and $(-64)^{\frac{1}{2}} \neq -64^{\frac{1}{2}}$.

78. Error Analysis Explain why the following simplification is incorrect.

$5\left(4 - 5^{\frac{1}{2}}\right) = 5(4) - 5\left(5^{\frac{1}{2}}\right) = 20 - 25^{\frac{1}{2}} = 15$

79. Open-Ended Find three nonzero numbers a such that $a\left(4 + 5^{\frac{1}{2}}\right)$ is a rational number. Can a itself be a rational number? Explain.

80. a. Reasoning Show that $\sqrt[4]{x^2} = \sqrt{x}$ by using the definition of fourth root.

    b. Reasoning Show that $\sqrt[4]{x^2} = \sqrt{x}$ by rewriting $\sqrt[4]{x^2}$ in exponential form.

 Challenge

Exponents that are irrational numbers can be defined so that all the properties of rational exponents are also true for irrational exponents. Use those properties to simplify each expression.

81. $\left(7^{\sqrt{2}}\right)^{\sqrt{2}}$ **82.** $\dfrac{3^{3+\sqrt{5}}}{3^{1+\sqrt{5}}}$ **83.** $\dfrac{x^{4\pi}}{x^{2\pi}}$

84. $5^{2\sqrt{3}} \cdot 25^{-\sqrt{3}}$ **85.** $9^{\frac{1}{\sqrt{2}}}$ **86.** $\left(3^{2+\sqrt{2}}\right)^{2-\sqrt{2}}$

Visit: PHSchool.com
Web Code: bbe-0704

87. Weather Using data for the effect of temperature and wind on an exposed face, the National Weather Service uses the following formula.

$$\text{Wind Chill Index} = 35.74 + 0.6215T - 35.75V^{0.16} + 0.4275TV^{0.16}$$

T is the temperature in degrees Fahrenheit and V is the velocity of the wind in miles per hour. Frostbite occurs in about 15 minutes when the wind chill index is about -20. Find the wind speed that produces a wind chill index of -20 when the temperature is $5°F$.

Multiple Choice Practice

For California Standards and CAHSEE Tutorials, visit PHSchool.com. Web Code: bbq-9045

ALG2 12.0 **88.** Which expression is equivalent to $\left(n^{\frac{3}{2}} \div n^{-\frac{1}{6}} \right)^{-3}$?

     A n^{27} **B** n^{-27} **C** n^{-4} **D** n^{-5}

ALG2 12.0 **89.** Which equation represents a property of exponents?

     A $(a^m)^n = a^{m+n}$ **C** $\left(\dfrac{a}{b} \right)^m = \dfrac{a^m}{b}$

     B $a^{-m} = \dfrac{1}{a^m}$ **D** $a^m \cdot a^n = a^{mn}$

ALG2 1.0 **90.** Which is the graph of $y - 2 = 2|x - 2|$?

A

C

B

D

Mixed Review

Lesson 7-3 **Simplify. Rationalize all denominators.**

91. $6\sqrt[3]{3} - 2\sqrt[3]{3}$ **92.** $3\sqrt{18} + 2\sqrt{72}$ **93.** $(\sqrt{5} - 1)(\sqrt{5} + 4)$

94. $(\sqrt{8} - \sqrt{7})^2$ **95.** $\dfrac{2 + \sqrt{10}}{2 - 3\sqrt{5}}$ **96.** $\dfrac{-2 + \sqrt{8}}{-3 - \sqrt{2}}$

Lesson 5-4 **Factor each expression.**

97. $4x^3 - 8x^2 + 16x$ **98.** $x^2 + 4x + 4$ **99.** $x^2 - 18x + 81$

100. $16a^2 - 9b^2$ **101.** $25x^2 - 40xy + 16y^2$ **102.** $9x^2 + 48x + 64$

7-5

Solving Square Root and Other Radical Equations

California Content Standards

ALG2 8.0 Students solve quadratic equations by factoring. *Master*

What You'll Learn

- To solve square root and other radical equations

...And Why

To find the power from a circular solar cell, as in Example 3

✓ **Check Skills You'll Need**

Solve by factoring.

1. $x^2 = -x + 6$

2. $x^2 = 5x + 14$

3. $2x^2 + x = 3$

4. $3x^2 - 2 = 5x$

5. $4x^2 = -8x + 5$

6. $6x^2 = 5x + 6$

GO for Help Lesson 5-5

🔊 **New Vocabulary** • radical equation • square root equation

---

1 Solving Radical Equations

A **radical equation** is an equation that has a variable in a radicand (or a variable with a fractional exponent). If the radical has index 2, the equation is a **square root equation**. In this lesson, you may assume that all radicals have real-number values.

$3 + \sqrt{x} = 10$ **square root equation** $\sqrt{3} + x = 10$ **not a square root equation**

To solve a radical equation, isolate the radical on one side of the equation and then raise both sides of the equation to the same power.

If $\sqrt[n]{x} = k$, then $(\sqrt[n]{x})^n = k^n$ and $x = k^n$.

1 EXAMPLE Solving Square Root Equations

Solve $2 + \sqrt{3x - 2} = 6$.

$2 + \sqrt{3x - 2} = 6$

$\sqrt{3x - 2} = 4$ **Isolate the radical.**

$(\sqrt{3x - 2})^2 = 4^2$ **Square each side.**

$3x - 2 = 16$

$3x = 18$

$x = 6$

Check $2 + \sqrt{3x - 2} = 6$

$2 + \sqrt{3(6) - 2} \overset{?}{=} 6$

$2 + \sqrt{16} \overset{?}{=} 6$

$2 + 4 \overset{?}{=} 6$

$6 = 6$ ✓

✓ **CA Standards Check** ① Solve $\sqrt{5x + 1} - 6 = 0$.

You can solve equations of the form $x^{\frac{m}{n}} = k$ by raising each side of the equation to the power $\frac{n}{m}$, the reciprocal of $\frac{m}{n}$. If the nth root of x is a real number, then $(x^{\frac{m}{n}})^{\frac{n}{m}} = |x|$.

2 EXAMPLE **Solving Radical Equations With Rational Exponents**

Solve $2(x - 2)^{\frac{2}{3}} = 50$.

$$2(x - 2)^{\frac{2}{3}} = 50$$

$$(x - 2)^{\frac{2}{3}} = 25 \qquad \text{Divide each side by 2.}$$

$$\left((x - 2)^{\frac{2}{3}}\right)^{\frac{3}{2}} = 25^{\frac{3}{2}} \qquad \text{Raise each side to the } \tfrac{3}{2} \text{ power.}$$

$$|x - 2|^1 = 25^{\frac{3}{2}} \qquad \text{Simplify.}$$

$$x - 2 = \pm 125 \qquad \text{Simplify.}$$

$$x = 127 \text{ or } x = -123$$

Check
$$2(x - 2)^{\frac{2}{3}} = 50 \qquad\qquad 2(x - 2)^{\frac{2}{3}} = 50$$
$$2(127 - 2)^{\frac{2}{3}} \stackrel{?}{=} 50 \qquad\qquad 2(-123 - 2)^{\frac{2}{3}} \stackrel{?}{=} 50$$
$$2(5^3)^{\frac{2}{3}} \stackrel{?}{=} 50 \qquad\qquad 2(-125)^{\frac{2}{3}} \stackrel{?}{=} 50$$
$$2(5)^2 \stackrel{?}{=} 50 \qquad\qquad 2(-5)^2 \stackrel{?}{=} 50$$
$$50 = 50 \checkmark \qquad\qquad 50 = 50 \checkmark$$

 CA Standards Check **2** Solve $2(x + 3)^{\frac{3}{2}} = 54$.

3 EXAMPLE **Real-World** **Connection**

Multiple Choice The power P in watts that a circular solar cell produces and the radius of the cell in centimeters are related by the square root equation

$r = \sqrt{\dfrac{P}{0.02\pi}}$. About how much power is produced by a cell with a radius of 10 cm?

Ⓐ 0.13 watt   Ⓑ 0.63 watt   Ⓒ 1.3 watts   Ⓓ 6.3 watts

$$r = \sqrt{\frac{P}{0.02\pi}}$$

$$10 = \sqrt{\frac{P}{0.02\pi}} \qquad \text{Substitute 10 for } r.$$

$$100 = \frac{P}{0.02\pi} \qquad \text{Square each side.}$$

$$100(0.02\pi) = P \qquad \text{Multiply each side by } 0.02\pi.$$

$$6.3 \approx P \qquad \text{Simplify. Round to one decimal place.}$$

A cell with radius 10 cm produces about 6.3 watts of power. The correct choice is D.

Real-World **Connection**

Solar cells convert sunlight directly into electricity. They power calculators, emergency road signs, satellites, and experimental vehicles.

 CA Standards Check **3** How much power is produced by a cell with radius 20 cm? How does this compare with the power produced by a 10-cm cell?

Extraneous solutions can be introduced when you raise both sides of an equation to a power. So check all possible solutions in the original equation.

4 EXAMPLE Checking for Extraneous Solutions

GO for Help

To review extraneous solutions, go to Lesson 1-5.

Solve $\sqrt{x-3} + 5 = x$. Check for extraneous solutions.

$$\sqrt{x-3} + 5 = x$$

$\sqrt{x-3} = x - 5$	Isolate the radical.
$(\sqrt{x-3})^2 = (x-5)^2$	Square each side.
$x - 3 = x^2 - 10x + 25$	Simplify.
$0 = x^2 - 11x + 28$	Combine like terms.
$0 = (x-4)(x-7)$	Factor.
$x - 4 = 0 \ \text{ or } \ x - 7 = 0$	Zero Product Theorem
$x = 4 \ \text{ or } \ x = 7$	

Check

$$\sqrt{x-3} + 5 = x \qquad\qquad \sqrt{x-3} + 5 = x$$
$$\sqrt{4-3} + 5 \overset{?}{=} 4 \qquad\qquad \sqrt{7-3} + 5 \overset{?}{=} 7$$
$$\sqrt{1} + 5 \overset{?}{=} 4 \qquad\qquad \sqrt{4} + 5 \overset{?}{=} 7$$
$$6 \neq 4 \qquad\qquad\qquad\qquad 7 = 7$$

● The only solution is 7.

✓ CA Standards Check ④ Solve $\sqrt{5x-1} + 3 = x$. Check for extraneous solutions.

If an equation contains two radical expressions (or two terms with rational exponents), isolate one of the radicals (or one of the terms).

5 EXAMPLE Solving Equations With Two Rational Exponents

Solve $(2x+1)^{0.5} - (3x+4)^{0.25} = 0$. Check for extraneous solutions.

$$(2x+1)^{0.5} - (3x+4)^{0.25} = 0$$

$(2x+1)^{0.5} = (3x+4)^{0.25}$	
$((2x+1)^{0.5})^4 = ((3x+4)^{0.25})^4$	Raise each side to the 4th power.
$(2x+1)^2 = 3x + 4$	Simplify exponents.
$4x^2 + 4x + 1 = 3x + 4$	Simplify.
$4x^2 + x - 3 = 0$	Combine like terms.
$(4x-3)(x+1) = 0$	Factor.
$x = \frac{3}{4} \ \text{ or } \ x = -1$	Zero Product Theorem

Test-Taking Tip

When you check a solution on a test, use the equation printed on the test rather than the one you've written on your paper. You could have copied the equation incorrectly.

Check

$$(2x+1)^{0.5} - (3x+4)^{0.25} = 0 \qquad\qquad (2x+1)^{0.5} - (3x+4)^{0.25} = 0$$
$$\left(2\cdot\tfrac{3}{4}+1\right)^{0.5} - \left(3\cdot\tfrac{3}{4}+4\right)^{0.25} \overset{?}{=} 0 \qquad (2(-1)+1)^{0.5} - (3(-1)+4)^{0.25} \overset{?}{=} 0$$
$$\left(\tfrac{5}{2}\right)^{0.5} - \left(\tfrac{25}{4}\right)^{0.25} \overset{?}{=} 0 \qquad\qquad\qquad (-1)^{0.5} - (1)^{0.25} \overset{?}{=} 0$$
$$\left(\tfrac{5}{2}\right)^{0.5} - \left(\left(\tfrac{5}{2}\right)^2\right)^{0.25} \overset{?}{=} 0 \qquad\qquad\qquad (-1)^{0.5} \text{ is not a real number.}$$
$$\left(\tfrac{5}{2}\right)^{0.5} - \left(\tfrac{5}{2}\right)^{0.5} = 0$$

● The only solution is $\frac{3}{4}$.

✓ CA Standards Check ⑤ Solve $\sqrt{3x+2} - \sqrt{2x+7} = 0$. Check for extraneous solutions.

Technology Activity: Checking for Extraneous Solutions

You can use a graphing calculator to check for extraneous solutions.

1. a. Solve $x = \sqrt{x + 7} + 5$. How many apparent solutions do you get?

   b. Any or all of the apparent solutions may be extraneous. One way to find out is to let y_1 equal the left side of the equation and let y_2 equal the right side. Graph the two equations. In how many points do they intersect?

   c. The x-values of the points of intersection are solutions of the original equation. Are any of the apparent solutions extraneous?

   d. Substitute the apparent solutions in the original equation. Does this algebraic check agree with the calculator check?

2. Use a graphing calculator to determine the number of solutions of each equation.

   a. $\sqrt{x} = x - 2$ b. $\sqrt{x^2 + 3} = 2x - 1$ c. $x + 8 = 4\sqrt{x + 5}$

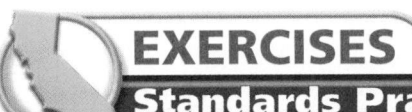

EXERCISES

For more exercises, see *Extra Skill and Word Problem Practice.*

Standards Practice

ALG2 8.0

A Practice by Example

Example 1
(page 397)

Solve.

1. $3\sqrt{x} + 3 = 15$

2. $4\sqrt{x} - 1 = 3$

3. $\sqrt{x + 3} = 5$

4. $\sqrt{3x + 4} = 4$

5. $\sqrt{2x + 3} - 7 = 0$

6. $\sqrt{6 - 3x} - 2 = 0$

Example 2
(page 398)

Solve.

7. $(x + 5)^{\frac{2}{3}} = 4$

8. $(x - 2)^{\frac{2}{3}} = 9$

9. $3(x - 2)^{\frac{3}{4}} = 24$

10. $3(x + 3)^{\frac{3}{4}} = 81$

11. $(x + 1)^{\frac{3}{2}} - 2 = 25$

12. $3 + (4 - x)^{\frac{3}{2}} = 11$

Example 3
(page 398)

13. **Volume** A spherical water tank holds 15,000 ft^3 of water. Find the diameter of the tank. (*Hint:* $V = \frac{\pi}{6}d^3$)

14. **Hydraulics** The maximum flow of water in a pipe is modeled by the formula $Q = Av$, where A is the cross-sectional area of the pipe and v is the velocity of the water. Find the diameter of a pipe that allows a maximum flow of 50 ft^3/min of water flowing at a velocity of 600 ft/min. Round your answer to the nearest inch.

Example 4
(page 399)

Solve. Check for extraneous solutions.

15. $\sqrt{11x + 3} - 2x = 0$

16. $(5x + 4)^{\frac{1}{2}} - 3x = 0$

17. $\sqrt{3x + 13} - 5 = x$

18. $\sqrt{x + 7} + 5 = x$

19. $(x + 3)^{\frac{1}{2}} - 1 = x$

20. $(5 - x)^{\frac{1}{2}} = x + 1$

400   Chapter 7   Radical Functions and Rational Exponents

Example 5
(page 399)

Solve. Check for extraneous solutions.

21. $\sqrt{3x} = \sqrt{x + 6}$

22. $(x + 5)^{\frac{1}{2}} - (5 - 2x)^{\frac{1}{4}} = 0$

23. $(7x + 6)^{\frac{1}{2}} = (9 + 4x)^{\frac{1}{2}}$

24. $\sqrt{3x + 7} = x - 1$

25. $\sqrt{x + 7} - x = 1$

26. $\sqrt{-3x - 5} = x + 3$

27. $(3x + 2)^{\frac{1}{2}} - (2x + 7)^{\frac{1}{2}} = 0$

28. $x + 8 = (x^2 + 16)^{\frac{1}{2}}$

29. $(2x)^{\frac{1}{2}} = (x + 5)^{\frac{1}{2}}$

30. $1 = (3 + x)^{\frac{1}{2}}$

B Apply Your Skills

31. a. Form a pair of simultaneous equations by letting y_1 equal the left side and y_2 equal the right side of $\sqrt{5} - x = 1$. Graph the equations.

   b. Repeat part (a) with the equivalent equation $\sqrt{5} = x + 1$.

   c. Repeat part (a) with the equivalent equation $\sqrt{5} - x - 1 = 0$.

    d. **Writing** Describe the similarities and differences among the graphs of the three sets of simultaneous equations.

32. a. **Package Design** The formula for the area A of a hexagon with a side s units long is $A = \frac{3s^2\sqrt{3}}{2}$. See the figure below. Solve the formula for s and rationalize the denominator.

   b. A package designer wants the hexagonal base of a hat box to have an area of about 200 in.^{2}. About how long is each side?

   c. What is the distance between opposite sides of the hat box?

33. Multiple Choice You can find the area A of a square whose side is s units as $A = s^2$. Find the best estimate for the side of a square with an area of 32 m^2.

   (A) 4.2 m   (B) 5.7 m   (C) 8.0 m   (D) 16 m

Solve. Check for extraneous solutions.

34. $3\sqrt{2x} - 3 = 9$

35. $2(2x)^{\frac{1}{3}} + 1 = 5$

36. $\sqrt{2x - 1} - 3 = 0$

37. $(2x + 3)^{\frac{1}{2}} - 7 = 0$

38. $\sqrt{x^2 + 3} = x + 1$

39. $(2x + 3)^{\frac{3}{4}} - 3 = 5$

40. $2(x - 1)^{\frac{4}{3}} + 4 = 36$

41. $x^{\frac{1}{2}} - (x - 5)^{\frac{1}{2}} = 2$

42. $\sqrt{x} = \sqrt{x - 8} + 2$

Homework Video Tutor

Visit: PHSchool.com
Web Code: bbe-0705

For each equation, let Y1 = left side and Y2 = right side. Display a graphing calculator table of X, Y1, and Y2 values. Find where Y1 = Y2. Use the Technology Activity steps on page 394 to check that you've found all solutions.

43. $\sqrt{5x + 1} - \sqrt{4x + 3} = 0$

44. $\sqrt{x + 10} + \sqrt{3 - x} = 5$

45. $(3x + 2)^{\frac{1}{2}} = 8(3x + 2)^{-\frac{1}{2}}$

46. $\sqrt{4x - 10} = 3\sqrt{x - 5}$

47. $(x - 9)^{\frac{1}{2}} + 1 = x^{\frac{1}{2}}$

48. $\sqrt{10x} - 2\sqrt{5x - 25} = 0$

49. $(2x + 1)^{\frac{1}{3}} = (2 + 3x)^{\frac{1}{3}}$

50. $(2x - 1)^{\frac{1}{3}} = (x + 1)^{\frac{1}{6}}$

51. Physics The velocity v of an object dropped from a tall building is given by the formula $v = \sqrt{64d}$, where d is the distance the object has dropped. Solve the formula for d.

52. Open-Ended Write an equation that has two radical expressions and no real roots.

 Challenge

Solve. Check for extraneous solutions.

53. $\sqrt{x + 1} + \sqrt{2x} = \sqrt{5x + 3}$

54. $\sqrt{x + \sqrt{2x}} = \sqrt{2x}$

55. $\sqrt{x + \sqrt{2x}} = 2$

56. $\sqrt{\sqrt{x + 25}} = \sqrt{x + 5}$

57. Critical Thinking Devise a plan to find the value of x.
$$x = \sqrt{2 + \sqrt{2 + \sqrt{2 + \ldots}}}$$

58. Critical Thinking You have solved equations containing square roots by squaring both sides. You were using the property that if $a = b$ then $a^2 = b^2$. Show that the following statements are *not* true for all real numbers.
  a. If $a^2 = b^2$ then $a = b$.
  b. If $a < b$ then $a^2 < b^2$.

Multiple Choice Practice

For California Standards and CAHSEE Tutorials, visit PHSchool.com. Web Code: bbq-9045

ALG2 8.0

59. Which quadratic equation has zeros at $x = 4$ and $x = -9$?
  Ⓐ $y = x^2 + 5x - 36$
  Ⓒ $y = x^2 - 5x - 36$
  Ⓑ $y = x^2 - 5x - 36$
  Ⓓ $y = x^2 + 5x + 36$

ALG2 12.0

60. Which expression best represents the simplification of $(6a^3b^4)(-2a^{-3}b^2)$?
  Ⓐ $\dfrac{12}{a^6b^6}$
  Ⓑ $-12a^6b^6$
  Ⓒ $-12b^6$
  Ⓓ $\dfrac{12}{b^6}$

ALG2 9.0

61. The graph of which function is NOT congruent to the graph of $y = 3x^2 - 1$?
  Ⓐ $y = -3x^2 - 1$
  Ⓒ $y = 3x^2 + 1$
  Ⓑ $y = x^2 - 1$
  Ⓓ $y = -3x^2 + 1$

Mixed Review

Lesson 7-4

Simplify each expression.

62. $64^{\frac{2}{3}}$ **63.** $25^{1.5}$ **64.** $6^{\frac{1}{2}} \cdot 12^{\frac{1}{2}}$ **65.** $8^{\frac{1}{2}} \cdot 40^{\frac{1}{2}}$ **66.** $3^{\frac{1}{3}} \cdot 18^{\frac{1}{3}}$

67. $81^{-0.25}$ **68.** $4^{3.5}$ **69.** $125 \cdot 125^{-\frac{1}{3}}$ **70.** $32 \cdot 256^{-\frac{1}{2}}$ **71.** $100^{-\frac{3}{2}} \cdot 0.01^{\frac{3}{2}}$

Lesson 6-7

Evaluate each expression.

72. $_7P_1$ **73.** $_7P_3$ **74.** $_5P_3$ **75.** $_8P_4$ **76.** $_4P_4$

77. $_5C_2$ **78.** $_7C_5$ **79.** $_5C_5$ **80.** $_6C_5$ **81.** $_7C_1$

Lesson 5-5

Solve each equation by factoring.

82. $x^2 - 7x + 12 = 0$ **83.** $x^2 - 8x + 15 = 0$ **84.** $x^2 + 9x + 20 = 0$

85. $3x^2 + 8x + 4 = 0$ **86.** $9x^2 + 15x + 4 = 0$ **87.** $4x^2 + 11x + 6 = 0$

You frequently need to use radical expressions in geometry formulas.

EXAMPLE

The cube at the right fits in (is inscribed in) the sphere. How much more than the cube does the sphere hold?

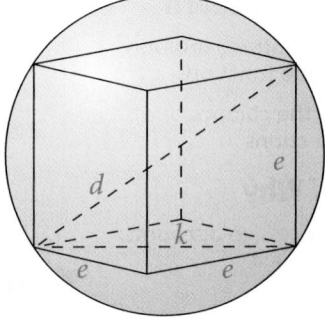

  Ⓐ 25% more   Ⓑ 50% more   Ⓒ 100% more   Ⓓ 150% more

Step 1 Find k.

k is the diagonal of the square that is the base of the cube. Use the Pythagorean Theorem.

$$k^2 = e^2 + e^2$$
$$= 2e^2$$
$$k = e\sqrt{2}$$

Step 2 Find the radius of the sphere.

The diameter d of the sphere is also the diagonal of the cube and the hypotenuse of a right triangle with legs k and e.

$$d^2 = k^2 + e^2$$
$$= (e\sqrt{2})^2 + e^2$$
$$= 2e^2 + e^2$$
$$= 3e^2$$
$$d = e\sqrt{3}.$$

So the radius of the sphere is $\frac{d}{2}$ or $\frac{e\sqrt{3}}{2}$.

Step 3 Find the ratio of the volume of the sphere to the volume of the cube.

The volume of a sphere is $V = \frac{4}{3}\pi r^3$.

The volume of the cube is e^3.

$$\frac{\text{volume of sphere}}{\text{volume of cube}} = \frac{\frac{4}{3}\pi\left(\frac{e\sqrt{3}}{2}\right)^3}{e^3}$$
$$= \frac{4\pi \cdot 3e^3\sqrt{3}}{3 \cdot 8 \cdot e^3}$$
$$= \frac{\pi\sqrt{3}}{2} \approx 2.7$$

The sphere holds about 2.7 times as much as the cube, so it holds 1.7 times more, or 170% more than the cube. If you chose answer D, you are a very good estimator!

EXERCISES

1. a. The cube at the right is inscribed in a cylinder. Estimate the percent by which the volume of the cylinder exceeds the volume of the cube. Then compute the percent. (For the volume of a cylinder: $V = \pi r^2 h$.)

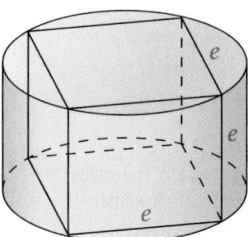

  b. Estimate the percent by which the surface area of the cylinder exceeds the surface area of the cube. Then compute the percent. (The formula for the surface area of a cylinder is S.A. $= 2\pi r^2 + 2\pi rh$.)

2. Estimate the percent by which the surface area of a sphere exceeds the surface area of its inscribed cube. Then compute the percent. (The formula for the surface area of a sphere is S.A. $= 4\pi r^2$.)

3. Estimate the percent by which the area and circumference of a circle exceed the area and perimeter of its inscribed square. Then compute the percents.

4. In the Example, suppose a smaller sphere is inscribed in the cube. Estimate the percent by which the volume of the outer sphere exceeds the volume of the inner sphere. Then compute the percent.

Function Operations

California Content Standards
ALG2 24.0 Students solve problems involving functional concepts, such as composition and performing arithmetic operations on functions. *Introduce, Develop*
ALG2 25.0 Students use properties from number systems to justify steps in combining and simplifying functions. *Introduce, Develop*

What You'll Learn

- To add, subtract, multiply, and divide functions
- To find the composite of two functions

...And Why

To find successive discounts, as in Example 4

 Check Skills You'll Need

 GO for Help Lesson 2-1

Find the domain and range of each function.

1. $\{(0, -5), (2, -3), (4, -1)\}$
2. $\{(-1, 0), (0, 0), (1, 0)\}$
3. $f(x) = 2x - 12$
4. $g(x) = x^2$

Evaluate each function for the given value of x.

5. Let $f(x) = 3x + 4$. Find $f(2)$.
6. Let $g(x) = 2x^2 - 3x + 1$. Find $g(-3)$.

New Vocabulary • composite function

---

1 Operations With Functions

If an airplane has an airspeed of 415 mi/h, then $f(x) = 415x$ represents the distance traveled by the plane in still air in x hours. If the wind speed is 30 mi/h, then $g(x) = 30x$ represents the motion of the wind, and $f(x) + g(x) = 415x + 30x$ represents the distance traveled by the airplane flying with the wind.

You can add, subtract, multiply, and divide functions.

 Key Concepts

Definition	Function Operations
Addition	$(f + g)(x) = f(x) + g(x)$
Multiplication	$(f \cdot g)(x) = f(x) \cdot g(x)$
Subtraction	$(f - g)(x) = f(x) - g(x)$
Division	$\left(\dfrac{f}{g}\right)(x) = \dfrac{f(x)}{g(x)}, \; g(x) \neq 0$

Vocabulary Tip

The domain of a function is the set of all possible inputs of the function.

The range of a function is the set of all possible outputs of the function.

The domains of the sum, difference, product, and quotient functions consist of the x-values that are in the domains of both f and g. However, the domain of a quotient function does not contain any x-value for which $g(x) = 0$.

1 EXAMPLE Adding and Subtracting Functions

Let $f(x) = 3x + 8$ and $g(x) = 2x - 12$. Find $f + g$ and $f - g$ and their domains.

$(f + g)(x) = f(x) + g(x) = (3x + 8) + (2x - 12) = 5x - 4$
$(f - g)(x) = f(x) - g(x) = (3x + 8) - (2x - 12) = x + 20$

The domain of both $f + g$ and $f - g$ is the set of real numbers.

CA Standards Check 1 Let $f(x) = 5x^2 - 4x$ and $g(x) = 5x + 1$. Find $f + g$ and $f - g$ and their domains.

---

2 EXAMPLE **Multiplying and Dividing Functions**

Let $f(x) = x^2 - 1$ and $g(x) = x + 1$. Find $f \cdot g$ and $\dfrac{f}{g}$ and their domains.

$(f \cdot g)(x) = f(x) \cdot g(x) = (x^2 - 1)(x + 1) = x^3 + x^2 - x - 1$

$\left(\dfrac{f}{g}\right)(x) = \dfrac{f(x)}{g(x)} = \dfrac{x^2 - 1}{x + 1} = \dfrac{(x + 1)(x - 1)}{x + 1} = x - 1, x \neq -1$

The domains of f and g are the set of real numbers, so the domain of $f \cdot g$ is also.

The domain of $\dfrac{f}{g}$ does not include -1 because $g(-1) = 0$.

✓ **CA Standards Check** **2** Let $f(x) = 6x^2 + 7x - 5$ and $g(x) = 2x - 1$. Find $f \cdot g$ and $\dfrac{f}{g}$ and their domains.

2 Composition of Functions

The diagram below shows what happens when you apply one function $g(x)$ after another function $f(x)$.

$$\begin{array}{c} f(x) \\ \text{1st} \qquad\qquad \text{1st} \quad \text{2nd} \qquad\qquad\quad g(x) \\ \text{Input} \Rightarrow \boxed{x^2} \Rightarrow \text{Output} \quad \text{Input} \Rightarrow \boxed{x + 4} \Rightarrow \text{2nd Output} \\ x \qquad\qquad x^2 \qquad x^2 \qquad\qquad\qquad x^2 + 4 \end{array}$$

Vocabulary Tip

Composite means
"put together."

The output from the first function becomes the input for the second function. When you combine two functions as in the diagram above, you form a **composite function.**

 Key Concepts

Definition	**Composition of Functions**

The composition of function g with function f is written as $g \circ f$ and is defined as $(g \circ f)(x) = g(f(x))$. The domain of $g \circ f$ consists of the values a in the domain of f for which $f(a)$ is in the domain of g.

$$(g \circ f)(x) = g(\underbrace{f(x)}_{①})$$
$$②$$

① **Evaluate the inner function $f(x)$ first.**

② **Then use your result as the input of the outer function $g(x)$.**

3 EXAMPLE **Composition of Functions**

Let $f(x) = x - 2$ and $g(x) = x^2$. Find $(g \circ f)(-5)$.

Method 1
$(g \circ f)(x) = g(f(x)) = g(x - 2) = (x - 2)^2$
$(g \circ f)(-5) = (-5 - 2)^2$
$\qquad\qquad = (-7)^2$
$\qquad\qquad = 49$

Method 2
$(g \circ f)(x) = g(f(x))$
$g(f(-5)) = g(-5 - 2)$
$\qquad\quad = g(-7)$
$\qquad\quad = (-7)^2 = 49$

✓ **CA Standards Check** **3** **a.** Find $(f \circ g)(x)$ and evaluate $(f \circ g)(-5)$ for the functions f and g defined in Example 3.

b. Critical Thinking Is a composition of functions commutative? Explain.

4 EXAMPLE   Real-World ⊕ Connection

Consumer Issues Suppose you are shopping in
the store in the photo. You have a coupon
worth $5 off any item.

a. Use functions to model discounting an item
by 20% and to model applying the coupon.

Let x = the original price.

Cost with 20% discount:

$$f(x) = x - 0.2x = 0.8x$$

Cost with a coupon for $5:

$$g(x) = x - 5$$

b. Use a composition of your two functions to model how much you would pay for
an item if the clerk applies the discount first and then the coupon.

$$(g \circ f)(x) = g(f(x)) \qquad \textbf{applying the discount first}$$
$$= g(0.8x)$$
$$= 0.8x - 5$$

c. Use a composition of your two functions to model how much you would pay for
an item if the clerk applies the coupon first and then the discount.

$$(f \circ g)(x) = f(g(x)) \qquad \textbf{applying the coupon first}$$
$$= f(x - 5)$$
$$= 0.8(x - 5)$$
$$= 0.8x - 4$$

d. How much more is any item if the clerk applies the coupon first?

$$(f \circ g)(x) - (g \circ f)(x) = (0.8x - 4) - (0.8x - 5) \qquad \textbf{Subtract the functions.}$$
$$= 1$$

Any item will cost $1 more.

✓ **CA Standards Check** ④ A store is offering a 10% discount on all items. In addition, employees get a
25% discount.
a. Write a composite function to model taking the 10% discount first.
b. Write a composite function to model taking the 25% discount first.
c. Suppose you are an employee. Which discount would you prefer to take first?

For more exercises, see *Extra Skill and Word Problem Practice.*
ALG2 24.0, 25.0

A Practice by Example

Examples 1 and 2
(pages 404, 405)
GO for Help

Let $f(x) = 3x + 5$ and $g(x) = x^2$. Perform each function operation.

1. $f(x) + g(x)$

2. $g(x) - f(x)$

3. $f(x) - g(x)$

4. $f(x) \cdot g(x)$

5. $\dfrac{f(x)}{g(x)}$

6. $\dfrac{g(x)}{f(x)}$

7. $(f + g)(x)$

8. $(f - g)(x)$

9. $(g - f)(x)$

10. $(f \cdot g)(x)$

11. $\left(\dfrac{f}{g}\right)(x)$

12. $\left(\dfrac{g}{f}\right)(x)$

Let $f(x) = 2x^2 + x - 3$ and $g(x) = x - 1$. **Perform each function operation and then find the domain.**

13. $f(x) + g(x)$ **14.** $g(x) - f(x)$ **15.** $f(x) - g(x)$

16. $f(x) \cdot g(x)$ **17.** $\dfrac{f(x)}{g(x)}$ **18.** $\dfrac{g(x)}{f(x)}$

19. Let $f(x) = 9x$ and $g(x) = 3x$. Find $(f \cdot g)(x)$ and $\left(\dfrac{f}{g}\right)(x)$ and their domains.

Example 3
(page 405)

Use each diagram to find $(g \circ f)(x)$. Then evaluate $(g \circ f)(3)$ and $(g \circ f)(-2)$.

20.

$f(x) = 2x$ $g(x) = x + 3$

21.

$f(x) = x^2$ $g(x) = |x + 5|$

Let $g(x) = 2x$ and $h(x) = x^2 + 4$. **Evaluate each expression.**

22. $(h \circ g)(1)$ **23.** $(h \circ g)(-5)$ **24.** $(h \circ g)(-2)$

25. $(g \circ h)(-2)$ **26.** $(g \circ h)(0)$ **27.** $(g \circ h)(-1)$

28. $(g \circ g)(3)$ **29.** $(h \circ h)(2)$ **30.** $(h \circ h)(-4)$

Let $f(x) = x^2$ and $g(x) = x - 3$. **Find each value or expression.**

31. $(g \circ f)(-2)$ **32.** $(f \circ g)(-2)$ **33.** $(g \circ f)(0)$

34. $(f \circ g)(0)$ **35.** $(g \circ f)(3.5)$ **36.** $(f \circ g)(3.5)$

37. $(f \circ g)\left(\dfrac{1}{2}\right)$ **38.** $(g \circ f)\left(\dfrac{1}{2}\right)$ **39.** $(f \circ g)(c)$

40. $(g \circ f)(c)$ **41.** $(f \circ g)(-a)$ **42.** $(g \circ f)(-a)$

Example 4
(page 406)

43. Sales A car dealer offers a 10% discount off the list price x for any car on the lot. At the same time, the manufacturer offers a $2000 rebate for each purchase of a car.
  a. Write a function $f(x)$ to represent the price after the discount.
  b. Write a function $g(x)$ to represent the price after the $2000 rebate.
  c. Suppose the list price of a car is $18,000. Use a composite function to find the price of the car if the discount is applied before the rebate.
  d. Suppose the list price of a car is $18,000. Use a composite function to find the price of the car if the rebate is applied before the discount.

44. Economics Suppose the function $f(x) = 0.12x$ represents the number of U.S. dollars equivalent to x Chinese yuan and the function $g(x) = 9.14x$ represents the number of Mexican pesos equivalent to x U.S. dollars.
  a. Write a composite function that represents the number of Mexican pesos equivalent to x Chinese yuan.
  b. Find the value in Mexican pesos of an item that costs 15 Chinese yuan.

Apply Your Skills

Let $f(x) = 2x + 5$ and $g(x) = x^2 - 3x + 2$. Perform each function operation.

45. $f(x) + g(x)$ **46.** $3f(x) - 2$ **47.** $g(x) - f(x)$

48. $-2g(x) + f(x)$ **49.** $f(x) - g(x) + 10$ **50.** $4f(x) + 2g(x)$

Let $f(x) = 3x^2 + 2x - 8$ and $g(x) = x + 2$. Perform each function operation and then find the domain.

51. $-f(x) + 4g(x)$ **52.** $f(x) - 2g(x)$ **53.** $f(x) \cdot g(x)$

54. $-3f(x) \cdot g(x)$ **55.** $\dfrac{f(x)}{g(x)}$ **56.** $\dfrac{5f(x)}{g(x)}$

57. Writing Evaluate $(g \circ f)(3)$, when $f(x) = 2x$ and $g(x) = x + 1$. Explain and justify your steps.

Let $g(x) = 3x + 2$ and $f(x) = \dfrac{x - 2}{3}$. Find each value.

58. $f(g(1))$ **59.** $g(f(-4))$ **60.** $f(g(0))$ **61.** $g(f(2))$

 for Help

For a guide to solving Exercise 62a, see p. 411.

62. Geometry You toss a pebble into a pool of water and watch the circular ripples radiate outward. You find that the function $r(x) = 12.5x$ describes the radius r in inches of a circle x seconds after it was formed. The function $A(x) = \pi x^2$ describes the area A of a circle with radius x.
a. Find $(A \circ r)(x)$ when $x = 2$. Interpret your answer.
b. Find the area of a circle 4 seconds after it was formed.

For each pair of functions, find $f(g(x))$ and $g(f(x))$.

63. $f(x) = 3x, g(x) = x^2$ **64.** $f(x) = x + 3, g(x) = x - 5$

65. $f(x) = 3x^2 + 2, g(x) = 2x$ **66.** $f(x) = \dfrac{x - 3}{2}, g(x) = 2x - 3$

67. $f(x) = -x - 7, g(x) = 4x$ **68.** $f(x) = \dfrac{x + 5}{2}, g(x) = x^2$

69. Open-Ended Write a function rule that approximates each value.
a. The amount you save is a percent of what you earn. (You choose the percent.)
b. The amount you earn depends on how many hours you work. (You choose the hourly wage.)
c. Write and simplify a composite function that expresses your savings as a function of the number of hours you work. Interpret your results.

70. a. Technology Suppose $f(x) = 3x$ and $g(x) = x^2 + 3$. In the spreadsheet, values for x are in Column A. What do the formulas in B and C represent?

	A	B	C	D	E
1		=3*A1	=A1^2+3	■	■
2	0	■	■	■	■
3	5	■	■	■	■
4	10	■	■	■	■

b. If the formulas in columns B and C are copied down the columns, what numbers will appear?
c. Find $(f \circ g)(x)$.
d. Complete column D for $(f \circ g)(x)$.
e. Find $(g \circ f)(x)$.
f. Complete column E for $(g \circ f)(x)$.

 Homework Video Tutor

Visit: PHSchool.com
Web Code: bbe-0706

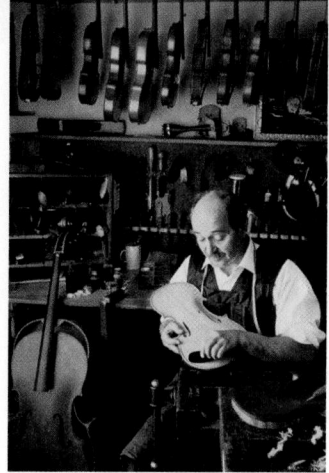

71. Profit A craftsman makes and sells violins. The function $C(x) = 1000 + 700x$ represents his cost in dollars to produce x violins. The function $I(x) = 5995x$ represents the income in dollars from selling x violins.

   a. Write and simplify a function $P(x) = I(x) - C(x)$.

   b. Find $P(30)$, the profit earned when he makes and sells 30 violins.

 72. Writing A salesperson earns a 3% bonus on weekly sales over $5000.

$$g(x) = 0.03x$$
$$h(x) = x - 5000$$

   a. Explain what each function above represents.

   b. Which composition, $(h \circ g)(x)$ or $(g \circ h)(x)$, represents the weekly bonus? Explain.

Real-World Connection

The profit a craftsman will make is the difference between the price and cost to produce his product.

Let $f(x) = 3x - 2$ and $g(x) = x^2 + 1$. Perform each function operation and use the properties of real numbers to justify each step in simplifying your answer.

73. $(f + g)(x)$ **74.** $(f - g)(x)$ **75.** $(f \circ g)(x)$

76. Grades Suppose your teacher offers to give the whole class a bonus if everyone passes the next math test. The teacher says she will (1) give everyone a 10-point bonus and (2) increase everyone's grade by 9% of their score.

   a. Let x represent the original test scores. Write statements (1) and (2) as the functions $f(x)$ and $g(x)$, respectively.

   b. Explain the meaning of $f(g(x))$. Evaluate $f(g(75))$.

   c. Explain the meaning of $g(f(x))$. Evaluate $g(f(75))$.

   d. Does $g(f(x)) = f(g(x))$?

C Challenge

Let $f(x) = x^4 + 2x^3 - 5x^2 - 10x$ and $g(x) = x^3 - 3x^2 - 5x + 15$. Perform each function operation and simplify, and then find the domain.

77. $f(x) \cdot g(x)$ **78.** $\dfrac{f(x)}{g(x)}$ **79.** $\dfrac{g(x)}{f(x)}$

Find each composition of functions. Simplify your answer.

80. Let $f(x) = \dfrac{1}{x}$. Find $f(f(x))$.

81. Let $f(x) = \dfrac{1}{x}$. Find $f(f(f(x)))$.

82. Let $f(x) = 1 - \dfrac{x}{2}$. Find $f(f(f(x)))$.

83. Let $f(x) = 2x - 3$. Find $\dfrac{f(1 + h) - f(1)}{h}, h \neq 0$.

84. Let $f(x) = 4x - 1$. Find $\dfrac{f(a + h) - f(a)}{h}, h \neq 0$.

Multiple Choice Practice

For California Standards and CAHSEE Tutorials, visit PHSchool.com. Web Code: bbq-9045

ALG2 24.0

85. A bakery sells pies and cakes. The function $p(x) = 1.5x + 3$ represents the cost in dollars to bake x pies. The function $c(x) = 0.75x + 2$ represents the cost in dollars to bake x cookies. Which function represents the total cost of baking x pies and x cakes?

   Ⓐ $p(x) + c(x) = 7.25x$ Ⓒ $p(x) - c(x) = 0.75x + 1$

   Ⓑ $p(x) + c(x) = 2.25x + 5$ Ⓓ $p(c(x)) = 1.125x + 6$

ALG2 25.0   **86.** If $f(x) = 2(x - 2)^2$ and $g(x) = x^2 - 5x + 4$, which is an equivalent form of $f(x) - g(x)$?

      Ⓐ $3x^2 - 13x + 12$ Ⓒ $x^2 + 3x - 4$

      Ⓑ $3x^2 + 13x - 12$ Ⓓ $x^2 - 3x + 4$

ALG2 2.0   **87.** Reyna wants to hire one of two local handymen, Andy and Tim. The graph shows the relationship between the total cost of each handyman's labor and the hours he spent working. According to the graph, which of these statements is true?

      Ⓐ If the job would take more than 2 hours, Andy's work would cost less than Tim's.

      Ⓑ If the job would take less than 2 hours, Tim's work would cost less than Andy's.

      Ⓒ If the job would take exactly 2 hours, Andy's work would cost less than Tim's.

      Ⓓ If the job would take more than 2 hours, Tim's work would cost less than Andy's.

Mixed Review

Lesson 7-5   **Solve. Check for extraneous solutions.**

88. $\sqrt{x^2 + 3} = x + 1$ **89.** $x + 8 = (x^2 + 16)^{\frac{1}{2}}$ **90.** $\sqrt{x^2 + 9} = x + 1$

91. $(x^2 - 9)^{\frac{1}{2}} - x = -3$ **92.** $\sqrt{x^2 + 12} - 2 = x$ **93.** $(3x)^{\frac{1}{2}} = (x + 6)^{\frac{1}{2}}$

Lesson 6-8   **Expand each binomial.**

94. $(x + 4)^8$ **95.** $(x + y)^6$ **96.** $(2x - y)^4$ **97.** $(2x - 3y)^7$

98. $(9 - 2x)^5$ **99.** $(4x - y)^5$ **100.** $(x^2 + x)^4$ **101.** $(x^2 + 2y^3)^6$

Lesson 5-6   **Simplify each expression.**

102. $(2 - 3\sqrt{-4}) + (4 + 2\sqrt{-16})$ **103.** $3\sqrt{-50} - (2 - \sqrt{-32})$

104. $(6 + \sqrt{-20}) - (-7 - \sqrt{-45})$ **105.** $(5 - \sqrt{-9})(2 - \sqrt{-36})$

Checkpoint Quiz 2   Lessons 7-4 through 7-6

Simplify each expression.

1. $(-27x^3)^{\frac{4}{3}}$ **2.** $(32y^5)^{-0.4}$

Solve each equation.

3. $\sqrt{3x + 1} - 4 = 0$ **4.** $(5x + 2)^{\frac{2}{3}} = 9$

Solve each equation. Check for extraneous solutions.

5. $\sqrt{3x + 3} - 3 = 3x$ **6.** $(2 - x)^{0.5} - x = 4$

Let $f(x) = 2x + 3$ and $g(x) = x^2 - x$. Find each value.

7. $(f + g)\left(\frac{1}{2}\right)$ **8.** $(f \cdot g)(1)$ **9.** $\left(\frac{f}{g}\right)(2)$ **10.** $(f \circ g)(5)$

Understanding Word Problems Read the problem below. It has two parts. Let the explanations guide you through both solutions. Check your understanding with the exercises at the bottom of the page.

Geometry You toss a pebble into a pool of water and watch the circular ripples radiate outward. You find that the function $r(x) = 12.5x$ describes the radius r in inches of a circle x seconds after it was formed. The function $A(x) = \pi x^2$ describes the area A of a circle with radius x.

a. Find $(A \circ r)(x)$ when $x = 2$. Interpret your answer.

The problem uses function notation. Here is the way to read function notation.

Write	$A(x)$	$A(r(x))$	$(A \circ r)(x) = A(r(x))$
Read	A of x	A of r of x	The composition of A with r equals A of r of x.

Solve For $A(x) = \pi x^2$ and $r(x) = 12.5x$, find $(A \circ r)(2)$.

$(A \circ r)(2) = A(r(2))$

$r(2) = 12.5(2) = 25$ **Find r(2) first.**

$A(25) = \pi(25)^2$ **Use the output r(2) = 25 as the input for $A(x)$.**

$= 625\pi \approx 1963$

$$r \qquad\qquad A$$
$$2 \longrightarrow 12.5(2) \longrightarrow 25 \longrightarrow \pi(25)^2 \longrightarrow 625\pi$$

To interpret your answer is to explain what your answer means in terms of the problem. The problem tells you that $A(x)$ is the area of a circle with radius x and that $r(x)$ is the radius of a circle x seconds after it was formed.

So $(A \circ r)(2)$ is the area of a circle after 2 seconds. The area is about 1963 in.^{2}.

b. Find the area of a circle 4 seconds after it was formed.

Similar to part (a), $(A \circ r)(4)$ is the area. Using part (a) as a guide,

$(A \circ r)(4) = A(r(4))$

$r(4) = 12.5(4) = 50$

$A(50) = \pi(50)^2$

$= 2500\pi \approx 7854$

The area of a circle after 4 seconds is about 7854 in.^{2}.

EXERCISES

1. You toss a pebble into a pool of water and watch the circular ripples radiate outward. You find that the function $r(x) = 12.5x$ describes the radius of the first circle r in inches after x seconds. The function $C(x) = 2\pi x$ describes the circumference C of a circle with radius x. Find $(C \circ r)(x)$ when $x = 3$. Interpret your answer.

2. A tanker leaks a small amount of crude oil into the bay. The function $d(x) = 2.3x$ models the length d, in kilometers, of the oval oil slick after x hours. $A(x) = \frac{3}{8}\pi x^2$ models the area of a slick x km long. Find the area of the oil slick after 10.5 hours.

7-7

Inverse Relations and Functions

 California Content Standards

ALG2 24.0 Students solve problems involving functional concepts, such as composition and defining the inverse function. *Master*
ALG2 25.0 Students use properties from number systems to justify steps in combining and simplifying functions. *Master*

What You'll Learn

• To find the inverse of a relation or function

. . . And Why

To estimate the speed of a car, as in Example 5

✓ **Check Skills You'll Need**

 for Help Lesson 3-1

Graph each pair of functions on a single coordinate plane.

1. $y = x - 6$
$y = x + 6$

2. $y = \dfrac{x - 7}{2}$
$y = 2x + 7$

3. $y = 3x - 1$
$y = \dfrac{x + 1}{3}$

4. $y = 0.5x + 1$
$y = 2x - 2$

5. $y = -x + 4$
$y = \dfrac{-x + 4}{-1}$

6. $y = \dfrac{x + 4}{5}$
$y = 5x - 4$

🔊 **New Vocabulary** • inverse relation • inverse functions

---

1 **The Inverse of a Function**

Activity: Inverses

• Function *f* doubles the input and then subtracts 8. $f(x) = 2x - 8$

• Function *g* adds 8 to the input and then divides by 2. $g(x) = \dfrac{x + 8}{2}$

$$f(x) \qquad\qquad g(x)$$
$$10 \rightarrow \boxed{2x - 8} \rightarrow \rightarrow \boxed{\dfrac{x + 8}{2}} \rightarrow ?$$

1. a. Find $f(10)$ and $g(f(10))$.
  b. Find $f(0)$ and $g(f(0))$.
  c. Find $f(-7)$ and $g(f(-7))$.
  d. Without computing, use the pattern in parts (a)–(c) to find $g(f(-1496))$.

$$g(x) \qquad\qquad f(x)$$
$$6 \rightarrow \boxed{\dfrac{x + 8}{2}} \rightarrow \rightarrow \boxed{2x - 8} \rightarrow ?$$

2. a. Find $g(6)$ and $f(g(6))$.
  b. Find $g(0)$ and $f(g(0))$.
  c. Find $g(-32)$ and $f(g(-32))$.
  d. Without computing, use the pattern in parts (a)–(c) to find $f(g(\pi))$.

3. a. Interchange the x and y variables in $y = 2x - 8$ and solve for y.
  b. Graph your two equations in part (a) on the same coordinate axes. Fold your graph paper so the two lines coincide. How are the two graphs related?

If a relation pairs element a of its domain to element b of its range, the **inverse relation** pairs b with a. So, if (a, b) is an ordered pair of a relation, then (b, a) is an ordered pair of its inverse.

This diagram shows a relation r and its inverse.

The range of the relation is the domain of the inverse, and the domain of the relation is the range of the inverse.

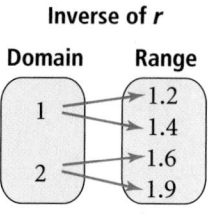

1 EXAMPLE   Finding the Inverse of a Relation

a. Find the inverse of relation s.

Relation s

x	1	2	3	4
y	−1	0	1	1

Interchange the x and y values to get the inverse.

Inverse of Relation s

x	−1	0	1	1
y	1	2	3	4

b. Graph s and its inverse.

Relation s

Reversing the Ordered Pairs

Inverse of s

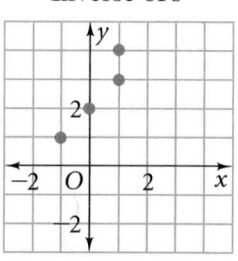

✓ **CA Standards Check** **1 a.** Describe how the line $y = x$ is related to the graphs of s and its inverse.
b. In Example 1, is relation s a function? Is the inverse of s a function?

As shown in Example 1, the graph of the inverse of a relation is the reflection in the line $y = x$ of the graph of the relation. If a relation or function is described by an equation in x and y, you can interchange x and y to get the inverse.

2 EXAMPLE   Interchanging x and y

Find the inverse of $y = x^2 + 3$.

$$y = x^2 + 3$$
$$x = y^2 + 3 \qquad \text{Interchange } x \text{ and } y.$$
$$x - 3 = y^2 \qquad \text{Solve for } y.$$
$$\pm\sqrt{x - 3} = y \qquad \text{Find the square root of each side.}$$

✓ **CA Standards Check** **2 a.** Does $y = x^2 + 3$ define a function? Is its inverse a function? Explain.
b. Find the inverse of $y = 3x - 10$. Is the inverse a function? Explain.

3 EXAMPLE Graphing a Relation and Its Inverse

Graph $y = x^2 + 3$ and its inverse, $y = \pm\sqrt{x - 3}$.

The graph of $y = x^2 + 3$ is a parabola that opens upward with vertex $(0, 3)$. The reflection of the parabola in the line $y = x$ is the graph of the inverse.

You can also find points on the graph of the inverse by reversing the coordinates of points on $y = x^2 + 3$.

✓ CA Standards Check ❸ Graph $y = 3x - 10$ and its inverse.

The inverse of function f is denoted by f^{-1}. Read f^{-1} as "the inverse of f" or as "f inverse." The notation $f(x)$ is used for functions, but the relation f^{-1} may not even be a function.

> **Vocabulary Tip**
>
> For a nonzero number x, x^{-1} is the multiplicative inverse of x, or $\frac{1}{x}$.
>
> For a function f, f^{-1} is the relation that is the inverse of f.

4 EXAMPLE Finding an Inverse Function

Consider the function $f(x) = \sqrt{x + 1}$.

a. Find the domain and range of f.

Since the radicand cannot be negative, the domain is the set of numbers greater than or equal to -1. Since the principal square root is nonnegative, the range is the set of nonnegative numbers.

b. Find f^{-1}.

> **Problem Solving Hint**
>
> If the graph of a function f does not have two points in line horizontally, then f^{-1} is also a function.

$$f(x) = \sqrt{x + 1}$$
$$y = \sqrt{x + 1} \quad \text{Rewrite the equation using } y.$$
$$x = \sqrt{y + 1} \quad \text{Interchange } x \text{ and } y. \text{ Since } x \text{ equals a principal square root, } x \geq 0.$$
$$x^2 = y + 1 \quad \text{Square both sides.}$$
$$y = x^2 - 1 \quad \text{Solve for } y.$$

So, $f^{-1}(x) = x^2 - 1$, $x \geq 0$.

c. Find the domain and range of f^{-1}.

The domain of f^{-1} equals the range of f, which is the set of nonnegative numbers. Since $x^2 \geq 0$, $x^2 - 1 \geq -1$. Thus the range of f^{-1} is the set of numbers greater than or equal to -1. Note that the range of f^{-1} is the same as the domain of f.

d. Is f^{-1} a function? Explain.

For each x in the domain of f^{-1}, there is only one value of $f^{-1}(x)$. So f^{-1} is a function.

✓ CA Standards Check ❹ Let $f(x) = 10 - 3x$. Find each of the following.
a. the domain and range of f **b.** f^{-1}
c. the domain and range of f^{-1} **d.** $f^{-1}(f(3))$
e. $f(f^{-1}(2))$

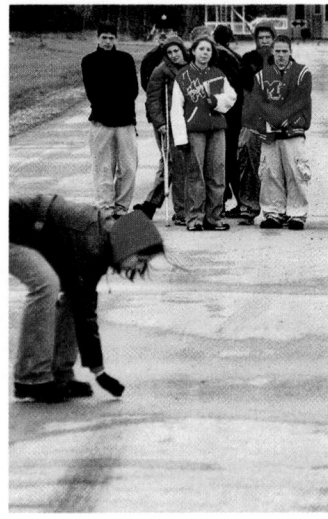

Functions that model real-life situations are frequently expressed as formulas with letters that remind you of the variables they represent. When finding the inverse of a formula, it would be very confusing to interchange the letters. Keep the letters the same and just solve the formula for the other variable.

5 EXAMPLE Real-World Connection

Multiple Choice The function $d = \frac{r^2}{24}$ is a model for the distance d in feet that a car with locked brakes skids in coming to a complete stop from a speed of r mi/h. Find the inverse of the function. What is the best estimate of the speed of a car that made skid marks 114 feet long?

　Ⓐ 5 mi/h 　　　Ⓑ 12 mi/h 　　　Ⓒ 23 mi/h 　　　Ⓓ 52 mi/h

$d = \frac{r^2}{24}$

$r^2 = 24d$ 　　　　　**Solve for r. Do not interchange the variables.**

$r = \sqrt{24d}$ 　　　　**Rate of speed must be positive.**

　$= \sqrt{24 \cdot 114}$ 　　**Substitute 114 for d.**

　≈ 52 　　　　　　**Use a calculator.**

● The car was traveling about 52 mi/h. The correct choice is D.

Real-World **Connection**

Many safe driving programs include experience with braking distance.

✓ **CA Standards Check** ⑤ The function $d = \frac{v^2}{64}$ is a model relating the distance d a stone has fallen in feet to its velocity v in feet per second (ft/s). Find the inverse of the function and use it to find the velocity of a stone that has fallen 30 ft.

If f and f^{-1} are both functions, and if f maps a to b, then f^{-1} must map b to a.

Domain of f 　　　Range of f
Range of f^{-1} 　　Domain of f^{-1}

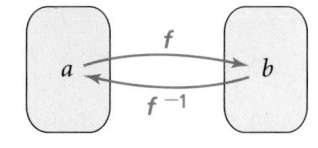

If f and f^{-1} are functions, they are called **inverse functions.** For inverse functions, $f^{-1}(f(x)) = x$ and $f(f^{-1}(x)) = x$.

 Key Concepts

Property	Composition of Inverse Functions

If f and f^{-1} are inverse functions, then

$(f^{-1} \circ f)(x) = x$ and $(f \circ f^{-1})(x) = x.$

6 EXAMPLE Composition of Inverse Functions

For the function $f(x) = \frac{x-7}{6}$, find $(f^{-1} \circ f)(374)$ and $(f \circ f^{-1})(-99\pi)$.

Since f is a linear function with nonzero slope, f^{-1} is also a linear function.

● So $(f^{-1} \circ f)(374) = 374$ and $(f \circ f^{-1})(-99\pi) = -99\pi.$

✓ **CA Standards Check** ⑥ For $f(x) = 5x + 11$, find $(f^{-1} \circ f)(777)$ and $(f \circ f^{-1})(-5802)$.

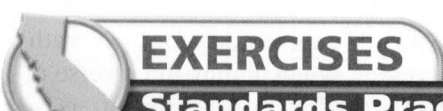

EXERCISES
Standards Practice

For more exercises, see *Extra Skill and Word Problem Practice*.

ALG2 24.0, 25.0

A Practice by Example

Example 1
(page 413)

GO for Help

Find the inverse of each relation. Graph the given relation and its inverse.

1.

x	1	2	3	4
y	0	1	0	2

2.

x	1	2	3	4
y	0	1	2	3

3.

x	0	1	2	3
y	0	1	4	9

4.

x	−3	−2	−1	0
y	2	2	2	2

Example 2
(page 413)

Find the inverse of each function. Is the inverse a function?

5. $y = 3x + 1$

6. $y = 2x - 1$

7. $y = 4 - 3x$

8. $y = 5 - 2x^2$

9. $y = x^2 + 4$

10. $y = 3x^2 - 5$

11. $y = (x + 1)^2$

12. $y = (3x - 4)^2$

13. $y = (1 - 2x)^2 + 5$

Example 3
(page 414)

Graph each relation and its inverse.

14. $y = 2x - 3$

15. $y = 3 - 7x$

16. $y = -x$

17. $y = 3x^2$

18. $y = -x^2$

19. $y = 4x^2 - 2$

20. $y = (x - 1)^2$

21. $y = (2 - x)^2$

22. $y = (3 - 2x)^2 - 1$

Example 4
(page 414)

For each function f, find f^{-1} and the domain and range of f and f^{-1}. Determine whether f^{-1} is a function.

23. $f(x) = 3x + 4$

24. $f(x) = \sqrt{x - 5}$

25. $f(x) = \sqrt{x + 7}$

26. $f(x) = \sqrt{-2x + 3}$

27. $f(x) = 2x^2 + 2$

28. $f(x) = -x^2 + 1$

Example 5
(page 415)

29. The formula for converting from Celsius to Fahrenheit temperatures is $C = \frac{9}{5}F + 32$.

   a. Find the inverse of the formula. Is the inverse a function?
   b. Use the inverse to find the Fahrenheit temperature that corresponds to 25°C.

30. Geometry The formula for the volume of a sphere is $V = \frac{4}{3}\pi r^3$.

   a. Find the inverse of the formula. Is the inverse a function?
   b. Use the inverse to find the radius of a sphere that has a volume of 35,000 ft³.

Example 6
(page 415)

For Exercises 31–34, $f(x) = 10x - 10$. Find each value.

31. $(f^{-1} \circ f)(10)$

32. $(f \circ f^{-1})(-10)$

33. $(f^{-1} \circ f)(0.2)$

34. $(f \circ f^{-1})(d)$

B Apply Your Skills

Find the inverse of each function. Is the inverse a function?

35. $f(x) = 1.5x^2 - 4$

36. $f(x) = \frac{3x^2}{4}$

37. $f(x) = \sqrt{2x - 1} + 3$

38. $f(x) = (x + 1)^2$

39. $f(x) = (2x - 1)^2$

40. $f(x) = (x + 1)^2 - 1$

41. $f(x) = x^3$

42. $f(x) = x^4$

43. $f(x) = \frac{2x^2}{5} + 1$

Real-World **Connection**

Water towers are tall because each foot of height provides 0.43 lb/in.² of pressure. A typical tower holds about a one-day supply for users.

44. Water Supply The velocity of the water that flows from an opening at the base of a tank depends on the height of water above the opening. The function $v(x) = \sqrt{2gx}$ models the velocity v in feet per second where g, the acceleration due to gravity, is about 32 ft/s² and x is the height in feet of the water. Find the inverse function and use it to find the depth of water when the flow is 40 ft/s, and when the flow is 20 ft/s.

45. Writing Explain how you can find the range of the inverse of $f(x) = \sqrt{x-1}$ without finding the inverse itself.

46. A function consists of the pairs $(2, 3)$, $(x, 4)$ and $(5, 6)$. What values, if any, may x not assume?

For each function f, find f^{-1}, the domain and range of f and f^{-1}, and determine whether f^{-1} is a function.

47. $f(x) = -\sqrt{x}$ **48.** $f(x) = \sqrt{x} + 3$ **49.** $f(x) = \sqrt{-x+3}$

50. $f(x) = \sqrt{x+2}$ **51.** $f(x) = \frac{x^2}{2}$ **52.** $f(x) = \frac{1}{x^2}$

53. $f(x) = (x-4)^2$ **54.** $f(x) = (7-x)^2$ **55.** $f(x) = \frac{1}{(x+1)^2}$

56. $f(x) = 4 - 2\sqrt{x}$ **57.** $f(x) = \frac{3}{\sqrt{x}}$ **58.** $f(x) = \frac{1}{\sqrt{-2x}}$

59. a. Copy the mapping diagram at the right. Complete it by writing members of the domain and range and connecting them with arrows so that r is a function and r^{-1} is not a function.

b. Repeat part (a) so that r is not a function and r^{-1} is a function.

Relation r

Domain   Range

60. Critical Thinking Relation r has one element in its domain and two elements in its range. Is r a function? Is the inverse of r a function? Explain.

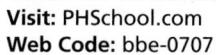

Visit: PHSchool.com
Web Code: bbe-0707

61. Geometry Write a function that gives the length of the hypotenuse of an isosceles right triangle with side length s. Evaluate the inverse of the function to find the side length of an isosceles right triangle with a hypotenuse of 6 in.

62. Open-Ended Write a function f such that the graph of f^{-1} lies in Quadrants III and IV.

 Challenge

Find the inverse of each function. Is the inverse a function?

63. $f(x) = \frac{1}{5}x^3$ **64.** $f(x) = \sqrt[3]{x-5}$ **65.** $f(x) = \frac{\sqrt[3]{x}}{3}$

66. $f(x) = (x-2)^3$ **67.** $f(x) = \sqrt[4]{x}$ **68.** $f(x) = 1.2x^4$

For California Standards and CAHSEE Tutorials, visit PHSchool.com. Web Code: bbq-9045

ALG2 25.0

69. Which expression represents $(f \circ g)(x) + h(x)$ if $f(x) = 4x$, $g(x) = \frac{1}{2}x + 7$, and $h(x) = |-2x + 4|$?

Ⓐ $2x^2 + 28x + |-2x + 4|$ Ⓒ $2x + 28 + |-2x + 4|$

Ⓑ $2x + 7 + |-2x + 4|$ Ⓓ $2x + 28 + 4|-2x + 4|$

ALG2 24.0   **70.** If $f(x) = 4x - 3$, what is $(f^{-1} \circ f)(10)$?

      (A) $\frac{13}{4}$ (C) 37

      (B) 10   (D) $\frac{481}{4}$

ALG2 20.0   **71.** What is the expanded form of $(x^3 + x)^4$?

      (A) $x^{12} + 4x^{10} + 6x^8 + 4x^6 + x^4$ (C) $x^7 + x^4$

      (B) $x^{12} - 4x^{10} - 6x^8 - 4x^6 - x^4$ (D) $x^{12} + 6x^{10} + 4x^8 + 6x^6 + x^4$

Mixed Review

for Help

Lesson 7-6   Let $f(x) = 4x$, $g(x) = \frac{1}{2}x + 7$, and $h(x) = |-2x + 4|$. Simplify each function.

72. $(f \circ g)(x)$ **73.** $(g \circ f)(x)$ **74.** $(h \circ g)(x)$

75. $g(x) + g(x)$ **76.** $(h \circ (g \circ f))(x)$ **77.** $(f \circ g)(x) + h(x)$

Lesson 7-1   **Find each indicated root if it is a real number.**

78. $\sqrt[4]{16}$ **79.** $-\sqrt[4]{16}$ **80.** $\sqrt[4]{-16}$ **81.** $\sqrt[5]{243}$

82. $-\sqrt[5]{243}$ **83.** $\sqrt[5]{-243}$ **84.** $\sqrt[3]{0.064}$ **85.** $\sqrt[4]{810,000}$

Lesson 6-5   **List all possible rational roots for each equation. Then use the Rational Root Theorem to find each root.**

86. $2x^3 + 3x^2 - 8x - 12 = 0$ **87.** $3x^3 - 5x^2 - 4x + 4 = 0$

88. $3x^3 + 10x^2 - x - 12 = 0$ **89.** $2x^3 - 11x^2 - x + 30 = 0$

90. $x^3 - 6x^2 + 11x - 6 = 0$ **91.** $x^3 + 3x^2 - 4x - 12 = 0$

Algebra at Work

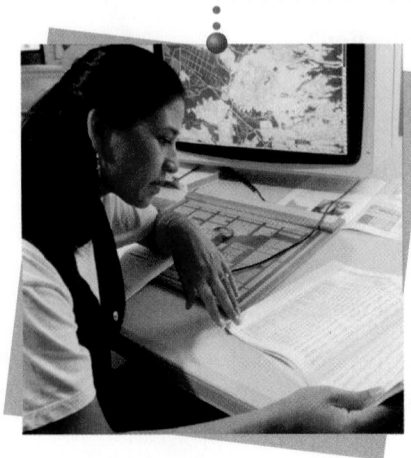

····················· **Demographer**

Demographers study human populations. They collect, analyze, and present data relating to the basic life cycle: birth, marriage, divorce, family formation, employment, aging, migration, and death.
Demographers draw on the related disciplines of sociology, economics, political science, anthropology, psychology, public health, and ecology.
    Demography is also concerned with the broader nature of social and economic change and its impact on the natural environment. It includes studying family structure, the role of women, and the value of children, as well as the social, cultural, and institutional context of demographic change. Demography is an essential component of many activities, such as planning government policies and market research.

Go Online
PHSchool.com
For: Information about demography
Web Code: bbb-2031

Graphing Inverses

ALG2 24.0 Students solve problems involving functional concepts, such as composition and defining the inverse function. *Master*

You can graph inverses of functions on a graphing calculator by using the DrawInv feature or by using parametric equations. It takes more keystrokes to set up parametric equations, but once you do you can easily change from one function to another and quickly see the graphs of the new function and its inverse.

ACTIVITY

Graph $y = 0.3x^2 + 1$ and its inverse.

Method 1 Use the DrawInv feature.

Step 1 Press Y= and enter the equation. Press ZOOM 5 to see a graph of the function with equal x- and y-intervals.

Step 2 Press 2nd DRAW 8. You will see DrawInv followed by a flashing cursor. Select equation Y_1 by pressing VARS ▶ 1 1. Press ENTER to see the graph of the function and its inverse.

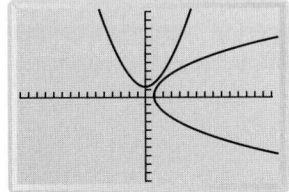

Method 2 Use parametric equations.

Step 1 Set to parametric mode. Press MODE, select **Par**, and press 2nd QUIT.

Step 2 Enter the given equation in parametric form. Press Y= and enter the equations $X_{1T} = T$ and $Y_{1T} = .3T^2 + 1$.

Step 3 Now use $X_{2T} = Y_{1T}$ and $Y_{2T} = X_{1T}$ to interchange the x- and y-values of the first parametric equation. Press Y= and move the cursor to follow $X_{2T} =$. Select Y_{1T} by pressing VARS ▶ 2 2. Enter the equation $Y_{2T} = X_{1T}$ in a similar fashion.

Step 4 Press ZOOM 5. Adjust the Window so that Tmin and Tmax approximately agree with Xmin and Xmax. Press GRAPH to see the graph of the function and its inverse.

EXERCISES

Graph each function and its inverse with a graphing calculator. Then sketch the graphs.

1. $y = x^2 - 5$ **2.** $y = (x - 3)^2$ **3.** $y = 0.01x^4$ **4.** $y = 0.5x^3 - 3$

5. Critical Thinking In Method 2, suppose you added a third pair of parametric equations that interchanged the x- and y-values of the second pair ($X_{3T} = Y_{2T}$ and $Y_{3T} = X_{2T}$). What would be the effect on the graphs? Explain.

6. Writing Change the parametric equation $X_{2T} = Y_{1T}$ in Method 2, Step 3 to $X_{2T} = -Y_{1T}$. Describe the graph that results.

7. Explain how, once you set up parametric equations, you can change from one function to another and quickly see the graphs of the new function and its inverse.

7-8

Graphing Square Root and Other Radical Functions

What You'll Learn

- To graph square root and other radical functions

. . . And Why

To estimate the initial height of a falling object, as in Example 5

✓ **Check Skills You'll Need**

GO for Help Lesson 5-3

Graph each equation.

1. $y = (x + 2)^2$ **2.** $y = (x - 3)^2$ **3.** $y = -(x + 4)^2$

4. $y = -x^2 - 1$ **5.** $y = -(x + 1)^2 + 1$ **6.** $y = 3x^2 + 3$

 New Vocabulary • radical function • square root function

---

1   Radical Functions

GO for Help

To review the vertical line test, go to Lesson 2-1.

A horizontal line can intersect the graph of $f(x) = x^2$ in two points. For example, $f(-2) = f(2)$. Therefore, a vertical line can intersect the graph of the inverse of $f(x) = x^2$ in two points, and f^{-1} is *not* a function.

$f(x) = x^2$ $f^{-1}(x) = \pm\sqrt{x}$

     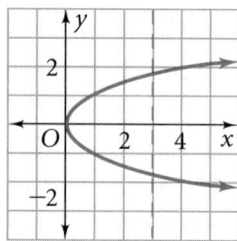

You can restrict the domain of f so that its inverse is a function.

$f(x) = x^2, x \geq 0$ $f^{-1}(x) = \sqrt{x}$

     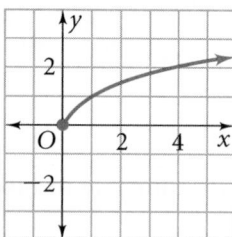

The inverse of $g(x) = x^3$ is a function.

$g(x) = x^3$ $g^{-1}(x) = \sqrt[3]{x}$

     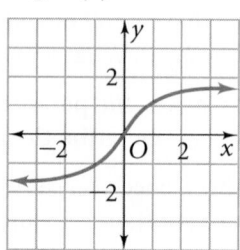

Inverses of functions of the form $y = x^n$ (with domains restricted as needed) form parent functions $y = \sqrt[n]{x}$ of families of **radical functions.** In particular, $f(x) = \sqrt{x}$ is the parent for the family of **square root functions.** Members of this family have the form $f(x) = a\sqrt{x - h} + k$.

🔑 **Key Concepts**

Summary	Families of Radical Functions Including the Square Root Function	
	Square Root	**Radical**
Parent function:	$y = \sqrt{x}$	$y = \sqrt[n]{x}$
Reflection in x-axis:	$y = -\sqrt{x}$	$y = -\sqrt[n]{x}$
Stretch ($a > 1$), shrink ($0 < a < 1$) by factor a:	$y = a\sqrt{x}$	$y = a\sqrt[n]{x}$
Reflection in x-axis:	$y = -a\sqrt{x}$	$y = -a\sqrt[n]{x}$
Translation: Horizontal by h	$y = \sqrt{x - h}$	$y = \sqrt[n]{x - h}$
Vertical by k	$y = \sqrt{x} + k$	$y = \sqrt[n]{x} + k$
Combined:	$y = \sqrt{x - h} + k$	$y = \sqrt[n]{x - h} + k$

1 EXAMPLE Translating Square Root Functions Vertically

Graph $y = \sqrt{x} + 2$ and $y = \sqrt{x} - 1$.

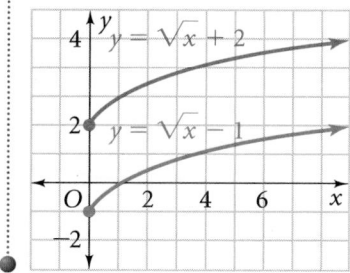

The graph of $y = \sqrt{x} + 2$ is the graph of $y = \sqrt{x}$ shifted up 2 units. The graph of $y = \sqrt{x} - 1$ is the graph of $y = \sqrt{x}$ shifted down 1 unit.

The domains of both functions are the set of nonnegative numbers, but their ranges differ.

✓ **CA Standards Check** **1** Graph $y = \sqrt{x} - 3$ and $y = \sqrt{x} + 3$.

The graph of $y = \sqrt{x - h}$ is a horizontal translation of $y = \sqrt{x}$. If h is positive, translate h units to the right. If h is negative, translate $|h|$ units to the left.

2 EXAMPLE Translating Square Root Functions Horizontally

Graph $y = \sqrt{x + 3}$ and $y = \sqrt{x - 2}$.

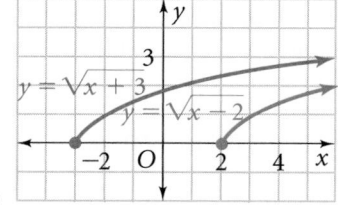

The graph of $y = \sqrt{x + 3}$ is the graph of $y = \sqrt{x}$ shifted left 3 units. The graph of $y = \sqrt{x - 2}$ is the graph of $y = \sqrt{x}$ shifted right 2 units.

The ranges of both functions are the set of nonnegative numbers, but their domains differ.

✓ **CA Standards Check** **2** Graph $y = \sqrt{x - 1}$ and $y = \sqrt{x + 4}$.

For the combined transformation $y = a\sqrt{x - h} + k$, a indicates a vertical stretch $(a > 1)$ or shrink $(0 < a < 1)$. A negative sign indicates reflection in the x-axis.

3 EXAMPLE Graphing Square Root Functions

Graph $y = -2\sqrt{x + 1} - 3$.

The graph of $y = -2\sqrt{x}$ is a stretch of $y = \sqrt{x}$ by a factor of 2 and a reflection across the x-axis (in black). Then translate left 1 unit and down 3 units.

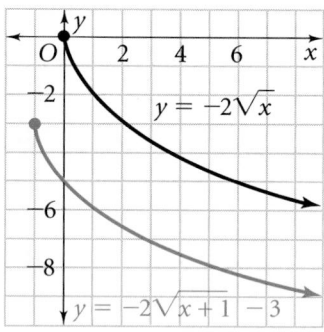

CA Standards Check ③ Graph $y = \frac{1}{4}\sqrt{x - 2} - 4$.

The pattern for graphing square root functions applies to other radical functions.

4 EXAMPLE Graphing Cube Root Functions

Graph $y = 2\sqrt[3]{x + 3} - 1$.

The graph of $y = 2\sqrt[3]{x + 3} - 1$ is the graph of $y = 2\sqrt[3]{x}$ translated 3 units left and 1 unit down.

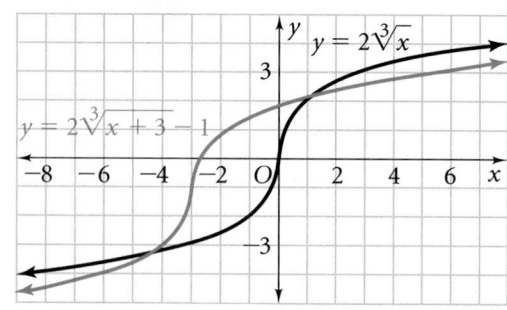

CA Standards Check ④ Graph $y = 3 - \sqrt[3]{x + 1}$.

5 EXAMPLE Solving Square Root Equations by Graphing

Physics You can model the time t, in seconds, an object takes to reach the ground falling from height H, in meters, by $t(H) = \sqrt{\dfrac{2H}{g}}$. The value of g is 9.81 m/s². From what height does an object fall if it takes 7 seconds to reach the ground?

For $t = 7$, solve the equation $7 = \sqrt{\dfrac{2H}{9.81}}$.

Graph Y1 $= \sqrt{(2X/9.81)}$ and Y2 $= 7$. Adjust the window to find where the graphs intersect. Use the Intersect feature to find the x-coordinate of the intersection.

The height for a 7-second fall is about 240 m.

CA Standards Check ⑤ How far does an object fall if it takes 3.5 seconds to reach the ground? How does this compare with the height of a 7-second fall?

Sometimes you have to rewrite a radical function so you can graph it using transformations.

6 EXAMPLE Rewriting Radical Functions

Rewrite $y = \sqrt{4x - 12}$ to make it easy to graph using transformations. Describe the graph.

$$y = \sqrt{4x - 12} = \sqrt{4(x - 3)} = 2\sqrt{x - 3}$$

● The graph of $y = \sqrt{4x - 12}$ is the graph of $y = 2\sqrt{x}$ translated 3 units right.

✓ **CA Standards Check** ⑥ Rewrite $y = \sqrt[3]{8x - 24} + 3$ to make it easy to graph using transformations. Describe the graph.

EXERCISES

For more exercises, see *Extra Skill and Word Problem Practice.*

Standards Practice

Ⓐ **Practice by Example**

Examples 1 and 2
(page 421)

GO for Help

Graph each function.

1. $y = \sqrt{x} + 1$ **2.** $y = \sqrt{x} - 2$ **3.** $y = \sqrt{x} - 4$ **4.** $y = \sqrt{x} + 5$

5. $y = \sqrt{x - 3}$ **6.** $y = \sqrt{x + 1}$ **7.** $y = \sqrt{x + 6}$ **8.** $y = \sqrt{x - 4}$

Example 3
(page 422)

Graph each function.

9. $y = 3\sqrt{x}$ **10.** $y = -0.25\sqrt{x}$ **11.** $y = \frac{1}{3}\sqrt{x}$

12. $y = -\sqrt{x - 1}$ **13.** $y = -5\sqrt{x + 2}$ **14.** $y = -0.75\sqrt{x} + 3$

15. $y = -\sqrt{x - 3} + 2$ **16.** $y = \frac{1}{4}\sqrt{x + 2} - 1$ **17.** $y = 3\sqrt{x + 1} + 4$

Example 4
(page 422)

Graph each function.

18. $y = \sqrt[3]{x} + 5$ **19.** $y = \sqrt[3]{x} - 4$ **20.** $y = \sqrt[3]{x + 2} - 7$

21. $y = -\sqrt[3]{x + 3} - 1$ **22.** $y = 2\sqrt[3]{x - 6} - 9$ **23.** $y = \frac{1}{2}\sqrt[3]{x - 1} + 3$

Example 5
(page 422)

24. Agriculture A center-pivot irrigation system can water from 1 to 130 acres of crop land. The length ℓ in feet of rotating pipe needed to irrigate A acres is given by the function $\ell = 117.75\sqrt{A}$.
 a. Graph the equation on your calculator. Make a sketch of the graph.
 b. Find the lengths of pipe needed to irrigate 40, 80, and 130 acres.

🖩 **Solve each square root equation by graphing. Round the answer to the nearest hundredth if necessary. If there is no solution, explain why.**

25. $\sqrt{x - 3} = 12$ **26.** $\sqrt{2x - 3} = 4$ **27.** $3\sqrt{3 - x} = 10$

28. $2.5\sqrt{2x - 1.3} = -1$ **29.** $2\sqrt{x + 4} = 3\sqrt{x - 1}$ **30.** $\sqrt{2x + 5} = \sqrt{2 - x}$

Example 6
(page 423)

Rewrite each function to make it easy to graph using transformations of its parent function. Describe the graph.

31. $y = \sqrt{9x - 9}$ **32.** $y = -\sqrt{16x + 32}$ **33.** $y = -2\sqrt{49x + 49}$

34. $y = \sqrt[3]{64x + 128}$ **35.** $y = \sqrt{64x - 128} - 3$ **36.** $y = \sqrt[3]{27x - 54} + 1$

Graph. Find the domain and the range of each function.

37. $y = \sqrt{x} + 7$ **38.** $y = \sqrt{x} - 6$ **39.** $y = \sqrt{x - 6}$

40. $y = -3\sqrt{x} + 2$ **41.** $y = -\frac{4}{5}\sqrt{x}$ **42.** $y = 7 - \sqrt{2x - 1}$

43. $y = 4\sqrt[3]{x - 2} + 1$ **44.** $y = \frac{1}{2}\sqrt{x - 1} + 3$ **45.** $y = -3\sqrt[3]{x - 4} - 3$

46. $y = -\sqrt{x + \frac{1}{2}}$ **47.** $y = -\sqrt[3]{8x} + 5$ **48.** $y = -2\sqrt[3]{x - 4}$

49. $y = -1 - \sqrt{4x + 20}$ **50.** $y = 4 - \sqrt[3]{x + 2.5}$ **51.** $y = -3\sqrt{x - \frac{3}{4}} + 7$

52. Circus The time t in seconds for a trapeze to complete one full cycle is given by the function $t = 1.11\sqrt{\ell}$, where ℓ is the length of the trapeze in feet.
  a. Graph the equation on your calculator. Make a sketch of the graph.
  b. How long is a full cycle if the trapeze is 15 ft. long? 30 ft. long?

53. a. Graph $y = \sqrt{x - 2} - 2$.
  b. Find the domain and the range.
  c. At what coordinate point does the graph start?
  d. Critical Thinking What is the relationship of the point at which the graph starts to the domain and the range?

54. a. The graph of $y = \sqrt{x}$ is translated five units to the right and two units down. Write an equation of the translated function.
  b. The translated graph from part (a) is again translated, this time four units left and three units down. Write an equation of the translated function.

55. a. Graph $y = \sqrt{x - 2} + 1$ and $y = -\sqrt{x - 2} + 1$.
  b. Find the domain and the range of each function.

Real-World Connection

The length of the pendulum formed by an aerialist on a trapeze depends on how far he hangs below the bar.

Rewrite each function to make it easy to graph using transformations of its parent function. Describe the graph.

56. $y = \sqrt{25x - 100} - 1$ **57.** $y = \sqrt{36x + 108} + 4$ **58.** $y = -\sqrt[3]{8x - 2}$

59. $y = \sqrt{\frac{x - 1}{4}} - 2$ **60.** $y = 10 - \sqrt[3]{\frac{x + 3}{27}}$ **61.** $y = \sqrt{\frac{x}{9} + 1} + 5$

62. Open-Ended Write a cube root function in which the vertical translation of $y = \sqrt[3]{x}$ is twice the horizontal translation.

63. Electronics The size of a television screen is the length of the screen's diagonal d in inches. The equation $d = \sqrt{2A}$ models the length of a diagonal of a television screen with area A.
  a. Graph the equation on your calculator.
  b. Suppose you want to buy a new television that has twice the area of your old television. Your old television has an area of 100 in.^{2}. What size screen should you buy?

 64. Writing Explain the effect that a has on the graph of $y = a\sqrt{x}$.

 Challenge

Rewrite each function to make it easy to graph using transformations of its parent function. Describe the graph. Find the domain and the range of each function.

65. $y = -\sqrt{2x + 8}$ **66.** $y = -\sqrt{2(4x - 3)}$

67. $y = \sqrt{3x - 5} + 6$ **68.** $y = -3 - \sqrt{12x + 18}$

Homework Video Tutor

Visit: PHSchool.com
Web Code: bbe-0708

69. a. Graph $y = \sqrt{-x}$, $y = \sqrt{1 - x}$, and $y = \sqrt{2 - x}$.

   b. Make a Conjecture How does the graph of $y = \sqrt{h - x}$ differ from the graph of $y = \sqrt{x - h}$?

70. For what positive integers n are the domain and range of $y = \sqrt[n]{x}$ the set of real numbers? Assume that x is a real number.

Multiple Choice Practice

For California Standards and CAHSEE Tutorials, visit PHSchool.com. Web Code: bbq-9045

ALG2 9.0

71. The equation $y = \frac{1}{2}x^2$ is changed to $y = -3x^2$. Which statement describes the effect on the graph?

   Ⓐ The graph is wider and opens downward.

   Ⓑ The graph is congruent and is translated down.

   Ⓒ The graph is narrower and opens downward.

   Ⓓ The graph is congruent and is translated up.

ALG2 10.0

72. Which of the following statements is true of the graph at the right?

   Ⓐ The equation of the parabola is
   $y = \frac{1}{3}(x - 1)^2 + 2$ and the vertex is $\left(0, 2\frac{1}{3}\right)$.

   Ⓑ The equation of the parabola is
   $y = \frac{1}{3}(x - 1)^2 + 2$ and the vertex is $(1, 2)$.

   Ⓒ The equation of the parabola is
   $y = \frac{1}{3}(x + 1)^2 - 2$ and the vertex is $(1, 2)$.

   Ⓓ The equation of the parabola is $y = \frac{1}{3}(x + 1)^2 - 2$ and the vertex is $\left(0, 2\frac{1}{3}\right)$.

ALG2 25.0

73. Which expression represents $f(g(x))$ if $f(x) = 2x^2 - 5$ and $g(x) = x + 3$?

   Ⓐ $2x^2 - 12x - 13$ Ⓒ $2x^3 - 15$

   Ⓑ $2x^2 + 12x + 13$ Ⓓ $2x^3 + 6x^2 - 5x - 15$

Mixed Review

for Help

Lesson 7-7

Find the inverse of each function. Is the inverse a function?

74. $f(x) = 4x - 1$ **75.** $f(x) = \frac{2}{3}x - 3$ **76.** $f(x) = 2.4x^2 + 1$

77. $f(x) = \sqrt{x + 3} - 4$ **78.** $f(x) = (2x + 1)^2$ **79.** $f(x) = 2x^3$

Lesson 7-2

Rationalize the denominator of each expression. Assume that all variables are positive.

80. $\dfrac{\sqrt{36x^3}}{\sqrt{12x}}$ **81.** $\sqrt[3]{\dfrac{3x}{2y}}$ **82.** $\dfrac{\sqrt[3]{x}}{\sqrt[3]{3y}}$ **83.** $\sqrt[5]{\dfrac{3x^3}{2y}}$

Lesson 5-8

Solve using the Quadratic Formula.

84. $5x^2 + x = 3$ **85.** $3x^2 + 9x = 27$ **86.** $x^2 - 9x + 15 = 0$

87. $x^2 + 10x + 11 = 0$ **88.** $x^2 - 12x + 25 = 0$ **89.** $8x^2 + 2x - 15 = 0$

Solving radical inequalities can be challenging. The domain considerations can be subtle. Algebraic processes can introduce extraneous solutions.

1 ACTIVITY

Can a number be less than its own square root?

Many people rely on their number sense and answer "no" to this question. In their minds, they run through a table of values like the one shown here.

```
Plot1 Plot2 Plot3
\Y1 ▤X
\Y2 ▤√(X)
\Y3 =
\Y4 =
\Y5 =
\Y6 =
\Y7 =
```

X	Y1	Y2
0	0	0
1	1	1
2	2	1.4142
3	3	1.7321
4	4	2
5	5	2.2361
6	6	2.4495
X=0		

1. Why is there no need to start this table with an x-value less than zero?

2. For the table above, $y_1 = x$ and $y_2 = \sqrt{x}$.
   a. Enter a third function $Y_3 = Y_1 - Y_2$. What will this function show?
   b. Turn off Y_1 and Y_2. Then view a table of Y_3 values. Scroll down. What happens to Y_3 values as the value of X increases?

3. In the table above and in your Y_3 table, the first two rows are unique. They may lead you to wonder what happens between $x = 0$ and $x = 1$.
   a. To find out, go to TBLSET. Change ΔTbl to 0.2 and view a $Y_1 - Y_2$ table. How do the values of x and $\sqrt{x}$ compare for values of x between 0 and 1?
   b. What would you expect to see in the Y_3 table? Check your conjecture.

In Exercise 3, you should have discovered some numbers that are less than their own square roots. But can you find them all? It helps to compare $Y_1 = X$ and $Y_2 = \sqrt{(X)}$ graphically.

4. a. Use the window settings shown at the right. Graph Y_1 and Y_2.
   b. Give a convincing argument that only numbers between 0 and 1 are less than their own square roots.
   c. What would you expect to see in a graph of Y_3? Check your conjecture. (*Hint:* You'll have to change your window settings.)

```
WINDOW
Xmin = 0
Xmax = 3
Xscl = 1
Ymin = 0
Ymax = 2
Yscl = 1
Xres = 1▮
```

2 ACTIVITY

A graphing calculator provides a practical way to solve radical inequalities, but you must be careful to use appropriate table or window settings.

5. a. What are the domains of $Y_1 = f(x) = \sqrt{x - 3}$ and $Y_2 = g(x) = \sqrt{7 - x}$?
   b. What are the only values of x that you have to consider to solve the radical inequality $\sqrt{x - 3} \leq \sqrt{7 - x}$? (*Hint:* Both expressions must be real numbers.)
   c. Graph Y_1 and Y_2. Solve the inequality.
   d. Let TblStart = 2 and ΔTbl = 1. Predict what a table will show, then check.

6. You can square both sides of the inequality $\sqrt{x-3} \le \sqrt{7-x}$ and simplify to $x \le 5$. Are there any x-values that satisfy $x \le 5$ but are not solutions of $\sqrt{x-3} \le \sqrt{7-x}$?

3 ACTIVITY

A **truth function** for an equation or inequality in x is a function whose range is the two numbers 0 and 1 and whose domain is the set of real numbers that can be used in place of x in the equation or inequality. If a value for x makes the equation or inequality true, the truth-function value is 1. Otherwise, it is 0.

You can solve an inequality graphically by viewing the graph of its truth function.

7. With your calculator in DOT mode, enter $Y_1 = \sqrt{x-3} \le \sqrt{7-x}$. (Find "$\le$" in the TEST menu.) Graph the truth function Y_1 as shown here.

8. Explain how the screen on the right shows where $\sqrt{x-3} \le \sqrt{7-x}$ is true. Based on the graph, for what values of x is the inequality true? Does this agree with your result in Exercise 6(c)?

9. For what values of x is the inequality false? How can you tell from the graph?

10. Solve the inequality $\sqrt{8+x} + \sqrt{4x} \ge 3 + \sqrt{5-x}$ in two ways.
  a. by graphing it as a truth function
  b. by graphing and comparing the two related functions
  c. Compare your solutions from parts (a) and (b).

11. Solve the inequality $\sqrt{x} - \sqrt{x-3} \le \sqrt{6-x}$ in two ways.
  a. by graphing it as a truth function
  b. algebraically
  c. Explain why a truth function might be less useful for solving this inequality.

4 ACTIVITY

You can find the LOGIC menu next to the TEST menu. The **logical operators** in the LOGIC menu can help you find the domain of an equation or inequality—that is, the values of x to which the solutions of an equation or inequality are restricted.

12. Use the inequality $\sqrt{x} - \sqrt{x-3} \le \sqrt{6-x}$ from Exercise 11.
  a. For $\sqrt{x} - \sqrt{x-3} \le \sqrt{6-x}$ it must be true that $x \ge 0, x-3 \ge 0$, and $6-x \ge 0$. Why?
  b. The truth function Y_1 in the screen at the right uses the logical operator *and*. Explain why the graph of Y_1 will show the domain of the inequality $\sqrt{x} - \sqrt{x-3} \le \sqrt{6-x}$.
  c. How can graphing $Y_1, Y_2 = \sqrt{x} - \sqrt{x-3}$, and $Y_3 = \sqrt{6-x}$ in the same window help you solve the inequality $\sqrt{x} - \sqrt{x-3} \le \sqrt{6-x}$?

In some multiple-choice questions, there may be several correct answers.

1 EXAMPLE

Which of the following are true for all values of x?

I. $\sqrt[3]{2^x} = \left(\sqrt[3]{2}\right)^x$　　　　**II.** $\sqrt{x^2} = \sqrt[3]{x^3}$　　　　**III.** $\sqrt{x^2 + 1} = |x| + 1$

  Ⓐ I only　　　Ⓑ III only　　　Ⓒ I and II only　　Ⓓ I and III only　　Ⓔ II and III only

Determine whether each statement is true for all values of x.

Equation I　　　$\sqrt[3]{2^x} = (2^x)^{\frac{1}{3}} = \left(2^{\frac{1}{3}}\right)^x = \left(\sqrt[3]{2}\right)^x$　　　　*True*

Equation II　　　$\sqrt{x^2} = |x| \neq x = \sqrt[3]{x^3}$　　　　*False*

Equation III　　　Square each side to get
　　　　　　　　　$x^2 + 1 = x^2 + 2|x| + 1$,
　　　　　　　　　or $0 = 2|x|$, which is true only for $x = 0$.　　*False*

● Only statement I is true for all values of x. The correct choice is A.

2 EXAMPLE

Which of the following are equal to x for all nonzero values of x?

I. $\sqrt{x^2}$　　　　　　**II.** $\sqrt[3]{x^3}$　　　　　　**III.** $\dfrac{\sqrt[3]{x^4}}{\sqrt[3]{x}}$

  Ⓐ I only　　　Ⓑ II only　　　Ⓒ I and II only　　Ⓓ II and III only　　Ⓔ I, II, and III

Rewrite each statement.

Expression I　　　$\sqrt{x^2} = x$ only when x is positive.

Expression II　　　$\sqrt[3]{x^3} = x$ for all values of x.

Expression III　　　$\dfrac{\sqrt[3]{x^4}}{\sqrt[3]{x}} = \dfrac{x^{\frac{4}{3}}}{x^{\frac{1}{3}}} = x^{\frac{4}{3} - \frac{1}{3}} = x$ when $x \neq 0$.

● Expressions II and III are correct choices. The correct choice is D.

EXERCISES

1. Test each equation in Example 1 with $x = 2$ and $x = -2$. What do your results show about each of the three equations?

2. Critical Thinking Test each equation in Example 1 with $x = 0$ and $x = 1$. Explain whether these values help you answer the question.

3. Suppose Example 2 asked, "Which of the following are equal to x for some nonzero values of x?" What would be the correct answer choice?

4. Which of the following equations are true?

I. $\left(\sqrt[4]{\sqrt{3}}\right)^8 = 3$　　　　**II.** $\left(\sqrt[4]{\sqrt{3}}\right)^6 = 3$　　　　**III.** $\dfrac{1}{\left(\frac{3}{5}\right)^{-1}} = \dfrac{5}{3}$

  Ⓐ I only　　　Ⓑ II only　　　Ⓒ I and II only　　Ⓓ I and III only　　Ⓔ II and III only

Chapter 7 Review

Choose the correct vocabulary term to complete each sentence.

1. In the expression $\sqrt[3]{8}$, 8 is called the (*principal root, radicand*).

2. In the expression $\sqrt[3]{8}$, 3 is called the (*principal root, index*).

3. When you rewrite an expression so there are no radicals in any denominator and no denominators in any radical, you (*rationalize the denominator, compose two functions*).

4. The expressions $\sqrt{x}$ and $\sqrt[5]{x}$ (*are, are not*) examples of like radicals.

5. The definition of (*rational exponents, inverse functions*) allows us to write $7^{\frac{2}{3}} = \sqrt[3]{7^2}$.

6. If $g(x) = x - 4$ and $h(x) = x^2$, $(g \circ h)(x) = x^2 - 4$ is a (*radical function, composite function*).

7. To multiply expressions you sometimes add (*radicands, rational exponents*).

8. If f and f^{-1} are (*composite functions, inverse functions*), then $(f \circ f^{-1})(x) = x$ and $(f^{-1} \circ f)(x) = x$.

9. $(x - 7)^{\frac{1}{2}} + 2 = x$ is an example of (*a radical equation, an inverse relation*).

10. The positive even root of a number is called the (*principal root, rational exponent*).

Go Online
PHSchool.com

For: Vocabulary quiz
Web Code: bbj-0751

Skills and Concepts

Lessons 7-1 and 7-2

- To simplify *n*th roots (p. 375)
- To multiply radical expressions (p. 380)
- To divide radical expressions (p. 381)

🔷 **ALG2 15.0**

For any real numbers *a* and *b*, and any positive integer *n*, if $a^n = b$, then *a* is an *n*th root of *b*. The **principal root** of a number with two real roots is the positive root. The principal *n*th root of *b* is written as $\sqrt[n]{b}$. *b* is the **radicand** and *n* is the **index** of the radical.

For any negative real number *a*, $\sqrt[n]{a^n} = |a|$ when *n* is even.

If $\sqrt[n]{a}$ and $\sqrt[n]{b}$ are real numbers, then $\sqrt[n]{a} \cdot \sqrt[n]{b} = \sqrt[n]{ab}$, and, if $b \neq 0$, then $\dfrac{\sqrt[n]{a}}{\sqrt[n]{b}} = \sqrt[n]{\dfrac{a}{b}}$.

To **rationalize the denominator** of an expression, rewrite it so there are no radicals in any denominator and no denominators in any radical.

Find each indicated root if it is a real number.

11. $\sqrt{144}$ **12.** $\sqrt[3]{-0.064}$ **13.** $\sqrt[4]{7^4}$ **14.** $\sqrt{0.25}$ **15.** $-\sqrt[3]{27}$

Simplify each radical expression. Use absolute value symbols as needed.

16. $\sqrt{49x^2y^{10}}$ **17.** $\sqrt[3]{-64y^9}$ **18.** $\sqrt{(a-1)^4}$

19. $\sqrt[5]{243x^{15}}$ **20.** $\sqrt[3]{(y+3)^6}$ **21.** $\sqrt{32x^9y^5}$

Simplify each expression. Assume that all variables are positive.

22. $\sqrt{10} \cdot \sqrt{40}$ **23.** $\sqrt[3]{12} \cdot \sqrt[3]{36}$ **24.** $2\sqrt[3]{2x^2y} \cdot 5\sqrt[3]{6x^4y^4}$

25. $\sqrt{7x^3} \cdot \sqrt{14x}$ **26.** $\sqrt{5x^4y^3} \cdot \sqrt{45x^3y}$ **27.** $3\sqrt[4]{4x^3} \cdot \sqrt[4]{8xy^5}$

28. $\dfrac{\sqrt{128}}{\sqrt{8}}$ **29.** $\dfrac{\sqrt[3]{56y^5}}{\sqrt[3]{7y}}$ **30.** $\dfrac{\sqrt{75x^3}}{\sqrt{3x}}$ **31.** $\dfrac{\sqrt{216x^3y^2}}{\sqrt{2}}$ **32.** $\dfrac{\sqrt[3]{81a^8b^5}}{\sqrt[3]{3a^2b}}$

Simplify each expression. Rationalize all denominators. Assume that all variables are positive.

33. $\dfrac{\sqrt{8}}{\sqrt{6}}$ **34.** $\dfrac{\sqrt{3x^5}}{\sqrt{8x^2}}$ **35.** $\dfrac{\sqrt[3]{5}}{\sqrt[3]{x^4}}$ **36.** $\dfrac{\sqrt{2a^7b^2}}{\sqrt{32b^3}}$ **37.** $\dfrac{\sqrt[3]{6x^2y^4}}{2\sqrt[3]{5x^7y}}$

Lessons 7-3 and 7-4

- To add and subtract radical expressions (p. 386)
- To multiply and divide binomial radical expressions (p. 387)
- To simplify expressions with rational exponents (p. 391)

 ALG2 15.0, 12.0

Like radicals have the same index and the same radicand. Use the distributive property to add or subtract them. Simplify radicals to find all the like radicals.

Use FOIL to multiply binomial radical expressions.

Binomials such as $a + b$ and $a - b$ are called conjugate expressions.

If the denominator of a fraction is a binomial radical expression, multiply both the numerator and denominator of the fraction by the conjugate of the denominator to rationalize the denominator.

The definition of **rational exponents** states that if the nth root of a is a real number and m is an integer, then $a^{\frac{1}{n}} = \sqrt[n]{a}$ and $a^{\frac{m}{n}} = \sqrt[n]{a^m} = \left(\sqrt[n]{a}\right)^m$. If m is negative, $a \neq 0$. The usual properties of exponents hold for rational exponents.

Simplify each expression.

38. $\sqrt{27} + \sqrt{75} - \sqrt{12}$ **39.** $(5 + \sqrt{3})(2 - \sqrt{3})$ **40.** $(7 - \sqrt{6})(7 + \sqrt{6})$

Simplify each expression. Rationalize all denominators. Assume that all variables are positive.

41. $\sqrt{2x} - \sqrt{8x} + \sqrt{18x}$ **42.** $\dfrac{6}{7 + 2\sqrt{3}}$ **43.** $\dfrac{\sqrt{2}}{1 - \sqrt{5}}$

Write each expression in radical form.

44. $3^{\frac{1}{5}}$ **45.** $x^{\frac{2}{3}}$ **46.** $2^{-\frac{3}{4}}$ **47.** $3^{0.2}$ **48.** $p^{-2.25}$

Simplify each expression. Assume that all variables are positive.

49. $(243)^{\frac{4}{5}}$ **50.** $36^{\frac{3}{2}}$ **51.** $\left(x^{\frac{3}{4}}\right)^{\frac{4}{3}}$ **52.** $x^{\frac{1}{6}} \cdot x^{\frac{2}{3}}$ **53.** $\left(x^{-\frac{3}{8}}y^{\frac{1}{4}}\right)^{16}$

Lesson 7-5

- To solve square root and other radical equations (p. 397)

 ALG2 8.0

To solve a **square root equation** or any **radical equation,** isolate a radical on one side of the equation. Then raise both sides of the equation to the same power. Check all possible solutions in the original equation to eliminate extraneous solutions.

Solve each equation. Check for extraneous solutions.

54. $\sqrt[3]{3x + 1} = -5$ **55.** $\sqrt{x + 7} = x + 1$ **56.** $x^{\frac{1}{2}} - 3 = 8$

Lessons 7-6 and 7-7

- To add, subtract, multiply, and divide functions (p. 404)
- To find the composite of two functions (p. 405)
- To find the inverse of a relation or function (p. 412)

 ALG2 24.0, 25.0

The following are definitions of function operations.

Addition $(f + g)(x) = f(x) + g(x)$ Subtraction $(f - g)(x) = f(x) - g(x)$

Multiplication $(f \cdot g)(x) = f(x) \cdot g(x)$ Division $\left(\dfrac{f}{g}\right)(x) = \dfrac{f(x)}{g(x)}, g(x) \neq 0$

The composition of function g with function f is written as $g \circ f$ and is defined as $(g \circ f)(x) = g(f(x))$. The domain of the **composite function** $g \circ f$ consists of the values a in the domain of f such that $f(a)$ is in the domain of g.

If (a, b) is an ordered pair of a relation, then (b, a) is an ordered pair of its **inverse relation.** If a relation or function is described by an equation in x and y, you can interchange x and y to get the inverse. The inverse of a function is denoted by f^{-1}.

If f and f^{-1} are both functions, they are called **inverse functions,** and $(f^{-1} \circ f)(x) = x$ and $(f \circ f^{-1})(x) = x$.

Let $f(x) = 2x + 5$ and $g(x) = x^2 - 3x + 2$. Perform each function operation.

57. $(f + g)(x)$ **58.** $f(x) - g(x)$ **59.** $g(x) \cdot f(x)$ **60.** $(g - f)(x)$ **61.** $\dfrac{g(x)}{f(x)}$

Let $f(x) = x^2$ and $g(x) = x - 3$. Evaluate each expression.

62. $(g \circ f)(-2)$ **63.** $(f \circ g)(-2)$ **64.** $(f \circ g)(0)$ **65.** $(g \circ g)(7)$ **66.** $(f \circ g)(c)$

Find the inverse of each function. Is the inverse a function?

67. $y = 6x + 2$ **68.** $y = 2x^3 + 1$ **69.** $y = (x - 2)^4$ **70.** $y = \sqrt{x + 2}$

Let $f(x) = 3x + 1$. Find each value.

71. $(f^{-1} \circ f)(5)$ **72.** $(f^{-1} \circ f)(-5)$ **73.** $(f^{-1} \circ f)(6)$ **74.** $(f^{-1} \circ f)(t)$

Lesson 7-8

- To graph square root and other radical functions (p. 420)

The parent function $f(x) = \sqrt{x}$ defines a family of **square root functions** $f(x) = a\sqrt{x - h} + k$. The graph of $f(x) = a\sqrt{x}$ is a stretch $(a > 0)$ or a shrink $(0 < a < 1)$ of the parent function. The graph of $y = a\sqrt{x - h} + k$ is a translation h units horizontally and k units vertically of $y = a\sqrt{x}$.

Graph each function.

75. $y = \sqrt{x} + 3$ **76.** $y = \sqrt{x - 1}$

77. $y = -3\sqrt{x} + 6$ **78.** $y = \sqrt{x + 7} - 2$

Simplify each radical expression. Use absolute value symbols when they are needed.

1. $\sqrt[3]{-0.027}$

2. $\sqrt{54x^3y^5}$

3. $\sqrt[5]{-64x^{14}y^{20}}$

4. $\sqrt{(x-2)^4}$

Simplify each expression. Rationalize all denominators. Assume that all variables are positive.

5. $\sqrt{7x^3} \cdot \sqrt{14x}$

6. $\sqrt{3y^3} \cdot \sqrt{4xy^4} \cdot \sqrt{6x^5y^2}$

7. $\dfrac{\sqrt{7x^4y}}{\sqrt{63xy^2}}$

8. $\dfrac{1-\sqrt{3x}}{\sqrt{6x}}$

9. $\sqrt{48} + 2\sqrt{75} + 5\sqrt{12}$

10. $\sqrt{98} + \sqrt{50} - \sqrt{5}$

11. $(3 + 2\sqrt{5})(1 - \sqrt{20})$

12. $(7 + \sqrt{3})(3 + 5\sqrt{3})$

13. $\dfrac{5}{3 - 2\sqrt{6}}$

14. $\dfrac{1 + \sqrt{3}}{\sqrt{3} - \sqrt{2}}$

Simplify each expression. Assume that all variables are positive.

15. $(125)^{-\frac{2}{3}}$

16. $x^{\frac{1}{6}} \cdot x^{\frac{1}{3}}$

17. $\left(\dfrac{8x^9y^3}{27x^2y^{12}}\right)^{\frac{2}{3}}$

Solve each equation. Check for extraneous solutions.

18. $\sqrt{x-3} = x - 5$

19. $\sqrt{x+4} = \sqrt{3x}$

20. $(3x+4)^{\frac{1}{3}} = -5$

21. $x - 6 = (x-4)^{\frac{1}{2}}$

Let $f(x) = x - 2$ and $g(x) = x^2 - 3x + 2$. Perform each function operation and then find the domain.

22. $g(x) - f(x)$

23. $-2g(x) + f(x)$

24. $\dfrac{g(x)}{f(x)}$

25. $-f(x) \cdot g(x)$

For each pair of functions, find $f(g(x))$ and $g(f(x))$.

26. $f(x) = x^2 - 2, g(x) = 4x + 1$

27. $f(x) = 2x^2 + x - 7, g(x) = -3x - 1$

28. Writing Explain why -108 has no real 6th roots.

29. Discounts While purchasing a pair of shoes on sale for 50% off, you noticed that the price on the cash register was only 25% off. The cashier then took another 25% off that price.
  a. Write a function $f(x)$ to represent the 50%-off price of the shoes.
  b. Write a function $g(x)$ to represent the price the cash register rang up the first time.
  c. Write a composite function to represent the price of the shoes after the cashier's solution to the problem.
  d. Compare the result of the cashier's solution to the correct price of the shoes.

Rewrite each function to make it easy to graph using a translation. Describe the graph.

30. $y = \sqrt{16x + 80} - 1$

31. $y = \sqrt{9x + 3}$

Graph. Find the domain and range of each function.

32. $y = 2\sqrt{x} + 3$

33. $y = \sqrt{2x + 3}$

34. $y = -\frac{1}{2}\sqrt{x} - 4$

35. $y = \sqrt{x + 3} - 4$

Let $f(x) = x^3 + 1$ and $g(x) = 7x - 4$. Find each value.

36. $f(g(-2))$

37. $g(f(3))$

38. $f(g(0))$

Find the inverse of each function. Is the inverse a function?

39. $f(x) = 3x^3 - 2$

40. $g(x) = \sqrt{x + 3} - 1$

41. $g(x) = \sqrt{2x + 1}$

42. $f(x) = \frac{1}{4}x^4$

43. a. Geometry For a sphere, $V = \frac{4}{3}\pi r^3$. Find the volume of a sphere with radius 4 in.
  b. Solve the formula in part (a) for r.
  c. Find to the nearest hundredth the radius of a sphere of volume 100 in.^{3}.

44. Open-Ended Write a relation rule that is not a function, but whose inverse is a function.

45. Measurement The time t in seconds for a swinging pendulum to complete one full cycle is given by the function $t = 0.2\sqrt{\ell}$, where ℓ is the length of the pendulum in cm. How long is a full cycle if the pendulum is 10 cm long? 20 cm long?

Some problems require you to find the inverse of a function.

> What is the inverse of the function $y = x^2 + 3$?
>
> (A) $y = x - 3$
>
> (B) $y = \pm\sqrt{x - 3}$
>
> (C) $y = \pm\sqrt{x^2 + 3}$
>
> (D) $y = (x - 3)^2$

Tip 1
To find the inverse of a function, interchange x and y.

Tip 2
Make sure you solve the equation for y.

Think It Through
$y = x^2 + 3$
$x = y^2 + 3$
$x - 3 = y^2$
$\pm\sqrt{x - 3} = y$
$y = \pm\sqrt{x - 3}$
The correct answer is B.

Vocabulary Review

As you solve problems, you must understand the meanings of mathematical terms. Match each term with its mathematical meaning.

A. radicand

B. index

C. composite function

D. inverse function

E. radical function

I. the combination of two functions such that the output from the first becomes the input for the second

II. the degree of the root in a radical expression

III. the number under the radical sign in a radical expression

IV. a function that can be written in the form $f(x) = a\sqrt[n]{x - h} + k$

V. the range of one function is the domain of the other and vice versa

Multiple Choice

Read each question. Then write the letter of the correct answer on your paper.

1. If w is a real number, for what values of w is $(w^4)^{\frac{1}{4}} = (w^3)^{\frac{1}{3}}$ true? (Lesson 7-4)

   (A) all values of w

   (B) some values of w

   (C) no values of w

   (D) impossible to determine

2. Your friend tells you that $(x + 1)^2 = x^2 + 1$. Which of the following statements is correct about the equation she wrote? (Lesson 6-1)

   (A) The equation is always true.

   (B) The equation is always true when $x = 0$.

   (C) The equation is never true.

   (D) The equation is sometimes true when $x = 0$.

3. Given the equation $y = \sqrt[n]{x}$ where $x > 0$ and $n < 0$, which statement is valid for real values of y? (Lesson 7-1)

   (A) $y > 0$ (C) $y = 0$

   (B) $y < 0$ (D) $-1 \leq y \leq 0$

4. Which expression is NOT equivalent to $\sqrt[6]{81x^4y^8}$? (Lesson 7-1)

   (A) $(3xy^2)^{\frac{2}{3}}$

   (B) $(3x)^{\frac{2}{3}}y^{\frac{4}{3}}$

   (C) $(3x^2y^4)^{\frac{1}{3}}$

   (D) $\sqrt[3]{9x^2y^4}$

5. Which of the following is a solution to the equation $(x + 2)^{\frac{3}{4}} = 27$? (Lesson 7-4)

    Ⓐ 34   Ⓒ 79

    Ⓑ 36   Ⓓ 81

6. Which of the following can be expressed as an integer? (Lesson 7-4)

    Ⓐ $90^{\frac{2}{3}}$ Ⓒ $125^{\frac{3}{4}}$

    Ⓑ $27^{\frac{2}{3}}$ Ⓓ $5100^{\frac{3}{4}}$

7. Which expression is equivalent to $(6a^2)^{\frac{4}{5}}(b^3)^{\frac{1}{2}}$? (Lesson 7-4)

    Ⓐ $\left(\sqrt[5]{1296a^8}\right)(b^3)$

    Ⓑ $\left(\sqrt[5]{1296a^{10}}\right)(b^{12})$

    Ⓒ $\left(6a^{\frac{8}{5}}\right)\left(b^{\frac{3}{2}}\right)$

    Ⓓ $\left(\sqrt{1296a^8}\right)\left(\sqrt{b}\right)$

8. Lucinda is choosing between two cable television providers. The graph shows the relationship between the total cost per month of each cable provider and the number of premium channels selected.

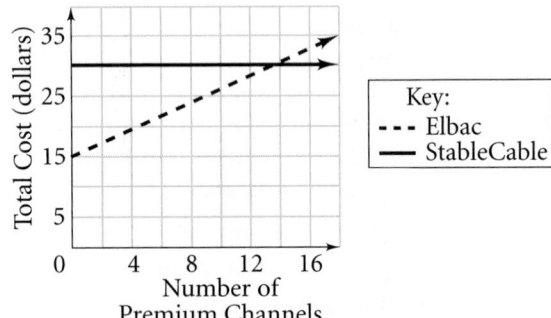

Key:
- - - Elbac
—— StableCable

According to the graph, which of these statements must be true? (Lesson 3-1)

    Ⓐ StableCable would cost more than Elbac if Lucinda used more than 12 channels per month.

    Ⓑ Elbac would cost less than StableCable if Lucinda used fewer than 12 channels per month.

    Ⓒ StableCable would cost less than Elbac if Lucinda used exactly 12 channels per month.

    Ⓓ Elbac would cost less than StableCable if Lucinda used more than 12 channels per month.

9. Solve the system. (Lesson 3-6)

$$\begin{cases} 2x + 3y - z = -2 \\ x - 4y + 2z = 18 \\ 5x + 2y - 6z = 8 \end{cases}$$

    Ⓐ $x = 3, y = 1, z = 2$

    Ⓑ $x = -3, y = 2, z = -1$

    Ⓒ $x = 4, y = -3, z = 1$

    Ⓓ $x = -1, y = 3, z = 2$

10. What is the inverse of $y = 5x - 1$? (Lesson 7-7)

    Ⓐ $y = 5x + 1$

    Ⓑ $y = \dfrac{x + 1}{5}$

    Ⓒ $y = \dfrac{x}{5} + 1$

    Ⓓ $y = \dfrac{x}{5} - 1$

11. If $(f \circ g)(x) = x^2 - 6x + 8$ and $g(x) = x - 3$, which expression could represent $f(x)$? (Lesson 7-6)

    Ⓐ $x - 4$ Ⓒ $x^2 - 1$

    Ⓑ $x - 1$ Ⓓ $x^2 - 6x + 5$

12. Let $g(x) = x - 3$ and $h(x) = x^2 + 6$. Find $(h \circ g)(1)$. (Lesson 7-6)

    Ⓐ -14 Ⓑ 4   Ⓒ 5   Ⓓ 10

13. A florist wants to make an arrangement using 15 flowers. She wants to use 9 roses and to use carnations for the rest. If she has 16 assorted roses and 21 assorted carnations in stock, how many different ways can she choose flowers for the arrangement? (Lesson 6-7)

    Ⓐ 135   Ⓑ 336   Ⓒ 50,200   Ⓓ 272,160

14. You decide to bring 2 pens and 4 pencils to class with you. There are 10 pencils and 11 pens in your locker. How many different ways can you choose pens and pencils for class? (Lesson 6-7)

    Ⓐ 8   Ⓑ 110   Ⓒ 265   Ⓓ 375

15. Which is the first *incorrect* step in simplifying $(x^3)^4 + (x^2)^3$? (Lesson 7-1)

Step 1: $(x^3)^4 + (x^2)^3 = x^{12} + (x^2)^3$
Step 2: $\qquad\qquad\qquad = x^{12} + x^5$
Step 3: $\qquad\qquad\qquad = x^{17}$

    Ⓐ Step 1

    Ⓑ Step 2

    Ⓒ Step 3

    Ⓓ Each step is correct.

16. Which is the first *incorrect* step in simplifying $\sqrt[3]{x^9 y^6 z}$? **(Lesson 7-1)**

Step 1: $\sqrt[3]{x^9 y^6 z} = \sqrt[3]{x^9} \cdot \sqrt[3]{y^6} \cdot \sqrt[3]{z}$

Step 2: $\qquad\quad = x^3 \cdot \sqrt[3]{y^6} \cdot \sqrt[3]{z}$

Step 3: $\qquad\quad = x^3 \cdot y^3 \cdot \sqrt[3]{z}$

- Ⓐ Step 1
- Ⓑ Step 2
- Ⓒ Step 3
- Ⓓ Each step is correct.

17. If $f(x) = 3x^2 - 5x + 3$ and $g(x) = (x - 1)^2$, which is an equivalent form of $f(x) - g(x)$? **(Lesson 7-6)**

- Ⓐ $2x^2 - 3x + 2$
- Ⓑ $2x^2 + 3x + 2$
- Ⓒ $4x^2 - 7x + 4$
- Ⓓ $4x^2 + 7x - 4$

18. If $f(x) = x - 1$ and $g(x) = (2x - 3)^2$, which is an equivalent form of $f(g(x))$? **(Lesson 7-6)**

- Ⓐ $4x^2 - 20x + 25$
- Ⓑ $4x^2 + 20x - 25$
- Ⓒ $4x^2 + 12x - 8$
- Ⓓ $4x^2 - 12x + 8$

19. What is the solution of $\begin{cases} 2x - y = 4 \\ y = 2 - x \end{cases}$? **(Lesson 3-2)**

- Ⓐ $(0, 2)$
- Ⓑ $(2, 0)$
- Ⓒ $(2, 4)$
- Ⓓ $(0, -4)$

20. Solve $3 + (x - 1)^{\frac{3}{4}} = 30$. **(Lesson 7-5)**

- Ⓐ 9
- Ⓑ 11
- Ⓒ 81
- Ⓓ 82

21. Which is NOT a solution of the system?
$\begin{cases} 2x - y > 3 \\ 2x + y \geq 5 \end{cases}$ **(Lesson 3-3)**

- Ⓐ $(3, 0)$
- Ⓑ $(6, 1)$
- Ⓒ $(4, -1)$
- Ⓓ $(0, -3)$

22. What is the inverse of $y = x^2 - 3$? **(Lesson 7-7)**

- Ⓐ $y = \pm\sqrt{x} + 3$
- Ⓑ $y = \pm\sqrt{x} - 3$
- Ⓒ $y = \pm\sqrt{x + 3}$
- Ⓓ $y = \pm\sqrt{x - 3}$

Standards Reference Guide

California Content Standard	Item Number(s)
ALG2 15.0	1–3
ALG2 12.0	4–7, 20
ALG2 2.0	8–9, 19, 21
ALG2 24.0	10–12, 22
ALG2 18.0	13–14
ALG2 11.2	15–16
ALG2 25.0	17–18

For additional review and practice, see the *California Standards Review and Practice Workbook* or go online to use the

California Standards Tutorials

Visit: PHschool.com, **Web Code:** bbq-9045

Exponential and Logarithmic Functions

 What You've Learned

California Content Standards

24.0 Students solve problems involving functional concepts, such as composition, defining the inverse function and performing arithmetic operations on functions.

25.0 Students use properties from number systems to justify steps in combining and simplifying functions.

15.0 Students determine whether a specific algebraic statement involving radical expressions is sometimes true, always true, or never true.

✓ Check Your Readiness **for Help** to the Lesson in green.

Evaluating Expressions (Lesson 1-2)

Evaluate each expression for $x = -2, -1, 0, 1,$ and 2.

1. 10^{x+1} **2.** $\left(\frac{3}{2}\right)^x$ **3.** $x^4 - x^2$

Using Linear Models (Lesson 2-4)

4. Each day, a squirrel buries three acorns.
   a. Write and graph a function to model the number n of acorns the squirrel buries in d days.
   b. Use your function to find the number of acorns buried in four weeks.
   c. Suppose the squirrel had started out with nine acorns already buried. Explain how this would change your function and its graph.

Using Quadratic Models (Lesson 5-1)

Find a quadratic function to model each set of values. Then graph the function.

5. $\{(0, 0), (2, -4), (3, -3)\}$ **6.** $\{(0, 7), (2, 15), (5, 72)\}$

Graphing Transformations (Lesson 5-3)

Identify the parent function of each equation. Graph each equation as a transformation of its parent function.

7. $y = -(x - 1)^2 + 4$ **8.** $y = 3(x + 2)^2 - 1$

Graphing Inverse Functions (Lesson 7-7)

Graph each function and its inverse on a coordinate plane.

9. $y = -5x$ **10.** $y = \sqrt{5x + 12}$ **11.** $y = 2x^3$

What You'll Learn Next

▲ If California poppies are planted in a suitable environment, the population can grow exponentially.

California Content Standards

12.0 Students understand exponential functions and use these functions in problems involving exponential growth and decay.

11.1 Students understand the inverse relationship between exponents and logarithms and use this relationship to solve problems involving logarithms and exponents.

14.0 Students understand and use the properties of logarithms to simplify logarithmic numeric expressions and to identify their approximate values.

New Vocabulary

🔊 **English and Spanish Audio Online**

- **asymptote** (p. 441)
- **Change of Base Formula** (p. 470)
- **common logarithm** (p. 455)
- **continuously compounded interest formula** (p. 449)
- **decay factor** (p. 441)
- **exponential equation** (p. 469)
- **exponential function** (p. 438)
- **growth factor** (p. 438)
- **logarithm** (p. 455)
- **logarithmic equation** (p. 471)
- **logarithmic function** (p. 456)
- **natural logarithmic function** (p. 478)

8-1

Exploring Exponential Models

 California Content Standards

ALG2 12.0 Students understand exponential functions and use these functions in problems involving exponential growth and decay. *Introduce, Develop*

What You'll Learn

- To model exponential growth
- To model exponential decay

... And Why

To model a car's depreciation, as in Example 6

 Check Skills You'll Need

GO for Help Lesson 1-2

Evaluate each expression for the given value of x.

1. 2^x for $x = 3$

2. 4^{x+1} for $x = 1$

3. 2^{3x+4} for $x = -1$

4. $3^x 3^{x-2}$ for $x = 2$

5. $\left(\frac{1}{2}\right)^x$ for $x = 0$

6. 2^x for $x = -2$

New Vocabulary • **exponential function** • **growth factor**
• **decay factor** • **asymptote**

---

1 Exponential Growth

For some data, the best model is a function that uses the independent variable as an exponent. An **exponential function** is a function with the general form $y = ab^x$, where x is a real number, $a \neq 0, b > 0,$ and $b \neq 1$.

You can use an exponential function with $b > 1$ to model growth. When $b > 1$, b is the **growth factor.**

Exponential Growth

Growth factor $b > 1$

1 EXAMPLE Graphing Exponential Growth

Graph $y = 2^x$.

Step 1 Make a table of values.

x	2^x	y
−3	2^{-3}	$\frac{1}{8} = 0.125$
−2	2^{-2}	$\frac{1}{4} = 0.25$
−1	2^{-1}	$\frac{1}{2} = 0.5$
0	2^0	1
1	2^1	2
2	2^2	4
3	2^3	8

Step 2 Graph the coordinates. Connect the points with a smooth curve.

 CA Standards Check **1** Graph each function.

a. $y = 4(2)^x$

b. $y = 3^x$

You can use an exponential function to model population growth. If you know the rate of increase r, you can find the growth factor by using the equation $b = 1 + r$.

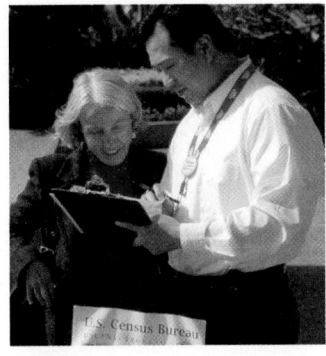

2 EXAMPLE Real-World Connection

Multiple Choice Refer to the graph. In 2000, the annual rate of increase in the U.S. population was about 1.24%. Suppose the rate of increase continues to be 1.24%. Which function best models U.S. population growth, in millions, after 2000?

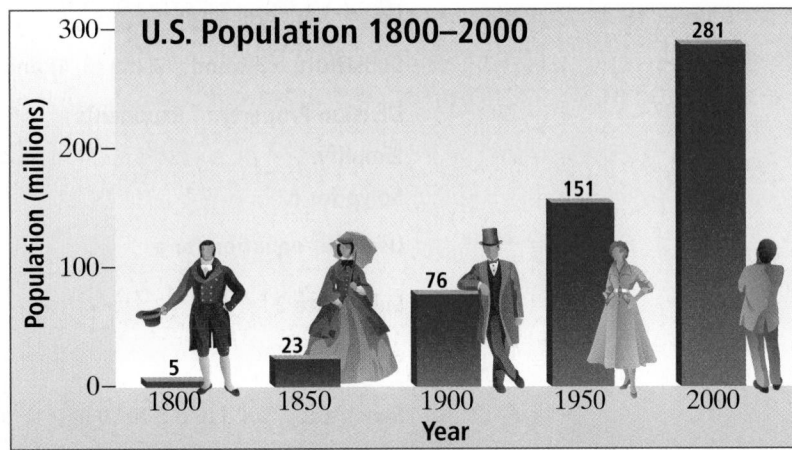

U.S. Population 1800–2000

Population (millions)

| 1800: 5 | 1850: 23 | 1900: 76 | 1950: 151 | 2000: 281 |

Year

Source: U.S. Census Bureau. Go to **www.PHSchool.com** for a data update. Web Code: bbg-9041

Ⓐ $281 + 1.0124^x$ Ⓑ $281(1.24)^x$ Ⓒ $281(1.024)^x$ Ⓓ $281(1.0124)^x$

First, find the growth factor.

$b = 1 + r$
$\quad = 1 + 0.0124$ **Substitute 1.24%, or 0.0124, for r.**
$\quad = 1.0124$ **Simplify.**

Then write a function.

Relate The population increases exponentially, so use the general form of an exponential function, $p(x) = ab^x$.

Define Let $\boxed{x}$ = number of years after 2000.

Let $\boxed{p(x)}$ = the population in millions.

Write $\boxed{p(x)} = a(1.0124)^x$

$281 = a(1.0124)^0$ **To find a, substitute the 2000 values: p(x) = 281, x = 0.**
$281 = a \cdot 1$ **Any nonzero number to the zero power equals 1.**
$281 = a$ **Simplify.**
$p(x) = 281(1.0124)^x$ **Substitute a and b into p(x) = ab^x.**

● The function $p(x) = 281(1.0124)^x$ models U.S. population growth. The answer is D.

✔ **CA Standards Check** ② **a.** Predict U.S. population in 2015 to the nearest million.

b. Critical Thinking Explain why the model and your prediction may not be valid for 2015.

c. Suppose the rate of population increase changes to 1.4%. Write a function to model population growth and use it to predict the 2015 population to the nearest million.

You can write an exponential function from two points on the function's graph.

3 EXAMPLE **Writing an Exponential Function**

Write an exponential function $y = ab^x$ for a graph that includes $(2, 2)$ and $(3, 4)$.

$y = ab^x$	**Use the general form.**
$2 = a \cdot b^2$	**Substitute for x and y using (2, 2).**
$\frac{2}{b^2} = a$	**Solve for a.**
$y = ab^x$	**Use the general form.**
$4 = \frac{2}{b^2}b^3$	**Substitute for x and y using (3, 4) and for a using $\frac{2}{b^2}$.**
$4 = 2b^{3-2}$	**Division Property of Exponents**
$4 = 2b$	**Simplify.**
$b = 2$	**Solve for b.**
$a = \frac{2}{b^2}$	**Use your equation for a.**
$a = \frac{2}{2^2}$	**Substitute 2 for b.**
$a = \frac{1}{2}$	**Simplify.**
$y = \frac{1}{2} \cdot 2^x$	**Substitute $\frac{1}{2}$ for a and 2 for b in $y = ab^x$.**

● The exponential function for a graph that includes $(2, 2)$ and $(3, 4)$ is $y = \frac{1}{2} \cdot 2^x$.

✓ **CA Standards Check** ❸ Write an exponential function $y = ab^x$ for a graph that includes $(2, 4)$ and $(3, 16)$.

2 Exponential Decay

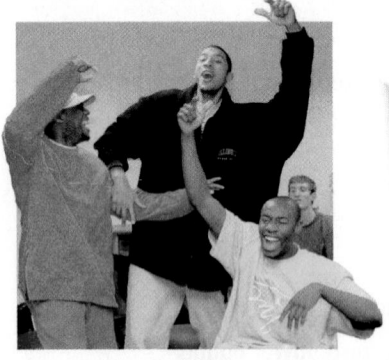

Real-World Connection

On a day in March, the NCAA announces the selection of 64 teams for its annual tournament.

Activity: Tournament Play

The National Collegiate Athletic Association (NCAA) holds an annual basketball tournament. The top 64 teams in Division I are invited to play each spring. When a team loses, it is out of the tournament.

1. How many teams are left in the tournament after the first round of basketball games?

2. a. Copy, complete, and extend the table until only one team is left.

After Round x	Number of Teams Left in Tournament (y)
0	64
1	■
2	■

   b. Graph the points from your table on graph paper.

3. How many rounds are played in the tournament?

4. Does the graph represent a linear function? Explain.

5. How does the number of teams left in each round compare to the number of teams in the previous round?

You can use an exponential function with $0 < b < 1$ to model decay. When $b < 1$, b is a **decay factor.**

Exponential Decay

Decay factor $b < 1$

4 EXAMPLE **Analyzing a Function**

Without graphing, determine whether the function $y = 14(0.95)^x$ represents exponential growth or exponential decay.

● In $y = 14(0.95)^x$, $b = 0.95$. Since $b < 1$, the function represents exponential decay.

✓ **CA Standards Check** ④ Without graphing, determine whether each function represents exponential growth or exponential decay.

a. $y = 100(0.12)^x$ **b.** $y = 0.2(5)^x$ **c.** $y = 16\left(\frac{1}{2}\right)^x$

Vocabulary Tip

Asymptote comes from the Greek word *asymptotos,* meaning "not meeting."

An **asymptote** is a line that a graph approaches as x or y increases in absolute value.

5 EXAMPLE **Graphing Exponential Decay**

Graph $y = 24\left(\frac{1}{2}\right)^x$. Identify the horizontal asymptote.

Step 1 Make a table of values.

x	−3	−2	−1	0	1	2	3
y	192	96	48	24	12	6	3

Step 2 Graph the coordinates. Connect the points with a smooth curve.

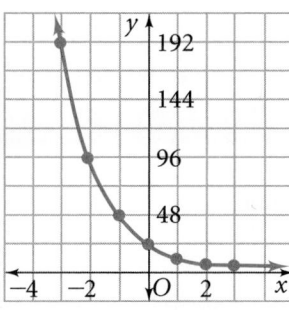

As x increases, y approaches 0.

● The asymptote is the x-axis, $y = 0$.

✓ **CA Standards Check** ⑤ Graph each decay function. Identify the horizontal asymptote.

a. $y = 24\left(\frac{1}{3}\right)^x$ **b.** $y = 100(0.1)^x$

Depreciation is the decline in an item's value resulting from age or wear. When an item loses about the same percent of its value each year, you can use an exponential function to model the depreciation.

6 EXAMPLE Real-World Connection

Depreciation The exponential decay graph shows the expected depreciation for a car over four years. Estimate the value of the car after six years.

The decay factor b equals $1 + r$, where r is the annual rate of decrease. The initial value of the car is $20,000. After one year the value of the car is about $17,000.

$$r = \frac{\text{final value} - \text{initial value}}{\text{initial value}}$$ **Write an equation for r.**

$$= \frac{17{,}000 - 20{,}000}{20{,}000}$$ **Substitute.**

$$= -0.15$$ **Simplify.**

$$b = 1 + r$$ **Use r to find b.**

$$= 1 + (-0.15) = 0.85$$ **Simplify.**

Expected Decrease in Value

[Graph: Value ($) vs Years since purchase, showing exponential decay from 20,000 at year 0 down through years 1–4]

Write a function, and then evaluate it for $x = 6$.

Relate The value of the car decreases exponentially; $b = 0.85$.

Define Let x = number of years. Let y = value of the car.

Write $y = ab^x$

$20{,}000 = a(0.85)^0$ **Substitute using (0, 20,000).**

$20{,}000 = a$ **Solve for a.**

$y = 20{,}000(0.85)^x$ **Substitute a and b into $y = ab^x$.**

$y = 20{,}000(0.85)^6$ **Evaluate for x = 6.**

≈ 7542.99 **Simplify.**

The car's value after six years will be about $7540.

✓ CA Standards Check **6** Estimate the value of the car from Example 6 after 10 years.

EXERCISES

For more exercises, see *Extra Skill and Word Problem Practice.*

Standards Practice

ALG2 12.0

A Practice by Example

Example 1
(page 438)

GO for Help

Graph each function.

1. $y = 6^x$
2. $y = 3(10)^x$
3. $y = 1000(2)^x$
4. $y = 9(3)^x$
5. $f(x) = 2(3)^x$
6. $s(t) = 1.5^t$
7. $y = 8(5)^x$
8. $y = 2^{2x}$

Example 2
(page 439)

9. Population The world population in 2000 was approximately 6.08 billion. The annual rate of increase was about 1.26%.
   a. Find the growth factor for the world population.
   b. Suppose the rate of increase continues to be 1.26%. Write a function to model world population growth.

Example 3
(page 440)

Write an exponential function $y = ab^x$ for a graph that includes the given points.

10. $(4, 8), (6, 32)$ **11.** $(2, 122.5), (3, 857.5)$ **12.** $(2, 18), (5, 60.75)$

13. $\left(-1, 8\frac{1}{3}\right), (2, 1.8)$ **14.** $(-3, 24), (-2, 12)$ **15.** $(0, 24), \left(3, \frac{8}{9}\right)$

Example 4
(page 441)

Without graphing, determine whether each function represents exponential growth or exponential decay.

16. $y = 129(1.63)^x$ **17.** $f(x) = 2(0.65)^x$ **18.** $y = 12\left(\frac{17}{10}\right)^x$ **19.** $y = 0.8\left(\frac{1}{8}\right)^x$

20. $f(x) = 4\left(\frac{5}{6}\right)^x$ **21.** $y = 0.45 \cdot 3^x$ **22.** $y = \frac{1}{100}\left(\frac{4}{3}\right)^x$ **23.** $f(x) = 2^{-x}$

Example 5
(page 441)

Graph each function.

24. $y = (0.75)^x$ **25.** $y = 2(0.5)^x$ **26.** $y = (0.25)^x$ **27.** $g(x) = 5(0.2)^x$

28. $f(x) = \left(\frac{1}{5}\right)^x$ **29.** $y = 81\left(\frac{1}{3}\right)^x$ **30.** $s(t) = \left(\frac{1}{10}\right)^t$ **31.** $y = \frac{1}{2}\left(\frac{1}{2}\right)^x$

Example 6
(page 442)

Write an exponential function for each graph. Evaluate the function for $x = 6$.

32.   **33.**   **34.**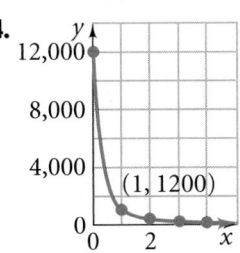

35. Business A computer valued at $6500 depreciates at the rate of 14.3% per year.
  a. Write a function that models the value of the computer.
  b. Find the value of the computer after three years.

B   **Apply Your Skills**

For each function, find the percent increase or decrease that the function models.

36. $y = 1298(1.63)^x$ **37.** $y = 0.65(1.3)^x$ **38.** $f(x) = 2(0.65)^x$

39. $y = 12\left(\frac{17}{10}\right)^x$ **40.** $y = 0.8\left(\frac{1}{8}\right)^x$ **41.** $y = 16\left(\frac{1}{4}\right)^x$

42. Multiple Choice According to the projected growth rate, how will these regions rank from largest to smallest populations in 2015?

World's Largest Metropolitan Regions Outside the U.S.

Rank in 2000	City	2000 Population	Projected Average Annual Growth
1	Tokyo, Japan	34,450,000	0.51%
2	Mexico City, Mexico	18,066,000	1.47%
3	Mumbai (Bombay), India	17,099,000	1.39%
4	Saõ Paulo, Brazil	16,086,000	2.62%

SOURCE: United Nations, Department for Economic and Social Information and Policy Analysis

  Ⓐ Tokyo, Mexico City, São Paulo, Mumbai
  Ⓑ Tokyo, Mexico City, Mumbai, São Paulo
  Ⓒ Tokyo, Mumbai, São Paulo, Mexico City
  Ⓓ Tokyo, São Paulo, Mexico City, Mumbai

Real-World **Connection**

In the aphotic zone of the ocean (1,000 m or deeper), there is not enough sunlight for plants to survive and animals are rare.

43. Oceanography The function $y = 20 \cdot 0.975^x$ models the intensity of sunlight beneath the surface of the ocean. The output y represents the percent of surface sunlight intensity that reaches a depth of x feet. The model is accurate from about 20 feet to about 600 feet beneath the surface.
a. Find the percent of sunlight 50 feet beneath the surface of the ocean.
b. Find the percent of sunlight at a depth of 370 ft.

44. a. Depreciation Each graph below shows the expected decrease in a car's value over the next five years. Write a function to model each car's depreciation. Determine which car will be worth more after 10 years.

b. Data Collection Find the initial value and the expected decrease in value of your favorite type of car. Write an exponential function to model the car's depreciation.

45. The population of a certain animal species decreases at a rate of 3.5% per year. You have counted 80 of the animals in the habitat you are studying.
a. Write a function that models the change in the animal population.
b. Graph the function. Estimate the number of years until the population first drops below 15 animals.

For each annual rate of change, find the corresponding growth or decay factor.

46. $+70\%$ **47.** $+500\%$ **48.** -75% **49.** -55%

50. $+12.5\%$ **51.** -0.1% **52.** $+0.1\%$ **53.** $+100\%$

54. Communications Cellular phone usage grew about 22% each year from 1995 (about 34 million) to 2003. Write a function to model U.S. cellular phone usage over that time period.

U.S. Cellular Phone Usage, 1995–2003

SOURCE: The CTIA Semi-Annual Wireless Survey

55. Open-Ended Write a problem that could be modeled with $y = 20(1.1)^x$.

C **Challenge**

56. The value of an industrial machine has a decay factor of 0.75 per year. After six years, the machine is worth $7500. What was the original value of the machine?

57. Multiple Choice Determine which situation best matches the graph.

  Ⓐ A population of 120 cougars decreases 98.75% yearly.
  Ⓑ A population of 125 cougars increases 1.25% yearly.
  Ⓒ A population of 115 cougars decreases 1.25% yearly.
  Ⓓ A population of 200 cougars decreases 50% yearly.

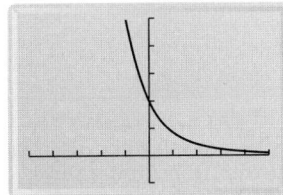

58. Critical Thinking Analyze the graph at the left to determine which function the graph represents. Explain your reasoning.

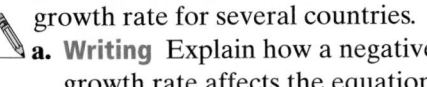

A. $y = \left(\frac{1}{3}\right)2^x$ **B.** $y = 2\left(\frac{1}{3}\right)^x$ **C.** $y = -2\left(\frac{1}{3}\right)^x$

59. Economics The table gives the 2003 gross domestic product and the real growth rate for several countries.

a. Writing Explain how a negative growth rate affects the equation for an exponential model.

b. Write a function for each country to model the GDP.

c. Suppose the given real growth rates continue. Predict the gross domestic product for each country in 2008.

Domestic Product Growth Rates

Country	2003 Gross Domestic Product (billions)	2003 Real Growth Rate
Armenia	$11.8	9.9%
Canada	$958.7	1.7%
Germany	$2271	−0.1%
Venezuela	$117.9	−9.2%

SOURCE: CIA, *The World Factbook*

Multiple Choice Practice

For California Standards and CAHSEE Tutorials, visit PHSchool.com. Web Code: bbq-9045

ALG2 12.0

60. Which function represents the value after x years of a delivery van that was purchased new for $17,500 and depreciates 11% each year?

Ⓐ $y = -11(17,500)^x$

Ⓑ $y = 17,500(0.89)^x$

Ⓒ $y = 35 \cdot (0.35)^x$

Ⓓ $y = 35 \div (1.35)^x$

ALG2 9.0

61. How does the graph of $y = x^2 - 2$ differ from the graph of $y = x^2 + 6$?

Ⓐ The graph of $y = x^2 - 2$ is 8 units above the graph of $y = x^2 + 6$.

Ⓑ The graph of $y = x^2 - 2$ is 8 units below the graph of $y = x^2 + 6$.

Ⓒ The graph of $y = x^2 - 2$ is 8 units to the left of the graph of $y = x^2 + 6$.

Ⓓ The graph of $y = x^2 - 2$ is 8 units to the right of the graph of $y = x^2 + 6$.

Mixed Review

GO for Help

Lesson 7-8

Graph each function.

62. $y = \sqrt{x + 2}$ **63.** $y = -2\sqrt[3]{x} + 4$ **64.** $y = \sqrt{9x - 153} - 5$

Lesson 7-2

Simplify each expression.

65. $\sqrt{180n^5}$ **66.** $3\sqrt[3]{72r^5} \cdot 2\sqrt[3]{343r^3}$ **67.** $\dfrac{\sqrt{64x^4}}{\sqrt{144x^5}}$

Lesson 6-2

Construct a polynomial function with the given zeros.

68. $x = 0, 1, 4$ **69.** $x = -2, -1, 3$ **70.** $x = 5, 0, 2$

Lesson 5-2

Each point lies on a parabola with vertex $(0, 2)$. Write the equation of the parabola.

71. $(1, 3)$ **72.** $(1, -3)$ **73.** $(-1, 4)$ **74.** $(2, 42)$

75. $(-2, 8)$ **76.** $(-1, 5)$ **77.** $(2, 0)$ **78.** $(2, -2)$

Fitting Exponential Curves to Data

PS 8.0 Students organize and describe distributions of data by using scatterplots.

You can use your graphing calculator to fit an exponential curve to data and find the exponential function.

ACTIVITY

The table at the right shows the number of degrees above room temperature for a cup of coffee after x minutes of cooling. Graph the data. Find the best-fitting exponential function.

Step 1 Press [STAT] [ENTER] to enter the data in lists.

Step 2 Use the **STAT PLOT** feature to draw a scatter plot.

Step 3 Find the equation for the best-fitting exponential function. Press [STAT] [▶] 0 [ENTER] to use the **ExpReg** feature. The line of best fit can be approximated by $f(x) = 133.458\ (0.942)^x$.

```
ExpReg
 y=a*b^x
 a=133.4584506
 b=.942405561
 r=-.9997925841
```

Step 4 Graph the function. Press [Y=] [CLEAR] [VARS] 5 [▶] [▶] [ENTER] to enter the **ExpReg** results. Press [GRAPH] to display the function and the scatter plot together.

Press [ZOOM] 9 to automatically adjust the window.

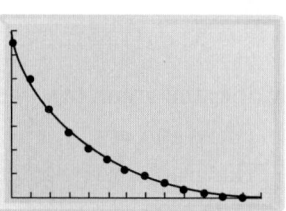

Cooling Coffee

Time (min)	°F Above Room Temperature
0	135
5	100
10	74
15	55
20	41
25	30
30	22
35	17
40	12
45	9
50	7
55	5
60	4

EXERCISES

Use a graphing calculator to find the exponential function that best fits each set of data. Graph each function. Sketch your graph.

1.

x	−3	−2	−1	0	1	2
y	50	25	12.5	6.25	3.13	1.56

2.

x	0	1	2	3	4	5
y	2	2.4	2.88	3.46	4.15	5

3.

x	1	2	3	4	5	6
y	1.2	4.8	19.2	76.8	307.2	1228.8

4.

x	−10	−9	−8	−7	−6	−5
y	0.03	0.07	0.14	0.27	0.55	1.09

5. Writing In the example above, the function appears to level off. Explain why this happens.

6. a. Find a linear function that models the data in Exercise 3.
   b. Which is a better fit, the linear function or the exponential function? Explain.

8-2

Properties of Exponential Functions

 California Content Standards

ALG2 12.0 Students understand exponential functions and use these functions in problems involving exponential growth and decay. *Master*

What You'll Learn

- To identify the role of constants in $y = ab^{cx}$
- To use e as a base

. . . And Why

To model the half-life of a radioactive substance, as in Example 3

✓ **Check Skills You'll Need**

GO for Help Lessons 2-6, 5-3, and 7-4

Write an equation for each translation.

1. $y = |x|$, 1 unit up, 2 units left

2. $y = -|x|$, 2 units down

3. $y = x^2$, 2 units down, 1 unit right

4. $y = -x^2$, 3 units up, 1 unit left

Write each equation in simplest form. Assume that all variables are positive.

5. $y = \left(x^{-\frac{5}{4}}\right)^4$

6. $y = \left(x^{-\frac{1}{7}}\right)^{-7}$

7. $y = \left(x^{\frac{5}{6}}\right)^6$

8. Use the formula for simple interest $I = Prt$. Find the interest for a principal of \$550 at a rate of 3% for 2 years.

🔊 **New Vocabulary** • continuously compounded interest formula

---

1 Comparing Graphs

The function $f(x) = b^x$ is the parent of a family of exponential functions for each value of b. The factor a in $y = ab^x$ stretches, shrinks, and/or reflects the parent.

GO for Help

To review function families, see Lesson 2-6 for absolute value functions, and Lesson 5-3 for quadratic functions.

1 EXAMPLE **Graphing $y = ab^x$ for $0 < |a| < 1$**

Graph $y = \frac{1}{2} \cdot 2^x$ and $y = -\frac{1}{2} \cdot 2^x$. Label the asymptote of each graph.

Step 1 Make a table of values.

x	$y = \frac{1}{2} \cdot 2^x$	$y = -\frac{1}{2} \cdot 2^x$
-2	$\frac{1}{8}$	$-\frac{1}{8}$
-1	$\frac{1}{4}$	$-\frac{1}{4}$
0	$\frac{1}{2}$	$-\frac{1}{2}$
1	1	-1
2	2	-2
3	4	-4

Step 2 Graph the functions.

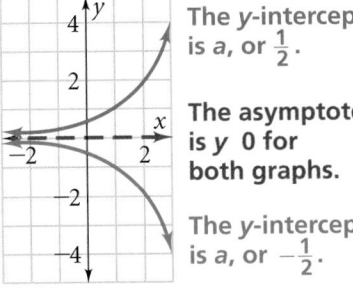

The y-intercept is a, or $\frac{1}{2}$.

The asymptote is y 0 for both graphs.

The y-intercept is a, or $-\frac{1}{2}$.

$y = \frac{1}{2} \cdot 2^x$ shrinks $y = 2^x$ by a factor of $\frac{1}{2}$.

$y = -\frac{1}{2} \cdot 2^x$ reflects $y = \frac{1}{2} \cdot 2^x$ in the x-axis.

✓ **CA Standards Check** Graph each function. **a.** $y = -4(2)^x$ **b.** $y = -3^x$

A horizontal shift $y = ab^{x-h}$ is the same as the vertical stretch or shrink $y = (ab^{-h})b^x$. A vertical shift $y = ab^x + k$ also shifts the horizontal asymptote from $y = 0$ to $y = k$.

2 EXAMPLE Translating $y = ab^x$

Graph the stretch $y = 8\left(\frac{1}{2}\right)^x$ and then the translation $y = 8\left(\frac{1}{2}\right)^{x+2} + 3$.

Step 1 Graph $y = 8\left(\frac{1}{2}\right)^x$. The horizontal asymptote is $y = 0$.

Step 2 For $y = 8\left(\frac{1}{2}\right)^{x+2} + 3$, $h = -2$ and $k = 3$. So shift the $y = 8\left(\frac{1}{2}\right)^x$ graph 2 units left and 3 units up. The horizontal asymptote is $y = 3$.

✓ CA Standards Check **2** Graph the stretch $y = 9(3)^x$ and then each translation.

    a. $y = 9(3)^{x+1}$
    b. $y = 9(3)^x - 4$
    c. $y = 9(3)^{x-3} - 1$

Some exponential functions are of the form $y = ab^{cx}$, where c is a nonzero constant.

3 EXAMPLE Real-World 🌐 Connection

Medicine The half-life of a radioactive substance is the time it takes for half of the material to decay. A hospital prepares a 100-mg supply of technetium-99m, which has a half-life of 6 hours. Make a table showing the amount of technetium-99m that remains at the end of each 6-hour interval for 36 hours. Then write an exponential function to find the amount of technetium-99m that remains after 75 hours.

The amount of technetium-99m is reduced by one half each 6 hours.

Real-World 🌐 Connection

As technetium-99m decays, it emits low-energy gamma rays. The rays are detected by a gamma camera to produce images like the one above.

Number of 6-h Intervals	0	1	2	3	4	5	6
Number of Hours Elapsed	0	6	12	18	24	30	36
Technetium-99m (mg)	100	50	25	12.5	6.25	3.13	1.56

Relate The amount of technetium-99m is an exponential function of the number of half-lives. The initial amount is 100 mg. The decay factor is $\frac{1}{2}$. One half-life equals 6 h.

Define Let $\boxed{y}$ = the amount of technetium-99m.

Let x = the number of hours elapsed. Then $\frac{1}{6}x$ = the number of half-lives.

Write $\boxed{y} = 100\left(\frac{1}{2}\right)^{\frac{1}{6}x}$

$y = 100\left(\frac{1}{2}\right)^{\frac{1}{6} \cdot 75}$ **Substitute 75 for x.**

$ = 100\left(\frac{1}{2}\right)^{12.5}$ **Simplify.**

$ \approx 0.017$ **Use a calculator.**

After 75 hours, about 0.017 mg of technetium-99m remains.

✓ CA Standards Check **3** Arsenic-74 is used to locate brain tumors. It has a half-life of 17.5 days. Write an exponential decay function for a 90-mg sample. Use the function to find the amount remaining after 6 days.

Key Concepts

Summary	**Families of Exponential Functions**
Parent functions ($b > 0, b \neq 1$):	$y = b^x$
Stretch ($\lvert a \rvert > 1$) Shrink ($0 < \lvert a \rvert < 1$) Reflection ($a < 0$) in x-axis	$y = ab^x$
Translation (horizontal by h; vertical by k):	$y = b^{x-h} + k$
Combined:	$y = ab^{x-h} + k$

2 The Number e

At the right is part of the graph of the function $y = \left(1 + \frac{1}{x}\right)^x$. One of the graph's asymptotes is $y = e$, where e is an irrational number approximately equal to 2.71828.

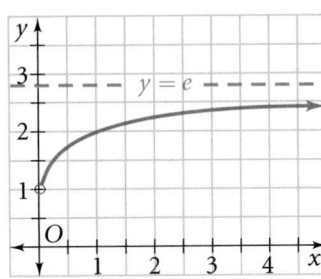

Exponential functions with a base of e are useful for describing continuous growth or decay. Your graphing calculator has a key for e^x.

4 EXAMPLE Evaluating e^x

Graph $y = e^x$. Evaluate e^2 to four decimal places.

Step 1 Graph $y = e^x$.

Step 2 Find y when $x = 2$.

Graphing Calculator Hint

After graphing e^x, press TRACE 2 ENTER to find y for $x = 2$.

The value of e^2 is about 7.3891.

CA Standards Check ④ Use the graph of $y = e^x$ to evaluate each expression to four decimal places.

a. e^4　　　　**b.** e^{-3}　　　　**c.** $e^{\frac{1}{2}}$

In past courses, you studied simple and compound interest. The more frequently interest is compounded, the more quickly the amount in an account increases. The formula for *continuously* compounded interest uses the number e.

Key Concepts

Definition	**Continuously Compounded Interest Formula**

amount in account　　　rate of interest (annual)

$$A = Pe^{rt} \longleftarrow \text{time in years}$$

principal

5 EXAMPLE **Real-World** **Connection**

Suppose you invest $1050 at an annual interest rate of 5.5% compounded continuously. How much money, to the nearest dollar, will you have in the account after five years?

$A = Pe^{rt}$

$= 1050 \cdot e^{0.055(5)}$	**Substitute 1050 for P, 0.055 for r, and 5 for t.**
$= 1050 \cdot e^{0.275}$	**Simplify.**
$\approx 1050(1.316531)$	**Evaluate $e^{0.275}$.**
≈ 1382.36	**Simplify.**

● You will have about $1382 in the account.

 CA Standards Check ● **5** Suppose you invest $1300 at an annual interest rate of 4.3% compounded continuously. Find the amount you will have in the account after three years.

EXERCISES

For more exercises, see *Extra Skill and Word Problem Practice*.

Standards Practice

ALG2 12.0

A **Practice by Example**

 GO **for Help**

Example 1
(page 447)

Graph each function. Label the asymptote of each graph.

1. $y = -5^x$
2. $y = -\left(\frac{1}{2}\right)^x$
3. $y = -2(4)^x$
4. $y = -9(3)^x$

5. $y = -3(2)^x$
6. $y = -24\left(\frac{1}{2}\right)^x$
7. $y = -4^x$
8. $y = -\left(\frac{1}{3}\right)^x$

Example 2
(page 448)

Graph each function as a transformation of its parent function.

9. $y = 8^x + 5$
10. $y = 15\left(\frac{4}{3}\right)^x - 8$
11. $y = -(0.3)^{x-2}$

12. $y = -2(5)^{x+3}$
13. $y = 52\left(\frac{2}{13}\right)^{x-1} + 26$
14. $y = 9\left(\frac{1}{3}\right)^{x+7} - 3$

Example 3
(page 448)

15. Botany Phosphorus-32 is used to study a plant's use of fertilizer. It has a half-life of 14.3 days. Write the exponential decay function for a 50-mg sample. Find the amount of phosporus-32 remaining after 84 days.

16. Public Works Iodine-131 is used to find leaks in water pipes. It has a half-life of 8.14 days. Write the exponential decay function for a 200-mg sample. Find the amount of iodine-131 remaining after 72 days.

17. Archaeology Carbon-14 is used to determine the age of artifacts in carbon dating. It has a half-life of 5730 years. Write the exponential decay function for a 24-mg sample. Find the amount of carbon-14 remaining after 30 millennia (1 millennium = 1000 years).

Example 4
(page 449)

 Use the graph of $y = e^x$ to evaluate each expression to four decimal places.

18. e^3
19. e^6
20. e^{-2}
21. e^0
22. $e^{\frac{5}{2}}$
23. e^e

Example 5
(page 450)

Find the amount in a continuously compounded account for the given conditions.

24. principal: $2000
annual interest 5.1%
time: 3 yr

25. principal: $400
annual interest 7.6%
time: 1.5 yr

26. principal: $950
annual interest 6.5%
time: 10 yr

27. Find the value of a for which the graph of $y = ab^x$ is a horizontal line.

28. Find the value of b for which the graph of $y = ab^x$ is a horizontal line.

29. Assume that a is positive and $b > 1$. Describe the effects of $c < 0$, $c = 0$, and $c > 0$ on the graph of the function $y = ab^{cx}$.

30. Savings A student wants to save $8000 for college in five years. How much should be put into an account that earns 5.2% annual interest compounded continuously?

31. When $a < 0$ and $b > 1$, $y = ab^x$ models negative exponential growth.
   a. Open-Ended Write an exponential function that models negative growth.
   b. Give an example of a situation that could be modeled by your function.
   c. Critical Thinking Explain one difference between negative exponential growth and exponential decay.

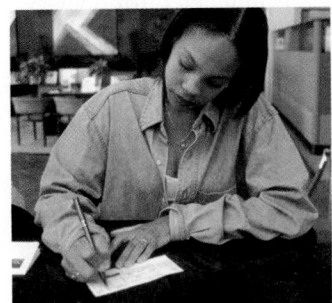

Real-World Connection

The amount of money you deposit into a savings account affects the interest you earn.

The parent function for each graph below is of the form $y = ab^x$. Write the parent function. Then write a function for the translation indicated.

32.
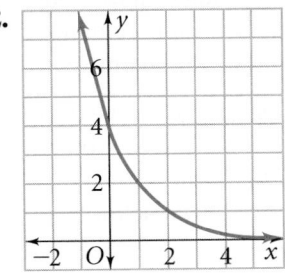
translation: left 4 units, up 3 units

33.
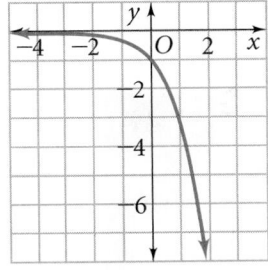
translation: right 8 units, up 2 units

34.
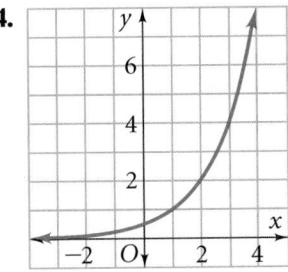
translation: right 6 units, down 7 units

35.

translation: left 5 units, down 1 unit

36. Physics At a constant temperature, the atmospheric pressure p in pascals is given by the formula $p = 101.3e^{-0.001h}$, where h is the altitude in meters. Find p at an altitude of 300 m.

37. Investment How long would it take to double your principal at an annual interest rate of 8% compounded continuously?

38. Writing Like a debt, a deficit is a negative amount of money. Explain how you would model a deficit that is growing exponentially. In $y = ab^{cx}$, would the values of a and c be positive or negative? Would the value of b be greater than 1 or less than 1?

39. Multiple Choice The gross domestic product, or GDP, of the United States was about $10.99 trillion in 2003. Assume that GDP grows 3.1% each year. Use an exponential model to find which percent best describes the GDP growth that occurs over 18 years.
   Ⓐ 19.0%   Ⓑ 74.7%   Ⓒ 129.1%   Ⓓ 173.2%

40. Suppose you invest \$2000 at an annual interest rate of 4.5%, compounded quarterly.
   a. How much will you have in the account after five years?
   b. Determine how much more you would have if the interest were compounded continuously.

41. An investor withdraws all \$525 from an account that was neglected for 8 years. It earned 3.4% annual interest, compounded continuously. How much was the initial deposit?

Without graphing, determine whether each equation represents exponential growth or exponential decay.

42. $s(t) = 5e^t$
43. $y = \frac{1}{6}e^x$
44. $y = \left(\frac{1}{e}\right)^x$

45. $y = \frac{7}{5}\left(\frac{e}{2}\right)^x$
46. $f(x) = \left(\frac{e}{3.7}\right)^x$
47. $y = -70e^t$

 Challenge

48. Biology A new flu virus is introduced when a stranger visits an isolated village of 8000 people. Every infected person infects two more each day.
   a. Write an exponential function to model the number of *uninfected* people.
   b. Determine how many people remain uninfected after one week.
   c. After how many days will the entire population be infected?

49. Psychology Psychologists use an exponential model of the learning process, $f(t) = c(1 - e^{-kt})$, where c is the total number of tasks to be learned, k is the rate of learning, t is time, and $f(t)$ is the number of tasks learned.
   a. Suppose you move to a new school, and you want to learn the names of 30 classmates in your homeroom. If your learning rate for new tasks is 20% per day, how many complete names will you know after 2 days? After 8 days?
   b. Graph the function on your graphing calculator. How many days will it take to learn everyone's name? Explain.
   c. Open-Ended Does this function seem to describe your own learning rate? If not, how could you adapt it to reflect your learning rate?

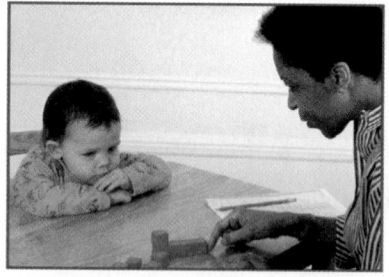

Real-World Connection

Psychologists use models to evaluate and predict learning rates.

50. Work begins on digging a moat on the perimeter of a property. After the first weekend, the first worker recruits a friend to help. After every succeeding weekend, each moat-digger recruits another friend. One person can dig 15 m³ of dirt per weekend. The moat should be 4 m wide and 3 m deep, and it must lie entirely within the 60 m-by-70 m property.
   a. Geometry Determine the volume of dirt that must be removed for the moat.
   b. Write an exponential function to model the volume of dirt remaining to be shoveled after x weekends.
   c. On which weekend will the moat be completed?

Multiple Choice Practice

For California Standards and CAHSEE Tutorials, visit PHSchool.com. Web Code: bbq-9045

ALG2 12.0

51. How is the graph of $y = 4 \cdot \left(\frac{1}{2}\right)^{x-3}$ translated from the graph of $y = 4 \cdot \left(\frac{1}{2}\right)^x$?
   Ⓐ 3 units right   Ⓑ 3 units left   Ⓒ 3 units down   Ⓓ 3 units up

ALG2 12.0

52. Sodium-24 has a half-life of 15 hours. How much sodium-24 will you have after 60 hours if your original sample is 64 mg?
   Ⓐ 4 mg   Ⓑ 16 mg   Ⓒ 32 mg   Ⓓ 64 mg

ALG2 1.0   **53.** The graph at the right shows which inequality?

    Ⓐ $y > |x + 4| - 4$

    Ⓑ $y > |x - 4| + 4$

    Ⓒ $y < |x + 4| - 4$

    Ⓓ $y < |x - 4| + 4$

Mixed Review

GO for Help

Lesson 8-1

Write an exponential equation $y = ab^x$ for a graph that includes the given points.

54. $(0, 1), (1, 3)$ **55.** $(1, -8), (2, -32)$ **56.** $(0, -5), (2, -20)$

57. $(-1, 16), (3, 1)$ **58.** $(-3, 0.07), (-1, 7)$ **59.** $(2, 6400), (4, 4096)$

Lesson 7-3

Simplify each expression.

60. $\cdot 5\sqrt{5} + \sqrt{5}$ **61.** $\sqrt[3]{4} - 2\sqrt[3]{4}$ **62.** $\sqrt{75} + \sqrt{125}$ **63.** $\sqrt[4]{32} + \sqrt[4]{128}$

64. $5\sqrt{3} - 2\sqrt{12}$ **65.** $3\sqrt{63} + \sqrt{28}$ **66.** $(3 - \sqrt{6})^2$ **67.** $\dfrac{-2 - 2\sqrt{5}}{1 - \sqrt{5}}$

Lesson 6-3

Divide using either long division or synthetic division.

68. $(x^2 - 3x - 1) \div x$ **69.** $(x^3 - 2x^2 - 5x + 6) \div (x - 1)$

70. $(x^3 + 4x^2 - x - 4) \div (x + 4)$ **71.** $(x^3 - 4x^2 - 4x - 5) \div (x - 5)$

72. $(13x^2 - 51x - 4) \div (x - 4)$ **73.** $(9x^3 - 18x^2 - x + 2) \div (3x + 1)$

Lesson 3-5

Find the equations of the traces of each graph.

74. $x - y + z = 5$ **75.** $x + y + 4z = -2$ **76.** $3x + 3y - 6z = 24$

77. $x - y + 2z = 8$ **78.** $3x + y + 9z = -18$ **79.** $-2x + y - 5z = 10$

✓ Checkpoint Quiz 1   Lessons 8-1 through 8-2

Identify each function as modeling either exponential growth or exponential decay. What percent of increase or decrease does the function model?

1. $y = 15(1.45)^x$ **2.** $y = 0.32(0.99)^x$ **3.** $y = 0.1(1.7)^x$ **4.** $y = 7.3(0.8)^x$

Graph each function.

5. $y = 3^x$ **6.** $y = 2^x + 1$ **7.** $y = (0.25)^x$ **8.** $y = 4^x - 5$

9. Open-Ended Describe a real-world problem that you could model with an exponential growth function.

10. Chemistry An element has a half-life of 30 hours. Write the exponential decay function for a 100-mg sample. Use the function to find the amount of the element remaining after 100 hours.

Logarithmic Functions as Inverses

 California Content Standards

ALG2 11.1 Students understand the inverse relationship between exponents and logarithms and use this information to solve problems involving logarithms and exponents. *Introduce, Develop*

What You'll Learn

- To write and evaluate logarithmic expressions
- To graph logarithmic functions

. . . And Why

To compare the acidities of milk and lemon juice, as in Example 4

Check Skills You'll Need

GO for Help Lessons 6-4 and 7-7

Solve each equation.

1. $8 = x^3$ **2.** $x^{\frac{1}{4}} = 2$ **3.** $27 = 3^x$ **4.** $4^6 = 4^{3x}$

Graph each relation and its inverse on a coordinate plane.

5. $y = 5x$ **6.** $y = 2x^2$ **7.** $y = -x^3$ **8.** $y = \frac{1}{2}x$

New Vocabulary • logarithm • common logarithm • logarithmic function

---

1 **Writing and Evaluating Logarithmic Expressions**

The magnitude of an earthquake is a measure of the amount of energy released at its source. The Richter scale is an exponential measure of earthquake magnitude. An earthquake of magnitude 5 releases about 30 times as much energy as an earthquake of magnitude 4.

The Richter Scale

Real-World Connection

The earthquake that struck Washington in 2001 measured 6.8 on the Richter scale.

1 **EXAMPLE** **Real-World Connection**

Seismology In 1995, an earthquake in Mexico registered 8.0 on the Richter scale. In 2001, an earthquake of magnitude 6.8 shook Washington state. Compare the amounts of energy released in the two earthquakes.

$\dfrac{E \cdot 30^{8.0}}{E \cdot 30^{6.8}}$ Write a ratio.

$= \dfrac{30^{8.0}}{30^{6.8}}$ Simplify.

$= 30^{8.0 - 6.8}$ Division Property of Exponents

$= 30^{1.2}$ Simplify.

≈ 59.2 Use a calculator.

The earthquake in Mexico released about 59 times as much energy as the earthquake in Washington.

 CA Standards Check **1** In 1997, an earthquake in Alabama registered 4.9 on the Richter scale. In 1999, one in California registered 7.0. Compare the energy released in the two quakes.

The exponents used by the Richter scale shown in Example 1 are called logarithms, or logs.

 Key Concepts

Definition	**Logarithm**

The **logarithm** to the base b of a positive number y is defined as follows:

$$\text{If } y = b^x, \text{then } \log_b y = x.$$

 Vocabulary Tip

Read $\log_b y$ as
"log base b of y."

The exponent x in the exponential expression b^x is the logarithm in the equation $\log_b y = x$. The base b in b^x is the same as the base b in the logarithm. In both cases, $b \neq 1$ and $b > 0$.

A positive number b raised to any power x cannot equal a number y less than or equal to zero. Therefore, the logarithm of a negative number or zero is undefined.

2 EXAMPLE **Writing in Logarithmic Form**

Write $25 = 5^2$ in logarithmic form.

If $y = b^x$, then $\log_b y = x$. **Write the definition.**
If $25 = 5^2$, then $\log_5 25 = 2$. **Substitute.**

● The logarithmic form of $25 = 5^2$ is $\log_5 25 = 2$.

✔ **CA Standards Check** **2** Write each equation in logarithmic form.
    a. $729 = 3^6$ **b.** $\left(\frac{1}{2}\right)^3 = \frac{1}{8}$ **c.** $10^0 = 1$

To evaluate logarithms, you can write them in exponential form.

3 EXAMPLE **Evaluating Logarithms**

Evaluate $\log_8 16$.

$\log_8 16 = x$ **Write an equation in logarithmic form.**
$16 = 8^x$ **Convert to exponential form.**
$2^4 = \left(2^3\right)^x$ **Write each side using base 2.**
$2^4 = 2^{3x}$ **Power Property of Exponents**
$4 = 3x$ **Set the exponents equal to each other.**
$\frac{4}{3} = x$ **Solve for x.**

● So $\log_8 16 = \frac{4}{3}$.

Video Tutor Help
Visit: PHSchool.com
Web Code: bbe-0775

✔ **CA Standards Check** **3** Evaluate each logarithm.
    a. $\log_{64} \frac{1}{32}$ **b.** $\log_9 27$ **c.** $\log_{10} 100$

A **common logarithm** is a logarithm that uses base 10. You can write the common logarithm $\log_{10} y$ as $\log y$.

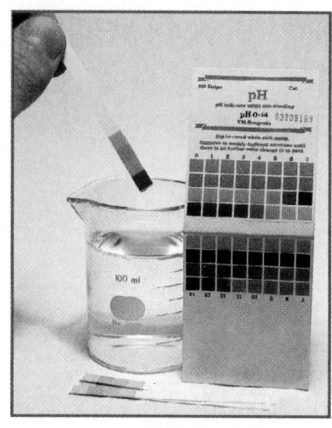

Scientists use common logarithms to measure acidity, which increases as the concentration of hydrogen ions in a substance increases. The pH of a substance equals $-\log[\text{H}^+]$, where $[\text{H}^+]$ is the concentration of hydrogen ions.

4 EXAMPLE Real-World Connection

Chemistry The pH of lemon juice is 2.3, while the pH of milk is 6.6. Find the concentration of hydrogen ions in each substance. Which substance is more acidic?

Real-World Connection

You can use pH strips to measure the acidity of a water solution. The pH scale ranges from 0 to 14.

Lemon juice	Milk
$\text{pH} = -\log[\text{H}^+]$	$\text{pH} = -\log[\text{H}^+]$
$2.3 = -\log[\text{H}^+]$	$6.6 = -\log[\text{H}^+]$
$\log[\text{H}^+] = -2.3$	$\log[\text{H}^+] = -6.6$
$[\text{H}^+] = 10^{-2.3}$	$[\text{H}^+] = 10^{-6.6}$
$\approx 5.0 \times 10^{-3}$	$\approx 2.5 \times 10^{-7}$

The $[\text{H}^+]$ of lemon juice is about 5.0×10^{-3}. The $[\text{H}^+]$ of milk is about 2.5×10^{-7}. Lemon juice has a higher concentration of hydrogen ions, so it is more acidic.

✓**CA Standards Check** **4** Find the concentration of hydrogen ions in seawater of pH 8.5.

2 Graphing Logarithmic Functions

A **logarithmic function** is the inverse of an exponential function. The graph shows $y = 10^x$ and $y = \log x$. Note that $(0, 1)$ and $(1, 10)$ lie on the graph of $y = 10^x$, and that $(1, 0)$ and $(10, 1)$ lie on the graph of $y = \log x$.

Recall that the graph of a function is symmetric to the graph of its inverse over the line $y = x$. You can graph $y = \log_b x$ as the inverse of $y = b^x$.

5 EXAMPLE Graphing a Logarithmic Function

Online active math

For: Log Functions Activity
Use: Interactive Textbook, 8-3

Graph $y = \log_2 x$.

By the definition of logarithm, $y = \log_2 x$ is the inverse of $y = 2^x$.

Step 1 Graph $y = 2^x$.

Step 2 Draw $y = x$.

Step 3 Choose a few points on $y = 2^x$. Reverse the coordinates and plot the points of $y = \log_2 x$.

✓**CA Standards Check** **5** Graph $y = \log_3 x$.

The function $y = \log_b x$ is the inverse of $y = b^x$. Since $(0, 1)$ and $(1, b)$ are points on the graph of $y = b^x$, $(1, 0)$ and $(b, 1)$ are points on the graph of $y = \log_b x$. Since the x-axis is an asymptote for $y = b^x$, the y-axis is an asymptote for $y = \log_b x$. Using these facts, you can sketch the graph of $y = \log_b x$.

You can graph $y = \log_b (x - h) + k$ by translating the graph of $y = \log_b x$ horizontally by h and vertically by k.

 Key Concepts

Summary	Families of Logarithmic Functions
Parent functions $(b > 0, b \neq 1)$:	$y = \log_b x, b > 0, b \neq 1$
Stretch $(\lvert a \rvert > 1)$ Shrink $(0 < \lvert a \rvert < 1)$ Reflection $(a < 0)$ in x-axis	$y = a \log_b x$
Translation (horizontal by h; vertical by k):	$y = \log_b(x - h) + k$
Combined:	$y = a \log_b (x - h) + k$

6 EXAMPLE Translating $y = \log_b x$

Graph $y = \log_6 (x - 2) + 3$.

Vocabulary Tip

A <u>parent function</u> is the simplest function in a family of functions.

Step 1 Make a table of values for the parent function.

x	$\log_6 x$	y
6	$\log_6 6 = 1$	1
1	$\log_6 1 = 0$	0
$\frac{1}{6}$	$\log_6 \frac{1}{6} = -1$	-1
$\frac{1}{36}$	$\log_6 \frac{1}{36} = -2$	-2
$\frac{1}{216}$	$\log_6 \frac{1}{216} = -3$	-3

Step 2 Graph the function by shifting the points from the table to the right 2 units and up 3 units.

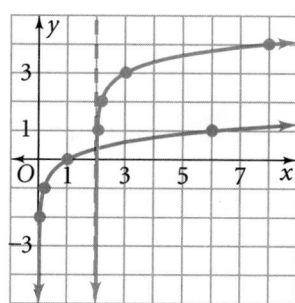

✓ CA Standards Check **6** Graph $y = \log_3 (x + 3)$.

 EXERCISES For more exercises, see *Extra Skill and Word Problem Practice.*

 Standards Practice ALG2 11.1

A Practice by Example

Example 1
(page 454)

 GO for Help

Seismology In 1812, an earthquake of magnitude 7.9 shook New Madrid, Missouri. Compare the amount of energy released by that earthquake to the amount of energy released by each earthquake below.

1. magnitude 7.7 in San Francisco, California, in 1906

2. magnitude 9.5 in Valdivia, Chile, in 1960

3. magnitude 3.2 in Charlottesville, Virginia, in 2001

4. magnitude 6.9 in Kobe, Japan, in 1995

5. magnitude 9.2 in Prince William Sound, Alaska, in 1964

Example 2
(page 455)

Write each equation in logarithmic form.

6. $49 = 7^2$ **7.** $10^3 = 1000$ **8.** $625 = 5^4$ **9.** $\frac{1}{10} = 10^{-1}$

10. $8^2 = 64$ **11.** $4 = \left(\frac{1}{2}\right)^{-2}$ **12.** $\left(\frac{1}{3}\right)^3 = \frac{1}{27}$ **13.** $10^{-2} = 0.01$

Example 3
(page 455)

Evaluate each logarithm.

14. $\log_2 16$ **15.** $\log_4 2$ **16.** $\log_8 8$ **17.** $\log_4 8$

18. $\log_2 8$ **19.** $\log_{49} 7$ **20.** $\log_5 (-25)$ **21.** $\log_3 9$

22. $\log_2 2^5$ **23.** $\log_{\frac{1}{2}} \frac{1}{2}$ **24.** $\log 10{,}000$ **25.** $\log_5 125$

Example 4
(page 456)

The pH of each food is given. Find the concentration of hydrogen ions $[H^+]$.

26. maple syrup, 5.2   **27.** lime juice, 2.2   **28.** egg white, 8.0

29. cider vinegar, 3.1   **30.** condensed milk, 6.3   **31.** soy sauce, 4.9

32. tomato juice, 4.0   **33.** watermelon, 5.4   **34.** mustard, 3.6

Examples 5 and 6
(pages 456 and 457)

Graph each logarithmic function.

35. $y = \log_4 x$ **36.** $y = \log_5 x$ **37.** $y = \log_8 x$

38. $y = \log_5 x + 1$ **39.** $y = \log_7 (x - 2)$ **40.** $y = \log_3 (x - 5) + 3$

 Apply Your Skills

Use your calculator to evaluate each logarithm to four decimal places. Then find the largest integer that is less than the value of the logarithm.

41. $\log 5$ **42.** $\log (6.1 \times 10^{-5})$ **43.** $\log 0.08$ **44.** $\log 200$

45. $\log \frac{1}{6}$ **46.** $\log 17.52$ **47.** $\log (1.3 \times 10^7)$ **48.** $\log \frac{13}{4}$

For a guide to solving Exercise 49, see p. 461.

49. Chemistry The pH scale ranges from 0 to 14. A pH level of 7 is neutral. A level greater than 7 is basic, and a level less than 7 is acidic. The table shows the hydrogen ion concentration $[H^+]$ for selected foods. Find the pH of each item. Determine whether it is basic or acidic.

Approximate $[H^+]$ of Foods

Food	$[H^+]$
Apple juice	3.2×10^{-4}
Buttermilk	2.5×10^{-5}
Cream	2.5×10^{-7}
Ketchup	1.3×10^{-4}
Shrimp sauce	7.9×10^{-8}
Strained peas	1.0×10^{-6}

50. Error Analysis Find the error in the following evaluation of $\log_{27} 3$. Then evaluate the logarithm correctly.

$$\log_{27} 3 = x$$
$$27 = x^3$$
$$3 = x$$
$$\log_{27} 3 = 3$$

 51. Writing Explain why the base b in $y = \log_b x$ cannot equal 1.

52. Open-Ended Write a logarithmic function of the form $y = \log_b x$. Find its inverse function. Graph both functions on one set of axes.

Write each equation in exponential form.

53. $\log_2 128 = 7$ **54.** $\log 0.0001 = -4$ **55.** $\log_7 16{,}807 = 5$

56. $\log_6 6 = 1$ **57.** $\log_4 1 = 0$ **58.** $\log_3 \frac{1}{9} = -2$

59. $\log_2 \frac{1}{2} = -1$ **60.** $\log 10 = 1$ **61.** $\log_2 8192 = 13$

Real-World Connection

Samples are loaded into a linear accelerator for carbon dating.

62. Archaeology One method of dating artifacts is radiocarbon dating. The artifacts in the table were found at a dig site near Kit Carson, Colorado. An artifact's age t in years is $t = 1.904 \times 10^4 \cdot \log\left(\frac{13.7}{R}\right)$, where R is the number of beta radiation emissions per minute per gram of carbon in the artifact.

Beta Emissions of Artifacts

Object	Mass of Carbon (g)	Beta Emissions per Minute
Buffalo bone	400	1640 ± 30
Bone fragment	15	61.5 ± 1.5
Pottery shard	25	342 ± 7
Charcoal	10	41.0 ± 1.3
Spear shaft	250	1020 ± 30

  a. For each artifact, use the range of beta emissions to find the artifact's maximum and minimum ages.
  b. Critical Thinking Which artifact is significantly different in age from the others? Give two possible explanations for the difference.

63. Multiple Choice Which function or functions are the inverse of $y = -\log_{0.25} x$?

  I. $y = 4^x$ **II.** $y = 4^{-x}$ **III.** $y = \left(\frac{1}{4}\right)^{-x}$

  Ⓐ II only   Ⓑ III only   Ⓒ I and III   Ⓓ II and III

Find the inverse of each function.

64. $y = \log_4 x$ **65.** $y = \log_{0.5} x$ **66.** $y = \log_{10} x$

67. $y = \log_2 2x$ **68.** $y = \log(x + 1)$ **69.** $y = \log 10x$

70. $y = \log(x - 2)$ **71.** $y = \log_5 x^2$ **72.** $y = \log_a(x - b)$

Graph each logarithmic function.

73. $y = \log 2x$ **74.** $y = 2\log_2 x$ **75.** $y = \log_4(2x + 3)$

Find the domain and the range of each function.

76. $y = \log_5 x$ **77.** $y = 3\log x$ **78.** $y = \log_2(x - 3)$

79. $y = 1 + \log x$ **80.** $y = \log(x - 2) + 1$ **81.** $y = \log_6(x + 1)$

82. $y = \log_8 x - 2$ **83.** $y = \log_2 x + \frac{1}{3}$ **84.** $y = \log(x - t)$

C Challenge

Sound The loudness in decibels (dB) of a sound is defined as $10 \log \frac{I}{I_0}$. I is the intensity of the sound. I_0 is 10^{-12}, the intensity of a barely audible sound. Complete the table.

Loudness of Sounds

	Type of Sound	Intensity (W/m²)	Loudness (dB)
	Pain-producing	1	120
85.	Jackhammer	10^{-2}	▪
86.	Busy street	10^{-5}	▪
87.	Conversation	10^{-6}	▪
88.	Whisper	10^{-10}	▪
89.	Rustle of leaves	10^{-11}	▪
	Barely audible sound	10^{-12}	0

90. Match each function with the graph of its inverse.
a. $y = \log_3 x$ **b.** $y = \log_2 4x$ **c.** $y = \log_{\frac{1}{2}} x$

I.   **II.**   **III.**

Multiple Choice Practice

For California Standards and CAHSEE Tutorials, visit PHSchool.com. Web Code: bbq-9045

ALG2 11.1

91. Which function is the inverse of $f(x) = 2^{x-1}$?
- **A** $f^{-1}(x) = \log_2 (x - 1)$
- **B** $f^{-1}(x) = \log_2 x - 1$
- **C** $f^{-1}(x) = \log_2 (x + 1)$
- **D** $f^{-1}(x) = \log_2 x + 1$

ALG2 11.1

92. Which of the following relationships is best represented by the graph at the right?
- **A** $y = \log_4 (x - 1) + 5$
- **B** $y = \log_4 (x - 1) - 2$
- **C** $y = \log_4 (x + 2) - 2$
- **D** $y = \log_4 (x - 1) - 1$

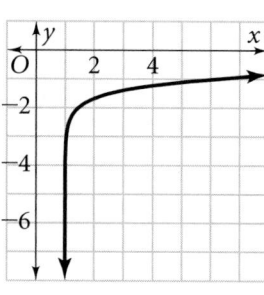

ALG2 9.0

93. The graph of $y = 5x^2 + c$ is a parabola with a vertex at the origin. Which of the following is true?
- **A** $c = 5$
- **C** $c > 0$
- **B** $c = 0$
- **D** $c < 0$

Mixed Review

Lesson 8-2

Sketch the graph of each function. Then locate the asymptote of the curve.

94. $y = 5^x - 100$ **95.** $y = -10(4)^{x+2}$ **96.** $y = -27(3)^{x-1} + 9$

Lesson 7-4

Write each expression in radical form.

97. $t^{\frac{2}{3}}$ **98.** $\left(16w^3\right)^{\frac{1}{2}}$ **99.** $z^{\frac{8}{5}}$ **100.** $x^{\frac{p}{n}}$

Lesson 6-4

Solve each equation by graphing. If necessary, round to the nearest thousandth.

101. $3x^2 + 18x + 24 = 0$ **102.** $1 - x = x^2 - 7x$ **103.** $x^4 = 7x^3 + 10x^2$

Lesson 5-4

Factor each expression.

104. $4x^2 - 8x + 3$ **105.** $\frac{1}{4}b^2 - 4$ **106.** $5x^2 + 13x - 6$

Understanding Word Problems Read the problem below. Let the explanations guide you through the use of the data table. Check your understanding with the exercise at the bottom of the page.

Chemistry The pH scale ranges from 0 to 14. A pH level of 7 is neutral. A level greater than 7 is basic, and a level less than 7 is acidic. The table shows the hydrogen ion concentration [H$^+$] for selected foods. Find the pH of each item. Determine whether it is basic or acidic.

Approximate [H+] of Selected Foods

Food	[H+]
Apple Juice	3.2×10^{-4}
Buttermilk	2.5×10^{-5}
Cream	2.5×10^{-7}
Ketchup	1.3×10^{-4}
Shrimp Sauce	7.9×10^{-8}
Strained Peas	1.0×10^{-6}

A table is a tool for organizing data.

The title of the table indicates the type of data represented. →

Approximate [H+] of Selected Foods

Food	[H+]
Apple Juice	3.2×10^{-4}
Buttermilk	2.5×10^{-5}

← Each row represents a different item. Row 1 contains data for apple juice.

Each column represents a different category of data. Column 2 lists the [H$^+$] of each food.

Now you can use the table.

$$\text{pH} = -\log [\text{H}^+] \qquad \text{Refer to page 456 for the formula for pH.}$$
$$\text{pH of apple juice} = -\log ([\text{H}^+] \text{ of apple juice}) \qquad \text{Use the formula.}$$
$$= -\log (3.2 \times 10^{-4}) \qquad \text{Substitute.}$$
$$\approx 3.49 \qquad \text{Simplify.}$$

Since the pH of apple juice is less than 7, it is acidic.

The problem asks you to find the pH and whether the item is basic or acidic. To organize the information, you can add two columns to the table.

Food	[H+]	pH	Acid or Base
Apple Juice	3.2×10^{-4}	3.49	Acid

EXERCISE

Copy and complete the table below.

[H+]	pH	Acid or Base
4.6×10^{-8}	■	■
3.7×10^{-3}	■	■
1.8×10^{-4}	■	■

Properties of Logarithms

 California Content Standards

ALG2 14.0 Students understand and use the properties of exponents to simplify logarithmic numeric expressions and to identify their approximate values. *Introduce, Develop*

ALG2 11.0 Students prove simple laws of logarithms. *Introduce, Develop*

What You'll Learn

- To use the properties of logarithms

. . . And Why

To relate sound intensity and decibel level, as in Example 4

 Check Skills You'll Need

GO for Help Lessons 8-3 and 1-2

Simplify each expression.

1. $\log_2 4 + \log_2 8$ **2.** $\log_3 9 - \log_3 27$ **3.** $\log_2 16 \div \log_2 64$

Evaluate each expression for $x = 3$.

4. $x^3 - x$ **5.** $x^5 \cdot x^2$ **6.** $\dfrac{x^6}{x^9}$ **7.** $x^3 + x^2$

1 Using the Properties of Logarithms

Activity: Properties of Logarithms

1. Complete the table. Round to the nearest thousandth.

x	1	2	3	4	5	6	7	8	9	10	15	20
log x	▢	▢	▢	▢	▢	▢	▢	▢	▢	▢	▢	▢

2. Complete each pair of statements. What do you notice?
   a. log 3 + log 5 = ▢ and log (3 · 5) = ▢
   b. log 1 + log 7 = ▢ and log (1 · 7) = ▢
   c. log 2 + log 4 = ▢ and log (2 · 4) = ▢
   d. log 10 + log 2 = ▢ and log (10 · 2) = ▢

3. Complete the statement: log M + log N = ▢.

4. **a. Make a Conjecture** How could you rewrite the expression log $\frac{M}{N}$ using the expressions log M and log N?
   b. Use your calculator to verify your conjecture for several values of M and N.

The properties of logarithms are summarized below.

 Key Concepts

Properties	**Properties of Logarithms**

For any positive numbers, M, N, and b, $b \neq 1$,

$\log_b MN = \log_b M + \log_b N$ **Product Property**

$\log_b \dfrac{M}{N} = \log_b M - \log_b N$ **Quotient Property**

$\log_b M^x = x \log_b M$ **Power Property**

You can use the properties of logarithms to rewrite logarithmic expressions.

1 EXAMPLE Identifying the Properties of Logarithms

State the property or properties used to rewrite each expression.

a. $\log_2 8 - \log_2 4 = \log_2 2$

Quotient Property: $\log_2 8 - \log_2 4 = \log_2 \frac{8}{4} = \log_2 2$

b. $\log_b x^3 y = 3 \log_b x + \log_b y$

Product Property: $\log_b x^3 y = \log_b x^3 + \log_b y$

Power Property: $\log_b x^3 + \log_b y = 3 \log_b x + \log_b y$

✓ **CA Standards Check** ❶ State the property or properties used to rewrite each expression.
a. $\log_5 2 + \log_5 6 = \log_5 12$
b. $3 \log_b 4 - 3 \log_b 2 = \log_b 8$

You can write the sum or difference of logarithms with the same base as a single logarithm.

2 EXAMPLE Simplifying Logarithms

Video Tutor Help
Visit: PHSchool.com
Web Code: bbe-0775

Write each logarithmic expression as a single logarithm.

a. $\log_3 20 - \log_3 4$

$\log_3 20 - \log_3 4 = \log_3 \frac{20}{4}$ **Quotient Property**

$= \log_3 5$ **Simplify.**

b. $3 \log_2 x + \log_2 y$

$3 \log_2 x + \log_2 y = \log_2 x^3 + \log_2 y$ **Power Property**

$= \log_2 \left(x^3 y \right)$ **Product Property**

So $\log_3 20 - \log_3 4 = \log_3 5$, and $3 \log_2 x + \log_2 y = \log_2 \left(x^3 y \right)$.

✓ **CA Standards Check** ❷ **a.** Write $3 \log 2 + \log 4 - \log 16$ as a single logarithm.
    b. Critical Thinking Can you write $3 \log_2 9 - \log_6 9$ as a single logarithm? Explain.

You can sometimes write a single logarithm as a sum or difference of two or more logarithms.

3 EXAMPLE Expanding Logarithms

Vocabulary Tip

In mathematics, <u>to expand</u> means "to show the full form of."

Expand each logarithm.

a. $\log_5 \frac{x}{y}$

$= \log_5 x - \log_5 y$ **Quotient Property**

b. $\log 3r^4$

$= \log 3 + \log r^4$ **Product Property**

$= \log 3 + 4 \log r$ **Power Property**

✓ **CA Standards Check** ❸ Expand each logarithm.
    a. $\log_2 7b$ **b.** $\log \left(\frac{y}{3} \right)^2$ **c.** $\log_7 a^3 b^4$

Logarithms are used to model sound. The intensity of a sound is a measure of the energy carried by the sound wave. The greater the intensity of a sound, the louder it seems. This apparent loudness L is measured in decibels.

You can use the formula $L = 10 \log \frac{I}{I_0}$, where I is the intensity of the sound in watts per square meter (W/m^2). I_0 is the lowest-intensity sound that the average human ear can detect.

Loudness of Sounds

150dB — Jet engine
Motorcycle
100dB
80dB — Vacuum cleaner
Hum of refrigerator
45dB
Breathing
Threshold of hearing — 10dB
0dB

4 EXAMPLE Real-World Connection

Noise Control A shipping company has started flying cargo planes out of the city airport. Residents in a nearby neighborhood have complained that the cargo planes are too loud. Suppose the shipping company hires you to design a way to reduce the intensity of the sound by half. By how many decibels would the loudness of the sound be decreased?

Relate The reduced intensity is one half of the present intensity.

Define Let I_1 = present intensity.
Let I_2 = reduced intensity.
Let L_1 = present loudness.
Let L_2 = reduced loudness.

Write $I_2 = 0.5\, I_1$

$$L_1 = 10 \log \frac{I_1}{I_0}$$

$$L_2 = 10 \log \frac{I_2}{I_0}$$

$$L_1 - L_2 = 10 \log \frac{I_1}{I_0} - 10 \log \frac{I_2}{I_0} \qquad \text{Find the decrease in loudness } L_1 - L_2.$$

$$= 10 \log \frac{I_1}{I_0} - 10 \log \frac{0.5 I_1}{I_0} \qquad \text{Substitute } I_2 = 0.5 I_1.$$

$$= 10 \log \frac{I_1}{I_0} - 10 \log \left(0.5 \cdot \frac{I_1}{I_0} \right)$$

$$= 10 \log \frac{I_1}{I_0} - 10 \left(\log 0.5 + \log \frac{I_1}{I_0} \right) \qquad \text{Product Property}$$

$$= 10 \log \frac{I_1}{I_0} - 10 \log 0.5 - 10 \log \frac{I_1}{I_0} \qquad \text{Distributive Property}$$

$$= -10 \log 0.5 \qquad \text{Combine like terms.}$$

$$\approx 3.0 \qquad \text{Use a calculator.}$$

● The decrease in loudness would be about three decibels.

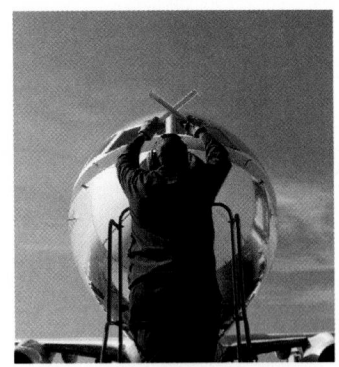

Real-World Connection

The workers who direct planes at airports must wear ear protection.

CA Standards Check ④ Suppose the shipping company wants you to reduce the sound intensity to 25% of the original intensity. By how many decibels would the loudness be reduced?

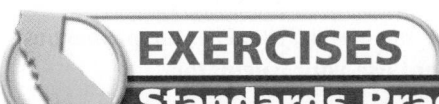

Standards Practice

A Practice by Example

Example 1
(page 463)

for Help

State the property or properties used to rewrite each expression.

1. $\log 4 + \log 5 = \log 20$

2. $\log_3 32 - \log_3 8 = \log_3 4$

3. $\log z^2 = 2 \log z$

4. $\log_6 \sqrt[n]{x^p} = \frac{p}{n} \log_6 x$

5. $8 \log 2 - 2 \log 8 = \log 4$

6. $\log \sqrt[3]{3x} = \frac{1}{3} \log 3x$

7. $3 \log_4 5 - 3 \log_4 3 = \log_4 \left(\frac{5}{3}\right)^3$

8. $2 \log w + 4 \log z = \log w^2 z^4$

9. $2 \log_2 m - 4 \log_2 n = \log_2 \frac{m^2}{n^4}$

10. $\log_b \frac{1}{8} + 3 \log_b 4 = \log_b 8$

Example 2
(page 463)

Write each logarithmic expression as a single logarithm.

11. $\log 7 + \log 2$

12. $\log_2 9 - \log_2 3$

13. $5 \log 3 + \log 4$

14. $\log 8 - 2 \log 6 + \log 3$

15. $4 \log m - \log n$

16. $\log 5 - k \log 2$

17. $\log_6 5 + \log_6 x$

18. $\log_7 x + \log_7 y - \log_7 z$

Example 3
(page 463)

Expand each logarithm.

19. $\log x^3 y^5$

20. $\log_7 22xyz$

21. $\log_4 5 \sqrt{x}$

22. $\log 3m^4 n^{-2}$

23. $\log_5 \frac{r}{s}$

24. $\log_3 (2x)^2$

25. $\log_3 7(2x - 3)^2$

26. $\log \frac{a^2 b^3}{c^4}$

27. $\log \sqrt{\frac{2x}{y}}$

28. $\log_8 8\sqrt{3a^5}$

29. $\log \frac{s\sqrt{7}}{t^2}$

30. $\log_b \frac{1}{x}$

Example 4
(page 464)

31. One brand of ear plugs claims to block the sound of snoring as loud as 22 dB. A second brand claims to block snoring that is eight times as intense. If the claims are true, for how many more decibels is the second brand effective?

32. A sound barrier along a highway reduced the intensity of the noise reaching a community by 95%. By how many decibels was the noise reduced?

B Apply Your Skills

Use the properties of logarithms to evaluate each expression.

33. $\log_2 4 - \log_2 16$

34. $3 \log_2 2 - \log_2 4$

35. $\log_3 3 + 5 \log_3 3$

36. $\log 1 + \log 100$

37. $\log_6 4 + \log_6 9$

38. $2 \log_8 4 - \frac{1}{3} \log_8 8$

39. $2 \log_3 3 - \log_3 3$

40. $\frac{1}{2} \log_5 1 - 2 \log_5 5$

41. $\log_9 \frac{1}{3} + 3 \log_9 3$

42. Error Analysis Explain why the expansion below of $\log_4 \sqrt{\frac{t}{s}}$ is incorrect. Then do the expansion correctly.

$$\log_4 \sqrt{\frac{t}{s}} = \frac{1}{2} \log_4 \frac{t}{s}$$
$$= \frac{1}{2} \log_4 t - \log_4 s$$

43. Open-Ended Write $\log 150$ as a sum or difference of two logarithms.

Assume that $\log 4 \approx 0.6021$, $\log 5 \approx 0.6990$, and $\log 6 \approx 0.7782$. Use the properties of logarithms to evaluate each expression. Do not use your calculator.

44. $\log 24$ **45.** $\log 30$ **46.** $\log 16$

47. $\log 125$ **48.** $\log 1.5$ **49.** $\log 0.8$

50. $\log \frac{1}{4}$ **51.** $\log \frac{1}{25}$ **52.** $\log 25$

53. $\log \frac{1}{6}$ **54.** $\log 36$ **55.** $\log \sqrt{5}$

Real-World Connection

Sound levels are measured using decibel meters.

56. Noise Control New components reduce the sound intensity of a certain model of vacuum cleaner from 10^{-4} W/m^2 to 6.31×10^{-6} W/m^2. By how many decibels do these new components reduce the vacuum cleaner's loudness?

57. Reasoning If $\log x = 5$, what is the value of $\frac{1}{x}$?

Write *true* or *false* for each statement. Justify your answer.

58. $\log_2 4 + \log_2 8 = 5$ **59.** $\log_3 \frac{3}{2} = \frac{1}{2}\log_3 3$

60. $\log_3 8 = 3 \log_3 2$ **61.** $\log_5 16 - \log 2 = \log_5 8$

62. $\log(x - 2) = \dfrac{\log x}{\log 2}$ **63.** $\dfrac{\log_b x}{\log_b y} = \log_b \dfrac{x}{y}$

64. $(\log x)^2 = \log x^2$ **65.** $\log_4 7 - \log_4 3 = \log_4 4$

66. $\log x + \log(x^2 + 2) = \log(x^3 + 2x)$ **67.** $\log_2 3 + \log_3 2 = \log_6 6$

68. $\log_2 x - 4 \log_2 y = \log_2 \dfrac{x}{y^4}$ **69.** $\log_b \frac{1}{8} + 3 \log_b 4 = \log_b 8$

70. Construction Suppose you are the supervisor on a road construction job. Your team is blasting rock to make way for a roadbed. One explosion has an intensity of 1.65×10^{-2} W/m^2. What is the loudness of the sound in decibels? (Use $I_0 = 10^{-12}$ W/m^2.)

71. Critical Thinking Can you expand $\log_3(2x + 1)$? Explain.

 72. Writing Explain why $\log(5 \cdot 2) \neq \log 5 \cdot \log 2$.

Write each logarithmic expression as a single logarithm.

73. $\frac{1}{4} \log_3 2 + \frac{1}{4} \log_3 x$ **74.** $\frac{1}{2}\left(\log_x 4 + \log_x y\right) - 3 \log_x z$

75. $2 \log 3 - \frac{1}{2} \log 4 + \frac{1}{2} \log 9$ **76.** $x \log_4 m + \frac{1}{y} \log_4 n - \log_4 p$

77. $\left(\dfrac{2 \log_b x}{3} + \dfrac{3 \log_b y}{4}\right) - 5 \log_b z$ **78.** $\dfrac{\log z - \log 3}{4} - 5 \dfrac{\log x}{2}$

Expand each logarithm.

79. $\log \left(\dfrac{2\sqrt{x}}{5}\right)^3$ **80.** $\log \dfrac{m^3}{n^4 p^{-2}}$ **81.** $\log 2 \sqrt{\dfrac{4r}{s^2}}$

82. $\log_b \dfrac{\sqrt{x}\,\sqrt[3]{y^2}}{\sqrt[5]{z^2}}$ **83.** $\log_4 \dfrac{\sqrt{x^5 y^7}}{zw^4}$ **84.** $\log \dfrac{\sqrt{x^2 - 4}}{(x + 3)^2}$

85. $\log \sqrt{\dfrac{x\sqrt{2}}{y^2}}$ **86.** $\log_3 \left[(xy)^{\frac{1}{3}} \div z^2\right]^3$ **87.** $\log_7 \dfrac{\sqrt{r + 9}}{s^2 t^{\frac{1}{3}}}$

88. Let $u = \log_b M$, and let $v = \log_b N$. Prove the Product Property of Logarithms by completing the equations below.

Statement	Reason
$u = \log_b M$	Given
$b^u = M$	Rewrite in exponential form.
$v = \blacksquare$	Given
$b^v = \blacksquare$	Rewrite in exponential form.
$MN = b^u b^v = b^{\blacksquare}$	Apply the Product Property of Exponents.
$\log_b MN = \blacksquare$	Take the logarithm of each side.
$\log_b MN = \log_b \blacksquare + \log_b \blacksquare$	Substitute $\log_b M$ for u and $\log_b N$ for v.

 Challenge

89. Let $u = \log_b M$. Prove the Power Property of logarithms.

90. Let $u = \log_b M$ and $v = \log_b N$. Prove the Quotient Property of logarithms.

Multiple Choice Practice

For California Standards and CAHSEE Tutorials, visit PHSchool.com. Web Code: bbq-9045

ALG2 14.0   **91.** Which expression is equal to $\log_5 x + 4 \cdot \log_5 y - 2 \cdot \log_5 z$?

Ⓐ $\log_5 (-8xyz)$ Ⓑ $-\log_5 \frac{4xy}{2z}$ Ⓒ $\log_5 \frac{(xy)^4}{z^2}$ Ⓓ $\log_5 \frac{xy^4}{z^2}$

ALG2 12.0   **92.** Which is the graph of $y = 5^x - 1$?

Mixed Review

Lesson 8-3   Write each equation in logarithmic form.

93. $49 = 7^2$ **94.** $5^3 = 125$ **95.** $\frac{1}{4} = 8^{-\frac{2}{3}}$ **96.** $5^{-3} = \frac{1}{125}$

Lesson 7-5   Solve each equation. Check for extraneous solutions.

97. $\sqrt[3]{y^4} = 16$ **98.** $\sqrt[3]{7x} - 4 = 0$ **99.** $2\sqrt{w - 1} = \sqrt{w + 2}$

Lesson 6-5   A polynomial equation with integer coefficients has the given roots. What additional roots can you identify?

100. $\sqrt{3}, -\sqrt{5}$ **101.** $-i, 4i$ **102.** $2i, -4 + i$

103. $\sqrt{2}, i - 1$ **104.** $-\sqrt{7}, -\sqrt{11}$ **105.** $-2i + 3, i$

Judging the Validity of an Argument

ALG2 11.2 Students judge the validity of an argument according to whether the properties of real numbers, exponents, and logarithms have been applied correctly at each step. *Develop, Master*

It is helpful to understand the properties of logarithms so that you can judge whether an argument or mathematical statement is valid.

1 EXAMPLE

Which is the first *incorrect* step in simplifying $\log_5 20$?

Step 1: $\log_5 20 \doteq \log_5 4 + \log_5 5$

Step 2: $\qquad = 4 + 5$

Step 3: $\qquad = 9$

- Ⓐ Step 1
- Ⓑ Step 2
- Ⓒ Step 3
- Ⓓ Each step is correct.

You must judge whether each step is correct to determine if a mistake was made.

Step 1: $\log_5 20 = \log_5 4 + \log_5 5$ is correct because of the Product Property of logarithms.

Step 2: $\log_5 4 + \log_5 5 = 4 + 5$ is incorrect because $\log_5 4 + \log_5 5 \approx 2.80 + 3.49 = 6.29$, which is not equal to $4 + 5 = 9$.

You do not need to check any other steps since Step 2 is the first incorrect step.

● The correct answer is B.

2 EXAMPLE

Angel and Margaret each worked the same problem at the chalkboard without using a calculator. Each student's work is shown below. Their teacher said only one of them was correct.

Angel's Work

$$\log_{10} \frac{500}{5} = \log_{10} 500 - \log_{10} 5$$
$$= 500 - 5$$
$$= 495$$

Margaret's Work

$$\log_{10} \frac{500}{5} = \log_{10} 100$$
$$\log_{10} 100 = x$$
$$100 = 10^x$$
$$x = 2$$

Which is the correct solution?

- Ⓐ Both are correct.
- Ⓑ Angel is correct.
- Ⓒ Margaret is correct.
- Ⓓ Neither are correct.

Check both answers to determine if the properties of logarithms were applied correctly. Angel's solution is incorrect because he did not apply the Quotient Property correctly. The correct answer is C.

Exponential and Logarithmic Equations

 California Content Standards

ALG2 13.0 Students translate between logarithms in any base. *Introduce, Develop*
ALG2 11.0 Students prove simple laws of logarithms. *Master*
ALG2 11.1 Students understand the inverse relationship between exponents and logarithms. *Master*

What You'll Learn

- To solve exponential equations
- To solve logarithmic equations

... And Why

To model animal populations, as in Example 4

 Check Skills You'll Need

Evaluate each logarithm.

GO **for Help** Lessons 8-3 and 7-4

1. $\log_9 81 \cdot \log_9 3$

2. $\log 10 \cdot \log_3 9$

3. $\log_2 16 \div \log_2 8$

4. Simplify $125^{-\frac{2}{3}}$.

New Vocabulary   • exponential equation   • Change of Base Formula
• logarithmic equation

---

1 | Solving Exponential Equations

An equation of the form $b^{cx} = a$, where the exponent includes a variable, is an **exponential equation.** If m and n are positive and $m = n$, then $\log m = \log n$. You can therefore solve an exponential equation by taking the logarithm of each side of the equation.

1 EXAMPLE Solving an Exponential Equation

Solve $7^{3x} = 20$.

$$7^{3x} = 20$$
$$\log 7^{3x} = \log 20 \quad \text{Take the common logarithm of each side.}$$
$$3x \log 7 = \log 20 \quad \text{Use the power property of logarithms.}$$
$$x = \frac{\log 20}{3 \log 7} \quad \text{Divide each side by 3 log 7.}$$
$$\approx 0.5132 \quad \text{Use a calculator.}$$

Check $7^{3x} = 20$
$$7^{3(0.5132)} \approx 20.00382 \approx 20 \; \checkmark$$

CA Standards Check **1** Solve each equation. Round to the nearest ten-thousandth. Check your answers.
a. $3^x = 4$
b. $6^{2x} = 21$
c. $3^{x+4} = 101$

2 EXAMPLE Solving an Exponential Equation by Graphing

Solve $6^{2x} = 1500$.

Graph the equations $y_1 = 6^{2x}$ and $y_2 = 1500$. Find the point of intersection.

Intersection
X=2.040793   Y=1500

The solution is $x \approx 2.0408$.

CA Standards Check **2** Solve $11^{6x} = 786$ by graphing.

3 EXAMPLE Solving an Exponential Equation by Tables

Solve the equation $2(1.5^x) = 6$ to the nearest hundredth.

Enter $y_1 = 2(1.5^x) - 6$. Use tabular zoom-in to find the sign change, as shown at the right.

● The solution is $x \approx 2.71$.

X	Y1
2.7060	−.0085
2.7070	−.0061
2.7080	−.0037
2.7090	−.0012
2.7100	.0012
2.7110	.0036
2.7120	.0061
X=2.709	

CA Standards Check ③ Solve $11^{6x} = 786$ using tables. Compare your result with your solution in Quick Check 2.

4 EXAMPLE Real-World Connection

Zoology Refer to the photo. Write an exponential equation to model the decline in the population. If the decay rate remains constant, in what year might only five peninsular bighorn sheep remain in the United States?

Step 1 Enter the data into your calculator. Let 0 represent the initial year, 1971.

Step 2 Use the **ExpReg** feature to find the exponential function that fits the data.

ExpReg
y = a*b^x
a = 1170
b = .9563175045

Step 3 Graph the function and the line $y = 5$.

Step 4 Find the point of intersection.

Intersection
X=122.13778   Y=5

The solution is $x \approx 122$, and $1971 + 122 = 2093$, so there may be only
● five peninsular bighorn sheep in 2093.

CA Standards Check ④ The population of peninsular bighorn sheep in Mexico was approximately 6200 in 1971. By 1999, about 2300 remained. Determine the year by which only 200 peninsular bighorn sheep might remain in Mexico.

Real-World Connection

The U.S. population of peninsular bighorn sheep was 1170 in 1971. By 1999, only 335 remained.

GO for Help

To review solving equations by tables, see Lesson 5-5.

---

2 Solving Logarithmic Equations

To evaluate a logarithm with any base, you can use the **Change of Base Formula.**

Key Concepts

Property	Change of Base Formula

For any positive numbers, M, b, and c, with $b \neq 1$ and $c \neq 1$,

$$\log_b M = \frac{\log_c M}{\log_c b}$$

5 EXAMPLE Using the Change of Base Formula

Use the Change of Base Formula to evaluate $\log_3 15$. Then convert $\log_3 15$ to a logarithm in base 2.

$$\log_3 15 = \frac{\log 15}{\log 3}$$ **Use the Change of Base Formula.**

$$\approx 2.4650$$ **Use a calculator.**

$$\log_3 15 = \log_2 x$$ **Write an equation.**

$$2.4650 \approx \log_2 x$$ **Substitute $\log_3 15 \approx 2.4650$.**

$$x \approx 2^{2.4650}$$ **Write in exponential form.**

$$\approx 5.5212$$ **Use a calculator.**

● The expression $\log_3 15$ is approximately equal to 2.4650, or $\log_2 5.5212$.

✓ **CA Standards Check** **⑤** **a.** Evaluate $\log_5 400$ and convert it to a logarithm in base 8.
  b. Critical Thinking Consider the equation $2.465 \approx \log_2 x$ from Example 2. How could you solve the equation without using the Change of Base Formula?

An equation that includes a logarithmic expression, such as $\log_3 15 = \log_2 x$ in Example 5, is called a **logarithmic equation.**

6 EXAMPLE Solving a Logarithmic Equation

Solve $\log (3x + 1) = 5$.

Method 1 $\log (3x + 1) = 5$

$$3x + 1 = 10^5$$ **Write in exponential form.**

$$3x + 1 = 100{,}000$$

$$x = 33{,}333$$ **Solve for x.**

Method 2 Graph the equations $y_1 = \log (3x + 1)$ and $y_2 = 5$. Use Xmin = 30000, Xmax = 40000, Ymin = 4.9, Ymax = 5.1.

Find the point of intersection.

The solution is $x = 33{,}333$.

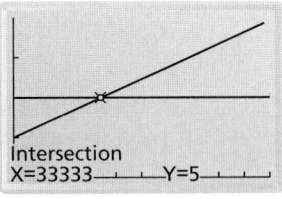

Intersection
X=33333   Y=5

Method 3 Enter $y_1 = \log (3x + 1) - 5$. Use tabular zoom-in to find the sign change. Use the information from Methods 1 or 2 to help you with your TblSet values.

The solution is $x = 33{,}333$.

X	Y1
33330	−4E−5
33331	−3E−5
33332	−1E−5
33333	0.0000
33334	1.3E−5
33335	2.6E−5
33336	3.9E−5

Y1=0

Check $\log (3x + 1) = 5$

$$\log (3 \cdot 33{,}333 + 1) \stackrel{?}{=} 5$$

$$\log 100{,}000 \stackrel{?}{=} 5$$

$$\log 10^5 = 5 \checkmark$$

✓ **CA Standards Check** **⑥** Solve $\log (7 - 2x) = -1$. Check your answer.

Sometimes the properties of logarithms will help solve an equation.

7 EXAMPLE Using Logarithmic Properties to Solve an Equation

Solve $2 \log x - \log 3 = 2$.

$2 \log x - \log 3 = 2$

$\log \left(\dfrac{x^2}{3} \right) = 2$ **Write as a single logarithm.**

$\dfrac{x^2}{3} = 10^2$ **Write in exponential form.**

$x^2 = 3(100)$ **Multiply each side by 3.**

$x = \pm 10\sqrt{3}$, or about ± 17.32

● Log x is defined only for $x > 0$, so the solution is $10\sqrt{3}$, or about 17.32.

✓ **CA Standards Check** **7** Solve $\log 6 - \log 3x = -2$.

EXERCISES

For more exercises, see *Extra Skill and Word Problem Practice.*

Standards Practice

ALG2 13.0, 11.0, 11.1

A Practice by Example

Example 1
(page 469)

for Help

Solve each equation. Round to the nearest ten-thousandth. Check your answers.

1. $2^x = 3$ **2.** $4^x = 19$ **3.** $5^x = 81.2$ **4.** $3^x = 27.3$

5. $8 + 10^x = 1008$ **6.** $5 - 3^x = -40$ **7.** $9^{2y} = 66$ **8.** $4^{2z} = 40$

9. $14^{x+1} = 36$ **10.** $12^{y-2} = 20$ **11.** $25^{2x+1} = 144$ **12.** $2^{3x-4} = 5$

Example 2
(page 469)

Solve by graphing.

13. $4^{7x} = 250$ **14.** $5^{3x} = 500$ **15.** $6^x = 4565$ **16.** $1.5^x = 356$

Example 3
(page 470)

Use a table to solve each equation. Round to the nearest hundredth.

17. $2^{x+3} = 512$ **18.** $3^{x-1} = 72$ **19.** $6^{2x} = 10$

20. $3^{x-2} = 12x - 1$ **21.** $4^{2x+1} = x^2$ **22.** $2^{2x-1} = 3^x$

Example 4
(page 470)

23. An investment of $2000 earns 5.75% interest, which is compounded quarterly. After approximately how many years will the investment be worth $3000?

24. The equation $y = 281(1.0124)^x$ models the U.S. population y, in millions of people, x years after the year 2000. Graph the function on your graphing calculator. Estimate when the U.S. population will reach 350 million.

Example 5
(page 471)

Use the Change of Base Formula to evaluate each expression. Then convert it to a logarithm in base 8.

25. $\log_2 9$ **26.** $\log_4 8$ **27.** $\log_3 54$ **28.** $\log_5 62$

29. $\log_3 33$ **30.** $\log_2 7$ **31.** $\log_5 510$ **32.** $\log_4 1.116$

Example 6
(page 471)

Solve each equation. Check your answers.

33. $\log 2x = -1$ **34.** $2 \log x = -1$ **35.** $\log (3x + 1) = 2$

36. $\log x + 4 = 8$ **37.** $\log 6x - 3 = -4$ **38.** $\log (x - 2) = 1$

39. $3 \log x = 1.5$ **40.** $2 \log (x + 1) = 5$ **41.** $\log (5 - 2x) = 0$

Example 7
(page 472)

Solve each equation.

42. $\log x - \log 3 = 8$

43. $\log 2x + \log x = 11$

44. $2 \log x + \log 4 = 2$

45. $\log 5 - \log 2x = 1$

46. $3 \log x - \log 6 + \log 2.4 = 9$

47. $\log (7x + 1) = \log (x - 2) + 1$

 Apply Your Skills

48. Consider the equation $2^{\frac{x}{3}} = 80$.
  a. Solve the equation by taking the logarithm in base 10 of each side.
  b. Solve the equation by taking the logarithm in base 2 of each side.
  c. Writing Compare your result in parts (a) and (b). What are the advantages of either method? Explain.

49. Seismology An earthquake of magnitude 7.9 occurred in 2001 in Gujarat, India. It was 11,600 times as strong as the greatest earthquake ever to hit Pennsylvania. Find the magnitude of the Pennsylvania earthquake. (*Hint*: Refer to the Richter Scale on page 454.)

Write an equation. Then solve the equation without graphing.

50. A parent raises a child's allowance by 20% each year. If the allowance is $8 now, when will it reach $20?

51. Protactinium-234*m*, a toxic radioactive metal with no known use, has a half-life of 1.17 minutes. How long does it take for a 10-mg sample to decay to 2 mg?

52. Multiple Choice As a town gets smaller, the population of its high school decreases by 12% each year. The student body has 125 students now. In how many years will it have about 75 students?

 Ⓐ 4 years   Ⓑ 7 years   Ⓒ 10 years   Ⓓ 11 years

Real-World Connection

Seismologists use models to determine the source, nature, and size of seismic events.

Mental Math Solve each equation.

53. $2^x = \frac{1}{2}$

54. $3^x = 27$

55. $\log_9 3 = x$

56. $\log_4 64 = x$

57. $\log_8 2 = x$

58. $10^x = \frac{1}{100}$

59. $\log_7 343 = x$

60. $25^x = \frac{1}{5}$

Population Use this "Most Populous States" table for Exercises 61–63.

Most Populous States

Rank in 2000	State	2000 Population	Average Annual Percentage Increase Since 1990
1	California	33,871,648	1.30%
2	Texas	20,851,820	2.08%
3	New York	18,976,457	0.54%
4	Florida	15,982,378	2.13%

SOURCE: U.S. Census Bureau. Go to www.PHSchool.com for a data update. Web Code: bbg-9041

61. a. Determine the growth factors for Florida and New York. Then write an equation to model each state's population growth.
  b. Estimate when Florida's population might exceed New York's population.

62. a. Determine the growth factors for Texas and California. Then write an equation to model each state's population growth.
  b. Estimate when Texas's population might exceed California's population.

63. Critical Thinking Is it likely that Florida's population will exceed that of Texas? Explain your reasoning.

64. Error Analysis What is wrong with the "proof" below that $2 = 1$?

$$2 = \frac{2}{1} = \frac{\log 10^2}{\log 10^1} = \log 10^{2-1} = \log 10^1 = 1$$

65. Open-Ended Write and solve a logarithmic equation.

66. Zoology Conservation efforts have increased the endangered Florida manatee population from 1465 in 1991 to 3276 in 2001. If this growth rate continues, when might there be 10,000 manatees? Explain the reasoning behind your choice of a model.

67. Consider the equation $a^x = b$.
   a. Solve the equation by using log base 10.
   b. Solve the equation by using log base a.
   c. Use your results in parts (a) and (b) to justify the Change of Base Formula.

Write each logarithm as the quotient of two common logarithms. Do not simplify the quotient.

68. $\log_7 2$ **69.** $\log_3 8$ **70.** $\log_5 140$ **71.** $\log_9 3.3$

72. $\log_4 3x$ **73.** $\log_6 (1 - x)$ **74.** $\log_x 5$ **75.** $\log_x (x + 1)$

Acoustics In Exercises 76–78, the loudness measured in decibels (dB) is defined by loudness $= 10 \log \frac{I}{I_0}$, where I is the intensity and $I_0 = 10^{-12}$ W/m^2.

76. The human threshold for pain is 120 dB. Instant perforation of the eardrum occurs at 160 dB.
   a. Find the intensity of each sound.
   b. How many times as intense is the noise that will perforate an eardrum as the noise that causes pain?

77. The noise level inside a convertible driving along the freeway with its top up is 70 dB. With the top down, the noise level is 95 dB.
   a. Find the intensity of the sound with the top up and with the top down.
   b. By what percent does leaving the top up reduce the intensity of the sound?

78. A screaming child can reach 90 dB. A launch of the space shuttle produces sound of 180 dB at the launch pad.
   a. Find the intensity of each sound.
   b. How many times as intense as the noise from a screaming child is the noise from a shuttle launch?

Solve each equation. If necessary, round to the nearest ten-thousandth.

79. $8^x = 444$ **80.** $14^{9x} = 146$

81. $3^{7x} = 120$ **82.** $\frac{1}{2} \log x + \log 4 = 2$

83. $4 \log_3 2 - 2 \log_3 x = 1$ **84.** $\log x^2 = 2$

85. $9^{2x} = 42$ **86.** $\log_8 (2x - 1) = \frac{1}{3}$

87. $1.3^x = 7$ **88.** $\log (5x - 4) = 3$

89. $2.1^x = 9$ **90.** $12^{4 - x} = 20$

91. $5^{3x} = 125$ **92.** $\log 4 + 2 \log x = 6$

93. $4^{3x} = 77.2$ **94.** $\log_7 3x = 3$

95. $3^x + 0.7 = 4.9$ **96.** $7^x - 1 = 371$

Real-World Connection

Many Florida manatees die after collisions with motorboats.

Homework Video Tutor

Visit: PHSchool.com
Web Code: bbe-0805

Bassoon
Guitar
Harp
Violin
Viola
Cello
Bass

−10 −5 0 5 10

C Challenge

97. Music The pitch, or frequency, of a piano note is related to its position on the keyboard by the function $F(n) = 440 \cdot 2^{\frac{n}{12}}$, where F is the frequency of the sound wave in cycles per second and n is the number of piano keys above or below Concert A, as shown above. If $n = 0$ at Concert A, which of the instruments shown in the diagram can sound notes of the given frequency?

a. 590   **b.** 120   **c.** 1440   **d.** 2093

98. Astronomy The brightness of an astronomical object is called its magnitude. A decrease of five magnitudes increases the brightness exactly 100 times. The sun is magnitude −26.7, and the full moon is magnitude −12.5. The sun is about how many times brighter than the moon?

99. Archaeology A scientist carbon-dates a piece of fossilized tree trunk that is thought to be over 5000 years old. The scientist determines that the sample contains 65% of the original amount of carbon-14. The half-life of carbon-14 is 5730 years. Is the reputed age of the tree correct? Explain.

Solve each equation.

100. $\log_7 (2x - 3)^2 = 2$ **101.** $\log_2 (x^2 + 2x) = 3$

102. $\log_4 (x^2 - 17) = 3$ **103.** $\frac{3}{2} \log_2 4 - \frac{1}{2} \log_2 x = 3$

104. In the formula $P = P_0 \left(\frac{1}{2}\right)^{\frac{h}{4795}}$, P is the atmospheric pressure in millimeters of mercury at elevation h meters above sea level. P_0 is the atmospheric pressure at sea level. If P_0 equals 760 mm, at what elevation is the pressure 42 mm?

105. Chemistry A technician found 12 mg of a radon isotope in a soil sample. After 24 hours, another measurement revealed 10 mg of the isotope.
   a. Estimate the length of the isotope's half-life to the nearest hour and to the nearest day.
   b. For each estimate, determine the amount of the isotope after two weeks.
   c. Compare your answers to part (b). Which is more accurate? Explain.

Multiple Choice Practice

For California Standards and CAHSEE Tutorials, visit PHSchool.com. Web Code: bbq-9045

ALG2 13.0   **106.** What is the solution to the equation $\log_5 x = \log_3 20$, to the nearest tenth?

      Ⓐ 2.7   Ⓑ 13.6   Ⓒ 80.5   Ⓓ 125

107. Which expression is equivalent to $\left(\frac{1}{64}\right)^{-\frac{1}{6}}$?

　　　Ⓐ $\left(\frac{1}{2}\right)^{-6}$　　　　Ⓑ 4^3　　　　Ⓒ 2　　　　Ⓓ 64^6

108. Which expression is equivalent to $2x^4 - 3x + 6$?

　　　Ⓐ $(x^4 - 2x^2 + 3) - (x^4 - x^2 - 9)$　　Ⓒ $2x^4 - 3(x + 6)$

　　　Ⓑ $(3x^4 - x + 3) + (3 - 2x - x^4)$　　Ⓓ $x(2x^3 - 3x) + 6$

Mixed Review

Lesson 8-4

Expand each logarithm.

109. $\log 2x^3y^{-2}$　　　**110.** $\log_3 \frac{x}{y}$　　　**111.** $\log_2 (3x)^3$

112. $\log_3 7(2x - 3)^2$　　**113.** $\log_4 5\sqrt{x}$　　**114.** $\log_2 \left(\frac{5a}{b^2}\right)$

Lesson 7-6

Let $f(x) = 3x$ and $g(x) = x^2 - 1$. Perform each function operation.

115. $(f + g)(x)$　　　**116.** $(g - f)(x)$　　　**117.** $(f \cdot g)(x)$

Lesson 6-6

Find all the zeros of each function.

118. $y = x^3 - x^2 + x - 1$　　　**119.** $f(x) = x^4 - 16$

120. $f(x) = x^4 - 5x^2 + 6$　　　**121.** $y = 3x^3 - 21x - 18$

Lesson 1-3

Write an equation to solve each problem.

122. A customer at a hardware store mentions that he is buying fencing for a vegetable garden that is 12 ft longer than it is wide. He buys 128 ft of fencing. What is the width of the garden?

123. A bowler has an average of 133. In a set of games one night, her scores are 135, 127, 119, 142, and 156. What score must she bowl in the sixth game to maintain her average?

✓ Checkpoint Quiz 2　　　　　Lessons 8-3 through 8-5

Graph each logarithmic function.

1. $y = \log_6 x$　　　　　　**2.** $y = \log (x - 2)$

Expand each logarithm.

3. $\log \frac{s^3}{r^5}$　　　**4.** $\log_6 (3xy)^2$　　　**5.** $\log_6 4\sqrt{x}$

Solve each equation.

6. $7 - 2^x = -1$　　　**7.** $\log 5x = 2$　　　**8.** $3 \log x = 9$

9. Evaluate the expressions below and order them from least to greatest.

　　2^3　　　　$\log_2 3$　　　$\log_3 2$　　　3^2　　　$\log 2$

 10. Writing Explain how to use the Change of Base Formula to rewrite $\log_2 10$ as a logarithmic expression with base 3.

You can transform an exponential function into a linear function by taking the logarithm of each side. Since linear models are easy to recognize, you can then determine whether an exponential function is a good model for a set of values.

$$y = ab^x$$ **Write the general form of an exponential function.**

$$\log y = \log ab^x$$ **Take the logarithm of each side.**

$$\log y = \log a + x(\log b)$$ **Product Property and Power Property**

$$\log y = (\log b)x + \log a$$ **Rewrite.**

If $\log b$ and $\log a$ are constants, then $\log y = (\log b)x + \log a$ is a linear equation in slope-intercept form. To confirm that $\log b$ is a constant, check that the graph of $\log y = (\log b)x + \log a$ is a line.

ACTIVITY

Determine whether an exponential function is a good model for the values in the table.

x	0	2	4	6	8	10
y	3.0	5.1	8.6	14.5	24.5	41.4

Step 1 Enter the values into STAT lists L_1 and L_2. To enter the values of $\log y$, place the cursor in the heading of L_3 and press LOG L_2 ENTER.

Step 2 To graph $\log y$, access the STAT PLOT feature and press 1. Then enter L_3 next to Ylist:. Then press ZOOM 9.

L1	L2	L3 1
0	3	0.47712
2	5.1	0.70757
4	8.6	0.9345
6	14.5	1.1614
8	24.5	1.3892
10	41.4	1.617
L1(1) = 0		

Since the graph of $\log y = (\log b)x + \log a$ is linear, the slope $\log b$ is constant, and b also is constant. An exponential function therefore is a suitable model.

Step 3 Press STAT ▶ 0 ENTER to find the exponential function: $y = 3(1.3)^x$.

EXERCISES

For each set of values, determine whether an exponential function is a good model. If so, find the function.

1.

x	1	3	5	7	9
y	6	22	54	102	145

2.

x	−1	0	1	2	3
y	40.2	19.8	9.9	5.1	2.5

3. Writing Explain how you could determine whether a logarithmic function is a good model for a set of values.

8-6 Natural Logarithms

 California Content Standards

ALG2 14.0 Students understand and use the properties of exponents to simplify logarithmic numeric expressions and to identify their approximate values. *Master*
ALG2 15.0 Students determine whether a specific algebraic statement involving logarithmic or exponential functions is sometimes true, always true, or never true. *Master*
ALG2 13.0 Students translate between logarithms in any base. *Master*

What You'll Learn

• To evaluate natural logarithmic expressions

• To solve equations using natural logarithms

... And Why

To model the velocity of a rocket, as in Example 2

✓ Check Skills You'll Need

GO for Help Lessons 8-2 and 8-5

Use your calculator to evaluate each expression to the nearest thousandth.

1. e^5 **2.** $2e^3$ **3.** e^{-2} **4.** $\frac{1}{e}$ **5.** $4.2e$

Solve.

6. $\log_3 x = 4$ **7.** $\log_{16} 4 = x$ **8.** $\log_{16} x = 4$

◀)) **New Vocabulary** • natural logarithmic function

---

1 Natural Logarithms

In Lesson 8-2, you learned that the number $e \approx 2.71828$ can be used as a base for exponents. The function $y = e^x$ has an inverse, the **natural logarithmic function.**

 Key Concepts

Definition **Natural Logarithmic Function**
If $y = e^x$, then $\log_e y = x$, which is commonly written as $\ln y = x$.   The natural logarithmic function is the inverse, written as $y = \ln x$.   ① $y = e^x$ ② $y = \ln x$

Vocabulary Tip

ln y means "the natural logarithm of y." The l stands for "logarithm" and the n stands for "natural."

The properties of common logarithms apply to natural logarithms also.

1 EXAMPLE **Simplifying Natural Logarithms**

Write $3 \ln 6 - \ln 8$ as a single natural logarithm.

$3 \ln 6 - \ln 8 = \ln 6^3 - \ln 8$ **Power Property**

$\qquad\qquad\quad = \ln \frac{6^3}{8}$ **Quotient Property**

$\qquad\qquad\quad = \ln 27$ **Simplify.**

✓ **CA Standards Check** ① Write each expression as a single natural logarithm.

a. $5 \ln 2 - \ln 4$ **b.** $3 \ln x + \ln y$ **c.** $\frac{1}{4} \ln 3 + \frac{1}{4} \ln x$

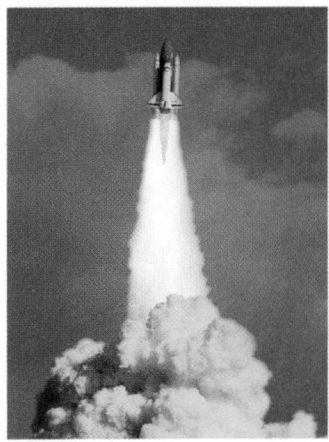

Natural logarithms are useful because they help express many relationships in the physical world.

2 EXAMPLE **Real-World Connection**

Space A spacecraft can attain a stable orbit 300 km above Earth if it reaches a velocity of 7.7 km/s. The formula for a rocket's maximum velocity v in kilometers per second is $v = -0.0098t + c \ln R$. The booster rocket fires for t seconds and the velocity of the exhaust is c km/s. The ratio of the mass of the rocket filled with fuel to its mass without fuel is R. Suppose a rocket used to propel a spacecraft has a mass ratio of 25, an exhaust velocity of 2.8 km/s, and a firing time of 100 s. Can the spacecraft attain a stable orbit 300 km above Earth?

Real-World Connection

A space shuttle must reach an escape velocity of about 11.2 km/s to exit Earth's gravitational field.

Let $R = 25$, $c = 2.8$, and $t = 100$. Find v.

$v = -0.0098t + c \ln R$	**Use the formula.**
$\quad = -0.0098(100) + 2.8 \ln 25$	**Substitute.**
$\quad \approx -0.98 + 2.8(3.219)$	**Use a calculator.**
$\quad \approx 8.0$	**Simplify.**

The maximum velocity of 8.0 km/s is greater than the 7.7 km/s needed for a stable orbit. Therefore, the spacecraft can attain a stable orbit 300 km above Earth.

✓ CA Standards Check **2** **a.** A booster rocket for a spacecraft has a mass ratio of about 15, an exhaust velocity of 2.1 km/s, and a firing time of 30 s. Find the maximum velocity of the spacecraft. Can the spacecraft achieve a stable orbit 300 km above Earth?
b. Critical Thinking Suppose a rocket, as designed, cannot provide enough velocity to achieve a stable orbit. Look at the variables in the velocity formula. What alterations could be made to the rocket so that a stable orbit could be achieved?

2 Natural Logarithmic and Exponential Equations

You can use the properties of logarithms to solve natural logarithmic equations.

3 EXAMPLE **Solving a Natural Logarithmic Equation**

Solve $\ln (3x + 5)^2 = 4$.

$\ln (3x + 5)^2 = 4$	
$(3x + 5)^2 = e^4$	**Rewrite in exponential form.**
$(3x + 5)^2 \approx 54.60$	**Use a calculator.**
$3x + 5 \approx \pm \sqrt{54.60}$	**Take the square root of each side.**
$3x + 5 \approx 7.39 \text{ or } -7.39$	**Use a calculator.**
$x \approx 0.797 \text{ or } -4.130$	**Solve for } x.**

Check $\ln (3 \cdot 0.797 + 5)^2 \overset{?}{=} 4 \qquad\qquad \ln (3 \cdot (-4.130) + 5)^2 \overset{?}{=} 4$

$\qquad\qquad\qquad \ln 54.6 \overset{?}{=} 4 \qquad\qquad\qquad\qquad \ln 54.6 \overset{?}{=} 4$

$\qquad\qquad\qquad 4.000 \approx 4 \checkmark \qquad\qquad\qquad\qquad 4.000 \approx 4 \checkmark$

✓ CA Standards Check **3** Solve each equation. Check your answers.

a. $\ln x = 0.1$ **b.** $\ln (3x - 9) = 21$ **c.** $\ln \left(\frac{x + 2}{3} \right) = 12$

You can use natural logarithms to solve exponential equations.

4 EXAMPLE **Solving an Exponential Equation**

Use natural logarithms to solve $7e^{2x} + 2.5 = 20$.

$7e^{2x} + 2.5 = 20$

$\quad 7e^{2x} = 17.5$ **Subtract 2.5 from each side.**

$\quad\quad e^{2x} = 2.5$ **Divide each side by 7.**

$\quad \ln e^{2x} = \ln 2.5$ **Take the natural logarithm of each side.**

$\quad\quad\quad 2x = \ln 2.5$ **Simplify.**

$\quad\quad\quad x = \dfrac{\ln 2.5}{2}$ **Solve for x.**

$\quad\quad\quad x \approx 0.458$ **Use a calculator.**

✓ **CA Standards Check** ④ Use natural logarithms to solve each equation.

a. $e^{x+1} = 30$ **b.** $e^{\frac{2x}{5}} + 7.2 = 9.1$

5 EXAMPLE **Real-World Connection**

Test-Taking Tip

If you perform an operation on one side of an equation, remember to perform the same operation on the other side.

Multiple Choice An investment of $100 is now valued at $149.18. The interest rate is 8%, compounded continuously. About how long has the money been invested?

Ⓐ 2 years   Ⓑ 5 years   Ⓒ 7 years   Ⓓ 19 years

$\quad\quad A = Pe^{rt}$ **Continuously compounded interest formula**

$149.18 = 100e^{0.08t}$ **Substitute 149.18 for A, 100 for P, and 0.08 for r.**

$1.4918 = e^{0.08t}$ **Divide each side by 100.**

$\ln 1.4918 = \ln e^{0.08t}$ **Take the natural logarithm of each side.**

$\ln 1.4918 = 0.08t$ **Simplify.**

$\dfrac{\ln 1.4918}{0.08} = t$ **Solve for t.**

$\quad\quad 5 \approx t$ **Use a calculator.**

The money has been invested for about five years. The answer is B.

✓ **CA Standards Check** ⑤ An initial investment of $200 is worth $315.24 after seven years of continuous compounding. Find the interest rate.

EXERCISES

For more exercises, see *Extra Skill and Word Problem Practice*.

Standards Practice

ALG2 14.0, 15.0, 13.0

A **Practice by Example**

Example 1
(page 478)

Write each expression as a single natural logarithm.

1. $3 \ln 5$ **2.** $\ln 9 + \ln 2$ **3.** $\ln 24 - \ln 6$

4. $4 \ln 8 + \ln 10$ **5.** $\ln 3 - 5 \ln 3$ **6.** $2 \ln 8 - 3 \ln 4$

7. $5 \ln m - 3 \ln n$ **8.** $\frac{1}{3}(\ln x + \ln y) - 4 \ln z$ **9.** $\ln a - 2 \ln b + \frac{1}{2} \ln c$

Example 2
(page 479)

Find the value of y for the given value of x.

10. $y = 15 + 3 \ln x$, for $x = 7.2$ **11.** $y = 0.05 - 10 \ln x$, for $x = 0.09$

For Exercises 12 and 13, use $v = -0.0098t + c \ln R$.

12. **Space** Find the velocity of a spacecraft whose booster rocket has a mass ratio of 20, an exhaust velocity of 2.7 km/s, and a firing time of 30 s. Can the spacecraft achieve a stable orbit 300 km above Earth?

13. A rocket has a mass ratio of 24 and an exhaust velocity of 2.5 km/s. Determine the minimum firing time for a stable orbit 300 km above Earth.

Example 3
(page 479)

Solve each equation. Check your answers.

14. $\ln 3x = 6$ 15. $\ln x = -2$ 16. $\ln (4x - 1) = 36$

17. $\ln (2m + 3) = 8$ 18. $\ln (t - 1)^2 = 3$ 19. $1.1 + \ln x^2 = 6$

20. $\ln \frac{x - 1}{2} = 4$ 21. $\ln 4r^2 = 3$ 22. $2 \ln 2x^2 = 1$

Example 4
(page 480)

Use natural logarithms to solve each equation.

23. $e^x = 18$ 24. $e^{2x} = 10$ 25. $e^{x + 1} = 30$

26. $e^{\frac{x}{5}} + 4 = 7$ 27. $e^{2x} = 12$ 28. $e^{\frac{x}{9}} - 8 = 6$

Example 5
(page 480)

29. **Investing** An initial deposit of $200 is now worth $331.07. The account earns 8.4% interest, compounded continuously. Determine how long the money has been in the account.

30. An investor sold 100 shares of stock valued at $34.50 per share. The stock was purchased at $7.25 per share two years ago. Find the rate of continuously compounded interest that would be necessary in a banking account for the investor to make the same profit.

 Apply Your Skills

Mental Math **Simplify each expression.**

31. $\ln e$ 32. $\ln e^2$ 33. $\ln e^{10}$ 34. $10 \ln e$

35. $\ln 1$ 36. $\frac{\ln e}{4}$ 37. $\frac{\ln e^2}{2}$ 38. $\ln e^{83}$

To review formulas and literal equations, see Skills Handbook, page 886.

39. The battery power available to run a satellite is given by the formula $P = 50 e^{-\frac{t}{250}}$, where P is power in watts and t is time in days. For how many days can the satellite run if it requires 15 watts?

40. **Space** Use the formula for maximum velocity $v = -0.0098t + c \ln R$. Find the mass ratio of a rocket with an exhaust velocity of 3.1 km/s, a firing time of 50 s, and a maximum shuttle velocity of 6.9 km/s.

Determine whether each statement is *always* true, *sometimes* true, or *never* true.

41. $\ln e^x > 1$ 42. $\ln e^x = \ln e^x + 1$ 43. $\ln t = \log_e t$

Biology For Exercises 44–46, use the formula $H = \left(\frac{1}{r}\right)(\ln P - \ln A)$. H is the number of hours, r is the rate of decline, P is the initial bacteria population, and A is the reduced bacteria population.

44. A scientist determines that an antibiotic reduces a population of 20,000 bacteria to 5000 in 24 hours. Find the rate of decline caused by the antibiotic.

45. A laboratory assistant tests an antibiotic that causes a rate of decline of 0.14. How long should it take for a population of 8000 bacteria to shrink to 500?

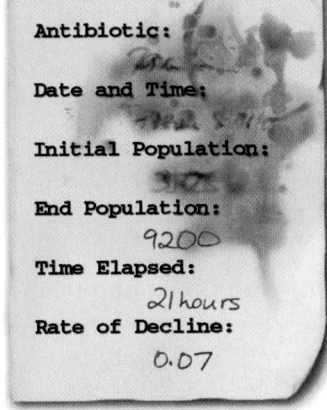

Antibiotic:

Date and Time:

Initial Population:

End Population:
9200

Time Elapsed:
21 hours

Rate of Decline:
0.07

46. A scientist spilled coffee on the lab report shown at the left. Determine the initial population of the bacteria.

Savings Suppose you invest $500 at 5% interest compounded continuously. Copy and complete the table to find how long it will take to reach each amount.

Homework Video Tutor

Visit: PHSchool.com
Web Code: bbe-0806

	Amount (A)	Time (years)
47.	$600	■
48.	$700	■
49.	$800	■
50.	$900	■
51.	$1000	■
52.	$1100	■
53.	$1200	■
54.	$1300	■

Solve each equation.

55. $\ln x - 3 \ln 3 = 3$ **56.** $\ln (2x - 1) = 0$ **57.** $4e^{x+2} = 32$

58. $\ln (5x - 3)^{\frac{1}{3}} = 2$ **59.** $2e^{3x-2} + 4 = 16$ **60.** $2e^{x-2} = e^x + 7$

61. $\frac{1}{3} \ln x + \ln 2 - \ln 3 = 3$ **62.** $\ln (x + 2) - \ln 4 = 3$

C **Challenge**   **63. Critical Thinking** Can $\ln 5 + \log_2 10$ be written as a single logarithm? Explain.

64. In 2000, there were about 300 million Internet users. That number is projected to grow to 1 billion in 2005.
  a. Let t represent the time, in years, since 2000. Write a function of the form $y = ae^{ct}$ that models the expected growth in the population of Internet users.
  b. In what year might there be 500 million Internet users?
  c. In what year might there be 1.5 billion Internet users?
  d. Solve your equation for t.
  e. Writing Explain how you can use your equation from part (d) to verify your answers to parts (b) and (c).

65. Physics The function $T(t) = T_r + (T_i - T_r)e^{kt}$ models Newton's Law of Cooling. $T(t)$ is the temperature of a heated substance t minutes after it has been removed from a heat (or cooling) source. T_i is the substance's initial temperature, k is a constant for that substance, and T_r is room temperature.
  a. The initial surface temperature of a beef roast is 236°F and room temperature is 72°F. If $k = -0.041$, how long will it take for this roast to cool to 100°F?
  b. Write and graph an equation that you can use to check your answer to part (a). Use your graph to complete the table below.

Temperature (°F)	225	200	175	150	125	100	75
Minutes Later	■	■	■	■	■	■	■

Physics students test Newton's Law of Cooling in laboratory settings.

66. Open-Ended Write a real-world problem that you can answer using Newton's Law of Cooling. Then answer it.

Multiple Choice Practice

For California Standards and CAHSEE Tutorials, visit PHSchool.com. Web Code: bbq-9045

ALG2 14.0   **67.** What is the value of x if $17e^{4x} = 85$?

  A $\frac{5}{4}$ **B** $\frac{\ln 85}{17 \cdot \ln 4}$ **C** $\frac{\ln 5}{4}$ **D** $\frac{\ln 85 - \ln 17}{\ln 4}$

ALG2 14.0   **68.** The table below shows the values of an investment after the given number of years of continuously compounded interest.

Years	0	1	2	3	4
Value	$500.00	$541.64	$586.76	$635.62	$688.56

Using the formula $A = Pe^{rt}$, to the nearest year, when will the investment be worth $1800?

    Ⓐ 4 years   Ⓑ 12 years   Ⓒ 16 years   Ⓓ 20 years

ALG2 24.0   **69.** Let $f(x) = -4x + 1$ and $g(x) = 2x - 6$. Find $(g - f)(x)$.

    Ⓐ $6x - 5$ Ⓑ $6x - 7$ Ⓒ $-6x + 5$ Ⓓ $-6x + 7$

ALG2 9.0   **70.** Which statement describes what happens to the graph of $y = ax^2$ when the value of a is changed from 1 to 4?

    Ⓐ The graph narrows.   Ⓒ The graph translates 4 units right.

    Ⓑ The graph widens.   Ⓓ The graph translates 4 units down.

Mixed Review

GO for Help

Lesson 8-5   **Solve each equation.**

71. $3^{2x} = 6561$ **72.** $7^x - 2 = 252$ **73.** $25^{2x+1} = 144$

74. $\log 3x = 4$ **75.** $\log 5x + 3 = 3.7$ **76.** $\log 9 - \log x + 1 = 6$

Lesson 7-7   **Find the inverse of each function. Is the inverse a function?**

77. $y = 5x + 7$ **78.** $y = 2x^3 + 10$ **79.** $y = -x^2 + 5$

Lesson 6-7   **80.** The Nut Shop carries 30 different types of nuts. The shop special is the Triple Play, a made-to-order mixture of any three different types of nuts. How many different Triple Plays are possible?

A Point in Time

1500   1600   1700   1800   1900   2000

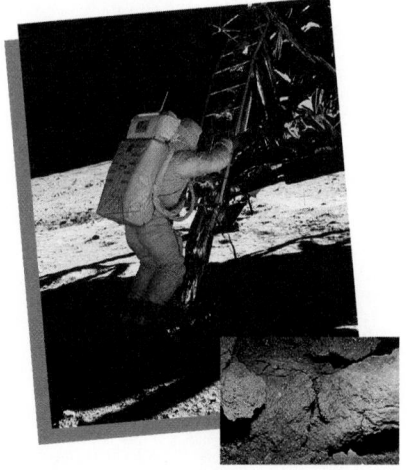

The first manned moon landing on July 20, 1969, gave scientists a unique opportunity to test their theories about the moon's geologic history.

A logarithmic function was used to date lunar rocks. Radioactive rubidium-87 decays into stable strontium-87 at a fixed rate. The ratio r of the two isotopes in a sample can be measured and used in the equation $T = -h \frac{\ln(r + 1)}{\ln 0.5}$, where T is the age in years and h is the half-life of rubidium-87, 4.7×10^{10} years. For the lunar sample, r was measured at 0.0588, giving an approximate age of 3.87 billion years.

For: Information about space exploration
PHSchool.com **Web Code:** bbe-2032

You can solve problems using exponential equations and inequalities.

1 ACTIVITY

Legend tells of a Roman general who was so successful in his campaigns that the emperor offered the general his choice of reward. The general asked the emperor for all the silver that he could carry out of the imperial treasury in one month. The emperor agreed, but offered a condition.

On the first day, the general would receive 1 silver denarius. On the second day, he would receive a coin valued at 2 denarii. Each day, the general was to come to the treasury and the treasurer would mint a special coin that would be twice as heavy and worth twice as much as the coin the general got a day earlier.

1. a. What function $V(x)$ gives the value of the coin that the general received on day x?
   b. What is the domain and range of this function?

One denarius coin weighed about 0.006 kg.

2. Write a function $M(x)$ that gives the mass of each coin in kilograms as a function of day x.

The largest object the general could carry or roll without help could weigh no more than 300 kg.

3. a. Use $M(x)$ from Exercise 2 to write an inequality that describes the mass of a coin that the general could carry or roll out of the treasury.
   b. Make a table of values of this function.
   c. Use the table to solve the inequality.

4. What is the total value of the coins that the general would receive?

2 ACTIVITY

Scientists are growing bacteria in a laboratory. They start with a known population of bacteria and measure how long it takes this population to double.

5. Sample A starts with 200,000 bacteria. The population doubles every hour. Write an exponential function that models the population in Sample A as a function of time in hours.

6. Sample B starts with 50,000 bacteria. The population doubles every half hour. Write an exponential function that models the population growth in Sample B as a function of time in hours.

7. a. Write an inequality that models the population in Sample B overtaking the population in Sample A.
   b. Use a graphing calculator to solve the inequality.

You can also use logarithmic equations and inequalities to solve problems.

3 ACTIVITY

Average barometric pressure varies with the altitude of a location.
The greater the altitude is, the lower the pressure. The altitude A is
measured in feet above sea level. The barometric pressure P is
measured in inches of mercury (in. Hg). The altitude can be
modeled by the function $A(P) = 90{,}000 - 26{,}500 \ln P$.

Mt. Kilimanjaro

8. What is the reasonable domain of the function? What is the
range of the function?

9. Use a graphing calculator to make a table of function values.
Use TblStart = 30 and ΔTbl = -1.

10. Write an equation to find what average pressure the model
predicts at sea level, or $A = 0$. Use your table to solve
the equation.

11. Kilimanjaro is a mountain in Tanzania that formed from three
extinct volcanoes. The base of the mountain is at 3000 ft above
sea level. The peak is at 19,340 ft above sea level. On
Kilimanjaro, $3000 \le A(P) \le 19{,}340$ is true for the altitude.
Write an inequality from which you can find minimum and
maximum values of normal barometric pressure on Kilimanjaro.
Use a table and solve the inequality for P.

12. Denver, Colorado, is nicknamed the "Mile High City" because its elevation is
about 1 mile, or 5280 ft, above sea level. The lowest point in Phoenix, Arizona,
is 1070 ft above sea level. Write an inequality that describes the range of $A(P)$
as you drive from Phoenix to Denver. Then solve the inequality for P.

4 ACTIVITY

Carbon-14 is a radioisotope that is produced when cosmic radiation penetrates
Earth's atmosphere. Plants absorb carbon-14 with carbon dioxide from the air.
Animals ingest carbon-14 when they eat plants.

The concentration of carbon-14 in a living organism is the same as its
concentration in the atmosphere. When an organism dies, it stops replacing
carbon-14. The remaining carbon-14 begins to decay. Scientists use the ratio of the
concentration of the remaining carbon-14 to its original concentration to estimate
the age of organic material. Let r represent this ratio.

13. The age of a fossil $g(r)$, in years, can be modeled as a function of r as
$g(r) = -5730 \log_2 r$ or $g(r) = -8266.64 \ln r$. What is the domain of the
function? What is the range of the function?

14. Graph the function.

15. Describe the behavior of the function as r becomes very small.

16. A paleontologist found an animal bone fossil and measured r to be 0.01. What
is the approximate age of the bone to the nearest thousand years?

17. Write an inequality that models the carbon-14 ratio in fossils that are more
than 50,000 years old. Then solve the inequality by graphing the corresponding
function on your calculator. What does your solution mean?

One advantage of a multiple-choice item is that the correct answer is among the choices. A frequently useful strategy is to test a choice in the original problem.

EXAMPLE

What number is the solution to $\left(\frac{1}{4}\right)^x = 8$?

(A) -2 (B) $-\frac{3}{2}$ (C) 0 (D) $\frac{1}{2}$

You can answer the question without solving the equation. Substitute each answer choice into the equation until you find the right one.

If $x = -2$, then $\left(\frac{1}{4}\right)^x = \left(\frac{1}{4}\right)^{-2} = 4^2 = 16$. Since $16 \neq 8$, answer A is wrong.

If $x = -\frac{3}{2}$, then $\left(\frac{1}{4}\right)^x = \left(\frac{1}{4}\right)^{-\frac{3}{2}} = 4^{\frac{3}{2}} = 8$. Since $8 = 8$, the correct answer is B.

You don't have to test the two other choices.

When answering a multiple-choice question that involves solving a difficult equation, you often can save time and effort by working backward from the answers to the question.

EXERCISES

Answer each question by testing the choices.

1. Which statement is always a correct conclusion about the quantities in the function $y = -x^2$?

    (A) Each value of y is less than the corresponding value of x.

    (B) As the values of x increase, the values of y increase.

    (C) Each value of y is greater than the corresponding value of x.

    (D) When the value of x is negative, the value of y is also negative.

2. The table at the right shows the height of a ball that was tossed into the air. Which equation best represents the relationship between time t and the height of the ball h?

    (A) $h = 26t + 4$

    (B) $h = -16t^2 + 30t + 4$

    (C) $h = 4t^2$

    (D) $h = -16t^2 + 4$

Time (seconds)	Height (feet)
0	4
0.25	10.5
0.5	15
0.75	17.5

3. What are the x-intercepts of the graph of the function $y = x^2 - 112x + 3072$?

    (A) $x = 0, x = 3072$ (C) $x = 36, x = 112$

    (B) $x = 64, x = 144$ (D) $x = 48, x = 64$

4. Two tickets to a concert cost \$78. Which expression represents the cost of n tickets?

    (A) $78 + n$ (B) $\frac{78 + n}{2}$ (C) $78n$ (D) $\frac{78n}{2}$

Chapter 8 Review

Vocabulary Review

🔊 **English and Spanish Audio Online**

asymptote (p. 441)
Change of Base Formula (p. 470)
common logarithm (p. 455)
continuously compounded interest
   formula (p. 449)

decay factor (p. 441)
exponential equation (p. 469)
exponential function (p. 438)
growth factor (p. 438)
logarithm (p. 455)

logarithmic equation (p. 471)
logarithmic function (p. 456)
natural logarithmic function (p. 478)

Choose the correct term to complete each sentence.

1. In the exponential function $y = ab^x$, when $b > 1$, b is the __?__.

Go Online
PHSchool.com
For: Vocabulary quiz
Web Code: bbj-0851

2. A __?__ is a logarithm that uses base 10.

3. The line $x = 2$ is a(n) __?__ of the function $f(x) = \frac{2}{x - 2}$.

4. The Change of Base Formula can be used to evaluate a __?__ with any base.

5. An __?__ can be solved by taking the logarithm of each side of the equation.

Skills and Concepts

Lesson 8-1

- To model exponential growth (p. 438)
- To model exponential decay (p. 440)

 ALG2 12.0

The general form of an **exponential function** is $y = ab^x$, where x is a real number, $a \neq 0$, $b > 0$, and $b \neq 1$. When $b > 1$, the function models exponential growth, and b is the **growth factor**. When $0 < b < 1$, the function models exponential decay, and b is the **decay factor**.

Determine whether each equation represents exponential growth or exponential decay. Find the rate of increase or decrease for each model. Graph each equation.

6. $y = 5^x$ **7.** $y = 2(4)^x$ **8.** $y = 0.2(3.8)^x$ **9.** $y = 3(0.25)^x$

Write an exponential equation whose graph passes through the given points.

10. $(1, 5), (2, 7)$ **11.** $(3, 1.5), (4, 15)$ **12.** $\left(-1, 6\frac{3}{4}\right), \left(2, \frac{1}{4}\right)$ **13.** $(-2, 9), (0, 1)$

Write an exponential function to model each situation. Find the value of each function after five years, to the nearest dollar.

14. A $12,500 car depreciates 9% each year.

15. A baseball card bought for $50 increases 3% in value each year.

Write an exponential equation for each graph. Evaluate the equation for $x = 4$.

16.

17.

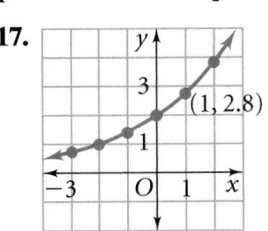

Lesson 8-2

- To identify the role of constants in $y = ab^{cx}$ (p. 447)
- To use e as a base (p. 449)

 ALG2 12.0

Exponential functions can be translated, stretched, shrunk, and reflected. The graph of $y = ab^{x-h} + k$ is the graph of $y = b^x$ stretched by a factor $|a|$, and translated $|h|$ units horizontally and $|k|$ units vertically.

The **continuously compounded interest** formula is $A = Pe^{rt}$, where P is the principal, r is the annual rate, and t is time in years.

Describe how the graph of each function relates to the graph of its parent function. Then graph each function.

18. $y = -3^x + 1$

19. $y = 8^x - 1$

20. $y = 2(2)^{x+1} + 3$

21. $y = -2\left(\frac{1}{3}\right)^{x-2}$

Find the amount in a continuously compounded account for the given conditions.

22. principal: $1000, annual interest rate: 4.8%, time: 2 yr

23. principal: $250, annual interest rate: 6.2%, time: 2.5 yr

24. principal: $500, annual interest rate: 8.5%, time: 3 yr

Evaluate to four decimal places.

25. e^1 **26.** e^{-1} **27.** e^5 **28.** $e^{-\frac{1}{2}}$

29. Physics Radium has a half-life of 1620 years. Write the decay function for a 3-mg sample. Find the amount of radium remaining after 50 years.

Lesson 8-3

- To write and evaluate logarithmic expressions (p. 454)
- To graph logarithmic functions (p. 456)

 ALG2 11.1

If $y = b^x$, then $\log_b y = x$. The **logarithmic function** is the inverse of the exponential function, so the graphs of the functions are reflections of one another over the line $y = x$. Logarithmic functions can be translated, stretched, shrunk, and reflected.

When $b = 10$, the logarithm is called a **common logarithm**, which you can write as $\log y$.

30. Chemistry The pH of a substance equals $-\log[H^+]$, where $[H^+]$ is the concentration of hydrogen ions. A sample of well water has a pH of 5.7. Find the concentration of hydrogen ions in the sample.

31. The concentration of hydrogen ions in water is 10^{-7}. Find the pH of water.

Write each equation in logarithmic form.

32. $6^2 = 36$

33. $2^{-3} = 0.125$

34. $3^3 = 27$

35. $10^{-3} = 0.001$

Evaluate each logarithm.

36. $\log_2 64$ **37.** $\log_3 \frac{1}{9}$ **38.** $\log 0.00001$ **39.** $\log_2 1$

Graph each logarithmic function.

40. $y = \log_3 x$

41. $y = \log(x + 2)$

42. $y = \log_2 2x$

43. $y = \log_5(x + 1)$

Lesson 8-4

- To use the properties of logarithms (p. 462)

 ALG2 14.0, 11.0

For any positive numbers, M, N, and b, $b \neq 1$, each of the following statements is true. Each can be used to rewrite a logarithmic expression.

- $\log_b MN = \log_b M + \log_b N$, by the Product Property
- $\log_b \dfrac{M}{N} = \log_b M - \log_b N$, by the Quotient Property
- $\log_b M^x = x \log_b M$, by the Power Property

Write each logarithmic expression as a single logarithm.

44. $\log 8 + \log 3$

45. $\log_2 5 - \log_2 3$

46. $4 \log_3 x + \log_3 7$

47. $\log z - \log y$

Expand each logarithm. State the properties of logarithms that you use.

48. $\log_4 x^2 y^3$

49. $\log 4s^4 t$

50. $\log_3 \dfrac{2}{x}$

51. $\log (x + 3)^2$

52. Use the formula $L = 10 \log \dfrac{I}{I_0}$. Suppose the sound intensity of a fan must be reduced by one third. By how many decibels would the loudness be decreased?

Lesson 8-5

- To solve exponential equations (p. 469)
- To solve logarithmic equations (p. 470)

 ALG2 13.0, 11.0, 11.1

An equation in the form $b^{cx} = a$, where the exponent includes a variable, is called an **exponential equation**. You can solve exponential equations by taking the logarithm of each side of the equation. An equation that includes a logarithmic expression is called a **logarithmic equation**.

Solve each equation. Round your answers to the nearest hundredth.

53. $4^x = 27$

54. $3^x = 36$

55. $7^{x-3} = 25$

56. $5^x = 9$

Solve by graphing.

57. $5^{2x} = 25$

58. $3^{7x} = 160$

59. $6^{3x+1} = 215$

60. $0.5^x = 0.12$

Solve each logarithmic equation. Leave your answer in exact form.

61. $\log 3x = 1$

62. $\log_2 4x = 5$

63. $\log x = \log 2x^2 - 2$

64. $2 \log_3 x = 54$

65. Convert $\log_2 7$ to a logarithm in base 5.

66. Biology A culture of 10 bacteria is started, and the number of bacteria will double every hour. In about how many hours will there be 3,000,000 bacteria?

Lesson 8-6

- To evaluate natural logarithmic expressions (p. 478)
- To solve equations using natural logarithms (p. 479)

 ALG2 14.0, 15.0, 13.0

The inverse of $y = e^x$ is the **natural logarithmic function** $y = \log_e x = \ln x$. You solve natural logarithm equations in the same way as common logarithm equations.

Solve each equation.

67. $e^{3x} = 12$

68. $\ln x + \ln(x + 1) = 2$

69. $2 \ln x + 3 \ln 2 = 5$

70. $\ln 4 - \ln x = 10$

71. $4e^{(x-1)} = 64$

72. $3 \ln x + \ln 5 = 7$

73. Savings An initial investment of $350 is worth $429.20 after six years of continuous compounding. Find the interest rate.

Evaluate each function to the nearest hundredth for for $x = 0, 1, 2, 3, 4, 5$. Graph each function.

1. $y = 3(0.25)^x$

2. $f(x) = -(6)^x$

3. $y = 0.1(10)^x$

4. $f(x) = 100(2)^x$

5. Open-Ended Give an example of an exponential function that models exponential growth and an example of an exponential function that models exponential decay.

Write an exponential function of the form $y = ab^x$ that has a graph through the given points.

6. $(1, 1), (2, 3)$

7. $\left(-2, \frac{2}{25}\right), (1, 10)$

8. $\left(-3, \frac{1}{16}\right), (-1, 1)$

9. Investment You put $1500 into an account earning 7% annual interest compounded continuously. How long will it be until you have $2000 in your account?

Describe how the graph of each function is related to the graph of its parent function.

10. $y = 3^x + 2$

11. $y = \left(\frac{1}{2}\right)^{x+1}$

12. $y = 5^{x-2} - 1$

13. $y = -(2)^{x+2}$

Evaluate each logarithm.

14. $\log_2 8$

15. $\log_7 7$

16. $\log_5 25$

17. $\log_3 27$

18. $\log_{11} 1$

19. $\log_4 256$

Graph each logarithmic function.

20. $y = \log_9 x$

21. $y = \log_3 (x - 1)$

22. $y = \frac{1}{2} \log_3 (x + 2)$

23. $y = 1 - \log_2 x$

Use the properties of logarithms to rewrite each logarithmic expression.

24. $\log_2 4 + 3 \log_2 9$

25. $3 \log a - 2 \log b$

26. $\log_7 \frac{a}{b}$

27. $\log 3x^3 y^2$

Use the properties of logarithms to evaluate each expression.

28. $\log_3 27 - \log_3 9$

29. $2 \log_2 64 + \log_2 2$

30. $-\log_4 \frac{1}{16} - \log_4 64$

31. $2 \log 5 + \log 40$

 32. Writing Show that solving the equation $3^{2x} = 4$ by taking common logarithms of both sides is equivalent to solving it by taking logarithms to the base 3 of both sides.

Solve each equation.

33. $\left(\frac{3}{4}\right)^x = 81$

34. $3^{x-1} = 24$

35. $\log 4x = 3$

36. $2 \log x = -4$

Use the Change of Base Formula to rewrite each expression using common logarithms.

37. $\log_3 16$

38. $\log_2 10$

39. $\log_7 8$

Use the properties of logarithms to simplify each equation and solve it. Round to thousandths.

40. $\ln 2 + \ln x = 1$

41. $\ln (x + 1) + \ln (x - 1) = 4$

42. $\ln (2x - 1)^2 = 7$

43. $3 \ln x - \ln 2 = 4$

44. Physics Seawater absorbs light. In some instances, this relationship is modeled by $\ln I = \ln I_0 - 0.014d$. I_0 is the intensity of the light at the surface of the water, and I is the intensity at a depth of d cm. At what depth will the intensity of the light in the water be 25% of the surface intensity?

Some problems ask you to find lengths of arcs or areas of sectors.

Tip 1
Draw a diagram.

6 cm   60°

Let $f(x) = \pi r^2$ represent the area of a circle with radius, $r = 6$ cm. Let $g(x) = \frac{60x}{360}$ represent the area of a 60° sector of that circle. What is the area, $(g \circ f)(x)$?

- Ⓐ 6π cm^2
- Ⓑ 12π cm^2
- Ⓒ 24π cm^2
- Ⓓ 36π cm^2

Tip 2
Find $f(x)$ first.

Think It Through

$$f(x) = \pi r^2$$
$$= \pi \cdot 6^2 = 36\pi$$
$$g(x) = \frac{60x}{360} = \frac{60 \cdot 36\pi}{360}$$
$$= \frac{36\pi}{6} = 6\pi$$

The correct answer is A.

Vocabulary Review

As you solve problems, you must understand the meanings of mathematical terms. Match each term with its mathematical meaning.

A. natural logarithmic function

B. asymptote

C. logarithmic function

D. exponential function

I. the inverse of an exponential function

II. a line that a graph approaches as x or y increases in absolute value

III. the inverse of $y = e^x$

IV. an equation of the form $b^{cx} = a$, where the exponent includes a variable

Multiple Choice

Read each question. Then write the letter of the correct answer on your paper.

1. What is the solution to the equation $\log_9 x = \log_6 x$, to the nearest tenth? (Lesson 8-5)

- Ⓐ 0.7
- Ⓒ 27.7
- Ⓑ 1.2
- Ⓓ 54.0

2. Which expression is equivalent to $\log_5 32$? (Lesson 8-5)

- Ⓐ $\log_{10} 5 + \log_{10} 32$
- Ⓑ $\log_{10} 5 - \log_{10} 32$
- Ⓒ $(\log_{10} 5)(\log_{10} 32)$
- Ⓓ $\frac{\log_{10} 32}{\log_{10} 5}$

3. Which equation has a solution of 0.9 when rounded to the nearest tenth? (Lesson 8-5)

- Ⓐ $\log_9 5 = \log_6 x$
- Ⓑ $\log_9 x = \log_6 5$
- Ⓒ $\log_9 x = \log_5 6$
- Ⓓ $\log_x 9 = \log_6 5$

4. Which expression is equivalent to $\frac{\log_{10} 4}{\log_{10} 7}$? (Lesson 8-5)

- Ⓐ $\log_{10} 7 - \log_{10} 4$
- Ⓑ $\log_{10} 7 + \log_{10} 4$
- Ⓒ $\log_7 4$
- Ⓓ $\log_{10} \frac{4}{7}$

5. If $i = \sqrt{-1}$, then which expression is equal to $9i(13i)$? (Lesson 5-6)

- Ⓐ -117
- Ⓒ 117
- Ⓑ $117i$
- Ⓓ $-117i$

Cumulative Practice (continued)

6. What is an equivalent form of $\frac{3}{7 + i}$? (Lesson 5-6)

   Ⓐ $\frac{21 + 3i}{50}$

   Ⓑ $\frac{21 - 3i}{50}$

   Ⓒ $\frac{21 - i}{50}$

   Ⓓ $\frac{21 - 3i}{48}$

7. What is the product of the complex numbers $(4 - i)$ and $(5 + i)$? (Lesson 5-6)

   Ⓐ 9

   Ⓑ 20

   Ⓒ $21 - i$

   Ⓓ $21 + i$

8. What is the solution of the system? $\begin{cases} 5x + 6y = -24 \\ -2x + 3y = 15 \end{cases}$ (Lesson 3-2)

   Ⓐ $(6, -1)$

   Ⓑ $(6, 1)$

   Ⓒ $(-6, 1)$

   Ⓓ $(-6, -1)$

9. Which solution is correct for this system of linear equations? (Lesson 3-1)

   $$2x - 4y = 5$$
   $$6x - 12y = 15$$

   Ⓐ $(0, -3)$

   Ⓑ $(8, 4)$

   Ⓒ There are no solutions because the lines are parallel.

   Ⓓ There are infinitely many solutions because the lines are the same.

10. On a certain night, a restaurant employs x servers at $25 per hour and y bus persons at $8 per hour. The total hourly cost for the restaurant's 12 employees that night is $249. The following system of equations can be used to find the number of servers and the number of bus persons at work.

    $$25x + 8y = 249$$
    $$x + y = 12$$

    Which of the following can you conclude, based on the solution of the system of equations? (Lesson 3-2)

    Ⓐ Fewer than 2 bus persons were working.

    Ⓑ More than 10 servers were working.

    Ⓒ 50% of the people working were bus persons.

    Ⓓ 75% of the people working were servers.

11. If $\log_{10} x = 3$, what is the value of x? (Lesson 8-3)

    Ⓐ 100

    Ⓑ 1,000

    Ⓒ 0.001

    Ⓓ 0.01

12. What is the solution to the equation $4^{2x} = 7$? (Lesson 8-5)

    Ⓐ $x = \frac{\log_{10} 7}{2 \log_{10} 4}$

    Ⓑ $x = \frac{2 \log_{10} 4}{\log_{10} 7}$

    Ⓒ $x = \frac{\log_{10} 7}{\log_{10} 8}$

    Ⓓ $x = \frac{2 \log_{10} 7}{\log_{10} 4}$

13. Which equation is equivalent to $\log_2 8 = y$? (Lesson 8-3)

    Ⓐ $8^y = 2$

    Ⓑ $2^y = 8$

    Ⓒ $8^2 = y$

    Ⓓ $y^8 = 2$

14. A savings account earns 4.62% annual interest, compounded continuously. After approximately how many years will a principal of $500 double? (Lesson 8-2)

    Ⓐ 2 years

    Ⓑ 10 years

    Ⓒ 15 years

    Ⓓ 44 years

15. How is the graph of $y = 4 \cdot \left(\frac{1}{2}\right)^x + 3$ translated from the graph of $y = 4 \cdot \left(\frac{1}{2}\right)^x$? (Lesson 8-2)

    Ⓐ 3 units right

    Ⓑ 3 units left

    Ⓒ 3 units down

    Ⓓ 3 units up

16. Which expression is equal to $\log_7 5 + \log_7 3$? (Lesson 8-4)

    Ⓐ $\log_7 8$

    Ⓑ $\log_7 15$

    Ⓒ $\log_7 125$

    Ⓓ $\log_{49} 15$

17. What is the value of $\log_4 256$? **(Lesson 8-3)**

Ⓐ 4

Ⓑ 8

Ⓒ 64

Ⓓ 252

18. If $\log 3 \approx 0.477$ and $\log 4 \approx 0.602$, what is the approximate value of $\log 144$? **(Lesson 8-4)**

Ⓐ 0.287

Ⓑ 1.079

Ⓒ 1.149

Ⓓ 2.158

19. If $\log 16 \approx 1.204$ and $\log 2 \approx 0.301$, what is the approximate value of $\log 8$? **(Lesson 8-4)**

Ⓐ 0.027

Ⓑ 0.602

Ⓒ 0.903

Ⓓ 4

20. If $f(x) = 2x - 3$ and $g(x) = -x^2 - 1$. Find $(g \circ f)(x)$. **(Lesson 7-6)**

Ⓐ $-2x^3 + 3x^2 - 2x + 3$

Ⓑ $-4x^2 + 12x - 10$

Ⓒ $-x^2 + 2x - 4$

Ⓓ $-x^2 - 2x + 2$

21. If $f(x) = 3 - x$ and $g(x) = -x^2 - 3$, which expression has the greatest value? **(Lesson 7-6)**

Ⓐ $(g \circ f)(-3)$

Ⓑ $(f \circ g)(-3)$

Ⓒ $(g \cdot f)(-3)$

Ⓓ $(g - f)(-3)$

22. What is the solution to $4(x + 3)^{\frac{5}{4}} = 128$? **(Lesson 7-5)**

Ⓐ $x = 12$

Ⓑ $x = 13$

Ⓒ $x = 16$

Ⓓ $x = 73$

23. Which point is a solution of the following system? **(Lesson 3-3)**

$$\begin{cases} y \le 3x - 2 \\ y < 2x \\ x \ge -1 \\ y \ge -4 \end{cases}$$

Ⓐ $(0, 7)$

Ⓑ $(-4, 1)$

Ⓒ $(3, 1)$

Ⓓ $(-1, -5)$

Standards Reference Guide

California Content Standard	Item Number(s)
ALG2 13.0	1–4
ALG2 6.0	5–7
ALG2 2.0	8–10, 23
ALG2 11.1	11–13
ALG2 12.0	14–15, 22
ALG2 14.0	16–19
ALG2 25.0	20–21

For additional review and practice, see the *California Standards Review and Practice Workbook* or go online to use the

California Standards Tutorials

Visit: PHSchool.com, **Web Code:** bbq-9045

What You've Learned

California Content Standards

4.0 Students factor polynomials representing the difference of squares, perfect square trinomials, and the sum and difference of two cubes.

12.0 Students know the laws of fractional exponents, understand exponential functions, and use these functions in problems involving exponential growth and decay.

25.0 Students use properties from number systems to justify steps in combining and simplifying functions.

✓ **Check Your Readiness**

 for Help to the Lesson in green.

Finding Theoretical Probabilities (Lesson 1-6)

A bookshelf contains 18 math books, 27 science books, 21 history books, and 15 grammar books. You pick one book at random from the shelf. Find each theoretical probability.

1. $P(\text{history})$ **2.** $P(\text{science})$ **3.** $P(\text{math or science})$

4. $P(\text{math or science or history})$ **5.** $P(\text{not grammar})$ **6.** $P(\text{not math and not science})$

Using Direct Variation (Lesson 2-3)

For each direct variation, find the constant of variation. Then find the value of y when $x = -3$.

7. $y = 4$ when $x = 3$ **8.** $y = 1$ when $x = -1.5$

9. $y = -5$ when $x = \frac{3}{2}$ **10.** $y = -16$ when $x = 7$

Factoring Quadratic Expressions (Lesson 5-4)

Factor each expression.

11. $x^2 + x - 6$ **12.** $4x^2 + 17x + 15$ **13.** $9x^2 - 25$

14. $x^2 - 12x + 36$ **15.** $3x^2 + 10x + 8$ **16.** $x^2 - 5x + 6$

Solving Quadratic Equations (Lesson 5-5)

Solve each equation.

17. $x^2 + 7x - 8 = 0$ **18.** $\frac{1}{4}x^2 + \frac{7}{2}x = -12$ **19.** $3x^2 = 18x - 24$

20. $9x^2 + 6x = 0$ **21.** $4x^2 + 16 = 34x$ **22.** $x^2 - 13x - 30 = 0$

What You'll Learn Next

▲ In Lesson 9-5, you will use rational expressions to determine the focal length of a camera lens.

California Content Standards

7.0 Students add, subtract, multiply, divide, reduce, and evaluate rational expressions with monomial and polynomial denominators and simplify complicated rational expressions.

6.0 Students find the roots and poles of a rational function and can graph the function and locate its asymptotes. *Mathematical Analysis*

1.0 Students know the definition of the notion of *independent events* and can use the rules of addition, multiplication and complementation to solve for probabilities. *Probability and Statistics*

New Vocabulary

🔊 **English and Spanish Audio Online**

- **branch** (p. 503)
- **complex fraction** (p. 524)
- **dependent events** (p. 539)
- **independent events** (p. 539)
- **inverse variation** (p. 496)
- **joint variation** (p. 498)
- **mutually exclusive events** (p. 541)
- **point of discontinuity** (p. 509)
- **rational function** (p. 509)
- **reciprocal function** (p. 503)
- **simplest form** (p. 517)

Inverse Variation

What You'll Learn

• To use inverse variation

• To use joint and other variations

. . . And Why

To find the life spans of mammals, as in Example 3

✓ **Check Skills You'll Need**

GO▶ for Help Lesson 2-3

In Exercises 1–3, y varies directly with x.

1. Given that $x = 2$ when $y = 4$, find y when $x = 5$.

2. Given that $x = 1$ when $y = 5$, find y when $x = 3$.

3. Given that $x = 10$ when $y = 3$, find y when $x = 4$.

◀)) **New Vocabulary**   • inverse variation   • joint variation

---

1 Using Inverse Variation

In Chapter 2, you studied direct variation. You can model a direct variation with an equation of the form $y = kx$, where $k \neq 0$. You can model an **inverse variation** with any of the equations $xy = k$, $y = \frac{k}{x}$, or $x = \frac{k}{y}$, where $k \neq 0$. As with direct variation, k is the constant of variation.

The table and graph below show the times needed to ride a bike 24 miles at different rates.

Rate (mi/h)	Time (h)
3	8
6	4
12	2
24	1

Notice that as the rate increases, the time decreases. Doubling the rate halves the time. The inverse variation $rt = 24$, or $t = \frac{24}{r}$, models this situation.

1 EXAMPLE Modeling Inverse Variation

Suppose that x and y vary inversely, and $x = 3$ when $y = -5$. Write the function that models the inverse variation.

$y = \frac{k}{x}$ **x and y vary inversely.**

$-5 = \frac{k}{3}$ **Substitute the given values of x and y.**

$-15 = k$ **Find k.**

$y = \frac{-15}{x}$ **Use the value of k to write the function.**

Vocabulary Tip

You can describe an <u>inverse</u> variation as "y varies inversely as x" or as "y is inversely proportional to x."

CA Standards Check **1** Suppose that x and y vary inversely, and $x = 0.3$ when $y = 1.4$. Write the function that models the inverse variation.

2 EXAMPLE Identifying Direct and Inverse Variations

For: Variation Activity
Use: Interactive Textbook, 9-1

Is the relationship between the variables in each table a direct variation, an inverse variation, or neither? Write functions to model the direct and inverse variations.

a.

x	0.5	2	6
y	1.5	6	18

As x increases, y increases. Since each y-value is 3 times the corresponding x-value, y varies directly with x, the constant of variation is 3, and the function is $y = 3x$.

b.

x	0.2	0.6	1.2
y	12	4	2

As x increases, y decreases. The product of each pair of x- and y-values is 2.4. y varies inversely with x and the constant of variation is 2.4. So $xy = 2.4$ and the function is $y = \frac{2.4}{x}$.

c.

x	1	2	3
y	2	1	0.5

As x increases, y decreases, but this is not an inverse variation. Not all the products of x and y are the same ($2 \cdot 1 \neq 3 \cdot 0.5$). This is neither a direct variation nor an inverse variation.

CA Standards Check **2** Is the relationship between the values in each table a direct variation, an inverse variation, or neither? Write functions to model the direct and inverse variations.

a.

x	0.8	0.6	0.4
y	0.9	1.2	1.8

b.

x	2	4	6
y	3.2	1.6	1.1

c.

x	1.2	1.4	1.6
y	18	21	24

3 EXAMPLE Real-World Connection

Real-World Connection

Horses have a life span of about 30 years.

Zoology Heart rates and life spans of most mammals are inversely related. Use the data to write a function that models this inverse variation. Use your function to estimate the average life span of a cat with a heart rate of 126 beats/min.

Heart Rate and Life Span

Mammal	Heart rate (beats/min)	Life span (min)
Mouse	634	1,576,800
Rabbit	158	6,307,200
Lion	76	13,140,000
Horse	63	15,768,000

SOURCE: *The Handy Science Answer Book*

Relate heart rate · life span = a constant

Define Let r = heart rate (beats/min).

Let s = life span (min).

Let k = constant of variation (beats in a life span).

Write r s = k

For each of the four mammals in the table, $rs \approx 1,000,000,000$.

$rs = 1,000,000,000$ **Substitute 1,000,000,000 for k.**

$126s = 1,000,000,000$ **Substitute 126 for r.**

$s \approx 8,000,000$

A cat's life span is about 8 million minutes, or about 15.2 years.

CA Standards Check **3** **a.** A squirrel's heart rate is 190 beats per minute. Estimate its life span.
b. An elephant's life span is about 70 years. Estimate its average heart rate.

Quantities can vary with respect to each other in different ways. For example, y can vary directly with x^3 ($y = kx^3$) or inversely with x^2 ($y = \frac{k}{x^2}$).

It is possible for three or more variables to be related. When one quantity varies with respect to two or more other quantities, the result is a combined variation. For example, a variable z can vary directly with both x and y. You can model such a **joint variation** with the equation $z = kxy$, where $k \neq 0$.

Vocabulary Tip

z varies jointly with x and y means z varies directly with the product of x and y.

Examples of Combined Variations

Combined Variation	Equation Form
z varies jointly with x and y.	$z = kxy$
z varies jointly with x and y and inversely with w.	$z = \frac{kxy}{w}$
z varies directly with x and inversely with the product wy.	$z = \frac{kx}{wy}$

Test-Taking Tip

Use dimensional analysis to check that a formula makes sense. For example, in.$^2 \cdot$ in. = in.^{3} suggests that $V = Bh$ is correct.

4 **EXAMPLE** **Real-World Connection**

Physics Newton's Law of Universal Gravitation is modeled by the formula $F = \frac{Gm_1m_2}{d^2}$. F is the gravitational force between two objects with masses m_1 and m_2, and d is the distance between the objects. G is the gravitational constant. Describe Newton's law as a combined variation.

$F = \dfrac{Gm_1m_2}{d^2}$ ← F varies jointly with the masses m_1 and m_2, and
                ← F varies inversely with the square of the distance d.

 CA Standards Check **4** **Geometry** The formula for the area of a trapezoid is $A = \frac{1}{2}h(b_1 + b_2)$. Describe this relationship as a combined variation.

5 **EXAMPLE** **Finding a Formula**

Multiple Choice The volume V of a tetrahedron varies jointly with its altitude h and base area B. A tetrahedron with a 5-cm altitude and 6-in.^{2} base has volume of 10 cm^3. Which formula models this joint variation?

   Ⓐ $V = 3Bh$ Ⓑ $V = \frac{1}{3}Bh$ Ⓒ $h = \frac{1}{12}VB$ Ⓓ $Vh = 5B$

$V = kBh$ **V varies jointly with B and h.**

$10 = k(6)(5)$ **Substitute given values for V, B, and h.**

$\frac{1}{3} = k$ **Solve for k.**

$V = \frac{1}{3}Bh$ **Substitute the value for k.**

  The correct choice is B.

 CA Standards Check **5** The volume of a square pyramid with congruent edges varies directly as the cube of the length of an edge. The volume of a square pyramid with edge length 4 is $\frac{32\sqrt{2}}{3}$. Find the formula for the volume of a square pyramid with congruent edges.

For more exercises, see *Extra Skill and Word Problem Practice*.

A Practice by Example

Example 1
(page 496)

GO for Help

Suppose that x and y vary inversely. Write a function that models each inverse variation.

1. $x = 1$ when $y = 11$ **2.** $x = -13$ when $y = 100$ **3.** $x = 1$ when $y = 1$

4. $x = 28$ when $y = -2$ **5.** $x = 1.2$ when $y = 3$ **6.** $x = 2.5$ when $y = 100$

Example 2
(page 497)

Is the relationship between the values in each table a direct variation, an inverse variation, or neither? Write equations to model the direct and inverse variations.

7.

x	3	8	10	22
y	15	40	50	110

8.

x	3	5	7	10.5
y	14	8.4	6	4

9.

x	0.5	2.1	3.5	11
y	1	4.2	7	22

10.

x	0.1	3	6	24
y	3	0.1	0.05	0.0125

11.

x	7	3	1	$\frac{1}{5}$
y	$\frac{1}{7}$	$\frac{1}{3}$	1	5

12.

x	10	12	20	23
y	2	$2\frac{2}{5}$	4	$5\frac{3}{5}$

Example 3
(page 497)

Suppose that x and y vary inversely. Write a function that models each inverse variation and find y when $x = 10$.

13. $x = 20$ when $y = 5$ **14.** $x = 20$ when $y = -4$ **15.** $x = 5$ when $y = -\frac{1}{3}$

Example 4
(page 498)

Describe the combined variation that is modeled by each formula.

16. $A = \pi r^2$ **17.** $A = 0.5bh$ **18.** $h = \frac{2A}{b}$ **19.** $V = \frac{Bh}{3}$

20. $V = \pi r^2 h$ **21.** $h = \frac{V}{\pi r^2}$ **22.** $V = \ell w h$ **23.** $\ell = \frac{V}{wh}$

Example 5
(page 498)

Write the function that models each variation. Find z when $x = 4$ and $y = 9$.

24. z varies directly with x and inversely with y. When $x = 6$ and $y = 2$, $z = 15$.

25. z varies jointly with x and y. When $x = 2$ and $y = 3$, $z = 60$.

26. z varies directly with the square of x and inversely with y. When $x = 2$ and $y = 4$, $z = 3$.

27. z varies inversely with the product of x and y. When $x = 2$ and $y = 4$, $z = 0.5$.

B Apply Your Skills

28. a. The spreadsheet shows data that could be modeled by an equation of the form $PV = k$. Estimate the value of k.
     b. Estimate P when $V = 62$.

Each ordered pair is from an inverse variation. Find the constant of variation.

29. $(6, 3)$ **30.** $(0.9, 4)$ **31.** $\left(\frac{3}{8}, \frac{2}{3}\right)$

32. $\left(\sqrt{2}, \sqrt{18}\right)$ **33.** $\left(\sqrt{3}, \sqrt{27}\right)$ **34.** $\left(\sqrt{8}, \sqrt{32}\right)$

	A	B	
1	P	V	
2	140.00	100	
3	147.30	95	
4	155.60	90	
5	164.70	85	
6	175.00	80	
7	186.70	75	

Visit: PHSchool.com
Web Code: bbe-0901

35. Mechanics Gear A drives Gear B. Gear A has
a teeth and speed r_A in revolutions per minute
(rpm). Gear B has *b* teeth and speed r_B. The
quantities are related by the formula $ar_A = br_B$.
Gear A has 60 teeth and speed 5400 rpm.
Gear B has 45 teeth. Find the speed of Gear B.

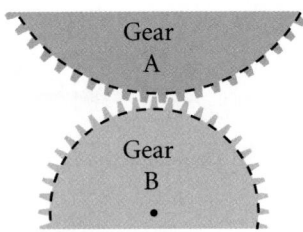

36. Physics The force *F* of gravity on a rocket varies
directly with its mass *m* and inversely with the square of its distance
d from Earth. Write a model for this combined variation.

Each pair of values is from a direct variation. Find the missing value.

37. $(3, 7), (8, y)$ **38.** $(2, 5), (4, y)$ **39.** $(4, 6), (x, 3)$

40. $(9, 5), (x, 3)$ **41.** $(8.3, 7.1), (5, y)$ **42.** $(2.6, 4.5), (x, 6.3)$

Each pair of values is from an inverse variation. Find the missing value.

43. $(3, 7), (8, y)$ **44.** $(2, 5), (4, y)$ **45.** $(4, 6), (x, 3)$

46. $(9, 5), (x, 3)$ **47.** $(8.3, 7.1), (5, y)$ **48.** $(2.6, 4.5), (x, 6.3)$

49. Suppose that *y* varies inversely with the square of *x*, and $y = 50$ when $x = 4$.
Find *y* when $x = 5$.

50. Suppose that *c* varies jointly with *d* and the square of *g*, and $c = 30$ when
$d = 15$ and $g = 2$. Find *d* when $c = 6$ and $g = 8$.

51. Suppose that *d* varies jointly with *r* and *t*, and $d = 110$ when $r = 55$ and $t = 2$.
Find *r* when $d = 40$ and $t = 3$.

52. Construction A concrete supplier sells premixed concrete in 300-ft³ truckloads.
The area *A* that the concrete will cover is inversely proportional to the depth *d*
of the concrete.
  a. Write a model for the relationship between the area and the depth of a
truckload of poured concrete.
  b. What area will the concrete cover if it is poured to a depth of 0.5 ft? A depth
of 1 ft? A depth of 1.5 ft?
  c. When the concrete is poured into a circular area, the depth of the concrete is
inversely proportional to the square of the radius *r*. Write a model for this
relationship.

Exercise 52

53. Suppose that *y* varies directly with *x* and inversely with z^2, and $x = 48$
when $y = 8$ and $z = 3$. Find *x* when $y = 12$ and $z = 2$.

54. Suppose that *t* varies directly with *s* and inversely with the square of *r*. How is
the value of *t* changed when the value of *s* is doubled? Is tripled?

55. Suppose that *x* varies directly with the square of *y* and inversely with *z*. How is
the value of *x* changed if the value of *y* is halved? Is quartered?

 Challenge   **56. Writing** Explain why 0 cannot be in the domain of an inverse variation.

57. Critical Thinking Suppose that (x_1, y_1) and (x_2, y_2) are values from an inverse
variation. Show that $\frac{x_1}{x_2} = \frac{y_2}{y_1}$.

58. Open-Ended The height *h* of a cylinder varies directly with its volume *V* and
inversely with the square of its radius *r*. Find at least four ways to change the
volume and radius of a cylinder so that its height is quadrupled.

59. Health Health care professionals use the body mass index (BMI) to establish guidelines for determining any possible risks of their patients and for planning any useful preventative programs. The BMI varies directly with weight and inversely with the square of height. Use this portion of the BMI chart to determine the BMI formula.

Weights and Body Mass Index (BMI)

Height	Range of Weight (pounds)			
	BMI 19–24.9	BMI 25–29.9	BMI 30–39.9	BMI ≥ 40
5'6"	118–154	155–185	186–246	≥247
5'7"	121–158	159–190	191–254	≥255
5'8"	125–163	164–196	197–261	≥262
5'9"	128–168	169–202	203–269	≥270
5'10"	132–173	174–208	209–277	≥278
5'11"	136–178	179–214	215–285	≥286
6'0"	140–183	184–220	221–293	≥294

Multiple Choice Practice

For California Standards and CAHSEE Tutorials, visit PHSchool.com. Web Code: bbq-9045

ALG2 10.0

60. Which equation is represented by the parabola shown at the right?

- Ⓐ $y = -\frac{3}{4}(x + 3)^2 - 5$
- Ⓑ $y = -\frac{3}{4}(x - 3)^2 + 5$
- Ⓒ $y = \frac{3}{4}(x + 3)^2 + 5$
- Ⓓ $y = \frac{3}{4}(x - 3)^2 - 5$

(3, 5)

(1, 2)

ALG2 8.0

61. Laura found that one root of the quadratic equation $0 = x^2 - 8x - 84$ is -6. What is the other root of the equation?

- Ⓐ -14
- Ⓑ -2
- Ⓒ 2
- Ⓓ 14

Mixed Review

Lesson 8-6

Solve each equation.

62. $\ln 4 + \ln x = 5$　　　**63.** $\ln x - \ln 3 = 4$　　　**64.** $2\ln x + 3\ln 4 = 4$

Lesson 7-2

Multiply and simplify. Assume that all variables are positive.

65. $-5\sqrt{6x} \cdot 3\sqrt{6x^2}$　　　**66.** $3\sqrt[3]{4x^2} \cdot 7\sqrt[3]{12x^4}$　　　**67.** $\sqrt{5x^3} \cdot \sqrt{40xy^7}$

Lesson 7-1

Simplify each radical expression. Use absolute value bars where they are needed.

68. $\sqrt{x^{10}y^{100}}$　　　**69.** $\sqrt[3]{-64a^3b^6}$　　　**70.** $\sqrt[4]{64m^8n^4}$　　　**71.** $\sqrt[4]{x^4}$

Graphing Rational Functions

You can use your graphing calculator to graph members of the reciprocal function family and other rational functions. It is sometimes preferable to use the Dot plotting mode rather than the Connected plotting mode. The Connected mode can join branches of a graph that should be separated. Try both modes to get the best graph.

EXAMPLE

Graph $y = \dfrac{4}{x - 3} - 1.5$.

Step 1 Press the MODE key. Scroll down to highlight the word Dot. Then press ENTER.

Step 2 Enter the function. Use parentheses to enter the denominator accurately.

Step 3 Graph the function.

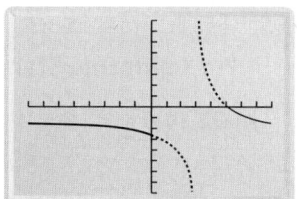

EXERCISES

1. a. Graph the parent reciprocal function $y = \frac{1}{x}$. Sketch the graph on paper.
   b. Examine both negative and positive values of x. Describe what happens to the y-values as x approaches zero.
   c. What happens to the y-values as x increases? As x decreases?

2. a. Change the mode on your graphing calculator to **Connected**. Graph the function from the example. Sketch the graph.
   b. Press the TRACE key and trace the function. What happens between $x \approx 2.9$ and $x \approx 3.2$?
   c. **Critical Thinking** How does your graph differ from the graph in the example? Explain the differences.

Use a graphing calculator to graph each function. Then sketch the graph.

3. $y = \dfrac{7}{x}$

4. $y = \dfrac{3}{x + 4} - 2$

5. $y = \dfrac{x + 2}{(x + 1)(x + 3)}$

6. $y = \dfrac{4x + 1}{x - 3}$

7. $y = \dfrac{2}{x - 2}$

8. $y = \dfrac{1}{x + 2} + 3$

9. $y = \dfrac{2x}{x + 3}$

10. $y = \dfrac{x^2}{x^2 - 5}$

11. $y = \dfrac{20}{x^2 + 5}$

12. $y = \dfrac{1}{x - 3} - 6$

13. $y = \dfrac{10}{x^2 - 5x - 10}$

14. $y = \dfrac{x}{x^2 - 1}$

9-2

The Reciprocal Function Family

 California Content Standards

MA 6.0 Students find the roots and poles of a rational function and can graph the function and locate its asymptotes.

What You'll Learn

- To graph reciprocal functions
- To graph translations of reciprocal functions

. . . And Why

To analyze musical pitch and the size of the instrument, as in Example 3

✓ **Check Skills You'll Need**

GO for Help Lesson 2-6

Each of the following equations is a translation of $y = |x|$. Describe each translation.

1. $y = |x| + 2$ **2.** $y = |x + 2|$

3. $y = |x| - 3$ **4.** $y = |x - 3|$

5. $y = |x + 4| - 5$ **6.** $y = |x - 10| + 7$

🔊 **New Vocabulary** • reciprocal function • branch

1   Graphing Reciprocal Functions

Functions that model inverse variations belong to a family whose parent is the **reciprocal function** $f(x) = \frac{1}{x}$, where $x \neq 0$. The general form of a family member is $y = \frac{a}{x - h} + k$, with a single real number h missing from its domain.

The inverse variations $y = \frac{a}{x}$ are the stretches and shrinks of the parent reciprocal function.

1 EXAMPLE   Graphing an Inverse Variation

Sketch a graph of $y = \frac{6}{x}, x \neq 0$.

Make a table of values that includes positive and negative values of x.

x	-12	-6	-3	-2	-1	$-\frac{1}{2}$	$\frac{1}{2}$	1	2	3	6	12
y	$-\frac{1}{2}$	-1	-2	-3	-6	-12	12	6	3	2	1	$\frac{1}{2}$

Vocabulary Tip

In a graph, a <u>branch</u> is a distinct part of a curve, just as, in nature, a branch is a distinct part of a river.

Graph the points. Connect them with a smooth curve to the left of where $x = 0$ and another smooth curve to the right of where $x = 0$. Each part of the graph is called a **branch.**

The x-axis is a horizontal asymptote.

The y-axis is a vertical asymptote.

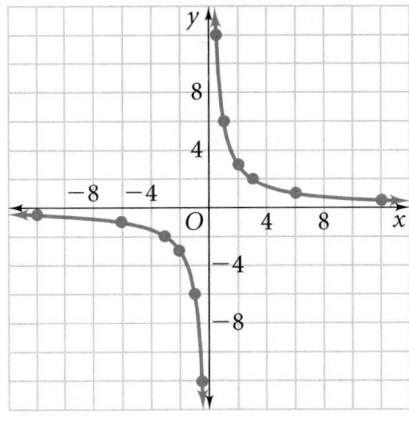

✓ **CA Standards Check** ① Sketch a graph of $y = \frac{16}{x}$.

Quadrant II	Quadrant I
Quadrant III	Quadrant IV

The branches of $y = \frac{1}{x}$ are in Quadrants I and III. Stretches of the parent function have the form $y = \frac{a}{x}$, where $a > 0$, and remain in Quadrants I and III. Their reflections, $y = \frac{-a}{x}$, are in Quadrants II and IV.

2 EXAMPLE Graphing Reciprocal Functions

Draw the graph of $f(x) = \frac{-4}{x}$. Describe properties of the graph.

The graph of $y = \frac{4}{x}$ is a stretch of $y = \frac{1}{x}$ by a factor of 4.

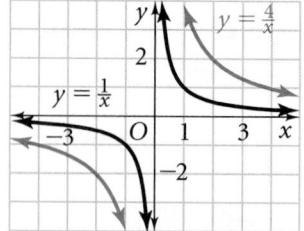

The graph of $y = \frac{-4}{x}$ is a reflection of $y = \frac{4}{x}$ in the x-axis.

The axes are asymptotes for each graph. Each graph is symmetric with respect to $y = x$ and $y = -x$.

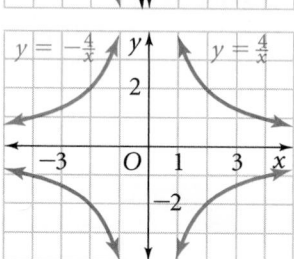

☑ **CA Standards Check** ② Use a graphing calculator. Set Xmin = −3, Xmax = 3, Ymin = −2, and Ymax = 2. Draw and compare the graphs of $y = \frac{1}{x}$, $y = \frac{2}{x}$, $y = \frac{-2}{x}$, $y = \frac{0.5}{x}$, and $y = \frac{-0.5}{x}$.

A situation in which an increase in one quantity is related to a proportional decrease in another quantity suggests inverse variation.

3 EXAMPLE Real-World 🌐 Connection

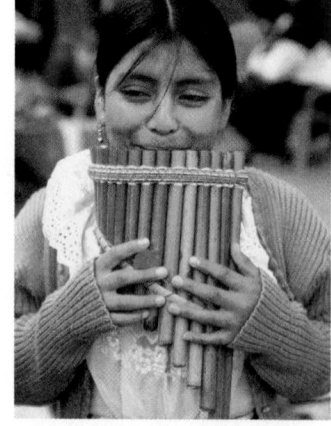

Real-World 🌐 Connection

The length, not the diameter, of a panpipe or organ pipe determines its pitch.

Music A musical pitch is determined by the frequency of vibration of the sound waves reaching the ear. The greater the frequency, the higher is the pitch. Frequency is measured in vibrations per second, or hertz (Hz).

The pitch y produced by a panpipe varies inversely with the length x of the pipe. The function $y = \frac{564}{x}$ models the inverse variation where x is the length in feet. Find the length of the pipe that produces a pitch of 277 Hz.

Graph the functions $y = \frac{564}{x}$ and $y = 277$. Use the **Intersect** feature.

Xmin=0	Ymin=−75
Xmax=40	Ymax=300
Xscl=5	Yscl=50

Intersection
X=2.0361011 Y=277

The pipe should be about 2.0 ft long.

☑ **CA Standards Check** ③ **a.** Pitches of 247 Hz, 311 Hz, and 370 Hz form a musical chord. Find the length of pipe that will produce each pitch.

b. Writing The asymptotes of $y = \frac{564}{x}$ are $x = 0$ and $y = 0$. Explain why this makes sense in terms of the panpipe.

The graphs at the right show the parent function $y = \frac{1}{x}$ and two of its translations, $y = \frac{1}{x-1}$ and $y = \frac{1}{x+2}$.

The vertical asymptotes of the graphs are $x = 0$, $x = 1$, and $x = -2$.

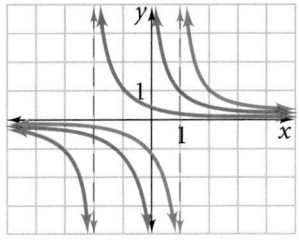

The graphs at the right show the parent function $y = \frac{1}{x}$ and two of its translations, $y = \frac{1}{x} + 1$ and $y = \frac{1}{x} - 2$.

The horizontal asymptotes of the graphs are $y = 0$, $y = 1$, and $y = -2$.

Key Concepts

Summary	The Reciprocal Function Family
Parent function:	$y = \frac{1}{x}, x \neq 0$
Stretch $(\lvert a \rvert > 1)$ Shrink $(0 < \lvert a \rvert < 1)$ Reflection $(a < 0)$ in x-axis	$y = \frac{a}{x}$
Translation (horizontal by h; vertical by k) with vertical asymptote $x = h$, horizontal asymptote $y = k$:	$y = \frac{1}{x-h} + k$
Combined:	$y = \frac{a}{x-h} + k$

You can use asymptotes to graph translations of the parent function.

For: Translation Activity
Use: Interactive Textbook, 9-2

4 EXAMPLE   Graphing a Translation

Sketch the graph of $y = \frac{1}{x-2} - 3$.

Step 1   Draw the asymptotes.
For $y = \frac{1}{x-2} + (-3)$,
$h = 2$ and $k = -3$.
The vertical asymptote is $x = 2$.
The horizontal asymptote is $y = -3$.

Step 2   Translate $y = \frac{1}{x}$.
The graph of $y = \frac{1}{x}$ includes $(1, 1)$ and $(-1, -1)$. Translate these points 2 units to the right and 3 units down to $(3, -2)$ and $(1, -4)$. Draw the branches through these points.

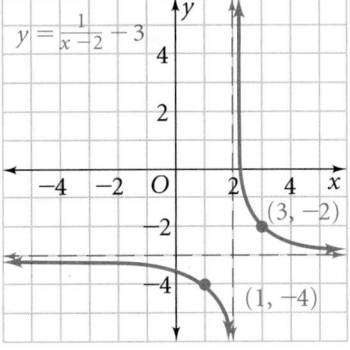

✓ **CA Standards Check**   ④ Find the asymptotes and sketch the graph of $y = -\frac{1}{x+7} - 3$.

If you know the translations or asymptotes of a stretch or shrink, $y = \frac{a}{x}$, then you can write its equation.

5 EXAMPLE **Writing the Equation of a Transformation**

Write an equation for the translation of $y = \frac{5}{x}$ that has asymptotes at $x = -2$ and $y = 3$.

$y = \dfrac{5}{x - h} + k$ Use the general form of a translation.

  $= \dfrac{5}{x - (-2)} + 3$ Substitute −2 for h and 3 for k.

  $= \dfrac{5}{x + 2} + 3$ Simplify.

An equation for the translation is $y = \frac{5}{x + 2} + 3$.

✔ **CA Standards Check** **5 a.** Write an equation for the translation of $y = -\frac{1}{x}$ that is 4 units left and 5 units up.
b. Check your work by graphing your solution to part (a).

EXERCISES

For more exercises, see *Extra Skill and Word Problem Practice*.

Standards Practice

MA 6.0

A Practice by Example

GO for Help

Example 1
(page 503)

Make a table of values. Then sketch a graph of each inverse variation.

1. $y = \frac{2}{x}$ **2.** $y = \frac{10}{x}$ **3.** $y = -\frac{10}{x}$

Example 2
(page 504)

Draw a graph of each function. Describe properties of the graph.

4. $y = \frac{0.2}{x}$ **5.** $y = \frac{-3}{x}$ **6.** $y = \frac{8}{x}$

7. $y = \frac{-5}{x}$ **8.** $y = \frac{100}{x}$ **9.** $y = \frac{-0.1}{x}$

Example 3
(page 504)

The weight P in pounds that a beam can safely carry is inversely proportional to the distance D in feet between the supports of the beam. For a certain type of wooden beam, $P = \frac{9200}{D}$. Use a graphing calculator and the Intersect feature to find the distance between supports that is needed to carry each given weight.

10. 500 lb   **11.** 1200 lb   **12.** 2400 lb   **13.** 5000 lb

Example 4
(page 505)

Sketch the asymptotes and the graph of each equation.

14. $y = \frac{1}{x} - 3$ **15.** $y = \frac{-2}{x} - 3$ **16.** $y = \frac{1}{x - 2} + 5$ **17.** $y = \frac{1}{x - 3} + 4$

18. $y = \frac{2}{x + 6} - 1$ **19.** $y = \frac{-10}{x + 1} - 8$ **20.** $y = \frac{1}{x} + 2$ **21.** $y = \frac{-8}{x + 5} - 6$

Example 5
(page 506)

Write an equation for the translation of $y = \frac{2}{x}$ that has the given asymptotes.

22. $x = 0$ and $y = 4$ **23.** $x = -2$ and $y = 3$ **24.** $x = 4$ and $y = -8$

B Apply Your Skills

25. Budgeting A high school spends $750 each year on student academic achievement awards. The amount spent per award depends on how many awards are given. Write and graph a function that models the relationship between the number a of awards given and the cost c of each award. What are a reasonable domain and range for the function?

26. Open-Ended Write an equation for a horizontal translation of $y = \frac{2}{x}$. Then write an equation for a vertical translation of $y = \frac{2}{x}$. Identify the horizontal and vertical asymptotes of the graph of each function.

Write each equation in the form $y = \frac{k}{x}$.

27. $y = \frac{1}{2x}$

28. $y = \frac{3}{4x}$

29. $y = -\frac{25}{3x}$

30. $xy = -0.01$

31. $3xy = 12$

32. $-7 = 5xy$

Sketch the graph of each function.

33. $xy = 3$

34. $xy + 5 = 0$

35. $3xy = 1$

36. $5xy = 2$

37. $10xy = -4$

38. $3xy = -17$

 39. Writing Explain how knowing the asymptotes of a translation of $y = \frac{k}{x}$ can help you graph the function. Include an example.

40. Multiple Choice The formula $p = \frac{69.1}{a + 2.3}$ models the relation between atmospheric pressure p in inches of mercury and altitude a in miles.

Use the data in the photo at the right. At which location does the model predict the pressure to be about 23.93 in. of mercury?

Sahara Desert
average alt. 1500 ft

Kalahari Desert
average alt. 3100 ft

Mt. Kilimanjaro
alt. 19,340 ft

Vinson Massif
alt. 16,860 ft

Ⓐ Sahara Desert

Ⓑ Kalahari Desert

Ⓒ Mt. Kilimanjaro

Ⓓ Vinson Massif

Problem Solving Hint

1 mi = 5280 ft

 Graph each pair of functions. Find the approximate point(s) of intersection.

41. $y = \frac{6}{x - 2}, y = 6$

42. $y = -\frac{1}{x - 3} - 6, y = 6.2$

43. $y = \frac{3}{x + 1}, y = -4$

44. $y = -\frac{2}{x^2}, y = -10$

45. $y = -\frac{1}{x - 4}, y = 4.2$

46. $y = \frac{4}{x^2} + 2, y = 9$

47. a. Gasoline Mileage Suppose you drive an average of 10,000 miles each year. Your gasoline mileage (mi/gal) varies inversely with the number of gallons of gasoline you use each year. Write and graph a model for your average mileage m in terms of the gallons g of gasoline used.

b. After you begin driving on the highway more often, you use 50 gal less per year. Write and graph a new model to include this information.

c. Calculate your old and new mileage assuming that you originally used 400 gal of gasoline per year.

Homework Video Tutor

Visit: PHSchool.com
Web Code: bbe-0902

Ⓒ **Challenge**

Critical Thinking Compare each pair of graphs and find any points of intersection.

 48. $y = \frac{1}{x}$ and $y = \left| \frac{1}{x} \right|$

49. $y = \frac{1}{x}$ and $y = \frac{1}{x^2}$

50. $y = \left| \frac{1}{x} \right|$ and $y = \frac{1}{x^2}$

51. Find two reciprocal functions such that the minimum distance from the origin to the graph of each function is $4\sqrt{2}$.

52. Write each equation in the form $y = \dfrac{k}{x - b} + c$, and sketch the graph.

   a. $y = \dfrac{2}{3x - 6}$ **b.** $y = \dfrac{1}{2 - 4x}$ **c.** $y = \dfrac{3 - x}{x + 2}$

   d. $y = \dfrac{2x + 1}{2x - 1}$ **e.** $xy + 2x = 1$ **f.** $xy - y = 1$

Multiple Choice Practice

For California Standards and CAHSEE Tutorials, visit PHSchool.com. Web Code: bbq-9045

ALG2 2.0

53. The graph at the right shows two boundaries of a city park. Which pair of inequalities represents these boundaries?

   Ⓐ $y > 2x - 3$ and $y > -x - 4$

   Ⓑ $y \le 2x - 3$ and $y \le -x - 4$

   Ⓒ $y \ge 2x - 3$ and $y \ge -x - 4$

   Ⓓ $y \ge -2x - 3$ and $y \ge x - 4$

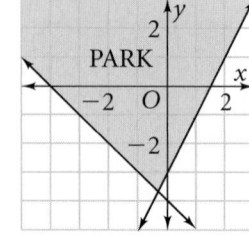

ALG2 6.0

54. Which expression is equivalent to $(3 - i)(1 + 2i)$?

   Ⓐ $5 + 4i$ Ⓒ $1 + 5i$

   Ⓑ $5 + 5i$ Ⓓ $1 + 4i$

ALG2 9.0

55. What is the effect on the graph when the equation $y = x^2 + 5$ is changed to $y = x^2 + 8$?

   Ⓐ The graph narrows.

   Ⓑ The graph keeps its shape but translates up the y-axis.

   Ⓒ The graph widens.

   Ⓓ The graph keeps its shape but translates in the positive x direction.

Mixed Review

Lesson 9-1

Describe the variation that is modeled by each formula.

56. $V = \dfrac{s^2 h}{3}$ **57.** $h = \dfrac{3V}{s^2}$ **58.** $B = \dfrac{3V}{h}$ **59.** $w = \dfrac{V}{\ell h}$ **60.** $b = \dfrac{2A}{h}$

Lesson 8-1

Identify each function as exponential growth or decay, and find the growth or decay factor.

61. $y = 3 \cdot 4^x$ **62.** $y = 0.1 \cdot 2^x$ **63.** $y = 5 \cdot (0.8)^x$ **64.** $y = 3 \cdot \left(\dfrac{1}{2}\right)^x$

Lesson 7-3

Multiply.

65. $\left(5\sqrt{3} - 2\right)^2$ **66.** $\left(\sqrt{3} + \sqrt{5}\right)\left(\sqrt{3} - \sqrt{5}\right)$

67. $\left(3\sqrt{5} + 2\sqrt{10}\right)\left(2\sqrt{5} + \sqrt{10}\right)$ **68.** $\left(4 + 2\sqrt{3}\right)\left(6 - 3\sqrt{3}\right)$

Rational Functions and Their Graphs

 California Content Standards

MA 8.0 Students are familiar with the notion of the limit of a function as the independent variable approaches a number or infinity.

What You'll Learn

• To identify properties of rational functions

• To graph rational functions

...And Why

To find the average cost of producing CD-ROMs, as in Example 5

✓ Check Skills You'll Need

 for Help Lessons 5-4 and 5-5

Factor.

1. $x^2 + 5x + 6$ **2.** $x^2 - 6x + 8$ **3.** $x^2 - 12x + 27$

4. $2x^2 + x - 28$ **5.** $2x^2 - 11x + 15$ **6.** $2x^2 - 19x + 24$

Solve.

7. $x^2 + x - 12 = 0$ **8.** $x^2 - 3x - 28 = 0$ **9.** $x^2 - 9x + 18 = 0$

🔊 **New Vocabulary**   • rational function   • point of discontinuity

---

1   Properties of Rational Functions

Members of the reciprocal function family are rational functions.

 Key Concepts

Definition	**Rational Function**

A **rational function** $f(x)$ is a function that can be written as

$$f(x) = \frac{P(x)}{Q(x)},$$

where $P(x)$ and $Q(x)$ are polynomial functions. The domain of $f(x)$ is all real numbers except those for which $Q(x) = 0$.

Vocabulary Tip

A rational function is a ratio of functions, just as a rational number is a ratio of numbers.

The graphs of the rational functions $y = \frac{-2x}{x^2 + 1}$, $y = \frac{1}{x^2 - 4}$, and $y = \frac{(x + 2)(x - 1)}{x + 1}$ are shown below.

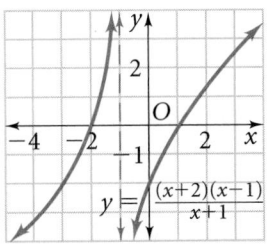

In the first rational function, there is no value of x that makes the denominator 0. The graph is continuous because it has no jumps, breaks, or holes in it. It can be drawn with a pencil that never leaves the paper.

In the second rational function, x cannot be 2 or -2. In the third, x cannot be -1. The last two graphs are discontinuous.

If a is a real number for which the denominator of a rational function f is zero, then a is not in the domain of f. The graph of f is not continuous at $x = a$ and the function has a **point of discontinuity** at $x = a$.

To find points of discontinuity, find the values of x that make the denominator 0.

1 EXAMPLE **Finding Points of Discontinuity**

For each rational function, find any points of discontinuity.

a. $y = \dfrac{1}{x^2 + 2x + 1}$

The function is undefined at value(s) of x for which $x^2 + 2x + 1 = 0$.

$x^2 + 2x + 1 = 0$	**Set the denominator equal to zero.**
$(x + 1)(x + 1) = 0$	**Solve by factoring or using the Quadratic Formula.**
$x + 1 = 0$	**Zero Product Property**
$x = -1$	**Solve for x.**

There is a point of discontinuity at $x = -1$.

b. $y = \dfrac{-x + 1}{x^2 + 1}$

The function is undefined at value(s) of x for which $x^2 + 1 = 0$.

$x^2 + 1 = 0$	**Set the denominator equal to zero.**
$x^2 = -1$	**Solve for x.**
$x = \pm \sqrt{-1}$	

Since $\sqrt{-1}$ is not a real number, there is no real value for x for which the function $y = \dfrac{-x + 1}{x^2 + 1}$ is undefined. There is no point of discontinuity.

✓ CA Standards Check **1** For each rational function, find any points of discontinuity.

a. $y = \dfrac{1}{x^2 - 16}$ **b.** $y = \dfrac{x^2 - 1}{x^2 + 3}$ **c.** $y = \dfrac{x + 1}{x^2 + 2x - 8}$

The graph of $y = \dfrac{x + 1}{(x - 1)(x + 2)}$ is shown at the right. The zeros of the denominator are 1 and -2. The graph has vertical asymptotes at those points.

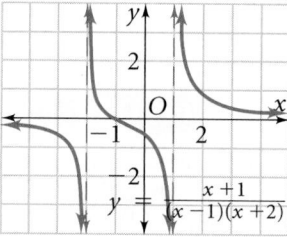

Graphing Calculator Hint

A hole in a graph is not displayed on a graphing calculator.

2 is a zero of both the numerator and the denominator of the rational function $y = \dfrac{(x - 2)(x + 1)}{x - 2}$. The graph of this function is the same as the graph of $y = x + 1$, except it has a hole at $x = 2$.

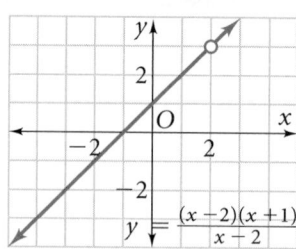

2 is a zero of both the numerator and the denominator of the rational function $y = \dfrac{x - 2}{(x - 2)(x - 1)}$. The graph of this function is the same as the graph of $y = \dfrac{1}{x - 1}$, except it has a hole at $x = 2$.

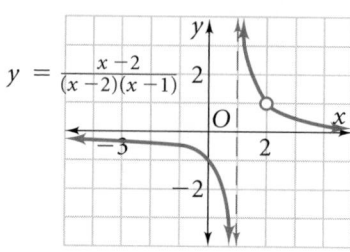

2 is a zero of both the numerator and the denominator of the rational function $y = \frac{x-2}{(x-2)^2}$.

The graph of this function is exactly the same as the graph of $y = \frac{1}{x-2}$. The vertical asymptote is $x = 2$ and there is no hole.

Properties	**Vertical Asymptotes**

The rational function $f(x) = \frac{P(x)}{Q(x)}$ has a point of discontinuity for each real zero of $Q(x)$.

If $P(x)$ and $Q(x)$ have no common real zeros, then the graph of $f(x)$ has a vertical asymptote at each real zero of $Q(x)$.

If $P(x)$ and $Q(x)$ have a common real zero a, then there is a hole in the graph or a vertical asymptote at $x = a$.

2 EXAMPLE **Finding Vertical Asymptotes**

Describe the vertical asymptotes and holes for the graph of each rational function.

a. $y = \frac{x+1}{(x-2)(x-3)}$

Since 2 and 3 are the zeros of the denominator and neither is a zero of the numerator, $x = 2$ and $x = 3$ are vertical asymptotes.

b. $y = \frac{(x-2)(x-1)}{x-2}$

The graph of this function is the same as the graph of $y = x - 1$, except it has a hole at $x = 2$.

c. $y = \frac{(x-3)(x+4)}{(x-3)(x-3)(x+4)}$

The graph of this function is the same as the graph of $y = \frac{1}{x-3}$, except it has a hole at $x = -4$. The vertical asymptote is $x = 3$.

 CA Standards Check **2** Describe the vertical asymptotes and holes for the graph of each rational function.

a. $y = \frac{x-2}{(x-1)(x+3)}$ **b.** $y = \frac{x-2}{(x-2)(x+3)}$ **c.** $y = \frac{x^2-1}{x+1}$

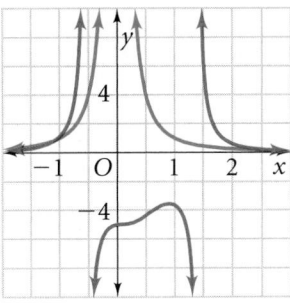

For the graphs of rational functions such as $y = \frac{1}{x}$ and $y = \frac{1}{x^2}$, the horizontal asymptote is $y = 0$. As shown at the left, when the absolute value of x is large, the graph of $y = \frac{2x^2 - x + 10}{5x^4 - 7x^3 + x^2 - 2}$ is very close to the graph of $y = \frac{1}{x^2}$. So $y = 0$ is the horizontal asymptote of both graphs.

In fact, $y = 0$ is the horizontal asymptote of the graph of any rational function, if the degree of the denominator is greater than the degree of the numerator.

If the degree of the numerator equals the degree of the denominator, then the horizontal asymptote can be found as shown in Example 3.

EXAMPLE **Finding Horizontal Asymptotes**

Find the horizontal asymptote of $y = \frac{3x + 5}{x - 2}$.

Divide the numerator by the denominator as shown at the right. The function $y = \frac{3x + 5}{x - 2}$ can be written as $y = \frac{11}{x - 2} + 3$. Its graph is a translation of $y = \frac{11}{x}$. The horizontal asymptote of the graph of $y = \frac{3x + 5}{x - 2}$ is $y = 3$.

$$
\begin{array}{r}
3 \\
x - 2 \overline{)3x + 5} \\
\underline{3x - 6} \\
11
\end{array}
$$

 CA Standards Check ❸ Find the horizontal asymptote of the graph of each rational function.

a. $y = \frac{-2x + 6}{x - 1}$ **b.** $y = \frac{2x^2 + 5}{x^2 + 1}$

Key Concepts

| **Properties** | **Horizontal Asymptotes** |

The graph of a rational function has at most one horizontal asymptote.

The graph of a rational function has a horizontal asymptote at $y = 0$ if the degree of the denominator is greater than the degree of the numerator.

If the degrees of the numerator and the denominator are equal, then the graph has a horizontal asymptote at $y = \frac{a}{b}$. a is the coefficient of the term of highest degree in the numerator and b is the coefficient of the term of highest degree in the denominator.

If the degree of the numerator is greater than the degree of the denominator, then the graph has no horizontal asymptote.

---

2 **Graphing Rational Functions**

You can use asymptotes to sketch the graphs of rational functions.

For: Rational Functions Activity
Use: Interactive Textbook, 9-3

4 **EXAMPLE** **Sketching Graphs of Rational Functions**

Sketch the graph of $y = \frac{x + 2}{(x + 3)(x - 4)}$.

The degree of the denominator is greater than the degree of the numerator, so the y-axis is the horizontal asymptote. When $x > 4$, y is positive. So as x increases, the graph approaches the y-axis from above. When $x < -3$, y is negative. So as x decreases, the graph approaches the y-axis from below.

Since -2 is the zero of the numerator, the x-intercept is at -2. Since -3 and 4 are the zeros of the denominator, the vertical asymptotes are at $x = -3$ and $x = 4$.

Calculate the values of y for values of x near the asymptotes. Plot those points and sketch the graph.

 CA Standards Check ❹ Sketch the graph of $y = \frac{x + 3}{(x - 1)(x - 5)}$.

5 **EXAMPLE** Real-World Connection

Business The CD-ROMs for a computer game can be manufactured for $.25 each. The development cost is $124,000. The first 100 discs are samples and will not be sold.

a. Write a function for the average cost of a salable disc. Graph the function.

Relate average cost $= \dfrac{\text{manufacturing cost of discs } + \text{ development cost}}{\text{number of salable discs}}$

Define Let $x =$ number of CD-ROMs produced.
Let $y =$ average cost of one salable disc.

Write $y = \dfrac{0.25x + 124{,}000}{x - 100}$

Graph the function. Adjust the viewing window.

Xmin=0   Ymin=−10
Xmax=15000 Ymax=100
Xscl=1000   Yscl=10

b. What is the average cost if 2000 discs are produced? If 12,800 discs are produced?

Use the **CALC** feature to evaluate the function at $x = 2000$ and at $x = 12{,}800$. If 2000 discs are produced, the average cost will be about $65.53. If 12,800 discs are produced, the average cost will be about $10.02.

Real-World Connection

Video game programmers' salaries are part of a game's development cost.

✓ **CA Standards Check** **5** **a. Critical Thinking** How could you find the number of discs that must be produced to bring the average cost under $8?
b. What is the vertical asymptote of the graph of the function in Example 5? What is the horizontal asymptote?
c. Describe how the asymptotes are related to the information given in Example 5.

EXERCISES

Standards Practice

For more exercises, see *Extra Skill and Word Problem Practice*.

MA 8.0

A Practice by Example

Example 1
(page 510)

Find any points of discontinuity for each rational function.

1. $y = \dfrac{2x^2 + 5}{x^2 - 2x}$

2. $y = \dfrac{x^2 + 2x}{x^2 + 2}$

3. $y = \dfrac{3x - 3}{x^2 - 1}$

4. $y = \dfrac{6 - 3x}{x^2 - 5x + 6}$

5. $y = \dfrac{x^2 + 5x + 6}{x^2 + 6x + 9}$

6. $y = \dfrac{x^2 + 4x + 3}{2x^2 + 5x - 7}$

7. $y = \dfrac{x^3 - 8}{x^3 - 8}$

8. $y = \dfrac{x^2}{x^2 + 1}$

9. $y = \dfrac{1}{2x^2 + 3x - 7}$

Example 2
(page 511)

Describe the vertical asymptotes and holes for the graph of each rational function.

10. $y = \dfrac{3}{x + 2}$

11. $y = \dfrac{x + 5}{x + 5}$

12. $y = \dfrac{x + 3}{(2x + 3)(x - 1)}$

13. $y = \dfrac{(x + 3)(x - 2)}{(x - 2)(x + 1)}$

14. $y = \dfrac{x^2 - 4}{x + 2}$

15. $y = \dfrac{x + 5}{x^2 + 9}$

16. $y = \dfrac{9 - x^2}{x^2 - 9}$

17. $y = \dfrac{2x^2}{2x^2 + 2}$

18. $y = \dfrac{6x^2 + x - 2}{3x^2 + 17x + 10}$

Example 3
(page 512)

Find the horizontal asymptote of the graph of each rational function.

19. $y = \dfrac{5}{x + 6}$

20. $y = \dfrac{x + 2}{2x^2 - 4}$

21. $y = \dfrac{x + 1}{x + 5}$

22. $y = \dfrac{x^2 + 2}{2x^2 - 1}$

23. $y = \dfrac{5x^3 + 2x}{2x^5 - 4x^3}$

24. $y = \dfrac{3x - 4}{4x + 1}$

Example 4
(page 512)

Graph each rational function. State the domain and range.

25. $y = \dfrac{x^2 - 4}{3x - 6}$

26. $y = \dfrac{4x}{x^3 - 4x}$

27. $y = \dfrac{x + 4}{x - 4}$

28. $y = \dfrac{x(x + 1)}{x + 1}$

29. $y = \dfrac{x + 6}{(x - 2)(x + 3)}$

30. $y = \dfrac{3x}{(x + 2)^2}$

Example 5
(page 513)

31. Business CDs can be manufactured for $.19 each. The development cost is $210,000. The first 500 discs are samples and will not be sold.
   a. Write a function for the average cost of a salable disc. Graph the function.
   b. What is the average cost if 5000 discs are produced? If 15,000 discs are produced?
   c. How many discs must be produced to bring the average cost under $10?
   d. What are the vertical and horizontal asymptotes of the graph of the function?

B **Apply Your Skills**

Find the vertical and horizontal asymptotes, if any, of the graph of each rational function.

32.

33.

34.

Sketch the graph of each rational function.

35. $y = \dfrac{2x + 3}{x - 5}$

36. $y = \dfrac{x^2 + 6x + 9}{x + 3}$

37. $y = \dfrac{4x^2 - 100}{2x^2 + x - 15}$

38. $y = -\dfrac{x}{(x - 1)^2}$

39. $y = \dfrac{2x}{3x - 1}$

40. $y = \dfrac{2}{x^2 - 4}$

 41. Writing Describe the conditions that will produce a rational function with a graph that has no vertical asymptotes.

42. Basketball A basketball player has made 21 of her last 30 free throws—an average of 70%. To model the player's rate of success if she makes x more consecutive free throws, use the function $y = \dfrac{21 + x}{30 + x}$.
   a. Graph the function.
   b. Use the graph to find the number of consecutive free throws the player needs to raise her success rate to 75%.

43. Data Analysis The president of XYZ Company earns $200,000 a year. Each of the other x employees earns $20,000 a year.
   a. Write and graph a function that models the average salary of all employees of XYZ.
   b. What is the average salary if there are three employees? If there are 30 employees?
   c. Critical Thinking Is the average salary the best measure of the workers' pay? Explain. What other measure could you use?

44. Reasoning Look for a pattern in the sequence of shells below.

   a. Write a model for the number of purple shells $P(n)$ at each step n.
   b. Write a model for the number of red shells $R(n)$ at each step n.
   c. Write a model for the ratio of $P(n)$ to $R(n)$. Use it to predict the ratio of purple shells to red shells in the next figure. Verify your answer.

45. Wage Policy The graph below compares the average hourly wage for production workers and the minimum hourly wage from 1950 to 2000.

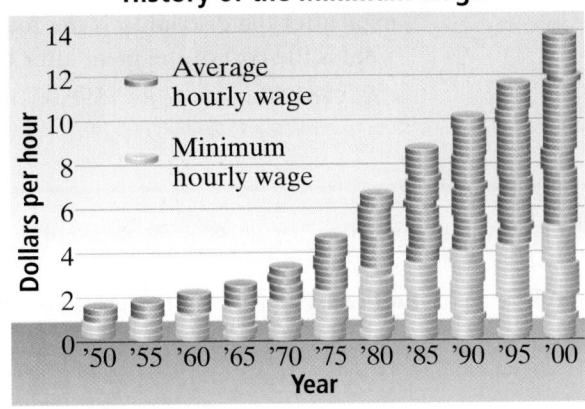

History of the Minimum Wage

SOURCE: Bureau of Labor Statistics.
Go to **www.PHSchool.com** for a data update.
Web Code: bbg-9041

   a. How has the comparison of the minimum wage to the production workers' wage changed over the years?
   b. If the minimum wage and the production workers' wage are modeled by polynomials, what type of function would model their ratio?
   c. The quadratic function $M(x) = 0.00081x^2 + 0.049x + 0.68$ models the minimum wage, where x is the number of years since 1950. The quadratic function $A(x) = 0.0043x^2 + 0.04x + 1.21$ models the average wage. Write a model for the ratio of these two functions.
   d. Graph your model. If the present trends continue, when will the minimum wage decrease to 25% of the average wage?

Multiple Choice Practice

For California Standards and CAHSEE Tutorials, visit PHSchool.com. Web Code: bbq-9045

ALG2 12.0

46. Suppose you invest \$775 at an annual interest rate of 4.75% compounded continuously. How much will you have in the account after 10 years?

   (A) \$812.70   (C) \$1,106.67

   (B) \$982.76   (D) \$1,246.26

ALG2 1.0

47. Which of the following represents the solution to $|x - 1| > 2$?

Ⓐ ![number line from -5 to 5 with open circle at 3, shaded right]

Ⓑ ![number line from -5 to 5 with open circle at -1, shaded right]

Ⓒ ![number line from -5 to 5 with open circles at -1 and 3, shaded between]

Ⓓ ![number line from -5 to 5 with open circles at -1 and 3, shaded outside]

ALG2 12.0

48. Bret is buying a car for $25,000. The equation $y = 25{,}000(0.775)^x$ approximates the value of the car after x number of years. Which is the best approximation of the car's value after 5 years?

Ⓐ $11,637　　Ⓑ $9,019　　Ⓒ $6,990　　Ⓓ $5,417

ALG2 24.0

49. Jason is treating his family to dinner with the coupon shown at the right. Including Jason, there are 7 people in his family. The equations $f(x) = x - 10$ and $g(x) = x - 0.25x$ model the discounts, and $(g \circ f)(x)$ models the cost of the meal after the discounts. If the total bill is $130, what is the cost of the meal after the discounts?

> **$10 OFF**
> **Toni's Restaurant**
>
> Bonus offer: Parties of 6 or more get an additional 25% off.

Ⓐ $87.50　　Ⓑ $90.00　　Ⓒ $97.50　　Ⓓ $120.00

Mixed Review

Lesson 9-2

Find the asymptotes of the graph of each equation.

50. $y = \frac{3}{x} + 4$

51. $y = \frac{2}{x + 3}$

52. $y = \frac{-1}{x + 1} + 1$

53. $y = \frac{5}{x - 7} - 3$

54. $y = \frac{5}{2 - x}$

55. $y = \frac{-2}{5 - x} - 6$

Lesson 8-2

Describe how the graph of each function relates to the graph of $y = 4(0.8)^x$.

56. $y = 4(0.8)^{x-1}$

57. $y = 4(0.8)^x + 3$

58. $y = 4(0.8)^{x+1} - 5$

✓ Checkpoint Quiz 1　　　　　Lessons 9-1 through 9-3

If $z = 30$ when $x = 3$ and $y = 2$, write the function that models each relationship.

1. z varies jointly with x and y.

2. z varies directly with x and inversely with y.

3. z varies inversely with the product of x and y.

Explain how the graph of y_2 is related to the graph of y_1.

4. $y_1 = \frac{4}{x}$ and $y_2 = \frac{9}{x}$

5. $y_1 = \frac{1}{x}$ and $y_2 = \frac{1}{x} + 5$

6. $y_1 = \frac{1}{x - 1} + 2$ and $y_2 = \frac{1}{x + 1} - 2$

Sketch the graph of each rational function.

7. $y = \frac{x^2 - 9}{2x + 6}$

8. $y = \frac{3x}{x^3 - x}$

9. $y = \frac{x + 3}{x - 3}$

10. $y = \frac{x^2 - 2x}{x - 2}$

Rational Expressions

 California Content Standards

ALG2 7.0 Students multiply, divide, reduce, and evaluate rational expressions with monomial and polynomial denominators and simplify complicated rational expressions, including those with negative exponents in the denominator. *Introduce*

What You'll Learn

- To simplify rational expressions
- To multiply and divide rational expressions

. . . And Why

To compute ratios of volume to surface area, as in Exercise 26

✓ **Check Skills You'll Need**

GO for Help Lesson 5-4 and Skills Handbook page 883

Factor.

1. $2x^2 - 3x + 1$

2. $4x^2 - 9$

3. $5x^2 + 6x + 1$

4. $10x^2 - 10$

Multiply or divide.

5. $\frac{3}{8} \cdot \frac{5}{6}$

6. $\frac{1}{2} \cdot \frac{4}{6}$

7. $\frac{8}{3} \cdot \frac{2}{16}$

8. $\frac{2}{5} \cdot \frac{3}{7}$

9. $\frac{5}{8} \div 4$

10. $\frac{3}{4} \div \frac{1}{2}$

11. $\frac{9}{16} \div \frac{3}{4}$

12. $\frac{5}{4} \div \frac{15}{8}$

🔊 **New Vocabulary** • simplest form

1 Simplifying Rational Expressions

A rational expression is in **simplest form** when its numerator and denominator are polynomials that have no common divisors.

In simplest form	Not in simplest form

$$\frac{x}{x-1} \qquad \frac{2}{x^2+3} \qquad\qquad \frac{x}{x^2} \qquad \frac{\frac{1}{x}}{x+1} \qquad \frac{2(x-3)}{3(x-3)}$$

You can simplify some expressions by dividing out common factors.

1 EXAMPLE **Simplifying Rational Expressions**

Simplify $\frac{x^2 + 10x + 25}{x^2 + 9x + 20}$. State any restrictions on the variable.

$$\frac{x^2 + 10x + 25}{x^2 + 9x + 20} = \frac{(x+5)(x+5)}{(x+4)(x+5)} \qquad \text{Factor the polynomials. Notice that } x \neq -4 \text{ or } -5.$$

$$= \frac{(x+5)(x+5)}{(x+4)(x+5)} \qquad \text{Divide out common factors.}$$

$$= \frac{x+5}{x+4}$$

The simplified expression is $\frac{x+5}{x+4}$ for $x \neq -4$ or -5. The restrictions on x are needed to prevent the denominator of the original expression from being zero.

✓ **CA Standards Check** **1.** Simplify each expression. State any restrictions on the variables.

a. $\frac{-27x^3y}{9x^4y}$

b. $\frac{-6 - 3x}{x^2 - 6x + 8}$

c. $\frac{2x^2 - 3x - 2}{x^2 - 5x + 6}$

To simplify rational expressions with negative exponents in the denominator, recall that $a^{-n} = \frac{1}{a^n}$ and $\frac{a^m}{a^n} = a^{m-n}$.

2 EXAMPLE **Simplifying Negative Exponents**

Simplify $\frac{2a^2b^3c}{(2a^{-1}bc^2)^2}$.

$$\frac{2a^2b^3c}{(2a^{-1}bc^2)^2} = \frac{2a^2b^3c}{2^2(a^{-1})^2b^2(c^2)^2}$$ **Raise each power in parentheses to the 2nd power.**

$$= \frac{2a^2b^3c}{2^2a^{-2}b^2c^4}$$ **Multiply exponents of a power raised to a power.**

$$= 2^{1-2}a^{2--2}b^{3-2}c^{1-4}$$ **Subtract exponents when dividing powers with the same base.**

$$= 2^{-1}a^4b^1c^{-3}$$ **Simplify.**

$$= \frac{a^4b}{2c^3}$$ **Rewrite using positive exponents.**

✓ **CA Standards Check** **2** **2.** Simplify each expression.

a. $\frac{4x^3y^4z^5}{2x^{-2}y^{-1}z^6}$ **b.** $\frac{x^2 - 4}{(x + 2)(x - 2)^{-1}}$ **c.** $\frac{(2a)^{-2}b^3c}{3b^{-4}c^5}$

---

2   Multiplying and Dividing Rational Expressions

You can use what you know about simplifying rational expressions when you multiply and divide them.

3 EXAMPLE **Multiplying Rational Expressions**

Multiply $\frac{2x^2 + 7x + 3}{x - 4}$ and $\frac{x^2 - 16}{x^2 + 8x + 15}$. State any restrictions on the variable.

Step 1   Factor both expressions.
$$\frac{2x^2 + 7x + 3}{x - 4} = \frac{(2x + 1)(x + 3)}{x - 4}$$
$$\frac{x^2 - 16}{x^2 + 8x + 15} = \frac{(x - 4)(x + 4)}{(x + 3)(x + 5)}$$

Step 2   Multiply the factored expressions.
$$\frac{2x^2 + 7x + 3}{x - 4} \cdot \frac{x^2 - 16}{x^2 + 8x + 15} = \frac{(2x + 1)(x + 3)}{x - 4} \cdot \frac{(x - 4)(x + 4)}{(x + 3)(x + 5)}$$

Step 3   Divide out the common factors.
$$\frac{(2x + 1)(\overset{1}{\cancel{x + 3}})}{\underset{1}{\cancel{x - 4}}} \cdot \frac{(\overset{1}{\cancel{x - 4}})(x + 4)}{(\underset{1}{\cancel{x + 3}})(x + 5)} = \frac{(2x + 1)(x + 4)}{x + 5}$$

The product is $\frac{(2x + 1)(x + 4)}{x + 5}$ for $x \neq 4, -3,$ or -5.

✓ **CA Standards Check** **3** Multiply $\frac{a^2 - 4}{a^2 - 1}$ and $\frac{a + 1}{a^2 + 2a}$. State any restrictions on the variable.

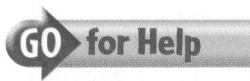

For practice in dividing fractions, go to p. 883.

Video Tutor Help

Visit: PHSchool.com
Web Code: bbe-0775

To divide rational expressions, remember to multiply by the reciprocal of the divisor, just as you did when dividing rational numbers.

4 EXAMPLE Dividing Rational Expressions

Divide $\dfrac{4 - x}{(3x + 2)(x - 2)}$ by $\dfrac{5(x - 4)}{(x - 2)(7y - 5)}$. State any restrictions on the variables.

$$\dfrac{4 - x}{(3x + 2)(x - 2)} \div \dfrac{5(x - 4)}{(x - 2)(7y - 5)}$$

$$= \dfrac{4 - x}{(3x + 2)(x - 2)} \cdot \dfrac{(x - 2)(7y - 5)}{5(x - 4)} \qquad \text{Multiply by the reciprocal.}$$

$$= \dfrac{-(x - 4)}{(3x + 2)(x - 2)} \cdot \dfrac{(x - 2)(7y - 5)}{5(x - 4)} \qquad \text{Divide out common factors.}$$

$$= \dfrac{-1}{3x + 2} \cdot \dfrac{7y - 5}{5} \qquad \text{Rewrite the expression.}$$

$$= \dfrac{-(7y - 5)}{5(3x + 2)} \qquad \text{Multiply.}$$

The quotient is $\dfrac{-(7y - 5)}{5(3x + 2)}$ for $x \neq -\dfrac{2}{3}$, 2, or 4, and $y \neq \dfrac{5}{7}$.

CA Standards Check ④ Divide $\dfrac{a^2 + 2a - 15}{a^2 - 16}$ by $\dfrac{a + 1}{3a - 12}$. State any restrictions on the variable.

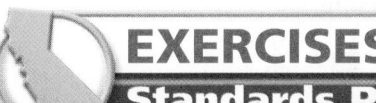

EXERCISES

Standards Practice

For more exercises, see *Extra Skill and Word Problem Practice*.

ALG2 7.0

A Practice by Example

Examples 1 and 2
(pages 517–518)

for Help

Simplify each rational expression. State any restrictions on the variable.

1. $\dfrac{2x}{4x^2 - 2x}$

2. $\dfrac{6c^2 + 9c}{3c}$

3. $\dfrac{a^2 b^3}{a^{-1} b^2}$

4. $\dfrac{z^2 - 49}{z + 7}$

5. $\dfrac{2x + 10}{4x^{-2}}$

6. $\dfrac{x^2 + 8x + 16}{x^2 - 2x - 24}$

Example 3
(page 518)

Multiply. State any restrictions on the variables.

7. $\dfrac{4x^2}{5y} \cdot \dfrac{7y}{12x^4}$

8. $\dfrac{2x^4}{10y^{-2}} \cdot \dfrac{5y^3}{4x^3}$

9. $\dfrac{8y - 4}{10y - 5} \cdot \dfrac{5y - 15}{3y - 9}$

10. $\dfrac{2x + 12}{3x - 9} \cdot \dfrac{2x - 6}{3x + 8}$

11. $\dfrac{x^2 - 4}{x^2 - 1} \cdot \dfrac{x + 1}{x^2 + 2x}$

12. $\dfrac{x^2 - 5x + 6}{x^2 - 4} \cdot \dfrac{x^2 + 3x + 2}{x^2 - 2x - 3}$

Example 4
(page 519)

Divide. State any restrictions on the variables.

13. $\dfrac{7x}{4y^3} \div \dfrac{21x^3}{8y}$

14. $\dfrac{3x^3}{5y^2} \div \dfrac{6y^{-3}}{5x^{-5}}$

15. $\dfrac{6x + 6y}{x - y} \div \dfrac{18}{5x - 5y}$

16. $\dfrac{3y - 12}{2y + 4} \div \dfrac{6y - 24}{4y + 8}$

17. $\dfrac{x^2}{x^2 + 2x + 1} \div \dfrac{3x}{x^2 - 1}$

18. $\dfrac{y^2 - 5y + 6}{y^3} \div \dfrac{y^2 + 3y - 10}{4y^2}$

Simplify each rational expression. State any restrictions on the variables.

19. $\dfrac{x^2 - 5x - 24}{x^2 - 7x - 30}$

20. $\dfrac{2y^2 + 8y - 24}{2y^2 - 8y + 8}$

21. $\dfrac{xy^3 - 9xy}{12xy^2 + 12xy - 144x}$

22. Write an expression for the area of the rectangle at the right.

$\dfrac{4a + 4}{a + 3}$

$\dfrac{3a + 9}{2a - 6}$

23. Error Analysis A student claims that $x = 2$ is the only solution of the equation $\dfrac{x}{x - 2} = \dfrac{1}{2} + \dfrac{2}{x - 2}$. Is the student correct? Explain.

24. Open-Ended Write three rational expressions that simplify to $\dfrac{x}{x + 1}$.

25. Writing How can you tell whether a rational expression is in simplest form? Include an example with your explanation.

26. Industrial Design A storage tank will have a circular base of radius r and a height of r. The tank can be either cylindrical or hemispherical (half a sphere).
 a. Write and simplify an expression for the ratio of the volume of the hemispherical tank to its surface area (including the base). For a sphere, $V = \frac{4}{3}\pi r^3$ and S.A. $= 4\pi r^2$.
 b. Write and simplify an expression for the ratio of the volume of the cylindrical tank to its surface area (including the bases).
 c. Compare the ratios of volume to surface area for the two tanks.
 d. Compare the volumes of the two tanks.

Exercise 26

Multiply or divide. State any restrictions on the variable.

27. $\dfrac{a + 3}{a^2 + a - 12} \div \dfrac{a^2 - 9}{a^2 + 7a + 12}$

28. $\dfrac{b^2 - 25}{(b + 5)^2} \div \dfrac{2b + 10}{4b + 20}$

29. $\dfrac{6x^3 - 6x^2}{x^4 + 5x^3} \div \dfrac{3x^2 - 15x + 12}{2x^2 + 2x - 40}$

30. $\dfrac{2x^2 - 6x}{x^2 + 18x + 81} \cdot \dfrac{9x + 81}{x^2 - 9}$

31. $\dfrac{x^2 - x - 2}{2x^2 - 5x + 2} \div \dfrac{x^2 - x - 12}{2x^2 + 5x - 3}$

32. $\dfrac{2x^2 + 5x + 2}{4x^2 - 1} \cdot \dfrac{2x^2 + x - 1}{x^2 + x - 2}$

Simplify. State any restrictions on the variables.

33. $\dfrac{(x^2 - x)^2}{x(x - 1)^{-2}(x^2 + 3x - 4)}$

34. $\dfrac{2x + 6}{(x - 1)^{-1}(x^2 + 2x - 3)}$

35. $\dfrac{54x^3 y^{-1}}{3x^{-2} y}$

36. The width of the rectangle at the right is $\dfrac{a + 10}{3a + 24}$. Write an expression for the length of the rectangle.

$A = \dfrac{2a + 20}{6a + 15}$

37. Physics The acceleration of an object is a measure of how much its velocity changes in a given period of time.

$$\text{acceleration} = \frac{\text{final velocity} - \text{initial velocity}}{\text{time}}$$

Suppose you are riding a bicycle at 6 m/s. You step hard on the pedals and increase your speed to 12 m/s in about 5 s.
 a. Find your acceleration in meters per second per second.
 b. A sedan can go from 0 to 60 mi/h in about 10 s. What is the acceleration in meters per second per second? (*Hints:* 1 mi ≈ 1609 m; 1 h = 3600 s.)

Homework Video Tutor

Visit: PHSchool.com
Web Code: bbe-0904

C **Challenge**

38. a. Critical Thinking Simplify $\dfrac{(2x^n)^2 - 1}{2x^n - 1}$, where x is an integer and n is a positive integer. (*Hint:* Factor the numerator.)
 b. Use the result from part (a) to show that the value of the given expression is always an odd integer.

Use the fact that $\dfrac{\frac{a}{b}}{\frac{c}{d}} = \dfrac{a}{b} \div \dfrac{c}{d}$ to simplify each rational expression. State any restrictions on the variables.

39. $\dfrac{\frac{8x^2y}{x+1}}{\frac{6xy^2}{x+1}}$

40. $\dfrac{\frac{3a^3b^3}{a-b}}{\frac{4ab}{b-a}}$

41. $\dfrac{\frac{9m+6n}{m^2n^2}}{\frac{12m+8n}{5m^2}}$

Multiple Choice Practice

For California Standards and CAHSEE Tutorials, visit PHSchool.com. **Web Code: bbq-9045**

ALG2 7.0   **42.** Which expression is equivalent to $\dfrac{x^2 - x - 12}{x^2 - 6x + 8}$?

Ⓐ $\dfrac{x-4}{x-2}$ for $x \neq 4$ or 2

Ⓑ $\dfrac{x+2}{x-4}$ for $x \neq 4$ or -2

Ⓒ $\dfrac{x+4}{x-3}$ for $x \neq -4$ or 3

Ⓓ $\dfrac{x+3}{x-2}$ for $x \neq 4$ or 2

ALG2 7.0   **43.** The area of the rectangle below can be represented by $x^4y^6z^2$.

$x^2y^8z^{-1}$

Which of the following expressions represents the width of the rectangle?

Ⓐ $\dfrac{x^2z^3}{y^2}$ Ⓒ $x^2y^2z^3$

Ⓑ $\dfrac{x^2z}{y^2}$ Ⓓ $x^6y^{14}z$

ALG2 11.1   **44.** Which is equivalent to $3^{-5} = \frac{1}{243}$?

Ⓐ $\log_{-5} 3 = \frac{1}{243}$ Ⓒ $\log_3 \frac{1}{243} = -5$

Ⓑ $\log_3 -5 = \frac{1}{243}$ Ⓓ $\log_3 243 = -5$

Mixed Review

GO for Help

Lesson 9-3   Describe the vertical asymptotes and holes for the graph of each rational function.

45. $y = \dfrac{x-3}{x-3}$ **46.** $y = \dfrac{x-1}{(3x+2)(x+1)}$ **47.** $y = \dfrac{(x-4)(x+5)}{(x+3)(x-4)}$

Lesson 8-3   Evaluate each logarithm.

48. $\log_4 64$ **49.** $\log_2 \frac{1}{32}$ **50.** $\log_5 5\sqrt{5}$ **51.** $\log_{16} 8$

Lesson 7-5   Solve each equation.

52. $\sqrt{x+3} - 1 = 4$ **53.** $\sqrt{7x+1} - \sqrt{6x+7} = 0$

9-5

Adding and Subtracting Rational Expressions

 California Content Standards

ALG2 7.0 Students add, subtract, reduce, and evaluate rational expressions with monomial and polynomial denominators and simplify complicated rational expressions, including those with negative exponents in the denominator. *Develop*

What You'll Learn

- To add and subtract rational expressions
- To simplify complex fractions

. . . And Why

To find the focal length of a camera lens, as in Example 1

 Check Skills You'll Need

GO for Help Skills Handbook page 883

Find the least common multiple of the two numbers.
1. $7, 21$ **2.** $6, 10$ **3.** $11, 17$ **4.** $30, 105$

Add or subtract.
5. $\frac{5}{19} + \frac{7}{38}$ **6.** $\frac{2}{15} + \frac{3}{25}$ **7.** $\frac{7}{24} - \frac{5}{36}$ **8.** $\frac{11}{12} - \frac{7}{45}$

 New Vocabulary • complex fraction

---

1   Adding and Subtracting Rational Expressions

Activity: Adding Fractions—Extended

1. Add. Simplify where possible.

   a. $\frac{2}{x} + \frac{3}{x}$ **b.** $\frac{4}{3x} + \frac{2}{3x}$ **c.** $\frac{3c}{2c - 1} + \frac{5c + 1}{2c - 1}$

2. Explain the steps you followed in Question 1.

3. How is adding rational expressions similar to adding fractions?

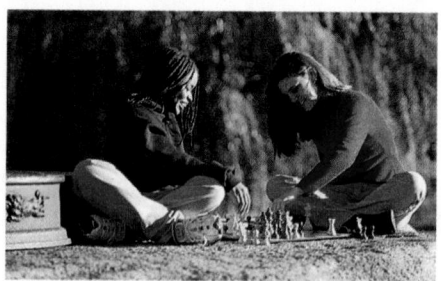

To produce a clear photograph, light rays must be focused on the film. The focal length of a camera lens is the distance from the lens to the point where parallel rays of light are focused.

When you focus a camera, you change the distance from the lens to the film.

The lens equation is $\frac{1}{f} = \frac{1}{d_i} + \frac{1}{d_o}$.

f = focal length of the lens

d_i = distance from the lens to the film

d_o = distance from the lens to the object

1 EXAMPLE Real-World 🌐 Connection

An object is 15 cm from a camera lens. The object is in focus on the film when the lens is 10 cm from the film. Find the focal length of the lens in centimeters.

$$\frac{1}{f} = \frac{1}{d_i} + \frac{1}{d_o}$$ **Use the lens equation.**

$$\frac{1}{f} = \frac{1}{10} + \frac{1}{15}$$ **Substitute.**

$$= \frac{3}{30} + \frac{2}{30}$$ **Write equivalent fractions with the LCD.**

$$= \frac{5}{30} = \frac{1}{6}$$ **Add and simplify.**

Since $\frac{1}{f} = \frac{1}{6}$, the focal length of the lens is 6 cm.

✓ **CA Standards Check** **1** Suppose an object is 20 cm from a camera lens. When the object is properly focused, the lens is 5 cm from the film. Find the focal length of the lens.

For practice in adding and subtracting fractions, go to p. 883.

To add or subtract rational expressions with different denominators, it is easiest to use the least common multiple of the denominators as a common denominator.

2 EXAMPLE Finding Least Common Multiples

Find the least common multiple of $4x^2 - 36$ and $6x^2 + 36x + 54$.

Step 1 Find the prime factors of each expression.

$$4x^2 - 36 = 4(x^2 - 9) = (2)(2)(x - 3)(x + 3)$$

$$6x^2 + 36x + 54 = 6(x^2 + 6x + 9) = (2)(3)(x + 3)(x + 3)$$

Step 2 Write each prime factor the greatest number of times it appears in either expression. Simplify where possible.

$$(2)(2)(3)(x - 3)(x + 3)(x + 3) = 12(x - 3)(x + 3)^2$$

The least common multiple is $12(x - 3)(x + 3)^2$.

✓ **CA Standards Check** **2** Find the least common multiple of each pair of expressions.
a. $3x^2 - 9x - 30$ and $6x + 30$ **b.** $5x^2 + 15x + 10$ and $2x^2 - 8$

3 EXAMPLE Adding Rational Expressions

Simplify $\dfrac{1}{x^2 + 5x + 4} + \dfrac{5x}{3x + 3}$.

$$\frac{1}{x^2 + 5x + 4} + \frac{5x}{3x + 3} = \frac{1}{(x + 1)(x + 4)} + \frac{5x}{3(x + 1)}$$ **Factor the denominators.**

$$= \frac{1}{(x + 1)(x + 4)} \cdot \frac{3}{3} + \frac{5x}{3(x + 1)} \cdot \frac{x + 4}{x + 4}$$ **identity for multiplication**

$$= \frac{3}{3(x + 1)(x + 4)} + \frac{5x(x + 4)}{3(x + 1)(x + 4)}$$ **Multiply.**

$$= \frac{3 + 5x(x + 4)}{3(x + 1)(x + 4)}$$ **Add.**

$$= \frac{5x^2 + 20x + 3}{3(x + 1)(x + 4)}$$ **Simplify the numerator.**

✓ **CA Standards Check** ③ Simplify $\dfrac{1}{x^2 - 4x - 12} + \dfrac{3x}{4x + 8}$.

Video Tutor Help

Visit: PHSchool.com
Web Code: bbe-0775

④ **EXAMPLE** **Subtracting Rational Expressions**

Simplify $\dfrac{7y}{5y^2 - 125} - \dfrac{4}{3y + 15}$.

$\dfrac{7y}{5y^2 - 125} - \dfrac{4}{3y + 15} = \dfrac{7y}{5(y + 5)(y - 5)} - \dfrac{4}{3(y + 5)}$ **Factor the denominators.**

$= \dfrac{7y}{5(y + 5)(y - 5)} \cdot \dfrac{3}{3} - \dfrac{4}{3(y + 5)} \cdot \dfrac{5(y - 5)}{5(y - 5)}$ **identity for multiplication**

$= \dfrac{(3)(7y)}{(3)(5)(y + 5)(y - 5)} - \dfrac{(4)(5)(y - 5)}{(3)(5)(y + 5)(y - 5)}$ **Multiply.**

$= \dfrac{(3)(7y) - (4)(5)(y - 5)}{(3)(5)(y + 5)(y - 5)}$ **Simplify.**

$= \dfrac{y + 100}{15(y + 5)(y - 5)}$ **Simplify.**

✓ **CA Standards Check** ④ Simplify each expression.

   a. $\dfrac{-2}{3x^2 + 36x + 105} - \dfrac{3x}{6x + 30}$ **b.** $\dfrac{x}{3x^2 - 9x + 6} - \dfrac{2x + 1}{3x^2 + 3x - 6}$

2   Simplifying Complex Fractions

A **complex fraction** is a fraction that has a fraction in its numerator or denominator or in both its numerator and denominator. Here are some examples.

$$\dfrac{\frac{1}{x}}{y} \qquad\qquad \dfrac{3}{1 - \frac{1}{2y}} \qquad\qquad \dfrac{\frac{x - 2}{x} - \frac{2}{x + 1}}{\frac{3}{x - 1} - \frac{1}{x + 1}}$$

Problem Solving Hint

Note that the complex fractions below are *not* equivalent.

$$\dfrac{\frac{a}{b}}{c} \qquad \dfrac{a}{\frac{b}{c}}$$

To simplify a complex fraction such as $\dfrac{\frac{a}{b}}{\frac{c}{d}}$ you can multiply the numerator $\frac{a}{b}$ and denominator $\frac{c}{d}$ by their least common denominator (LCD) *bd*. Or you can divide the numerator $\frac{a}{b}$ by the denominator $\frac{c}{d}$.

⑤ **EXAMPLE** **Simplifying Complex Fractions**

Simplify $\dfrac{\frac{1}{x} + 3}{\frac{5}{y} + 4}$.

Method I First find the LCD of all the rational expressions.

$\dfrac{\frac{1}{x} + 3}{\frac{5}{y} + 4} = \dfrac{\left(\frac{1}{x} + 3\right) \cdot xy}{\left(\frac{5}{y} + 4\right) \cdot xy}$ **The LCD is *xy*. Multiply the numerator and denominator by *xy*.**

$= \dfrac{\frac{1}{x} \cdot xy + 3 \cdot xy}{\frac{5}{y} \cdot xy + 4 \cdot xy}$ **Use the Distributive Property.**

$= \dfrac{y + 3xy}{5x + 4xy}$ **Simplify.**

Method 2 First simplify the numerator and denominator.

$$\frac{\frac{1}{x} + 3}{\frac{5}{y} + 4} = \frac{\frac{1}{x} + \frac{3x}{x}}{\frac{5}{y} + \frac{4y}{y}}$$ Write equivalent expressions with common denominators.

$$= \frac{\frac{1 + 3x}{x}}{\frac{5 + 4y}{y}}$$ Add.

$$= \frac{1 + 3x}{x} \div \frac{5 + 4y}{y}$$ Divide the numerator fraction by the denominator fraction.

$$= \frac{1 + 3x}{x} \cdot \frac{y}{5 + 4y}$$ Multiply by the reciprocal.

$$= \frac{(1 + 3x)y}{x(5 + 4y)}$$

$$= \frac{y + 3xy}{5x + 4xy}$$

 CA Standards Check **5** Simplify each complex fraction.

a. $\dfrac{\frac{1}{x}}{y}$

b. $\dfrac{3}{1 - \frac{1}{2y}}$

c. $\dfrac{\frac{x-2}{x} - \frac{2}{x+1}}{\frac{3}{x-1} - \frac{1}{x+1}}$

EXERCISES

Standards Practice

For more exercises, see *Extra Skill and Word Problem Practice.*

ALG2 7.0

 A Practice by Example

Example 1
(page 523)

 for Help

The focal length f of a camera lens is 2 in. The lens equation is $\frac{1}{f} = \frac{1}{d_i} + \frac{1}{d_o}$, where d_i is the distance between the lens and the film and d_o is the distance between the lens and the object.

1. The object to be photographed is 10 ft away. How far should the lens be from the film?

2. The object to be photographed is 20 ft away. How far should the lens be from the film?

3. Critical Thinking Explain why one setting on the camera is used for photographing all objects that are more than 10 ft from the camera.

Example 2
(page 523)

Find the least common multiple of each pair of polynomials.

4. $9(x + 2)(2x - 1)$ and $3(x + 2)$

5. $x^2 - 1$ and $x^2 + 2x + 1$

6. $(x - 2)(x + 3)$ and $10(x + 3)^2$

7. $12x^2 - 6x - 126$ and $18x - 63$

8. $5y^2 - 80$ and $y + 4$

9. $x^2 - 32x - 10$ and $2x + 10$

Example 3
(page 523)

Simplify each sum.

10. $\dfrac{1}{2x} + \dfrac{1}{2x}$

11. $\dfrac{d - 3}{2d + 1} + \dfrac{d - 1}{2d + 1}$

12. $\dfrac{5y + 2}{xy^2} + \dfrac{2x - 4}{4xy}$

13. $\dfrac{5x}{x^2 - 9} + \dfrac{2}{x + 4}$

14. $\dfrac{-3x}{x^2 - 9} + \dfrac{4}{2x - 6}$

15. $\dfrac{5x}{x^2 - x - 6} + \dfrac{4}{x^2 + 4x + 4}$

Example 4
(page 524)

Simplify each difference.

16. $\dfrac{-2}{x} - \dfrac{1}{x}$

17. $\dfrac{-5y}{2y - 1} - \dfrac{y + 3}{2y - 1}$

18. $\dfrac{y}{2y + 4} - \dfrac{3}{y + 2}$

19. $\dfrac{x}{3x + 9} - \dfrac{8}{x^2 + 3x}$

20. $\dfrac{3y}{y^2 - 25} - \dfrac{8}{y - 5}$

21. $\dfrac{2x}{x^2 - x - 2} - \dfrac{4x}{x^2 - 3x + 2}$

Example 5
(page 524)

Simplify each complex fraction.

22. $\dfrac{\frac{1}{x}}{\frac{2}{y}}$

23. $\dfrac{1 - \frac{1}{4}}{2 - \frac{3}{5}}$

24. $\dfrac{\frac{2}{x + y}}{3}$

25. $\dfrac{\frac{1}{3}}{\frac{3}{b}}$

26. $\dfrac{1}{1 + \frac{x}{y}}$

27. $\dfrac{3}{\frac{2}{x} + y}$

28. $\dfrac{\frac{2}{x + y}}{\frac{5}{x + y}}$

29. $\dfrac{\frac{3}{x - 4}}{1 - \frac{2}{x - 4}}$

30. $\dfrac{-3}{\frac{5}{x} + y}$

B Apply Your Skills

Add or subtract. Simplify where possible.

31. $\dfrac{3}{4x} - \dfrac{2}{x^2}$

32. $\dfrac{3}{x + 1} + \dfrac{x}{x - 1}$

33. $\dfrac{2x}{x^2 - 1} - \dfrac{1}{x^2}$

34. $\dfrac{4}{x^2 - 9} + \dfrac{7}{x + 3}$

35. $\dfrac{x + 2}{x - 1} - \dfrac{x - 3}{2x + 1}$

36. $\dfrac{x}{2x^2 - x} + \dfrac{1}{2x}$

37. $\dfrac{5x}{x^2 - x - 6} - \dfrac{4}{x^2 + 4x + 4}$

38. $3x + \dfrac{x^2 + 5x}{x^2 - 2}$

39. $4y - \dfrac{y + 2}{y^2 + 3y}$

40. $\dfrac{5y}{y^2 - 7y} - \dfrac{4}{2y - 14} + \dfrac{9}{y}$

41. Open-Ended Write two rational expressions whose sum is $\frac{x - 2}{x + 4}$.

42. Writing Explain how factoring is used when adding or subtracting rational expressions. Include an example in your explanation.

43. Error Analysis How would you convince a student that $\frac{7x + 25}{x^2 - 9}$ is *not* the sum of $\frac{4}{x^2 - 9}$ and $\frac{7}{x + 3}$?

Simplify each complex fraction.

44. $\dfrac{\frac{2}{x} + \frac{3}{y}}{\frac{-5}{x} + \frac{7}{y}}$

45. $\dfrac{\frac{5}{x} - \frac{2}{y}}{\frac{-4}{x} - \frac{6}{y}}$

46. $\dfrac{1 + \frac{2}{x}}{2 + \frac{3}{2x}}$

47. $\dfrac{\frac{1}{xy} - \frac{1}{y^2}}{\frac{1}{x^2 y} - \frac{1}{xy^2}}$

48. $\dfrac{\frac{2}{x + 4} + 2}{1 + \frac{3}{x + 4}}$

49. $\dfrac{\frac{3}{x - 2} - 5}{2 - \frac{4}{x - 2}}$

50. Open-Ended Write two different complex fractions that simplify to $\frac{x - 2}{x + 4}$.

51. Critical Thinking What real numbers are not in the domain of function f? Explain.
$$f(x) = \dfrac{\frac{x + 1}{x + 2}}{\frac{x + 3}{x + 4}}$$

Homework Video Tutor

Visit: PHSchool.com
Web Code: bbe-0905

Real-World **Connection**

Shortening a guitar string to $\frac{1}{2}$ or $\frac{2}{3}$ of its original length produces a sound in harmony with the original pitch.

C Challenge

52. Music The harmonic mean of two numbers a and b equals $\dfrac{2}{\frac{1}{a} + \frac{1}{b}}$. As you vary the length of a violin or guitar string, its pitch changes. If a full-length string is 1 unit long, then many lengths that are simple fractions produce pitches that harmonize, or sound pleasing together. The harmonic mean relates three lengths that produce harmonious sounds. For example, $\frac{1}{3}$ is the harmonic mean of $\frac{1}{2}$ and $\frac{1}{4}$, and strings of these lengths produce harmonious sounds. Find the harmonic mean for strings of lengths 1 and $\frac{1}{2}$, $\frac{3}{4}$ and $\frac{1}{2}$, and $\frac{3}{4}$ and $\frac{3}{5}$.

53. a. If you jog 12 mi at an average rate of 4 mi/h and walk the same route back at an average rate of 3 mi/h, you have traveled 24 mi in 7 h and your overall rate is $\frac{24}{7}$ mi/h. What is your overall average rate if you travel d mi at 3 mi/h and d mi at 4 mi/h?
   b. Harmonic Mean Find the harmonic mean (see Exercise 52) of 3 and 4.
   c. If you travel any distance at x mi/h and the same distance at y mi/h then your average rate for the trip is the harmonic mean of x and y. Find the average rate of speed if you travel to a distant city at 50 mi/h and return at 40 mi/h.
   d. You travel to a city at x mi/h and the return trip is a mi/h faster. Express your average rate in terms of x and a.

54. Electricity The total resistance R for a parallel circuit with three bulbs is $R = \dfrac{1}{\frac{1}{R_1} + \frac{1}{R_2} + \frac{1}{R_3}}$.
   a. Simplify the right side of the equation.
   b. Find the total resistance R of a parallel circuit with bulbs that have resistances of 3 ohms, 2.5 ohms, and 2.5 ohms.

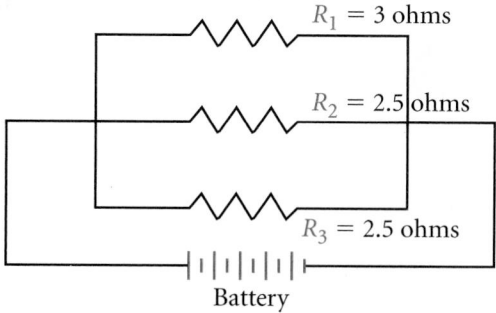

$R_1 = 3$ ohms
$R_2 = 2.5$ ohms
$R_3 = 2.5$ ohms
Battery

55. Physics Use the camera lens equation $\frac{1}{f} = \frac{1}{d_i} + \frac{1}{d_o}$, where d_i is the distance from the lens to the film and d_o is the distance from the lens to an object.
   a. Solve the lens equation for f by taking the reciprocal of each side of the equation. Simplify the equation so it contains no complex fraction.
   b. When an object is in focus, a lens is x cm from the object and $(2x + 1)$ cm from the film. Find the focal length of the lens.

Multiple Choice Practice

For California Standards and CAHSEE Tutorials, visit PHSchool.com. Web Code: bbq-9045

ALG2 7.0 **56.** Which expression equals $\dfrac{1}{x^2 - 2x - 3} + \dfrac{1}{x^2 - 4x + 3}$?

   (A) $\dfrac{2x - 1}{(x - 1)(x + 3)(x + 1)}$

   (B) $\dfrac{2x}{(x - 1)(x + 1)(x - 3)}$

   (C) $\dfrac{2x + 1}{(x - 1)(x + 1)(x - 3)}$

   (D) $\dfrac{2x}{(x + 3)(x - 1)(x + 1)}$

ALG2 2.0 **57.** For which system of equations can you eliminate the variable y by first multiplying one equation by 2 and then adding the equations?

   (A) $\begin{cases} 3x - 4y = 7 \\ x + 2y = 9 \end{cases}$

   (B) $\begin{cases} x + y = 2 \\ x - y = 1 \end{cases}$

   (C) $\begin{cases} 2x + 6y = 1 \\ 2x - 4y = -3 \end{cases}$

   (D) $\begin{cases} 2.5x + 6y = 0 \\ 5x - 9y = 14 \end{cases}$

 GO ●nline Lesson Quiz Visit: PHSchool.com, **Web Code:** bba-0905

ALG2 4.0 **58.** What is the factored form of $2x^3 + 5x^2 - 12x$?

    Ⓐ $x(2x - 3)(x + 4)$

    Ⓑ $(2x^2 - 3)(x + 4)$

    Ⓒ $x(2x + 4)(x - 3)$

    Ⓓ $(2x - 4)(x + 3)$

ALG2 5.0 **59.** If $i = \sqrt{-1}$, which point shows the location of $2 - i$ on the plane?

    Ⓐ point A

    Ⓑ point B

    Ⓒ point C

    Ⓓ point D

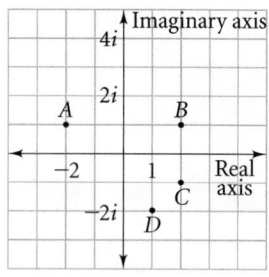

Mixed Review

Lesson 9-4

Divide. State any restrictions on the variables.

60. $\dfrac{4x^3}{3y^4} \div \dfrac{16x^2}{9y^2}$

61. $\dfrac{7ax^3}{8by^2} \div \dfrac{14ax^4}{4by}$

62. $\dfrac{6x^2}{y} \div \dfrac{12x^4}{y^3}$

63. $\dfrac{3x^2 - 9x}{x - 2} \div \dfrac{x^2 - 9}{4x - 8}$

64. $\dfrac{3x - 6}{12x + 24} \div \dfrac{x^2 - 5x + 6}{3x^2 - 12}$

65. $\dfrac{5x + 15}{10x - 10} \div \dfrac{x^2 + 6x + 9}{3x^2 - 3}$

Lesson 8-4 **Write each expression as a single logarithm.**

66. $\log_3 y + 4 \log_3 t$ **67.** $7 \log_{10} p + \log_{10} q$ **68.** $\log_5 x - \frac{1}{5} \log_5 y$

Lesson 7-6 **Let $f(x) = x^2 + 1$ and $g(x) = 3x$. Find each value.**

69. $(g \circ f)(-3)$ **70.** $(f \circ g)(-3)$ **71.** $(g \circ f)\left(\frac{1}{2}\right)$ **72.** $(f \circ f)(3)$

✓ Checkpoint Quiz 2   Lessons 9-4 through 9-5

Simplify each expression.

1. $\dfrac{3x - 6}{5x - 20} \cdot \dfrac{x - 8}{5x - 10}$

2. $\dfrac{14x + 7}{4x - 6} \cdot \dfrac{8x - 12}{42x + 21}$

3. $\dfrac{y^2 - 25}{(y + 5)^2} \div \dfrac{2y - 10}{4y + 20}$

4. $\dfrac{y^2 - 25}{y^2 - 16} \div \dfrac{2y + 10}{y^2 - 4y}$

5. $\dfrac{8}{3x^3y} + \dfrac{4}{9xy^3}$

6. $\dfrac{7}{5y + 25} + \dfrac{4}{3y + 15}$

7. $\dfrac{5x}{2y + 4} - \dfrac{6}{y^2 + 2y}$

8. $3x - \dfrac{x^2 + 5x}{x^2 - 2}$

9. $\dfrac{\frac{3}{2y}}{\frac{6}{8x}}$

10. $\dfrac{\frac{1}{x} + 3}{4 + \frac{5}{y}}$

Since division by zero is undefined, strange and illogical things can happen when division by zero sneaks unnoticed into algebraic procedures.

Does $2 = 1$? Study the proof below.

① $\qquad a = b$

② $\qquad a^2 = ab$

③ $\qquad a^2 - b^2 = ab - b^2$

④ $\quad (a - b)(a + b) = b(a - b)$

⑤ $\quad \dfrac{(a - b)(a + b)}{a - b} = \dfrac{b(a - b)}{a - b}$

⑥ $\qquad a + b = b$

⑦ $\qquad b + b = b$

⑧ $\qquad 2b = b$

⑨ $\qquad 2 = 1$

1. a. Describe each step of the proof.
   b. Check equation ① by replacing a and b with a number such as 3. Do the same for each of the other equations. Which equations are true?
   c. Equation ⑤ seems to be derived by using the Division Property of Equality: If $a = b$ and $c \neq 0$, then $\frac{a}{c} = \frac{b}{c}$. Explain why the property is not used correctly.

2. a. Justify each step of the solution to $\frac{1}{x^2} = \frac{2}{x}$.

   ① $\qquad \dfrac{1}{x^2} = \dfrac{2}{x}$

   ② $\qquad 2x^2 = x$

   ③ $\qquad 2x^2 - x = 0$

   ④ $\quad x(2x - 1) = 0$

   ⑤ $\quad x = 0 \text{ or } x = \frac{1}{2}$

   b. Check the solution $x = \frac{1}{2}$ in equations ④, ③, ②, and ①.
   c. Check the solution $x = 0$ in equations ④, ③, ②, and ①.
   d. How are the checks different? Explain.
   e. If equations ④ and ① have the same solutions, then you can work backward to derive equation ① from ④. What goes wrong when you try?
   f. Critical Thinking Explain why equation ③ can be derived from ②, and ② from ③, thereby ensuring that they have the same solutions.
   g. Equation ② is derived from equation ① using the Multiplication Property of Equality: If $a = b$ then $ac = bc$. Both sides of equation ① are multiplied by x^3 to obtain equation ②. Is there anything wrong with this step?
   h. Critical Thinking Explain why equation ② can be derived from ①, but ① cannot be derived from ②.

9-6 ## Solving Rational Equations

 California Content Standards

ALG2 7.0 Students add, subtract, reduce, and evaluate rational expressions with monomial and polynomial denominators. *Master*

What You'll Learn

• To solve rational equations

• To use rational equations in solving problems

. . . And Why

To find the average speed of a bicycle trip, as in Example 3

☑ **Check Skills You'll Need**

GO for Help   Skills Handbook page 883

Find the LCD of each pair of fractions.

1. $\dfrac{1}{3t}, \dfrac{1}{5t^2}$

2. $\dfrac{x}{2}, \dfrac{3x}{8}$

3. $\dfrac{4}{3h^2}, \dfrac{2h}{h^3}$

4. $\dfrac{4}{y+2}, \dfrac{3}{y-1}$

5. $\dfrac{z}{2z+1}, \dfrac{1}{z}$

6. $\dfrac{1}{k+2}, \dfrac{3k}{k^2-4}$

---

1 Solving Rational Equations

Extraneous solutions can be introduced when you multiply both sides of an equation by the same algebraic expression. An extraneous solution is a solution of the derived equation, but not of the original equation.

You must check all solutions of the derived equation in the original equation to find whether any of them are not solutions of the original equation.

1 EXAMPLE **Solving Rational Equations**

Solve $\dfrac{5}{2x-2} = \dfrac{15}{x^2-1}$. Check each solution.

$$\dfrac{5}{2x-2} = \dfrac{15}{x^2-1}$$

$5(x^2-1) = 15(2x-2)$ **Write the cross products.**

$5x^2 - 5 = 30x - 30$ **Distributive Property**

$5x^2 - 30x + 25 = 0$ **Write in standard form.**

$x^2 - 6x + 5 = 0$ **Divide each side by 5.**

$(x-1)(x-5) = 0$ **Factor.**

$x = 1 \text{ or } x = 5$ **Zero-Product Property**

Problem Solving Hint

In a proportion, the cross products are equal.

If $\frac{a}{b} = \frac{c}{d}$, then $ad = cb$ ($b \neq 0$, $d \neq 0$).

Check When $x = 1$, both denominators in the original equation are zero. The original equation is undefined at $x = 1$. So $x = 1$ is not a solution.

When 5 is substituted for x in the original equation, both sides equal $\frac{5}{8}$.

● The solution is $x = 5$.

☑ **CA Standards Check** ① Solve each equation. Check each solution.

a. $\dfrac{-4}{5(x+2)} = \dfrac{3}{x+2}$

b. $\dfrac{-2}{x^2-2} = \dfrac{2}{x-4}$

When an equation has a sum or difference of two rational expressions, you can use the least common denominator (LCD) to simplify the equation.

2 EXAMPLE **Solving Rational Equations**

Solve $\frac{1}{2x} - \frac{2}{5x} = \frac{1}{2}$.

$$\frac{1}{2x} - \frac{2}{5x} = \frac{1}{2}$$

$10x\left(\frac{1}{2x} - \frac{2}{5x}\right) = 10x\left(\frac{1}{2}\right)$ **Multiply each side by the LCD, 10x.**

$\frac{10x}{2x} - \frac{10x(2)}{5x} = \frac{10x}{2}$ **Distributive Property**

$5 - 4 = 5x$ **Simplify.**

$x = \frac{1}{5}$

Since $\frac{1}{5}$ makes the original equation true, the solution is $x = \frac{1}{5}$.

✓ **CA Standards Check** **2** Solve $\frac{4}{x} - \frac{3}{x+1} = 1$. Check your solution.

---

2 **Using Rational Equations**

3 EXAMPLE **Real-World 🌐 Connection**

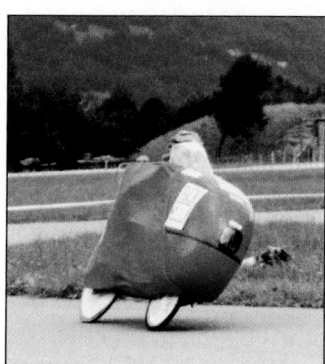

Real-World 🌐 Connection

This high-performance bicycle has the aerodynamic design of a custom racing bicycle, but is practical enough for everyday riding.

Aerodynamics The aerodynamic covering on this bicycle increases a cyclist's average speed by 10 mi/h. The time for a 75-mi trip is reduced by 2 h. What is the average speed for the trip using the aerodynamic covering?

Relate speed with aerodynamic covering = speed without covering + 10

Define

	Distance (mi)	Rate (mi/h)	Time (h)
Without Covering	75	$\frac{75}{t}$	t
With Covering	75	$\frac{75}{t-2}$	$t - 2$

Write $\frac{75}{t-2} = \frac{75}{t} + 10$

$$\frac{75}{t-2} = \frac{75}{t} + 10$$

$t(t-2)\left(\frac{75}{t-2}\right) = t(t-2)\left(\frac{75}{t}\right) + t(t-2)(10)$ **Multiply by the LCD,**
t(t − 2).

$t(75) = (t-2)(75) + 10t(t-2)$ **Simplify.**

$75t = 75t - 150 + 10t^2 - 20t$ **Distributive Property**

$0 = 10t^2 - 20t - 150$ **Simplify.**

$0 = t^2 - 2t - 15$ **Divide each side by 10.**

$0 = (t-5)(t+3)$ **Factor.**

$t = 5$ or $t = -3$ The time must be positive, so $\frac{75}{t-2} = \frac{75}{5-2} = 25$.

The average speed with the aerodynamic covering is 25 mi/h.

✓ **CA Standards Check** **3** Rosa can jog 5 mi downhill in the same time it takes her to jog 3 mi uphill. She jogs downhill 4 mi/h faster than she jogs uphill. Find her jogging rate each way.

4 EXAMPLE **Real-World** **Connection**

Volunteerism Tim can stuff envelopes three times as fast as his daughter Georgia. They have to stuff 5000 envelopes for a fund-raiser. Working together, Tim and Georgia can complete the job in about four hours. How many hours would it take each of them working alone?

Relate Tim's rate + Georgia's rate = combined rate

Define

	Time (hr)	Rate (envelopes per hour)
Tim	x	$\dfrac{5000}{x}$
Georgia	$3x$	$\dfrac{5000}{3x}$
Combined	4	$\dfrac{5000}{4} = 1250$

Write $\dfrac{5000}{x} + \dfrac{5000}{3x} = 1250$

Method 1 Use a graphing calculator. Graph $y_1 = \dfrac{5000}{x} + \dfrac{5000}{3x}$ and $y_2 = 1250$ in a window with Xmin = 3, Xmax = 10, Ymin = 0, and Ymax = 2000. Then use the INTERSECT feature to find the intersections of the two graphs. The graphs intersect at $x \approx 5.33$.

Method 2 Use a graphing calculator and $y_1 = \dfrac{5000}{x} + \dfrac{5000}{3x} - 1250$. Use the TABLE feature and "zoom in" on the point where the function changes sign. This occurs at $x \approx 5.33$.

Tim could stuff 5000 envelopes in about 5.33 hours.

Georgia could stuff 5000 envelopes in 3(5.33) hours, or about 16 hours.

For help with solving equations by tables, see Lesson 5-5.

✓ CA Standards Check **4** **a.** Suppose Maria can stuff envelopes twice as fast as her friend Paco. Together, they can stuff 6750 envelopes in 4.5 hours. How long would it take each of them working alone?

b. Suppose Adrian can weed the garden twice as fast as his son Phillip. Together they can weed the garden in 3 hours. How long would it take each of them working alone?

EXERCISES

For more exercises, see *Extra Skill and Word Problem Practice.*

Standards Practice

ALG2 7.0

A **Practice by Example**

Example 1
(page 530)

Solve each equation. Check each solution.

1. $\dfrac{x}{5} = \dfrac{x+3}{8}$

2. $\dfrac{1}{5x} = \dfrac{1}{9x}$

3. $\dfrac{4}{3x+3} = \dfrac{12}{x^2-1}$

4. $\dfrac{2}{x-1} = \dfrac{x+4}{3}$

5. $\dfrac{3}{x+1} = \dfrac{1}{x^2-1}$

6. $\dfrac{4}{2x-3} = \dfrac{x}{5}$

7. $\dfrac{3}{x} = \dfrac{12}{x+7}$

8. $\dfrac{10}{6x+7} = \dfrac{6}{2x+9}$

9. $\dfrac{2}{3x-5} = \dfrac{4}{x-15}$

Example 2
(page 531)

Solve each equation. Check each solution.

10. $\frac{1}{4} - x = \frac{x}{8}$

11. $\frac{y}{5} + \frac{y}{2} = 7$

12. $\frac{2x}{3} - \frac{1}{2} = \frac{2x + 5}{6}$

13. $\frac{3x - 2}{12} - \frac{1}{6} = \frac{1}{6}$

14. $\frac{1}{x} + \frac{x}{2} = \frac{x + 4}{2x}$

15. $\frac{11}{3x} - \frac{1}{3} = \frac{-4}{x^2}$

16. $\frac{3}{2x} - \frac{5}{3x} = 2$

17. $\frac{5x}{4} - \frac{3}{x} = \frac{1}{4}$

18. $\frac{2}{y} + \frac{1}{2} = \frac{5}{2y}$

19. $x + \frac{6}{x} = -5$

20. $\frac{1}{4x} - \frac{3}{4} = \frac{7}{x}$

21. $\frac{5}{2x} - \frac{2}{3} = \frac{1}{x} + \frac{5}{6}$

Examples 3 and 4
(pages 531 and 532)

22. Carlos can travel 40 mi on his motorbike in the same time it takes Paul to travel 15 mi on his bicycle. If Paul rides his bike 20 mi/h slower than Carlos rides his motorbike, find the speed for each bike.

23. A passenger train travels 392 mi in the same time that it takes a freight train to travel 322 mi. If the passenger train travels 20 mi/h faster than the freight train, find the speed of each train.

24. Shelley can paint a fence in 8 hours. Karen can do it in 4 hours. How long will it take them to do the job if they work together?

25. One pump can fill a tank with oil in 4 hours. A second pump can fill the same tank in 3 hours. If both pumps are used at the same time, how long will they take to fill the tank?

 Apply Your Skills

Solve each equation for the given variable.

26. $m = \frac{2E}{V^2}$; E

27. $\frac{c}{E} - \frac{1}{mc} = 0$; E

28. $\frac{m}{F} = \frac{1}{a}$; F

29. $\frac{1}{c} - \frac{c}{a^2 - b^2} = 0$; c

30. $\frac{\ell}{T^2} = \frac{g}{4\pi^2}$; T

31. $\frac{q}{m} = \frac{2V}{B^2 r^2}$; B

GO for Help

For a guide to solving
Exercise 32, see page 538.

32. Anita and Fran have volunteered to contact every member of their organization by phone to inform them of an upcoming event. Fran can complete the calls in six days if she works alone. Anita can complete them in four days. How long will they take to complete the calls working together?

33. **Multiple Choice** On the first four tests of the term your average is 84%. You think you can score 96% on each of the remaining tests. How many consecutive test scores of 96% would you need to bring your average up to 90% for the term?

Ⓐ 1   Ⓑ 2   Ⓒ 3   Ⓓ 4

34. You are planning a school field trip to a local theater. It costs $60 to rent the bus. Each theater ticket costs $5.50.
   a. Write a function $c(x)$ to represent the cost per student if x students sign up.
   b. How many students must sign up if the cost is to be no more than $10 per student?

35. **Woodworking** A tapered cylinder is made by decreasing the radius of a rod continuously as you move from one end to the other. The rate at which it tapers is the taper per foot. You can calculate the taper per foot using the formula $T = \frac{24(R - r)}{L}$. The lengths R, r, and L are measured in inches.

   a. Solve this equation for L.
   b. Find L if $R = 4$ in.; $r = 3$ in.; and $T = 0.75, 0.85,$ and 0.95.

Homework Video Tutor

Visit: PHSchool.com
Web Code: bbe-0906

36. Fuel Economy Suppose you drive an average of 15,000 miles per year, and your car gets 24 miles per gallon. Suppose gasoline costs $1.60 a gallon.

   a. How much money do you spend each year on gasoline?

   b. You plan to trade in your car for one that gets x more miles per gallon. Write an expression to represent the new yearly cost of gasoline.

   c. Write an expression to represent your savings on gasoline.

   d. Suppose you save $200 a year with the new car. How many miles per gallon does the new car get?

37. Open-Ended Write a rational equation that has the same solution as the question in the cartoon.

38. Industry The average hourly wage $H(x)$ of workers in an industry is modeled by the function $H(x) = \frac{16.24x}{0.062x + 39.42}$, where x represents the number of years since 1970.

   a. In what year does the model predict that wages will be $25/h?

   b. Critical Thinking Is the prediction reasonable? Explain.

The Family Circus *by Bil Keane*

4-25

"What's 129 divided by 4?"

Solve each equation. Check each solution.

39. $\frac{15}{x} + \frac{9x - 7}{x + 2} = 9$

40. $\frac{2}{x + 2} - \frac{1}{x} = \frac{-4}{x(x + 2)}$

41. $\frac{1}{b + 1} + \frac{1}{b - 1} = \frac{2}{b^2 - 1}$

42. $c - \frac{c}{3} + \frac{c}{5} = 26$

43. $\frac{2}{x - 3} - \frac{4}{x + 3} = \frac{8}{x^2 - 9}$

44. $\frac{1}{8} + \frac{5x}{x + 2} = \frac{5}{2}$

45. $\frac{1}{x - 5} = \frac{x}{x^2 - 25}$

46. $\frac{k}{k + 1} + \frac{k}{k - 2} = 2$

47. $\frac{3}{x + 5} + \frac{2}{5 - x} = \frac{-4}{x^2 - 25}$

48. $\frac{5}{x + 2} = \frac{-1}{x^2 + 7x + 10} + \frac{3}{-x - 5}$

49. $\frac{5}{x^2 - 7x + 12} - \frac{2}{3 - x} = \frac{5}{x - 4}$

50. $\frac{10}{2y + 8} - \frac{7y + 8}{y^2 - 16} = \frac{-8}{2y - 8}$

51. $\frac{7x + 3}{x^2 - 8x + 15} + \frac{3x}{x - 5} = \frac{1}{3 - x}$

52. $\frac{2}{x + 3} - \frac{3}{4 - x} = \frac{2x - 2}{x^2 - x - 12}$

53. Landscape Design Suppose you want to double the area of the patio shown at the right. Find the increase x of both the length and width of the patio.

54. Writing Write and solve a problem that can be modeled by a rational equation.

55. Transportation A plane flies from New York to Chicago (about 700 miles) at a speed of 360 mi/h.

   a. The speed s of the plane is given by $s = \frac{d}{t}$. d represents the distance and t is the time. Solve the equation for t.

   b. Find the time for the trip.

   c. On the return trip from Chicago to New York, a tail wind helps the plane move faster. Write an expression for the speed of the plane on the return trip. Let x represent the speed of the tail wind.

   d. The total flying time for the round trip is 3.5 h. Write a rational equation for the sum of the flying times. Find the speed x of the tail wind.

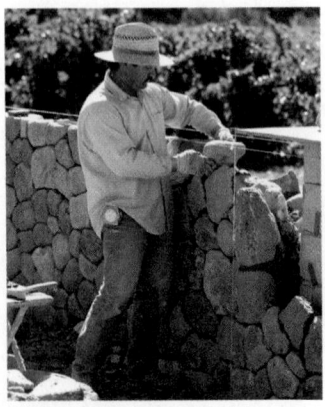

Real-World **Connection**

The area of a structure determines how many stones a mason needs.

Challenge

56. Open-Ended Write a rational equation that has the following.
    a. one solution   **b.** two solutions   **c.** no real solution

57. A salesman drove from his home to a nearby city at an average speed of 40 mi/h. He returned home at an average speed of 50 mi/h. What was his average speed for the entire trip?

58. An automatic pitching machine can pitch all its baseballs in $1\frac{1}{4}$ hours. One attendant can retrieve all the baseballs pitched by one machine in $3\frac{1}{2}$ hours. At least how many attendants working at the same rate should be hired so that the baseballs from 10 machines are all retrieved in fewer than 8 hours?

Multiple Choice Practice

For California Standards and CAHSEE Tutorials, visit PHSchool.com. Web Code: bbq-9045

ALG2 7.0

59. What is the complete solution set of $\dfrac{3}{x^2 - 1} + \dfrac{4x}{x + 1} = \dfrac{1.5}{x - 1}$?

    Ⓐ 1, −1   Ⓑ 1, 0.375   Ⓒ 0.375   Ⓓ 0.375, 3

ALG2 10.0

60. The graph at the right represents which function?

    Ⓐ $y = \dfrac{x^2 - 4}{x + 4}$

    Ⓑ $y = x^2 - 4x + 1$

    Ⓒ $y = |x + 4|$

    Ⓓ $y = x^3 + x^2 - 4$

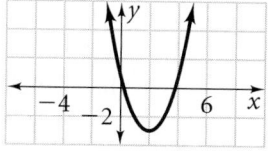

ALG2 9.0

61. Which list orders the functions from widest to narrowest graph?

    Ⓐ $y = -\frac{1}{5}x^2,\ y = \frac{4}{5}x^2,\ y = 3x^2,\ y = -5x^2$

    Ⓑ $y = -5x^2,\ y = 3x^2,\ y = \frac{4}{5}x^2,\ y = -\frac{1}{5}x^2$

    Ⓒ $y = \frac{4}{5}x^2,\ y = 3x^2,\ y = -5x^2,\ y = -\frac{1}{5}x^2$

    Ⓓ $y = -5x^2,\ y = -\frac{1}{5}x^2,\ y = \frac{4}{5}x^2,\ y = 3x^2$

Mixed Review

Lesson 9-5

Simplify each difference.

62. $\dfrac{3y + 1}{4y + 4} - \dfrac{2y + 7}{2y + 2}$ **63.** $\dfrac{5x}{2y + 4} - \dfrac{6}{y^2 + 2y}$ **64.** $\dfrac{x + 1}{2x - 2} - \dfrac{2x}{x^2 + 2x - 3}$

Lesson 8-5

Solve each equation.

65. $\log_{10} 0.001 = x$ **66.** $\log_3 27 = 3x + 6$

67. $\log_{0.1}(x + 1) = 3$ **68.** $\log_3 \frac{1}{9} = \frac{x}{3}$

Lesson 7-7

Find the inverse of each function. Is the inverse a function?

69. $y = 5 - 2x$ **70.** $y = x^2 + 1$ **71.** $y = x^3 - 4$

Rational Inequalities

You can multiply both sides of a rational inequality by the same algebraic expression just as you have done with equations. However, not only can you introduce extraneous solutions, you can also lose solutions!

1 ACTIVITY

1. Here is Alice's solution of the rational inequality $\frac{N}{4 - N} < 3$.
   Read it carefully.

$$\frac{N}{4 - N} < 3$$

$$N < 3(4 - N)$$

$$N < 12 - 3N$$

$$4N < 12$$

$$N < 3$$

Alice concluded that the solution consists of all integers less than 3. Or so it would seem. Does Alice's solution appear to be correct?

2. **a.** Choose an integer less than 3. Does it make the inequality true?
   b. Pick an integer greater than 4. Does it make the inequality true?
   c. What happens to the inequality when $N = 3$? $N = 4$?
   d. Make a conjecture about the solution based on your results in parts (a)–(c).

3. Enter the function $y_1 = x/(4 - x)$ in your graphing calculator. Set up a table as shown below. Scroll down through the table. All the x-values are integers greater than 3. Find one that fails to satisfy the inequality $\frac{N}{4 - N} < 3$. Does this finding agree with your results from Exercise 2?

2 ACTIVITY

It would appear that Alice's algebraic solution was only partially successful. It correctly concludes that any integer less than 3 satisfies the inequality. Unfortunately, it fails to identify other values that satisfy the inequality.

4. **Error Analysis** Alice made an error in one step in her solution. Where is the error? What erroneous assumption did Alice make?

5. What is the first change you would make to correct Alice's error.

6. Show how the assumption $N > 4$ leads to solutions of the inequality that Alice did not find. (*Hint:* What is important about the value of $4 - N$?)

7. Now, write a complete solution of the inequality $\frac{N}{4 - N} < 3$.

As you can see, the algebraic solution to the simple-looking rational inequality $\frac{N}{4 - N} < 3$ is not all that simple. You might find it easier to solve this inequality (and other rational inequalities) graphically.

8. Graph two functions $y_1 = \frac{x}{4 - x}$ and $y_2 = 3$ using the settings at the right. Explain how you can use the graph to solve the inequality $\frac{N}{4 - N} < 3$.

9. Graph the function $y_3 = \frac{x}{4 - x} - 3$ (or $y_3 = y_1 - y_2$) in the window used in Exercise 8. How can you use this graph to solve the inequality $\frac{N}{4 - N} < 3$?

```
WINDOW
 Xmin = -4.7
 Xmax = 9.4
 Xscl = 1
 Ymin = -8
 Ymax = 5
 Yscl = 1
 Xres = 1■
```

10. Show how to solve $\frac{N}{4 - N} < 3$ by using y_1 and y_2 and tables, or y_3 and tables.

EXERCISES

Use the settings from Exercise 8. Solve each of 11–13 using your choice of two graphs (Exercise 8), one graph (Exercise 9), or tables (Exercise 10).

11. $\frac{2}{x - 1} < x$

12. $x + 1 > \frac{x + 5}{x + 2}$

13. $\frac{2x}{(x - 2)(x + 3)} < 1$

14. For Exercises 11–13, check your work by using a different method to solve each inequality.

15. Multiple Choice Which graph can you use to solve the inequality $\frac{1}{x - 2} < -3$

Ⓐ 　　Ⓑ 　　Ⓒ 　　Ⓓ

16. Mr. Huerta has 600 minutes per week to give individual help to students. He averages 20 min per student. If he reduces the time per student by t min to $(20 - t)$ min, he can meet with $\frac{600}{20 - t}$ students. Write an inequality that describes each situation below and solve the inequality.

  a. How many fewer minutes per student will allow Mr. Huerta to work with at least 36 students?

  b. How many more minutes per student will allow Mr. Huerta to work with no more than 27 students?

17. The equation $d = rt$ relates the distance d you travel, the time t it takes to travel that distance, and the rate r at which you travel. So the time it takes is $t = \frac{d}{r}$. If you increase your rate by a to $r + a$, then it takes less time, $t = \frac{d}{r + a}$. In fact, the time you save by going at the faster rate is $T = \frac{d}{r} - \frac{d}{r + a}$.

  a. You normally take a 500-mi trip, averaging 45 mi/h. You want to increase the rate so that your travel time is at least 1 h shorter. Write an inequality that describes the situation.

  b. Solve the inequality you wrote in part (a).

Understanding Word Problems Read the problem below. Then let Ahmed's thinking guide you through the solution. Check your understanding with the exercises at the bottom of the page.

Anita and Fran have volunteered to contact every member of their organization by phone to inform them of an upcoming event. Fran can complete the calls in six days if she works alone. Anita can complete them in four days. How long will they take to complete the calls working together?

What Ahmed Thinks

I'll write the information in my own words.

Work problems involve rates. Even though I don't know the number of calls Fran and Anita are making, maybe I can just consider the entire job, or total amount of work, being done.

I'll define variables, t for time and w for work.

Now I can write an equation.

The variable w is going to cancel out of the equation, so I can just solve for t.

I can write my answer in a sentence now.

What Ahmed Writes

Fran can complete the work in 6 days.
Anita can complete the work in 4 days.

$$\text{rate} = \frac{\text{work being done}}{\text{time}}$$

$$\frac{\text{Fran's}}{\text{rate}} = \frac{\text{work being done}}{\text{time}} = \frac{\text{total work}}{6}$$

$$\frac{\text{Anita's}}{\text{rate}} = \frac{\text{work being done}}{\text{time}} = \frac{\text{total work}}{4}$$

w = total work
t = time working together

$$\frac{\text{Fran's}}{\text{rate}} + \frac{\text{Anita's}}{\text{rate}} = \frac{\text{combined}}{\text{rate}}$$

$$\frac{\text{total work}}{6} + \frac{\text{total work}}{4} = \frac{\text{total work}}{\text{time together}}$$

$$\frac{w}{6} + \frac{w}{4} = \frac{w}{t}$$

$$\frac{1}{6} + \frac{1}{4} = \frac{1}{t}$$

$$2t + 3t = 12$$

$$5t = \frac{12}{5} = 2\frac{2}{5}$$

It will take Anita and Fran, working together, $2\frac{2}{5}$ days to complete all the calls.

EXERCISES

1. Charlene can wash a car in 15 minutes, and Robert can wash the same size car in 12 minutes. How long will it take them to wash a car if they work together?
2. It takes 12 min to fill a bathtub with the drain closed. If the tap is closed, it takes 20 min to drain the bathtub. How long does it take to fill the bathtub with both the tap and the drain open?

Probability of Multiple Events

 California Content Standards

PS 1.0 Students know the definition of the notion of *independent events* and can use the rules of addition, multiplication, and complementation to solve for probabilities of particular events in finite sample spaces.

What You'll Learn

- To find the probabilities of events *A* and *B*
- To find the probabilities of events *A* or *B*

. . . And Why

To solve problems involving radio call-in shows, as in Example 2

 Check Skills You'll Need

 for Help Lesson 1-6

A bag contains 24 green marbles, 22 blue marbles, 14 yellow marbles, and 12 red marbles. Suppose you pick one marble at random. Find each probability.

1. P(yellow)　　**2.** P(not blue)　　**3.** P(green or red)

4. Of 300 senior students at Taft High, 150 have taken physics, 192 have taken chemistry, and 30 have taken neither physics nor chemistry. How many students have taken both physics and chemistry?

 New Vocabulary ● **dependent events** ● **independent events**
● **mutually exclusive events**

1　Finding *P*(*A* and *B*)

Hands-On Activity: Multiple Events

- Work with a partner to analyze the game Primarily Odd.

- **Partner A:** Roll two standard number cubes. If the sum is either odd *or* a prime number, score a point.

- **Partner B:** Roll two standard number cubes. If the sum is both odd *and* a prime number, score a point.

- Alternate turns rolling the number cubes.

1. a. List all the possible outcomes of rolling two number cubes.
　b. How many outcomes result in an odd sum? Calculate the probability of getting an odd sum.
　c. How many outcomes result in a prime sum? Calculate the probability of getting a prime sum.

2. Predict which partner is more likely to score points in Primarily Odd. Justify your reasoning.

3. Play the game with your partner. Take 10 turns each. Keep track of each player's score. How do your results compare with the prediction you made in Question 2?

When the outcome of one event affects the outcome of a second event, the two events are **dependent events.** When the outcome of one event does *not* affect the outcome of a second event, the two events are **independent events.**

1 EXAMPLE **Classifying Events**

Classify each pair of events as *dependent* or *independent*.

a. Roll a number cube. Then toss a coin.
Since the two events do not affect each other, they are independent.

b. Pick a flower from a garden. Then pick another flower from the same garden.
Picking the first flower affects the possible outcomes of picking the second flower. So the events are dependent.

✓ CA Standards Check **①** Suppose you select a marble from a bag of marbles. You replace the marble and then select again. Are your selections dependent or independent events? Explain.

You can find the probability that two independent events will both occur by multiplying probabilities.

 Key Concepts

Property	**Probability of *A* and *B***

If *A* and *B* are independent events, then $P(A \text{ and } B) = P(A) \cdot P(B)$.

Example: If $P(A) = \frac{1}{2}$ and $P(B) = \frac{1}{3}$, then $P(A \text{ and } B) = \frac{1}{2} \cdot \frac{1}{3} = \frac{1}{6}$.

2 EXAMPLE **Real-World** 🌐 **Connection**

Radio Suppose your favorite radio station is running a promotional campaign. Every hour, four callers chosen at random get to select two songs each. You call the station once after 7:00 A.M. and again after 3:00 P.M. What is the probability that you will be one of the four callers both times you call?

WKW Radio Statistics

Hour	Calls Received That Hour
7:00 A.M.	125
3:00 P.M.	200

Relate probability of both events **is** probability of first event **times** probability of second event

Define Event *A* = you are one of the four callers after 7:00 A.M. Then $P(A) = \frac{4}{125}$.

Event *B* = you are one of the four callers after 3:00 P.M. Then $P(B) = \frac{4}{200}$.

Write $P(A \text{ and } B) = P(A) \cdot P(B)$

$P(A \text{ and } B) = \frac{4}{125} \cdot \frac{4}{200}$

$= \frac{16}{25,000}$ **Multiply.**

$= \frac{2}{3125}$ **Simplify.**

The probability of being one of the four callers selected at random both times you call is $\frac{2}{3125}$, or 0.064%.

Real-World 🌐 **Connection**

In the United States, the peak hours for radio-listening are 7–8 A.M., 12–1 P.M., and 3–4 P.M.

✓ CA Standards Check **②** Suppose the radio station changes the promotional campaign. Now it chooses five callers at random each hour.
a. What is the probability of being one of the five callers after 7 A.M? After 3 P.M.?
b. Find the probability of being one of the five callers both times you call.

When two events cannot happen at the same time, the events are **mutually exclusive events.** If *A* and *B* are mutually exclusive events, then *P(A and B)* = 0.

EXAMPLE Mutually Exclusive Events

Are the events mutually exclusive? Explain.

a. rolling a 2 or a 3 on a number cube

Since you cannot roll a 2 and a 3 at the same time, the events are mutually exclusive.

b. rolling an even number or a multiple of 3 on a number cube

By rolling a 6, you can roll an even number and a multiple of 3 at the same time. So the events are not mutually exclusive.

Vocabulary Tip

Events that are not mutually exclusive are sometimes called <u>inclusive</u> events, or <u>non-mutually exclusive</u> events.

 CA Standards Check **3** Are the events mutually exclusive? Explain.
  a. rolling an even number and rolling a prime number on a number cube
  b. rolling an even number and rolling a number less than 2 on a number cube

You need to determine whether events *A* and *B* are mutually exclusive before you can find the probability of (*A* or *B*).

Key Concepts

Property	Probability of (*A or B*)
	If *A* and *B* are mutually exclusive events, then $P(A \text{ or } B) = P(A) + P(B)$.
	If *A* and *B* are not mutually exclusive events, then $P(A \text{ or } B) = P(A) + P(B) - P(A \text{ and } B)$.

Many statistical measures are based on probabilities of the form *P(A or B)*.

4 **EXAMPLE** Real-World 🌐 Connection

College Enrollment About 53% of U.S. college students are under 25 years old. About 21% of U.S. college students are over 34 years old. What is the probability that a U.S. college student chosen at random is under 25 or over 34?

Since a student cannot be under 25 and over 34, the events are mutually exclusive.

$P(\text{under } 25 \text{ or over } 34) = P(\text{under } 25) + P(\text{over } 34)$ **Use the *P(A or B)* formula for mutually exclusive events.**

$= 0.53 + 0.21$

$= 0.74$

The probability that a U.S. college student chosen at random is under 25 or over 34 is about 0.74, or about 74%.

CA Standards Check **4** A U.S. college student is chosen at random. Find the probability for each age range of the student.
  a. 25−34   **b.** 25−34 or over 34   **c.** 34 or under

When two events are *not* mutually exclusive, you need to subtract the probability of the common outcomes.

5 EXAMPLE Probabilities of Events

Multiple Choice Suppose you reach into the bowl at the left and select a piece of fruit at random. What is the probability that the fruit is an apple or green?

① $\frac{2}{9}$ ② $\frac{3}{9}$ ③ $\frac{6}{9}$ ④ $\frac{8}{9}$

$P(\text{apple or green}) = P(\text{apple}) + P(\text{green}) - P(\text{apple and green})$

$$= \frac{5}{9} + \frac{3}{9} - \frac{2}{9}$$

$$= \frac{6}{9}$$

The probability of picking a piece of fruit that is an apple or green is $\frac{6}{9}$, or $\frac{2}{3}$. The correct choice is C.

CA Standards Check ④ Find each probability.   **a.** $P(\text{apple or red})$ **b.** $P(\text{green or citrus fruit})$

EXERCISES
For more exercises, see *Extra Skill and Word Problem Practice.*

Standards Practice   PS 1.0

A Practice by Example

Example 1
(page 540)

Classify each pair of events as *dependent* or *independent*.

1. A month is selected at random; a number from 1 to 30 is selected at random.

2. A month is selected at random; a day of that month is selected at random.

3. A letter of the alphabet is selected at random; one of the remaining letters is selected at random.

4. The color of a car is selected at random; the type of transmission is selected at random.

Example 2
(page 540)

Q and R are independent events. Find $P(Q \text{ and } R)$.

5. $P(Q) = \frac{1}{4}, P(R) = \frac{2}{3}$ **6.** $P(Q) = \frac{12}{17}, P(R) = \frac{3}{8}$

7. $P(Q) = 0.6, P(R) = 0.9$ **8.** $P(Q) = \frac{1}{3}, P(R) = \frac{6}{x}$

9. Suppose you have five books in your book bag. Three are novels, one is a biography, and one is a poetry book. Today you grab one book out of your bag without looking, and return it later. Tomorrow you do the same thing. What is the probability that you grab a novel both days?

Example 3
(page 541)

Two standard number cubes are tossed. State whether the events are mutually exclusive. Explain your reasoning.

10. The sum is a prime number; the sum is less than 4.

11. The numbers are equal; the sum is odd.

12. The product is greater than 20; the product is a multiple of 3.

Example 4
(page 541)

13. Population About 30% of the U.S. population is under 20 years old. About 17% of the population is over 60. What is the probability that a person chosen at random is under 20 or over 60?

S and T are mutually exclusive events. Find P(S or T).

14. $P(S) = \frac{5}{8}, P(T) = \frac{1}{8}$

15. $P(S) = \frac{3}{5}, P(T) = \frac{1}{3}$

16. $P(S) = 12\%, P(T) = 27\%$

17. $P(S) = \frac{1}{7}, P(T) = 60\%$

Example 5
(page 542)

A standard number cube is tossed. Find each probability.

18. P(3 or odd)

19. P(4 or even)

20. P(even or less than 4)

21. P(odd or greater than 2)

22. P(odd or prime)

23. P(even or prime)

24. P(4 or less than 6)

25. P(greater than 1 or less than 5)

 Apply Your Skills

C and D are not mutually exclusive events. Copy and complete the table below to find each missing probability.

	P(C)	P(D)	P(C and D)	P(C or D)
26.	$\frac{4}{9}$	$\frac{4}{9}$	▨	$\frac{5}{9}$
27.	$\frac{1}{2}$	$\frac{1}{3}$	$\frac{1}{4}$	▨
28.	$\frac{2}{3}$	$\frac{3}{5}$	▨	$\frac{13}{15}$
29.	$\frac{3}{7}$	$\frac{1}{4}$	$\frac{1}{8}$	▨

Test-Taking Tip

In $P(C$ or $D)$, C or D means that C occurs by itself, D occurs by itself, or possibly both C and D occur together.

30. Multiple Choice Suppose a number from 1 to 100 is selected at random. What is the probability that a multiple of 4 or 5 is chosen?

Ⓐ $\frac{1}{20}$ Ⓑ 0.36   Ⓒ $\frac{2}{5}$ Ⓓ 45%

Statistics **The graph at the right shows the types of jobs held by people in the United States. Find each probability.**

31. A person is in a service occupation.

32. A person is in service or sales.

33. A person is not in production or transportation.

34. A person is neither in sales nor in service, nor in managerial nor professional occupations.

35. A person is neither in service nor in sales.

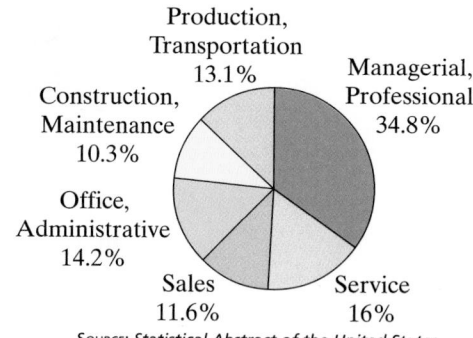

U.S. Employment, by Occupation

Production, Transportation 13.1%
Managerial, Professional 34.8%
Construction, Maintenance 10.3%
Office, Administrative 14.2%
Sales 11.6%
Service 16%

SOURCE: *Statistical Abstract of the United States.*
Go to **www.PHSchool.com** for a data update.
Web Code: bbg-9041

A jar contains four blue marbles and two red marbles. Suppose you choose a marble at random and do not replace it. Then you choose a second marble. Find the probability of each event.

36. You select a blue marble and then a red marble.

37. You select a red marble and then a blue marble.

38. One of the marbles you select is blue and the other is red.

39. Both of the marbles you select are red.

40. You select two red marbles or two blue marbles.

Homework Video Tutor

Visit: PHSchool.com
Web Code: bbe-0907

H and J are not mutually exclusive events. Copy and complete the table below to find each missing probability.

	P(H)	P(J)	P(H and J)	P(H or J)
41.	$\frac{7}{11}$	$\frac{3}{11}$	▪	$\frac{9}{11}$
42.	$\frac{1}{2}$	▪	$\frac{1}{4}$	$\frac{2}{3}$
43.	▪	$\frac{2}{5}$	$\frac{1}{5}$	$\frac{2}{3}$
44.	$\frac{2}{x}$	$\frac{3}{2x}$	$\frac{1}{x}$	▪

45. **Tests** A multiple-choice test has four choices for each answer.
   a. What is the probability that a random guess on a question will yield the correct answer?
   b. Suppose you need to make a random guess on three of the ten test questions. What is the probability that you will answer all three correctly?

46. **Open-Ended** Describe two events that are not mutually exclusive. Estimate the probability of both events occurring.

47. **Error Analysis** Events F and G are mutually exclusive independent events. A student says that $P(F$ and $G)$ is greater than $P(F$ or $G)$. Explain how you can tell that the student is wrong.

 Challenge

Use the tables below for Exercises 48–50. One student from each school is chosen at random to be on a committee. Find each probability.

School A

Freshman	Sophomore	Junior	Senior
30%	27%	25%	18%

School B

Freshman	Sophomore	Junior	Senior
28%	28%	24%	20%

48. a junior from School A and a senior from School B

49. two juniors

50. a freshman or sophomore from School A and a senior from School B

51. Two number cubes are rolled. What is the probability that the sum is greater than 9 or less than 6?

52. **Critical Thinking** Tatyana has $x + 2$ pens in the pocket of her backpack. Samuel has $2x - 1$ pens in the pocket of his backpack.
   a. Tatyana has 2 blue pens. Find the probability that she pulls out a blue pen at random.
   b. Samuel has $x - 3$ blue pens. Find the probability that he pulls out a blue pen at random.
   c. Find the probability that both Tatyana and Samuel pull out blue pens at random.
   d. Find the probability that either Tatyana or Samuel pulls out a blue pen at random.

Multiple Choice Practice

For California Standards and CAHSEE Tutorials, visit PHSchool.com. Web Code: bbq-9045

PS 1.0
53. Rachel is playing a game that involves rolling two standard number cubes. She needs to roll two of the same number in order to win the game. In one roll of the two number cubes, what is the probability that the faces on the number cubes will be the same?

(A) $\frac{1}{36}$ (B) $\frac{1}{12}$ (C) $\frac{1}{6}$ (D) $\frac{1}{3}$

ALG2 1.0
54. Which inequality is represented by the graph?

(A) $y \geq |x + 1| - 3$
(B) $y \geq -|x + 1| + 3$
(C) $y \leq |x - 1| - 3$
(D) $y > |x - 1| + 3$

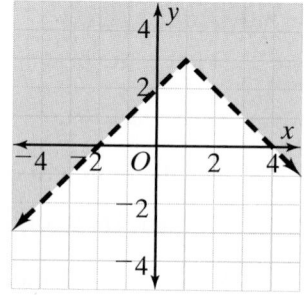

Mixed Review

Lesson 9-6   **Solve each equation. Check your answer.**

55. $\frac{1}{2} - x = \frac{x}{6}$ **56.** $\frac{2}{2x - 1} = \frac{x}{3}$ **57.** $\frac{3}{2x} - \frac{2}{3x} = 5$

GO **for Help**

Lesson 8-6   **Solve each equation.**

58. $\ln 2x = 3$ **59.** $\ln x + \ln 2 = 6$ **60.** $\ln x - \ln 4 = 5$

61. $\ln x^2 + 1 = 5$ **62.** $\ln x^2 + \ln x = 6$ **63.** $e^x = 12$

64. $e^{x+1} = 8$ **65.** $e^{x^2} = 3$ **66.** $2e^{2x} + 1 = 5$

Algebra at Work

············ Economist

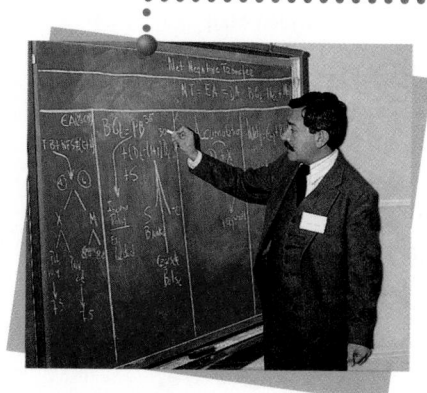

Economists study the relationship between the supply of a product and public demand for it. A supply curve shows that the number of units a manufacturer produces will increase as the price of the item increases. A demand curve shows that the number of units sold will decrease as the price increases. The curves cross at a point that establishes a stable equilibrium price.

For: Information about economists
Web Code: bbb-2031

Before you try to find the answer to a problem, you may be able to eliminate some answer choices.

1 EXAMPLE

What is the best approximation to $\sqrt{105} - \dfrac{3}{2 - \sqrt{27}}$?

A -5.1 **B** 8.3 **C** 11.2 **D** 12.5

The denominator of $\dfrac{3}{2 - \sqrt{27}}$ is a negative number, so $\sqrt{105} - \dfrac{3}{2 - \sqrt{27}}$ is a positive number. Therefore, you can eliminate A.

Since $\sqrt{105}$ is close to 10, and $-\dfrac{3}{2 - \sqrt{27}}$ is a positive number close to 1, $\sqrt{105} - \dfrac{3}{2 - \sqrt{27}}$ is close to 11. You can eliminate B and D.

● The correct answer must be C.

2 EXAMPLE

Solve $\dfrac{2x}{x + 2} = 1 + \dfrac{x}{x - 2}$.

A $x = \dfrac{2}{3}, x = -2,$ or $x = 2$ **C** $x = 2$ or $x = -2$

B $x = \dfrac{2}{3}$ **D** $x = \dfrac{3}{2}$

The equation has denominators $x + 2$ and $x - 2$. Since the denominators cannot equal zero, you know that x cannot equal -2 or 2. You can eliminate A and C.

EXERCISES

Explain how you can eliminate at least two choices for each problem.

1. The expression $6x^2 + 9x - 60$ represents the volume of a rectangular prism. If $3x + 12$ represents the area of the base, which expression best describes the height of the prism?

    A $3x - 5$ **B** $2x - 5$ **C** $3x + 5$ **D** $2x + 5$

2. How many miles could Tracy save by driving from home to the Alden Mall on Route 6 rather than by traveling on Howe Avenue and then Elm Street?

    A 1.6 miles   **C** 2.5 miles

    B 2.0 miles   **D** 2.9 miles

3. A jar contains 3 red, 3 green, and 3 yellow chips. Two chips are drawn at random from the jar, without replacement. What is the probability that one chip is red and the other is green?

    A $\dfrac{1}{8}$ **B** $\dfrac{2}{9}$ **C** $\dfrac{1}{4}$ **D** $\dfrac{2}{3}$

Vocabulary Review

◀) **English and Spanish Audio Online**

branch (p. 503)
complex fraction (p. 524)
dependent events (p. 539)
independent events (p. 539)

inverse variation (p. 496)
joint variation (p. 498)
mutually exclusive events (p. 541)
point of discontinuity (p. 509)

rational function (p. 509)
reciprocal function (p. 503)
simplest form (p. 517)

Choose the correct vocabulary term to complete each sentence.

1. Two events are __?__ if they cannot happen at the same time.

2. When the numerator and denominator of a rational expression are polynomials with no common divisors, the rational expression is in __?__ .

3. When the outcome of one event does not affect the outcome of a second event, the two events are __?__ .

4. A part of the graph of an inverse variation is called a(n) __?__ .

5. If a is a zero of the denominator of a function, the function has a(n) __?__ at $x = a$.

Go Online
PHSchool.com
For: Vocabulary quiz
Web Code: bbj-0951

Skills and Concepts

Lesson 9-1

• To use inverse variation (p. 496)

• To use joint and other variations (p. 498)

An equation in two variables of the form
$$xy = k, y = \frac{k}{x}, \text{ or } x = \frac{k}{y}, \text{ where } k \neq 0,$$
is an **inverse variation**. Extensions of direct and inverse variations to more complicated relationships are combined variations.

Suppose that x and y vary inversely. Write a function that models each inverse variation. Find y when $x = 5$.

6. $x = 10$ when $y = 15$ 　　7. $x = 30$ when $y = 2$ 　　8. $x = 6$ when $y = 30$

If possible, write direct or inverse variation equations to model each relation.

9.

x	3	4	8
y	24	18	9

10.

x	11	13	15
y	15	13	11

11.

x	5	7	9
y	30	42	54

Write the function that models each relationship. Find z when $x = 4$ and $y = 8$.

12. z varies jointly with x and y. When $x = 2$ and $y = 2$, $z = 7$.

13. z varies directly with x and inversely with y. When $x = 5$ and $y = 2$, $z = 10$.

14. z varies directly with the cube of x and inversely with y. When $x = 3$ and $y = 3$, $z = 9$.

Describe the variation modeled by each equation.

15. $R = kmn^2$ 　　16. $W = \frac{k}{d^2}$ 　　17. $P = \frac{kx}{y^2 z}$

Lesson 9-2

- To graph reciprocal functions (p. 503)
- To graph translations of reciprocal functions (p. 505)

 MA 6.0

The graph of an inverse variation has two parts called **branches**. The graph of $y = \frac{k}{x - b} + c$ is a translation of $y = \frac{k}{x}$ by b units horizontally and c units vertically. It has a vertical asymptote at $x = b$ and a horizontal asymptote at $y = c$.

Sketch the graph of each equation.

18. $y = \frac{1}{x}$ **19.** $y = \frac{-2}{x^2}$ **20.** $y = \frac{-1}{x} - 4$ **21.** $y = \frac{3}{x - 2} + 1$

Write an equation for the translation of $xy = 4$ that has the given asymptotes.

22. $x = 0, y = 3$ **23.** $x = 2, y = 2$ **24.** $x = -3, y = -4$

Lesson 9-3

- To identify properties of rational functions (p. 509)
- To graph rational functions (p. 512)

 MA 8.0

The rational function $f(x) = \frac{P(x)}{Q(x)}$ has a **point of discontinuity** for each real zero of $Q(x)$. If $P(x)$ and $Q(x)$ have no common factors, then the graph of $f(x)$ has a vertical asymptote when $Q(x) = 0$. If $P(x)$ and $Q(x)$ have a common real zero a, then there is a hole or a vertical asymptote at $x = a$.

If the degree of $Q(x)$ is greater than the degree of $P(x)$, then the graph of $f(x)$ has a horizontal asymptote at $y = 0$.

If $P(x)$ and $Q(x)$ have equal degrees, then there is a horizontal asymptote at $y = \frac{a}{b}$, where a and b are the coefficients of the terms of greatest degree in $P(x)$ and $Q(x)$.

If the degree of $P(x)$ is greater than the degree of $Q(x)$, then there is no horizontal asymptote.

25. A headset can be manufactured for \$.17. The development cost is \$150,000. Graph the function that represents the average cost of a headset. About how many must be manufactured to result in a cost of less than \$5 per headset?

Find any points of discontinuity for each rational function. Sketch the graph. Describe any vertical or horizontal asymptotes and any holes.

26. $y = \frac{2.5}{x + 7}$ **27.** $y = \frac{x - 1}{(x + 2)(x - 1)}$

28. $y = \frac{x^3 - 1}{x^2 - 1}$ **29.** $y = \frac{2x^2 + 3}{x^2 + 2}$

Lessons 9-4 and 9-5

- To simplify rational expressions (p. 517)
- To multiply and divide rational expressions (p. 518)
- To add and subtract rational expressions (p. 522)
- To simplify complex fractions (p. 524)

 ALG2 7.0

A rational expression is in **simplest form** when its numerator and denominator are polynomials that have no common divisors. To add or subtract rational expressions with different denominators, write each expression with the least common denominator.

A fraction that has a fraction in its numerator or denominator or in both is called a **complex fraction**. You can simplify a complex fraction by multiplying the numerator and denominator by the LCD of all the rational expressions.

Simplify each rational expression. State any restrictions on the variable.

30. $\frac{x^2 - 2x - 24}{x^2 + 7x + 12} \cdot \frac{x^2 - 1}{x - 6}$ **31.** $\frac{4x^2 - 2x}{x^2 + 5x + 4} \div \frac{2x}{x^2 + 2x + 1}$

32. What is the ratio of the volume of a sphere to its surface area?

33. A camera's focal length is 4 cm. If the lens is 6 cm from the film, what is the distance from the lens to an object that is in focus?

Simplify each expression.

34. $\dfrac{3x}{x^2 - 4} + \dfrac{6}{x + 2}$ **35.** $\dfrac{1}{x^2 - 1} - \dfrac{2}{x^2 + 3x}$ **36.** $\dfrac{2 - \frac{2}{3}}{3 - \frac{1}{2}}$ **37.** $\dfrac{\frac{1}{x + y}}{4}$

Lesson 9-6

- To solve rational equations (p. 530)
- To use rational equations in solving problems (p. 531)

 ALG2 7.0

Solving a rational equation often requires multiplying both sides by an algebraic expression. This may introduce an extraneous solution—a solution of a derived equation but not of the original equation. Check all possible solutions in the original equation.

Solve each equation. Check each solution.

38. $\dfrac{1}{x} = \dfrac{5}{x - 4}$ **39.** $\dfrac{2}{x + 3} - \dfrac{1}{x} = \dfrac{-6}{x(x + 3)}$ **40.** $\dfrac{1}{2} + \dfrac{x}{6} = \dfrac{18}{x}$

41. One pump can fill a water cistern twice as fast as a second pump. Working together, the two pumps can fill the cistern in 5 hours. Find how long it takes each pump to fill the cistern when working alone.

Lesson 9-7

- To find the probabilities of events A and B (p. 539)
- To find the probabilities of events A or B (p. 541)

 PS 1.0

When the occurrence of one event affects the probability of another event, the two events are **dependent events.** When the occurrence of one event does not affect the probability of another event, the two events are **independent events.** When two events cannot happen at the same time, the events are **mutually exclusive events.**

If A and B are independent, then $P(A \text{ and } B) = P(A) \cdot P(B)$.

If A and B are mutually exclusive, then $P(A \text{ and } B) = 0$.

If A and B are mutually exclusive, then $P(A \text{ or } B) = P(A) + P(B)$.

If A and B are not mutually exclusive, then
$P(A \text{ or } B) = P(A) + P(B) - P(A \text{ and } B)$.

Classify each pair of events as *dependent* or *independent*.

42. A student in your algebra class is selected at random. One of the remaining students is selected at random.

43. A number 1 through 6 is chosen by tossing a standard number cube. The same number cube is tossed again to select a number 1 through 6.

Two standard number cubes are tossed. State whether the events are mutually exclusive.

44. One of the numbers is 1 less than the other. The sum is odd.

45. The sum is greater than 10. Six is one of the numbers.

A standard number cube is tossed. Find each probability.

46. a 5 or a 6   **47.** an even number or a number greater than 4

48. an odd number or a number less than or equal to 5

Chapter 9 Test

Go Online
PHSchool.com
For: Chapter Test
Web Code: bba-0952

Write a function that models each variation.

1. $x = 2$ when $y = -8$. y varies inversely with x.

2. $x = 0.2$ and $y = 3$ when $z = 2$. z varies jointly with x and y.

3. $x = \frac{1}{3}$, $y = \frac{1}{5}$, and $r = 3$ when $z = \frac{1}{2}$. z varies directly with x and inversely with the product of r^2 and y.

Is the relationship between the values in each table a direct variation, an inverse variation, or neither? Write an equation to model any direct or inverse variation.

4.

x	3	5	7	9
y	6	8	10	12

5.

x	4	6	8	10
y	10	8	6	4

6.

x	4	8	16	32
y	32	16	8	4

Graph the translation of $y = \frac{7}{x}$ with the given asymptotes. Write the equation of the translation.

7. $x = 1$; $y = 2$

8. $x = -3$; $y = -2$

For each rational function, identify any holes, or horizontal or vertical asymptotes of its graph.

9. $y = \frac{x + 1}{x - 1}$

10. $y = \frac{x + 3}{x + 3}$

11. $y = \frac{x - 2}{(x + 1)(x - 2)}$

12. $y = \frac{2x^2}{x^2 - 4x}$

13. $y = \frac{1}{x + 2} - 3$

14. $y = \frac{5}{x - 2} + 1$

15. $y = \frac{x^2 + 5}{x - 5}$

16. $y = \frac{x + 2}{(x + 2)(x - 3)}$

Simplify each rational expression. State any restrictions on the variable.

17. $\frac{x^2 + 7x + 12}{x^2 - 9}$

18. $\frac{(x + 3)(2x - 1)}{x(x + 4)} \div \frac{(-x - 3)(2x + 1)}{x}$

19. Open-Ended Write a function whose graph has a horizontal asymptote but no vertical asymptote.

Find the least common multiple of each pair of polynomials.

20. $3x + 5$ and $9x^2 - 25$

21. $5(x + 3)(x + 1)$ and $2(x + 1)(x - 3)$

Simplify each sum or difference.

22. $\frac{x + 2}{(x - 3)(x + 1)} + \frac{(x - 1)(x + 2)}{x - 3}$

23. $\frac{x^2 - 1}{(x - 2)(3x - 1)} - \frac{x + 1}{x + 3}$

24. $\frac{x(x + 4)}{x - 2} + \frac{x - 1}{x^2 - 4}$

Simplify each complex fraction.

25. $\dfrac{\frac{2}{x}}{1 - \frac{1}{y}}$

26. $\dfrac{3 - \frac{3}{4}}{\frac{1}{2} - \frac{1}{4}}$

Solve each equation. Check each solution.

27. $\frac{x}{2} = \frac{x + 1}{4}$

28. $\frac{3}{x - 1} = \frac{4}{3x + 2}$

29. $\frac{3x}{x + 1} = 0$

30. $\frac{3}{x + 1} = \frac{1}{x^2 - 1}$

31. $\frac{1}{x} + \frac{1}{3} = \frac{6}{x^2}$

32. $\frac{1}{x} + \frac{x}{x + 2} = 1$

33. Almir can seal a driveway in 4 hours. Working together, he and Louis can seal it in 2.3 hours. How long would it take Louis to seal it working alone?

Two standard number cubes are tossed. State whether the events are mutually exclusive. Then find $P(A \text{ or } B)$.

34. A means their sum is 12; B means both are odd

35. A means they are equal; B means their sum is a multiple of 3

36. a. Writing Suppose you select a number at random from the set $\{90, 91, 92, \ldots, 99\}$. Event A is selecting a multiple of 3. Event B is selecting a multiple of 4. Are these two events mutually exclusive? Explain.
   b. Find $P(A \text{ and } B)$.
   c. Find $P(A \text{ or } B)$.

Some problems ask you to find the lateral area or the (total) surface area of a three-dimensional figure.

Tip 1
Use the formula for the lateral area of a cone:
$S = \pi r l$.

What is the approximate lateral area of the cone shown below?

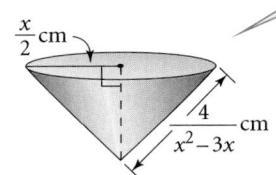

$\frac{x}{2}$ cm

4 cm

$x^2 - 3x$

A $\frac{3}{x + 3}$

B $\frac{6}{x - 3}$

C $\frac{3}{x - 3}$

D $\frac{6}{x + 3}$

Tip 2
Use the information from the diagram for the values you need in the formula.

Think It Through

radius: $r = \frac{x}{2}$ cm

slant height: $l = \dfrac{4}{x^2 - 3x}$ cm

$$S = \pi r l$$
$$= \pi\left(\frac{x}{2}\right)\left(\frac{4}{x^2 - 3x}\right)$$
$$\approx \frac{6}{x - 3}$$

The correct answer is B.

Vocabulary Review

As you solve problems, you must understand the meanings of mathematical terms. Match each term with its mathematical meaning.

A. joint variation

B. branch

C. point of discontinuity

D. inverse variation

E. reciprocal function

I. the x-coordinate of a point where the graph of a function breaks into branches

II. each piece of a discontinuous graph

III. a relation represented by an equation of the form $y = \frac{k}{x}$ or $xy = k$, where $k \neq 0$ and is the constant of variation

IV. a function that can be written in the form $f(x) = \dfrac{a}{x - h} + k$, where $a \neq 0$

V. one variable varies directly with respect to each of two or more other variables

Multiple Choice

Read each question. Then write the letter of the correct answer on your paper.

1. Which expression equals $\dfrac{5x}{x^2 - 9} - \dfrac{4x}{x^2 + 5x + 6}$?
(Lesson 9-5)

A $\dfrac{7x}{(x - 3)(x + 3)(x + 2)}$

B $\dfrac{x^2 - 2x}{(x - 3)(x + 3)(x + 2)}$

C $\dfrac{x^2 + 22x}{(x - 3)(x + 3)(x + 2)}$

D $\dfrac{9x^2 - 2x}{(x - 3)(x + 3)(x + 2)}$

2. What is the least common denominator of the rational expressions $\dfrac{1}{x^2 - 5x - 6}$ and $\dfrac{1}{x^2 - 12x + 36}$?
(Lesson 9-5)

A $x - 6$

B $x^2 - 5x + 6$

C $x^3 + 11x^2 - 24x - 36$

D $x^3 - 11x^2 + 24x + 36$

3. Which expression can be simplified to $\frac{x - 1}{x - 3}$?
(Lesson 9-4)

A $\dfrac{x^2 - x - 6}{x^2 - x - 2}$

B $\dfrac{x^2 - 4x + 3}{x^2 - 6x + 9}$

C $\dfrac{x^2 - 3x - 4}{x^2 - 7x + 12}$

D $\dfrac{x^2 - 2x + 1}{x^2 + 2x - 3}$

4. Which binomial is NOT a factor of
$x^3 - x^2 - 17x - 15$? **(Lesson 6-3)**

   Ⓐ $x - 5$

   Ⓑ $x + 1$

   Ⓒ $x + 3$

   Ⓓ $x + 5$

5. Which is the first *incorrect* step in simplifying
$\log_9 243$? **(Lesson 8-3)**
Step 1: $\log_9 243 = x$
Step 2: $9^x = 243$
Step 3: $x = 243 \div 9$
Step 4: $= 27$

   Ⓐ   Step 1

   Ⓑ   Step 2

   Ⓒ   Step 3

   Ⓓ   Step 4

6. Ana and Matthew each worked out the same
problem, as shown below. Which statement is true of
their solutions? **(Lesson 9-4)**

Ana's work	Matthew's work
$\dfrac{a^2b}{a^{-3}b^4} = \dfrac{a^2}{a^{-3}} \cdot \dfrac{b}{b^4}$	$\dfrac{a^2b}{a^{-3}b^4} = \dfrac{a^2b^1}{a^{-3}b^4}$
$= a^{2-3}\,b^{0-4}$	$= a^{2--3}\,b^{1-4}$
$= a^{-1}\,b^{-4}$	$= a^5\,b^{-3}$
$= \dfrac{1}{ab^4}$	$= \dfrac{a^5}{b^3}$

   Ⓐ   Ana is correct.

   Ⓑ   Matthew is correct.

   Ⓒ   Both answers are incorrect.

   Ⓓ   Both answers are correct.

7. Let $f(x) = -5x$ and $g(x) = 1 - 2x^2$. Which is an
equivalent form of $(g \circ f)(1)$? **(Lesson 7-6)**

   Ⓐ -49

   Ⓑ -5

   Ⓒ 5

   Ⓓ 51

8. If $i = \sqrt{-1}$, what is the value of $-i^4$? **(Lesson 5-6)**

   Ⓐ i

   Ⓑ $-i$

   Ⓒ 1

   Ⓓ -1

9. Which rational expression represents the area of the
triangle below? **(Lesson 9-4)**

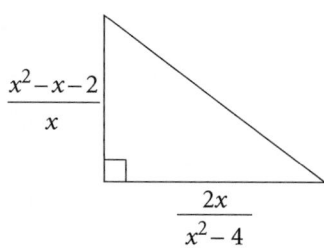

   Ⓐ $\dfrac{x+1}{x-2}$

   Ⓑ $\dfrac{x+1}{x+2}$

   Ⓒ $\dfrac{1}{2}$

   Ⓓ $\dfrac{2x+2}{x+2}$

10. Which expression is in simplest form? **(Lesson 9-4)**

   Ⓐ $\dfrac{x^2-x}{x^2-1}$

   Ⓑ $\dfrac{x^2-1}{x+1}$

   Ⓒ $\dfrac{x^2-1}{x^2+1}$

   Ⓓ $\dfrac{x+3}{x^2+4x+3}$

11. On a recent homework assignment, Laura wrote the
equation $\dfrac{x^2 - 2x - 15}{x^2 - 9} = \dfrac{x - 5}{x - 3}$. Which of the
following statements is correct about the equation
she wrote? **(Lesson 9-6)**

   Ⓐ   The equation is always true.

   Ⓑ   The equation is always true, except when
$x = 3$ or -3.

   Ⓒ   The equation is never true.

   Ⓓ   The equation is sometimes true when
$x = 3$ or -3.

12. If $i = \sqrt{-1}$, what is the value of i^5? **(Lesson 5-6)**

   Ⓐ i Ⓒ 1

   Ⓑ $-i$ Ⓓ -1

13. Which of the following expressions is equivalent
to $(a - 3)^4$? **(Lesson 6-8)**

   Ⓐ $a^4 - 54a^3 + 12a^2 - 108a - 81$

   Ⓑ $a^4 + 54a^3 + 12a^2 + 108a - 81$

   Ⓒ $a^4 - 12a^3 + 54a^2 - 108a - 81$

   Ⓓ $a^4 + 12a^3 + 54a^2 + 108a - 81$

14. Which of the following expressions is equivalent to $x^5 + 10x^4y + 40x^3y^2 + 80x^2y^3 + 80xy^4 + 32y^5$?
(Lesson 6-8)

Ⓐ $(x - 2y)^5$

Ⓑ $(x + 2y)^5$

Ⓒ $(x + 2y)^6$

Ⓓ $(2x + y)^5$

15. If x is a real number, for what values of x is the equation $\frac{2x - 8}{4x^{-1}} = \frac{x^2 - 4x}{2}$ true? (Lesson 9-6)

Ⓐ all values of x

Ⓑ some values of x

Ⓒ no values of x

Ⓓ impossible to determine

16. Given the equation $y = \log_x n$ where $y > 0$ and $n < 0$, which statement is valid for real values of x?
(Lesson 8-3)

Ⓐ $x < 0$

Ⓑ $x \leq 0$

Ⓒ $x \geq 0$

Ⓓ $x > 0$

17. Which expression is NOT equivalent to $(3 - (2 - x)) - 2(1 + x)$? (Lesson 6-1)

Ⓐ $1 + x$

Ⓑ $(1 + x) - (2 + 2x)$

Ⓒ $-x - 1$

Ⓓ $-(-(-1 - x))$

18. If $f(x) = x^2$ and $g(x) = x - 1$, which statement is true? (Lesson 7-6)

Ⓐ $(f \circ g)(x) \geq (g \circ f)(x)$ for all values of x.

Ⓑ $(f \circ g)(x) \leq (g \circ f)(x)$ for all values of x.

Ⓒ $(f \circ g)(x) = (g \circ f)(x)$ only for $x = 1$.

Ⓓ $(f \circ g)(x) \neq (g \circ f)(x)$ for any value of x.

19. If $g(x) = x^2 - 4$ and $h(x) = 4x - 6$, which expression is equal to $\left(\frac{g}{h}\right)(x)$? (Lesson 7-6)

Ⓐ $\frac{4x - 6}{x^2 - 4}$

Ⓑ $\frac{x^2 - 2}{4x - 3}$

Ⓒ $x^2 - 4 - (4x - 6)$

Ⓓ $\frac{x^2 - 4}{4x - 6}$

20. What is the third term in the expansion of $(a - b)^7$? (Lesson 6-8)

Ⓐ $-21a^5b^2$

Ⓑ $-7a^6a$

Ⓒ $7a^6b$

Ⓓ $21a^5b^2$

21. Which polynomial represents $(x - 1)(3x^2 + 2x - 4)$? (Lesson 6-1)

Ⓐ $3x^3 + x^2 - 6x - 4$

Ⓑ $3x^3 - x^2 - 6x + 4$

Ⓒ $4x^3 - 3x^2 - 4x + 4$

Ⓓ $4x^3 + 3x^2 + 6x - 4$

California Content Standard	Item Number(s)
ALG2 7.0	1–3, 9–10
ALG2 20.0	13–14, 20
ALG2 5.0	8, 12
ALG2 11.2	5–6
ALG2 3.0	4, 17, 21
ALG2 15.0	11, 15–16
ALG2 25.0	7, 18–19

For additional review and practice, see the *California Standards Review and Practice Workbook* or go online to use the

California Standards Tutorials

Visit: PHSchool.com, **Web Code:** bbq-9045

Quadratic Relations and Conic Sections

 What You've Learned

California Content Standards

7.0 Students add, subtract, multiply, divide, reduce, and evaluate rational expressions with monomial and polynomial denominators and simplify complicated rational expressions, including those with negative exponents in the denominator.

9.0 Students demonstrate the effect that changing a coefficient has on the graph of quadratic functions; that is, students can determine how the graph of a parabola changes as a, b, and c vary in the equation $y = a(x - b)^2 + c$.

✓ **Check Your Readiness**   **for Help** to the Lesson in green.

Identifying Quadratic Functions (Lesson 5-1)

Determine whether each function is linear or quadratic. Identify the quadratic, linear, and constant terms.

1. $y = 6x - x^2 + 1$ **2.** $f(x) = -2(3 + x)^2 + 2x^2$ **3.** $y = 2x - y - 13$

4. $y = 4x(7 - 2x)$ **5.** $g(x) = -2x^2 - 3(x - 2)$ **6.** $y = x - 2(x + 5)$

Graphing Quadratic Functions (Lesson 5-2)

Graph each function.

7. $y = -x^2$ **8.** $y = \frac{1}{3}x^2$ **9.** $y = 2x^2 + 5$ **10.** $y = x^2 + 6x + 8$

Completing the Square (Lesson 5-7)

Complete the square.

11. $x^2 + 8x + \blacksquare$ **12.** $x^2 - 5x + \blacksquare$ **13.** $x^2 + 14x + \blacksquare$

Rewrite each function in vertex form. Then graph the function.

14. $y = x^2 + 6x + 7$ **15.** $y = 2x^2 - 4x + 10$ **16.** $y = -3x^2 + x$

Solving Polynomial Equations (Lesson 6-5)

Find all the roots of each polynomial equation.

17. $2x^3 - x^2 + 10x - 5 = 0$ **18.** $2x^3 - 5x^2 + 4x - 1 = 0$

Graphing Exponential Decay (Lesson 8-1)

Sketch the graph for each decay function. Label the asymptote.

19. $y = 8\left(\frac{1}{2}\right)^x$ **20.** $y = 2(0.4)^x$ **21.** $y = \left(\frac{3}{4}\right)^x$

What You'll Learn Next

The architecture of the Getty Center in Los Angeles incorporates conic sections.

California Content Standards

16.0 Students demonstrate and explain how the geometry of the graph of a conic section (e.g., asymptotes, foci, eccentricity) depends on the coefficients of the quadratic equation representing it.

17.0 Given a quadratic equation of the form $ax^2 + by^2 + cx + dy + e = 0$, students can use the method for completing the square to put the equation into standard form and can recognize whether the graph of the equation is a circle, ellipse, parabola, or hyperbola. Students can then graph the equation.

New Vocabulary

🔊 **English and Spanish Audio Online**

- **center** (p. 571)
- **circle** (p. 571)
- **conic section** (p. 557)
- **co-vertices** (p. 578)
- **directrix** (p. 565)
- **ellipse** (p. 578)

- **focus of a parabola** (p. 565)
- **focus of an ellipse** (p. 578)
- **focus of a hyperbola** (p. 585)
- **hyperbola** (p. 585)
- **major axis** (p. 578)
- **minor axis** (p. 578)

- **radius** (p. 571)
- **standard form of an equation of a circle** (p. 571)
- **transverse axis** (p. 585)
- **vertices of an ellipse** (p. 578)
- **vertices of a hyperbola** (p. 585)

A conic section is a special curve formed by the intersection of a cone and a plane. You can use paper cutouts to investigate conic sections.

Step 1   Draw two circular areas, each one measuring four inches in diameter. Cut out each circular area, and then cut it in half. Roll each half into a cone and secure it with tape.

Step 2   Trace the three templates below onto a sheet of paper. Cut out the parts corresponding to the white areas. The remaining parts corresponding to the blue areas are the templates. Label each one.

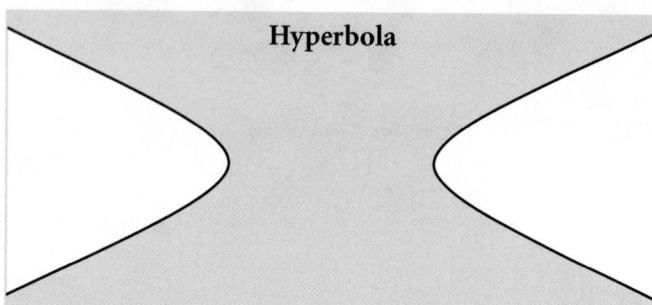

Step 3   Make a fourth template for a circle. Use a compass or a coin of any size to draw the circle.

Step 4   Fit each template around the cones so that the template stays flat, like a plane. The ellipse is shown at the right. Sketch each result.

EXERCISES

1. a. The template for a hyperbola has two parts. Explain how you must position the cones to use this template as a model of a hyperbola.
   b. Suppose you tried to fit your other three templates around a double cone. Would the results change? Explain.

2. a. Fold the template for each curve so that two halves coincide. In how many ways can you do this for each of the four templates?
   b. How many axes of symmetry does each template have?

3. Which templates have rotational symmetry? Explain.

Exploring Conic Sections

 California Content Standards

ALG2 17.0 Given a quadratic equation, students can recognize whether the graph of the equation is a circle, ellipse, parabola, or hyperbola and then graph the equation. *Introduce* **MA 5.0** Students are familiar with conic sections, both analytically and geometrically.

What You'll Learn

• To graph conic sections

• To identify conic sections

. . . And Why

To analyze Moiré patterns, as in Example 5

 Check Skills You'll Need

GO for Help Lessons 2-2, 5-2, and 5-5

Find the *x*- and *y*-intercepts of the graph of each function.

1. $y = 3x + 6$ **2.** $2y = -x - 3$

3. $3x - 4y = -12$ **4.** $y = x^2 - 4$

5. $y = (x - 3)^2$ **6.** $y = -4x^2 + 1$

🔊 **New Vocabulary** • conic section

---

1 Graphing Equations of Conic Sections

Vocabulary Tip

<u>Cone</u> comes from the Indo-European word for "sharpen." <u>Section</u> comes from the word for "cut."

A **conic section** is a curve formed by the intersection of a plane and a double cone. By changing the inclination of the plane, you can create a circle, a parabola, an ellipse, or a hyperbola. You can use lines of symmetry to graph a conic section.

 1 EXAMPLE Graphing a Circle

Graph the equation $x^2 + y^2 = 25$. Describe the graph and its lines of symmetry. Then find the domain and range.

Make a table of values.

x	−5	−4	−3	0	3	4	5
y	0	±3	±4	±5	±4	±3	0

Plot the points and connect them with a smooth curve.

The graph is a circle of radius 5. Its center is at the origin. Every line through the center is a line of symmetry.

Recall from Chapter 2 that you can use set notation to describe a domain or a range. In this example, the domain is $\{x \mid -5 \le x \le 5\}$. The range is $\{y \mid -5 \le y \le 5\}$.

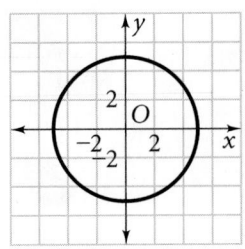

The photograph shows a double cone of illuminated smoke being intersected by a laser to produce a circle.

1 **a.** Graph the functions $y = \sqrt{25 - x^2}$ and $y = -\sqrt{25 - x^2}$ on the same screen. Compare this graph to the one in Example 1.

b. Explain how you can get the equations in part (a) from $x^2 + y^2 = 25$.

c. **Critical Thinking** Why is there no point on the graph of Example 1 with an x-coordinate of 6?

An ellipse is similar to a circle, but it has only two lines of symmetry.

2 **EXAMPLE** **Graphing an Ellipse**

Graph the equation $9x^2 + 16y^2 = 144$. Describe the graph and the lines of symmetry. Then find the domain and range.

Make a table of values.

x	−4	−3	0	3	4
y	0	±2.0	±3	±2.0	0

Plot the points and connect them with a smooth curve.

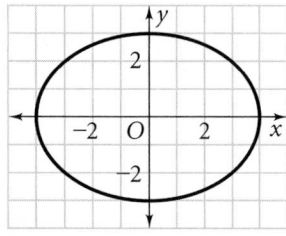

The graph is an ellipse. The center is at the origin. It has two lines of symmetry, the x-axis and the y-axis.

The domain is $\{x \mid -4 \le x \le 4\}$.
The range is $\{y \mid -3 \le y \le 3\}$.

Here the laser intersects the smoke to produce an ellipse.

✅ **CA Standards Check** **2** **a.** How far are the x-intercepts from the center of the ellipse? How far are the y-intercepts from the center? Describe how an ellipse differs from a circle.

b. The point $(1, 2.9)$ is an approximation of a point on the graph in Example 2. Use symmetry to find three other approximate points on the ellipse.

c. Graph the equation $2x^2 + y^2 = 18$. Describe the graph and give the coordinates of the x- and y-intercepts.

Not all conic sections consist of one smooth curve. Note the unique shape of the hyperbola.

3 **EXAMPLE** **Graphing a Hyperbola**

Graph the equation $x^2 - y^2 = 9$. Describe the graph and its lines of symmetry. Then find the domain and range.

Make a table of values.

x	−5	−4	−3	−2	−1	0	1	2	3	4	5
y	±4	±2.6	0	−	−	−	−	−	0	±2.6	±4

Plot the points and connect them with smooth curves.

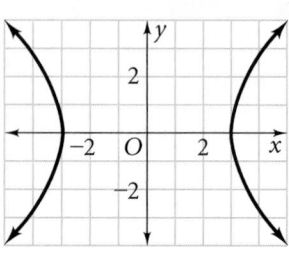

The graph is a hyperbola that consists of two branches. Its center is at the origin. It has two lines of symmetry, the x-axis and the y-axis.

The domain is $\{x \mid x \le -3 \text{ or } x \ge 3\}$. The range is all real numbers.

Here the laser intersects the smoke to produce a hyperbola.

3 **a.** Does the graph in Example 3 represent a function? Explain.
b. In the table in Example 3, why is the *y*-value undefined when
$x = -2, -1, 0, 1,$ or 2?
c. Critical Thinking What two lines does each branch of this hyperbola get
very close to? What are these lines called?

2 / Identifying Conic Sections

The center and the intercepts are important points to identify on the graph of
some conic sections.

4 **EXAMPLE** **Identifying Graphs of Conic Sections**

Identify the center and intercepts of each conic section. Then find the domain and
range. In part (b), each interval on the graph represents one unit.

a.

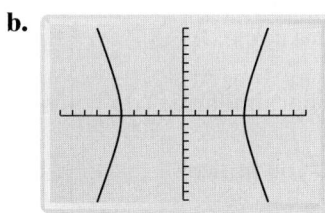

The center of the ellipse is $(0, 0)$. The *x*-intercepts are $(-6, 0)$ and $(6, 0)$, and
the *y*-intercepts are $(0, -4)$ and $(0, 4)$. The domain is $\{x \mid -6 \leq x \leq 6\}$, and the
range is $\{y \mid -4 \leq y \leq 4\}$.

b.

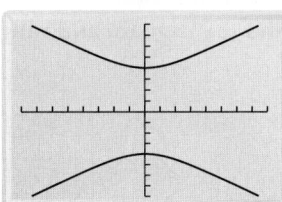

The center of the hyperbola is $(0, 0)$. The *x*-intercepts are $(-5, 0)$ and $(5, 0)$, and
there are no *y*-intercepts. The domain is $\{x \mid x \geq 5 \text{ or } x \leq -5\}$, and the range is
all real numbers.

✓ **CA Standards Check** **4** Identify the center and intercepts of the conic section. Then find the domain and
range. Each interval represents one unit.

You will study each conic section in detail later in this chapter. Even before you
learn the details of the equations of conic sections, you can match the equations
with their graphs.

5 EXAMPLE **Real-World** **Connection**

Design Moiré patterns are formed when two patterns, such as arrays of dots or lines, overlap to produce a third, unintended pattern. Moiré patterns cause problems for printers and video technicians. Describe each unintended pattern. Match it with one of these possible equations: $x^2 - y^2 = 1$, $x^2 + y^2 = 16$, or $9x^2 + 25y^2 = 225$.

a.   **b.**   **c.**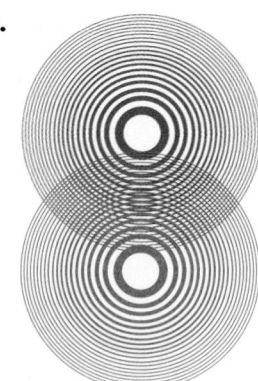

a. Ellipse: The equation $9x^2 + 25y^2 = 225$ represents a conic section with two sets of intercepts, $(\pm 5, 0)$ and $(0, \pm 3)$. Since the intercepts are not equidistant from the center, the equation models an ellipse.

b. Hyperbola: The equation $x^2 - y^2 = 1$ represents a conic section with one set of intercepts, $(\pm 1, 0)$, so the equation must model a hyperbola.

c. Circle: The equation $x^2 + y^2 = 16$ represents a conic section with two sets of intercepts, $(\pm 4, 0)$ and $(0, \pm 4)$. Since each intercept is 4 units from the center, the equation models a circle.

✓ **CA Standards Check** **5** **a.** **Critical Thinking** What similarities do you notice among the three equations in Example 5?
b. What differences do you notice?

 EXERCISES   For more exercises, see *Extra Skill and Word Problem Practice.*

Standards Practice   **ALG2 17.0, MA 5.0**

 A **Practice by Example**

Examples 1, 2, and 3
(pages 557 and 558)

 GO **for Help**

Graph each equation. Identify the conic section and describe the graph and its lines of symmetry. Then find the domain and range.

1. $3y^2 - x^2 = 25$
2. $2x^2 + y^2 = 36$

3. $x^2 + y^2 = 16$
4. $3y^2 - x^2 = 9$

5. $4x^2 + 25y^2 = 100$
6. $x^2 + y^2 = 49$

7. $x^2 - y^2 + 1 = 0$
8. $x^2 - 2y^2 = 4$

9. $6x^2 + 6y^2 = 600$
10. $x^2 + y^2 - 4 = 0$

11. $6x^2 + 24y^2 - 96 = 0$
12. $4x^2 + 4y^2 - 20 = 0$

13. $x^2 + 9y^2 = 1$
14. $4x^2 - 36y^2 = 144$

15. $4y^2 - 36x^2 = 1$
16. $36x^2 + 4y^2 = 144$

Example 4
(page 559)

Identify the center and intercepts of each conic section. Give the domain and range of each graph. On graphing calculator screens, each interval represents one unit.

17.

18.

19.

20.

21.

22.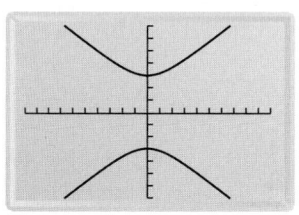

Example 5
(page 560)

Match each equation with a graph in Exercises 17–22.

23. $x^2 - y^2 = 9$ **24.** $4x^2 + 9y^2 = 36$

25. $y^2 - x^2 = 4$ **26.** $x^2 + 4y^2 = 64$

27. $25x^2 + 9y^2 = 225$ **28.** $y^2 - x^2 = 9$

B Apply Your Skills

Graph each equation. Describe the graph and its lines of symmetry. Then find the domain and range.

29. $9x^2 - y^2 = 144$ **30.** $11x^2 + 11y^2 = 44$

31. $-8x^2 + 32y^2 - 128 = 0$ **32.** $25x^2 + 16y^2 - 320 = 0$

33. Light The light emitted from a lamp with a shade forms a shadow on the wall. Explain how you could turn the lamp in relation to the wall so that the shadow cast by the shade forms each conic section.
   a. hyperbola   **b.** parabola   **c.** ellipse   **d.** circle

34. a. Writing Describe the relationship between the center of a circle and the axes of symmetry of the circle.
   b. Make a Conjecture Where is the center of an ellipse or a hyperbola located in relation to the axes of symmetry? Verify your conjectures with examples.

Graph each circle so that the center is at the origin. Then write the equation.

35. radius 6   **36.** radius $\frac{1}{2}$ **37.** diameter 8   **38.** diameter 2.5

39. Multiple Choice The sharpened part of the pencil at the right meets each painted surface in a curved path. What is the best name for such a path?
   Ⓐ circle   Ⓑ ellipse   Ⓒ parabola   Ⓓ hyperbola

Homework Video Tutor

Visit: PHSchool.com
Web Code: bbe-1001

Mental Math **Each given point is on the graph of the given equation. Use symmetry to find at least one more point on the graph.**

40. $(2, -4), y^2 = 8x$

41. $\left(-\sqrt{2}, 1\right), x^2 + y^2 = 3$

42. $\left(2, 2\sqrt{2}\right), x^2 + 4y^2 = 36$

43. $(-2, 0), 9x^2 + 9y^2 - 36 = 0$

44. $\left(-3, -\sqrt{51}\right), 6y^2 - 9x^2 - 225 = 0$

45. $\left(0, \sqrt{7}\right), x^2 + 2y^2 = 14$

46. Open-Ended Describe any other figures you can imagine that can be formed by the intersection of a plane and other shapes.

 Challenge

47. a. Graph the equation $xy = 16$. Use both positive and negative values for x.
   b. Which conic section does the equation appear to model?
   c. Identify any intercepts and lines of symmetry.
   d. Does your graph represent a function? If so, rewrite the equation using function notation.

 48. An xy term has an interesting effect on the graph of a conic section. Sketch the graph of each conic section below using your graphing calculator.
(*Hint:* To solve for y, you will need to complete a square.)
   a. $4x^2 + 2xy + y^2 = 9$
   b. $4x^2 + 2xy - y^2 = 9$

49. Sound An airplane flying faster than the speed of sound creates a cone-shaped pressure disturbance in the air. This is heard by people on the ground as a sonic boom. What is the shape of the path on the ground?

Multiple Choice Practice

For California Standards and CAHSEE Tutorials, visit PHSchool.com. Web Code: bbq-9045

ALG2 17.0

50. Which is the graph of $4x^2 - y^2 = 4$?

A.

C.

B.

D.
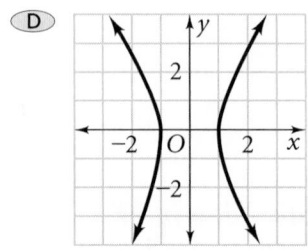

51. What is the simplified form of $\frac{3 - \sqrt{5}}{\sqrt{5}}$?

Ⓐ $\frac{3\sqrt{5} - 5}{5}$

Ⓒ $\frac{5\sqrt{3} - 5}{5}$

Ⓑ $\frac{3\sqrt{3} - \sqrt{15}}{5}$

Ⓓ $\frac{14 - 6\sqrt{5}}{5}$

Mixed Review

GO for Help

Lesson 9-7

Suppose you toss a standard number cube. Find each probability.

52. $P(5$ or greater than $3)$ **53.** $P(\text{even or } 6)$

54. $P(\text{even or } 7)$ **55.** $P(\text{prime or } 2)$

Lesson 9-1

Suppose z varies jointly with x and y. Write a function that models each relationship. Find the value of z when $x = -2$ and $y = 3$.

56. $z = -5$ when $x = -1$ and $y = -1$ **57.** $z = 72$ when $x = 3$ and $y = -6$

58. $z = 32$ when $x = 0.1$ and $y = 8$ **59.** $z = 5$ when $x = -4$ and $y = 2.5$

Lesson 8-1

Write an exponential equation $y = ab^x$ whose graph passes through the given points.

60. $(-1, 2)$ and $(3, 32)$ **61.** $\left(0, \frac{1}{2}\right)$ and $(2, 8)$ **62.** $(1, 6)$ and $(2, 12)$

63. $\left(0, \frac{1}{3}\right)$ and $(2, 3)$ **64.** $\left(-1, \frac{2}{3}\right)$ and $(2, 18)$ **65.** $\left(-1, \frac{1}{8}\right)$ and $(4, 4)$

Lesson 6-8

Expand each binomial.

66. $(x - y)^3$ **67.** $(p + q)^6$ **68.** $(x - 2)^4$ **69.** $(3 - x)^5$

·······A P●int in Time

1500   1600   1700   1800   1900   2000

Titanic was the largest passenger liner that had yet been built. On its maiden voyage in 1912, it struck an iceberg and sank. More than 1500 people died.

In 1985 a French and American team searched for *Titanic*. Research vessels combed the area with sonar. Transmitters aboard each ship sent out powerful spherical sound waves. Each wave reflected off any object in a half-mile-wide strip of ocean floor and returned to a receiver. The receiver then converted the echo to a picture of the object and calculated its depth. Two months after the search began, *Titanic* was discovered lying in two sections at a depth of some 13,000 feet.

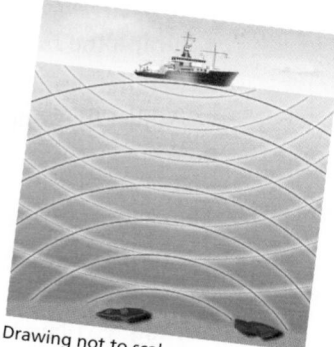

Drawing not to scale

Go ●nline
PHSchool.com   **For:** Information about *Titanic*
Web Code: bbe-2032

Graphing Conic Sections

Ellipses and hyperbolas described by equations of the form $Ax^2 + By^2 = C$ are symmetric about the x-axis. You can use your graphing calculator to graph these conic sections.

ACTIVITY

Graph the ellipse $\frac{x^2}{16} + \frac{y^2}{9} = 1$.

Step 1 Solve the equation for y.

$$\frac{x^2}{16} + \frac{y^2}{9} = 1$$

$$\frac{y^2}{9} = 1 - \frac{x^2}{16}$$

$$y^2 = 9\left(1 - \frac{x^2}{16}\right)$$

$$y = \pm 3\sqrt{1 - \frac{x^2}{16}}$$

Step 2 Enter the equations as Y_1 and Y_2.

Step 3 Select a square window.

Step 4 Graph.

EXERCISES

Graph each conic section.

1. $x^2 + y^2 = 25$

2. $4x^2 + y^2 = 16$

3. $9x^2 - 16y^2 = 144$

4. $x^2 - y^2 = 3$

5. $\frac{x^2}{4} - \frac{y^2}{9} = 1$

6. $x^2 + \frac{y^2}{4} = 16$

7. a. Graph the functions $y = \sqrt{\frac{81}{4} - x^2}$ and $y = -\sqrt{\frac{81}{4} - x^2}$.

   b. Estimate the x-intercepts and find the y-intercepts.
   c. Adjust the window to $-9.3 \le x \le 9.5$. Verify the x-intercepts.
   d. What conic section does the graph represent?

Graph each conic section. Find the x- and y-intercepts.

8. $4x^2 + y^2 = 25$

9. $x^2 + y^2 = 30$

10. $9x^2 - 4y^2 = 72$

11. Writing Explain how to use a graphing calculator to graph the relation $x = |y - 3|$.

12. Critical Thinking Which conic sections can you graph using only one function? Explain.

Parabolas

 California Content Standards

ALG2 16.0 Students demonstrate and explain how the geometry of the graph of a conic section depends on the coefficients of the quadratic equation representing it. ***Introduce***
MA 5.2 Students can take a geometric description of a conic section and derive a quadratic equation representing it.

What You'll Learn

- To write the equation of a parabola
- To graph parabolas

. . . And Why

To model a solar collector, as in Example 3

 Check Skills You'll Need **GO for Help** Skills Handbook pages 884 and 896

Solve for c.

1. $\frac{1}{8} = \frac{1}{c}$ **2.** $\frac{1}{8} = \frac{1}{2c}$ **3.** $\frac{1}{12} = \frac{1}{4c}$ **4.** $2 = \frac{1}{4c}$

Find the distance between the given points.

5. $(2, 3)$ and $(4, 1)$ **6.** $(4, 6)$ and $(3, -2)$ **7.** $(-1, 5)$ and $(2, -3)$

New Vocabulary • focus of a parabola • directrix

---

 1 **Writing the Equation of a Parabola**

In Chapter 5 you learned that a parabola is the graph of a quadratic equation. By definition, a parabola is the set of all points in a plane that are the same distance from a fixed line and a fixed point not on the line. The fixed point is the **focus of a parabola.** The fixed line is the **directrix.** The line through the focus and perpendicular to the directrix is the axis of symmetry.

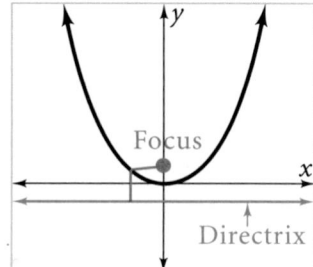

1 EXAMPLE **Using the Definition of a Parabola**

Write an equation for a graph that is the set of all points in the plane that are equidistant from the point $F(0, 3)$ and the line $y = -3$.

You need to find all points $P(x, y)$ such that FP and the distance from P to the given line are equal.

Problem Solving Hint

The distance between $P_1(x_1, y_1)$ and $P_2(x_2, y_2)$ is $\sqrt{(x_2 - x_1)^2 + (y_2 - y_1)^2}$.

$$FP = PQ$$
$$\sqrt{(x - 0)^2 + (y - 3)^2} =$$
$$\sqrt{(x - x)^2 + (y - (-3))^2}$$
$$x^2 + (y - 3)^2 = 0^2 + (y + 3)^2$$
$$x^2 + y^2 - 6y + 9 = y^2 + 6y + 9$$
$$x^2 = 12y$$
$$y = \frac{1}{12}x^2$$

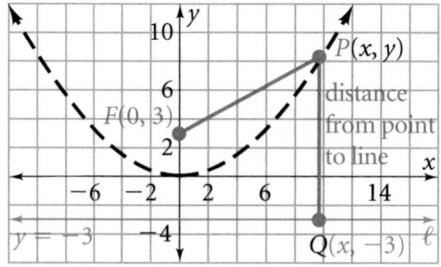

● An equation of the set of all points equidistant from $F(0, 3)$ and $y = -3$ is $y = \frac{1}{12}x^2$.

✓ CA Standards Check **1** Write an equation for a graph that is the set of all points in the plane that are equidistant from the point $F(2, 0)$ and the line $x = -2$.

In Chapter 5 you learned about the special relationship between the value of a and the graph of a quadratic function in the form $y = ax^2$. Now you will learn about the relationship between the value of a and the graph of a quadratic relation in the form $y = ax^2$ or $x = ay^2$.

If c is the distance from the vertex to the focus of a parabola, then $|a| = \frac{1}{4c}$.

Consider any parabola with equation $y = ax^2$ and vertex at the origin.

GO for Help

To review graphing parabolas, go to Lesson 5-2.

If $a > 0$, then
- the parabola opens upward
- the focus is at $(0, c)$
- the directrix is $y = -c$

If $a < 0$, then
- the parabola opens downward
- the focus is at $(0, -c)$
- the directrix is at $y = c$

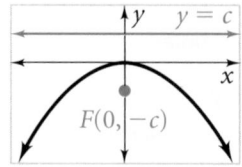

Consider any parabola with equation $x = ay^2$.

If $a > 0$, then
- the parabola opens to the right
- the focus is at $(c, 0)$
- the directrix is at $x = -c$

If $a < 0$, then
- the parabola opens to the left
- the focus is at $(-c, 0)$
- the directrix is at $x = c$

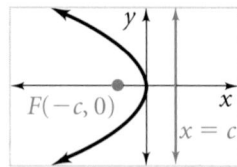

You can use the information above to write an equation of a parabola.

2 EXAMPLE Writing the Equation of a Parabola

Multiple Choice Which equation represents a parabola with a vertex at the origin and a focus at $(-5, 0)$?

(A) $y = \frac{1}{20}x^2$ (B) $x = \frac{1}{20}y^2$ (C) $y = -\frac{1}{20}x^2$ (D) $x = -\frac{1}{20}y^2$

Test-Taking Tip

When you identify or graph a relation, be sure you correctly match the equation variables and the graph variables.

Step 1 Determine the orientation of the parabola. Make a sketch. Since the focus is located to the left of the vertex, the parabola must open to the left. Use $x = ay^2$.

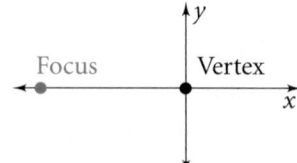

Step 2 Find a.

$$|a| = \frac{1}{4c}$$

$$= \frac{1}{4(5)} \quad \text{Since the focus is a distance of 5 units from the vertex, } c = 5.$$

$$= \frac{1}{20}$$

Since the parabola opens to the left, a is negative. So $a = -\frac{1}{20}$.

An equation for the parabola is $x = -\frac{1}{20}y^2$. The correct choice is D.

✓ CA Standards Check ② Write an equation of a parabola with a vertex at the origin and a focus at $\left(\frac{1}{2}, 0\right)$.

You can find the equation of a parabola that models a real-world situation.

3 **EXAMPLE** Real-World 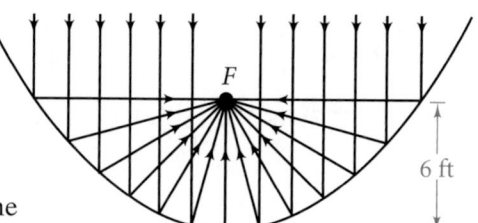 Connection

Solar Energy In some solar collectors, a mirror with a parabolic cross section is used to concentrate sunlight on a pipe, which is located at the focus of the mirror.

Real-World 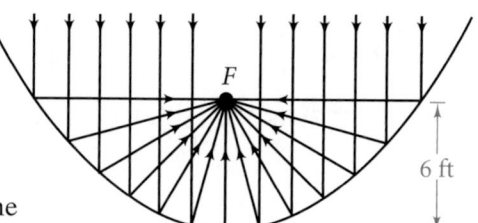 **Connection**

Parabolic solar mirrors focus the sun's energy to produce steam that drives electric generators.

a. Suppose the pipe is located 6 ft from the vertex of the mirror. Write an equation of the parabola that models the cross section of the mirror.

The distance from the vertex to the focus is 6 ft, so $c = 6$. Find the value of a.

$$a = \frac{1}{4c}$$

$$= \frac{1}{4(6)}$$

$$= \frac{1}{24} \quad \text{Since the parabola opens upward, } a \text{ is positive.}$$

The equation of the parabola is $y = \frac{1}{24}x^2$.

b. Suppose you stretch the equation of the mirror (and the mirror itself upward) by a factor of 2 to become $y = \frac{1}{12}x^2$. How should you move the pipe so that it remains at the focus?

In $a = \frac{1}{4c}$, if a doubles, the value of c must halve. The distance to the focus would change from 6 ft to 3 ft.

✓ **CA Standards Check** **3** Suppose the pipe is located 8.25 ft from the vertex of the mirror. Write an equation of the parabola to model the cross section of the mirror.

2 Graphing Parabolas

You can use the value of a to identify the focus and directrix of a parabola.

4 **EXAMPLE** **Identifying Focus and Directrix**

Identify the focus and the directrix of the graph of the equation $y = -\frac{1}{16}x^2$.

The parabola is of the form $y = ax^2$, so the vertex is at the origin and the parabola has a vertical axis of symmetry. Since $a < 0$, the parabola opens downward.

Test-Taking Tip

Forgetting a negative sign is one of the most common mistakes on tests.

$$|a| = \frac{1}{4c}$$

$$\left|-\frac{1}{16}\right| = \frac{1}{4c} \quad \text{Substitute } -\frac{1}{16} \text{ for } a.$$

$$4c = 16 \quad \text{Solve for } c.$$

$$c = 4$$

The focus is at $(0, -4)$. The equation of the directrix is $y = 4$.

✓ **CA Standards Check** **4** Identify the focus and the directrix of the graph of the equation $y = \frac{1}{12}x^2$.

You can use the focus and directrix to graph the equation of a parabola.

5 EXAMPLE Graphing the Equation of a Parabola

Identify the vertex, the focus, and the directrix of the graph of the equation $y^2 - 4x - 4y + 16 = 0$. Then graph the parabola.

$$y^2 - 4x - 4y + 16 = 0$$

$4x = y^2 - 4y + 16$	**Solve for x, since x is in only one term.**
$4x = (y^2 - 4y + 4) + 16 - 4$	**Complete the square in y.**
$x = \frac{1}{4}(y^2 - 4y + 4) + 4 - 1$	**Divide both sides of the equation by 4.**
$x = \frac{1}{4}(y - 2)^2 + 3$	**vertex form**

The parabola is of the form $x = a(y - k)^2 + h$. This is a translation of $x = ay^2$. All of the graph's features—axis of symmetry, vertex, focus, and directrix—translate with the parabola. The parabola has a horizontal axis of symmetry. $a > 0$, so the parabola opens to the right. Its vertex is at $(h, k) = (3, 2)$.

$$|a| = \frac{1}{4c}$$
$$\left|\frac{1}{4}\right| = \frac{1}{4c} \quad \textbf{Substitute } \frac{1}{4} \textbf{ for } a.$$
$$4c = 4 \quad \textbf{Solve for } c.$$
$$c = 1$$

The focus is at $(4, 2)$. The directrix is $x = 2$.

Locate one or more points on the parabola. Select a value for y, such as 4. The point on the parabola with a y-value of 4 is $(4, 4)$. Use the symmetric nature of a parabola to find the corresponding point, $(4, 0)$.

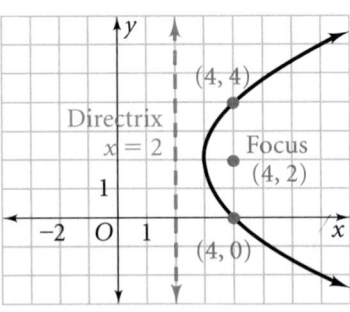

CA Standards Check 5 Identify the vertex, the focus, and the directrix of the graph of $x^2 + 6x + 3y + 12 = 0$. Then graph the equation.

EXERCISES For more exercises, see *Extra Skill and Word Problem Practice*.

Standards Practice   ALG2 16.0, MA 5.2

Write an equation for a graph that is the set of all points in the plane that are equidistant from the given point and the given line.

1. $F(0, 2), y = -2$ **2.** $F(0, -1), y = 1$ **3.** $F(-3, 0), x = 3$

4. $F(0, -8), y = 8$ **5.** $F(0, 4), y = 0$ **6.** $F\left(\frac{1}{2}, 0\right), x = -\frac{1}{2}$

Example 2
(page 566)

Write an equation of a parabola with a vertex at the origin and the given focus.

7. focus at $(6, 0)$ **8.** focus at $(0, -4)$ **9.** focus at $(0, 7)$

10. focus at $(-1, 0)$ **11.** focus at $(2, 0)$ **12.** focus at $(0, -5)$

Example 3
(page 567)

Write an equation of a parabola opening upward with a vertex at the origin.

13. focus 1.5 units from vertex   **14.** focus $\frac{1}{8}$ of a unit from vertex

15. Optics A cross section of a flashlight reflector is a parabola. The bulb is located at the focus. Suppose the bulb is located $\frac{1}{4}$ in. from the vertex of the reflector. Model a cross section of the reflector by writing an equation of a parabola that opens upward and has its vertex at the origin. What is an advantage of this parabolic design?

Example 4
(page 567)

Identify the focus and the directrix of the graph of each equation.

16. $y = \frac{1}{4}x^2$ **17.** $y = x^2$ **18.** $y = -\frac{1}{8}x^2$ **19.** $x = \frac{1}{2}y^2$

20. $y = \frac{1}{2}x^2$ **21.** $x = \frac{1}{36}y^2$ **22.** $x = -\frac{1}{18}y^2$ **23.** $y = -2x^2$

Example 5
(page 568)

Identify the vertex, the focus, and the directrix of each graph. Then sketch the graph.

24. $x = \frac{1}{24}y^2$ **25.** $y = -\frac{1}{4}x^2$ **26.** $x = \frac{1}{12}y^2$

27. $y^2 - 25x = 0$ **28.** $x^2 = 4y$ **29.** $x^2 = -4y$

30. $(x - 2)^2 = 4y$ **31.** $-8x = y^2$ **32.** $(x + 2)^2 = y - 4$

33. $y^2 - 6x = 18$ **34.** $x^2 + 24y - 8x = -16$ **35.** $y^2 - 12x + 2y = -37$

B   **Apply Your Skills**

Write an equation of a parabola with a vertex at the origin.

36. directrix $x = -3$ **37.** focus at $(0, 100)$ **38.** directrix $y = 5$

39. focus at $(-7, 0)$ **40.** directrix $x = 9$ **41.** directrix $y = 2.8$

42. Earth Science The equation $d = \frac{1}{10}s^2$ relates the depth d (in meters) of the ocean to the speed s (in meters per second) at which tsunamis travel. Graph the equation.

Use the information in each graph to write the equation for the graph.

43.   **44.**   **45.**

Graph each equation.

46. $y^2 - 8x = 0$ **47.** $y^2 - 8y + 8x = -16$ **48.** $2x^2 - y + 20x = -53$

49. $x^2 = 12y$ **50.** $y = 4(x - 3)^2 - 2$ **51.** $(y - 2)^2 = 4(x + 3)$

Write an equation of a parabola with a vertex at (1, 1).

52. directrix $y = -\frac{1}{2}$ **53.** directrix $x = \frac{3}{2}$ **54.** focus at $(1, 0)$

55. Open-Ended Write an equation for a parabola that opens to the left. Give the focus and directrix of the parabola.

56. Writing Explain how to find the distance from the focus to the directrix of the parabola $x = 2y^2$.

57. Multiple Choice The focus of a parabola is at $(-3, 3)$. The vertex is at $(0, 3)$. What is the equation of the parabola?

Ⓐ $y - 3 = \frac{1}{12}x^2$ Ⓒ $y = -\frac{1}{12}(x - 3)^2$

Ⓑ $x = -\frac{1}{12}(y - 3)^2$ Ⓓ $x = \frac{1}{12}(y + 3)^2$

58. Critical Thinking Use the definition of a parabola to show that the parabola with vertex (h, k) and focus $(h, k + c)$ has the equation $(x - h)^2 = 4c(y - k)$.

59. Modeling Draw a cross section of a parabolic mirror modeled by the equation $y = 0.002323x^2$.

60. a. What part of a parabola is modeled by the function $y = -\sqrt{x}$?
   b. State the domain and range for the function in part (a).

61. The directrix of a parabola is the line $y = -2$. The focus is the point $(0, 2)$.
   a. Suppose the directrix remains fixed, but the focus is shifted along the y-axis farther away from the directrix. Explain what happens to the vertex and the shape of the parabola.
   b. Suppose the focus moves along the y-axis toward the directrix. Explain what happens to the vertex and the shape of the parabola.
   c. What would happen if the focus moved down all the way to the directrix?

Multiple Choice Practice

For California Standards and CAHSEE Tutorials, visit PHSchool.com. Web Code: bbq-9045

ALG2 16.0

62. What is the equation of the parabola with a vertex at the origin and a focus at $\left(0, \frac{5}{2}\right)$?

   A $x = -\frac{1}{10}y^2$ **C** $y = -\frac{1}{10}x^2$

   B $x = \frac{1}{10}y^2$ **D** $y = \frac{1}{10}x^2$

ALG2 3.0

63. What is the remainder when $x^2 - 5x + 7$ is divided by $x + 1$?

   A -13 **B** -1 **C** 1 **D** 13

ALG2 11.2

64. Which equation represents the inverse of the graph at the right?

   A $y = \log_3 x$
   B $x = \log_3 y$
   C $y = \log_x 3$
   D $x = \log_y 3$

Mixed Review

 GO for Help

Lesson 10-1

Graph each equation.

65. $x^2 + y^2 = 64$ **66.** $x^2 + 9y^2 = 9$ **67.** $4x^2 - 9y^2 = 36$

Lesson 9-2

Find the asymptotes of the graph of each equation.

68. $y = \frac{3}{x}$ **69.** $y = \frac{1}{x} + 4$ **70.** $y = \frac{4}{x + 1}$

71. $y = -\frac{1}{x - 1}$ **72.** $y = \frac{5}{x + 5} + 2$ **73.** $y = \frac{2}{x - 3} - 1$

Lesson 8-2

74. Investing Suppose you have a continuously compounding account with a beginning principal of $3,800 and an interest rate of 8.1%. What is the balance after 4 years?

Circles

10-3

 California Content Standards

ALG2 16.0 Students demonstrate and explain how the geometry of the graph of a conic section depends on the coefficients of the quadratic equation representing it. *Develop*

What You'll Learn

- To wite and graph the equation of a circle
- To find the center and radius of a circle and use it to graph the circle

... And Why

To model gears in machinery, as in Example 3

---

1 Writing the Equation of a Circle

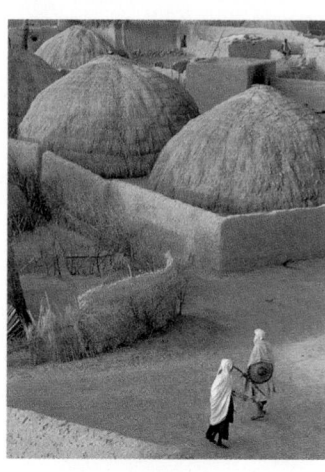

Real-World Connection

People of many cultures use circular dwellings, like those shown above in Mali, to maximize volume for a given surface area.

A **circle** is the set of all points in a plane that are a distance r from a given point, called the **center.** The distance r is the **radius** of the circle.

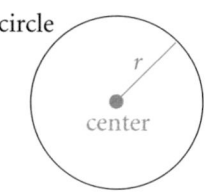

In the coordinate plane, if r is the radius of a circle with a center at the origin, then the equation of the circle can be written in the form $x^2 + y^2 = r^2$.

Not every circle has its center at the origin. You can use the distance formula to find an equation of a circle with a radius r and a center at the point (h, k).

Let (x, y) be any point on the circle. The distance from (h, k) to (x, y) is the radius.

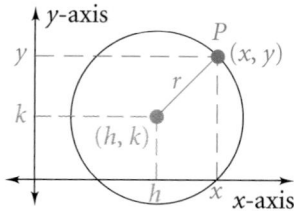

$d = \sqrt{(x_2 - x_2)^2 + (y_2 - y_1)^2}$ **Distance Formula**

$r = \sqrt{(x - h)^2 + (y - k)^2}$ Substitute r for d, (h, k) for (x_1, y_1), and (x, y) for (x_2, y_2).

$r^2 = (x - h)^2 + (y - k)^2$ Square each side.

This derivation leads to a definition.

 Key Concepts

Definition	**Standard Form of an Equation of a Circle**

The standard form of an equation of a circle with center (h, k) and radius r is

$$(x - h)^2 + (y - k)^2 = r^2.$$

You can use the center and the radius of a circle to write an equation for a circle.

1 EXAMPLE Writing the Equation of a Circle

Write an equation of a circle with center $(-4, 3)$ and radius 4.

$(x - h)^2 + (y - k)^2 = r^2$ **Use the standard form of the equation of a circle.**

$(x - (-4))^2 + (y - 3)^2 = 4^2$ **Substitute −4 for h, 3 for k, and 4 for r.**

$(x + 4)^2 + (y - 3)^2 = 16$ **Simplify.**

An equation for the circle is $(x + 4)^2 + (y - 3)^2 = 16$.

Check   Solve the equation for y and enter both functions into your graphing calculator.

$(x + 4)^2 + (y - 3)^2 = 16$

$(y - 3)^2 = 16 - (x + 4)^2$

$y - 3 = \pm \sqrt{16 - (x + 4)^2}$

$y = 3 \pm \sqrt{16 - (x + 4)^2}$

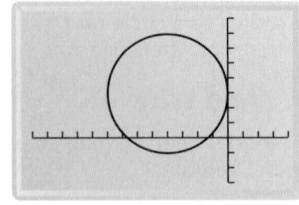

✓ **CA Standards Check** ① Write an equation for a circle with center at $(5, -2)$ and radius 8. Check your answer.

You can use parameters h and k to translate the circle $x^2 + y^2 = r^2$ with center $(0, 0)$ to the circle $(x - h)^2 + (y - k)^2 = r^2$ with center (h, k). Translate to the right when h is positive; to the left when h is negative. Translate up when k is positive; down when k is negative.

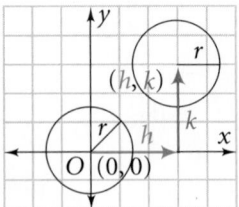

2 EXAMPLE Using Translations to Write an Equation

Write an equation for the translation of $x^2 + y^2 = 9$ four units left and three units up. Then graph the translation.

$(x - h)^2 + (y - k)^2 = r^2$ **Use standard form.**

$(x - (-4))^2 + (y - 3)^2 = 9$ **Substitute −4 for h, 3 for k, and 9 for r^2.**

$(x + 4)^2 + (y - 3)^2 = 9$ **Simplify.**

✓ **CA Standards Check** ② Write an equation for each translation.
   a. $x^2 + y^2 = 1$; left 5 and down 3   **b.** $x^2 + y^2 = 9$; right 2 and up 3

You can write an equation of a circle to model a real-world situation.

3 EXAMPLE Real-World Connection

Machinery The diagram below shows four gears in a motor assembly. Gear B rotates 8 times for each rotation of gear A. Gears B and C share the same shaft, with centers at the origin. The radius of gear C is 6 times the radius of gear B. The radius of gear D is $\frac{1}{3}$ the radius of gear C. Write the equation of the circle that represents each gear.

Make a table. Let the radius of gear $B = \frac{1}{2}$. The radius of gear A must be 8 times the radius of gear B, or 4.

Gear	(h, k)	r	Equation
A	$\left(-4\frac{1}{2}, 0\right)$	4	$\left(x + \frac{9}{2}\right)^2 + y^2 = 16$
B	$(0, 0)$	$\frac{1}{2}$	$x^2 + y^2 = \frac{1}{4}$
C	$(0, 0)$	3	$x^2 + y^2 = 9$
D	$(4, 0)$	1	$(x - 4)^2 + y^2 = 1$

✓ **CA Standards Check** **3** Write the equation of a circle for a gear that is the same size as gear D and has center $(0, -4)$.

---

2 Using the Center and Radius of a Circle

You can find the center and radius of a circle by rewriting the equation in the standard form of a circle.

4 EXAMPLE Finding the Center and Radius

Find the center and radius of the circle with equation $(x - 16)^2 + (y + 9)^2 = 144$.

$(x - h)^2 + (y - k)^2 = r^2$ **Write the standard form.**

$(x - 16)^2 + (y + 9)^2 = 144$ **Write the equation.**

$(x - 16)^2 + (y - (-9))^2 = 12^2$ **Rewrite the equation in standard form.**

$h = 16 \quad k = -9 \quad r = 12$ **Find h, k, and r.**

The center of the circle is $(16, -9)$. The radius is 12.

✓ **CA Standards Check** **4** Find the center and radius of the circle with equation $(x + 8)^2 + (y + 3)^2 = 121$.

You can use the center and the radius to graph a circle.

⑤ **EXAMPLE** Graphing a Circle Using Center and Radius

Graph $(x + 1)^2 + (y - 3)^2 = 25$.

$$(x - h)^2 + (y - k)^2 = r^2 \qquad \textbf{Find the center and the radius of the circle.}$$
$$(x - (-1))^2 + (y - 3)^2 = 25$$
$$h = -1 \qquad k = 3 \qquad r^2 = 25, \text{ or } r = 5$$

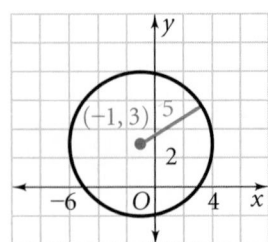

Draw the center $(-1, 3)$ and
radius 5. Draw a smooth curve.

✓ **CA Standards Check** ⑤ Graph $(x - 4)^2 + (y + 2)^2 = 49$.

EXERCISES

For more exercises, see *Extra Skill and Word Problem Practice*.

Standards Practice

ALG2 16.0

A **Practice by Example**

Example 1
(page 572)

Write an equation of a circle with the given center and radius. Check your answers.

1. $(0, 0), 10$ **2.** $(-4, -6), 7$ **3.** $(2, 3), 4.5$ **4.** $(-6, 10), 1$

5. $(1, -3), 10$ **6.** $(-5, -1), 6$ **7.** $(-3, 0), 8$ **8.** $(-1.5, -3), 2$

Example 2
(page 572)

Write an equation for each translation.

9. $x^2 + y^2 = 9$; down 1   **10.** $x^2 + y^2 = 1$; left 1

11. $x^2 + y^2 = 25$; right 2 and down 4   **12.** $x^2 + y^2 = 81$; left 1 and up 3

13. $x^2 + y^2 = 100$; down 5   **14.** $x^2 + y^2 = 49$; right 3 and up 2

15. $x^2 + y^2 = 20$; left 6 and up 1   **16.** $x^2 + y^2 = 50$; right 5

Example 3
(page 573)

Write an equation for each circle. Each interval represents one unit.

17.

18.
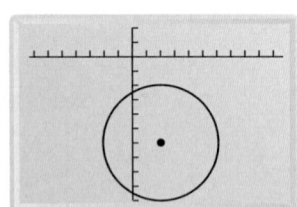

Example 4
(page 573)

For each equation, find the center and radius of the circle.

19. $(x - 1)^2 + (y - 1)^2 = 1$ **20.** $(x + 2)^2 + (y - 10)^2 = 4$

21. $(x - 3)^2 + (y + 1)^2 = 36$ **22.** $(x + 3)^2 + (y - 5)^2 = 81$

23. $x^2 + (y + 3)^2 = 25$ **24.** $(x + 6)^2 + y^2 = 121$

25. $(x + 2)^2 + (y + 4)^2 = 256$ **26.** $(x - 3)^2 + (y - 7)^2 = 96$

Example 5
(page 574)

Use the center and the radius to graph each circle.

27. $(x + 9)^2 + (y + 2)^2 = 100$ **28.** $(x + 4)^2 + (y - 4)^2 = 4$

29. $(x - 6)^2 + y^2 = 64$ **30.** $(x - 1)^2 + (y + 3)^2 = 16$

31. $x^2 + y^2 = 9$ **32.** $(x + 3)^2 + (y - 9)^2 = 49$

33. $(x - 7)^2 + (y - 1)^2 = 100$ **34.** $x^2 + (y + 4)^2 = 144$

B   **Apply Your Skills**

Write the equation of the circle that passes through the given point and has a center at the origin. (*Hint:* You can use the distance formula to find the radius.)

35. $(0, 4)$ **36.** $(0, -3)$ **37.** $(-5, 0)$ **38.** $(\sqrt{3}, 0)$ **39.** $(4, -3)$

40. $(-5, -12)$ **41.** $(12, -5)$ **42.** $(-2, 3)$ **43.** $(1, -5)$ **44.** $(-6, -4)$

Use the given information to write an equation of the circle.

45. radius 7, center $(-6, 13)$ **46.** area 25π, center $(5, -3)$

47. center $(-2, 7.5)$, circumference 3π **48.** center $(1, -2)$, through $(0, 1)$

49. center $(2, 1)$, through $(6, 4)$ **50.** center $(6, 4)$, through $(2, 1)$

51. translation of $(x - 1)^2 + (y + 3)^2 = 36$, 2 units left and 4 units down

52. Multiple Choice Which equation models the circular fountain at the right?

   Ⓐ $(x - 24)^2 + (y - 22)^2 = 100$

   Ⓑ $(x + 22)^2 + (y + 24)^2 = 100$

   Ⓒ $(x - 24)^2 + (y - 22)^2 = 10$

   Ⓓ $(x + 24)^2 + (y + 22)^2 = 10$

53. Open-Ended Write two functions that together represent a circle.

54. Error Analysis A student claims that the circle $(x + 7)^2 + (y - 7)^2 = 8$ is a translation of the circle $x^2 + y^2 = 8$, 7 right and 7 down. What is the student's mistake?

Find the center and the radius of each circle.

55. $x^2 + y^2 = 2$ **56.** $x^2 + (y + 1)^2 = 5$

57. $x^2 + y^2 = 14$ **58.** $x^2 + (y - 4)^2 = 11$

59. $(x + 5)^2 + y^2 = 18$ **60.** $(x + 2)^2 + (y + 4)^2 = 50$

61. $(x + 3)^2 + (y - 5)^2 = 38$ **62.** $x^2 + 2x + 1 + y^2 = 4$

63. $x^2 + y^2 - 6x - 2y + 4 = 0$ **64.** $x^2 + y^2 - 4y - 16 = 0$

Homework Video Tutor

Visit: PHSchool.com
Web Code: bbe-1003

Graph each pair of equations. Identify the conic section represented by the graph. Then write the equation of the conic section.

65. $y = 3 + \sqrt{16 - (x - 4)^2}$ **66.** $y = -2 + \sqrt{x - 3}$

     $y = 3 - \sqrt{16 - (x - 4)^2}$ $y = -2 - \sqrt{x - 3}$

C   **Challenge**

67. Reasoning Let $P(x, y)$ be any point on the circle with center $(0, 0)$ and radius r. Choose a method for proving that $x^2 + y^2 = r^2$.

nline Lesson Quiz   Visit: PHSchool.com, **Web Code:** bba-1003

68. a. Writing Explain why $x^2 + y^2 = 0$ does not represent a circle.
b. Critical Thinking What does the equation represent?

69. The table gives the diameters of four planets.
a. Use a center of $(0, 0)$ to graph a circle that represents the size of each planet.
b. Write an equation representing the circular cross section through the center of each planet.

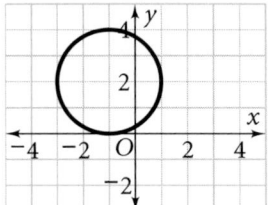

Planet	Diameter (miles)
Mercury	3031
Mars	4222
Venus	7520
Earth	7926

70. a. A circle contains $(0, 0), (6, 8),$ and $(7, 7)$. Find its equation by solving a system of three equations.
b. Several parabolas contain the three points of part (a), but only one is described by a quadratic function. Find that function.

Multiple Choice Practice

For California Standards and CAHSEE Tutorials, visit PHSchool.com. Web Code: bbq-9045

ALG2 16.0

71. Which equation is most likely represented by the circle shown?

Ⓐ $(x - 1)^2 + (y + 2)^2 = 4$
Ⓑ $(x + 1)^2 + (y - 2)^2 = 4$
Ⓒ $(x + 2)^2 + (y - 1)^2 = 4$
Ⓓ $(x - 2)^2 + (y + 1)^2 = 4$

ALG2 2.0

72. Which point represents a solution to the following system of linear equations?

$$\begin{cases} y = \frac{4}{3}x - 1 \\ 2x + y = -11 \end{cases}$$

Ⓐ $\left(\frac{11}{3}, 2\right)$ Ⓑ $\left(-2, -\frac{4}{3}\right)$ Ⓒ $(-3, 5)$ Ⓓ $(-3, -5)$

Mixed Review

Lesson 10-2

73. Write an equation of a parabola opening left with vertex $(0, 0)$ and focus $(-3, 0)$.

Lesson 9-3

For each rational function, find any points of discontinuity.

74. $y = \dfrac{2}{x + 1}$ **75.** $y = \dfrac{1}{x^2 - 5x + 6}$ **76.** $y = \dfrac{2x - 1}{x^2 + 4}$

Lesson 8-3

Evaluate each logarithm.

77. $\log_2 16$ **78.** $\log_5 25$ **79.** $\log_3 \frac{1}{27}$

80. $\log 10,000$ **81.** $\log_{36} 6$ **82.** $\log_{100} 100$

Checkpoint Quiz 1   Lessons 10-1 through 10-3

Identify the vertex, focus, and directrix of each parabola. Then graph the parabola.

1. $y = 3x^2$ **2.** $x = 4(y + 2)^2$ **3.** $y + 1 = (x - 3)^2$

4. Write an equation in standard form of the circle with center $(-6, 3)$ and radius 8.

5. What translation of $x^2 + y^2 = 18$ results in $(x + 4)^2 + (y - 6)^2 = 18$?

Using Parametric Equations

MA 7.0 Students demonstrate an understanding of functions and equations defined parametrically and can graph them.

The graphing calculator program below uses parametric equations (Activity Lab, page 124) to graph a circle. To enter the program, use the QUIT **NEW** menu. Name your program **CIRCLE**.

Note that you find the **Disp**, **Prompt**, and **DispGraph** features in the QUIT **I/O** menu, and X_{1T} and Y_{1T} in the VARS **Y-Vars Parametric** menu. You can find **Par** and **Radian** under MODE, and **Tmin**, **Tmax**, and **Tstep** in the VARS **Window T/θ** menu.

Use ALPHA keys to enter words, quotation marks, and variables $H, K, R,$ and T.

```
PROGRAM:CIRCLE
:Disp "CENTER (H,K)"
:Disp "RADIUS R"
:Prompt H,K,R
:"Rcos(T)+H"→X₁T
■
```

```
PROGRAM:CIRCLE
:"Rsin(T)+K"→Y₁T
:Param
:Radian
:0→Tmin
:2π→Tmax
:.05→Tstep
:DispGraph■
```

The screens below show the program being run for a circle with a center at $(-2, 3)$ and a radius of 5. Enter appropriate square-window values with the calculator in function mode. Then choose the program from the QUIT **EXEC** menu.

```
WINDOW
 Xmin=-12
 Xmax=12
 Xscl=1
 Ymin=-8
 Ymax=8
 Yscl=1
 Xres=1■
```

```
prgmCIRCLE
CENTER (H,K)
RADIUS R
H=?-2
K=?3
R=?5■
```

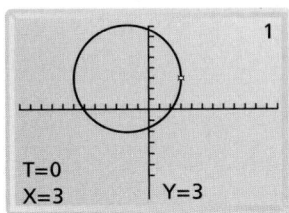

T=0
X=3   Y=3

Note that you can trace to find the coordinates of points on the circle.

EXERCISES

Use your program to graph each circle. Use an appropriate square window for each graph.

1. center $(0, 2)$, radius 4

2. center $(5, -2)$, radius 5

3. center $(-1, 3)$, radius 8

4. $(x - 2)^2 + (y + 1)^2 = 25$

5. $(x + 4)^2 + (y - 3)^2 = 100$

6. $x^2 + (y + 2)^2 = 49$

7. $(x - 1)^2 + (y + 2)^2 = 36$

8. $(x - 6)^2 + y^2 = 100$

9. Open-Ended Use TRACE to find four points in Quadrant III that lie on the circle described by the equation $(x + 5)^2 + (y - 2)^2 = 16$.

10. Writing Describe how to change your program to work in degrees and plot a point every 5° of rotation.

Ellipses

 California Content Standards

ALG2 16.0 Students demonstrate and explain how the geometry of the graph of a conic section depends on the coefficients of the quadratic equation representing it. **Master**

What You'll Learn

- To write the equation of an ellipse

- To find the foci of an ellipse and to graph an ellipse

. . . And Why

To model NASA's Transonic Tunnel, as in Example 2

 Check Skills You'll Need **GO for Help** Lesson 5-5 and Skills Handbook page 886

Solve each equation.

1. $27 = x^2 + 11$ **2.** $x^2 = 48$ **3.** $84 = 120 - x^2$

Evaluate each expression for $a = 3$ and $b = 5$.

4. $a^2 + b^2$ **5.** $a^2 - b^2$ **6.** $b^2 - 2a^2$

◀») **New Vocabulary** • ellipse • focus of an ellipse • major axis • vertices of an ellipse • minor axis • co-vertices

---

1   Writing the Equation of an Ellipse

Ellipses play an important role in science. For example, the planets follow elliptical, not circular, orbits around the sun.

 Key Concepts

| **Definition** | **Ellipse** |

An **ellipse** is a set of points P in a plane such that the sum of the distances from P to two fixed points F_1 and F_2 is a given constant k.

$$PF_1 + PF_2 = k, \text{ where } k > F_1F_2$$

Vocabulary Tip

Ellipse comes from a Greek word for "smaller." The cutting plane of an ellipse makes a smaller angle with the base than does the side of the cone. See p. 547.

Each fixed point F is a **focus of an ellipse** (plural: foci). The **major axis** is the segment that contains the foci and has its endpoints on the ellipse. The endpoints of the major axis are **vertices of an ellipse.** The midpoint of the major axis is the center of the ellipse. The **minor axis** is perpendicular to the major axis at the center. The endpoints of the minor axis are **co-vertices.**

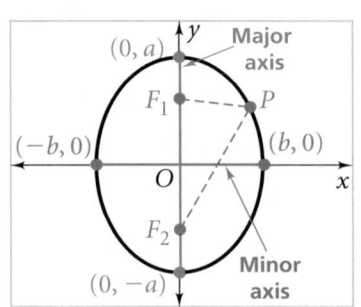

$$\frac{x^2}{a^2} + \frac{y^2}{b^2} = 1$$
major axis: horizontal
vertices: $(\pm a, 0)$
co-vertices: $(0, \pm b)$

← standard forms of an equation of an ellipse, with center at the origin and $a > b > 0$ →

$$\frac{x^2}{b^2} + \frac{y^2}{a^2} = 1$$
major axis: vertical
vertices: $(0, \pm a)$
co-vertices: $(\pm b, 0)$

You can write the equation of an ellipse with a center at the origin if you know an *x*-intercept and a *y*-intercept.

1 EXAMPLE Writing the Equation of an Ellipse

Write an equation in standard form of an ellipse that has a vertex at $(0, 5)$, a co-vertex at $(2, 0)$, and a center at the origin.

Since $(0, 5)$ is a vertex of the ellipse, the other vertex is at $(0, -5)$, and the major axis is vertical. Since $(2, 0)$ is a co-vertex, the other co-vertex is at $(-2, 0)$, and the minor axis is horizontal. So $a = 5, b = 2, a^2 = 25,$ and $b^2 = 4$.

$\dfrac{x^2}{b^2} + \dfrac{y^2}{a^2} = 1$ **standard form of an equation of an ellipse with a vertical major axis**

$\dfrac{x^2}{4} + \dfrac{y^2}{25} = 1$ **Substitute 4 for b^2 and 25 for a^2.**

● An equation of the ellipse is $\dfrac{x^2}{4} + \dfrac{y^2}{25} = 1$.

✓ CA Standards Check ❶ Write an equation in standard form for an ellipse that has a vertex at $(0, -6)$, a co-vertex at $(3, 0)$, and a center at the origin.

You can write an equation for an ellipse with a center at the origin if you know the length of both axes.

2 EXAMPLE Real-World 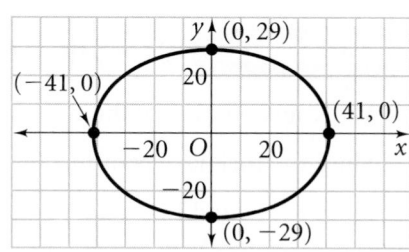 Connection

Aerodynamics Scientists used the Transonic Tunnel at NASA Langley Research Center, Virginia, to study the dynamics of air flow. The elliptical opening of the Transonic Tunnel is 82 ft wide and 58 ft high. Find an equation of the ellipse.

Imagine a large coordinate grid placed over the elliptical opening. Since the widest part of the ellipse is horizontal and the width is 82 ft, place the vertices at $(\pm 41, 0)$. Place the co-vertices at $(0, \pm 29)$.

So $a = 41, b = 29, a^2 = 1681,$ and $b^2 = 841$.

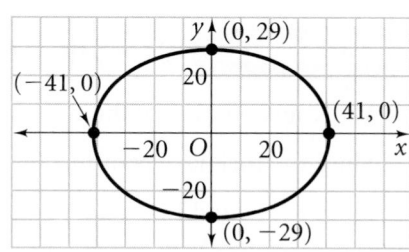

$\dfrac{x^2}{a^2} + \dfrac{y^2}{b^2} = 1$ **standard form for an ellipse with a horizontal major axis**

$\dfrac{x^2}{1681} + \dfrac{y^2}{841} = 1$ **Substitute 1681 for a^2 and 841 for b^2.**

● An equation of the ellipse is $\dfrac{x^2}{1681} + \dfrac{y^2}{841} = 1$.

✓ CA Standards Check ❷ Find an equation of an ellipse centered at the origin that is 12 units wide and 30 units high.

Real-World 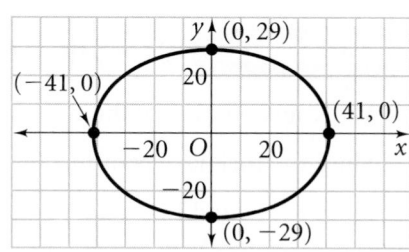 Connection

The guide vanes in the elliptical opening of the Transonic Tunnel allow a smooth flow of air through the passageway.

The foci are important points in an ellipse. For example, the sun is at a focus, not at the center, of Earth's orbit around the sun.

The foci of an ellipse are always on the major axis at c units from the center.

There is an important and useful relationship among a, b, and c: $c^2 = a^2 - b^2$.

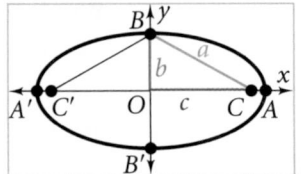

You can use the relationship to find the foci of an ellipse.

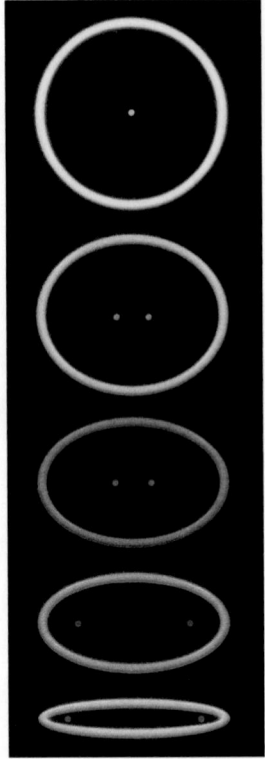

The figure above shows the relationship between the center of a circle and the foci of an ellipse.

3 **EXAMPLE** **Finding the Foci of an Ellipse**

Find the foci of the ellipse with the equation $25x^2 + 9y^2 = 225$. Graph the ellipse.

$$25x^2 + 9y^2 = 225$$

$$\frac{x^2}{9} + \frac{y^2}{25} = 1 \quad \text{Write in standard form.}$$

Since $25 > 9$ and 25 is with y^2, the major axis is vertical, $a^2 = 25$, and $b^2 = 9$.

$$c^2 = a^2 - b^2 \quad \text{Find } c.$$

$$= 25 - 9 \quad \text{Substitute 25 for } a^2 \text{ and 9 for } b^2.$$

$$= 16$$

$$c = 4$$

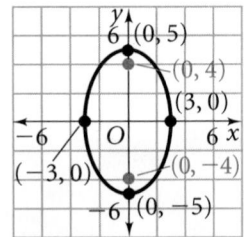

The major axis is vertical, so the coordinates of the foci are $(0, \pm c)$. The foci are $(0, 4)$ and $(0, -4)$.

The vertices are $(0, \pm 5)$. The co-vertices are $(\pm 3, 0)$.

CA Standards Check **3** Find the foci of the ellipse with the equation $x^2 + 9y^2 = 9$. Graph the ellipse.

You can use the relationship among a, b, and c to write the equation of an ellipse.

4 **EXAMPLE** **Using the Foci of an Ellipse**

Write an equation of the ellipse with foci at $(\pm 7, 0)$ and co-vertices at $(0, \pm 6)$.

Since the foci have coordinates $(\pm 7, 0)$, the major axis is horizontal.

Since $c = 7$ and $b = 6$, $c^2 = 49$ and $b^2 = 36$.

$$c^2 = a^2 - b^2 \quad \text{Use the equation to find } a^2.$$

$$49 = a^2 - 36 \quad \text{Substitute 49 for } c^2 \text{ and 36 for } b^2.$$

$$a^2 = 85 \quad \text{Simplify.}$$

$$\frac{x^2}{85} + \frac{y^2}{36} = 1 \quad \text{Substitute 85 for } a^2 \text{ and 36 for } b^2.$$

An equation of the ellipse is $\frac{x^2}{85} + \frac{y^2}{36} = 1$.

Online **active math**

For: Ellipse Activity
Use: Interactive Textbook, 10-4

CA Standards Check **4** Write an equation of the ellipse with foci at $\left(0, \pm\sqrt{17}\right)$ and co-vertices at $(\pm 8, 0)$.

A Practice by Example

Example 1
(page 579)

Write an equation of an ellipse in standard form with center at the origin and with the given vertex and co-vertex.

1. $(4, 0), (0, 3)$ **2.** $(0, 1), (2, 0)$ **3.** $(3, 0), (0, -1)$ **4.** $(0, 6), (1, 0)$

5. $(0, -7), (4, 0)$ **6.** $(-6, 0), (0, 5)$ **7.** $(-9, 0), (0, -2)$ **8.** $(0, 5), (-3, 0)$

Example 2
(page 579)

Find an equation of an ellipse for each given height and width. Assume that the center of the ellipse is $(0, 0)$.

9. $h = 1\,\text{m}, w = 3\,\text{m}$ **10.** $h = 32\,\text{ft}, w = 16\,\text{ft}$ **11.** $h = 20\,\text{ft}, w = 12\,\text{ft}$

12. $h = 10\,\text{cm}, w = 7\,\text{cm}$ **13.** $h = 14\,\text{yd}, w = 28\,\text{yd}$ **14.** $h = 8\,\text{ft}, w = 2\,\text{ft}$

15. $h = 15\,\text{ft}, w = 32\,\text{ft}$ **16.** $h = 40\,\text{mi}, w = 60\,\text{mi}$ **17.** $h = 5\,\text{m}, w = 2\,\text{m}$

Example 3
(page 580)

Find the foci for each equation of an ellipse. Then graph the ellipse.

18. $\frac{x^2}{4} + \frac{y^2}{9} = 1$ **19.** $\frac{x^2}{9} + \frac{y^2}{25} = 1$ **20.** $\frac{x^2}{81} + \frac{y^2}{49} = 1$

21. $\frac{x^2}{100} + \frac{y^2}{36} = 1$ **22.** $\frac{x^2}{64} + \frac{y^2}{100} = 1$ **23.** $3x^2 + y^2 = 9$

24. $x^2 + 4y^2 = 16$ **25.** $\frac{x^2}{225} + \frac{y^2}{144} = 1$ **26.** $\frac{x^2}{256} + \frac{y^2}{121} = 1$

Example 4
(page 580)

Write an equation of an ellipse for the given foci and co-vertices.

27. foci $(\pm 6, 0)$, co-vertices $(0, \pm 8)$ **28.** foci $(0, \pm 8)$, co-vertices $(\pm 8, 0)$

29. foci $(\pm 5, 0)$, co-vertices $(0, \pm 8)$ **30.** foci $(0, \pm 4)$, co-vertices $(\pm 2, 0)$

31. foci $(\pm 14, 0)$, co-vertices $(0, \pm 7)$ **32.** foci $(\pm 17, 0)$, co-vertices $(0, \pm 15)$

B Apply Your Skills

Find the foci for each equation of an ellipse.

33. $4x^2 + 9y^2 = 36$ **34.** $16x^2 + 4y^2 = 64$ **35.** $36x^2 + 4y^2 = 144$

36. $25x^2 + 4y^2 = 100$ **37.** $36x^2 + 8y^2 = 288$ **38.** $25x^2 + 24y^2 = 600$

39. $25x^2 + 16y^2 + 150x = 160y - 225$ **40.** $2x^2 + 8x + y^2 + 4 = 0$

Vocabulary Tip

Eccentric means "out of center."

41. The eccentricity of an ellipse is a measure of how nearly circular it is. Eccentricity is defined as $\frac{c}{a}$, where c is the distance from the center to a focus and a is the distance from the center to a vertex.
  a. Find the eccentricity of an ellipse with foci $(\pm 9, 0)$ and vertices $(\pm 10, 0)$. Sketch the graph.
  b. Find the eccentricity of an ellipse with foci $(\pm 1, 0)$ and vertices $(\pm 10, 0)$. Sketch the graph.
  c. Describe the shape of an ellipse that has an eccentricity close to 0.
  d. Describe the shape of an ellipse that has an eccentricity close to 1.

42. Multiple Choice Which equation represents the ellipse with foci on the x-axis, major axis 9 units long, minor axis 4 units long, and center at the origin?

Ⓐ $\frac{x^2}{4} + \frac{y^2}{9} = 1$ Ⓑ $\frac{x^2}{20.25} + \frac{y^2}{4} = 1$ Ⓒ $\frac{x^2}{9} + \frac{y^2}{4} = 1$ Ⓓ $\frac{x^2}{4} + \frac{y^2}{20.25} = 1$

43. a. Critical Thinking An ellipse has foci very close to the center. Its minor axis has length 2. Explain why its shape is close to that of a circle.
  b. Is a circle also an ellipse? Explain.

Write an equation for each ellipse.

44.

45.

46.

47.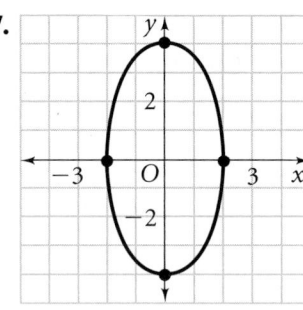

48. Error Analysis A student claims that an ellipse has vertices at $(\pm 3, 0)$ and co-vertices at $(0, \pm 7)$. What is the student's error?

49. Open-Ended Find a real-world design that uses ellipses. Place a coordinate grid over the design and write an equation of the ellipse.

Write an equation of an ellipse in standard form with center at the origin and with the given characteristics.

50. focus $(1, 0)$, width 4

51. $a = 5, b = 2$, width 10

52. vertex $(-11, 0)$, co-vertex $(0, 9)$

53. height 29, width 53

54. focus $(-5, 0)$, co-vertex $(0, -12)$

55. $c^2 = 68$, vertex $(0, -18)$

56. focus $\left(0, 3\sqrt{2}\right)$, height 19

57. focus $\left(10\sqrt{3}, 0\right)$, width 40

58. focus $(2, 0)$, x-intercept 4

59. focus $(0, 3)$, y-intercept 5

60. focus $(0, -5)$, y-intercept 8

61. focus $(3, 0)$, x-intercept -6

62. $a = 3, b = 2$, width 4

63. $a = 2\sqrt{5}, b = 3\sqrt{2}$, width $6\sqrt{2}$

64. Draw an ellipse by placing two tacks in a piece of graph paper laid over a piece of cardboard. Place a loop of string around the tacks. With your pencil keeping the string taut, draw around the tacks. Mark the center of your ellipse $(0, 0)$ and draw the x- and y-axes.

  a. Where are the vertices and co-vertices of your ellipse?

  b. Where are the foci?

  c. Write the equation of your ellipse.

Homework Video Tutor

Visit: PHSchool.com
Web Code: bbe-1004

 Challenge ✎ **65. Writing** The area of a circle is πr^2. The area of an ellipse is πab. Explain the connection.

66. Astronomy The sun is at a focus of Earth's elliptical orbit.

a. Find the distance from the sun to the other focus.

b. Refer to Exercise 41 for the definition of eccentricity. What is the eccentricity of the orbit?

c. Write an equation of Earth's orbit. Assume that the major axis is horizontal.

9.45 × 10⁷ mi from sun (farthest)

9.15 × 10⁷ mi from sun (nearest)

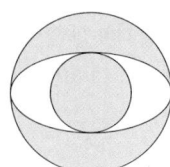

67. An ellipse and two circles share a center. The major axis of the ellipse is twice as long as its minor axis. The diameter of the larger circle is the same length as the major axis of the ellipse. The diameter of the smaller circle is the same length as the minor axis of the ellipse. The area of an ellipse is πab. Compare the areas of the blue and white regions at the left.

68. Acoustics In "whispering galleries" a sound made at one focus can be clearly heard at the other focus, even though very little can be heard by someone in between. Suppose an elliptical room measures 320 ft long and 150 ft wide. How far would the listener have to be from the source of the sound in order to hear it?

Multiple Choice Practice

For California Standards and CAHSEE Tutorials, visit PHSchool.com. Web Code: bbq-9045

ALG2 16.0

69. The point $A(-10, 0)$ is on the ellipse with equation $\frac{x^2}{100} + \frac{y^2}{64} = 1$. What is the sum of the distances $AF_1 + AF_2$, where F_1 and F_2 are the foci?

(A) 10   (B) 12   (C) 14   (D) 20

ALG2 12.0

70. Which function generates the table of values below?

x	-2	-1	0	1	2	3
y	243	81	27	9	3	1

(A) $y = 9\left(\frac{2}{3}\right)^x$

(B) $y = 27\left(\frac{1}{3}\right)^x$

(C) $y = 81\left(\frac{3}{4}\right)^x$

(D) $y = 3\left(\frac{5}{3}\right)^x$

Mixed Review

Lesson 10-3

Write an equation of a circle with the given center and radius.

71. center $(2, -3)$, radius 6

72. center $(-4, 7)$, radius 11

Lesson 9-4

Simplify each expression. What are the restrictions on the variable?

73. $\dfrac{3x}{6x^2 - 9x^5}$

74. $\dfrac{x^2 - 36}{x^2 + 5x - 6}$

75. $\dfrac{x^2 - 3x - 10}{x^3 + 8}$

Lesson 8-4

Write each logarithmic expression as a single logarithm.

76. $\log 3 + \log 5$

77. $\log_3 12 - \log_3 2$

78. $3 \log 2 - \log 4$

79. $5 \log 2 + \log 10$

80. $\log x - \log y$

81. $k \log 5 - \log 4$

Hyperbolas

 California Content Standards

ALG2 16.0 Students demonstrate and explain how the geometry of the graph of a conic section depends on the coefficients of the quadratic equation representing it. *Master*

What You'll Learn

• To graph hyperbolas

• To find and use the foci of a hyperbola

. . . And Why

To write an equation that models the path of Voyager 2 around Saturn, as in Example 3

 Check Skills You'll Need **GO for Help** Lesson 2-2 and Skills Handbook page 886

Write an equation of a line in slope-intercept form using the given information.

1. rise -5, run 2, through the origin   **2.** through $(3, 1)$ and $(9, 3)$

Solve each equation for y.

3. $\dfrac{x^2}{4} - \dfrac{y^2}{16} = 1$ **4.** $\dfrac{y^2}{9} - \dfrac{x^2}{25} = 1$ **5.** $\dfrac{x^2}{36} - \dfrac{y^2}{81} = 1$

New Vocabulary • hyperbola • transverse axis • focus of a hyperbola
• vertices of a hyperbola

---

1 Graphing Hyperbolas Centered at the Origin

Vocabulary Tip

Hyperbola comes from a Greek word for "greater." The cutting plane of a hyperbola makes a greater angle with the base than does the side of the cone. See p. 557.

Activity: Analyzing Hyperbolas

1. The diagram below shows the shape of a hyperbola. Measure the distances to the nearest millimeter to complete the table.

2. **Make a Conjecture** What is the relationship between the distances from the points F_1 and F_2 to any point on the hyperbola?

Distance	P_1	P_2	P_3	...
Distance From F_1	■	■	■	■
Distance From F_2	■	■	■	■
$\lvert PF_1 - PF_2 \rvert$	■	■	■	■

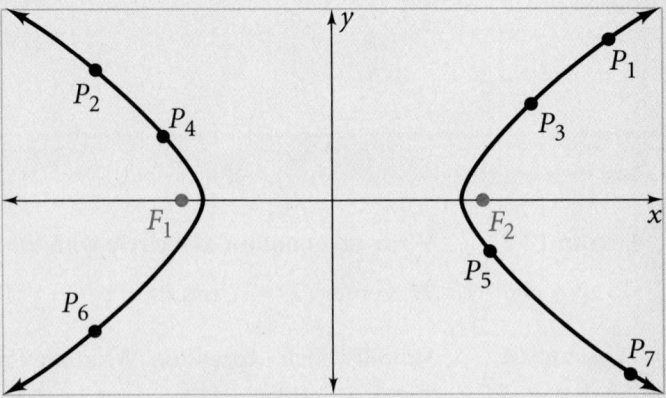

Hyperbolas play an important role in science and navigation. Some comets follow hyperbolic paths.

Definition | **Hyperbola**

A **hyperbola** is a set of points P in a plane such that the absolute value of the difference between the distances from P to two fixed points F_1 and F_2 is a constant k.

$$|PF_1 - PF_2| = k, \text{ where } k < F_1F_2.$$

Each fixed point F is a **focus of a hyperbola.** The segment that lies on the line containing the foci and has endpoints on a hyperbola is the **transverse axis.** The endpoints are the **vertices of a hyperbola.** The midpoint of the segment is the center of a hyperbola.

Below are the standard forms of the equation of a hyperbola centered at $(0, 0)$.

$$\frac{x^2}{a^2} - \frac{y^2}{b^2} = 1$$ **standard form of an equation of a hyperbola with a horizontal transverse axis**

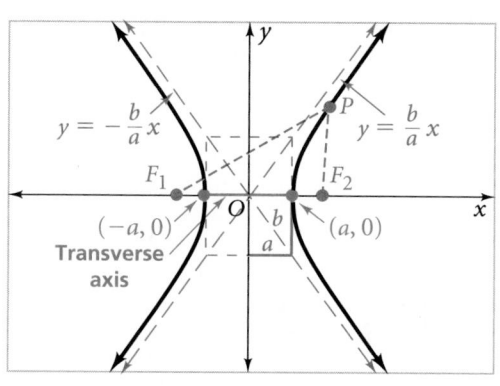

foci: F_1, F_2

vertices: $(\pm a, 0)$

asymptotes: $y = \pm \frac{b}{a}x$

x-intercepts: $\pm a$

y-intercepts: none

Vocabulary Tip

An <u>asymptote</u> is a line that a graph approaches.

$$\frac{y^2}{a^2} - \frac{x^2}{b^2} = 1$$ **standard form of an equation of a hyperbola with a vertical transverse axis**

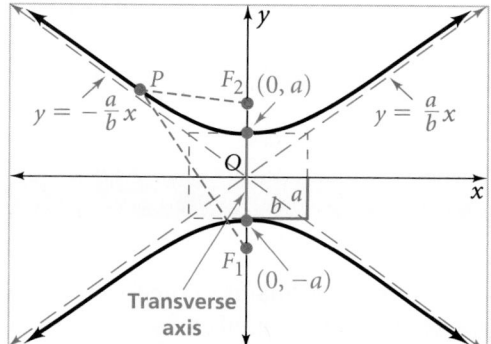

foci: F_1, F_2

vertices: $(0, \pm a)$

asymptotes: $y = \pm \frac{a}{b}x$

x-intercepts: none

y-intercepts: $\pm a$

To graph a hyperbola, use the standard form of the equation to find the values of a and b. You can use a and b to find and graph the vertices and to draw a central rectangle that is used to guide the graph.

Draw the asymptotes through the diagonals of the central rectangle. Then draw the branches of the hyperbola through the vertices so they approach the asymptotes.

1 EXAMPLE Graphing a Hyperbola

Graph $9x^2 - 25y^2 = 225$.

$9x^2 - 25y^2 = 225$

$\dfrac{x^2}{25} - \dfrac{y^2}{9} = 1$ **Rewrite the equation in standard form.**

The equation is of the form $\dfrac{x^2}{a^2} - \dfrac{y^2}{b^2} = 1$, so the transverse axis is horizontal. Since $a^2 = 25$ and $b^2 = 9$, $a = 5$ and $b = 3$.

Step 1 Graph the vertices. Since the transverse axis is horizontal, the vertices lie on the x-axis. The coordinates are $(\pm a, 0)$, or $(\pm 5, 0)$.

Step 2 Use the values of a and b to draw the central rectangle. The lengths of its sides are $2a$ and $2b$, or 10 and 6.

Step 3 Draw the asymptotes. The equations of the asymptotes are $y = \pm \dfrac{b}{a}x$ or $y = \pm \dfrac{3}{5}x$. The asymptotes contain the diagonals of the central rectangle.

Step 4 Sketch the branches of the hyperbola through the vertices so they approach the asymptotes.

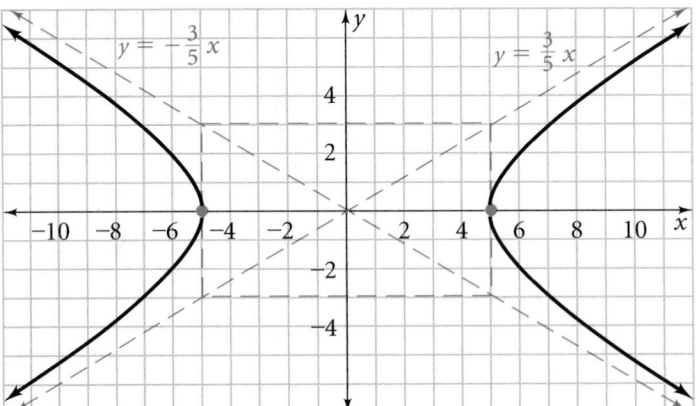

✔ CA Standards Check **1** Graph the hyperbola with equation $\dfrac{y^2}{16} - \dfrac{x^2}{9} = 1$.

---

2 Using the Foci of a Hyperbola

Use $(\pm c, 0)$ for the coordinates of the foci if the transverse axis is horizontal or $(0, \pm c)$ if it is vertical.

The distance between the foci, $2c$, is also the length of the diagonal of the central rectangle.

You can find the value of c using the Pythagorean Theorem.

$$c^2 = a^2 + b^2$$

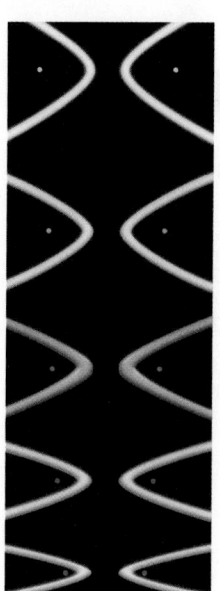

The figures above show how the shape of a hyperbola changes with decreased distances between the foci and the vertices.

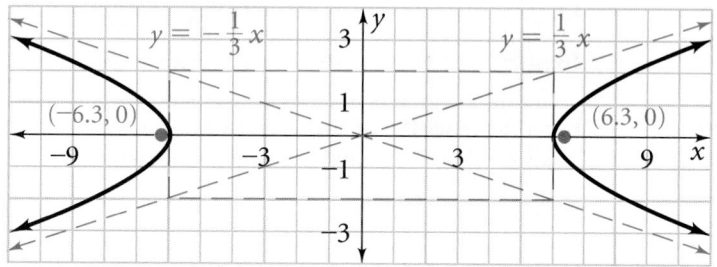

2 EXAMPLE Finding the Foci of a Hyperbola

Find the foci of the graph $\frac{x^2}{36} - \frac{y^2}{4} = 1$. Draw the graph.

The equation is in the form $\frac{x^2}{a^2} - \frac{y^2}{b^2} = 1$, so the transverse axis is horizontal; $a^2 = 36$ and $b^2 = 4$.

$$c^2 = a^2 + b^2 \qquad \textbf{Use the Pythagorean Theorem.}$$
$$= 36 + 4 \qquad \textbf{Substitute 36 for } a^2 \textbf{ and 4 for } b^2.$$
$$c = \sqrt{40} \approx 6.3 \qquad \textbf{Find the square root of each side of the equation.}$$

The foci $(\pm c, 0)$ are approximately $(-6.3, 0)$ and $(6.3, 0)$. The vertices $(\pm a, 0)$ are $(6, 0)$ and $(-6, 0)$. The asymptotes are the lines $y = \pm\frac{b}{a}x$, or $y = \pm\frac{1}{3}x$.

 CA Standards Check ② Find the foci of $\frac{x^2}{25} - \frac{y^2}{9} = 1$. Draw the graph.

You can use the value of c to write the equation of a hyperbola.

3 EXAMPLE Real-World 🌎 Connection

Online active math

For: Hyperbola Activity
Use: Interactive Textbook, 10-5

Space As a spacecraft approaches a planet, the gravitational pull of the planet changes the spacecraft's path to a hyperbola that diverges from its asymptote. Find an equation that models the path of Voyager 2 around Saturn, given that $a = 332{,}965$ km and $c = 492{,}788.2$ km.

Assume that the center of the hyperbola is at the origin and that the transverse axis is horizontal. The equation will be in the form $\frac{x^2}{a^2} - \frac{y^2}{b^2} = 1$.

$$c^2 = a^2 + b^2 \qquad\qquad\qquad \textbf{Use the Pythagorean Theorem.}$$
$$(492{,}788.2)^2 = (332{,}965)^2 + b^2 \qquad\qquad \textbf{Substitute.}$$
$$b^2 = (492{,}788.2)^2 - (332{,}965)^2 \qquad \textbf{Solve for } b^2.$$
$$\approx 1.320 \times 10^{11} \qquad\qquad \textbf{Use a calculator.}$$

$$\frac{x^2}{1.109 \times 10^{11}} - \frac{y^2}{1.320 \times 10^{11}} = 1 \quad \textbf{Substitute } a^2 \textbf{ and } b^2.$$

The path of Voyager 2 around Saturn can be modeled by

$$\frac{x^2}{1.109 \times 10^{11}} - \frac{y^2}{1.320 \times 10^{11}} = 1.$$

 CA Standards Check ③ Find an equation that models the path of Voyager 2 around Jupiter, given that $a = 2{,}184{,}140$ km and $c = 2{,}904{,}906.2$ km.

EXERCISES For more exercises, see *Extra Skill and Word Problem Practice*.

Standards Practice ALG2 16.0

A Practice by Example

Example 1
(page 586)

Graph each equation.

1. $\frac{x^2}{16} - \frac{y^2}{4} = 1$ **2.** $\frac{y^2}{169} - \frac{x^2}{16} = 1$ **3.** $\frac{x^2}{25} - \frac{y^2}{36} = 1$

4. $x^2 - 4y^2 = 4$ **5.** $36y^2 - 9x^2 = 324$ **6.** $25x^2 - 16y^2 = 400$

7. $9x^2 - 49y^2 = 441$ **8.** $25x^2 - 35y^2 = 875$ **9.** $81y^2 - 9x^2 = 729$

Example 2
(page 587)

Find the foci of each hyperbola. Then draw the graph.

10. $\frac{y^2}{81} - \frac{x^2}{16} = 1$ **11.** $\frac{y^2}{49} - \frac{x^2}{64} = 1$ **12.** $\frac{x^2}{121} - \frac{y^2}{144} = 1$

13. $\frac{x^2}{64} - \frac{y^2}{36} = 1$ **14.** $\frac{y^2}{25} - \frac{x^2}{100} = 1$ **15.** $\frac{x^2}{36} - \frac{y^2}{169} = 1$

16. $4y^2 - 25x^2 = 100$ **17.** $36x^2 - 8y^2 = 288$ **18.** $14y^2 - 28x^2 = 448$

Example 3
(page 587)

For Exercises 19–21, find the equation of a hyperbola with the given values. Assume that the transverse axis is horizontal.

19. $a = 263, c = 407$ **20.** $b = 100, c = 500$ **21.** $a = 13{,}872, c = 19{,}043$

22. Find an equation that models the path of Voyager 2 around Jupiter, given that $a = 1{,}362{,}450$ km and $c = 1{,}543{,}781$ km.

B Apply Your Skills

Write the equation of a hyperbola with the given foci and vertices.

23. foci $(\pm 5, 0)$, vertices $(\pm 3, 0)$ **24.** foci $(0, \pm 13)$, vertices $(0, \pm 5)$

25. foci $(0, \pm 2)$, vertices $(0, \pm 1)$ **26.** foci $(\pm \sqrt{5}, 0)$, vertices $(\pm 2, 0)$

Graph each equation.

27. $5x^2 - 12y^2 = 120$ **28.** $16x^2 - 20y^2 = 560$ **29.** $\frac{y^2}{20} - \frac{x^2}{5} = 1$

Write the equation of a hyperbola from the given information. Graph the equation. Place the center of each hyperbola at the origin of the coordinate plane.

30. Transverse axis is vertical and is 9 units; central rectangle is 9 units by 4 units.

31. Perimeter of central rectangle is 16 units; vertices are at $(0, 3)$ and $(0, -3)$.

For a guide to solving
Exercise 32, see p. 591.

32. (Distance from the center of a hyperbola to a focus)$^2 = 96$; endpoints of the transverse axis are at $\left(-\sqrt{32}, 0\right)$ and $\left(\sqrt{32}, 0\right)$.

Solve each equation for y. Graph each relation on your graphing calculator. Use the TRACE feature to locate the vertices.

33. $x^2 - 2y^2 = 4$ **34.** $x^2 - y^2 = 1$ **35.** $3x^2 - y^2 = 2$

36. Rewrite the equation $4x^2 - 9y^2 = 36$ in standard form. Then write the equation for a translation right 3 units and down 5 units. Draw the graph of each.

37. Open-Ended Choose two points on an axis to be the vertices of a hyperbola. Choose two other points on the same axis to be the foci. Write the equation of your hyperbola and draw its graph.

Visit: PHSchool.com
Web Code: bbe-1005

38. List the properties of a hyperbola that allow you to sketch its graph.

39. Writing Describe the similarities and differences between hyperbolas and ellipses.

Find the vertices and the asymptotes of each hyperbola.

40. $y^2 - x^2 = 1$ **41.** $x^2 - 9y^2 = 1$ **42.** $y^2 - 4x^2 = 64$

43. $16x^2 - 25y^2 = 400$ **44.** $9y^2 - 36x^2 = 144$ **45.** $25x^2 - 49y^2 = 1225$

46. a. Prove that the hyperbola $\dfrac{y^2}{a^2} - \dfrac{x^2}{b^2} = 1$ never intersects its asymptotes.

    b. Is $\dfrac{y^2}{16} - \dfrac{x^2}{9} = 4$ a hyperbola? Is $\dfrac{y^2}{16} - \dfrac{x^2}{9} = -1$ a hyperbola? Explain.

C Challenge

47. Air Traffic Control Suppose you are an air traffic controller directing the pilot of a plane on a hyperbolic flight path. You and another air traffic controller from a different airport send radio signals to the pilot simultaneously. The two airports are 48 km apart. The pilot's instrument panel tells him that the signal from your airport always arrives 100 μs (microseconds) before the signal from the other airport.

a. To which airport is the plane closer?

b. If the signals travel at a rate of 300 m/μs, what is the difference in distances from the plane to the two airports?

c. Write the equation of the flight path. (*Hint: k = 2a*)

d. Draw the hyperbola. Which branch represents the flight path?

Real-World Connection

Air traffic controllers coordinate the flow of air traffic by the use of radar and visual observation.

48. The function $y = \sqrt{x^2 - 9}$ represents part of a hyperbola. The tables at the right show the coordinates of several points on the graph.

a. Explain why ERROR appears for some entries.

b. Describe the relationship between the x- and y-coordinates as x gets larger.

c. Critical Thinking Do you think that the x- and y-coordinates will ever be equal? Explain.

d. Make a Conjecture What are the equations of the asymptotes of this hyperbola? Verify your answer by drawing the complete graph.

X	Y1
0	ERROR
1	ERROR
2	ERROR
3	0
4	2.6458
5	4
6	5.1962
X=0	

X	Y1
10	9.5394
20	19.774
30	29.85
40	39.887
50	49.91
60	59.925
70	69.936
X=10	

 Multiple Choice Practice

For California Standards and CAHSEE Tutorials, visit PHSchool.com. Web Code: bbq-9045

ALG2 16.0   **49.** The graph of $\dfrac{x^2}{16} - \dfrac{y^2}{4} = 1$ is a hyperbola. Which set of equations represents the asymptotes of the hyperbola's graph?

    Ⓐ $y = \frac{1}{2}x, \ y = -\frac{1}{2}x$ Ⓒ $x = \frac{1}{2}y, \ x = -\frac{1}{2}y$

    Ⓑ $y = 2x, \ y = -2x$ Ⓓ $y = \frac{1}{4}x, \ y = -\frac{1}{4}x$

ALG2 4.0   **50.** What is the factored form of $16x^2 + 48x + 36$?

    Ⓐ $(4x + 6)^2$ Ⓒ $4(2x + 3)^2$

    Ⓑ $2(2x + 3)^2$ Ⓓ $4(2x + 3)(2x - 3)$

ALG2 11.2

51. Mr. Gonzalez asks two students to work out the same problem. Each student's work is shown below.

Steven's Work
$$\frac{ab^3}{a^{-2}b^4} = a^{0-2}b^{3-4}$$
$$= a^{-2}b^{-1}$$
$$= \frac{1}{a^2b}, \, a,b \neq 0$$

Gabrielle's Work
$$\frac{ab^3}{a^{-2}b^4} = a^{1--2}b^{3-4}$$
$$= a^3b^{-1}$$
$$= \frac{a^3}{b}, \, b \neq 0$$

Which statement about their solutions is true?

    Ⓐ   Both are correct.   Ⓒ   Gabrielle is correct.

    Ⓑ   Steven is correct.   Ⓓ   Neither are correct.

ALG2 20.0

52. What is the expanded form of $(a - b)^3$?

    Ⓐ $a^3 + a^2b + ab^2 + b^3$ Ⓒ $a^3 + 3a^2b + 3ab^2 + b^3$

    Ⓑ $a^3 - a^2b + ab^2 - b^3$ Ⓓ $a^3 - 3a^2b + 3ab^2 - b^3$

Mixed Review

Lesson 10-4

GO for Help

Find the vertices and co-vertices of each ellipse.

53. $\frac{x^2}{34} + \frac{y^2}{25} = 1$ **54.** $3x^2 + 2y^2 = 6$ **55.** $25x^2 + 16y^2 = 1600$

Lesson 9-5

Simplify each expression.

56. $\frac{1}{5x} + \frac{1}{10x}$ **57.** $\frac{2x}{x^2 - 2x - 3} - \frac{7}{x^2 - 9}$ **58.** $\frac{4}{2x - 6} + \frac{x + 1}{x - 3}$

Lesson 8-5

Solve each equation.

59. $8^{2x} = 4$ **60.** $\log 8x = 3$ **61.** $2 \log_3 x - \log_3 4 = 2$

✓ Checkpoint Quiz 2   Lessons 10-4 through 10-5

Write an equation for each ellipse with the given foci and co-vertices.

1. foci $(\pm 3, 0)$
    co-vertices $(0, \pm 4)$

2. foci $(0, \pm 2)$
    co-vertices $(\pm 5, 0)$

3. foci $(0, \pm 7)$
    co-vertices $(\pm 10, 0)$

Find the foci for each conic section. Then draw the graph.

4. $\frac{x^2}{16} - \frac{y^2}{49} = 1$ **5.** $\frac{y^2}{100} - \frac{x^2}{36} = 1$ **6.** $\frac{x^2}{4} - \frac{y^2}{81} = 1$ **7.** $\frac{y^2}{25} - \frac{x^2}{64} = 1$

Write an equation for a hyperbola centered at the origin with the given characteristics.

8. horizontal transverse axis, $a = 11, c = 15$

9. vertices $(\pm 4, 0)$, perimeter of central rectangle 28 units

10. Transverse axis is vertical, 16 units long; central rectangle is 16 units by 7 units.

Understanding Math Problems Read the problem below. Then let Michelle's thinking guide you through the solution. Check your understanding with the exercise at the bottom of the page.

Write the equation of a hyperbola from the given information. Graph the equation. Place the center of the hyperbola at the origin of the coordinate plane.

> (Distance from the center of a hyperbola to a focus)$^2 = 96$; endpoints of the transverse axis are at $(-\sqrt{32}, 0)$ and $(\sqrt{32}, 0)$.

What Michelle Thinks

There is a lot of information here. I'll start with the second part. The endpoints of the transverse axis of a hyperbola are its vertices.

I know that the hyperbola opens horizontally, because the transverse axis lies on the *x*-axis. The vertices are at $(-a, 0)$ and $(a, 0)$, so I know the value of a^2.

Now I'll work on the first part of the given information. The distance from the center to the focus is c, which is also half the length of the diagonal of the central rectangle. I'll draw what I know so far.

Knowing c will help me find b! I can use the Pythagorean Theorem.

I'm ready to fill in the rest of the standard form of the equation for the hyperbola. Then I'll graph the hyperbola.

What Michelle Writes

Vertices: $(-\sqrt{32}, 0)$ and $(\sqrt{32}, 0)$

The transverse axis is horizontal, so the equation will look like $\dfrac{x^2}{a^2} - \dfrac{y^2}{b^2} = 1$.

$a = \sqrt{32}$, so $a^2 = 32$.
c = distance from center to focus
 = half length of diagonal
$c^2 = 96$, so $c = \sqrt{96}$

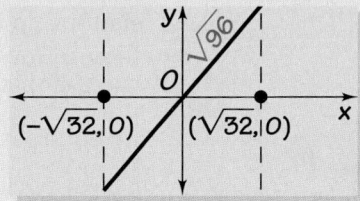

$b^2 = c^2 - a^2 = 96 - 32 = 64$

Equation:
$\dfrac{x^2}{32} - \dfrac{y^2}{64} = 1$

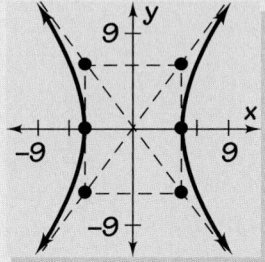

EXERCISE

Write the equation of a hyperbola from the given information. Graph the equation. Place the center of the hyperbola at the origin of the coordinate plane.

(Distance from the center of a hyperbola to a focus)$^2 = 40$; endpoints of the transverse axis are at $(-4, 0)$ and $(4, 0)$.

Translating Conic Sections

 California Content Standards

ALG2 17.0 Given a quadratic equation of the form $ax^2 + by^2 + cx + dy + e = 0$, students can use the method for completing the square to put the equation into standard form and can recognize whether the graph of the equation is a circle, ellipse, parabola, or hyperbola. *Develop, Master*

What You'll Learn

- To write the equation of a translated conic section
- To identify a translated conic section from an equation

...And Why

To explore the LORAN navigation system, as in Example 3

 Check Skills You'll Need

 for Help Lesson 5-3

Name the parent function for the equations in Exercises 1–4. Describe each equation as a translation of the parent function.

1. $y = x^2 + 4$ **2.** $y = (x - 3)^2 - 2$

3. $y - 1 = x^2$ **4.** $y = (x + 5)^2 + 6$

Rewrite each equation in vertex form.

5. $y = x^2 - 6x + 1$ **6.** $y = x^2 + 10x - 7$

7. $y = 2x^2 + 8x + 5$ **8.** $y = 4x^2 - 12x + 3$

---

1   Writing Equations of Translated Conic Sections

Technology Activity: Translating Conic Sections

1. Examine the calculator screen at the right. Describe the relationship between the two ellipses. How are they similar? How are they different?

2. The equation of ellipse ① is $\frac{x^2}{36} + \frac{y^2}{16} = 1$. Use what you know about translations to write the equation of ellipse ②.

3. The graph at the right shows the hyperbola with equation $\frac{x^2}{9} - \frac{y^2}{4} = 1$. Write the equation of the hyperbola that has been shifted four units left and one unit up.

Xmin=–9   Ymin=–9
Xmax=12   Ymax=5
Xscl=1   Yscl=1

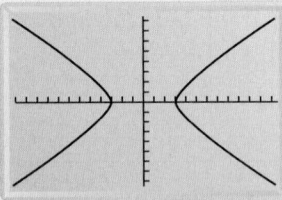

Xmin=–12   Ymin=–8
Xmax=12   Ymax=8
Xscl=1   Yscl=1

Vocabulary Tip

A <u>translation</u> shifts a graph horizontally, vertically, or both.

Just as you have translated parabolas in Chapter 5 and circles in Lesson 10-3, you can also use parameters h and k to translate ellipses and hyperbolas. A translated ellipse or hyperbola has center (h, k).

Conic Section		Standard Form of Equation	
Parabola	Vertex $(0,0)$ $y = ax^2$ $x = ay^2$	Vertex (h,k) $y - k = a(x - h)^2$ or $y = a(x - h)^2 + k$ $x - h = a(y - k)^2$ or $x = a(y - k)^2 + h$	
Circle	Center $(0,0)$ $x^2 + y^2 = r^2$	Center (h,k) $(x - h)^2 + (y - k)^2 = r^2$	
Ellipse	Center $(0,0)$ $\dfrac{x^2}{a^2} + \dfrac{y^2}{b^2} = 1$ $\dfrac{x^2}{b^2} + \dfrac{y^2}{a^2} = 1$	Center (h,k) $\dfrac{(x - h)^2}{a^2} + \dfrac{(y - k)^2}{b^2} = 1$ $\dfrac{(x - h)^2}{b^2} + \dfrac{(y - k)^2}{a^2} = 1$	
Hyperbola	Center $(0,0)$ $\dfrac{x^2}{a^2} - \dfrac{y^2}{b^2} = 1$ $\dfrac{y^2}{a^2} - \dfrac{x^2}{b^2} = 1$	Center (h,k) $\dfrac{(x - h)^2}{a^2} - \dfrac{(y - k)^2}{b^2} = 1$ $\dfrac{(y - k)^2}{a^2} - \dfrac{(x - h)^2}{b^2} = 1$	

Summary — Families of Conic Sections

1 EXAMPLE Writing the Equation of a Translated Ellipse

Write an equation of an ellipse with center $(-3, -2)$, vertical major axis of length 8, and minor axis of length 6.

The length of the major axis is $2a$. So $2a = 8$ and $a = 4$. The length of the minor axis is $2b$. So $2b = 6$ and $b = 3$. Since the center is $(-3, -2)$, $h = -3$ and $k = -2$.

The major axis is vertical, so the equation has the form $\dfrac{(x - h)^2}{b^2} + \dfrac{(y - k)^2}{a^2} = 1$.

$\dfrac{(x - (-3))^2}{3^2} + \dfrac{(y - (-2))^2}{4^2} = 1$ **Substitute -3 for h and -2 for k.**

The equation of the ellipse is $\dfrac{(x + 3)^2}{9} + \dfrac{(y + 2)^2}{16} = 1$.

Check Solve the equation for y and graph both equations.

$$\frac{(x + 3)^2}{9} + \frac{(y + 2)^2}{16} = 1$$
$$16(x + 3)^2 + 9(y + 2)^2 = 144$$
$$9(y + 2)^2 = 144 - 16(x + 3)^2$$
$$(y + 2)^2 = \frac{1}{9}(144 - 16(x + 3)^2)$$
$$y + 2 = \pm\sqrt{\frac{1}{9}\left(144 - 16(x + 3)^2\right)}$$
$$y = -2 \pm \frac{1}{3}\sqrt{144 - 16(x + 3)^2}$$

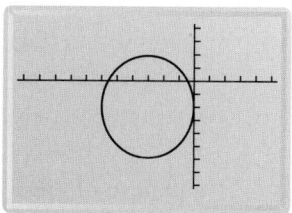

✓ CA Standards Check ① Write an equation of an ellipse with center $(1, -4)$, horizontal major axis of length 10, and minor axis of length 4. Check your answer.

2 EXAMPLE **Writing the Equation of a Translated Hyperbola**

Write an equation of a hyperbola with vertices $(0, 1)$ and $(6, 1)$, and foci $(-1, 1)$ and $(7, 1)$.

Draw a sketch. The center is the midpoint of the line joining the vertices. Its coordinates are $(3, 1)$.

The distance between the vertices is $2a$ and the distance between the foci is $2c$. $2a = 6$, so $a = 3$; $2c = 8$, so $c = 4$.

Find b^2 using the Pythagorean Theorem.

$c^2 = a^2 + b^2$

$16 = 9 + b^2$

$b^2 = 7$

The transverse axis is horizontal. The equation has form $\dfrac{(x - h)^2}{a^2} - \dfrac{(y - k)^2}{b^2} = 1$.

The equation of the hyperbola is $\dfrac{(x - 3)^2}{9} - \dfrac{(y - 1)^2}{7} = 1$.

> **Problem Solving Hint**
>
> The midpoint of the segment joining (x_1, y_1) and (x_2, y_2) is $\left(\dfrac{x_1 + x_2}{2}, \dfrac{y_1 + y_2}{2}\right)$.

✓ **CA Standards Check** ② Write an equation of a hyperbola with vertices $(2, -1)$ and $(2, 7)$, and foci $(2, 10)$ and $(2, -4)$.

3 EXAMPLE **Real-World Connection**

Navigation Some ships navigate using LORAN. The ship's equipment calculates the difference between the arrival times of simultaneously broadcast radio signals. The difference in arrival times indicates how much closer the ship is to one transmitter than to the other. The navigator then locates the ship on a hyperbola shown in red. The process is repeated using a second pair of transmitters to locate the ship on a hyperbola shown in blue.

All points on hyperbola #25800 as shown in the diagram are 48 mi closer to one transmitter than the other. The transmitters, at the foci, are 200 mi apart and are located at $(0, 0)$ and $(200, 0)$. Find the equation of hyperbola #25800.

Step 1 Find c. Since the foci are 200 mi apart, $2c = 200$, $c = 100$, and the center of the hyperbola is at $(100, 0)$.

Step 2 Find a by calculating the difference in the distances from the vertex at $(a + 100, 0)$ to the two foci.

$48 = (a + 100) - [200 - (a + 100)]$

$\quad = 2a$

$24 = a$

Step 3 Find b^2.

$c^2 = a^2 + b^2$

$(100)^2 = (24)^2 + b^2$

$10{,}000 = 576 + b^2$

$b^2 = 9424$

The equation of the hyperbola is $\dfrac{(x - 100)^2}{24^2} - \dfrac{y^2}{9424} = 1$ or $\dfrac{(x - 100)^2}{576} - \dfrac{y^2}{9424} = 1$.

> **Real-World Connection**
>
> LORAN stands for *long range navigation*. It uses simultaneously broadcast radio signals from three transmitters to locate the ship's position at the intersection of the red and the blue hyperbolas.

✓ **CA Standards Check** ③ Use the information from Example 3. Find the equation of the hyperbola with all points 56 mi closer to one transmitter than the other.

for Help

To review completing the square, go to page 291 and Lesson 5-7.

The equation $Ax^2 + Bxy + Cy^2 + Dx + Ey + F = 0$ is the general equation for all conic sections, where A and C are not both equal to zero. To determine which conic section the equation represents, write the equation in standard form by completing the square for the x- and y-terms.

4 EXAMPLE Identifying a Translated Conic Section

Multiple Choice Identify the conic section with equation $4x^2 + y^2 - 24x + 6y + 9 = 0$.

Ⓐ circle; center $(3, -3)$
Ⓒ ellipse; foci $(3, -3 - 3\sqrt{3})$ and $(3, -3 + 3\sqrt{3})$
Ⓑ circle; center $(-3\sqrt{3}, 3\sqrt{3})$
Ⓓ ellipse; foci $(0, 3)$ and $(0, -3)$

Complete the square for the x- and y-terms to write the equation in standard form.

$$4x^2 + y^2 - 24x + 6y + 9 = 0$$

$$4x^2 - 24x + y^2 + 6y = -9 \qquad \text{Group the } x\text{- and } y\text{-terms.}$$

$$4(x^2 - 6x + \blacksquare) + (y^2 + 6y + \blacksquare) = -9 \qquad \text{Complete the square.}$$

$$4(x^2 - 6x + (-3)^2) + (y^2 + 6y + 3^2) = -9 + 4(-3)^2 + 3^2 \qquad \text{Add } 4(-3)^2 \text{ and } 3^2 \text{ to each side.}$$

$$4(x^2 - 6x + 9) + (y^2 + 6y + 9) = -9 + 36 + 9 \qquad \text{Simplify.}$$

$$4(x - 3)^2 + (y + 3)^2 = 36 \qquad \text{Write the trinomials as binomials squared.}$$

$$\frac{4(x - 3)^2}{36} + \frac{(y + 3)^2}{36} = 1 \qquad \text{Divide each side by 36.}$$

$$\frac{(x - 3)^2}{9} + \frac{(y + 3)^2}{36} = 1 \qquad \text{Simplify.}$$

The equation represents an ellipse. The center is $(3, -3)$. The major axis is vertical. Since $b^2 = 9$, $b = 3$. Since $a^2 = 36$, $a = 6$.

$$c^2 = a^2 - b^2 = 36 - 9$$
$$= 27$$
$$c = 3\sqrt{3}$$

The distance from the center of the ellipse to the foci is $3\sqrt{3}$. Since the ellipse is centered at $(3, -3)$ and the major axis is vertical, the foci are located $3\sqrt{3}$ above and below this center. The foci are at $(3, -3 + 3\sqrt{3})$ and $(3, -3 - 3\sqrt{3})$. The correct choice is C.

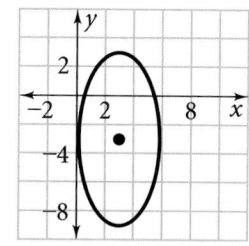

✓ CA Standards Check ④ Identify the conic section represented by $x^2 + y^2 - 12x + 4y = 8$. Sketch the graph.

For more exercises, see *Extra Skill and Word Problem Practice.*

Standards Practice
ALG2 17.0

Ⓐ **Practice by Example**

 for Help

Example 1
(page 593)

Write an equation of an ellipse with the given characteristics. Check your answers.

1. center $(-2, 1)$, horizontal major axis of length 6, minor axis of length 4

2. center $(5, 3)$, vertical major axis of length 12, minor axis of length 8

3. center $(0, -4)$, horizontal major axis of length 12, minor axis of length 10

4. center $(3, -6)$, vertical major axis of length 14, minor axis of length 6

Example 2
(page 594)

Write an equation of a hyperbola with the given characteristics.

5. vertices $(1, -3)$ and $(-7, -3)$, foci $(2, -3)$ and $(-8, -3)$

6. vertices $(4, -1)$ and $(4, -5)$, foci $(4, 3)$ and $(4, -9)$

7. vertices $(2, 2)$ and $(-4, 2)$, foci $(6, 2)$ and $(-8, 2)$

8. vertices $(-1, 4)$ and $(-1, -6)$, foci $(-1, 8)$ and $(-1, -10)$

9. vertices $(0, -2)$ and $(0, 4)$, foci $(0, 6)$ and $(0, -4)$

Example 3
(page 594)

For Exercises 10–11, find the equation of each hyperbola described.

10. All points on the hyperbola are 72 units closer to one focus than the other. The foci are located at $(0, 0)$ and $(300, 0)$.

11. All points on the hyperbola are 88 units closer to one focus than the other. The foci are located at $(0, 0)$ and $(350, 0)$.

Example 4
(page 595)

Identify the conic section represented by each equation by writing the equation in standard form. For a parabola, give the vertex. For a circle, give the center and the radius. For an ellipse or a hyperbola, give the center and the foci. Sketch the graph.

12. $x^2 - 8x - y + 19 = 0$

13. $x^2 + y^2 + 12x = 45$

14. $3x^2 + 6x + y^2 - 6y = -3$

15. $x^2 + y^2 - 2x + 6y = 3$

16. $y^2 - x^2 + 6x - 4y = 6$

17. $x^2 - 4y^2 - 2x - 8y = 7$

18. $x^2 + y^2 + 14y = -13$

19. $y^2 - 2x - 4y = -10$

20. $4x^2 + 9y^2 + 16x - 54y = -61$

21. $x^2 - y^2 + 6x + 10y = 17$

22. $x^2 + 4y^2 - 2x - 15 = 0$

23. $9x^2 - 4y^2 - 24y = 72$

 Apply Your Skills

24. A conic section centered at the origin is translated. Describe the translation that would produce the equation $x^2 - 2y^2 + 6x - 7 = 0$.

25. Critical Thinking Use the equation $Ax^2 + Bxy + Cy^2 + Dx + Ey + F = 0$ to identify the shape of the graph that results in each case.
a. $A = C = D = E = 0, B \neq 0, F \neq 0$
b. $A = B = C = 0, D \neq 0, E \neq 0, F \neq 0$

26. Multiple Choice How does the translation of an ellipse affect the lengths of its axes?
(A) Both increase in length.   (C) Both stay the same length.
(B) Both decrease in length.   (D) One increases; the other decreases.

 27. Writing Describe how the translation of a hyperbola affects the equations of its asymptotes.

28. Critical Thinking Campbell claims that $\frac{x^2}{10} + \frac{y^2}{10} = 1$ represents an ellipse. Monique disagrees. Whom do you support? Give a reasoned argument.

Write an equation for each conic section. Then sketch the graph.

29. circle with center $(-6, 9)$ and radius 9

30. ellipse with center $(3, 2)$, vertices $(9, 2)$ and $(-3, 2)$, and co-vertices $(3, 5)$ and $(3, -1)$

31. parabola with vertex $(2, -3)$ and focus $(2, 5)$

32. hyperbola with center $(6, -3)$, one focus $(6, 0)$, and one vertex $(6, -1)$

Homework Video Tutor

Visit: PHSchool.com
Web Code: bbe-1006

Write the equation of each graph. In Exercise 35, each interval represents one unit.

33.

34.

35.

36.

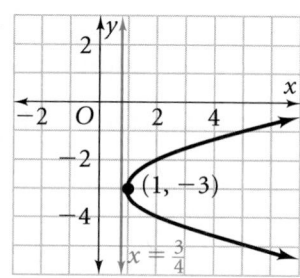

The graph of each equation is to be translated 3 units right and 5 units up. Write each new equation.

37. $(x - 5)^2 + (y + 3)^2 = 4$

38. $\dfrac{(x - 3)^2}{64} + \dfrac{(y + 3)^2}{36} = 1$

39. $y = 4x^2$

40. $9x^2 + 3x + 10 = 16y^2 + 154 + 3x$

41. $\dfrac{(x - 2)^2}{36} - \dfrac{(y - 3)^2}{25} = 1$

42. $\dfrac{(x - 3)^2}{4} + \dfrac{(y - 4)^2}{9} = 1$

43. $9x^2 + 16y^2 + 18x = 64y + 71$

44. $x^2 + 4y^2 + 6x - 7 = 0$

45. $x^2 - 16y^2 - 2x + 128y = 271$

46. $(x - 5)^2 = 12(y - 6)$

47. $25x^2 + 16y^2 + 150x = 160y - 225$

48. $x^2 - y^2 + 6x + 10y = 17$

Graph each pair of functions. Identify the conic section represented by the graph and write each equation in standard form.

49. $y = \sqrt{36 - 4x^2}$
$y = -\sqrt{36 - 4x^2}$

50. $y = \sqrt{4x^2 - 36}$
$y = -\sqrt{4x^2 - 36}$

51. $y = \sqrt{4x^2 + 36}$
$y = -\sqrt{4x^2 + 36}$

52. $y = \sqrt{36 - x^2}$
$y = -\sqrt{36 - x^2}$

53. $y = 0.5\sqrt{36 - x^2}$
$y = -0.5\sqrt{36 - x^2}$

54. $y = \sqrt{x - 4}$
$y = -\sqrt{x - 4}$

Challenge

Real-World Connection

This Nigerian cloth combines writing symbols and patterns.

55. Open-Ended On a graphing calculator, create a design using three translated quadratic relations.

56. History Some symbols of the writing system of the Ejagham, people who lived in Nigeria and Cameroon, are shown. The symbol for marriage consists of two parabolic shapes. Reproduce this symbol on a graphing calculator. What equations did you use?

57. Consider equations of the form $Ax^2 + By^2 + Cx + Dy + E = 0$.
  a. What must be true about A and B for the graph of the equation to be a circle? To be an ellipse? To be a hyperbola? To be a parabola?
  b. Suppose $A = 1$ and $B = 1$. Must the graph be a circle? Explain.
  c. Suppose $A = 1, B = -1$, and $C = D = E = 0$. Describe the graph.

58. Astronomy The dimensions of the elliptical orbits of three planets are given in millions of kilometers in the table. The sun is at one focus. The other focus is on the positive *x*-axis.

a. Write an equation for each orbit and draw the curves on your graphing calculator. (Remember to adjust the viewing window.)

b. Reasoning Which orbit is most circular? Justify your reasoning.

Planet	*a*	*b*
Earth	149.60	149.58
Mars	227.9	226.9
Mercury	57.9	56.6

 Multiple Choice Practice

For California Standards and CAHSEE Tutorials, visit PHSchool.com. Web Code: bbq-9045

ALG2 17.0 **59.** Which graph of a conic section represents the equation $x^2 + y^2 = 6x - 14y - 9$?

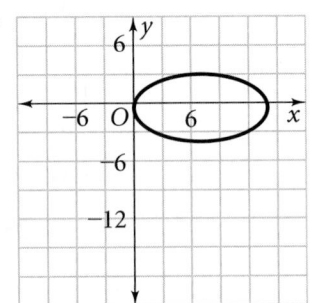

ALG2 17.0 **60.** What is the standard form of the equation of the conic given below?
$$2x^2 + 2y^2 + 4x - 12y - 22 = 0$$

Ⓐ $\dfrac{(x + 1)^2}{21} - \dfrac{(y - 3)^2}{21} = 1$ Ⓒ $\dfrac{(x - 3)^2}{21} + \dfrac{(y + 1)^2}{21} = 1$

Ⓑ $\dfrac{(x + 1)^2}{21} + \dfrac{(y - 3)^2}{21} = 1$ Ⓓ $\dfrac{(x - 1)^2}{7} + \dfrac{(y + 3)^2}{3} = 1$

Mixed Review

Lesson 10-5   **Find the foci of each hyperbola. Draw the graph.**

61. $\dfrac{x^2}{49} - \dfrac{y^2}{36} = 1$ **62.** $8y^2 - 6x^2 = 72$ **63.** $4y^2 - 100x^2 = 400$

 Lesson 9-6   **Solve each equation. Check your answers.**

64. $\dfrac{1}{3x + 1} = \dfrac{1}{x^2 - 3}$ **65.** $\dfrac{2}{x + 2} = \dfrac{6}{x^2 - 4}$ **66.** $\dfrac{5}{x^2 - x} + \dfrac{3}{x - 1} = 6$

Lesson 8-6   **Simplify each expression.**

67. $\ln e$ **68.** $2 \ln e$ **69.** $\ln e^3$ **70.** $4 \ln e^2$

Solving Quadratic Systems

ALG2 8.0 Students solve and graph quadratic equations. *Master*

In Chapter 3 you solved systems of linear equations. You can use the same methods to solve systems that include quadratic equations.

1 ACTIVITY Solving Algebraically

Solve the system algebraically. $\begin{cases} x^2 - y^2 = 9 \\ x^2 + 9y^2 = 169 \end{cases}$

$x^2 - y^2 = 9$

$\underline{x^2 + 9y^2 = 169}$

$-10y^2 = -160$ **Subtract like terms to eliminate the x^2 terms.**

$y = 4 \text{ or } y = -4$ **Solve for y.**

$x^2 - (4)^2 = 9$ **Substitute the values of y into** $x^2 - (-4)^2 = 9$
one of the original equations.
$x^2 = 25$ $x^2 = 25$

$x = 5 \text{ or } x = -5$ **Solve for x.** $x = 5 \text{ or } x = -5$

● The ordered pairs $(5, 4), (-5, 4), (5, -4),$ and $(-5, -4)$ are solutions to the system.

2 ACTIVITY Solving Graphically

Solve the system by graphing. $\begin{cases} x^2 + y^2 = 36 \\ y = (x - 2)^2 - 3 \end{cases}$

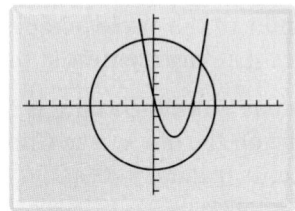

$x^2 + y^2 = 36$

$y = \pm\sqrt{36 - x^2}$ **Solve the first equation for y.**

Graph the equations and find the point(s) of intersection.
● The solutions are approximately $(-1.0, 5.9)$ and $(4.6, 3.8)$.

EXERCISES

Solve each quadratic system.

1. $\begin{cases} x^2 + 64y^2 = 64 \\ x^2 + y^2 = 64 \end{cases}$ **2.** $\begin{cases} 2x^2 - y^2 = 2 \\ x^2 + y^2 = 25 \end{cases}$ **3.** $\begin{cases} 9x^2 + 25y^2 = 225 \\ y = -x^2 + 5 \end{cases}$ **4.** $\begin{cases} 4x^2 + 4y^2 = 100 \\ 3x^2 + 3y^2 = 27 \end{cases}$

5. a. Writing The system that consists of $y = -3x + 6$ and $y = x^2 - 4x$ is a linear-quadratic system. How would you solve the system algebraically? Graphically?
b. Solve the system in part (a).

Identify each system as linear-quadratic or quadratic-quadratic. Then solve.

6. $\begin{cases} y = x - 1 \\ x^2 + y^2 = 25 \end{cases}$ **7.** $\begin{cases} 9x^2 + 4y^2 = 36 \\ x^2 - y^2 = 4 \end{cases}$ **8.** $\begin{cases} -x + y = 4 \\ y = x^2 - 4x + 2 \end{cases}$ **9.** $\begin{cases} 4x^2 + 25y^2 = 100 \\ y = x + 2 \end{cases}$

10. $\begin{cases} y^2 = 5x - 3 \\ 3x^2 - 3y^2 = 1 \end{cases}$ **11.** $\begin{cases} y = 3x + 1 \\ x^2 + y^2 = 3 \end{cases}$ **12.** $\begin{cases} (x - 1)^2 = (y + 2)^2 \\ y = 2x^2 - 4 \end{cases}$ **13.** $\begin{cases} x^2 + y^2 = 25 \\ (x - 3)^2 + (y - 3)^2 = 100 \end{cases}$

Some multiple-choice questions cannot be solved. If so, then one of the answer choices will be *cannot be determined*. Be careful, however. Sometimes the answer choice *cannot be determined* is included as a distractor.

1 EXAMPLE

Find an equation of a circle that passes through the points $(0, 0)$, $(1, 0)$ and $(2, 0)$.

Ⓐ $(x - 1)^2 + y^2 = 1$

Ⓒ $\left(x - \frac{1}{2}\right)^2 + y^2 = \frac{1}{4}$

Ⓑ $\left(x - \frac{3}{2}\right)^2 + y^2 = \frac{1}{4}$

Ⓓ cannot be determined

Since the y-coordinates of all three points are zero, the points are collinear. A circle cannot pass through three collinear points. The correct answer is D.

2 EXAMPLE

Which of the following completely describes the graphs of $(x - d)^2 + (y - d)^2 = 2d^2$?

Ⓐ circles of radius d with centers on the line $y = x$

Ⓑ circles with centers (d, d)

Ⓒ circles with centers on the line $y = x$ and passing through $(0, 0)$

Ⓓ cannot be determined

The standard form of an equation of a circle is $(x - h)^2 + (y - k)^2 = r^2$, where (h, k) is the center of the circle and r is the radius. So the equation in Example 2 describes circles that have centers at (d, d) and have radius $\sqrt{2d^2}$, or $|d|\sqrt{2}$.

Eliminate choice A, since the radius is incorrect. Since the centers of the circles are (d, d), they all lie on the line $y = x$. Choices B and C could be correct. Test choice C by substituting $x = 0$ and $y = 0$.

$(0 - d)^2 + (0 - d)^2 \stackrel{?}{=} 2d^2$ **Substitute (0, 0) for *x* and *y*.**

$(-d)^2 + (-d)^2 \stackrel{?}{=} 2d^2$ **Simplify.**

$2d^2 = 2d^2$

The circles pass through the point $(0, 0)$. The correct answer is C. Choice D is a distractor.

EXERCISES

If the answer to an exercise can be determined, write the answer. If not, write *cannot be determined* and explain your reasoning.

1. Find the radius of the circle defined by $x^2 + y^2 - 4x - 2y + 14 = 0$.

2. Find the number of points of intersection of the graphs of $y = x^2$ and $y = 2ax - a^2$.

3. Given that $x^2 - y^2 = 12$, find y when $x = 3$.

4. The focus of a parabola is $(0, 3)$. Find the equation of the directrix.

Chapter 10 Review

Vocabulary Review

◀)) **English and Spanish Audio Online**

center (p. 571)	focus of a parabola (p. 565)	radius (p. 571)
circle (p. 571)	focus of an ellipse (p. 578)	standard form of an equation of a
conic section (p. 557)	focus of a hyperbola (p. 585)	circle (p. 571)
co-vertices (p. 578)	hyperbola (p. 585)	transverse axis (p. 585)
directrix (p. 565)	major axis (p. 578)	vertices of an ellipse (p. 578)
ellipse (p. 578)	minor axis (p. 578)	vertices of a hyperbola (p. 585)

Go **Online**
PHSchool.com

For: Vocabulary quiz
Web Code: bbj-1051

Choose the correct vocabulary term to complete each sentence.

1. In the definition of a parabola, the fixed line is the __?__ .

2. The vertices of an ellipse are on its __?__ .

3. $(x - h)^2 + (y - k)^2 = r^2$ is the __?__ .

4. The distance from a point on a circle to its center is the __?__ of the circle.

5. The vertices of a hyperbola are on its __?__ .

Skills and Concepts

Lesson 10-1

- To graph conic sections (p. 557)
- To identify conic sections (p. 559)

 ALG2 17.0, MA 5.0

A **conic section** is a curve formed by the intersection of a plane and a double cone. Circles, ellipses, parabolas, and hyperbolas are all conic sections.

Graph each equation. Identify the conic section and describe the graph and its lines of symmetry. Then find the domain and range.

6. $\frac{x^2}{49} + \frac{y^2}{121} = 1$ **7.** $x^2 + y^2 = 4$ **8.** $\frac{x^2}{25} - \frac{y^2}{4} = 1$ **9.** $x = 2y^2 + 5$

Identify the center, the intercepts, and the domain and range of each graph.

10.   **11.**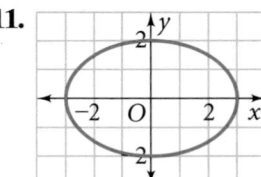

Lesson 10-2

- To write the equation of a parabola (p. 565)
- To graph parabolas (p. 567)

 ALG2 16.0, MA 5.2

In a plane, a parabola is the set of all points that are the same distance c from a fixed line, the **directrix,** and a fixed point not on the line, the **focus.**

For $y = ax^2$ when $a > 0$, the parabola opens upward. The focus is $(0, c)$ and the directrix is $y = -c$. When $a < 0$, the parabola opens downward. The focus is $(0, -c)$ and the directrix is $y = c$. For $x = ay^2$, when $a > 0$, the parabola opens to the right. The focus is $(c, 0)$ and directrix is $x = -c$. When $a < 0$, the parabola opens to the left. The focus is $(-c, 0)$ and the directrix is $x = c$. Always, $|a| = \frac{1}{4c}$.

Write an equation for a graph that is the set of all points in the plane that are equidistant from the given point and the given line.

12. $F(0, 3), y = -1$ **13.** $F(-2, 0), x = 4$

Write an equation of a parabola with a vertex at the origin and the given focus.

14. focus at $(5, 0)$ **15.** focus at $(0, -5)$ **16.** focus at $(0, 6)$

Write an equation of a parabola opening upward with a vertex at the origin.

17. focus is 2.5 units from the vertex   **18.** focus is $\frac{1}{12}$ of a unit from the vertex

Find the focus and the directrix of the graph of each equation. Sketch the graph.

19. $y = 5x^2$ **20.** $x = 2y^2$ **21.** $x = -\frac{1}{8}y^2$

Lesson 10-3

- To write and graph the equation of a circle (p. 571)
- To find the center and radius of a circle and use it to graph the circle (p. 573)

 ALG2 16.0

In a plane, a **circle** is the set of all points at a given distance, the **radius** r, from a given point, the **center** (h, k). The **standard form of an equation of a circle** is $(x - h)^2 + (y - k)^2 = r^2$.

Write an equation in standard form of the circle with the given center and radius.

22. center $(0, 0)$, radius 4   **23.** center $(8, 1)$, radius 5

Write an equation for each translation of $x^2 + y^2 = r^2$ with the given radius.

24. left 3 units, up 2 units; radius 10   **25.** right 5 units, down 3 units; radius 8

Write an equation for each circle. Each interval represents one unit.

26.   **27.**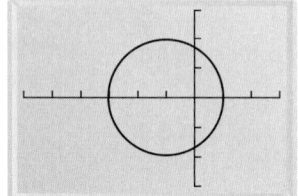

Find the center and the radius of each circle. Sketch the graph.

28. $(x - 1)^2 + y^2 = 64$ **29.** $(x + 7)^2 + (y + 3)^2 = 49$

Lesson 10-4

- To write the equation of an ellipse (p. 578)
- To find the foci of an ellipse and to graph an ellipse (p. 580)

 ALG2 16.0

In a plane, an **ellipse** is the set of all points P, the sum of whose distances to two fixed points, the **foci**, is constant. The **major axis** is the segment that contains the foci and has endpoints called the **vertices of an ellipse**. The **minor axis** is perpendicular to the major axis and has endpoints called the **co-vertices**.

There are two standard forms of an ellipse centered at the origin. If $\frac{x^2}{a^2} + \frac{y^2}{b^2} = 1$, the major axis is horizontal with vertices $(\pm a, 0)$ and co-vertices $(0, \pm b)$, where $a > b > 0$.

If $\frac{x^2}{b^2} + \frac{y^2}{a^2} = 1$, the major axis is vertical with vertices $(0, \pm a)$ and co-vertices $(\pm b, 0)$. In either case, you can find the foci c using the relationship $c^2 = a^2 - b^2$.

Write an equation of an ellipse in standard form with a center at the origin and with the given characteristics.

30. foci $(\pm1, 0)$, co-vertices $(0, \pm4)$

31. vertex $(0, \sqrt{29})$, co-vertex $(-5, 0)$

32. focus $(0, 1)$, vertex $(0, \sqrt{10})$

33. foci $(\pm2, 0)$, co-vertices $(0, \pm6)$

34. Write the equation of an ellipse centered at the origin with height 8 units and width 16 units.

35. Graph $\frac{x^2}{4} + \frac{y^2}{9} = 1$. Identify the foci.

Lesson 10-5

- To graph hyperbolas (p. 584)
- To find and use the foci of a hyperbola (p. 586)

 ALG2 16.0

In a plane, a **hyperbola** is the set of all points P such that difference between the distances from P to two fixed points, the **foci**, is constant. The foci lie on the line containing the **transverse axis**. Each branch of a hyperbola intersects the transverse axis at a **vertex of the hyperbola**. Each branch approaches the two asymptotes, which contain the diagonals of the central rectangle.

There are two standard forms of hyperbolas centered at the origin. If $\frac{x^2}{a^2} - \frac{y^2}{b^2} = 1$, the asymptotes are $y = \pm\frac{b}{a}x$, the transverse axis is horizontal with vertices $(\pm a, 0)$, and the foci are $(\pm c, 0)$. If $\frac{y^2}{a^2} - \frac{x^2}{b^2} = 1$, the asymptotes are $y = \pm\frac{a}{b}x$, the transverse axis is vertical with vertices $(0, \pm a)$, and the foci are $(0, \pm c)$. In either case, you can find the value of b using the relationship $c^2 = a^2 + b^2$.

Find the foci of each hyperbola. Draw the graph.

36. $\frac{x^2}{36} - \frac{y^2}{225} = 1$

37. $\frac{y^2}{400} - \frac{x^2}{169} = 1$

38. $\frac{x^2}{121} - \frac{y^2}{81} = 1$

39. Find an equation that models the path of a spacecraft around a planet if $a = 107{,}124$ and $c = 213{,}125.9$.

Lesson 10-6

- To write the equation of a translated conic section (p. 592)
- To identify a translated conic section from an equation (p. 595)

 ALG2 17.0

You can substitute $(x - h)$ for x and $(y - k)$ for y to translate graphs of an ellipse or a hyperbola. A translated ellipse or hyperbola has center (h, k).

Write an equation of a conic section with the given characteristics.

40. an ellipse with center $(3, -2)$, vertical major axis of length 6; minor axis of length 4

41. a hyperbola with vertices $(3, 3)$ and $(9, 3)$, foci $(1, 3)$ and $(11, 3)$

42. All points on the hyperbola are 81 units closer to one focus than the other. The foci are at $(0, 0)$ and $(155, 0)$.

Identify the conic section represented by each equation by writing the equation in standard form. For a parabola, give the vertex. For a circle, give the center and the radius. For an ellipse or a hyperbola, give the center and the foci. Sketch the graph.

43. $-x^2 + y^2 + 4y - 16 = 0$

44. $x^2 + y^2 + 3x - 4y - 9 = 0$

45. $x^2 + x - y - 42 = 0$

46. $2x^2 + 3y^2 - 4x + 12y - 20 = 0$

Identify the center and intercepts of each conic section. Give the domain and range of each graph.

1.

2.

3.

4.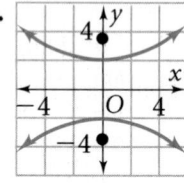

5. Writing Explain how you can tell what kind of conic section a quadratic equation describes without graphing the equation.

Identify the focus and the directrix of the graph of each equation.

6. $y = 3x^2$

7. $x = -2y^2$

8. $x + 5y^2 = 0$

9. $9x^2 - 2y = 0$

Write an equation of a parabola with a vertex at the origin and the given characteristic.

10. focus at $(0, -2)$

11. focus at $(3, 0)$

12. directrix $x = 7$

13. directrix $y = -1$

Find the center and radius of the circle. Sketch the circle.

14. $(x - 2)^2 + (y - 3)^2 = 36$

15. $(x + 5)^2 + (y + 8)^2 = 100$

16. $(x - 1)^2 + (y + 7)^2 = 81$

17. $(x + 4)^2 + (y - 10)^2 = 121$

Find an equation of an ellipse for each given height and width. Assume that the center of the ellipse is (0, 0).

18. height 10 units, width 16 units

19. height 2 units, width 12 units

20. height 9 units, width 5 units

Find the foci for each ellipse. Sketch the ellipse.

21. $\frac{x^2}{81} + \frac{y^2}{36} = 1$

22. $\frac{x^2}{25} + \frac{y^2}{121} = 1$

23. $x^2 + \frac{y^2}{49} = 1$

24. $4x^2 + y^2 = 4$

25. Critical Thinking What is the shape of an ellipse whose height and width are equal?

Find the foci for each hyperbola. Sketch the hyperbola.

26. $\frac{x^2}{144} - \frac{y^2}{100} = 1$

27. $\frac{y^2}{169} - \frac{x^2}{400} = 1$

28. $\frac{x^2}{64} - \frac{y^2}{4} = 1$

29. $y^2 - \frac{x^2}{225} = 1$

30. Open-Ended Write the equation of a hyperbola with a transverse axis on the x-axis.

Write an equation of an ellipse with the given characteristics.

31. center $(0, 0)$, vertex $(4, 0)$, co-vertex $(0, -3)$

32. center $(-2, 7)$, horizontal major axis of length 8, minor axis of length 6

33. center $(3, -2)$, vertical major axis of length 12, minor axis of length 10

Write an equation of a hyperbola with the given characteristics.

34. vertices $(\pm 3, 7)$, foci $(\pm 5, 7)$

35. vertices $(2, \pm 5)$, foci $(2, -7), (2, 7)$

36. vertices $(-3, -1), (-5, -1)$, foci $(0, -1), (-8, -1)$

Identify the conic section represented by each equation. If it is a parabola, give the vertex. If it is a circle, give the center and radius. If it is an ellipse or a hyperbola, give the center and foci. Sketch the graph.

37. $3y^2 - x - 6y + 5 = 0$

38. $x^2 + y^2 - 4x - 6y + 4 = 0$

39. $4x^2 + y^2 - 16x - 6y + 9 = 0$

40. $4x^2 - y^2 - 16x + 6y - 9 = 0$

Some problems ask you to interpret a graph of a quadratic function.

Tip 1
Read the labels on the axes to understand the meaning of a point on the graph.

A stone falls from a 56-foot cliff. The graph shows the height of the stone h, in feet, after t seconds. In about how many seconds does the stone reach the ground?

A) 0.9 second   C) 1.5 seconds
B) 1.0 second   D) 1.9 seconds

Tip 2
Use the graph to determine when $h = 0$.

Think It Through
Find the point where the graph crosses the horizontal axis.

The graph crosses the horizontal axis at about $(1.9, 0)$. So the stone reaches the ground in about 1.9 seconds.

The correct answer is D.

Vocabulary Review

As you solve problems, you must understand the meanings of mathematical terms. Choose the correct term for each sentence.

1. A (parabola, hyperbola) is a set of points P in a plane such that the absolute value of the difference between the distances from P to two fixed points F_1 and F_2 is a constant k.

2. A(n) (ellipse, circle) is a set of points P in a plane such that the sum of the distances from P to two fixed points F_1 and F_2 is a constant k.

3. A (circle, parabola) is the set of all points in a plane that are a distance r from a given point.

4. A (parabola, conic section) is a curve formed by the intersection of a plane and a double cone.

5. A (focus, directrix) is the fixed line that all points on a plane are the same distance from in a parabola.

Multiple Choice

Read each question. Then write the letter of the correct answer on your paper.

1. An acrobat landed on a teeterboard and launched his partner into the air. The graph below shows the height h of the partner, in yards, at t seconds after the launch.

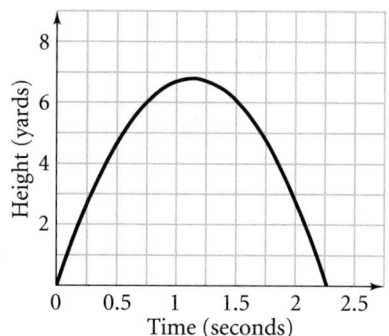

Which value is the best approximation of the maximum height of the partner? **(Lesson 5-1)**

A) 6.0 yards

B) 6.4 yards

C) 6.8 yards

D) 7.2 yards

2. The graph of $\frac{x^2}{21} - \frac{y^2}{4} = 1$ is a hyperbola. Which set of coordinates represents the foci of the hyperbola's graph? **(Lesson 10-5)**

Ⓐ $(0, 5)$ and $(0, -5)$

Ⓑ $(5, 0)$ and $(0, -5)$

Ⓒ $(0, 5)$ and $(-5, 0)$

Ⓓ $(5, 0)$ and $(-5, 0)$

3. If the equation $y = 4^x$ is graphed, which of the following values of x would produce a point closest to the x-axis? **(Lesson 8-2)**

Ⓐ -3 Ⓒ 0

Ⓑ -1 Ⓓ 4

4. The bacteria in a petri dish are growing exponentially with time, as shown in the table below.

Bacteria Growth

Day	Bacteria
0	50
1	150
2	450

Which of the following equations expresses the number of y bacteria present at any time t? **(Lesson 8-2)**

Ⓐ $y = (3)^x$

Ⓑ $y = 50 + (3)^x$

Ⓒ $y = 50 \cdot (3)^x$

Ⓓ $y = 150 \cdot (3)^x$

5. What is the standard form of the equation of the conic section given below? **(Lesson 10-6)**
$$25x^2 - 49y^2 - 1225 = 0$$

Ⓐ $\frac{x^2}{49} - \frac{y^2}{25} = 1$

Ⓑ $\frac{x^2}{49} + \frac{y^2}{25} = 1$

Ⓒ $25x^2 - 49y^2 = 1225$

Ⓓ $49x^2 - 25y^2 = 1$

6. Alexandra dives from a 30-foot board into a swimming pool. The graph below shows her height h, in feet, at t seconds after jumping.

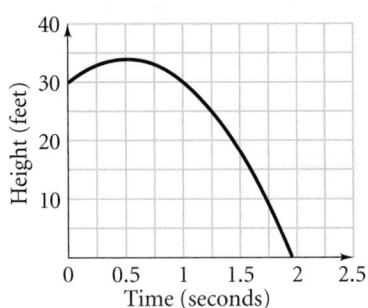

After leaving the board, in how many seconds is Alexandra at the height of 30 feet again? **(Lesson 5-1)**

Ⓐ 0.5 second

Ⓑ 1.0 second

Ⓒ 1.5 seconds

Ⓓ 2.0 seconds

7. An employer is selecting 4 out of 30 workers as employees of the month. How many different selections are possible? **(Lesson 6-7)**

Ⓐ 120   Ⓒ 164,430

Ⓑ 27,405   Ⓓ 657,720

8. Owen threw a ball straight up into the air from an initial height of 5 feet. The graph below shows the height h of the ball, in feet, at t seconds after Owen threw it. Of the following times, when was the ball closest to the ground? **(Lesson 5-1)**

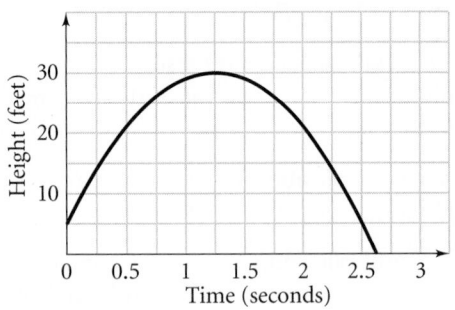

Ⓐ 0.6 second

Ⓑ 1 second

Ⓒ 1.6 seconds

Ⓓ 2 seconds

9. What are the coordinates of the foci of $4x^2 - 24x = 64 - 25y^2$? **(Lesson 10-6)**

  (A) $(\sqrt{21} - 3, 0), (\sqrt{21} + 3, 0)$

  (B) $(0, \sqrt{21} - 3), (0, \sqrt{21} + 3)$

  (C) $(3 - \sqrt{21}, 0), (3 + \sqrt{21}, 0)$

  (D) $(0, 3 - \sqrt{21}), (0, 3 + \sqrt{21})$

10. Which is the first *incorrect* step in simplifying $\dfrac{4}{(x - 1)^{-1}(x^2 + 3x - 4)}$? **(Lesson 9-4)**

Step 1: $\dfrac{4(x - 1)}{x^2 + 3x - 4}$

Step 2: $\dfrac{4(x - 1)}{(x + 4)(x - 1)}$

Step 3: $\dfrac{4(x - 1)}{(x + 4)(x - 1)} \div \dfrac{x - 1}{x - 1}$

Step 4: $\dfrac{4}{x + 4} \div \dfrac{4}{4} = \dfrac{1}{x}$

  (A) Step 1   **(C)** Step 3

  (B) Step 2   **(D)** Step 4

11. What is the distance between the foci of the ellipse with the equation $\dfrac{x^2}{36} + \dfrac{(y - 2)^2}{100} = 1$? **(Lesson 10-4)**

  (A) 4   **(B)** 8   **(C)** 12   **(D)** 16

12. Which of the following is the graph of the quadratic parent function? **(Lesson 5-3)**

  (A)

  (C)

  (B)

  (D)
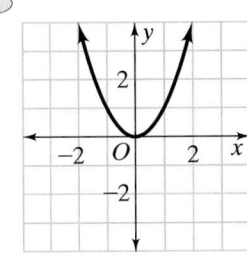

13. Which conic section is represented by the equation $x^2 + y^2 = 6x - 14y - 9$? **(Lesson 10-6)**

  (A) circle   **(C)** parabola

  (B) ellipse   **(D)** hyperbola

14. If x is a real number, for what values of x is the equation $(3x - 6)(x - 2)^{-1} = 3$ true? **(Lesson 9-4)**

  (A) all values of x

  (B) some values of x

  (C) no values of x

  (D) impossible to determine

15. Your homework assignment is to graph four linear equations and three quadratic equations. Your teacher gives you eight linear equations and eight quadratic equations to choose from. How many different combinations are possible? **(Lesson 6-7)**

  (A) 64   **(C)** 336

  (B) 126   **(D)** 1680

Standards Reference Guide

California Content Standard	Item Number(s)
ALG2 10.0	1, 6, 8, 12
ALG2 16.0	2, 9, 11
ALG2 12.0	3–4
ALG2 17.0	5, 13
ALG2 18.0	7, 15
ALG2 11.2	10
ALG2 15.0	14

For additional review and practice, see the *California Standards Review and Practice Workbook* or go online to use the

California Standards Tutorials

Visit: PHSchool.com, **Web Code:** bbq-9045

CHAPTER 11

Sequences and Series

What You've Learned

California Content Standards

8.0 Students are familiar with the notion of the limit of a function as the independent variable approaches a number or infinity. *Mathematical Analysis*

20.0 Students know the binomial theorem and use it to expand binomial expressions that are raised to positive integer powers.

✓ **Check Your Readiness**   **for Help** to the Lesson in green.

Evaluating Functions (Lesson 2-1)

For each function, find $f(1), f(2), f(3),$ and $f(4)$.

1. $f(x) = 2x + 7$ **2.** $f(x) = 5x - 4$ **3.** $f(x) = 0.2x + 0.7$

4. $f(x) = -5x + 3$ **5.** $f(x) = 4x - \frac{2}{3}$ **6.** $f(x) = -3x - 9$

Graphing Quadratic Functions (Lesson 5-2)

Graph each function.

7. $y = x^2 + 3$ **8.** $y = -\frac{1}{2}x^2 + 2$ **9.** $y = 4x^2 - 1$

10. $y = 2x^2 - 7x + 3$ **11.** $y = -4x^2 + 8x + 5$ **12.** $y = x^2 + 3x + 4$

Evaluating Radical Expressions (Lesson 7-1)

Find each real-number root.

13. $\sqrt{16}$ **14.** $-\sqrt{16}$ **15.** $\sqrt{0.16}$ **16.** $\sqrt{2500}$

Simplify each radical expression. Use absolute value symbols as needed.

17. $\sqrt{25x^4}$ **18.** $-\sqrt{0.09y^8}$ **19.** $\sqrt{x^6y^{10}}$ **20.** $\sqrt{121y^{24}}$

Simplifying Complex Fractions (Lesson 9-5)

Simplify each complex fraction.

21. $\dfrac{1 - \frac{1}{3}}{\frac{1}{2}}$ **22.** $\dfrac{\frac{1}{3} + \frac{1}{6}}{\frac{2}{3}}$ **23.** $\dfrac{1}{1 - \frac{2}{5}}$ **24.** $\dfrac{1 - \frac{3}{8}}{2 + \frac{1}{4}}$

What You'll Learn Next

▲ In Lesson 11-6, you will find the distance traveled by a peregrine falcon in a high-speed dive.

California Content Standards

21.0 Students apply the method of mathematical induction to prove general statements about the positive integers.

22.0 Students find the general term and the sums of arithmetic series and of both finite and infinite geometric series.

23.0 Students derive the summation formulas for arithmetic series and for both finite and infinite geometric series.

New Vocabulary

🔊 **English and Spanish Audio Online**

- **arithmetic mean** (p. 617)
- **arithmetic sequence** (p. 616)
- **arithmetic series** (p. 630)
- **circumscribed rectangles** (p. 645)
- **common difference** (p. 616)
- **common ratio** (p. 622)
- **converge** (p. 637)
- **diverge** (p. 637)
- **explicit formula** (p. 612)
- **geometric mean** (p. 624)
- **geometric sequence** (p. 622)
- **geometric series** (p. 636)
- **inscribed rectangles** (p. 645)
- **limit** (p. 631)
- **recursive formula** (p. 612)
- **sequence** (p. 610)
- **series** (p. 629)
- **term** (p. 610)

11-1

Mathematical Patterns

California Content Standards

Prepares for ALG2 22.0 Students find the general term of arithmetic series and of both finite and infinite geometric series.

What You'll Learn

• To identify mathematical patterns
• To use a formula for finding the nth term of a sequence

... And Why

To predict the height of a bouncing ball, as in Example 2

✓ Check Skills You'll Need

GO for Help Skills Handbook p. 878

Find the next two numbers of each pattern. Then write a rule to describe the pattern.

1. $1, 3, 5, 7, 9, 11, \ldots$

2. $-2, -4, -6, -8, -10, -12, \ldots$

3. $0.2, 1, 5, 25, 125, 625, \ldots$

4. $50, 45, 40, 35, 30, 25, \ldots$

5. $512, 256, 128, 64, 32, 16, \ldots$

6. $2, 5, 8, 11, 14, 17, \ldots$

7. $16, 32, 64, \ldots$

8. $-3, -7, -11, -15, \ldots$

◀)) **New Vocabulary** • sequence • term • recursive formula • explicit formula

1 Identifying Mathematical Patterns

Activity: Generating a Pattern

Suppose each student in your math class has a phone conversation with every other member of the class. What is the minimum number of calls required?

Instead of actually making the calls, you can represent telephone conversations by drawing diagrams like the ones below.

1. How many calls are necessary for two people to have a conversation?

2. How many calls are necessary for everyone to talk to everyone else in a group of three people? In a group of four people?

3. Use a diagram to find the number of calls needed for five people.

4. **Reasoning** Which of the following expressions represents the pattern for numbers of telephone calls?

   A. $2n - 3$ **B.** $n(n - 1) - 5$ **C.** $\dfrac{n(n - 1)}{2}$

5. Use the expression from Question 4 to find the number of calls needed for a group of seven students.

6. How many calls would be needed for your class?

Sometimes steps in a process form a pattern. You can describe some patterns with a **sequence,** or ordered list of numbers. Each number in a sequence is a **term.**

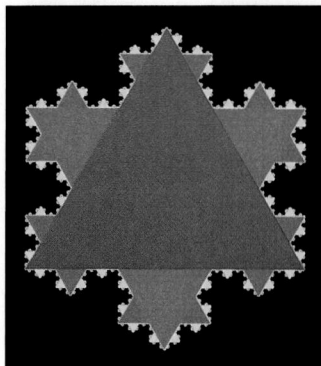

When you apply the construction from Example 1 to an equilateral triangle, you form the Koch snowflake.

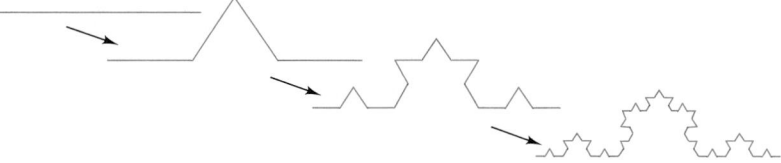

1 EXAMPLE **Generating a Sequence**

a. To create one side of the Koch snowflake, replace each _____ with _/_ . Draw the first four figures of the pattern.

b. Write the number of segments in each figure above as a sequence.

$1, 4, 16, 64, \ldots$

c. Predict the next term of the sequence. Explain your choice.

Each term is 4 times the preceding term. The next term is $64 \cdot 4$, or 256. There will be 256 segments in the next figure in the pattern.

✓ CA Standards Check **1** Describe the pattern formed. Find the next three terms.
   a. $27, 34, 41, 48, \ldots$ **b.** $243, 81, 27, 9, \ldots$

Sometimes you can find the next term in a sequence by using a pattern from the terms that come before it.

2 EXAMPLE **Real-World** **Connection**

Test-Taking Tip

When you have to repeat a step several times, be careful to use the correct number of steps.

Multiple Choice Suppose you drop a handball from a height of 10 ft. After the ball hits the floor, it rebounds to 85% of its previous height. About how high will the ball rebound after its fourth bounce?

  Ⓐ 10 ft   Ⓑ 8.5 ft   Ⓒ 6.1 ft   Ⓓ 5.2 ft

Original height of ball: 10 ft →

After 1st bounce: 85% of $10 = 0.85(10) = 8.5 →$

After 2nd bounce: $0.85(8.5) = 7.225 →$

After 3rd bounce: $0.85(7.225) \approx 6.141 →$

After 4th bounce: $0.85(6.141) \approx 5.220 →$

The ball will rebound about 5.2 ft after the fourth bounce. The correct choice is D.

✓ CA Standards Check **2** **a.** About how high will the ball rebound after the seventh bounce?
   b. After what bounce will the rebound height be less than 2 ft?

You can use a variable, such as a, with positive integer subscripts to represent the terms in a sequence.

1st term	2nd term	3rd term	$\ldots$	$n-1$ term	nth term	$n+1$ term	$\ldots$
↓	↓	↓		↓	↓	↓	
a_1	a_2	a_3	$\ldots$	a_{n-1}	a_n	a_{n+1}	$\ldots$

A **recursive formula** defines the terms in a sequence by relating each term to the ones before it. The pattern in Example 2 was recursive because the height of the ball after each bounce was 85% of its previous height. The recursive formula that describes the ball's height is $a_n = 0.85a_{n-1}$, where $a_1 = 10$.

3 **EXAMPLE** **Using a Recursive Formula**

a. Describe the pattern that allows you to find the next term in the sequence $2, 4, 6, 8, 10, \ldots$ Write a recursive formula for the sequence.

The terms of the sequence are the even numbers. Add 2 to a term to find the next term. A recursive formula is $a_n = a_{n-1} + 2$, where $a_1 = 2$.

b. Find the sixth and seventh terms in the sequence.

Since $a_5 = 10$, $a_6 = 10 + 2 = 12$, and $a_7 = 12 + 2 = 14$.

c. Find the value of term a_9 in the sequence.

Term a_9 is the ninth term. $a_9 = a_8 + 2 = (a_7 + 2) + 2 = (14 + 2) + 2 = 18$

✓**CA Standards Check** **3** Find terms a_{11} and a_{15} in the sequence.

Sometimes you can find the value of a term of a sequence without knowing the preceding term. Instead, you can use the number of the term to calculate its value. A formula that expresses the *n*th term in terms of *n* is an **explicit formula.**

4 **EXAMPLE** **Real-World Connection**

Geometry The spreadsheet below shows the perimeters of squares with sides from 1 to 6 units long. The numbers in each row form a sequence.

	A	B	C	D	E	F	G	H
1		a1	a2	a3	a4	a5	a6	...
2	Length of a Side	1	2	3	4	5	6	...
3	Perimeter	4	8	12	16	20	24	...

a. For each sequence, find the next term (a_7) and the twenty-fifth term (a_{25}).

In the sequence in row 2, each term is the same as its subscript. Therefore, $a_7 = 7$ and $a_{25} = 25$.
In the sequence in row 3, each term is 4 times its subscript. Therefore, $a_7 = 4(7) = 28$ and $a_{25} = 4(25) = 100$.

b. Write an explicit formula for each sequence.

The explicit formula for the sequence in row 2 is $a_n = n$. The explicit formula for the sequence in row 3 is $a_n = 4n$.

✓**CA Standards Check** **4** **a.** Write the first six terms in the sequence showing the areas of the squares in Example 4. Then find a_{20}.
b. Write an explicit formula for the sequence from part (a).
c. **Critical Thinking** Given the recursive formula $a_n = a_{n-1} + 3$, can you find the fourth term in the sequence? Explain.

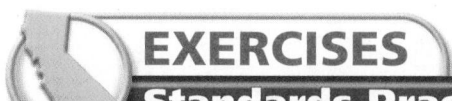

EXERCISES
Standards Practice

A Practice by Example

Examples 1 and 2
(page 611)

GO for Help

Describe each pattern formed. Find the next three terms.

1. $80, 77, 74, 71, 68, \ldots$ **2.** $4, 8, 16, 32, 64, \ldots$ **3.** $0, 3, 7, 12, 18, \ldots$

4. $1, 4, 7, 10, 13, \ldots$ **5.** $100, 10, 1, 0.1, 0.01, \ldots$ **6.** $\frac{1}{2}, \frac{1}{4}, \frac{1}{8}, \frac{1}{16}, \frac{1}{32}, \ldots$

7. $4, -8, 16, -32, 64, \ldots$ **8.** $1, 2, 6, 24, 120, \ldots$ **9.** $0, 1, 0, \frac{1}{3}, 0, \frac{1}{5}, \ldots$

Fractal Geometry **Draw the first four figures of the sequence described.**

10. ——— is replaced by .   **11.** is replaced by.

Example 3
(page 612)

Write a recursive formula for each sequence. Then find the next term.

12. $-2, -1, 0, 1, 2, \ldots$ **13.** $43, 41, 39, 37, 35, \ldots$ **14.** $40, 20, 10, 5, \frac{5}{2}, \ldots$

15. $6, 1, -4, -9, \ldots$ **16.** $144, 36, 9, \frac{9}{4}, \ldots$ **17.** $\frac{1}{2}, \frac{1}{4}, \frac{1}{8}, \frac{1}{16}, \frac{1}{32}, \ldots$

Example 4
(page 612)

Write an explicit formula for each sequence. Then find a_{12}.

18. $4, 5, 6, 7, 8, \ldots$ **19.** $\frac{1}{2}, \frac{1}{3}, \frac{1}{4}, \frac{1}{5}, \frac{1}{6}, \ldots$ **20.** $4, 7, 10, 13, 16, \ldots$

21. $3, 7, 11, 15, 19, \ldots$ **22.** $-2\frac{1}{2}, -2, -1\frac{1}{2}, -1, \ldots$ **23.** $2, 5, 10, 17, 26, \ldots$

B Apply Your Skills

Decide whether each formula is *explicit* or *recursive*. Then find the first five terms of each sequence.

24. $a_n = 2a_{n-1} + 3$, where $a_1 = 3$ **25.** $a_n = \frac{1}{2}(n)(n-1)$

26. $(n-5)(n+5) = a_n$ **27.** $a_n = -3a_{n-1}$, where $a_1 = -2$

28. $a_n = -4n^2 - 2$ **29.** $a_n = 2n^2 + 1$

30. $a_n = 5n$ **31.** $a_n = a_{n-1} - 17$, where $a_1 = 340$

32. Entertainment Suppose you are building a tower of cards with levels as displayed below. Complete the table, assuming the pattern continues.

Levels	1	2	3	4	5
Cards Needed	2	7	■	■	■

Find the next two terms in each sequence. Write a formula for the nth term. Identify each formula as *explicit* or *recursive*.

33. $5, 8, 11, 14, 17, \ldots$ **34.** $3, 6, 12, 24, 48, \ldots$ **35.** $1, 8, 27, 64, 125, \ldots$

36. $4, 16, 64, 256, 1024, \ldots$ **37.** $49, 64, 81, 100, 121, \ldots$ **38.** $-1, 1, -1, 1, -1, 1, \ldots$

39. $-16, -8, -4, -2, \ldots$ **40.** $-75, -68, -61, -54, \ldots$ **41.** $21, 13, 5, -3, \ldots$

42. Suppose the cartoon at the right included one sheep to the left and another sheep to the right of the three shown. What "names" would you give these sheep?

WHEN MATHEMATICIANS CAN'T SLEEP

 43. Writing Explain the difference between a recursive formula and an explicit formula.

44. a. Open-Ended Write four terms of a sequence of numbers that you can describe both recursively and explicitly.
   b. Write a recursive formula and an explicit formula for your sequence.
   c. Find the 20th term of the sequence by evaluating one of your formulas. Use the other formula to check your work.

Use the given rule to write the 4th, 5th, 6th, and 7th terms of each sequence.

45. $a_1 = -1, a_n = a_{n-1} + n^2$

46. $a_1 = -2, a_n = 3(a_{n-1} + 2)$

47. $a_n = (n + 1)^2$

48. $a_n = 2(n - 1)^3$

49. $a_n = \dfrac{n^2}{n + 1}$

50. $a_n = \dfrac{n + 1}{n + 2}$

 51. Geometry Suppose you are stacking boxes in levels that form squares. The numbers of boxes in successive levels form a sequence. The figure at the left shows the top four levels as viewed from above.
   a. How many boxes of equal size would you need for the next lower level?
   b. How many boxes of equal size would you need to add three levels?
   c. Suppose you are stacking a total of 285 boxes. How many levels will you have?

C Challenge

Use each recursive formula to write an explicit formula for the sequence.

52. $a_1 = 10, a_n = 2a_{n-1}$

53. $a_1 = -5, a_n = a_{n-1} - 1$

54. $a_1 = -2, a_n = \frac{1}{2}a_{n-1}$

55. $a_1 = 1, a_n = a_{n-1} + 4$

56. Finance Use the information in the ad.
   a. Suppose you start a savings account at Mun e-Bank. Write both a recursive formula and an explicit formula for the amount of money you would have in the bank at the end of any week.
   b. How much money would you have in the bank after four weeks?
   c. Assume the bank pays interest every four weeks. To calculate your interest, multiply the balance at the end of the four weeks by 0.005. Then add that much to your account on the last day of the four-week period. Write a recursive formula for the amount of money you have after each interest payment.
   d. Critical Thinking What is the bank's annual interest rate?

57. Geometry The triangular numbers form a sequence. The diagram represents the first three triangular numbers: 1, 3, and 6.

a. Find the fifth and sixth triangular numbers.
b. Write a recursive formula for the nth triangular number.
c. Is the explicit formula $a_n = \frac{1}{2}(n^2 + n)$ the correct formula for this sequence? How do you know?

$n = 1 \qquad n = 2 \qquad n = 3$

 Multiple Choice Practice

For California Standards and CAHSEE Tutorials, visit PHSchool.com. Web Code: bbq-9045

ALG2 12.0

58. Which is the graph of an exponential function?

Ⓐ

Ⓒ

Ⓑ

Ⓓ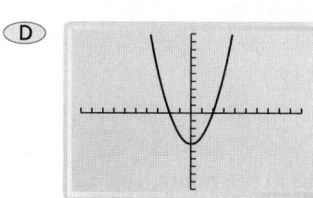

ALG2 9.0

59. What is the equation of the graphed function when translated 3 units up and 4 units left?

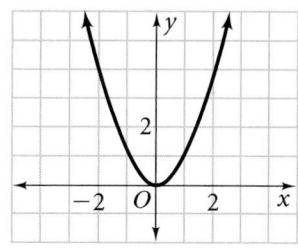

Ⓐ $y = (x - 3)^2 - 4$ 　　　　Ⓒ $y = (x + 4)^2 + 3$
Ⓑ $y = (x - 4)^2 + 3$ 　　　　Ⓓ $y = (x + 3)^2 - 4$

Mixed Review

Lesson 10-6

The graph of each equation is translated 2 units left and 3 units down. Write each new equation.

60. $(x + 2)^2 + (y - 1)^2 = 5$ 　　　　**61.** $\dfrac{(x - 1)^2}{36} + \dfrac{(y - 1)^2}{36} = 1$

Lesson 9-1

Each point is from an inverse variation. Write an equation to model the data.

62. $(1, 20)$ 　　**63.** $(5, 2)$ 　　**64.** $(9, 13)$ 　　**65.** $(-3, -9)$

66. $(2, 5)$ 　　**67.** $(-6, -12)$ 　　**68.** $\left(\frac{1}{2}, -\frac{1}{2}\right)$ 　　**69.** $(-10, -10)$

Arithmetic Sequences

 California Content Standards

ALG2 22.0 Students find the general term of arithmetic series. *Introduce, Develop*

What You'll Learn

- To identify and generate arithmetic sequences

. . . And Why

To determine the amount of money raised during a fund-raiser, as in Example 2

✓ **Check Skills You'll Need**

 for Help Skills Handbook p. 878

Describe the pattern in each sequence. Use at least one of the words *add*, *subtract*, or *difference*.

1. $10, 8, 6, 4, 2, 0, \ldots$

2. $100, 117, 134, 151, 168, \ldots$

3. $\frac{5}{7}, \frac{8}{7}, \frac{11}{7}, 2, \ldots$

4. $-\frac{1}{4}, -\frac{1}{2}, -\frac{3}{4}, -1, -\frac{5}{4}, -\frac{3}{2}, \ldots$

🔊 **New Vocabulary** • arithmetic sequence • common difference • arithmetic mean

---

1 Identifying and Generating Arithmetic Sequences

Vocabulary Tip

The stress in the noun <u>arithmetic</u> is on the second syllable (uh RITH muh tik). The stress in the adjective <u>arithmetic</u> is on the third syllable (ar ith MET ik).

In an **arithmetic sequence,** the difference between consecutive terms is constant. This difference is called the **common difference.** The common difference can be positive (the terms of the sequence are increasing in value) or negative (the terms of the sequence are decreasing in value).

Online
active math

For: Sequences Activity
Use: Interactive Textbook, 11-2

1 EXAMPLE **Identifying an Arithmetic Sequence**

Is the given sequence arithmetic?

a. $2, 4, 8, 16, \ldots$

$$2, \quad 4, \quad 8, \quad 16, \ldots$$
$$+2 \qquad +4 \qquad +8$$
$$4 - 2 = 2 \quad 8 - 4 = 4 \quad 16 - 8 = 8$$

There is no common difference. This is *not* an arithmetic sequence.

b. the golf ball pattern at the right

$$6, \quad 12, \quad 18, \ldots$$
$$+6 \qquad +6$$
$$12 - 6 = 6 \quad 18 - 12 = 6$$

The common difference is 6. The dots on the golf ball form an arithmetic sequence.

✓ **CA Standards Check** ① Is the given sequence arithmetic? If so, identify the common difference.
a. $2, 5, 7, 12, \ldots$ **b.** $48, 45, 42, 39, \ldots$

You can use an explicit formula to find the value of the *n*th term of an arithmetic sequence when the previous term is unknown.

| Property | Arithmetic Sequence Formulas |

Recursive Formula

$a_1 = $ a given value, $a_n = a_{n-1} + d$

Explicit Formula

$a_n = a_1 + (n-1)d$

In these formulas, a_n is the nth term ($n > 1$), a_1 is the first term, n is the number of the term, and d is the common difference.

Real-World Connection

Participants in a bike-a-thon receive pledges based on the number of miles they will bike.

2 EXAMPLE Real-World Connection

Fund-Raising Suppose you participate in a bike-a-thon for charity. The charity starts with $1100 in donations. Each participant must raise at least $35 in pledges. What is the minimum amount of money raised if there are 75 participants?

Find the 76th term of the sequence $1100, 1135, 1170, \ldots$

$a_n = a_1 + (n-1)d$ **Use the explicit formula.**

$a_{76} = 1100 + (76 - 1)(35)$ **Substitute $a_1 = 1100$, $n = 76$, and $d = 35$.**

$= 1100 + (75)(35)$ **Subtract within parentheses.**

$= 3725$ **Simplify.**

● With 75 participants, the bike-a-thon will raise a minimum of $3725.

 CA Standards Check **2 a. Critical Thinking** In Example 2, why find the value of the 76th term, not the 75th term?

b. Use the explicit formula to find the 25th term in the sequence $5, 11, 17, 23, 29, \ldots$

Video Tutor Help

Visit: PHSchool.com
Web Code: bbe-0775

The **arithmetic mean** of any two numbers is the average of the two numbers.

$$\text{arithmetic mean} = \frac{\text{sum of two numbers}}{2}$$

For any three sequential terms in an arithmetic sequence, the middle term is the arithmetic mean of the first and third terms.

Graphs of arithmetic sequences are linear. Two terms of an arithmetic sequence and their arithmetic mean lie on the same line.

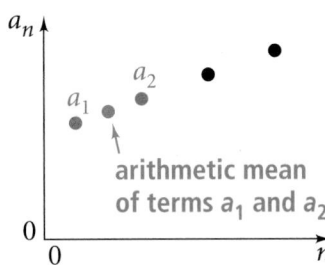

arithmetic mean of terms a_1 and a_2

You can use the arithmetic mean to find a missing term of an arithmetic sequence.

3 EXAMPLE Using the Arithmetic Mean

Find the missing term of the arithmetic sequence $84, \blacksquare, 110$.

$\text{arithmetic mean} = \dfrac{84 + 110}{2}$ **Write the average.**

$= 97$ **Simplify.**

● The missing term is 97.

 CA Standards Check **3 a.** Find the missing term of the arithmetic sequence $24, \blacksquare, 57$.

b. Write an expression for the arithmetic mean of a_6 and a_7.

EXERCISES
Standards Practice

For more exercises, see *Extra Skill and Word Problem Practice*.

A Practice by Example

Example 1
(page 616)

 for Help

Is the given sequence arithmetic? If so, identify the common difference.

1. $1, 4, 9, 16, \ldots$　　　　　　　**2.** $10, 20, 30, 40, \ldots$

3. $1, 1, 2, 3, 5, 8, \ldots$　　　　　　**4.** $0, 1, 3, 6, 10, \ldots$

5. $-21, -18, -15, -12, \ldots$　　　**6.** $97, 86, 75, 64, \ldots$

7. $3, 7, 11, 15, \ldots$　　　　　　　**8.** $100, 10, 1, 0.1, \ldots$

9. $\frac{1}{2}, \frac{1}{4}, \frac{1}{8}, \frac{1}{16}, \ldots$　　　　　　　**10.** $-5, 5, -5, 5, -5, \ldots$

Example 2
(page 617)

Find the 32nd term of each sequence.

11. $34, 37, 40, 43, \ldots$　　　　　　**12.** $-9, -8.7, -8.4, \ldots$

13. $0.1, 0.5, 0.9, 1.3, \ldots$　　　　**14.** $0.0023, 0.0025, 0.0027, \ldots$

15. $101, 105, 109, 113, \ldots$　　　**16.** $213, 201, 189, 177, \ldots$

17. $3, 1, -1, -3, \ldots$　　　　　　**18.** $23, 30, 37, 44, \ldots$

19. $9, 4, -1, -6, -11, \ldots$　　　**20.** $13, 17, 21, 25, \ldots$

Example 3
(page 617)

Find the missing term of each arithmetic sequence.

21. $-16, \blacksquare, 1, \ldots$　　　　　　**22.** $14, \blacksquare, 28, \ldots$

23. $\ldots 5, \blacksquare, 21, \ldots$　　　　　**24.** $\frac{13}{2}, \blacksquare, \frac{51}{2}, \ldots$

25. $101, \blacksquare, -115, \ldots$　　　　**26.** $203, \blacksquare, 1117, \ldots$

27. $25, \blacksquare, -10, \ldots$　　　　　**28.** $\ldots 65, \blacksquare, -60, \ldots$

29. $\ldots a_{10}, \blacksquare, a_{12}, \ldots$　　　**30.** $\ldots 99, \blacksquare, 66, \ldots$

B Apply Your Skills

Find the arithmetic mean a_n of the given terms.

31. $a_{n-1} = 7, a_{n+1} = 1$　　　　**32.** $a_{n-1} = 4, a_{n+1} = -3$

33. $a_{n-1} = 21, a_{n+1} = 5$　　　　**34.** $a_{n-1} = 100, a_{n+1} = 140$

35. $a_{n-1} = -18, a_{n+1} = -21$　　**36.** $a_{n-1} = 0.3, a_{n+1} = 1.9$

37. $a_{n-1} = 9, a_{n+1} = -11$　　　**38.** $a_{n-1} = \frac{3}{5}, a_{n+1} = 1$

39. $a_{n-1} = r, a_{n+1} = s$　　　　　**40.** $a_{n-1} = r, a_{n+1} = r + s$

41. $a_{n-1} = -2x, a_{n+1} = 2x$　　　**42.** $a_{n-1} = x + 3, a_{n+1} = 3x - 1$

43. Error Analysis A student claims that the next term of the arithmetic sequence $0, 2, 4, \ldots$ is 8. What error did the student make?

44. a. Open-Ended Use your calculator to generate an arithmetic sequence with a common difference of -7. How could you use a calculator to find the 6th term? The 8th term? The 20th term?

　b. Critical Thinking Explain how your answer to part (a) relates to the explicit formula $a_n = a_1 + (n-1)d$.

Homework Video Tutor

Visit: PHSchool.com
Web Code: bbe-1102

45. Writing Describe some advantages and some disadvantages of a recursive formula and an explicit formula.

618　Chapter 11　Sequences and Series

Find the 17th term of each sequence.

46. $a_{16} = 18, d = 5$

47. $a_{16} = 18, d = -3$

48. $a_{16} = 18, d = \frac{1}{2}$

49. $a_{18} = 18, d = -4$

50. $a_{18} = 18, d = 12$

51. $a_{18} = 18, d = -11$

Write an explicit and a recursive formula for each sequence.

52. $2, 4, 6, 8, 10, \ldots$

53. $0, 6, 12, 18, 24, \ldots$

54. $-5, -4, -3, -2, -1, \ldots$

55. $-4, -8, -12, -16, -20, \ldots$

56. $-2, 5, 12, 19, 26, 33, \ldots$

57. $27, 15, 3, -9, -21, \ldots$

58. $-5, -3.5, -2, -0.5, 1, \ldots$

59. $-32, -20, -8, 4, 16, \ldots$

60. $1, 1\frac{1}{3}, 1\frac{2}{3}, 2, \ldots$

61. $0, \frac{1}{8}, \frac{1}{4}, \frac{3}{8}, \ldots$

62. Transportation Suppose a trolley stops at a certain intersection every 14 min. The first trolley of the day gets to the stop at 6:43 A.M. How long do you have to wait for a trolley if you get to the stop at 8:15 A.M.? At 3:20 P.M.?

Find the missing terms of each arithmetic sequence. (*Hint:* The arithmetic mean of the first and fifth terms is the third term.)

63. $2, \blacksquare, \blacksquare, \blacksquare, -22, \ldots$

64. $10, \blacksquare, \blacksquare, \blacksquare, -11.6, \ldots$

65. $1, \blacksquare, \blacksquare, \blacksquare, -35, \ldots$

66. $\ldots \frac{13}{5}, \blacksquare, \blacksquare, \blacksquare, \frac{37}{5}, \ldots$

67. $17, \blacksquare, \blacksquare, \blacksquare, 17, \ldots$

68. $660, \blacksquare, \blacksquare, \blacksquare, 744, \ldots$

69. $\ldots -17, \blacksquare, \blacksquare, \blacksquare, 1, \ldots$

70. $\ldots a + 1, \blacksquare, \blacksquare, \blacksquare, a + 17, \ldots$

71. Savings In February you start a holiday savings account with a deposit of $20. You increase each monthly deposit by five dollars until the end of the year.

a. Write the amount in the account after each deposit.

b. Write a recursive formula for the sequence of balances.

c. How much money will you have saved by the end of the year?

Graph the arithmetic sequence generated by each formula over the domain $1 \le n \le 10$.

72. $a_1 = -60, a_n = a_{n-1} + 9$

73. $a_n = 50 - 7n$

74. Critical Thinking Suppose you turn the water on in an empty bathtub with vertical sides. After 20 s, the water has reached a level of 1.15 in. You then leave the room. You want to turn the water off when the level in the bathtub is 8.5 in. How many minutes later should you return? (*Hint:* Begin by identifying two terms of an arithmetic sequence.)

75. The arithmetic mean of two terms in an arithmetic sequence is 42. One term is 30. Find the other term.

76. The arithmetic mean of two terms in an arithmetic sequence is -6. One term is -20. Find the other term.

77. In an arithmetic sequence with $a_1 = 4$ and $d = 9$, which term is 184?

78. In an arithmetic sequence with $a_1 = 2$ and $d = -2$, which term is -82?

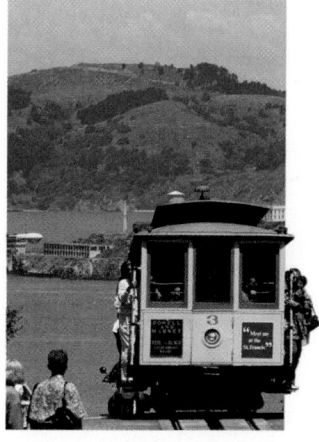

Real-World Connection

At some intersections in San Francisco, trolleys stop every 3 to 6 minutes during rush hour.

C Challenge

Given two terms of each arithmetic sequence, find a_1 and d.

79. $a_3 = 5$ and $a_5 = 11$ **80.** $a_4 = 8$ and $a_7 = 20$

81. $a_3 = 32$ and $a_7 = -8$ **82.** $a_{10} = 17$ and $a_{14} = 34$

83. $a_4 = -34.5$ and $a_5 = -12.5$ **84.** $a_4 = -2.4$ and $a_6 = 2$

Find the indicated term of each arithmetic series.

85. $a_1 = k, d = k + 4; a_9$ **86.** $a_1 = k + 7, d = 2k - 5; a_{11}$

Multiple Choice Practice

For California Standards and CAHSEE Tutorials, visit PHSchool.com. Web Code: bbq-9045

ALG2 22.0 **87.** What is the 30th term of the sequence $7, 16, 25, 34, \ldots$?

    Ⓐ 261 Ⓑ 268 Ⓒ 270 Ⓓ 277

ALG2 16.0 **88.** The equation for the circle at the right is $x^2 + y^2 = 9$. If the graph is translated one unit up and two units to the left, what is the new equation?

    Ⓐ $(x - 1)^2 + (y + 2)^2 = 9$
    Ⓑ $(x + 1)^2 + (y - 2)^2 = 9$
    Ⓒ $(x - 2)^2 + (y + 1)^2 = 9$
    Ⓓ $(x + 2)^2 + (y - 1)^2 = 9$

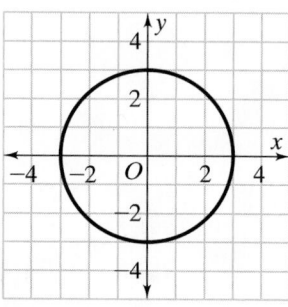

ALG2 15.0 **89.** On a recent homework assignment, Sam wrote the equation $\frac{b^2 - 4b + 3}{b - 3} = b - 1$. Which of the following statements is correct about the equation he wrote?

    Ⓐ The equation is always true.
    Ⓑ The equation is always true, except when $b = 3$.
    Ⓒ The equation is never true.
    Ⓓ The equation is sometimes true when $b = 3$.

Mixed Review

GO for Help

Lesson 11-1 **Decide whether each formula is *explicit* or *recursive*. Then find the first five terms of each sequence.**

90. $a_1 = -2, a_n = a_{n-1} - 5$ **91.** $a_n = 3n(n + 1)$

92. $a_n = n^2 - 1$ **93.** $a_1 = -121, a_n = a_{n-1} + 13$

Lesson 10-6 **Find the foci of each ellipse.**

94. $\frac{x^2}{4} + \frac{y^2}{9} = 1$ **95.** $\frac{x^2}{36} + \frac{y^2}{4} = 1$

96. $\frac{(x - 1)^2}{121} + \frac{y^2}{100} = 1$ **97.** $\frac{(x - 1)^2}{64} + \frac{(y - 3)^2}{25} = 1$

Lesson 7-2 **98. Geometry** The formula for volume V of a sphere with radius r is $V = \frac{4}{3}\pi r^3$. Find the radius of a sphere as a function of its volume. Rationalize the denominator.

The Fibonacci Sequence

ALG2 22.0 Students find the general term of arithmetic series.
Develop, Master

One famous mathematical sequence is the Fibonacci sequence. You can find each term of the sequence using addition, but the sequence is not arithmetic. The recursive formula for the Fibonacci sequence is $F_n = F_{n-2} + F_{n-1}$, with $F_1 = 1$ and $F_2 = 1$.

You can use the formula to generate the first five terms of the sequence.

$F_1 = 1$

$F_2 = 1$

$F_3 = F_1 + F_2 = 1 + 1 = 2$

$F_4 = F_2 + F_3 = 1 + 2 = 3$

$F_5 = F_3 + F_4 = 2 + 3 = 5$

The first five terms of the Fibonacci sequence are $1, 1, 2, 3, 5$.

1. **Nature** The numbers of the Fibonacci sequence are often found in other areas, especially in nature. Which term of the Fibonacci sequence does each picture represent?

a.   **b.**   **c.**   **d.**

2. **a.** Describe a recursive rule for constructing Pascal's Triangle at the right. How is your rule similar to the process for generating the Fibonacci sequence? (*Hint:* How can you find the numbers in the last row?)

   b. Find "diagonals" in Pascal's Triangle by starting with the first 1 in each row and moving one row up and one number to the right. For example, the diagonal starting in the fifth row is $1, 3, 1$. The diagonal starting in the sixth row is $1, 4, 3$. For each diagonal, write the sum of its entries. What pattern do the sums form?

```
        1
       1 1
      1 2 1
     1 3 3 1
    1 4 6 4 1
  1 5 10 10 5 1
1 ■ ■ ■ ■ ■ ■
```

3. **a.** Generate the first ten terms of the Fibonacci sequence.

   b. Find the sum of the first ten terms of the Fibonacci sequence. Divide the sum by 11. What do you notice?

   c. **Open-Ended** Choose two numbers other than 1 and 1. Generate a Fibonacci-like sequence from them. Write the first ten terms of your sequence, find the sum, and divide the sum by 11. What do you notice?

   d. **Make a Conjecture** What is the sum of the first ten terms of any Fibonacci-like sequence?

4. **a.** Study the pattern at the right. Write the next line.

   b. Without calculating, use the pattern to predict the sum of squares of the first ten terms of the Fibonacci sequence.

   c. Verify the prediction you made in part (b).

$$1^2 + 1^2 = 2 = 1 \cdot 2$$
$$1^2 + 1^2 + 2^2 = 6 = 2 \cdot 3$$
$$1^2 + 1^2 + 2^2 + 3^2 = 15 = 3 \cdot 5$$
$$1^2 + 1^2 + 2^2 + 3^2 + 5^2 = 40 = 5 \cdot 8$$

5. Make a table with four columns, as shown as the right. Begin with $n = 2$ and complete the first 8 rows. Make a conjecture suggested by the numbers in the third and fourth columns.

n	F_n	$(F_n)^2$	$F_{n-1} \cdot F_{n+1}$

11-3 Geometric Sequences

 California Content Standards
ALG2 22.0 Students find the general term of geometric series *Introduce, Develop*

What You'll Learn

• To identify and generate geometric sequences

. . . And Why

To find the size of a reduced photograph, as in Example 2

 Check Skills You'll Need

Find the next term in each sequence.

1. $1, 2, 4, 8, \ldots$

2. $336, 168, 84, 42, \ldots$

3. $0.1, 1, 10, 100, \ldots$

4. $900, 300, 100, \ldots$

 for Help Lesson 11-1

◀)) **New Vocabulary** • geometric sequence • common ratio • geometric mean

---

1 Identifying and Generating Geometric Sequences

Activity: Geometric Sequences

• Make a large right isosceles triangle out of colored paper.

• Cut the triangle into two congruent isosceles triangles.

• Place one triangle on top of the other and repeat the previous step.

1. Complete the sequence for the numbers of triangles below.

$a_1 = \blacksquare$ $a_2 = \blacksquare$ $a_3 = \blacksquare$ $a_4 = \blacksquare$

2. Is the sequence in Question 1 arithmetic? Explain why or why not.

3. a. Find the sixth term, a_6, of the sequence.
   b. Write a formula for a_6 in terms of a_5.
   c. Write a general formula for a_n in terms of a_{n-1}.

4. a. Open-Ended Generate two sequences by multiplying by a constant factor. Write each sequence.
   b. Write a recursive formula for each sequence. What do these formulas and the formula for a_n from Question 3 have in common?
   c. Graph all three sequences. Then sketch each graph.
   d. Compare all three graphs. Write a description of the pattern.

Graphing Calculator Hint

Enter the values of n and a_n into lists. Then use the **STAT** and **2nd** STAT PLOT features to graph the sequences.

In a **geometric sequence,** the ratio between consecutive terms is constant. This ratio is called the **common ratio.** Unlike in an arithmetic sequence, the difference between consecutive terms varies.

Video Tutor Help

Visit: PHSchool.com
Web Code: bbe-0775

1 EXAMPLE Identifying a Geometric Sequence

Is the given sequence geometric? If so, identify the common ratio.

a. 5, 15, 45, 135, . . .

$$5, \qquad 15, \qquad 45, \qquad 135, \ldots$$
$$\times 3 \qquad \times 3 \qquad \times 3$$
$$15 \div 5 = 3 \qquad 45 \div 15 = 3 \qquad 135 \div 45 = 3$$

There is a common ratio of 3. This is a geometric sequence.

b. 15, 30, 45, 60, . . .

$$15, \qquad 30, \qquad 45, \qquad 60, \ldots$$
$$\times 2 \qquad \times 1\frac{1}{2} \qquad \times 1\frac{1}{3}$$
$$30 \div 15 = 2 \qquad 45 \div 30 = 1\frac{1}{2} \qquad 60 \div 45 = 1\frac{1}{3}$$

There is no common ratio. This is *not* a geometric sequence.

 CA Standards Check **1** **a.** Write the first ten terms of the geometric sequence from Example 1. Explain how you found the tenth term in the sequence, a_{10}.
b. Is the sequence 6, -24, 96, -384, . . . *arithmetic, geometric,* or *neither?* Explain.
c. Is the sequence 8, 20, 32, 44, . . . *arithmetic, geometric,* or *neither?* Explain.

Key Concepts

Property	**Geometric Sequence Formulas**

Recursive Formula   **Explicit Formula**

$a_1 = $ a given value, $a_n = a_{n-1} \cdot r$ $a_n = a_1 \cdot r^{n-1}$

In these formulas, a_n is the nth term, a_1 is the first term, n is the number of the term, and r is the common ratio.

As with an arithmetic sequence, you can use an explicit formula to find the value of the nth term when the previous term is unknown.

Real-World Connection

Graphic designers use math to determine a scale factor when reducing or enlarging photographs.

2 EXAMPLE Real-World Connection

Design Suppose you want a reduced copy of a photograph. The actual length of the photograph is 10 in. The smallest size the copier can make is 64% of the original. Find the length of the photograph after five reductions at 64%.

For five reductions, you need to find the 6th term of the geometric sequence 10, 6.4, . . .

$$a_n = a_1 \cdot r^{n-1} \qquad \textbf{Use the explicit formula.}$$
$$a_6 = 10 \cdot 0.64^{6-1} \qquad \textbf{Substitute } a_1 = 10, n = 6, \text{ and } r = 0.64.$$
$$= 10 \cdot 0.64^5 \qquad \textbf{Simplify the exponent.}$$
$$\approx 1.07 \qquad \textbf{Use a calculator.}$$

After five reductions of 64%, the photograph is about 1 in. long.

 CA Standards Check **2** Find the 19th term in each sequence.
a. 11, 33, 99, 297, . . .   **b.** 20, 17, 14, 11, 8, . . .

The graphs of arithmetic and geometric sequences have different shapes.

To review exponential curves, go to Lesson 8–2.

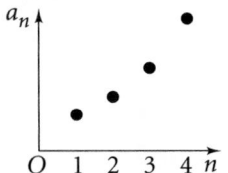

Arithmetic graphs are linear. Geometric graphs are exponential.

You can find the **geometric mean** of any two positive numbers by taking the positive square root of the product of the two numbers.

$$\text{geometric mean} = \sqrt{\text{product of the two numbers}}$$

You can use the geometric mean to find a missing term of a geometric sequence.

3 EXAMPLE Real-World Connection

Physics When a child swings without being pushed, air resistance causes the length of the arc of the swing to decrease geometrically. Find the missing arc length.

Find the geometric mean of the two arc lengths.

$$\text{geometric mean} = \sqrt{8 \cdot 6\tfrac{1}{8}}$$
$$= \sqrt{49}$$
$$= 7$$

• On the second swing, the length of the arc is 7 ft.

CA Standards Check ❸ Find the missing term of each geometric sequence. It could be the geometric mean or its opposite.
a. 20, ■, 80, . . . **b.** 3, ■, 18.75, . . . **c.** 28, ■, 5103, . . .

EXERCISES

For more exercises, see *Extra Skill and Word Problem Practice.*

Standards Practice
ALG2 22.0

A Practice by Example

Example 1
(page 623)

GO for Help

Is the sequence geometric? If so, find the common ratio and the next two terms.

1. $1, 2, 4, 8, \ldots$ **2.** $1, 2, 3, 4, \ldots$

3. $1, -2, 4, -8, \ldots$ **4.** $-1, 1, -1, 1, \ldots$

5. $10, 4, 1.6, 0.64, \ldots$ **6.** $7, 0.7, 0.07, 0.007, \ldots$

7. $18, -6, 2, -\frac{2}{3}, \ldots$ **8.** $1, \frac{1}{2}, \frac{1}{3}, \frac{1}{4}, \ldots$

9. $10, 15, 22.5, 33.75, \ldots$ **10.** $2, -10, 50, -250, \ldots$

11. $-1, -6, -36, -216, \ldots$ **12.** $\frac{1}{2}, \frac{1}{4}, \frac{1}{6}, \frac{1}{8}, \ldots$

Example 2
(page 623)

Write the explicit formula for each sequence. Then generate the first five terms.

13. $a_1 = 5, r = -3$ **14.** $a_1 = 0.0237, r = 10$ **15.** $a_1 = \frac{1}{2}, r = \frac{2}{3}$

16. $a_1 = 1, r = 0.5$ **17.** $a_1 = 100, r = -20$ **18.** $a_1 = 7, r = 1$

19. $a_1 = 1024, r = 0.5$ **20.** $a_1 = 4, r = 0.1$ **21.** $a_1 = 10, r = -1$

Example 3
(page 624)

Find the missing term of each geometric sequence. It could be the geometric mean or its opposite.

22. $5, \blacksquare, 911.25, \ldots$ **23.** $9180, \blacksquare, 255, \ldots$ **24.** $\frac{2}{5}, \blacksquare, \frac{8}{45}, \ldots$

25. $3, \blacksquare, 0.75, \ldots$ **26.** $5, \blacksquare, 2.8125, \ldots$ **27.** $12, \blacksquare, 3, \ldots$

 Apply Your Skills

Identify each sequence as *arithmetic, geometric,* or *neither.* Then find the next two terms.

28. $45, 90, 180, 360, \ldots$ **29.** $25, 50, 75, 100, \ldots$ **30.** $3, -3, 3, -3, \ldots$

31. $30, 35, 40, 45, \ldots$ **32.** $-5, 10, -20, 40, \ldots$ **33.** $2, 1, 0.5, 0.25, \ldots$

34. $5, 6, 8, 11, 15, \ldots$ **35.** $2, 2, 2, 2, \ldots$ **36.** $1, 4, 9, 16, \ldots$

Find the missing terms of each geometric sequence. (*Hint:* The geometric mean of the first and fifth terms is the third term. Some terms might be negative.)

37. $19,683; \blacksquare; \blacksquare; \blacksquare; 243; \ldots$ **38.** $2.5, \blacksquare, \blacksquare, \blacksquare, 202.5, \ldots$

39. $12.5, \blacksquare, \blacksquare, \blacksquare, 5.12, \ldots$ **40.** $-4, \blacksquare, \blacksquare, \blacksquare, -30\frac{3}{8}, \ldots$

 for Help

For a guide to solving Exercise 37, see p. 628.

41. a. Open-Ended Choose two positive numbers. Find their geometric mean.
    b. Find the common ratio for a geometric sequence that includes the terms from part (a) in order from least to greatest or from greatest to least.
    c. Find the 9th term of the geometric sequence from part (b).
    d. Find the geometric mean of the term from part (c) and the first term of your sequence. What term of the sequence have you just found?

For the geometric sequence 3, 12, 48, 192, . . . , find the indicated term.

42. 5th term   **43.** 7th term   **44.** 10th term

45. 14th term   **46.** 17th term   **47.** nth term

Find the 10th term of each geometric sequence.

48. $a_9 = 8, r = \frac{1}{2}$ **49.** $a_{11} = 8, r = \frac{1}{2}$

50. $a_9 = -5, r = -\frac{1}{2}$ **51.** $a_{11} = -5, r = -\frac{1}{2}$

52. $a_9 = -\frac{1}{3}, r = \frac{1}{2}$ **53.** $a_{11} = -\frac{1}{3}, r = \frac{1}{2}$

Homework Video Tutor

Visit: PHSchool.com
Web Code: bbe-1103

54. Writing Describe the similarities and differences between a common difference and a common ratio.

Challenge

55. Banking Copy and complete the table below. Use the geometric mean. Assume compound interest is earned and no withdrawals are made.

Period 1	$140.00	$600.00	$25.00	$57.50	$100.00	$250.00
Period 2	$\blacksquare$	$\blacksquare$	$\blacksquare$	$\blacksquare$	$\blacksquare$	$\blacksquare$
Period 3	$145.64	$627.49	$32.76	$60.37	$111.98	$276.55

56. Golf Each of the putts misses the hole and continues past it for half the distance.

　a. Write a sequence to represent the ball's distance from the hole before each of his first six putts.
　b. Is this sequence geometric? Explain your reasoning.
　c. Write a recursive formula for the sequence.

57. Critical Thinking How are the formulas for a geometric sequence similar to the formulas for an arithmetic sequence?

58. Suppose a balloon is filled with 5000 cm^3 of helium. It then loses one fourth of its helium each day.
　a. Write the geometric sequence that shows the amount of helium in the balloon at the start of each day for five days.
　b. What is the common ratio of the sequence?
　c. How much helium will be left in the balloon at the start of the tenth day?
　d. Graph the sequence. Then sketch the graph.
　e. Critical Thinking How does the common ratio affect the shape of the graph?

Find a_1 for a geometric sequence with the given terms.

59. $a_5 = 112$ and $a_7 = 448$　　　　　**60.** $a_9 = \frac{1}{2}$ and $a_{12} = \frac{1}{16}$

Multiple Choice Practice

For California Standards and CAHSEE Tutorials, visit PHSchool.com. Web Code: bbq-9045

ALG2 22.0　**61.** What is the common ratio in the geometric sequence 4, 10, 25, 62.5, …?
　　Ⓐ 0.4　　　　Ⓑ 2.5　　　　Ⓒ 15　　　　Ⓓ 25

ALG2 22.0　**62.** The first term of a geometric sequence is 1 and its common ratio is 6. What is the sixth term?
　　Ⓐ 31　　　　Ⓑ 3176　　　　Ⓒ 7776　　　　Ⓓ 46,656

ALG2 2.0　**63.** Zelda is choosing between two baby sitters, Maria and Lacy. Each graph shows the relationship between the total charge for services and the hours spent working. According to the two graphs, which of these statements is true?

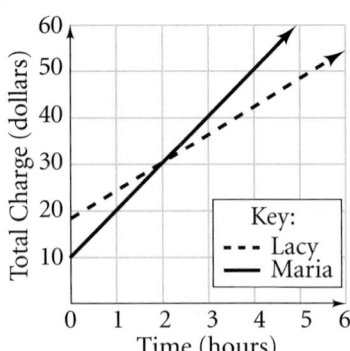

　　Ⓐ If the job takes more than 2 hours, Maria would charge less than Lacy.
　　Ⓑ If the job takes less than 2 hours, Lacy would charge less than Maria.
　　Ⓒ If the job takes exactly 2 hours, Maria would charge less than Lacy.
　　Ⓓ If the job takes more than 2 hours, Lacy would charge less than Maria.

ALG2 10.0

64. The graph of a quadratic function in the xy-plane opens downward and has x-intercepts at $x = -3$ and $x = 5$. For what x-value is the value of this function greatest?

   Ⓐ $x = -3$ Ⓑ $x = 1$ Ⓒ $x = 2$ Ⓓ $x = 5$

Mixed Review

GO for Help

Lesson 11-2

Write an explicit and a recursive formula for each arithmetic sequence.

65. $-3, 0, 3, 6, \ldots$ **66.** $17, 8, -1, \ldots$ **67.** $-2, -13, -24, \ldots$

Lesson 10-3

Write an equation of the circle with the given center and radius. Graph the circle.

68. center $(0, 0)$, radius 3   **69.** center $(-3, 1)$, radius 5   **70.** center $(1, 1)$, radius 2

Lesson 9-3

Find the vertical asymptotes of each function.

71. $y = \dfrac{x-3}{x+3}$ **72.** $y = \dfrac{x-3}{x+1}$ **73.** $y = \dfrac{x-3}{x(x-1)}$

✓ Checkpoint Quiz 1   Lessons 11-1 through 11-3

Identify each sequence as *arithmetic* or *geometric*. Then find the common difference or common ratio.

1. $15, 30, 45, 60, \ldots$ **2.** $2, 6, 18, 54, \ldots$ **3.** $37, 34, 31, 28, 25, \ldots$

4. $700, 350, 175, 87.5, \ldots$ **5.** $8, -4, 2, -1, 0.5, \ldots$ **6.** $4, 2, 0, -2, -4, \ldots$

Find the fifth term of each sequence.

7. $a_1 = 100, a_n = \frac{1}{2}a_{n-1}$ **8.** $a_1 = 2, a_n = 3a_{n-1} - 2$ **9.** $a_n = -n + 6$

10. Writing Explain how to compute the arithmetic mean and the geometric mean of two terms of a sequence.

A P•int in Time

1000   1200   1400   1600   1800   2000

In 1276, the Chinese astronomer Guo Shoujing built a device to study the sun. A hole in the tower of his observatory faced due south. At noon, a horizontal pole in the tower cast a shadow on a low wall that extended north from the building. Guo Shoujing learned about the sun's movements by studying the geometric pattern of the shadows on the wall.

Go Online
PHSchool.com

For: Information about techniques for measuring the sun's position
Web Code: bbe-2032

Understanding Math Problems Read the problem below. Then let Wanda's thinking guide you through the solution. Check your understanding with the exercises at the bottom of the page.

Find the missing terms of the geometric sequence. (*Hint:* The geometric mean of the first and fifth terms is the third term. Some terms might be negative.)

19,683; ■; ■; ■; 243; …

What Wanda Thinks

In this geometric sequence, the numbers decrease.

The hint tells me information about terms in the sequence. I'll label the terms.

The hint says that the geometric mean of the first and fifth terms is the third term. That makes sense, because the third term is the middle term. I'll write that relationship and substitute.

Perfect. I have the third term in the sequence.

I can rewrite the sequence to include the third term.

Now I can find the 2nd and 4th terms in the same way, because they are between terms I know.

I'll rewrite the sequence with the missing terms filled in.

What Wanda Writes

19,683; ■; ■; ■; 243; …

$$1^{st} \text{ term} = 19{,}683$$
$$2^{nd} \text{ term} = \blacksquare$$
$$3^{rd} \text{ term} = \blacksquare$$
$$4^{th} \text{ term} = \blacksquare$$
$$5^{th} \text{ term} = 243$$

Geometric mean of 1st and 5th terms is 3rd term

$$3^{rd} \text{ term} = \sqrt{19{,}683 \cdot 243}$$
$$3^{rd} \text{ term} = \sqrt{4{,}782{,}969}$$
$$3^{rd} \text{ term} = 2187$$

19,683; ■; 2187; ■; 243; …

$$2^{nd} \text{ term} = \pm\sqrt{19{,}683 \cdot 2187} = \pm 6561$$

$$4^{th} \text{ term} = \pm\sqrt{2187 \cdot 243} = \pm 729$$

The sequence is
19,683; 6561; 2187; 729; 243; …
or 19,683; −6561; 2187; −729; 243; …

EXERCISES

Find the missing terms of each geometric sequence.

1. 12,312; ■; ■; ■; 152; …

2. 1.7; ■; ■; ■; 11,153.7; …

3. −100; ■; ■; ■; −0.16; …

4. 5040; ■; ■; ■; $\frac{35}{9}$; …

5. Critical Thinking Explain why, in the worked example above, the second and fourth terms can be both positive or both negative but the third term must be positive.

Arithmetic Series

 California Content Standards

ALG2 22.0 Students find the sums of arithmetic series. *Develop, Master*

What You'll Learn

- To write and evaluate arithmetic series
- To use summation notation

. . . And Why

To find the number of stitches in a cross-stitch pattern, as in Example 2

✓ Check Skills You'll Need

GO for Help Lesson 11-1

Find each sum.

1. $2 + 3.5 + 5 + 6.5 + 8$

2. $-17 + (-13) + (-9) + (-5) + (-1) + 3$

Write an explicit formula for each sequence.

3. $4, 6, 8, 10, 12, \ldots$

4. $1, 4, 7, 10, 13, 16, \ldots$

5. $-17, -23, -29, -35, \ldots$

6. $10, 1, -8, -17, \ldots$

🔊 **New Vocabulary** • series • arithmetic series • limit

---

1 Writing and Evaluating Arithmetic Series

Activity: Arithmetic Series

Use the sequence 1, 2, 3, 4, . . . , 97, 98, 99, 100 to answer each question.

1. Is it *arithmetic, geometric,* or *neither?* Justify your reasoning.

2. a. Add the first and last terms of the sequence and write down the answer. Then add the second and next-to-last terms. Continue adding terms until you get to the middle of the sequence.

   b. Reasoning What patterns do you notice in your answers to part (a)?

3. Use your answer to Question 2 to find the sum of the terms of the sequence.

4. a. Describe a short method for finding the following sum.
   $5 + 10 + 15 + 20 + 25 + 30 + 35 + 40 + 45 + 50$

   b. Find the sum.

 Vocabulary Tip

Ellipsis points, as used here, indicate that the pattern continues.

A **series** is the expression for the sum of the terms of a sequence. Finite sequences and series have terms that you can count individually from 1 to a final whole number n. Infinite sequences and series continue without end. You indicate an infinite sequence or series with ellipsis points.

Finite sequence	**Finite series**
$6, 9, 12, 15, 18$	$6 + 9 + 12 + 15 + 18$
Infinite sequence	**Infinite series**
$3, 7, 11, 15, \ldots$	$3 + 7 + 11 + 15 + \ldots$

1 EXAMPLE Writing and Evaluating a Series

Use the finite sequence 2, 11, 20, 29, 38, 47. Write the related series. Then evaluate the series.

Related series → 2 + 11 + 20 + 29 + 38 + 47 = 147 ← **Add to evaluate.**

● The sum of the terms of the sequence is 147.

CA Standards Check ❶ Write the related series for each finite sequence. Then evaluate the series.
  a. 0.3, 0.6, 0.9, 1.2, 1.5, 1.8, 2.1, 2.4, 2.7, 3.0   **b.** 100, 125, 150, 175, 200, 225

An **arithmetic series** is a series whose terms form an arithmetic sequence. When a sequence has many terms, or when you know only the first and last terms of the sequence, you can use a formula to evaluate the related series quickly.

🔑 **Key Concepts**

Property	Sum of a Finite Arithmetic Series

The sum S_n of a finite arithmetic series $a_1 + a_2 + a_3 + \ldots + a_n$ is

$$S_n = \frac{n}{2}(a_1 + a_n)$$

where a_1 is the first term, a_n is the nth term, and n is the number of terms.

2 EXAMPLE Real-World 🌐 Connection

Crafts Embroidery such as cross-stitch frequently decorates table linens and clothing, although it was originally used to strengthen and repair woven fabric.

row 1
row 3
row 5

Several rows of cross-stitches make up the green roof. Find the total number of green cross-stitches in the roof.

Relate   sum of the series   is $\dfrac{\text{number of terms}}{2}$ times   (the first term   plus   the last term)

Define Let S_n = total number of cross-stitches,

and let n = the number of rows.

Then a_1 = the number of cross-stitches in the first row,

and a_n = the number of cross-stitches in the last row.

Write $S_n = \frac{n}{2}(a_1 + a_n)$ **Use the formula.**

  $= \frac{5}{2}(5 + 13)$ **Substitute $n = 5$, $a_1 = 5$, and $a_n = 13$.**

  $= 2.5(18)$ **Simplify.**

  $= 45$ **Multiply.**

● There are 45 cross-stitches in the green roof.

CA Standards Check ❷ Suppose the pattern from Example 2 extends to 14 rows of cross-stitches.
  a. Find the 14th term of the sequence.
  b. Use the formula to find the value of the series to the 14th term.

Vocabulary Tip

Σ is the Greek capital letter <u>sigma</u>, the equivalent of the English letter S (for summation).

You can use the summation symbol Σ to write a series. Then you can use limits to indicate how many terms you are adding. **Limits** are the least and greatest integral values of n.

upper limit, greatest value of n —————┐   ┌— explicit formula for the sequence

$$\sum_{n=1}^{3} (5n + 1)$$

lower limit, least value of n ————┘

3 EXAMPLE   **Writing a Series in Summation Notation**

Use summation notation to write the series $3 + 6 + 9 + \ldots$ for 33 terms.

$3 \cdot 1 = 3, 3 \cdot 2 = 6, 3 \cdot 3 = 9, \ldots$ **The explicit formula for the sequence is $3n$.**

$3 + 6 + 9 + \ldots + 99 = \displaystyle\sum_{n=1}^{33} 3n$ **The lower limit is 1 and the upper limit is 33.**

✓ CA Standards Check   **3** Use summation notation to write each series for the specified number of terms.
   a. $1 + 2 + 3 + \ldots ; n = 6$
   b. $3 + 8 + 13 + 18 + \ldots ; n = 9$

To expand a series from summation notation, you can substitute each value of n into the explicit formula and add the results.

4 EXAMPLE   **Finding the Sum of a Series**

GO Online

Video Tutor Help
Visit: PHSchool.com
Web Code: bbe-0775

Use the series $\displaystyle\sum_{n=1}^{3} (5n + 1)$.

a. Find the number of terms in the series.
   Since the values of n are 1, 2, and 3, there are three terms in the series.

b. Find the first and last terms of the series.
   The first term of the series is $5n + 1 = 5(1) + 1 = 6$.
   The last term of the series is $5n + 1 = 5(3) + 1 = 16$.

c. Evaluate the series.

$$\sum_{n=1}^{3} (5n + 1) = (5(1) + 1) + (5(2) + 1) + (5(3) + 1) \quad \textbf{Substitute.}$$

$$= 6 + 11 + 16 \quad \textbf{Simplify within parentheses.}$$

$$= 33 \quad \textbf{Add.}$$

The sum of the series is 33.

✓ CA Standards Check   **4** For each sum, find the number of terms, the first term, and the last term. Then evaluate the series.

   a. $\displaystyle\sum_{n=1}^{10} (n - 3)$ **b.** $\displaystyle\sum_{n=1}^{4} \left(\tfrac{1}{2}n + 1\right)$ **c.** $\displaystyle\sum_{n=2}^{5} n^2$

A Practice by Example

Example 1
(page 630)

Write the related series for each finite sequence. Then evaluate each series.

1. 21, 18, 15, 12, 9, 6, 3

2. −5, −15, −25, −35, −45

3. 100, 99, 98, . . . , 95

4. 0.5, 0.25, 0, . . . , −0.75

5. 17.3, 19.6, 21.9, 24.2, 26.5

6. 4.5, 5.6, 6.7, . . . , 11.1

Example 2
(page 630)

Each sequence has eight terms. Evaluate each related series.

7. $\frac{1}{2}, \frac{3}{2}, \frac{5}{2}, \ldots, \frac{15}{2}$

8. 1, −1, −3, . . . , −13

9. 5, 13, 21, . . . , 61

10. −3.5, −1.25, 1, . . . , 12.25

11. 1765, 1414, 1063, . . . , −692

12. −13, −14.5, −16, . . . , −23.5

Example 3
(page 631)

Use summation notation to write each arithmetic series for the specified number of terms.

13. 2 + 4 + 6 + . . . ; $n = 4$

14. 8 + 9 + 10 + . . . ; $n = 8$

15. 5 + 6 + 7 + . . . ; $n = 7$

16. 1 + 4 + 7 + 10 + . . . ; $n = 11$

17. 7 + 14 + 21 + . . . ; $n = 15$

18. (−3) + (−6) + (−9) + . . . ; $n = 5$

Example 4
(page 631)

For each sum, find the number of terms, the first term, and the last term. Then evaluate the series.

19. $\sum_{n=1}^{5} (2n - 1)$

20. $\sum_{n=1}^{5} (-2n - 1)$

21. $\sum_{n=3}^{8} (7 - n)$

22. $\sum_{n=1}^{5} (0.2n - 0.2)$

23. $\sum_{n=2}^{10} \frac{4n}{3}$

24. $\sum_{n=5}^{10} (20 - n)$

B Apply Your Skills

Tell whether each list is a *sequence* or a *series*. Then tell whether it is *finite* or *infinite*.

25. 1, 2, 4, 8, 16, 32, . . .

26. 1, 0.5, 0.25, 0.125, 0.0625

27. 5 + 10 + . . . + 25

28. −0.5 − 0.25 − 0.125 − . . .

29. $\frac{4}{3}, \frac{7}{3}, \frac{10}{3}, \frac{13}{3}, \frac{16}{3}, \ldots$

30. 2.3 + 4.6 + 9.2 + 18.4

31. Architecture A 20-row theater has three sections of seating. In each section, the number of seats in a row increases by one with each successive row. The first row of the middle section has 10 seats. The first row of each of the two side sections has 4 seats.
  a. Find the total number of chairs in each section. Then find the total seating capacity of the theater.
  b. Write an arithmetic series to represent each section.
  c. After every five rows, the ticket price goes down by $5. Front-row tickets cost $60. What is the total amount of money generated by a full house?

32. a. Consider the finite arithmetic series 10 + 13 + 16 + . . . + 31. How many terms are in it? Explain.
  b. Evaluate the series.

Real-World 🌎 **Connection**

The seats in a theater are staggered so people don't block the view of those in the row behind them.

33. Education Luis has taken three math tests so far this semester. The spreadsheet shows his grades.

	A	B	C	D
1	Student Name	Test 1	Test 2	Test 3
2	Luis Ortez	75	79	83
3	Marie Bova	78	85	84
4	Lasheha Brown	87	82	91

a. Suppose his test grades continue to improve at the same rate. What will be his grade on the fifth (and final) test?

b. What will his test average be for this grading period? (Assume each test is worth 100 points.)

34. a. A supermarket displays cans in a triangle. Write an explicit formula for the sequence of the number of cans.

b. Use summation notation to write the related series for a triangle with 10 cans in the bottom row.

c. Suppose the triangle had 17 rows. How many cans would be in the 17th row?

d. Critical Thinking Could the triangle have 110 cans? 140 cans? Justify your reasoning.

Evaluate each series to the given term.

35. $2 + 4 + 6 + 8 + \ldots$; 10th term

36. $-5 - 25 - 45 - \ldots$; 9th term

37. $2 + 3 + 4 + 5 + \ldots$; 100th term

38. $\frac{5}{2} + 1 - \frac{1}{2} - 2 - \ldots$; 8th term

39. $0.17 + 0.13 + 0.09 + 0.05 + \ldots$; 12th term

40. $1500 + 1499 + 1498 + 1497 + \ldots$; 1000th term

41. Technology A school committee has decided to spend a large portion of its annual technology budget on graphing calculators. This year, the technology coordinator bought 75 calculators, and plans to buy 25 new calculators each year from now on.

a. Suppose the school committee has decided that each student in the school should have access to a graphing calculator within seven years. The school population is 500. Will the technology coordinator meet this goal? Explain your reasoning.

b. Writing What are some pros and cons of buying calculators in this manner? If you could change the plan, would you? If so, how would you change it?

42. a. Open-Ended Write two explicit formulas for arithmetic sequences.

b. Write the first five terms of each related series.

c. Use summation notation to rewrite each series.

d. Evaluate each series.

Challenge

Use the values of a_1 and S_n to find the value of a_n.

43. $a_1 = 4$ and $S_{40} = 6080$; a_{40}

44. $a_1 = -6$ and $S_{50} = -5150$; a_{50}

Find a_1 for each arithmetic series.

45. $S_8 = 440$ and $d = 6$

46. $S_{30} = 240$ and $d = -2$

47. Evaluate S_{10} for the series $x + (x + y) + (x + 2y) + \ldots$

48. Evaluate S_{15} for the series $3x + (3x - 2y) + (3x - 4y) + \ldots$

Multiple Choice Practice

For California Standards and CAHSEE Tutorials, visit PHSchool.com. Web Code: bbq-9045

ALG2 22.0

49. The first term of an arithmetic series is 123. The common difference is 12 and the sum is 648. How many terms are in the series?

    (A) 7   (B) 8   (C) 9   (D) 10

ALG2 22.0

50. Which expression represents the sum of the arithmetic series below?
13, 16, 19, 22, 25, 28, 31

    (A) $\frac{7}{2}(13 + 31)$ (C) $4 + 3(n + 2)$

    (B) $7(13 + 31)$ (D) $\frac{7}{2}(13 - 31)$

ALG2 11.2

51. Elizabeth, Mario, Ling, and Andrew all worked the same math problem at the chalkboard. Each student's work is shown below. Their teacher said that while two of them had the correct answer, only one of them had arrived at the correct conclusion using correct steps.

Elizabeth's work

$$\log_4 12 = \frac{\log_{10} 12}{\log_{10} 4}$$
$$\approx 0.4771$$

Mario's work

$$\log_4 12 = \log_{10} 12 - \log_{10} 4$$
$$\approx 0.4771$$

Ling's work

$$\log_4 12 = \log_{10} 12 - \log_{10} 4$$
$$\approx 1.7925$$

Andrew's work

$$\log_4 12 = \frac{\log_{10} 12}{\log_{10} 4}$$
$$\approx 1.7925$$

Which is a completely correct solution?

    (A) Elizabeth's work   (C) Mario's work

    (B) Ling's work   (D) Andrew's work

Mixed Review

Lesson 11-3

Write the explicit formula for each geometric sequence. Then generate the first three terms.

52. $a_1 = 1, r = 2$ **53.** $a_1 = 1, r = 5$ **54.** $a_1 = -1, r = -1$

55. $a_1 = 3, r = \frac{3}{2}$ **56.** $a_1 = -7, r = 0.1$ **57.** $a_1 = 20, r = -0.5$

Lesson 10-1

Graph each equation. Describe each graph and its lines of symmetry. Give the domain and range for each graph.

58. $x^2 + 3y^2 = 36$ **59.** $x^2 - y^2 = 25$ **60.** $x^2 + y^2 = 4$

Lesson 9-4

Simplify each rational expression.

61. $\frac{x^2 + 4x + 3}{x^2 - 3x - 4}$ **62.** $\frac{c^2 - 8c + 12}{c^2 - 11c + 30}$ **63.** $\frac{3z^4 + 36z^3 + 60z^2}{3z^3 - 3z^2}$

Geometry and Infinite Series

ALG2 23.0 Students derive the summation formulas for series. *Introduce*
ALG2 21.0 Students apply the method of mathematical induction. *Introduce*

You can use geometric figures to model some infinite series.

1 ACTIVITY Modeling an Infinite Series

Geometry Draw a geometric figure to model the series.
$$\frac{1}{2} + \left(\frac{1}{2}\right)^2 + \left(\frac{1}{2}\right)^3 + \ldots + \left(\frac{1}{2}\right)^n + \ldots$$

Use a square grid. Shade one half of the grid. Then shade one half of the remaining area. Continue until the grid is full.

So the series

$$\frac{1}{2} + \left(\frac{1}{2}\right)^2 + \left(\frac{1}{2}\right)^3 + \ldots + \left(\frac{1}{2}\right)^n + \ldots$$

appears to have a sum of 1.

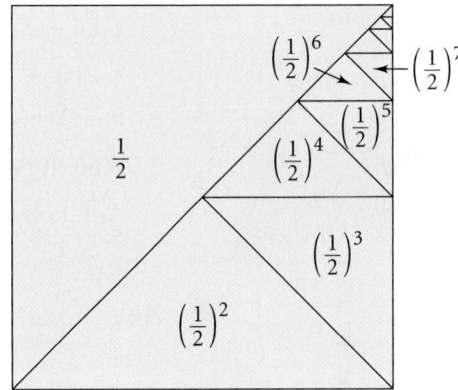

You can write an infinite series from a geometric model.

2 ACTIVITY Writing an Infinite Series

Geometry Write the series modeled by the trapezoids. Estimate the sum of the series. Explain your reasoning.

  $\frac{1}{4}$ + $\left(\frac{1}{4}\right)^2$ +   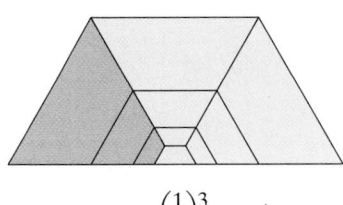 $\left(\frac{1}{4}\right)^3$ + . . .

The red area approaches one third of the figure.
So the series $\frac{1}{4} + \left(\frac{1}{4}\right)^2 + \left(\frac{1}{4}\right)^3 + \ldots + \left(\frac{1}{4}\right)^n + \ldots$ appears to have a sum of $\frac{1}{3}$.

EXERCISES

1. a. Write the series modeled by the figure at the right.
   b. Evaluate the series. Explain your reasoning.

2. Draw a figure to model the series. Begin with a 10 × 10 square.
$$\frac{1}{5} + \left(\frac{1}{5}\right)^2 + \left(\frac{1}{5}\right)^3 + \ldots + \left(\frac{1}{5}\right)^n + \ldots$$

3. Make a Conjecture Consider the series
$$\frac{1}{c} + \left(\frac{1}{c}\right)^2 + \left(\frac{1}{c}\right)^3 + \ldots + \left(\frac{1}{c}\right)^n + \ldots$$
What is the sum of the series? Explain your reasoning.

11-5

Geometric Series

 California Content Standards

ALG2 22.0 Students find the sums of both finite and infinite geometric series. *Develop, Master*
MA 8.0 Students are familiar with the notion of the limit of a sequence. They determine whether certain sequences converge or diverge.

What You'll Learn

- To evaluate a finite geometric series
- To evaluate an infinite geometric series

. . . And Why

To find the length of a chambered nautilus shell, as in Example 4

✓ **Check Skills You'll Need**   **GO for Help** Lesson 9-5

Find each sum or difference.

1. $100 + 50 + 25 + \frac{25}{2} + \frac{25}{4}$ **2.** $3 + 9 + 27 + 81$

3. $-2 + 4 - 8 + 16 - 32$ **4.** $-5 - 10 - 20 - 40$

Simplify each fraction.

5. $\dfrac{1 - \frac{1}{5}}{\frac{1}{3}}$ **6.** $\dfrac{1}{1 - \frac{1}{4}}$ **7.** $\dfrac{\frac{1}{2} - \frac{1}{3}}{\frac{1}{4}}$ **8.** $\dfrac{2 + \frac{1}{16}}{\frac{1}{3}}$

◀)) **New Vocabulary** • geometric series • converge • diverge

---

1 Evaluating a Finite Geometric Series

A **geometric series** is the expression for the sum of the terms of a geometric sequence. As with arithmetic series, you can use a formula to evaluate a finite geometric series.

 Key Concepts

Property	**Sum of a Finite Geometric Series**

The sum S_n of a finite geometric series $a_1 + a_2 + a_3 + \ldots + a_n, r \neq 1$, is

$$S_n = \frac{a_1(1 - r^n)}{1 - r}$$

where a_1 is the first term, r is the common ratio, and n is the number of terms.

1 EXAMPLE **Using the Geometric Series Formula**

Use the formula to evaluate the series $3 + 6 + 12 + 24 + 48 + 96$.

The first term is 3, and there are six terms in the series.

GO for Help

For more practice with ratios, see Skills Handbook p. 884.

The common ratio is $\frac{6}{3} = \frac{12}{6} = \frac{24}{12} = \frac{48}{24} = \frac{96}{48} = 2$.

So $a_1 = 3, r = 2$, and $n = 6$.

$S_n = \dfrac{a_1(1 - r^n)}{1 - r}$ **Write the formula.**

$S_6 = \dfrac{3(1 - 2^6)}{1 - 2}$ **Substitute $a_1 = 3, r = 2$, and $n = 6$.**

$= \dfrac{-189}{-1} = 189$ **Simplify.**

● The sum of the series is 189.

① Identify $a_1, r,$ and n for each series. Then evaluate each series.

    a. $-45 + 135 - 405 + 1215 - 3645$ **b.** $\frac{1}{3} + \frac{1}{9} + \frac{1}{27} + \frac{1}{81}$

You can use the formula to solve problems involving geometric series.

② EXAMPLE Real-World Connection

Financial Planning In March, the Floyd family starts saving for a vacation at the end of August. The Floyds expect the vacation to cost $1375. They start with $125. Each month they plan to deposit 20% more than the previous month. Will they have enough money for their trip?

Relate $S_n = \dfrac{a_1(1 - r^n)}{1 - r}$ **Write the formula for the sum of a geometric series.**

Define S_n = total amount saved

         $a_1 = 125$ **initial amount**

         $r = 1.2$ **common ratio**

         $n = 6$ **number of months (March through August)**

Write $S_6 = \dfrac{125(1 - 1.2^6)}{1 - 1.2}$ **Substitute.**

         $= 1241.24$ **Simplify.**

The final balance will be $1241.24. The Floyds will *not* have enough money for their trip in August.

CA Standards Check ② **a. Reasoning** Explain how the common ratio 1.2 was found.

    b. Suppose each month the Floyds deposit 25% more than the previous month. Describe how this changes the problem.

    c. At this rate of saving, will they have enough money for their trip? Explain.

② Evaluating an Infinite Geometric Series

In some cases you can evaluate an infinite geometric series. When $|r| < 1$, the series **converges,** or gets closer and closer, to the sum S. When $|r| \geq 1$, the series **diverges,** or approaches no limit.

③ EXAMPLE Determining Divergence and Convergence

Vocabulary Tip

In $\displaystyle\sum_{n=1}^{\infty}$, the symbol for infinity ∞ indicates that the series continues without end.

Decide whether each infinite geometric series *diverges* or *converges*. State whether the series has a sum.

a. $1 - \frac{1}{3} + \frac{1}{9} - \ldots$

     $a_1 = 1, a_2 = -\frac{1}{3}$

     $r = -\frac{1}{3} \div 1 = -\frac{1}{3}$

     Since $|r| < 1$, the series converges, and the series has a sum.

b. $\displaystyle\sum_{n=1}^{\infty} 5(2)^{n-1}$

     $a_1 = 5(2^0) = 5, a_2 = 5(2^1) = 10$

     $r = 10 \div 5 = 2$

     Since $|r| \geq 1$, the series diverges, and the series does not have a sum.

CA Standards Check ③ Determine whether each infinite series converges or diverges.

    a. $1 + \frac{1}{5} + \frac{1}{25} + \ldots$ **b.** $4 + 8 + 16 + \ldots$

Key Concepts

Definition	Sum of an Infinite Geometric Series

An infinite geometric series with $|r| < 1$ converges to the sum

$$S = \frac{a_1}{1 - r}$$

where a_1 is the first term and r is the common ratio.

You can use the sum formula to evaluate some infinite geometric series.

4 **EXAMPLE** **Real-World** 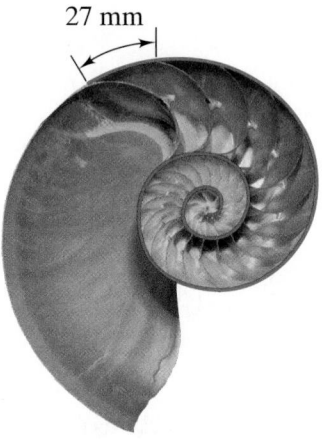 **Connection**

Multiple Choice The length of the outside shell of each closed chamber of a chambered nautilus is 0.9 times the length of the larger chamber next to it. What is the best estimate for the total length of the outside shell for the enclosed chambers?

27 mm

Ⓐ 24.3 mm   Ⓒ 243 mm
Ⓑ 30 mm   Ⓓ 270 mm

The outside edge of the largest enclosed chamber is 27 mm long, so $a_1 = 27$.

$S = \frac{a_1}{1 - r}$ **Use the formula.**

$= \frac{27}{1 - 0.9}$ **Substitute.**

$= 270$ **Simplify.**

● The estimate for the length is 270 mm. The correct choice is D.

☑ **CA Standards Check** **4** Evaluate each infinite geometric series.

a. $1 + \frac{1}{2} + \frac{1}{4} + \frac{1}{8} + \ldots$ **b.** $3 - \frac{3}{2} + \frac{3}{4} - \frac{3}{8} + \ldots$

EXERCISES

For more exercises, see *Extra Skill and Word Problem Practice.*

Standards Practice

ALG2 22.0

Ⓐ Practice by Example

Examples 1 and 2
(pages 636 and 637)

 for Help

Evaluate the finite series for the specified number of terms.

1. $1 + 2 + 4 + \ldots; n = 8$ **2.** $4 + 12 + 36 + \ldots; n = 6$

3. $3 + 6 + 12 + \ldots; n = 7$ **4.** $7 - 35 + 175 - \ldots; n = 5$

5. $-5 - 10 - 20 - \ldots; n = 11$ **6.** $-\frac{1}{6} + 1 - 6 + 36 - \ldots; n = 5$

7. $\frac{1}{2} + \frac{1}{4} + \frac{1}{8} + \ldots; n = 8$ **8.** $1 - 3 + 9 - 27 + \ldots; n = 8$

Example 3
(page 637)

Decide whether each infinite geometric series *diverges* or *converges*. State whether each series has a sum.

9. $1 + \frac{1}{4} + \frac{1}{16} + \ldots$ **10.** $1 - \frac{1}{2} + \frac{1}{4} - \ldots$ **11.** $4 + 2 + 1 + \ldots$

12. $1 + 2 + 4 + \ldots$ **13.** $6 + 18 + 54 + \ldots$ **14.** $-54 - 18 - 6 - \ldots$

15. $1 - 1 + 1 - \ldots$ **16.** $1 + \frac{1}{5} + \frac{1}{25} + \ldots$ **17.** $\frac{1}{4} + \frac{1}{2} + 1 + 2 + \ldots$

Example 4
(page 638)

Evaluate each infinite geometric series.

18. $1.1 + 0.11 + 0.011 + \ldots$

19. $1.1 - 0.11 + 0.011 - \ldots$

20. $1 - \frac{1}{5} + \frac{1}{25} - \frac{1}{125} + \ldots$

21. $3 + 1 + \frac{1}{3} + \frac{1}{9} + \ldots$

22. $3 + 2 + \frac{4}{3} + \frac{8}{9} + \ldots$

23. $3 - 2 + \frac{4}{3} - \frac{8}{9} + \ldots$

B Apply Your Skills

Determine whether each series is *arithmetic* or *geometric*. Then evaluate the finite series for the specified number of terms.

24. $2 + 4 + 8 + 16 + \ldots ; n = 10$

25. $2 + 4 + 6 + 8 + \ldots ; n = 20$

26. $-5 + 25 - 125 + 625 - \ldots ; n = 9$

27. $6.4 + 8 + 10 + 12.5 + \ldots ; n = 7$

28. $1 + 2 + 3 + 4 + \ldots ; n = 1000$

29. $81 + 27 + 9 + 3 + \ldots ; n = 200$

30. Communications Many companies use a telephone chain to notify employees of a closing due to bad weather. Suppose the first person in the chain calls four people. Then each of these people calls four others, and so on.
a. Make a tree diagram to show the first three stages in the telephone chain. How many calls are made at each stage?
b. Write the series that represents the total number of calls made through the first six stages.
c. How many employees have been notified after stage six?

 31. The graph shows the sum of the first n terms in the series with $a_1 = 20$ and $r = 0.9$.
a. Write the first four terms of the series.
b. Use the graph to evaluate the series to the 47th term.
c. Write and evaluate the formula for the sum of the series.
d. Graph the sum using the window values shown. Use the graph to verify your answer to part (c).

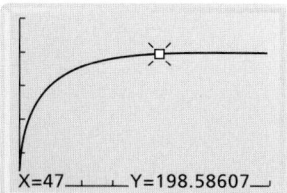

X=47 　　 Y=198.58607

Xmin=0　　　Ymin=0
Xmax=94　　Ymax=250
Xscl=10　　　Yscl=50

Evaluate each infinite series that has a sum.

32. $\displaystyle\sum_{n=1}^{\infty} \left(\frac{1}{5}\right)^{n-1}$

33. $\displaystyle\sum_{n=1}^{\infty} 3\left(\frac{1}{4}\right)^{n-1}$

34. $\displaystyle\sum_{n=1}^{\infty} \left(-\frac{1}{3}\right)^{n-1}$

35. $\displaystyle\sum_{n=1}^{\infty} 7(2)^{n-1}$

36. $\displaystyle\sum_{n=1}^{\infty} (-0.2)^{n-1}$

37. $\displaystyle\sum_{n=1}^{\infty} 2(1.2)^{n-1}$

38. A bouncing ball reaches heights of 16 cm, 12.8 cm, and 10.24 cm on three consecutive bounces.
a. If the ball started at a height of 25 cm, how many times has it bounced when it reaches a height of 16 cm?
b. Write a geometric series for the downward distances the ball travels from its release at 25 cm.
c. Write a geometric series for the upward distances the ball travels from its first bounce.
d. Find the total vertical distance the ball travels before it comes to rest.

39. Open-Ended Write an infinite geometric series that converges to 3. Use the formula to evaluate the series.

40. a. A classmate uses the formula for the sum of an infinite geometric series to evaluate $1 + 1.1 + 1.21 + 1.331 + \ldots$ and gets -10. Is your classmate's answer reasonable? Explain.

b. Error Analysis What did your classmate fail to check before using the formula?

Critical Thinking **Find the specified value for each infinite geometric series.**

41. $a_1 = 12, S = 96$; find r.

42. $S = 12, r = \frac{1}{6}$; find a_1.

43. Writing Suppose you are to receive an allowance each week for the next 26 weeks. Would you rather receive (a) \$1000 per week or (b) 2¢ the first week, 4¢ the second week, 8¢ the third week, and so on for the 26 weeks? Justify your answer.

44. The sum of an infinite geometric series is twice its first term.

a. Error Analysis A student says the common ratio of the series is $\frac{3}{2}$. What is the student's error?

b. Find the common ratio of the series.

 Technology **Create a spreadsheet to evaluate the first n terms of each series. Determine whether each infinite series converges to a sum. If so, estimate the sum.**

45. $\displaystyle\sum_{n=1}^{\infty} \frac{1}{2^n}$

46. $\displaystyle\sum_{n=1}^{\infty} \frac{100}{n}$

47. $\displaystyle\sum_{n=1}^{\infty} \frac{1}{(n-1)!}$

48. Physics Because of friction and air resistance, each swing of a pendulum is a little shorter than the previous one. The lengths of the swings form a geometric sequence. Suppose the first swing of a pendulum has a length of 100 cm and the return swing is 99 cm.

a. On which swing will the arc first have a length less than 50 cm?

b. Find the total distance traveled by the pendulum until it comes to rest.

49. a. Show that the infinite geometric series $0.142857 + 0.000000142857 + \ldots$ has a sum of $\frac{1}{7}$.

b. Find the fraction form of the repeating decimal $0.428571428571\ldots$.

50. The function $S(n) = \dfrac{10(1 - 0.8^n)}{0.2}$ represents the sum of the first n terms of an infinite geometric series.

a. What is the domain of the function?

b. Find $S(n)$ for $n = 1, 2, 3, \ldots, 10$. Sketch the graph of the function.

c. Find the sum S of the infinite geometric series.

Multiple Choice Practice

For California Standards and CAHSEE Tutorials, visit PHSchool.com. Web Code: bbq-9045

ALG2 22.0

51. What is the sum of the infinite geometric series below?

$$\frac{2}{5}, \frac{4}{25}, \frac{8}{125}, \ldots$$

Ⓐ 0 　　　　　 Ⓑ $\frac{2}{3}$ 　　　　　 Ⓒ 1 　　　　　 Ⓓ $\frac{3}{2}$

ALG2 2.0

52. A pet grooming company charges $7.50 to bathe a cat and $8.25 to bathe a dog. One day, the company made $159 from bathing 20 cats and dogs. Which system of equations could be used to find the numbers of cats c and dogs d that were bathed that day?

- (A) $c + d = 20$
  $7.50c + 8.25d = 1.59$
- (B) $c + d = 20$
  $7.50c + 8.25d = 159$
- (C) $c + d = 20$
  $750c + 825d = 159$
- (D) $c + d = 20$
  $750c + 825d = 1590$

ALG2 14.0

53. If $\log 4 \approx 0.60205$ and $\log 5 \approx 0.69897$, what is the approximate value of $\log 80$?

- (A) 0.2534
- (B) 0.2914
- (C) 1.903
- (D) 11.1835

Mixed Review

Lesson 11-4

Evaluate each series to the given term.

54. $12.5 + 15 + 17.5 + 20 + 22.5 + \ldots$; 7th term

55. $-100 - 95 - 90 - 85 - \ldots$; 11th term

56. $-17 - 11 - 5 + 1 + 7 + 13 + \ldots$; 25th term

Lesson 10-2

Identify the focus and directrix of each parabola. Then graph the parabola.

57. $y = \frac{1}{16}x^2$ **58.** $x = -\frac{1}{4}y^2$ **59.** $x^2 = -9y$

Lesson 9-5

Add or subtract. Simplify where possible.

60. $\frac{7}{2c} - \frac{2}{c^2}$ **61.** $\frac{5}{y+3} + \frac{15}{y-3}$

62. $\frac{4}{x^2 - 36} + \frac{x}{x-6}$ **63.** $\frac{15}{3-d} - \frac{-3}{9-d^2}$

Checkpoint Quiz 2

Lessons 11-4 through 11-5

Determine whether each series is *arithmetic* or *geometric*. Then evaluate the finite series for the specified number of terms.

1. $1 + 3 + 5 + 7 + \ldots$; $n = 30$ **2.** $1 + 3 + 9 + 27 + \ldots$; $n = 10$

3. $-4 - 2 - 1 - 0.5 - \ldots$; $n = 7$ **4.** $500 + 380 + 260 + 140 + \ldots$; $n = 6$

5. $120 + 60 + 30 + 15 + \ldots$; $n = 8$ **6.** $-175 - 50 + 75 + 200 + \ldots$; $n = 12$

Evaluate each infinite geometric series.

7. $\displaystyle\sum_{n=1}^{\infty} \left(\frac{1}{15}\right)^{n-1}$ **8.** $\displaystyle\sum_{n=1}^{\infty} 2(0.5)^{n-1}$

9. Open-Ended Write a finite geometric series with a sum less than 1.

10. Critical Thinking Can an infinite arithmetic series converge? Explain. Do not consider the series $0 + 0 + \ldots = 0$.

Mathematical Induction

ALG2 21.0 Students apply the method of mathematical induction to prove general statements about the positive integers. *Develop, Master*

MA 3.0 Students can give proofs of various formulas by using the technique of mathematical induction.

Consider the pattern in the following statements.

1	= 1
1 + 3	= 4
1 + 3 + 5	= 9
1 + 3 + 5 + 7	= 16
1 + 3 + 5 + 7 + 9	= 25

If this pattern continues without end, then the statement

$$1 + 3 + 5 + 7 + \ldots + (2n - 1) = n^2$$

is true for all positive integers n.

The general statement above is true for the first several values of n. There is, however, no number of examples that would prove it true for all positive integers. To prove such a statement true for all positive integers, you can use a method called mathematical induction.

Theorem | **Principle of Mathematical Induction**

Let S be a statement involving a positive integer n.

Then S is true for all positive integers if the following two conditions hold.

1. S is true for $n = 1$.

2. For any positive integer k, if S is true for k, then S is true for $k + 1$.

The principle of mathematical induction is like a chain reaction in an infinite line of dominoes. Proving that a statement is true for $n = 1$ is like knocking over the first domino. Knowing that if the statement is true for any value of k then it will be true for $k + 1$ is like knowing that if any domino is knocked over the one after it will be knocked over also.

EXAMPLE **Using Mathematical Induction**

Prove that the following statement is true for all positive integers n.

$1 + 3 + 5 + \ldots + (2n - 1) = n^2$

Proof First show that the statement is true for $n = 1$.

$2n - 1 = n^2$	**Use the statement.**
$2(1) - 1 \stackrel{?}{=} 1^2$	**Substitute 1 for n.**
$2 - 1 \stackrel{?}{=} 1^2$	**Multiply.**
$1 = 1 \checkmark$	**Simplify.**

The statement is true for $n = 1$.

Next, assume that the statement is true for k.

$$1 + 3 + 5 + \ldots + (2k - 1) = k^2$$

From this assumption, prove that the statement is true for $k + 1$.

$1 + 3 + 5 + \ldots + [2(k + 1) - 1] \stackrel{?}{=} (k + 1)^2$	**Write the statement for $k + 1$.**
$1 + 3 + 5 + \ldots + (2k + 1) \stackrel{?}{=} (k + 1)^2$	**Simplify the left side.**
$1 + 3 + 5 + \ldots + (2k - 1) + (2k + 1) \stackrel{?}{=} (k + 1)^2$	**Rewrite to show the odd number preceding $(2k + 1)$.**
$k^2 + (2k + 1) \stackrel{?}{=} (k + 1)^2$	**Substitute from the assumption.**
$(k + 1)^2 = (k + 1)^2$ ✓	**Factor the left side.**

The proof shows that conditions 1 and 2 of the principle of mathematical induction are true. By the principle, then, $1 + 3 + 5 + \ldots + (2n - 1) = n^2$ is true for all positive integers, which is what we wanted to prove.

EXERCISES

1. Test the statement from the example to verify that it is true for $n = 6, 7,$ and 8.

2. Complete the mathematical induction steps below to prove that
$$2 + 4 + 6 + \ldots + 2n = n(n + 1)$$
is true for all positive integers n.
   a. Show that the statement is true for $n = 1$.
   b. What statement will you assume to be true?
   c. What statement will you prove true using the assumption from part (b)?
   d. Express the sum in your statement from part (c) in terms of what you assumed. Then substitute and simplify to complete the proof.

Use mathematical induction to prove that each statement is true for all positive integers n.

3. $\dfrac{1}{1 \cdot 2} + \dfrac{1}{2 \cdot 3} + \dfrac{1}{3 \cdot 4} + \ldots + \dfrac{1}{n(n + 1)} = \dfrac{n}{n + 1}$

4. $1 + 2 + 3 + \ldots + n = \dfrac{n(n + 1)}{2}$

5. $1 + 4 + 7 + \ldots + (3n - 2) = \dfrac{n(3n - 1)}{2}$

6. $\dfrac{1}{2} + \left(\dfrac{1}{2}\right)^2 + \left(\dfrac{1}{2}\right)^3 + \left(\dfrac{1}{2}\right)^4 + \ldots + \left(\dfrac{1}{2}\right)^n = 1 - \left(\dfrac{1}{2}\right)^n$

7. $n^2 + n$ is divisible by 2.

8. $1 \cdot 2 + 2 \cdot 3 + 3 \cdot 4 + \ldots + n(n + 1) = \dfrac{n(n + 1)(n + 2)}{3}$

9. $1^2 + 2^2 + 3^2 + \ldots + n^2 = \dfrac{n(n + 1)(2n + 1)}{6}$

10. $a_1 + a_1 r + a_1 r^2 + a_1 r^3 + \ldots + a_1 r^{n-1} = \dfrac{a_1(1 - r^n)}{1 - r}, r \neq 1$
   (This is the formula for the sum of a finite geometric series, page 636.)

11. $1^3 + 2^3 + 3^3 + \ldots + n^3 = (1 + 2 + 3 + \ldots + n)^2$

> **ALG2 23.0** Students derive the summation formulas for arithmetic series and for both finite and infinite geometric series. *Develop, Master*

In Lessons 11-4 and 11-5, you used formulas to find the sums of arithmetic and geometric series. You can derive these formulas from a given series.

1 EXAMPLE Finite Arithmetic Series

Derive the summation formula for finite arithmetic series using the series $S_5 = 1, 3, 5, 7, 9$.

Step 1 Find the sum. $\qquad$ $1 + 3 + 5 + 7 + 9 = 25$

Step 2 Reverse the order of terms. $\qquad$ $9 + 7 + 5 + 3 + 1 = 25$

Step 3 Combine the equations above. $\qquad$ $10 + 10 + 10 + 10 + 10 = 2(25)$

Every pair has the same sum, which is equal to the sum of the first term and the last term. So,

$$2(25) = 5(1 + 9)$$

$$25 = \tfrac{5}{2}(1 + 9)$$

In general, the sum is equal to half the number of terms times the sum of the first and the last terms, or $S_n = \frac{n}{2}(a_1 + a_n)$.

2 EXAMPLE Finite Geometric Series

Derive the summation formula for finite geometric series using the series $S_5 = 3, 9, 27, 81, 243$.

Step 1 Write an equation for the sum. $\qquad$ $S_5 = 3 + 9 + 27 + 81 + 243$

Step 2 Multiply the equation by $-r$, where r is the common ratio. $\qquad$ $-3S_5 = -9 - 27 - 81 - 243 - 729$

Step 3 Combine the equations above. $\qquad$ $(1 - 3)S_5 = 3 - 729$

Step 4 Isolate S_5. $\qquad$ $\dfrac{(1 - 3)S_5}{(1 - 3)} = \dfrac{3 - 729}{1 - 3}$

Since $S_5 = \frac{3 - 729}{1 - 3} = \frac{3(1 - 243)}{1 - 3}$, we can derive that the sum of a finite geometric series is equal to the product of the first term and the difference of 1 and the common ratio raised the nth power divided by the difference of 1 and the common ratio. Therefore, $S_n = \frac{a_1(1 - r^n)}{1 - r}$.

EXERCISES

1. Derive the summation formula for an infinite geometric series using the series $S = \frac{1}{3}, \frac{1}{9}, \frac{1}{27}, \frac{1}{81}, \cdots$

2. The basis for many geometric series is the identity
$$x^n - y^n = (x - y)(x^{n-1} + x^{n-2}y + \ldots + xy^{n-2} + y^{n-1}).$$
Show that this is true for the following expressions.

    a. $2^4 - 5^4$ $\qquad$ **b.** $x^5 - 32$ $\qquad$ **c.** $1 - x^3$

Area Under a Curve

What You'll Learn

• To find area under a curve

. . . And Why

To estimate the distance traveled by a peregrine falcon, as in Example 1

✓ **Check Skills You'll Need**

GO for Help Skills Handbook page 887

Find the area of a rectangle with the given length and width.

1. $\ell = 4$ ft, $w = 1$ ft

2. $\ell = 5.5$ m, $w = 0.5$ m

3. $\ell = 6.2$ cm, $w = 0.1$ cm

4. $\ell = 9\frac{1}{2}$ in., $w = 3\frac{5}{8}$ in.

🔊 **New Vocabulary** • inscribed rectangles • circumscribed rectangles

---

1 Finding Area Under a Curve

You can easily calculate the exact area under part of a line parallel to the *x*-axis, but it is not so easy to calculate the exact area under part of a curve. You can use rectangles to estimate the area under a curve and analyze data.

Inscribed rectangles are completely under the curve. The approximation is less than the area.

 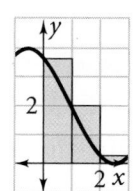

Circumscribed rectangles are partially above the curve. The approximation is greater than the area.

Real-World Connection

Adult peregrine falcons can reach speeds of 200 mi/h in a dive.

1 EXAMPLE Real-World Connection

Data Analysis The curve at the right approximates the speed of a peregrine falcon during the first 20 s of a high-speed dive.

a. What does the area under the curve represent?

$$\text{area} = \frac{\text{meters}}{\text{second}} \cdot \text{seconds} \qquad \textbf{Use dimensional analysis.}$$

$$= \text{meters} \qquad \textbf{Simplify.}$$

The area under the curve approximates the total distance traveled by the peregrine falcon.

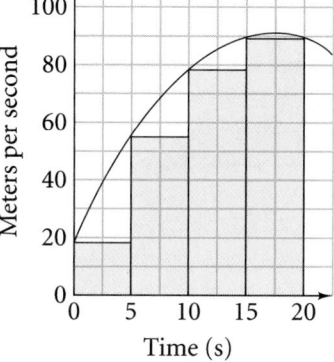

b. Use inscribed rectangles 5 units wide to estimate the area under the curve.

```
   ┌─ Width of each rectangle          ┌─ Total area
  5(18) + 5(54) + 5(78) + 5(89) = 1195
      ↑        ↑        ↑        ↑
```

Value of curve at upper edge of each rectangle

The area under the curve is about 1195 units². The peregrine falcon traveled about 1195 m during the first 20 s of its dive. The estimate is low because inscribed rectangles were used.

1 The graph at the right shows the curve from Example 1, but it shows circumscribed rectangles.

a. Estimate the area under the curve using circumscribed rectangles. How does your answer differ from the answer to Example 1?

b. Critical Thinking Find the mean of the answer using inscribed rectangles and the answer using circumscribed rectangles. Of the three answers, which is likely the most accurate? Explain.

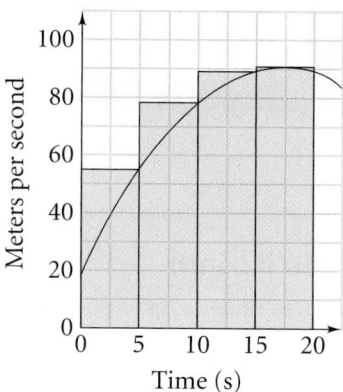

You can use summation notation to represent the area of a series of rectangles and to approximate the area under the curve $f(x)$. Let a_n represent the x-value of a point on the base of the nth rectangle.

$$A = \sum_{n=1}^{b} (w)f(a_n)$$

number of rectangles

width of each rectangle

function value at a_n

The expression $f(a_n)$ gives the height of the nth rectangle.

Online
active math

For: Area Under a Curve Activity
Use: Interactive Textbook, 11-6

2 EXAMPLE **Using a Sum to Estimate Area Under a Curve**

Estimate the area under the curve $f(x) = -x^2 + 5$ for the domain $0 \le x \le 2$ by evaluating the sum A.

$$A = \sum_{n=1}^{4} (0.5)f(a_n)$$

Evaluate the function at the right side of each rectangle.

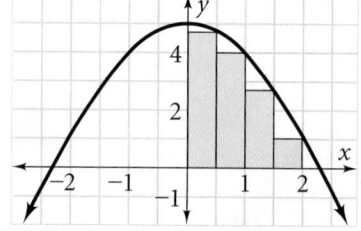

$a_1 = 0.5, a_2 = 1, a_3 = 1.5, a_4 = 2$ **Use the x-values on the right side of each rectangle.**

$A = 0.5f(0.5) + 0.5f(1) + 0.5f(1.5) + 0.5f(2)$ **Add the areas of the rectangles.**

$= 0.5(4.75 + 4 + 2.75 + 1)$ **total area = width of each rectangle · sum of the heights**

$= 0.5(12.5)$ **Add within parentheses.**

$= 6.25$ **Simplify.**

● The indicated area is about 6.25 units^2.

✓ **CA Standards Check** **2 a.** Sketch the graph from Example 2 and draw circumscribed rectangles for the domain $0 \le x \le 2$.

b. Critical Thinking To find the area using these rectangles, you should evaluate the function at the left side of each rectangle. Explain why.

c. Use the circumscribed rectangles to write and evaluate a sum that approximates the area under the curve for the domain $0 \le x \le 2$. Compare your answer to the answer in Example 2.

You can use a graphing calculator to find the exact area under a curve.

3 **EXAMPLE** **Using a Graphing Calculator**

Graph the function $f(x) = -2x^2 + 5$. Find the area under the curve for the domain $-1 \leq x \leq 1.5$.

Step 1 Input the equation. Adjust the window values.

Step 2 Access the $\int f(x)dx$ feature from the CALC menu.

Step 3 Use the lower limit of $x = -1$.

Step 4 Use the upper limit of $x = 1.5$.

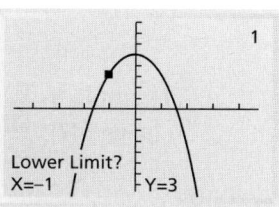

Xmin=–4.7 Ymin=–7
Xmax=4.7 Ymax=8
Xscl=1   Yscl=1

Graphing Calculator Hint

To move the cursor by tenths along the *x*-axis, set your *x* window values to multiples of 4.7 or press ZOOM 4.

● The area under the curve between $x = -1$ and $x = 1.5$ is $9.58\overline{3}$ units^2.

✓ **CA Standards Check** **3** Use the equation from Example 3 and a graphing calculator. Find the area under the curve for each domain.
   a. $0 \leq x \leq 1$ **b.** $-1 \leq x \leq 1$ **c.** $-1.5 \leq x \leq 0$

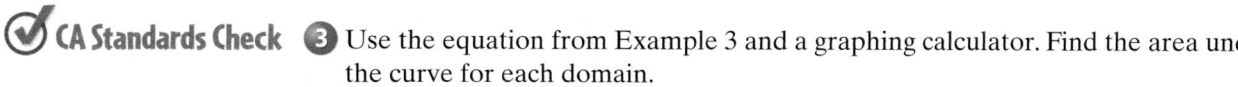

EXERCISES

For more exercises, see *Extra Skill and Word Problem Practice*.

Standards Practice

A Practice by Example

Example 1
(page 645)

GO for Help

Given each set of axes, what does the area under the curve represent?

1. *y*-axis: production rate, *x*-axis: time

2. *y*-axis: rate of growth, *x*-axis: time

3. *y*-axis: miles per gallon, *x*-axis: gallons

4. *y*-axis: distance traveled per year, *x*-axis: years

5. *y*-axis: price per pound of gold, *x*-axis: pounds of gold

Use the given rectangles to estimate area under the curve.

6.

7.

8.

Example 2
(page 646)

Write and evaluate a sum to estimate the area under each curve for the domain $0 \le x \le 2$.
a. Use inscribed rectangles 1 unit wide.
b. Use circumscribed rectangles 1 unit wide.

9. $f(x) = \frac{1}{2}x^2$ **10.** $y = -x^2 + 5$ **11.** $g(x) = x^2 + 1$

12. $y = -x^2 + 4$ **13.** $y = \frac{2}{3}x^2 + 5$ **14.** $h(x) = 5x^2$

15. $y = 4 - \frac{1}{4}x^2$ **16.** $h(x) = -(x-2)^2 + 5$ **17.** $y = (x-2)^2 + 2$

Example 3
(page 647)

Find the area under each curve for the domain $0 \le x \le 1$.

18. $y = -x^2 + 2$ **19.** $f(x) = x + 2$ **20.** $y = x^3$

21. $y = -x^4 + 2x^3 + 3$ **22.** $y = x^5 - x^2 + 2.5$ **23.** $y = -(x-1)^3 + 3$

B   **Apply Your Skills**

Graph each curve. Use inscribed rectangles to approximate the area under the curve for the interval and rectangle width given.

24. $y = x^2 + 1, 1 \le x \le 3, 0.5$ **25.** $y = 3x^2 + 2, 2 \le x \le 4, 1$

26. $y = x^2, 3 \le x \le 5, 0.5$ **27.** $y = 2x^2, 3 \le x \le 5, 1$

28. $y = x^3, 1 \le x \le 3, 0.25$ **29.** $y = x^2 + 4, -2 \le x \le 2, 0.5$

30. a. Graph the curve $y = \frac{1}{3}x^3$.
    b. Use inscribed rectangles to approximate the area under the curve for the interval $0 \le x \le 3$ and rectangle width of 1 unit.
    c. Repeat part (b) using circumscribed rectangles.
    d. Find the mean of the areas you found in parts (b) and (c). Of the three estimates, which best approximates the area for the interval? Explain.

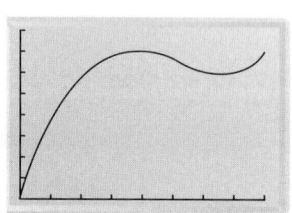

Homework Video Tutor

Visit: PHSchool.com
Web Code: bbe-1106

31. The graph at the left approximates the speed of a car as it enters a highway from a stopped position and merges with traffic. The x-axis represents time in seconds, and the y-axis represents miles per hour.
    a. Copy the graph. Use inscribed rectangles half the width of a grid square to estimate the total distance the car traveled in 50 s.
    b. Writing How does your choice of inscribed or circumscribed rectangles in part (a) affect your area estimate?

Xmin: 0   Ymin: 0
Xmax: 200   Ymax: 70
Xscl: 25   Yscl: 10

Evaluate the area under each curve for $-1 \le x \le 2$.

32. $f(x) = -x^2 + 4$ **33.** $y = (x - 0.5)^2 + 1.75$ **34.** $g(x) = 2 + 3x^2$

35. $y = \sqrt{1 + x}$ **36.** $g(x) = 2^x + 1$ **37.** $y = x^3 + 2$

38. $y = -(x-1)^2 + 4\frac{1}{3}$ **39.** $h(x) = \sqrt{x^2}$ **40.** $f(x) = -x^4 + 2x^3 + 3$

41. Open-Ended Write equations for three curves that are positive for $1 \le x \le 3$. Use your graphing calculator to find the area under each curve for this domain.

C   **Challenge**

42. Approximate the area under the curve $f(x) = x^2$ for the interval $0 \le x \le 4$ by evaluating each sum. Use inscribed rectangles.
    a. $\sum_{n=1}^{8} (0.5)f(a_n)$ **b.** $\sum_{n=1}^{4} (1)f(a_n)$
    c. Which estimate is closer to the actual area under the curve? Explain.

43. a. Graph $y = \frac{1}{4}x^3 + 1$ and $y = 1$ over the domain $-4.7 \le x \le 4.7$.
    b. Critical Thinking Evaluate the area under each curve for the interval $-1.5 \le x \le 1.5$. What do you notice? Explain.

44. Critical Thinking Use your graphing calculator to find the area of the triangle with vertices $(-3, 0)$, $(-1, 3)$, and $(1, 0)$. (*Hint:* First find the function whose graph makes a peak at $(-1, 3)$.)

 45. a. Write the equation $\frac{x^2}{25} + \frac{y^2}{9} = 1$ in calculator-ready form.
 b. Graph the top half of the ellipse. Calculate the area under the curve for the interval $-5 \le x \le 5$.
 c. Use symmetry to find the area of the entire ellipse.
 d. Open-Ended Find the area of another symmetric shape by graphing part of it. Sketch your graph and show your calculations.

 ## Multiple Choice Practice

For California Standards and CAHSEE Tutorials, visit PHSchool.com. Web Code: bbq-9045

ALG2 22.0

46. A sales associate at a shoe store stacked boxes of shoes to make the display shown at the right. The next day, he added two more rows of shoe boxes in the same pattern. What is the total number of shoe boxes in the larger display?

   Ⓐ 20   Ⓑ 28   Ⓒ 36   Ⓓ 56

ALG2 3.0

47. The length of a rectangle is $2x^2 - 4x + 1$. The width is $3x - 5$. Which polynomial represents the area of the rectangle?
   Ⓐ $6x^3 - 22x^2 + 23x - 5$ Ⓒ $3x^3 - 11x^2 + 11.5x - 2.5$
   Ⓑ $6x^3 + 22x^2 + 23x + 5$ Ⓓ $2x^2 - x - 4$

ALG2 10.0

48. The graph at the right shows the quadratic function $y = -\frac{1}{2}x^2 + x + 4$. Which point represents a solution to the equation $-\frac{1}{2}x^2 + x + 4 = 0$?
   Ⓐ $(0, 4)$
   Ⓑ $(1, 4)$
   Ⓒ $(2, 4)$
   Ⓓ $(4, 0)$

Mixed Review

Lesson 11-5

Determine whether the sum of each infinite geometric series exists.

49. $4 + 2 + 1 + \frac{1}{2} + \frac{1}{4} + \ldots$ **50.** $-972 - 324 - 108 - \ldots$

Lesson 10-5

Write the equation of each hyperbola in standard form. Sketch the graph.

51. $9x^2 - 16y^2 = 144$ **52.** $x^2 - 25y^2 = 25$ **53.** $16x^2 - 10y^2 = 160$

Lesson 9-6

Solve each equation. Check your solution.

54. $\frac{x}{4} = \frac{x-3}{8}$ **55.** $\frac{5}{2-x} = \frac{4}{2x+1}$ **56.** $\frac{x}{x+1} - \frac{x}{x-3} = 9$

Estimating the answer to a problem may help you eliminate one or more answers, find the answer, or check your answer.

1 EXAMPLE

A ball drops from a height of 2 m. After it hits the floor, it rebounds to 60% of its previous height. Find the total distance the ball travels before it comes to rest.

    (A) 3 m   (B) 3.5 m   (C) 5 m   (D) 10 m   (E) 20 m

Estimate the distance the ball travels before the second bounce. The ball rebounds about one-half its previous height, so it travels down 2 m, then up about 1 m, and then down about 1 m. Since $2 + 1 + 1 = 4$, the ball travels about 4 m before the second bounce. You can eliminate answer choices A and B.

Since the distance the ball travels on each bounce models a geometric sequence with $r < 1$, the final answer will be closer to 4 than to 10. The answer is C.

2 EXAMPLE

A student jogs 3.8 mi around a local reservoir five afternoons a week. The student claims to have run about 990 mi around the reservoir last year. Is the student correct? Explain.

$3.8 \cdot 5 \cdot 52 \approx 4 \cdot 5 \cdot 50$ **distance · days per week · weeks per year**

$= 20 \cdot 50 = 1000$ **Simplify and multiply.**

The student ran about 1000 mi around the reservoir last year. The student is correct.

EXERCISES

1. A square is inscribed in a circle. The square has side length 4 cm. What is the best estimate for the area of the circle?

    (A) 50 cm^2 (B) 25 cm^2 (C) 16 cm^2 (D) 15 cm^2 (E) 12 cm^2

2. Which is the best approximation of the area of the region between the graph of $y = (x - 1)^2$, the x-axis, and the y-axis?

    (A) 2 units^2 (B) 1.5 units^2 (C) 1 units^2 (D) 0.8 units^2 (E) 0.5 units^2

3. Which estimate is closest to the sum $1 + \frac{1}{4} + \frac{1}{16} + \ldots + \frac{1}{1024}$?

    (A) 2.00   (B) 1.50   (C) 1.33   (D) 0.5   (E) 0.33

Estimate the answer to each problem.

4. Suppose your aunt gives you $100 on your birthday, along with a promise to give you one half the previous year's amount each year until the amount reaches 1¢. What is the total amount of money that your aunt will give you?

5. If two numbers a and b are approximately equal, their arithmetic mean and their geometric mean are approximately equal. Use this fact to estimate the value of $\sqrt{56}$.

Chapter 11 Review

Vocabulary Review

arithmetic mean (p. 617)
arithmetic sequence (p. 616)
arithmetic series (p. 630)
circumscribed rectangles (p. 645)
common difference (p. 616)
common ratio (p. 622)

converge (p. 637)
diverge (p. 637)
explicit formula (p. 612)
geometric mean (p. 624)
geometric sequence (p. 622)
geometric series (p. 636)

inscribed rectangles (p. 645)
limit (p. 631)
recursive formula (p. 612)
sequence (p. 610)
series (p. 629)
term (p. 610)

For: Vocabulary quiz
Web Code: bbj-1151

Choose the correct vocabulary term to complete each sentence.

1. When using Σ to write a series, you can use ? to indicate how many terms you are adding.

2. Using ? to approximate the area under a curve will result in an approximation that is greater than the area.

3. An ordered list of terms is a ? .

4. If an infinite geometric series ? , then it must have a sum.

5. There is a ? between consecutive terms in a geometric sequence.

Skills and Concepts

Lesson 11-1

- To identify mathematical patterns (p. 610)
- To use a formula for finding the nth term of a sequence (p. 612)

A **sequence** is an ordered list of numbers called **terms**. A **recursive formula** gives the first term and defines the other terms in a sequence by relating each term to the one before it. An **explicit formula** expresses the nth term in a sequence in terms of n, where n is a positive integer.

Write a recursive formula for each sequence. Then find the next three terms.

6. $5, 22, 39, 56, \ldots$ **7.** $1, -7, 49, -343, \ldots$ **8.** $-2, 7, 16, 25, \ldots$

Write an explicit formula for each sequence. Then find a_{12}.

9. $1, 4, 7, 10, \ldots$ **10.** $2, 4, 8, 16, \ldots$ **11.** $-24, -6, 24, 66, \ldots$

 12. Writing Explain how you decide whether a formula is explicit or recursive.

Lesson 11-2

- To identify and generate arithmetic sequences (p. 616)

 ALG2 22.0

In an **arithmetic sequence,** the difference between consecutive terms is constant. The difference is the **common difference.** A recursive formula for an arithmetic sequence is $a_n = a_{n-1} + d$, given a_1. An explicit formula for an arithmetic sequence is $a_n = a_1 + (n-1)d$. In each case, a_n is the nth term, a_1 is the first term, n is the number of the term, and d is the common difference. The **arithmetic mean** of any two numbers (or terms in a sequence) is the average of the two numbers.

$$\text{arithmetic mean} = \frac{\text{sum of two numbers}}{2}$$

Is each given sequence arithmetic? If so, identify the common difference and find the 32nd term of the sequence.

13. $2, 4, 7, 10, 13, \ldots$ **14.** $3, 18, 33, 48, \ldots$ **15.** $7, 10, 13, 16, \ldots$

Find the missing term(s) of each arithmetic sequence.

16. $1, \blacksquare, 9, \ldots$ **17.** $104, \blacksquare, 99, \ldots$ **18.** $-4.6, \blacksquare, -5.2, \ldots$

19. $-1, \blacksquare, 11, \ldots$ **20.** $-13, \blacksquare, \blacksquare, \blacksquare, -3, \ldots$ **21.** $2, \blacksquare, \blacksquare, \blacksquare, -0.4, \ldots$

Find a_n, the arithmetic mean of the given terms.

22. $a_{n-1} = 7, a_{n+1} = 15$ **23.** $a_{n-1} = -2, a_{n+1} = 3$

 24. Writing Explain how you can determine if a sequence is arithmetic.

Lesson 11-3

• To identify and generate geometric sequences (p. 622)

 ALG2 22.0

In a **geometric sequence,** the ratio of consecutive terms is constant. The ratio is the **common ratio.** You can use recursive or explicit formulas to express a geometric sequence.

A recursive formula for a geometric sequence is $a_n = a_{n-1} \cdot r$, given a_1. An explicit formula for a geometric sequence is $a_n = a_1 \cdot r^{n-1}$. In each case, a_n is the nth term, a_1 is the first term, n is the number of the term, and r is the common ratio.

You can find the geometric mean of two positive numbers by taking the positive square root of the product of the two numbers.

$$\text{geometric mean} = \sqrt{\text{product of two numbers}}$$

The middle term of any three consecutive terms in a geometric sequence is the geometric mean of the first and third terms.

Is the given sequence geometric? If so, identify the common ratio, write the explicit formula for the sequence, and find the next two terms.

25. $1, \frac{1}{2}, \frac{1}{4}, \frac{1}{8}, \ldots$ **26.** $1, 3, 5, 7, \ldots$ **27.** $3, 3.6, 4.32, 5.184, \ldots$

Find the missing term(s) of each geometric sequence.

28. $3, \blacksquare, 12, \ldots$ **29.** $60, \blacksquare, \frac{20}{3}, \ldots$ **30.** $0.004, \blacksquare, 0.4, \ldots$

31. $-20, \blacksquare, \blacksquare, \blacksquare, -1.25, \ldots$ **32.** $-\frac{1}{6}, \blacksquare, \blacksquare, \blacksquare, -2\frac{2}{3}, \ldots$ **33.** $1, \blacksquare, \blacksquare, \blacksquare, 150\frac{1}{16}, \ldots$

Lesson 11-4

• To write and evaluate arithmetic series (p. 629)
• To use summation notation (p. 631)

 ALG2 22.0

A **series** is the expression for the sum of the terms of a sequence. Whether the sequence is finite or infinite determines whether the series is finite or infinite.

An **arithmetic series** is the expression for the sum of the terms of an arithmetic sequence. The sum S_n of the first n terms of an arithmetic series is $S_n = \frac{n}{2}(a_1 + a_n)$.

You can use a summation symbol, Σ, and **limits** to write a series. Limits are the least and greatest integral values of n.

Use summation notation to write each arithmetic series for the specified number of terms. Then evaluate the sum.

34. $10 + 7 + 4 + \ldots; n = 5$ **35.** $50 + 55 + 60 + \ldots; n = 7$

36. $6 + 7.4 + 8.8 + \ldots; n = 11$ **37.** $21 + 19 + 17 + \ldots; n = 8$

Find the number of terms in each series, the first term, and the last term. Then evaluate the sum.

38. $\displaystyle\sum_{n=1}^{3} (17n - 25)$

39. $\displaystyle\sum_{n=2}^{10} \left(\tfrac{1}{2}n + 3\right)$

40. $\displaystyle\sum_{n=5}^{15} \left(-\tfrac{2}{3}n\right)$

41. Business Deanna Jones opened a video rental store this year with 400 tapes. She plans to buy 150 new tapes each year from now on. Deanna expects to have 1300 tapes available during her fifth year in business. At her current purchasing rate, will she reach her goal? Explain.

Lesson 11-5

- To evaluate a finite geometric series (p. 636)
- To evaluate an infinite geometric series (p. 637)

 ALG2 22.0, MA 8.0

A **geometric series** is the sum of the terms of a geometric sequence. The sum S_n of the first n terms of a geometric series is $S_n = \dfrac{a_1(1 - r^n)}{1 - r}$.

You can find the sum of some infinite geometric series. When $|r| < 1$, the series gets closer and closer, or **converges**, to $S = \dfrac{a_1}{1 - r}$. When $|r| \geq 1$, the series **diverges**, or approaches no limit.

Evaluate the finite series for the specified number of terms.

42. $3 + 1 + \tfrac{1}{3} + \ldots ; n = 7$

43. $1 + 2 + 4 + \ldots ; n = 5$

44. $80 - 40 + 20 - \ldots ; n = 8$

45. $12 + 2 + \tfrac{1}{3} + \ldots ; n = 4$

Decide whether each infinite geometric series *converges* or *diverges*. Then state whether each series has a sum, and if it does, find the sum.

46. $150 + 30 + 6 + \ldots$

47. $2.2 + 2.42 + 2.662 + \ldots$

48. $-10 - 20 - 40 - \ldots$

49. $\tfrac{2}{3} + \tfrac{4}{9} + \tfrac{8}{27} + \ldots$

Lesson 11-6

- To find the area under a curve (p. 645)

You can approximate the area under a curve by using **inscribed rectangles** or **circumscribed rectangles**. If you use inscribed rectangles, the approximation is less than the area under the curve. If you use circumscribed rectangles, the approximation is greater than the area under the curve. You can use summation notation to represent the area of a series of rectangles and the approximate area under a curve $f(x)$:

$$A = \sum_{n=1}^{b} (w)f(a_n),$$

where b is the number of rectangles, w is the width of each rectangle, a_n is the x-value of a point on the base of the nth rectangle, and $f(a_n)$ is the function value at a_n.

Write and evaluate a sum to approximate the area under each curve for the domain $0 \leq x \leq 2$.

a. Use inscribed rectangles 1 unit wide.
b. Use circumscribed rectangles 1 unit wide.
c. Use a graphing calculator to find the exact area under the curve.

50. $y = x^2$

51. $y = x^3 + 1$

52. $y = -2x^2 + 8$

53. $y = -x + 5$

54. $y = x^3 + 4$

55. $y = x^2 + 3$

Chapter 11 Test

Write a recursive and an explicit formula for each sequence. Then find a_{12}.

1. $7, 13, 19, 25, 31, \ldots$ **2.** $10, 20, 40, 80, 160, \ldots$

3. After one month at a new job, you have saved $50. You decide to save $5 more each month.
   a. Write an explicit formula to model the amounts you save each month.
   b. How much will you save in the sixth month?

Determine whether each sequence is *arithmetic, geometric,* or *neither.* Then find the tenth term.

4. $23, 27, 31, 35, 39, \ldots$ **5.** $-12, -5, 2, 9, 16, \ldots$

6. $-5, 15, -45, 135, -405, \ldots$

Find the arithmetic mean a_n of the given terms.

7. $a_{n-1} = 4, a_{n+1} = 12$

8. $a_{n-1} = -11, a_{n+1} = 23$

9. Open-Ended Write an arithmetic sequence. Then write an explicit formula for it.

Determine whether each sequence is *arithmetic* or *geometric.* Then identify the common difference or the common ratio.

10. $1620, 540, 180, 60, 20, \ldots$

11. $78, 75, 72, 69, 66, 63, 60, \ldots$

12. $\frac{3}{32}, \frac{3}{16}, \frac{3}{8}, \frac{3}{4}, \frac{3}{2}, 3, 6, \ldots$

In Exercises 13–16, a_1 is the first term of a sequence, r is a common ratio, and d is a common difference. Write the first five terms.

13. $a_1 = 2, r = -2$ **14.** $a_1 = 3, d = 7$

15. $a_1 = -100, r = \frac{1}{5}$ **16.** $a_1 = 19, d = -4$

Find the missing term of each geometric sequence.

17. $2, \blacksquare, 0.5, \ldots$ **18.** $2, \blacksquare, 8, \ldots$

Find the sum of each infinite geometric series.

19. $0.5 + 0.05 + 0.005 + \ldots$

20. $1 - \frac{1}{2} + \frac{1}{4} - \ldots$ **21.** $6 + 5 + \frac{25}{6} + \ldots$

Determine whether each series is *arithmetic* or *geometric.* Then evaluate the finite series for the specified number of terms.

22. $2 + 7 + 12 + \ldots ; n = 8$

23. $5000 + 1000 + 200 + \ldots ; n = 15$

24. $1 + 0.01 - 0.98 - \ldots ; n = 5$

For each sum, find the number of terms, the first term, and the last term. Then evaluate the sum.

25. $\displaystyle\sum_{n=1}^{5} (3n + 1)$ **26.** $\displaystyle\sum_{n=1}^{8} \frac{2n}{3}$

27. $\displaystyle\sum_{n=4}^{10} (0.8n - 0.4)$ **28.** $\displaystyle\sum_{n=2}^{6} (-2)^{n-1}$

29. Critical Thinking How can you tell whether or not a geometric series converges? Include examples of both types of series. Evaluate the series that converges.

30. Investments A diamond is purchased for $2500. Suppose its value increases 5% each year. Find the value of the diamond after 8 years.

31. Physics A ball on a pendulum moves 40 cm on its first swing. On each succeeding swing back or forth it moves 90% of the distance of the previous swing. Write the first four terms of the sequence of swing lengths.

Given each set of axes, what does the area under the curve represent?

32. y-axis: miles per hour, x-axis: hours

33. y-axis: pounds per in.^{2}, x-axis: in.^{2}

34. y-axis: dollars per gallon, x-axis: gallons

Use left endpoints in the given interval and inscribed rectangles 1 unit wide to approximate the area under the curve $y = f(x)$.

35. $y = 2x^2; 0 \le x \le 2$ **36.** $y = x^3; 1 \le x \le 3$

37. $y = x^2 + 1; -1 \le x \le 2$

38. Writing Explain how you could use circumscribed and inscribed rectangles to estimate the area under a curve.

Some problems ask you to solve quadratic equations by using graphs.

The graph below shows the quadratic function $y = 2x^2 + 2x - 4$. Use the graph to find the solutions of $2x^2 + 2x - 4 = 0$.

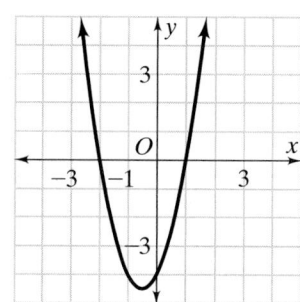

Tip 1
Find where $y = 0$.
These are the x-intercepts of the graph.

Think It Through
The x-intercepts of the graph are at $x = -2$ and $x = 1$. Substitute to verify your answers.

$$2(-2)^2 + 2(-2) - 4 = 2(4) - 4 - 4$$
$$= 0$$
$$2(1)^2 + 2(1) - 4 = 2 + 2 - 4$$
$$= 0$$

The correct answer is B.

Tip 2
Check your solutions in the original equation.

- (A) -4 and 0
- (B) -2 and 1
- (C) -1 and 2
- (D) 2 and -1

Vocabulary Review

As you solve problems, you must understand the meanings of mathematical terms. Match each term with its mathematical meaning.

A. recursive formula

B. limit

C. explicit formula

D. sequence

I. a formula that expresses the nth term in terms of n

II. an ordered list of numbers

III. the least or greatest integer value of n in a series

IV. a formula that defines terms in sequence by relating each one to the one before it

Multiple Choice

Read each question. Then write the letter of the correct answer on your paper.

1. What is the solution set of the equation $(2x - 4)(x + 6) = 0$? **(Lesson 5-5)**

- (A) $\{-4, -6\}$
- (B) $\{-4, 6\}$
- (C) $\{2, -6\}$
- (D) $\{-2, -6\}$

2. The graph below shows the quadratic function $y = x^2 + 2x - 3$. Use the graph to find all the solutions of $x^2 + 2x - 3 = 0$. **(Lesson 5-5)**

- (A) -3
- (B) -1
- (C) -3 and 1
- (D) 3 and -1

3. The table shows ordered pairs that satisfy the equation $y = -x^2 + 2x + 15$.

x	-3	0	2	3	5
y	0	15	15	12	0

Based on this table, what is the solution set of the equation $-x^2 + 2x + 15 = 0$? **(Lesson 5-5)**

- (A) $\{0, 15\}$
- (B) $\{-3, 15\}$
- (C) $\{5, 0\}$
- (D) $\{-3, 5\}$

Cumulative Practice (continued)

4. If $f(x) = 4x^4 - 9$ and $g(x) = 2x^2 + 3$, what is $\left(\frac{f}{g}\right)(x)$? **(Lesson 7-6)**

- (A) $2x^2 - 3$
- (B) $2x + 3$
- (C) $2x - 3$
- (D) $2x^2 + 3$

5. Marisol wants to start saving money for college. She sees the advertisement below in her local newspaper.

> **Start a savings account**
> **today and earn 4.7%**
> **annual interest!**
> Bonus Offer: After one year,
> an additional $50 will be
> added to your account!

The equations $f(x) = 0.047x$ and $g(x) = x + 50$ model the amount of money Marisol can earn and $(g \circ f)(x)$ models the balance Marisol would have after one year if she deposits x dollars. If she starts a savings account by depositing $120, what is her balance after one year? **(Lesson 7-6)**

- (A) $175.64
- (B) $182.58
- (C) $226.40
- (D) $249.90

6. What is the product of $\frac{x^2 + 5x + 4}{(x - 1)(x + 1)}$ and $\frac{x^2 - 5x + 6}{x - 2}$? **(Lesson 9-4)**

- (A) $\frac{x^2 + 7x + 12}{x - 1}$ for $x \neq 1$
- (B) $\frac{x^2 + x - 12}{x - 1}$ for $x \neq -1, 1,$ or 2
- (C) $\frac{x^2 + x - 12}{x - 1}$ for $x \neq 1$
- (D) $\frac{x^2 + 7x + 12}{x - 1}$ for $x \neq -1, 1,$ or 2

7. What is the sum of the following finite geometric series? **(Lesson 11-5)**

$$1, 4, 16, 64, 256$$

- (A) 341
- (B) 334
- (C) 331
- (D) 326

8. What is the sum of the following finite arithmetic series? **(Lesson 11-4)**

$$14, 20, 26, 32, 38, 44, 50$$

- (A) 2
- (B) 54
- (C) 224
- (D) 448

9. What is the common ratio in a geometric series if $a_2 = \frac{2}{5}$ and $a_5 = \frac{16}{135}$? **(Lesson 11-5)**

- (A) $\frac{2}{5}$
- (B) $\frac{2}{3}$
- (C) $\frac{6}{65}$
- (D) $\frac{8}{27}$

10. What is the sum of the infinite geometric series $\frac{1}{4}, \frac{1}{16}, \frac{1}{64}, \frac{1}{256}, \dots$? **(Lesson 11-5)**

- (A) $\frac{1}{4}$
- (B) $\frac{1}{3}$
- (C) $\frac{1}{2}$
- (D) 3

11. What is the value of $\log_4 256$? **(Lesson 8-5)**

- (A) 1
- (B) 2
- (C) 4
- (D) 64

12. If $\log 5 \approx 0.69897$ and $\log 6 \approx 0.77815$, what is the approximate value of $\log 150$? **(Lesson 8-4)**

- (A) 0.34188
- (B) 0.38017
- (C) 1.20412
- (D) 2.17609

13. There are 15 marbles in a bag: 2 are red, 8 are green, and 5 are blue. A marble is chosen at random and not replaced. A second marble is chosen at random. To the nearest whole percent, what is the probability that *neither* marble is green? **(Lesson 9-7)**

- (A) 19%
- (B) 20%
- (C) 89%
- (D) 90%

14. If a fair coin is tossed 5 times, what is the probability of the coin showing "tails" all 5 times? **(Lesson 9-7)**

  Ⓐ $\frac{2}{5}$

  Ⓑ $\frac{1}{5}$

  Ⓒ $\frac{1}{16}$

  Ⓓ $\frac{1}{32}$

15. Rachel is playing a game that involves rolling two standard number cubes. She needs to roll two of the same number in order to win the game. In one roll of two number cubes, what is the probability that the faces on the number cubes will be the same? **(Lesson 9-7)**

  Ⓐ $\frac{1}{36}$

  Ⓑ $\frac{1}{12}$

  Ⓒ $\frac{1}{6}$

  Ⓓ $\frac{1}{3}$

16. The total area of a sheet of paper can be represented by $27x^3 + 64y^3$. Which factors could represent the length times the width? **(Lesson 6-2)**

  Ⓐ $(3x + 4y)(3x^2 + 4y^2)$

  Ⓑ $(3x + 4y)(9x^2 - 12xy + 16y^2)$

  Ⓒ $(3x - 4y)(9x^2 - 12xy + 16y^2)$

  Ⓓ $(3x + 4y)(3x^2 - 3xy + 4y^2)$

17. What is the area of the parallelogram below? **(Lesson 9-4)**

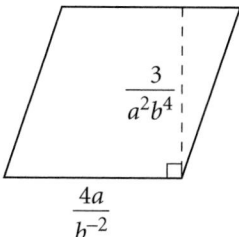

  Ⓐ $\frac{12}{ab^2}$

  Ⓑ $\frac{3}{ab^2}$

  Ⓒ $\frac{12b^2}{a}$

  Ⓓ $\frac{3b^6}{4a^3}$

18. What is $\frac{4x^2 - 1}{2x^2 - 5x - 3} \cdot \frac{x^2 - 6x + 9}{2x^2 + 5x - 3}$? **(Lesson 9-4)**

  Ⓐ 1 Ⓒ $x - 3$

  Ⓑ $x + 3$ Ⓓ $\frac{x - 3}{x + 3}$

19. Which is the factored form of $0.81p^2 - 0.09$? **(Lesson 5-4)**

  Ⓐ $(0.9p + 0.045)(0.9p - 0.045)$

  Ⓑ $(0.9p + 0.3)(0.9p - 0.3)$

  Ⓒ $(0.9p + 0.03)(0.9p - 0.03)$

  Ⓓ $(0.9p + 0.81)(0.9p - 0.81)$

20. Which arithmetic sequence does NOT include the term 33? **(Lesson 11-2)**

  Ⓐ $1, 5, 9, 13, \ldots$

  Ⓑ $3, 9, 15, \ldots$

  Ⓒ $1, 11, 21, \ldots$

  Ⓓ $85, 72, 59, \ldots$

Standards Reference Guide

California Content Standard	Item Number(s)
ALG2 8.0	1–3
ALG2 24.0	4–5
ALG2 7.0	6, 17–18
ALG2 22.0	7–10, 20
ALG2 14.0	11–12
PS 1.0	13–15
ALG2 4.0	16, 19

For additional review and practice, see the *California Standards Review and Practice Workbook* or go online to use the

California Standards Tutorials

Visit: PHSchool.com, **Web Code:** bbq-9045

CHAPTER 12

Probability and Statistics

 ## What You've Learned

California Content Standards

1.0 Students know the definition of the notion of *independent events* and can use the rules of addition, multiplication, and complementation to solve for probabilities of particular events in finite sample spaces. **Probability and Statistics**

18.0 Students use fundamental counting principles to compute combinations and permutations.

19.0 Students use combinations and permutations to compute probabilities.

✓ Check Your Readiness

GO for Help to the Lesson in green.

Evaluating Expressions (Lesson 6-7)

Evaluate each expression.

1. $5!$
2. $6!$
3. $4! \cdot 3!$
4. $_5C_5$
5. $_6C_1$
6. $_7C_4$

Expanding Binomials (Lesson 6-8)

Use Pascal's Triangle or the Binomial Theorem to expand each binomial.

7. $(a + b)^5$
8. $(j + 3k)^3$
9. $(m + 0.7)^2$
10. $(0.2 + t)^6$

Finding Real Roots (Lesson 7-1)

Find the real square roots of each number. Round to the nearest thousandth.

11. $\frac{1}{100}$
12. $\frac{1}{200}$
13. $\frac{1}{250}$
14. $\frac{1}{391}$
15. $\frac{1}{435}$
16. $\frac{1}{757}$

Finding Probability (Lesson 9-7)

A and B are independent events. Find $P(A \text{ and } B)$.

17. $P(A) = 0.4, P(B) = 0.2$
18. $P(A) = 0.25, P(B) = 0.5$
19. $P(A) = 0.85, P(B) = 0.10$

20. Find $P(A \text{ or } B)$ for the events in Exercise 19.

21. Data Analysis While processing a day's worth of new checkbook orders, a data entry operator notices that thirty percent of customers prefer the leather checkbook cover to the vinyl checkbook cover. Twenty percent prefer script lettering on their checks to any other kind of lettering. Find the probability that an order selected at random is for a leather checkbook cover with script lettering on the checks.

What You'll Learn Next

▲ The probability of a high-speed train arriving on time is not necessarily greater than that of a regular train.

California Content Standards

2.0 Students know the definition of *conditional probability* and use it to solve for probabilities in finite sample spaces. ***Probability and Statistics***

6.0 Students know the definitions of the *mean, median,* and *mode* of a distribution of data. ***Probability and Statistics***

7.0 Students compute the variance and the standard deviation of a distribution of data. ***Probability and Statistics***

New Vocabulary

◀)) **English and Spanish Audio Online**

- **binomial probability** (p. 699)
- **box-and-whisker plot** (p. 674)
- **conditional probability** (p. 666)
- **cumulative probability** (p. 660)
- **interquartile range** (p. 681)
- **margin of error** (p. 691)
- **measures of central tendency** (p. 672)
- **measures of variation** (p. 681)
- **normal distribution** (p. 704)
- **outlier** (p. 676)
- **percentile** (p. 675)
- **probability distribution** (p. 661)
- **quartiles** (p. 674)
- **sample** (p. 689)
- **sample proportion** (p. 689)
- **standard deviation** (p. 681)
- **standard normal curve** (p. 705)
- **z-score** (p. 683)

Probability Distributions

 California Content Standards

PS 8.0 Students organize and describe distributions of data by using a number of different methods, including frequency tables, histograms, and bar graphs.

What You'll Learn

• To make a probability distribution

• To use a probability distribution in conducting a simulation

. . . And Why

To conduct market research, as in Example 5

✓ **Check Skills You'll Need**

 for Help Lesson 1-6

Suppose you roll a standard number cube. State whether each set represents a sample space for the outcomes.

1. $\{1, 2, 3, 4, 5, 6\}$ **2.** $\{$less than $3, 4, 5, 6\}$ **3.** $\{$even, prime$\}$

Find each probability for two tosses of a number cube.

4. $P(4 \text{ and } 3)$ **5.** $P(\text{two odd numbers})$ **6.** $P(\text{two integers})$

◄)) **New Vocabulary** • frequency table • cumulative probability • probability distribution

---

1 Making a Probability Distribution

A **frequency table** is a list of the outcomes in a sample space and the number of times each outcome occurs.

1 EXAMPLE   Making a Frequency Table

Vocabulary Tip

Scalene comes from the Latin word for uneven.

Below are three types of triangles: equilateral, isosceles, and scalene. Make a frequency table. For isosceles, use triangles with exactly two congruent sides.

Step 1 Count the number of each type.

Equilateral	卌 I
Isosceles	卌 卌 I
Scalene	卌 III
Total number of triangles: 25	

Step 2 Make a table.

Type	Number
Equilateral	6
Isosceles	11
Scalene	8
Total	25

✓ **CA Standards Check** ❶ The triangles in Example 1 can also be described as acute, right, and obtuse. Make a frequency table using those categories.

Probability over a continuous range of events is **cumulative probability.** You can use a frequency table to find cumulative probability.

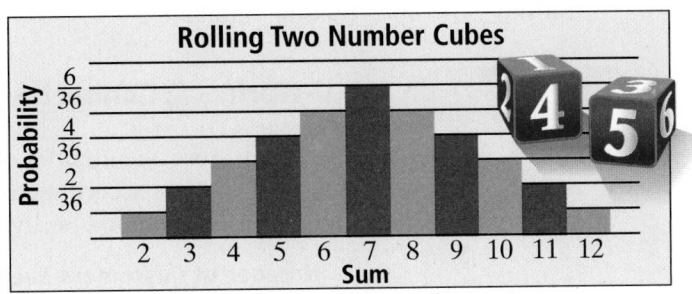
Vocabulary Tip

The <u>experimental probability</u> of an event is the ratio of the number of times the event occurs to the number of trials.

Social Science Use the frequency table. Find the probability that an elderly person living alone will have contact with his or her children more than once a week.

Contact Between Children and Elderly Who Live Alone

How Often Contact Is Made	Number of Elderly
7 times per week	680
2–6 times per week	276
1 time per week	236
Less than 1 time per week	199
Total	1391

SOURCE: *Statistical Handbook on the American Family*

$P(\text{7 times per week}) = \frac{680}{1391}$ — Find the experimental probability for each event in the table that represents contact more than once a week.

$P(\text{2–6 times per week}) = \frac{276}{1391}$

$\frac{680}{1391} + \frac{276}{1391} = \frac{956}{1391} \approx 0.687$ — Add to find cumulative probability.

● The probability of contact more than once a week is about 0.687, or 68.7%.

✓ **CA Standards Check** ② Find $P(\text{once a week or more})$.

A **probability distribution** is a function that gives the probability of each event in a sample space. You can use a table or a graph to show a probability distribution.

3 EXAMPLE Probability Distributions

Suppose you roll two number cubes. Show the probability distribution for the sum of the numbers.

Method 1 Make a frequency table. Then extend the table to include probabilities.

Rolling Two Number Cubes

Sum	2	3	4	5	6	7	8	9	10	11	12
Frequency	1	2	3	4	5	6	5	4	3	2	1
Probability	$\frac{1}{36}$	$\frac{2}{36}$	$\frac{3}{36}$	$\frac{4}{36}$	$\frac{5}{36}$	$\frac{6}{36}$	$\frac{5}{36}$	$\frac{4}{36}$	$\frac{3}{36}$	$\frac{2}{36}$	$\frac{1}{36}$

← There are 36 possible outcomes.
← Divide to find the probability.

Method 2 Draw a graph.

Rolling Two Number Cubes

✓ **CA Standards Check** ③ Use a table or a graph to show the probability distribution for the roll of one number cube.

A situation may be described by more than one sample space. In that case, each sample space has its own probability distribution.

4 EXAMPLE Real-World Connection

Genetics Use the information in the chart of inherited gene pairs. Graph the probability distribution for each sample space.

Inherited Gene Pairs From Two Hybrid Corn Plants

		Parent Plant	
		G	**w**
Parent Plant	**G**	GG	Gw
	w	Gw	ww

GG = dominant gene pair (green plant)
Gw = hybrid gene pair (green plant)
ww = recessive gene pair (white plant)

a. Genotype Distribution
{GG, Gw, ww}

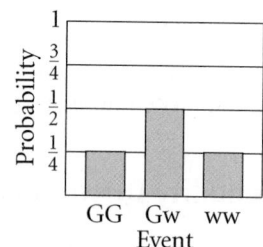

b. Plant Color Distribution
{green, white}

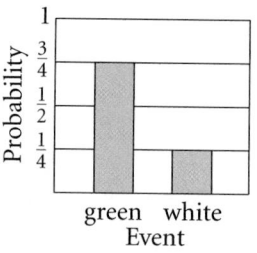

✓ **CA Standards Check** **4 a. Critical Thinking** Which probability distribution would be more useful to a farmer who wants to avoid raising white corn plants? Explain.

b. Make a probability distribution table for each sample space in Example 4.

2 Using a Probability Distribution

You can design a simulation based on a probability distribution. First, use the probabilities to assign numbers to each event in the sample space. For example, if $P(\text{event}) = 0.15$, assign 15 out of 100 numbers to that event. Then you can conduct trials by generating random numbers.

5 EXAMPLE Real-World Connection

Market Research At a certain store, the number of customers c who arrive at the checkout counters each minute varies according to the distribution below. Simulate the number of customers over a ten-minute period.

Number of Customers Each Minute

c	0	1	2	3	4	5	6
P(c)	0.15	0.24	0.28	0.17	0.09	0.05	0.02

Step 1 Define how the simulation will be done. Use random numbers. Assign numbers from 1 to 100 to the events, based on the probability of each event. Use cumulative probabilities to help you assign the numbers.

Graphing Calculator Hint

Use the command int(100*rand) + 1 to generate random numbers from 1 to 100. Press MATH and use the int option under the NUM menu and the rand option under the PRB menu.

Event	Probability	Cumulative Probability	Assigned Numbers
0	0.15	0.15	01–15
1	0.24	0.39	16–39
2	0.28	0.67	40–67
3	0.17	0.84	68–84
4	0.09	0.93	85–93
5	0.05	0.98	94–98
6	0.02	1.00	99–100

Since $P(0) = 0.15$, assign 15 numbers to this outcome.

There are 17 numbers from 68 to 84.

Step 2 Conduct the simulation. Model a ten-minute period by generating ten random numbers from 1 to 100.

Minute →	1st	2nd	3rd	4th	5th	6th	7th	8th	9th	10th
Random numbers →	81	29	83	93	18	9	40	97	47	16
Number of customers →	3	1	3	4	1	0	2	5	2	1

The random number 9 is assigned to the outcome 0 customers.

Step 3 Interpret the simulation. Based on this simulation, a total of 22 customers would arrive at checkout counters over a ten-minute period.

✓ CA Standards Check **5** Conduct a simulation for Example 5 over a 20-minute period.

EXERCISES
Standards Practice
PS 8.0

For more exercises, see *Extra Skill and Word Problem Practice*.

A Practice by Example

Example 1
(page 660)

GO for Help

In the game Rock-Paper-Scissors, the scissors cut the paper, the rock dulls the scissors, and the paper covers the rock. Use the results below for Exercises 1 and 2.

Rock-Paper-Scissors

Player 1	R	S	P	P	S	R	S	S	R	P	S	S	R	S	P	P	R	S
Player 2	S	P	R	S	P	P	R	S	R	S	R	R	P	P	R	S	S	S

R = Rock   P = Paper   S = Scissors   **Bold** = Winner

1. Make a frequency table for the objects played: rock, paper, or scissors.

2. Make a frequency table for the winning players: Player 1, Player 2, or tie.

Example 2
(page 661)

The table shows the frequency of responses to editorials. Find each probability.

Number of Responses	0	1	2	3	4	5	6 or more	Total
Number of Editorials	20	30	56	38	34	16	6	200

3. $P(5 \text{ or more responses})$ **4.** $P(\text{at most 4 responses})$ **5.** $P(0-2 \text{ responses})$

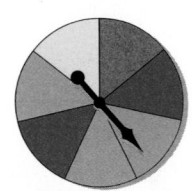

Example 3
(page 661)

6. Use a table and a graph to show the probability distribution for the spinner {red, green, blue, yellow}.

7. Use a table and a graph to show the probability distribution for the number of days {28, 29, 30, 31} in each of 48 consecutive months.

Example 4
(page 662)

Suppose you roll two number cubes. Graph the probability distribution for each sample space.

8. {sum of numbers even, sum of numbers odd}

9. {both numbers even, both numbers odd, one number even and the other odd}

Example 5
(pages 662–663)

10. Design and conduct a simulation to determine the ages of 20 licensed drivers chosen at random in the United States.

Licensed Drivers in the United States, by Age

a	< 20	20–29	30–39	40–49	50–59	60–69	70–79	≥80
P(a)	0.048	0.175	0.199	0.211	0.167	0.102	0.066	0.032

SOURCE: U.S. Department of Transportation. Go to **www.PHSchool.com** for a data update.
Web Code: bbg-9041

11. Design and conduct a simulation to determine the size and type of 30 cars purchased from U.S. car dealerships.

U.S. Car Sales by Vehicle Size and Type

t	Luxury	Large	Midsize	Small
P(t)	0.165	0.076	0.527	0.232

SOURCE: Ward's Communications

B **Apply Your Skills**

Graph the probability distribution described by each function.

12. $P(x) = \frac{x}{10}$ for $x = 1, 2, 3$, and 4

13. $P(x) = \frac{2x + 1}{15}$ for $x = 1, 2$, and 3

14. Weather Refer to the table at the left.
 a. Make a table showing the probability distribution for weather in Dayton.
 b. Define the independent and dependent variables.
 c. Find the probability that a day in Dayton will include rain or snow.

15. Data Collection Find weather data for a city near you. Draw a graph to show the probability distribution of weather conditions.

16. a. Transportation Sometimes a probability distribution is shown as a circle graph. Define the independent and dependent variables in the distribution at the right.
 b. Draw the distribution as a bar graph.
 c. Find P(the tank is at least half full when a driver buys gas).

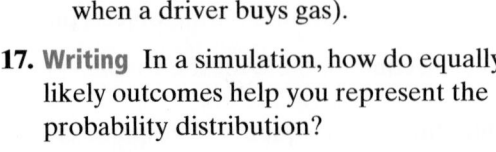

17. Writing In a simulation, how do equally likely outcomes help you represent the probability distribution?

18. Odds The odds in favor of an event equal the ratio of the number of times the event occurs to the number of times the event does not occur. The odds in favor of event A are 1 : 4. The odds in favor of event B are 2 : 3. The odds in favor of event C are 1 : 3. The odds in favor of event D are 3 : 17. Graph the probability distribution of events A, B, C, and D.

Weather Conditions in Dayton, Ohio

Type of Weather	Days Per Year
Clear	82
Partly Cloudy	118
Mostly Cloudy	34
Rain	75
Light Snow (< 1.5 in.)	45
Snow (≥1.5 in.)	11
Total	365

SOURCE: The USA Today Weather Almanac

Homework Video Tutor

Visit: PHSchool.com
Web Code: bbe-1201

Real-World 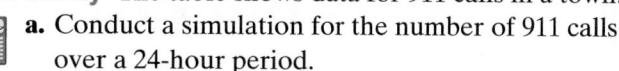 **Connection**

The highest volume of calls for most 911 services occur during late afternoon and early evening hours.

19. Safety The table shows data for 911 calls in a town.
   a. Conduct a simulation for the number of 911 calls over a 24-hour period.
   b. If there are two response teams available, and each response takes about an hour, how many callers in your simulation have to wait?
   c. Find P(caller will have to wait).
   d. Critical Thinking Use your simulation to determine whether additional response teams are needed for this town. Explain your reasoning.

20. Marketing A company includes instant-win tickets with 10,000,000 of its products. Of the prizes offered, one is a large cash prize, 1,600,000 are small cash prizes, and the other prizes are free samples of the company's products.
   a. Find the theoretical probability of winning each type of prize.
   b. Design and conduct a simulation to determine the prizes for 100 products.
   c. Find the experimental probability for winning each type of prize.

Probability Distribution for Number of 911 Calls Each Hour

c	P(c)
0	0.21
1	0.30
2	0.18
3	0.13
4	0.09
5	0.05
6	0.03
7	0.01

Multiple Choice Practice

For California Standards and CAHSEE Tutorials, visit PHSchool.com. Web Code: bbq-9045

PS 8.0   **21.** The table shows the number of cities in a region of the U.S. that are served by the given number of airlines. What is the probability that a city chosen at random is served by exactly 4 airlines?

A. $\frac{1}{18}$

B. $\frac{4}{21}$

C. $\frac{2}{11}$

D. $\frac{2}{9}$

Number of Airlines	Number of Cities
1	27
2	14
3	15
4	18
5	14
6	11

PS 1.0   **22.** A and B are independent but not mutually exclusive events. If $P(A) = \frac{1}{4}$ and $P(B) = \frac{1}{5}$, what is $P(A \text{ or } B)$?

A. $\frac{1}{20}$ B. $\frac{1}{9}$ C. $\frac{2}{9}$ D. $\frac{2}{5}$

Mixed Review

 for Help

Lesson 11-6 **Find the area under each curve for the domain $0 \le x \le 1$.**

23. $y = 3$ **24.** $y = 4x + 2$ **25.** $y = 4x^3 + 1$

Lesson 10-6 **Sketch the graph of each equation.**

26. $x^2 - 4y^2 + 2x + 24y = 51$ **27.** $20y^2 - 40y - x = -25$

Lesson 9-7 **Classify each pair of events as *dependent* or *independent*.**

28. Choose one item from a buffet. Then choose a different item from the buffet.

29. Choose a size for your drink. Then select a flavor.

Conditional Probability

 California Content Standards

PS 2.0 Students know the definition of *conditional probability* and use it to solve for probabilities in finite sample spaces.

What You'll Learn

- To find conditional probabilities
- To use formulas and tree diagrams

. . . And Why

To find the probability of school closings after snowfall, as in Example 4

 Check Skills You'll Need

GO for Help Lesson 9-7

A spinner has four equal sections that are red, blue, green, and yellow. Find each probability for two spins.

1. *P*(blue, then blue)
2. *P*(red, then yellow)
3. *P*(not yellow, then green)
4. *P*(not blue, then not red)
5. *P*(at least one green)
6. *P*(neither spin red)

New Vocabulary • conditional probability

---

1 Finding Conditional Probabilities

A **conditional probability** contains a condition that may limit the sample space for an event. You can write a conditional probability using the notation $P(B \mid A)$, read "the probability of event B, given event A."

1 EXAMPLE Finding Conditional Probability

The table shows the results of a class survey. Find P(did a chore | male).

The condition *male* limits the sample space to 15 possible outcomes. Of the 15 males, 7 did a chore. Therefore, P(did a chore | male) equals $\frac{7}{15}$.

Did you do a household chore last night?

	Yes	No	
Male	7	8	← 15 males
Female	7	6	← 13 females

CA Standards Check ❶ Use the data in Example 1 to find P(female | did a chore).

2 EXAMPLE Real-World Connection

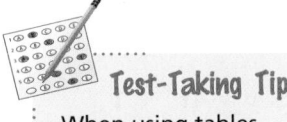 **Test-Taking Tip**

When using tables, mark on the table to help you keep track of the data you need.

Multiple Choice Americans recycle increasingly more materials through municipal waste collection each year. The table shows recycling data for a recent year. Find the probability that a sample of recycled waste was paper.

- Ⓐ 16 %
- Ⓑ 28%
- Ⓒ 36%
- Ⓓ 54%

Municipal Waste Collected (millions of tons)

Material	Recycled	Not Recycled
Paper	36.7	45.1
Metal	6.3	11.9
Glass	2.4	10.1
Plastic	1.4	24.0
Other	21.2	70.1

SOURCE: U.S. Environmental Protection Agency.
Go to **www.PHSchool.com** for a data update.
Web Code: bbg-9041

The given condition limits the sample space to *recycled* waste. A favorable outcome is recycled paper.

$$P(\text{paper} \mid \text{recycled}) = \frac{36.7}{36.7 + 6.3 + 2.4 + 1.4 + 21.2}$$
$$\approx 0.54$$

The probability that the recycled waste was paper is about 54%. The correct choice is D.

 CA Standards Check **2** Find the probability that a sample of recycled waste was plastic.

---

2 Using Formulas and Tree Diagrams

You can use a formula to find conditional probability.

🔑 **Key Concepts**

Property	**Conditional Probability Formula**

For any two events A and B from a sample space with $P(A) \neq 0$,

$$P(B \mid A) = \frac{P(A \text{ and } B)}{P(A)}$$

Using the formula, you can calculate a conditional probability from other probabilities.

3 EXAMPLE **Real-World 🌐 Connection**

Market Research Researchers asked shampoo users whether they apply shampoo directly to the head, or indirectly using a hand. Find the probability that a respondent applies shampoo directly to the head, given that the respondent is female.

Applying Shampoo

	Directly Onto Head	Into Hand First
Male	2	18
Female	6	24

Relate $P(\text{female}) = \frac{30}{50}$

$P(\text{female } and \text{ applies directly to head}) = \frac{6}{50}$

Define Let A = female.

Let B = applies directly to head.

Write $P(B \mid A) = \dfrac{P(A \text{ and } B)}{P(A)}$

$= \dfrac{\frac{6}{50}}{\frac{30}{50}}$ **Substitute.**

$= \dfrac{6}{30} = \dfrac{1}{5}$ **Simplify.**

The probability that a respondent applies shampoo directly to the head, given that the respondent is female, is $\frac{1}{5}$, or 20%.

 CA Standards Check **3** Eighty percent of an airline's flights depart on schedule. Seventy-two percent of its flights depart and arrive on schedule. Find the probability that a flight that departs on time also arrives on time.

You can use tree diagrams to solve problems involving conditional probabilities.

4 EXAMPLE Making a Tree Diagram

A student in Buffalo, New York, made the observations below.

- Of all snowfalls, 5% are heavy (at least 6 in.).
- After a heavy snowfall, schools are closed 67% of the time.
- After a light (less than 6 in.) snowfall, schools are closed 3% of the time.

Find the probability that the snowfall is light and the schools are open.

Make a tree diagram. Use H for heavy snowfall, L for light snowfall, C for schools closed, and O for schools open. Find $P(L$ and $O)$.

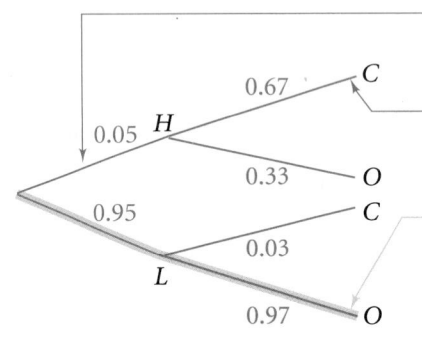

Each first branch represents a simple probability. $P(H) = 0.05$

Each second branch represents a conditional probability. $P(C|H) = 0.67$

The highlighted path represents $P(L$ and $O)$.
$$P(L \text{ and } O) = P(L) \cdot P(O|L)$$
$$= 0.95 \cdot 0.97$$
$$= 0.9215$$

The probability that the snowfall is light and the schools are open is about 92%.

 CA Standards Check 4 Find P(schools open, given heavy snow).

Real-World Connection

During some winters, Buffalo gets more than 100 inches of snow.

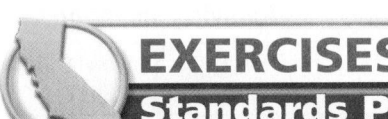 **EXERCISES**

For more exercises, see *Extra Skill and Word Problem Practice*.

Standards Practice
PS 2.0

A Practice by Example

Example 1
(page 666)

 GO for Help

Use the table to find each probability.

1. P(has diploma)

2. P(has diploma and experience)

3. P(has experience | has diploma)

4. P(has no diploma | has experience)

Characteristics of Job Applicants

		Has Experience	
		Yes	No
Has High School Diploma	**Yes**	54	27
	No	5	4

Example 2
(pages 666–667)

Use the table below to find each probability.

5. P(The recipient is male.)

6. P(The degree is a bachelor's.)

7. P(The recipient is female, given that the degree is advanced.)

8. P(The degree is *not* an associate's, given that the recipient is male.)

Projected Number of Degree Recipients in 2010 (thousands)

Degree	Male	Female
Associate's	245	433
Bachelor's	598	858
Advanced	293	376

Source: U.S. National Center for Education Statistics

Example 3
(page 667)

Use the survey results below for Exercises 9 and 10.

9. Find the probability that a respondent has a pet, given that the respondent has had a pet.

10. Find the probability that a respondent has never had a pet, given that the respondent does not have a pet now.

> 39% have a pet now and have had a pet.
>
> 61% do not have a pet now.
>
> 86% have had a pet.
>
> 14% do not have a pet now and have never had a pet.

Example 4
(page 668)

11. Make a tree diagram based on the survey results below . Then find P(a female respondent is left-handed) and P(a respondent is both male and right-handed).
   • Of all the respondents, 17% are male.
   • Of the male respondents, 33% are left-handed.
   • Of female respondents, 90% are right-handed.

12. A football team has a 70% chance of winning when it doesn't snow, but only a 40% chance of winning when it snows. Suppose there is a 50% chance of snow. Make a tree diagram to find the probability that the team will win.

B **Apply Your Skills**

13. Suppose A and B are independent events, with $P(A) = 0.60$ and $P(B) = 0.25$. Find each probability.
   a. $P(A$ and $B)$
   b. $P(A \mid B)$
   c. What do you notice about $P(A)$ and $P(A \mid B)$?
   d. Critical Thinking One way to describe A and B as independent events is *The occurrence of B has no effect on the probability of A.* Explain how the answer to part (c) illustrates this relationship.

Surveys **Conduct a survey in your class. Then find each probability.**

14. P(left-handed | left shoe)

15. P(left-handed | not the right shoe)

16. P(left shoe | right-handed)

17. P(first shoe picked up | right-handed)

18. P(don't know)

Which Shoe Do You Put on First?		Dominant Hand	
		Right	**Left**
First Shoe Put On	Right	▪	▪
	Left	▪	▪
	First One Grabbed	▪	▪
	Don't Know	▪	▪

Homework Video Tutor

Visit: PHSchool.com
Web Code: bbe-1202

Weather **Use probability notation to describe the chance of each event. Let S, C, W, and R represent sunny, cloudy, windy, and rainy weather, respectively.**

19. cloudy weather

20. sunny and windy weather

21. rainy weather if it is windy

22. windy weather if it is sunny

C **Challenge** ✎ 23. **a. Writing** Explain which branches of the tree diagram at the right represent conditional probabilities. Give a specific example.
   b. Are the event of having a license and the event of being an adult independent events? Justify your answer.
   c. Open-Ended Estimate probabilities for each branch of the tree diagram for your city or town. Then find $P(L)$.

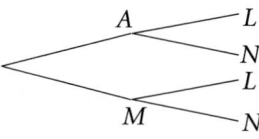

A = adult (21 or older)
M = minor (under 21)
L = licensed driver
N = not licensed to drive

24. Critical Thinking Sixty percent of a company's sales representatives have completed training seminars. Of these, 80% have had increased sales. Overall, 56% of the representatives (whether trained or not) have had increased sales. Use a tree diagram to find the probability of increased sales, given that a representative has not been trained.

Multiple Choice Practice

For California Standards and CAHSEE Tutorials, visit PHSchool.com. Web Code: bbq-9045

PS 2.0 **25.** In a library, the probability that a book is a hardback, given that it is illustrated, is 0.40. The probability that the book is hardback *and* illustrated is 0.20. What is the probability that a book in the library is illustrated?

    Ⓐ 0.20   Ⓑ 0.40   Ⓒ 0.50   Ⓓ 0.60

ALG2 16.0 **26.** Which parabola has focus $(3, 0)$ and directrix $x = -3$?

    Ⓐ $y = \frac{1}{12}x^2$ Ⓑ $x = \frac{1}{12}y^2$ Ⓒ $y = -\frac{1}{3}x^2$ Ⓓ $x = \frac{1}{3}y^2$

ALG2 10.0 **27.** Roland needs to solve the equation $x^2 = 5x + 6$ by graphing. Which method could he use to find the solution for x?

    Ⓐ Graph the parabola $y = x^2$ and the line $y = 5x + 6$ and find the y-coordinate of the intersection.

    Ⓑ Graph the parabola $y = x^2$ and the line $y = 5x + 6$ and find the difference of the two x-intercepts.

    Ⓒ Graph the parabola $y = x^2 - 5x - 6$ and find the y-intercept.

    Ⓓ Graph the parabola $y = x^2 - 5x - 6$ and find the x-intercepts.

ALG2 3.0 **28.** Which of the following expressions is equivalent to $3(n - 3)(n + 4)$?

    Ⓐ $3n^2 + 3n - 36$ Ⓒ $3n^2 - 3n - 36$

    Ⓑ $3n^2 - 3n + 36$ Ⓓ $3n^2 - 36$

Mixed Review

Lesson 12-1 **29.** Consider a February that is not in a leap year. Graph the probability distribution for the sample space {weekdays, weekend days}.

Lesson 11-1 **30. Construction** An earthmover purchased for $600,000 loses 18% of its value each year. What is the value of the earthmover after one year? After three years?

Lesson 10-1 **31.** Identify the center and intercepts of the conic section at the right. Then find the domain and range.

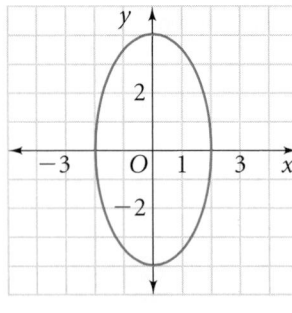

Lesson 8-5 **Solve each equation. If necessary, round to the nearest thousandth.**

32. $2^x = 4$ **33.** $4^{2x} = 10$ **34.** $4^{x+1} = 28$

35. $7 - 3^x = -38$ **36.** $\log x = -1$

37. $2 \log x = 1$ **38.** $\log (2x + 2) = 2$

You can use a tree diagram like the one at
the right to find the conditional probability
$P(P \mid D)$, which is the probability that a
person with a disease will test positive for it.
In this case, $P(P \mid D) = 0.99$.

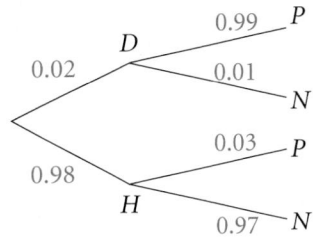

D = person has the disease
H = person is healthy
P = person tests positive
N = person tests negative

Scientists also look at $P(H \mid P)$, the
probability of a "false positive," which is the
probability that a person who tests positive is
actually healthy. Since this probability is not
found on a branch in the diagram, you must use the formula for conditional probability.

1 EXAMPLE

Use the tree diagram above to find $P(H \mid P)$.

Since $P(H \mid P) = \dfrac{P(H \text{ and } P)}{P(P)}$, find $P(H \text{ and } P)$ and $P(P)$.

$$P(H \text{ and } P) = 0.98 \cdot 0.03 \qquad P(P) = P(D \text{ and } P) \text{ or } P(H \text{ and } P)$$
$$= 0.0294 \qquad\qquad = 0.02 \cdot 0.99 + 0.98 \cdot 0.03 = 0.0492$$

So $P(H \mid P) = \dfrac{P(H \text{ and } P)}{P(P)}$

$\qquad = \dfrac{0.0294}{0.0492}$ **Substitute.**

$\qquad \approx 0.598$ **Simplify.**

About 60% of the people who test positive do not actually have the disease.

EXERCISES

Use the tree diagram in the Example to find each probability.

1. $P(N)$ **2.** $P(H \text{ and } N)$ **3.** $P(H \mid N)$ **4.** $P(D \mid N)$

5. Transportation You can take Bus 65 or Bus 79 to get to work. You take the
first bus that arrives. The probability that Bus 65 arrives first is 75%. There is a
40% chance that Bus 65 picks up passengers along the way. There is a 60%
chance that Bus 79 picks up passengers. Your bus picked up passengers. What is
the probability that it was Bus 65?

**The tree diagram relates snowfall and
school closings. Find each probability.**

6. $P(C)$ **7.** $P(H \text{ and } O)$

8. $P(H \mid C)$ **9.** $P(L \mid O)$

10. $P(L \mid C)$ **11.** $P(H \mid O)$

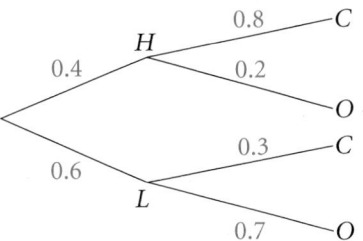

H = heavy snowfall
L = light snowfall
C = schools closed
O = schools open

12. Writing Explain the difference in
meaning between $P(P \mid D)$ and $P(D \mid P)$ for the test in the Example. Compare
the values of $P(P \mid D)$ and $P(D \mid P)$. What is the best use for this test? Explain.

Analyzing Data

 California Content Standards

PS 6.0 Students know the definitions of the *mean*, *median*, and *mode* of a distribution of data and can compute each in particular situations.
PS 8.0 Students organize and describe distributions of data by using a number of different methods, including histograms and box-and-whisker plots.

What You'll Learn

- To calculate measures of central tendency
- To draw and interpret box-and-whisker plots

. . . And Why

To analyze a set of water temperatures, as in Example 2

 Check Skills You'll Need

GO for Help Lesson 1-1

Order each set of values from least to greatest. Then find the middle value.

1. 0.2 0.3 0.6 1.2 0.7 0.9 0.8

2. 11 23 15 17 21 18 21

3. 7.8 2.6 3.9 15.6 9.1 11.7 10.4

4. 76 89 80 82 86 84 86

New Vocabulary • measures of central tendency • mean • median • mode • bimodal • quartiles • box-and-whisker plot • percentiles • outlier

---

1 Measures of Central Tendency

Statistics is the study of data analysis and interpretation. The mean, the median, and the mode are single, central values that help describe a set of data. They are called **measures of central tendency.**

 Key Concepts

Definition	**Measures of Central Tendency**	
Measure	**Definition**	**Example, using {1, 2, 2, 3, 5, 5}**
Mean	$\dfrac{\text{sum of the data values}}{\text{number of data values}}$	$\dfrac{1 + 2 + 2 + 3 + 5 + 5}{6} = \dfrac{18}{6} = 3$
Median	middle value *or* mean of the two middle values	$\dfrac{2 + 3}{2} = 2.5$
Mode	most frequently occurring value	2 and 5

A **bimodal** data set has two modes. If a data set has more than two modes, then the modes are probably not statistically useful. If no value occurs more frequently than any other, then there is no mode.

1 EXAMPLE Finding Measures of Central Tendency

Vocabulary Tip

Read $\bar{x}$ as "the mean of x" or "x bar."

Find the mean, median, and mode for these values: 98, 95, 99, 97, 89, 92, 97, 62, 90.

$$\bar{x} = \frac{98 + 95 + 99 + 97 + 89 + 92 + 97 + 62 + 90}{9} = \frac{819}{9} = 91$$

Use the symbol $\bar{x}$ to designate the mean.

$$62 \quad 89 \quad 90 \quad 92 \quad \underset{\uparrow}{95} \quad \underset{\uparrow}{97} \quad \underset{\uparrow}{97} \quad 98 \quad 99$$
$$\qquad\qquad\qquad \text{Median} \qquad \text{Mode}$$

Find the median and the mode by ordering the values numerically.

The mean is 91, the median is 95, and the mode is 97.

CA Standards Check ① Find the mean, median, and mode for these values: 2.4, 4.3, 3.7, 3.9, 2.8, 5.4, 2.8.

You can use a graphing calculator to find the measures of central tendency.

2 EXAMPLE Real-World Connection

Oceanography Find the mean, the median, and the mode of all the water temperatures listed for the eastern coast of the Gulf of Mexico.

Gulf of Mexico Eastern Coast Water Temperatures (°F)

Location	J	F	M	A	M	J	J	A	S	O	N	D
Pensacola, Florida	56	58	63	71	78	84	85	86	82	74	65	58
St. Petersburg, Florida	62	64	68	74	80	84	86	86	84	78	70	64
Key West, Florida	69	70	75	78	82	85	87	87	86	82	76	72
Dauphin Island, Alabama	51	53	60	70	75	82	84	84	80	72	62	56
Grand Isle, Louisiana	61	61	64	70	77	83	85	85	83	77	70	65

Step 1 Use the STAT feature to enter the data as L1 in your graphing calculator.

Step 2 Use the LIST feature to access the MATH menu. Find the mean.

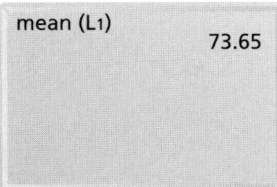

Step 3 Return to the same menu to find the median.

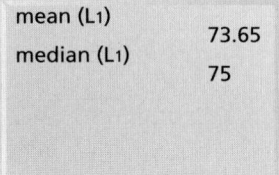

Step 4 Use the STAT PLOT feature to access **Plot 1**. Choose the histogram, L1, and Frequency 1 options. Then enter an appropriate viewing window.

Step 5 Graph the data. Use the TRACE feature to move the cursor to the highest points of the graph.

On the screen, the mode appears as the minimum value for the cursor. The modes are 70 and 84.

The modes both occur five times in the data.

● The mean is 73.65°F, the median is 75°F, and the modes are 70°F and 84°F.

✓ CA Standards Check ② Find the mean, median, and mode for the water temperatures in Grand Isle, Louisiana.

If you arrange data in increasing order, then the median divides the data set into two equal parts. You can use the median of each of the parts to divide the set further, into four equal parts. The values separating the four parts are called **quartiles.** Quartiles are shown below for the 12 water temperatures from Pensacola in Example 2.

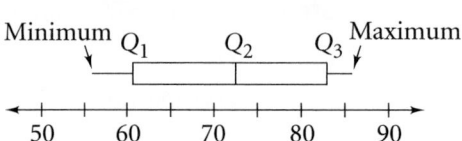

Median of lower part (Q_1) = 60.5   Median of upper part (Q_3) = 83

56   58   58   63   65   71   74   78   82   84   85   86

Median of data set (Q_2) = 72.5

Vocabulary Tip

Quartiles are sometimes called "hinges."

The values Q_1, Q_2, and Q_3 are the first, second, and third quartiles. A **box-and-whisker plot** is a method of displaying data that uses quartiles to form the center box and the minimum and maximum values to form the whiskers.

Minimum Q_1 Q_2 Q_3 Maximum

50   60   70   80   90

3 **EXAMPLE**   **Making a Box-and-Whisker Plot**

Make a box-and-whisker plot for these values: 84, 79, 90, 73, 95, 88, 92, 81, 67.

Step 1   Find the quartile values, the minimum value, and the maximum value.

67   73   79   81   84   88   90   92   95

Q_2 = median = 84

When the median is a value of the data set, it is removed for the calculation of Q_1 and Q_3.

67   73   79   81   88   90   92   95

$Q_1 = \dfrac{73 + 79}{2} = 76$ $Q_3 = \dfrac{90 + 92}{2} = 91$

The minimum value is 67, and the maximum value is 95.

Step 2   Draw a number line for the base of your box-and-whisker plot. Above the number line, plot the three quartiles, the minimum value, and the maximum value.

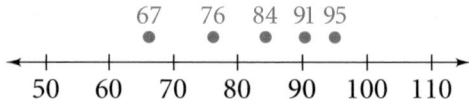

67   76   84   91 95

50   60   70   80   90   100   110

Step 3   Finish your box-and-whisker plot by drawing a box through Q_1 and Q_3, a vertical line through the median, and line segments from the box outward to the minimum and maximum values.

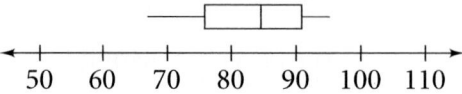

50   60   70   80   90   100   110

 CA Standards Check   **3** Make a box-and-whisker plot for these values: 34, 36, 47, 45, 28, 31, 29, 40.

4 **EXAMPLE** Real-World 🌐 Connection

Oceanography Use a graphing calculator to find the quartiles of the water temperature data in Example 2.

Use the **STAT PLOT** feature to select a box-and-whisker plot. Enter the window values. Graph the box-and-whisker plot.

● Use the **TRACE** feature to find the quartiles: $Q_1 = 64.5$, $Q_2 = 75$, and $Q_3 = 83.5$.

✓ **CA Standards Check** **④** Use the data for just the summer months, as shown in the graph below. Find the quartiles by graphing the box-and-whisker plot.

Let x be a value from a data set. A **percentile** is a number from 0 to 100 that you can associate with x to indicate the percent of the data that are less than or equal to x. If x is at the 63rd percentile, then 63% of the data are less than or equal to x.

5 **EXAMPLE** Using Percentiles

Find the values at the 20th and 65th percentiles for the values below.
54 98 45 87 98 64 21 61 71 82 93 65 62 98 87 24 65 97 31 47

Step 1 Order the values.
21 24 31 45 47 54 61 62 64 65 65 71 82 87 87 93 97 98 98 98

Step 2 Find the number of values that fall below the 20th percentile and the number that fall below the 65th percentile.

Of the 20 values, 20% should fall below the 20th percentile and 65% should fall below the 65th percentile.

$$20 \cdot 20\% = 20 \cdot 0.20 = 4 \qquad\qquad 20 \cdot 65\% = 20 \cdot 0.65 = 13$$

Since 47 is greater than 4 values, 47 is at the 20th percentile.

Since 87 is greater than 13 values, 87 is at the 65th percentile.

● The value at the 20th percentile is 47 and the value at the 65th percentile is 87.

✓ **CA Standards Check** **⑤** Find the value at each percentile for the data in Example 5.
  a. 0th percentile   **b.** 45th percentile   **c.** 55th percentile

An **outlier** is an item of data with a value substantially different from the rest of the items in the data set. Sometimes an outlier is an important part of the data. At other times it can represent a false reading. When you think an outlier has resulted from an error, you may remove it from the data set.

6 EXAMPLE **Identifying an Outlier**

Multiple Choice Which is an outlier for this set of values:
56 65 73 59 98 65 59?

Ⓐ 42   Ⓑ 65   Ⓒ 98   Ⓓ 59

| 56 | 59 | 59 | 65 | 65 | 73 | 98 | **Order the data.**

    3   0   6   0   8   25   **Find the differences between adjacent values.**

● 98 is substantially different, so 98 is an outlier. The correct choice is C.

✓ **CA Standards Check** **6 a.** Suppose the values in Example 6 are measurements of the water temperature of a lake. Would you discard the outlier? Explain.

b. Suppose the data represent the number of customers in a small restaurant each night during one week. Would you discard the outlier? Explain.

EXERCISES
Standards Practice
For more exercises, see *Extra Skill and Word Problem Practice.*

PS 6.0, 8.0

Ⓐ Practice by Example

Examples 1 and 2
(pages 672 and 673)

Find the mean, median, and mode of each set of values.

1. 5 9 4 2 7 3 4 8 8 4 3   **2.** 307 309 323 304 390 398

3. 475 722 499 572 402 809 499 828 405 499 800 422 672 800

Examples 3 and 4
(pages 674 and 675)

Make a box-and-whisker plot for each set of values.

4. 12 11 15 12 19 20 19   **5.** 120 145 133 105 117 150

6. 49 57.5 58 49.2 62 22.2 67 52.1 77 99.9 80 51.7 64

7. Weather The table shows the high temperatures for one day at different locations on the island of Maui, Hawaii. Make a box-and-whisker plot of the data.

High Temperatures on Maui

Location	Temperature
Kahului	88°F
Kihei	85°F
Lahaina	86°F
Hana	82°F
Haleakala	66°F
Kula	75°F

Example 5
(page 675)

Find the values at the 30th and 90th percentiles for each set of values.

8. 6283 5700 6381 6274 5700 5896 5972 6075 5993 5581

9. 7 12 3 14 17 20 5 3 17 4 13 2 15 9 15 18 16 9 1 6

Example 6
(page 676)

Identify the outlier of each set of values.

10. 3.4 4.5 2.3 5.9 9.8 3.3 2.1 3.0 2.9

11. 17 21 19 10 15 19 14 0 11 16

Dilbert

Apply Your Skills

12. a. What percent of the customers in the cartoon are exactly the median age?
   b. Must one item from a data set fall exactly at the median? Explain.
   c. Can the company do anything about the shocking discovery? Explain.

13. Meteorology On May 3, 1999, 59 tornadoes hit Oklahoma in the largest tornado outbreak ever recorded in the state. Sixteen of these were classified as strong (F2 or F3) or violent (F4 or F5).
   a. Make a box-and-whisker plot of the data for length of path.
   b. Identify the outliers. Remove them from the data set and make a revised box-and-whisker plot.
   c. Writing How does the removal of the outliers affect the box-and-whisker plot? How does it affect the median of the data set?

Identify the outlier of each set of values. Then describe how its value affects the mean of the data.

14. 947   757   103   619   661   582   626   900   869   728   1001   596   515

15. 87   104   381   215   174   199   233   186   142   228   9   53   117   129

For Exercises 16–18, use the set of values below.
1   1   1   1   1   1   2   3   5   8   13   21   34   55   89   89   89   89   89   89

16. At what percentile is 1?   **17.** At what percentile is 34?

18. Error Analysis A student claims that 89 is at the 100th percentile. Explain the student's error.

19. Geology The table below shows the number of major earthquakes (magnitude 7.0 or greater) worldwide in the ten-year period from 1991 through 2000.

Major Earthquakes Worldwide (Magnitude 7.0 and Greater)

Year	1991	1992	1993	1994	1995	1996	1997	1998	1999	2000
Earthquakes	11	23	16	15	25	22	20	16	23	18

SOURCE: U.S. Geological Survey National Earthquake Information Center

a. Find the mean and the median of the numbers of annual earthquakes.
b. Do the data include an outlier that you should discard? Explain.
c. Compare the box-and-whisker plots at the right. One shows the data above. The other shows worldwide earthquake data from 1900 through 2000. What conclusions can you draw about recent earthquakes? Justify your reasoning.

Xmin = 0   Ymin = 0
Xmax = 45   Ymax = 1
Xscl = 5   Yscl = 1

Major Tornadoes in Oklahoma, May 3, 1999

Length of Path (miles)	Intensity
6	F3
9	F3
4	F2
37	F5
7	F2
12	F3
8	F2
7	F2
15	F4
39	F4
1	F2
22	F3
15	F3
8	F2
13	F3
2	F2

SOURCE: National Oceanic & Atmospheric Administration

Homework Video Tutor

Visit: PHSchool.com
Web Code: bbe-1203

20. Critical Thinking Which measure better represents a data set with several outliers—the mean or the median? Justify your answer.

C Challenge

21. Track and Field The table shows the 36 best qualifying distances for the shot put events for both men and women during the 2004 Olympics.

2004 Olympic Qualifying Distances for Shot Put (meters)

Men	21.15	20.78	20.65	20.61	20.53	20.45	20.37	20.32	20.11
	20.06	20.06	20.04	19.69	19.68	19.67	19.60	19.55	19.50
	19.46	19.41	19.40	19.38	19.31	19.25	19.14	19.09	19.09
	19.07	19.04	19.02	19.02	18.91	18.89	18.67	18.52	18.44
Women	19.69	19.10	18.90	18.79	18.65	18.61	18.57	18.52	18.38
	18.33	18.16	18.03	18.00	17.99	17.89	17.78	17.44	17.34
	17.28	17.22	17.17	17.11	16.90	16.58	16.49	16.47	16.45
	16.35	15.99	15.91	15.86	15.33	15.20	15.06	14.88	14.60

Real-World Connection

The "shot" in shot put refers to cannonballs. For centuries, soldiers used them in throwing contests.

a. Using the same number line base for both plots, make a box-and-whisker plot for the men's results and another for the women's results.

 b. Writing Compare your box-and-whisker plots. Describe any conclusions you can draw about Olympic-level male and female shot-putters.

22. a. Government Make a box-and-whisker plot for the data from each of the three types of elections shown in the table below.

Voter Turnout (percent of voting-age population)

Presidential Year	1976	1980	1984	1988	1992	1996	2000
Voting for President	53.5	52.8	53.3	50.3	55.1	48.9	51.2
Voting for Representatives	48.9	47.6	47.8	44.9	50.8	45.7	47.2
Non-Presidential Year	1978	1982	1986	1990	1994	1998	2002
Voting for Representatives	34.9	38.0	33.5	33.1	36.6	32.7	34.2

SOURCE: U.S. Census Bureau. Go to **www.PHSchool.com** for a data update.
Web Code: bbg-9041

 b. Writing How does a Presidential election in the United States affect the voter turnout rate in elections for the House of Representatives? Use your box-and-whisker plots to describe any effect that you see.

Multiple Choice Practice

For California Standards and CAHSEE Tutorials, visit PHSchool.com. Web Code: bbq-9045

PS 6.0

23. A person checked her email four times each day. The table shows the number of new emails she received each time she checked during 5 days.

Day 1	Day 2	Day 3	Day 4	Day 5
6, 3, 1, 5	5, 3, 7, 2	6, 7, 3, 2	8, 2, 6, 9	7, 7, 6, 11

Which value is the greatest?

Ⓐ the mean number of emails for checks made on days 1–3

Ⓑ the mean number of emails for checks made on days 2–4

Ⓒ the mean number of emails for checks made on days 2–3

Ⓓ the mean number of emails for checks made on days 3–4

ALG2 8.0　　**24.** In the equation $y = 2x^2 - x - 21$, which is a value of x when $y = 0$?

ⓐ -21　　　ⓑ $1\frac{1}{2}$　　　ⓒ 3　　　ⓓ $3\frac{1}{2}$

ALG2 2.0　　**25.** The length of a rectangle is four times its width. If its perimeter is 15 inches, which system of equations can be used to find the dimensions of the rectangle?

ⓐ $\ell = w + 4$
　　$2(\ell + w) = 15$

ⓑ $\ell = w + 4$
　　$2\ell + 8w = 15$

ⓒ $\ell = 4w$
　　$2(\ell + w) = 15$

ⓓ $\ell = 4w$
　　$2\ell + 8w = 15$

Mixed Review

Lesson 12-2　　**Of all the respondents to a survey, 59% are girls. Of the girls, 61% read horror stories. Of the boys, 49% read horror stories.**

26. Find P(boy and reads horror stories).　　**27.** Find P(reads horror stories).

Lesson 11-2　　**Is the sequence arithmetic? If so, identify the common difference.**

28. $16, 7, -2, \ldots$　　**29.** $34, 51, 68, \ldots$　　**30.** $2, 2.2, 2.22, \ldots$　　**31.** $1, 1, 1, \ldots$

Lesson 10-2　　**Graph each equation.**

32. $y^2 - x - 2y + 1 = 0$　　　　**33.** $x^2 + 4x + 144y + 4 = 0$

Checkpoint Quiz 1　　　　　Lessons 12-1 through 12-3

In a poll, gymnasts were asked, "How many seconds long was your longest handstand on the balance beam?" Use the results below for Exercises 1 and 2.

Longest Handstand

Duration (seconds)	0–2	3–5	6–10	11–20	21–30	31–60	> 60	Total
Number of Respondents	14	27	19	18	13	15	24	130

1. Graph the probability distribution.　　**2.** Find $P(6-30$ seconds$)$.

　3. Writing Could the function $P(x) = \frac{x-2}{2}$ for $x = 1, 2, 3,$ or 4, represent a probability distribution? Explain.

Use the table at the right to find each probability.

4. P(teacher | yes)　　**5.** P(no | teacher)

6. P(student | no)　　**7.** P(yes | student)

Find the mean, median, and mode of each data set.

8. 7 4 9 3 5 4 4 7 9 10 3 1 8

9. 1.2 2.1 4.6 2.5 9.7 6.2 2.6 2.4 3.1 3.8

Did You Eat Breakfast Today?

	Yes	No
Teachers	12	20
Students	45	23

10. Open-Ended Write a data set that includes an outlier. Make a box-and-whisker plot of your data set with and without the outlier.

Standard Deviation

 California Content Standards
PS 7.0 Students compute the variance and the standard deviation of a distribution of data.

What You'll Learn
- To find the standard deviation of a set of values
- To use standard deviation in real-world situations

. . . And Why

To analyze energy demand, as in Example 3

 Check Skills You'll Need

 for Help Skills Handbook page 885

Simplify each expression. If necessary, round to the nearest hundredth.

1. $\frac{34.3}{7}$

2. $\frac{6}{2.4}$

3. $8.4 \cdot 1.25$

4. $12 - 6 \cdot 0.5$

5. $\frac{1}{3}[(2 - 6)^2 + (7 - 6)^2 + (8 - 6)^2]$

6. $\sqrt{\frac{1}{2}(4 - 3)^2 + (5 + 3)^2}$

New Vocabulary • measures of variation • range of a set of data • interquartile range • standard deviation • z-score

 Finding Standard Deviation

Activity: Analyzing Data Spread

1. a. Find the mean, the median, and the mode of each set of data.

Set 1	77	78	79	80	80	81	82	83
Set 2	20	60	70	80	80	90	100	140
Set 3	50	60	70	80	80	90	100	110
Set 4	20	30	40	80	80	120	130	140

b. Are the sets the same? Explain.

2. Find the difference between the greatest and least values in each set of data. What do these differences tell you about each set of data?

3. Find the quartiles of each set of data.

4. For each set, half of the data lie between Q_1 and Q_3. The value $Q_3 - Q_1$ gives you an idea of how the data are spread out. Find $Q_3 - Q_1$ for each set of data.

5. a. Give an example of two sets of data that are spread out differently, though the differences between their extreme values are the same.
b. Give an example of two sets of data that are spread out differently, though their values of $Q_3 - Q_1$ are the same.

6. a. Summarize the similarities and differences among the four sets in terms of central tendency and spread. Which is the most spread-out set? Which is the least? Explain.
b. Make box-and-whisker plots of the four sets of data. Do the plots support your conclusions from part (a)?

Statisticians use several **measures of variation** to describe how the data in a data set are spread out.

The **range of a set of data** is the difference between the greatest and least values. The **interquartile range** is the difference between the third and first quartiles.

1 EXAMPLE Real-World Connection

Thirteen men qualified for the 2002 U.S. Men's Alpine Ski Team. Find the range and the interquartile range of their ages at the time of qualification: 27, 28, 29, 23, 25, 26, 26, 28, 22, 23, 23, 21, 25.

greatest value − least value = 29 − 21   **Find the range.**
$$= 8$$

Median   **Find the median.**
$$\downarrow$$
21 22 23 23 23 25 25 26 26 27 28 28 29
          ↑   ↑
$$Q_1 = 23 \qquad\qquad Q_3 = \frac{27 + 28}{2} = 27.5 \quad \textbf{Find } \boldsymbol{Q_1} \textbf{ and } \boldsymbol{Q_3}.$$

$$Q_3 - Q_1 = 27.5 - 23 \qquad \textbf{Find the interquartile range.}$$
$$= 4.5$$

● The range is 8 years. The interquartile range is 4.5 years.

✓ CA Standards Check ① **a.** Seventeen women qualified for the 2002 U.S. Women's Alpine Ski Team. Find the range and the interquartile range of their ages: 24, 30, 29, 21, 22, 22, 28, 21, 16, 17, 25, 22, 21, 18, 19, 18, 19.
    b. Critical Thinking Can the variation, or spread, in two sets of data be different, even though they have the same range? Give an example.
    c. Can the variation in two sets of data be different, even though they have the same interquartile range? Give an example.

Another measure of variation is the **standard deviation,** a measure of how much the values in a data set vary, or deviate, from the mean. The Greek letter σ (sigma) represents standard deviation.

You can use the following procedure to calculate standard deviation.

 Key Concepts

Summary	Finding Standard Deviation

• Find the mean of the data set: $\bar{x}$.

• Find the difference between each value and the mean: $x - \bar{x}$.

• Square each difference: $(x - \bar{x})^2$.

• Find the average (mean) of these squares: $\dfrac{\sum (x - \bar{x})^2}{n}$.

• Take the square root to find the standard deviation:

$$\sigma = \sqrt{\frac{\sum (x - \bar{x})^2}{n}}.$$

Real-World Connection

By age 29, skier Paul Casey Puckett had made the U.S. Olympic teams of 1992, 1994, 1998, and 2002.

Vocabulary Tip

The Greek letter <u>sigma</u> (σ or Σ) corresponds to the English letter s. In the notation used in the Summary, Σ means "summation."

2 EXAMPLE Finding the Standard Deviation

Find the mean and the standard deviation for the values: 48.0, 53.2, 52.3, 46.6, 49.9.

$$\bar{x} = \frac{48.0 + 53.2 + 52.3 + 46.6 + 49.9}{5} = 50.0$$ **Find the mean.**

Organize the next steps in a table.

x	$\bar{x}$	$x - \bar{x}$	$(x - \bar{x})^2$
48.0	50.0	−2.0	4.00
53.2	50.0	3.2	10.24
52.3	50.0	2.3	5.29
46.6	50.0	−3.4	11.56
49.9	50.0	−0.1	0.01

Sum: 31.1

$$\sigma = \sqrt{\frac{\sum (x - \bar{x})^2}{n}}$$ **Find the standard deviation.**

$$= \sqrt{\frac{31.1}{5}} \approx 2.5$$

● The mean is 50.0, and the standard deviation is about 2.5.

✓ CA Standards Check **2** Find the mean and the standard deviation for these values: 50, 60, 70, 80, 80, 90, 100, 110.

Standard deviation is like a custom-made measuring stick for the variation in a set of data. A small standard deviation (compared to actual data values) indicates that the data are clustered tightly around the mean. As the data become more spread out, the standard deviation increases.

3 EXAMPLE Real-World 🌐 Connection

Energy Find the mean and the standard deviation of the data for daily energy demand in a small town during August.

Vocabulary Tip

The <u>watt</u> is the metric unit of measurement for power. One million watts of power delivered for one hour results in one <u>megawatt-hour</u> (MWh).

Daily Energy Demand During August (MWh)

Sun.	Mon.	Tues.	Wed.	Thurs.	Fri.	Sat.
		53	52	47	50	39
33	40	41	44	47	49	43
39	47	49	54	53	46	36
33	45	45	42	43	39	33
33	40	40	41	42		

Step 1 Use the STAT feature to enter the data as L1.

Step 2 Use the CALC menu of STAT to access the 1-Var Stats option.

The mean is about 43.2 MWh; the standard deviation is about 6.0 MWh.

```
1-Var Stats
  x̄=43.16129032  ←————— mean
  Σx=1338
  Σx²=58872
  Sx=6.116081394
  σx=6.016626288 ←————— standard
  ↓n=31                  deviation
```

2 Using Standard Deviation

In a data list, every value falls within some number of standard deviations of the mean. When a value falls within one standard deviation of the mean, it is in the range of values from one standard deviation below the mean to one standard deviation above. For example, if the mean is 50 and the standard deviation is 10, then a value x within one standard deviation of the mean must be in the range $40 \leq x \leq 60$.

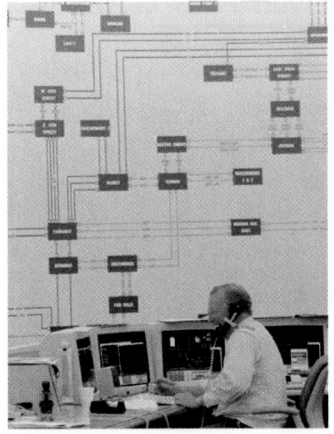

Real-World Connection

Dispatchers coordinate a utility's power supply and demand.

4 EXAMPLE Real-World Connection

Energy Use the energy demand data from Example 3. Within how many standard deviations of the mean do all of the values fall? How might the company supplying power to the town use this information?

Step 1 Draw a number line. Plot the data values and the mean.

Step 2 Mark off intervals of 6.0 on either side of the mean.

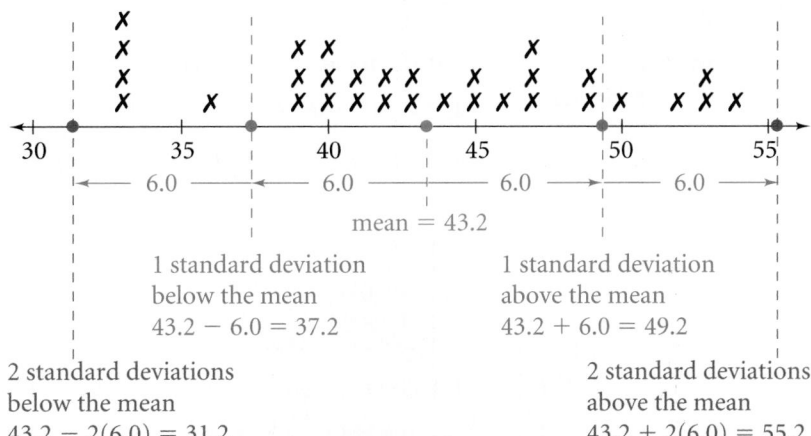

All of the values fall within two standard deviations of the mean. Therefore, the power company can expect that the daily demand on most days in August will fall within two standard deviations of the mean.

 CA Standards Check ④ **a.** Within how many standard deviations of the mean for August is a demand of 38.5 MWh?

b. In May, the mean daily energy demand is 35.8 MWh, with a standard deviation of 3.5 MWh. The power company prepares for any demand within three standard deviations of the mean. Are they prepared for a demand of 48 MWh? Explain.

The **z-score** is the number of standard deviations that a value is from the mean. In Example 4, the value 49.2 is one standard deviation above the mean, so it has a z-score of 1. The value 37.2, which is one standard deviation below the mean, has a z-score of -1.

5 **EXAMPLE** **Finding the z-score**

A set of values has a mean of 85 and a standard deviation of 6. Find the *z*-score of the value 76.

$$z\text{-score} = \frac{\text{value} - \text{mean}}{\text{standard deviation}}$$

$$= \frac{76 - 85}{6} \quad \textbf{Substitute.}$$

$$= \frac{-9}{6} \quad \textbf{Simplify.}$$

$$= -1.5$$

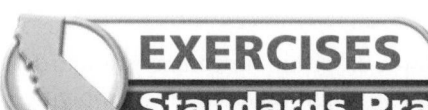 **CA Standards Check** **5** Use the mean and standard deviation from Example 5. Find the value that has a *z*-score of 2.5.

 EXERCISES

Standards Practice

For more exercises, see *Extra Skill and Word Problem Practice*.

PS 7.0

A **Practice by Example**

Example 1
(page 681)

GO for Help

Find the range and the interquartile range of each set of values.

1. 5 6 7 3 4 5 6 7 8
2. 56 78 125 34 67 91 20

3. 724 786 670 760 300 187 190 345 456 732 891 879 324

Examples 2 and 3
(page 682)

Find the mean and the standard deviation for each set of values.

4. 78 90 456 673 111 381 21
5. 13 15 17 18 12 21 10

6. The Dow Jones Industrial average for the last 24 weeks of 1994:

3735.04	3764.50	3747.02	3768.71	3755.11	3881.05
3885.58	3874.81	3933.35	3831.75	3843.19	3797.43
3910.47	3891.30	3930.66	3807.52	3801.47	3815.26
3708.27	3745.62	3691.11	3807.19	3833.43	3834.44

7. The Dow Jones Industrial average for the last 24 weeks of 2004:

9962.22	10,139.71	9815.33	9825.35	10,110.14	10,195.01
10,260.20	10,313.07	10,284.46	10,047.24	10,192.65	10,055.20
9933.38	9757.81	10,027.47	10,387.54	10,539.01	10,456.91
10,522.23	10,592.21	10,543.22	10,649.92	10,827.12	10,783.01

Example 4
(page 683)

Determine the whole number of standard deviations that includes all data values.

8. The mean price of the nonfiction books on a best-sellers list is $25.07; the standard deviation is $2.62.
$26.95, $22.95, $24.00, $24.95, $29.95, $19.95, $24.95, $24.00, $27.95, $25.00

9. The mean length of Beethoven's nine symphonies is 37 minutes; the standard deviation is 12 minutes.
27 min, 30 min, 47 min, 35 min, 30 min, 40 min, 35 min, 22 min, 65 min

Example 5
(page 684)

A data set has mean 25 and standard deviation 5. Find the z-score of each value.

10. 39   **11.** 18   **12.** 125   **13.** 25   **14.** 11

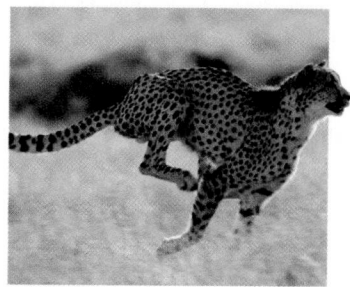

B **Apply Your Skills**

Find the standard deviation for each data set. Use the standard deviations to compare each pair of data sets.

15. fastest recorded speeds of various large wild cats (miles per hour):
70 50 30 40 35 30 30 40 15
fastest recorded speeds of various birds in flight (miles per hour):
217 106 95 56 65 37 50 31 53 25 25 25

16. the number of buttons on selected outfits:
11 5 12 8 3 12 10 10 0 5 0 2 7 10
the number of pockets in the same outfits:
5 5 5 2 2 5 3 2 0 2 0 0 5 5

Income **Use the chart at the right for Exercises 17–20.**

17. Find the mean income for each year.

 18. Writing Use the range of the data for each year to describe how farm income varied from 2001 to 2002.

19. Find the standard deviation for each year. In which year did farm income cluster more tightly around the mean?

20. Which state's 2001 income has a z-score of about 1.4?

Farm Income in Midwestern States (millions of dollars)

State	2001	2002
Iowa	10,653	10,834
Kansas	7979	7862
Minnesota	7537	7478
Missouri	4723	4402
Nebraska	9221	9589
North Dakota	2938	3223
South Dakota	3897	3779

SOURCE: U.S. Department of Agriculture

21. a. Energy Find the mean and the standard deviation for daily energy usage during ten days in June: 51.8 MWh, 53.6 MWh, 54.7 MWh, 51.9 MWh, 49.3 MWh, 52.0 MWh, 53.5 MWh, 51.2 MWh, 60.7 MWh, 59.3 MWh.
  b. How many items in the data set fall within one standard deviation of the mean? Within two standard deviations? Within three standard deviations?

GO **for Help**

For a guide to solving Exercise 21, see p. 687.

Another measure of variation is *variance*, **which equals** σ^2. **Find the variance and the standard deviation of each data set.**

22. 12 h 3 h 2 h 4 h 5 h 7 h

23. 60 m 40 m 35 m 45 m 39 m

24. $6.99 $5.50 $7.10 $9.22 $8.99

25. 0.7 g 0.84 g 0.9 g 0.8 g 0.69 g

26. Critical Thinking From your results in Exercises 22–25, which do you think is a better measure of variation—variance or standard deviation? Explain.

27. Error Analysis Minh says that the data below fall within three standard deviations of the mean. Marsha disagrees, saying that the data fall within six standard deviations of the mean. With whom do you agree? Explain.

28. a. Data Collection Make a table showing the number of siblings of each student in the class.
   b. Find the mean and standard deviation of the data.

 Challenge

Ages of the Members of the 2000 U.S. Olympic Soccer Teams

Men		Women	
23	32	32	29
29	23	29	22
23	23	32	28
22	23	25	23
21	18	22	22
19	22	20	24
20	23	32	25
23	21	29	27
26	22	24	22

29. a. Use the table at the left to find the range, the mean, and the standard deviation of the ages for each team.
   b. Critical Thinking For two data sets, does the set with the larger range necessarily have the larger standard deviation? Support your answer with your results from part (a).

30. Earnings The table at the right shows the median weekly earnings of union and nonunion workers in various occupations.
   a. Find the mean and the range of the data for union workers and for nonunion workers.
   b. Find the standard deviation for each set of data.
   c. Within how many standard deviations of the mean are earnings of $395 for union workers? For nonunion workers?
   d. Writing Compare the wages of union and nonunion workers. Use your results from parts (a) through (c).

Workers' Median Weekly Earnings, 1999

Occupation	Union	Nonunion
Construction	$778	$509
Transportation and public utilities	$748	$613
Trade	$499	$418
Manufacturing	$614	$561
Services	$554	$515
Finance, insurance, and real estate	$582	$599
Mining	$710	$735

SOURCE: U.S. Bureau of Labor Statistics.
Go to www.PHSchool.com for a data update.
Web Code: bbg-9041

Multiple Choice Practice

For California Standards and CAHSEE Tutorials, visit PHSchool.com. Web Code: bbq-9045

PS 7.0   **31.** Six members of a bowling team received the following scores: 175, 210, 180, 195, 208, 196. What is the standard deviation of these scores?

  Ⓐ 11   Ⓑ 13   Ⓒ 19   Ⓓ 31

ALG2 4.0   **32.** Which polynomial has $(x - 1)$ as a factor?

  Ⓐ $x^2 + 3x + 2$ Ⓒ $x^3 - x^2 - x + 1$
  Ⓑ $x^2 + 2x + 1$ Ⓓ $x^3 - 3x - 2$

Mixed Review

 GO for Help

Lesson 12-3   **Make a box-and-whisker plot for each set of values.**

33. 25, 25, 30, 35, 45, 45, 50, 55, 60, 60   **34.** 20, 23, 25, 36, 37, 38, 39, 50, 52, 55

Lesson 11-3   **Find the missing positive term in each geometric sequence.**

35. 64, ■, 4, . . .   **36.** 20, ■, 0.05, . . .   **37.** 29, ■, 65.25, . . .

Lesson 10-3   **Graph each circle.**

38. $(x - 2)^2 + (y + 1)^2 = 36$ **39.** $(x - 1)^2 + (y - 1)^2 = 4$

Understanding Math Problems Read the problem below. Let the explanation guide you through analyzing the data. Check your understanding by solving the exercises at the bottom of the page.

a. Energy Find the mean and the standard deviation for daily energy usage during ten days in June: 51.8 MWh, 53.6 MWh, 54.7 MWh, 51.9 MWh, 49.3 MWh, 52.0 MWh, 53.5 MWh, 51.2 MWh, 60.7 MWh, 59.3 MWh.

To find the mean, add the data entries and divide by the number of entries.

$$\overline{x} = \frac{51.8 + 53.6 + 54.7 + 51.9 + 49.3 + 52.0 + 53.5 + 51.2 + 60.7 + 59.3}{10} = 53.8$$

The mean energy usage for 10 days is 53.8 MWh.

To simplify finding standard deviation, enter the data into a table.

x	51.8	53.6	54.7	51.9	49.3	52.0	53.5	51.2	60.7	59.3
$\overline{x}$					53.8					
$x - \overline{x}$	−2.0	−0.2	0.9	−1.9	−4.5	−1.8	−0.3	−2.6	6.9	5.5
$(x - \overline{x})^2$	4.00	0.04	0.81	3.61	20.25	3.24	0.09	6.76	47.61	30.25

Now use the definition of standard deviation.

$$\sigma = \sqrt{\frac{\sum (x - \overline{x})^2}{n}}$$

$$= \sqrt{\frac{116.66}{10}}$$

$$\approx 3.4$$

The standard deviation is about 3.4 MWh.

b. How many items in the data set fall within one standard deviation of the mean? Within two standard deviations? Within three standard deviations?

Look at the $x - \overline{x}$ row in your table. Compare its values with the following.

$$1\sigma \approx 3.4 \qquad 2\sigma \approx 6.8 \qquad 3\sigma \approx 10.2$$

7 items are within 1σ of the mean, 9 items are within 2σ, and 10 items are within 3σ.

EXERCISES

Find the mean and the standard deviation of the data. List entries that are more than two standard deviations from the mean.

1. 1.1, 1.8, 2.1, 0.7, 1.8, 0.5, 0.9, 2.9, 5.0, 2.1

2. 122, 94, 111, 95, 137, 56, 89, 115, 119, 125

3. 1635, 1247, 1689, 1496, 1571, 1836, 1652

4. −0.6, 0.8, 1.1, 0.3, −0.8, −0.3, −1.6, 0.8, 0.4, −0.1

Most of the probability examples you study in this chapter are about discrete situations. These situations involve whole numbers of people, test scores, money amounts, and so on. You can apply probabilities to continuous situations as well.

ACTIVITY

A traffic signal is green for 20 seconds out of every minute. Find the probability that the signal will be green when you turn the corner and first see it.

You can model the signal's color intervals by using a number line.

Let an interval of 60 represent one cycle of green, yellow, and red. Inside that interval, an interval of 20 represents a green light. You come across the signal at a random point in time, so

$$P(\text{green}) = \frac{\text{time light is green}}{\text{total time of cycle}} = \frac{20}{60} = \frac{1}{3}$$

EXERCISES

1. The traffic signal is green when you first see it. What is the probability that it will turn yellow within 5 seconds?

2. The traffic signal is red when you first see it. What do you need to know to find the probability that it will not turn green for another 15 seconds?

The following continuous situations involve functions and conic sections that you have studied to this point. For each, assume that you pick real numbers a and b at random between 0 and 10. Find the probability of each of the following.

3. The line $y = ax$ intersects the segment joining $(0, 10)$ and $(5, 10)$. See graph at the right.

4. The circle $(x - a)^2 + (y - b)^2 = 1$ lies entirely within a square with opposite vertices $(0, 0)$ and $(10, 10)$.

5. The ellipse $\frac{x}{a^2} + \frac{y}{b^2} = 1$ has a vertical major axis.

6. The hyperbola $\frac{x}{a^2} - \frac{y}{b^2} = 1$ has a horizontal transverse axis.

7. The interval from 4 to 6 is a part of the domain of the function $y = \sqrt{x - a} + b$.

8. The function $y = ab^x$ models growth.

9. The function $y = \frac{1}{x - a} + b$ has a horizontal asymptote.

10. The point (a, b) is in the upper triangle formed by the diagonals of a square whose sides lie on the axes and the lines $x = 10$ and $y = 10$.

Working With Samples

What You'll Learn

• To find sample proportions

• To find the margin of error

. . . And Why

To analyze data from a poll, as in Example 5

✓ **Check Skills You'll Need**

Simplify each expression.

1. $\dfrac{1}{\sqrt{4}}$

2. $-\dfrac{1}{\sqrt{9}}$

3. $\dfrac{1}{\sqrt{36}}$

4. $-\dfrac{1}{\sqrt{121}}$

5. $\dfrac{1}{\sqrt{50}}$

6. $-\dfrac{1}{\sqrt{81}}$

GO for Help Lesson 7-1

🔊 **New Vocabulary** • **sample** • **sample proportion** • **random sample**
• **margin of error**

---

1 Sample Proportions

Suppose you want to know what percent of all teenagers recognize the word that means "to pass the summer in a state of slumber." Since it is too costly and time consuming to ask every teenager, use a sample. A **sample** gathers information from only part of a population.

Using any sample, you can find a sample proportion. The **sample proportion** is the ratio $\frac{x}{n}$, where x is the number of times an event occurs in a sample of size n.

> ── **Word Wise** ──
>
> Which word means "to pass the summer in a state of slumber"?
>
> **A. stridulate**
> **B. ruminate**
> **C. estivate**
> **D. somnambulate**

---

1 EXAMPLE **Finding the Sample Proportion**

In a sample of 350 teenagers, 294 have never made a snow sculpture. Find the sample proportion for those who have never made a snow sculpture. Write the answer as a percent.

sample proportion $= \dfrac{x}{n}$ **Write the formula.**

$\qquad\qquad = \dfrac{294}{350}$ **Substitute 294 for x and 350 for n.**

$\qquad\qquad = 0.84$ **Simplify.**

● The sample proportion is 84%.

✓ **CA Standards Check** ① In a poll of 1085 voters, 564 favor Candidate A. Find the sample proportion for those who favor Candidate A.

Samples vary in how well they reflect the entire population. In a **random sample,** all members of the population are equally likely to be chosen.

Vocabulary Tip

Bias means "slant."

When a part of a population is overrepresented or underrepresented in a sample, the sample is biased. A random sample can help avoid bias in gathering data.

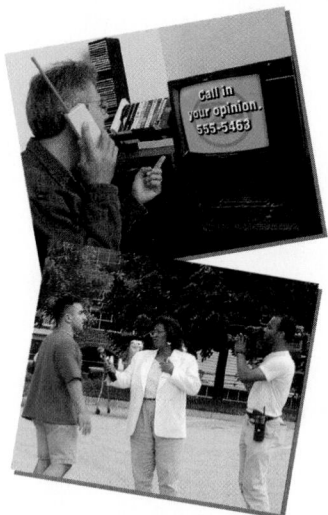

2 EXAMPLE   Real-World Connection

Public Opinion A news program reports on a proposed school dress code. The purpose of the program is to find out what percent of the population in its viewing area favors the dress code. Identify any bias in each sampling method.

a. Viewers are invited to call the program and express their preferences.

The people who decide to call in may over- or underrepresent some views. For example, members of a group favoring the new dress code might encourage its members to call in. This type of sample is called a "self-selected" sample.

b. A reporter interviews people on the street near the local high school.

This is a "convenience" sample, since it is convenient for the reporter to stay in one place. Because the location is near the school, students may be overrepresented in the sample and the results will be biased.

c. During the program, 300 people are selected at random from the viewing area. Then each person is contacted.

This sampling method contains the least bias. It is a random sample.

✓ **CA Standards Check** **2 a.** Suppose the 350 teenagers in Example 1 all live in Florida. Is there bias in this sample? Explain.
b. Critical Thinking The only way to know a true population proportion is to poll every person in the population. Such a poll is no longer a sample, but a census. Describe a situation in which a sample is unsatisfactory and a census is required.

---

2 Sample Size and Margin of Error

The size of a sample affects its reliability. With a small sample size, you are likely to get a wide range of sample proportions. For example, in some samples, no one will recognize the word that means "to pass the summer in a state of slumber." In other samples, everyone will recognize *estivate*. With larger sample sizes, you are less likely to have a sample containing an "all or nothing" result.

The Law of Large Numbers states that the variation in a data set decreases as the sample size increases. By comparing the variation in samples, you can get an idea of their relative sizes.

3 EXAMPLE   Comparing Sample Sizes

Each graph below shows the sample proportions for 20 samples. Match each graph to the most likely sample size.

a. 20 people per sample   **b.** 5 people per sample

Distributions of Sample Proportions

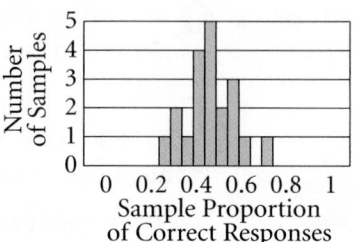

a. The graph on the right shows less variation, so it is more likely to be based on samples of a larger size, 20 people per sample.

b. The graph on the left shows more variation, so it is more likely to be based on 5 people per sample.

 CA Standards Check **3** A science class measured the heights of blades of grass behind the school. The class took three samples. Use the information in the table below to decide which sample most likely was the greatest in size. Explain your reasoning.

Sample	Standard Deviation (in.)
A	1.45
B	1.09
C	1.26

A sample proportion should be reported with an estimate of error, called the **margin of error.** The margin of error is based on the standard deviation in graphs like those in Example 3. The larger the sample size, the smaller the margin of error.

🔑 **Key Concepts**

Property	Margin of Error Formula

When a random sample of size n is taken from a large population, the sample proportion has a margin of error of approximately $\pm\dfrac{1}{\sqrt{n}}$.

4 **EXAMPLE** **Using the Margin of Error**

A poll reports that 56% of voters favor Candidate B, with a margin of error of $\pm 3\%$. Estimate the number of voters in the poll.

$$\text{margin of error} = \pm\frac{1}{\sqrt{n}} \qquad \textbf{Write the formula.}$$

$$\pm\sqrt{n} = \frac{1}{\text{margin of error}} \qquad \textbf{Rewrite the equation.}$$

$$= \frac{1}{0.03} \qquad \textbf{Substitute 0.03 for margin of error.}$$

$$\approx 33.33 \qquad \textbf{Simplify.}$$

$$n \approx 1111 \qquad \textbf{Square each side.}$$

The poll included about 1100 voters.

 CA Standards Check **4** Estimate the sample size for each margin of error.
 a. $\pm 10\%$ **b.** $\pm 4\%$ **c.** $\pm 2\%$

You can use the margin of error to determine the likely range for the true population proportion. The graph below shows the range for the population in Example 4.

5 **EXAMPLE** **Real-World** **Connection**

Genetics A survey of 2580 students found that 9% are left-handed.

a. Find the margin of error for the sample.

$$\text{margin of error} = \pm\frac{1}{\sqrt{n}} \quad \textbf{Use the formula.}$$

$$= \pm\frac{1}{\sqrt{2580}} \quad \textbf{Substitute.}$$

$$\approx \pm 0.0197 \quad \textbf{Use a calculator.}$$

The margin of error is about $\pm 2\%$.

b. Use the margin of error to find an interval that is likely to contain the true population proportion.

The margin of error forms an interval with the sample proportion at its midpoint.

Sample Proportion

$\longleftarrow -2\% \xrightarrow{} +2\% \longrightarrow$

7%   9%   11%

The proportion of students who are left-handed is likely to be from 7% to 11%.

Real-World **Connection**

<u>Southpaw</u> originated as a baseball term for a left-handed pitcher.

✓ **CA Standards Check** **5** In a poll of 123 students, 87 have never ridden a ferry. Find the sample proportion, the margin of error, and the interval likely to contain the true population proportion.

For more exercises, see *Extra Skill and Word Problem Practice*.

Standards Practice

A **Practice by Example**

For each sample, find the sample proportion. Write it as a percent.

Example 1
(page 689)

1. 837 out of 1150 insurance applicants have no citations on their driving record.

2. 27 out of 60 shoppers prefer generic brands when available.

3. 532 out of 580 households own a color television set.

Example 2
(page 690)

Identify any bias in each sampling method.

4. A supermarket wants to find the proportion of shoppers who use reduced-price coupons. A manager interviews every shopper entering the greeting card aisle.

5. A maintenance crew wants to estimate how many of 3000 air filters in an office building need replacing. The crew examines five filters chosen at random on each floor of the building.

6. The student government wants to find out how many students have after-school jobs. A pollster interviews students selected at random as they board buses at the end of the school day.

Example 3
(pages 690–691)

7. In a survey, teenagers were asked the importance of "making your own things." The response scale ranged from 1 to 5, with 5 being extremely important. Which sample most likely was largest? Explain.

Sample	Score	Standard Deviation
A	3.6	1.2
B	3.8	1.0
C	3.8	0.5

8. The table below shows the results of a poll asking students, "How many hours a week would you say you spend doing academic homework?" Which sample most likely was smaller? Explain.

Example 4
(page 691)

Find the margin of error for the sample proportion, given each sample of size *n*.

9. $n = 200$ **10.** $n = 800$ **11.** $n = 1200$

Find the sample size that produces each margin of error.

12. $\pm 8\%$ **13.** $\pm 5\%$ **14.** $\pm 1\%$

Example 5
(page 692)

For each situation, find the margin of error for the sample. Then find an interval likely to contain the true population proportion.

15. Of 750 teenagers polled, 59% think boys and girls are portrayed as equals on television.

16. Of 400 teenagers surveyed, 62% do not plan to stay in their community after finishing their education.

B Apply Your Skills

Surveys **For each sample, find (a) the sample proportion, (b) the margin of error, and (c) the interval likely to contain the true population proportion.**

17. In a random sample of 408 grocery shoppers, 258 prefer one large trip per week to several smaller ones.

18. Of 500 teenagers surveyed, 460 would like to see adults in their community do more to solve drug problems.

19. In a survey of 32 people, 30 return a milk carton to the refrigerator immediately after using it.

20. In a survey of 16 people, one person never locks his car.

21. Writing Write a news article describing the sample proportion and margin of error for the poll results shown at the right.

22. Reasoning How is the margin of error affected if you double the sample size? Explain.

23. a. Data Collection Write a survey question to find out the number of students at your school who plan to continue their education after high school
    b. Describe the sampling method you would use.
    c. Conduct your survey.

dailypoll

Do you save more than 5% of your income?

◯ yes   ◯ no

dailypoll
Results:
yes **370**
no **583**

Homework Video Tutor

Visit: PHSchool.com
Web Code: bbe-1205

24. Critical Thinking A sample proportion provides an estimate for the percent of an entire population that favors an event. Is a sample proportion an experimental or a theoretical probability? Explain.

25. **Computer Use** An online advertisement asks you to participate in a survey. The survey asks how much time you spend online each week. Identify any bias in this method. If appropriate, suggest a method more likely to produce a random sample.

An event occurs *x* times in a sample of size *n*. Find its sample proportion and margin of error.

26. $x = 96$	**27.** $x = 20$	**28.** $x = 100$	**29.** $x = 273$
$n = 900$	$n = 64$	$n = 250$	$n = 435$

 Challenge

30. **a.** It costs $20 to interview each person for a survey. Find the cost to obtain a ±3% margin of error.

    b. Critical Thinking Find the cost to obtain a ±2% margin of error. Why do you think polls with smaller margins of error are rare?

31. **a. Elections** A poll of 150 voters shows that a candidate is preferred by 56% of the voters while 44% prefer the opponent. Should the candidate be concerned? Explain.

    b. A later poll of 600 voters shows the candidate is preferred by 55% of the voters. Should this candidate feel more or less confident, given the results of the second poll? Explain.

Exercise 32

32. **Wildlife** Wild animal populations are often estimated through the use of the capture−tag−recapture method. Several animals are captured, tagged, and released back into the wild. The animals continue to roam freely. Then, some time later at the same site, several more animals are captured, and the number of tagged animals is recorded. An estimate of the population can then be calculated. This method of estimation assumes that the fraction of tagged animals in the second sample is equivalent to the fraction of tagged animals in the entire population.

$$\frac{\text{tagged animals in second sample}}{\text{animals in second sample}} = \frac{\text{tagged animals in population}}{\text{population } (P)}$$

Use the formula above to predict the black bear population of the northern coastal plain of South Carolina. Researchers tagged fourteen black bears in the fall and captured eleven bears the following summer. Of the eleven bears, three were tagged.

Multiple Choice Practice

For California Standards and CAHSEE Tutorials, visit PHSchool.com. Web Code: bbq-9045

ALG2 2.0

33. Mark swam *x* km/h in a stream with a current of *y* km/h. The system below shows the results of a 4-km swim upstream and a 4-km swim downstream.

$$4(x - y) = 4$$
$$2(x + y) = 4$$

Based on the solution of the system of equations, which of the following can be concluded?

Ⓐ Mark's rate was $\frac{1}{3}$ times the rate of the current.

Ⓑ Mark's rate was $\frac{1}{2}$ times the rate of the current.

Ⓒ Mark's rate was 2 times the rate of the current.

Ⓓ Mark's rate was 3 times the rate of the current.

ALG2 19.0

34. In a high school auditorium, 1 junior and 3 sophomores are seated randomly together in a row. What is the probability that the 3 sophomores are seated next to each other?

Ⓐ $\frac{1}{16}$　　Ⓑ $\frac{1}{4}$　　Ⓒ $\frac{3}{4}$　　Ⓓ Not here

ALG2 24.0

35. Which function is the inverse of $f(x) = (x - 3)^2$?

Ⓐ $g(x) = \dfrac{x^2}{(3x - 1)^2}$

Ⓑ $g(x) = \dfrac{1}{(x - 3)^2}$

Ⓒ $g(x) = \sqrt{x} + 3$

Ⓓ $g(x) = \sqrt{x} - 3$

Mixed Review

Lesson 12-4

Find the mean and the standard deviation for each data set.

36. 0 km, 1 km, 1 km, 1 km, 2 km, 2 km, 2 km, 3 km, 3 km, 4 km, 5 km, 10 km

37. 1 oz, 1 oz, 2 oz, 2 oz, 3 oz, 4 oz, 5 oz, 6 oz, 8 oz, 9 oz, 10 oz, 10 oz, 12 oz, 20 oz

Lesson 11-4

Use summation notation to write each arithmetic series for the specified number of terms.

38. $3 + 8 + 13 + \ldots; n = 5$　　　**39.** $41 + 33 + 25 + \ldots; n = 8$

40. $-14 + (-8) + (-2) + \ldots; n = 6$　　**41.** $-27 + (-21) + (-15) + \ldots; n = 10$

Lesson 10-4

Find the equation of each ellipse centered at the origin.

42. height: 20 units
width: 6 units

43. height: 12 units
width: 10 units

44. height: 24 units
width: 36 units

Algebra at Work

·············· **Market Researcher**

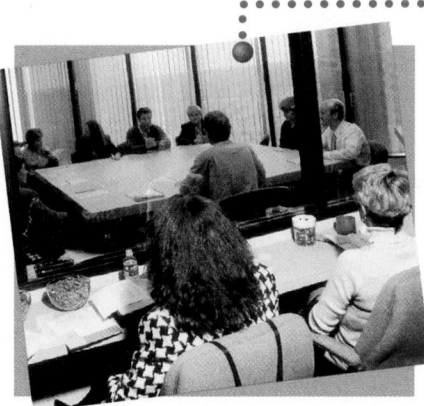

When questions arise about consumer products or services, a market researcher gathers statistical information to help answer the questions. The information a market researcher collects and analyzes helps companies improve their products and make decisions about their customer base. Quantitative research allows a market researcher to analyze data from a large population of potential customers. Market research strategies for gathering information include the following.

- mail surveys
- focus groups
- telephone surveys
- in-person interviews

For: Information about market research
Web Code: bbb-2031

For the equation $y = mx + b$, you may have heard x and y described as variables and m and b as parameters. In other situations, however, x and y may be parameters and m and b may be variables. At this time, you can perhaps better understand the distinction between *variable* and *parameter* by considering examples than by reading definitions of these terms.

EXAMPLE   The Family of Quadratic Functions

Distinguish between the variable x and the parameters a, h, and k as they appear in $f(x) = a(x - h)^2 + k$, the vertex form of a quadratic function.

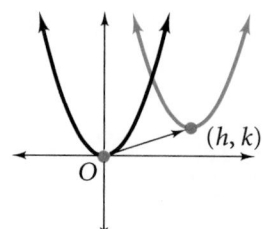

The variable x represents any value in the domain of the function f. Since the domain of a quadratic function is the set of real numbers, x represents any real number.

The parameters a, h, and k represent real numbers, but they are constant for any specific quadratic function. They give that function the stretch and translation characteristics that relate it to the parent quadratic function $y = x^2$.

EXERCISES

Describe the values given to the quadratic parameters in each vertex-form quadratic function below.

1. $f(x) = 2(x - 3)^2 + 4$

2. $g(x) = -(x + 1)^2 - 2$

3. $h(x) = -x^2 + 1$

4. You may not have noticed, but the "parent" exponential function $y = b^x$ is itself a family of functions, with each parent defined by the value of the parameter b. (That's why the Key Concepts Summary on page 449 uses the plural "Families" in its title "Families of Exponential Functions.")

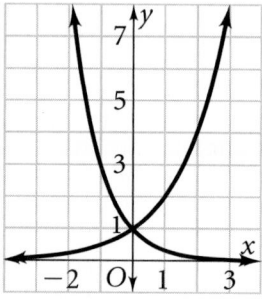

 a. What parameter values give the two parent exponential functions shown in the graph?

 b. Describe the domain of the parameter b for the exponential function $y = b^x$.

5. The function $V(k) = x^2 + k$ pairs a number k with a member of the family of quadratic functions. In other words, the inputs for V are the parameter values k; the outputs are quadratic functions. Describe this set of quadratic functions by their common characteristics.

The domain of each function is a set of real-number parameter values. The outputs are functions. Describe each set of outputs by their common characteristics.

6. $T(h) = (x - h)^2$

7. $S(a) = ax^2$

8. $V(k) = -x^2 + k$

9. $R(h) = \sqrt{x - h}$

10. $L(b) = \log_b x$

11. $V(h) = \pi r^2 h$

12. Probability Suppose k and n are whole numbers with $1 \le k \le n$.

 a. If you choose one number at random from 1 through n, what is $P(\text{choosing } k)$?

 b. For this situation, you can think of k as a variable and n as a parameter. How is your answer to part (a) affected by the value of the parameter n?

12-6

Binomial Distributions

 California Content Standards

PS 3.0 Students demonstrate an understanding of the notion of *discrete random variables*.
PS 4.0 Students are familiar with the binomial distribution.
ALG2 18.0 Students use fundamental counting principles to compute combinations and permutations. ***Master***
ALG2 19.0 Students use combinations and permutations to compute probabilities. ***Master***

What You'll Learn

- To find binomial probabilities
- To use binomial distributions

. . . And Why

To find the probability of winning a prize, as in Example 2

✓ **Check Skills You'll Need**

 for Help Lessons 6-7 and 6-8

Evaluate each expression.

1. $_4C_2$ **2.** $_3C_3$ **3.** $_5C_2$

Use the binomial theorem to expand each binomial.

4. $(x + 2)^3$ **5.** $(w - y)^4$
6. $(m + n)^3$ **7.** $(t + 3s)^4$
8. $(a + 2b)^5$ **9.** $(p + q)^6$

🔊 **New Vocabulary**   • binomial experiment   • binomial probability

1 Finding Binomial Probabilities

Activity: Binomial Probability

1. Examine the situations described in the chart below. What do the situations printed in blue have in common?

> receive a numerical grade
> receive a pass/fail grade
> wear soccer, running, basketball, or street shoes
> wear shoes with cleats or no cleats
> guess on a matching test
> guess on a true/false test

 Problem Solving Hint

You can use a coin, a number cube, or random numbers to conduct a simulation.

2. Suppose you guess each answer on a ten-question true-or-false test. Are you likely to get 70% or more right?
   a. Design and conduct a simulation for this situation.
   b. Run your simulation 10 times. Make a frequency table of the scores.
   c. Find *P*(70% or more right).

A **binomial experiment** has three important features:

- The situation involves repeated trials.

- Each trial has two possible outcomes (success or failure).

- The probability of success is constant throughout the trials. (The trials are independent.)

1 EXAMPLE Designing a Binomial Experiment

Suppose that you guess the answers to three questions of a multiple-choice test. Each question has five choices, with one correct choice.

a. Describe a trial for this situation. How many trials are there?

Each guess is a trial. Since you are guessing three times, there are three trials.

b. Describe a success. What is the probability of success on any single trial?

Each correct answer is a success. Since there are five possible answers, all of them equally likely, the probability of success on any single trial is 0.2.

c. Design and conduct a simulation to determine the probability of getting at least two answers correct. Run the simulation 10 times.

Assign each number from 1 to 5 to an outcome, based on each outcome's probability. Let 1 represent a correct response. Let 2−5 represent incorrect responses. Generate random numbers from 1 to 5.

Simulation	1	2	3	4	5	6	7	8	9	10
Number Generated, Trial 1	2	4	2	5	5	2	1	5	1	2
Number Generated, Trial 2	1	1	5	4	4	5	1	4	5	1
Number Generated, Trial 3	1	3	1	2	2	5	4	2	3	2
Number of Correct Guesses	2	1	1	0	0	0	2	0	1	1

Two of the simulations result in two or more correct guesses. So the experimental probability of getting at least two answers correct is $\frac{2}{10}$, or 20%.

 CA Standards Check **1** Run the simulation an additional 15 times. Use the results of all 25 simulations to find the experimental probability of getting at least two answers correct.

You can use a tree diagram to analyze binomial probabilities.

2 EXAMPLE Real-World 🌐 Connection

Merchandising As part of a promotion, a store is giving away scratch-off cards. Prizes are awarded on 40% of the game cards. Suppose you have three cards. Find the probability that exactly two of the three cards will reveal a prize.

Each card represents a trial with a probability of success of 0.4. The probability of failure is 0.6. The tree diagram below shows the probabilities along each path.

The probability that exactly two of three cards will reveal a prize is 0.288.

CA Standards Check **2** **a.** Complete the tree diagram in Example 2 by finding the probability of receiving one prize and the probability of receiving no prize.

b. Verify your work by adding the probabilities for three, two, one, and no prizes. What answer should you get?

The relationships you have seen are summarized in the following formula.

 Key Concepts

Definition	Binomial Probability

Suppose you have repeated independent trials, each with a probability of success p and a probability of failure q (with $p + q = 1$). Then the probability of x successes in n trials is the following product.

$$_nC_x p^x q^{n-x}$$

3 **EXAMPLE** **Real-World** **Connection**

Quality Control A calculator contains four batteries. With normal use, each battery has a 90% chance of lasting for one year. What is the probability that all four batteries will last a year?

Relate This is a binomial experiment.

• There are four batteries.

• Each battery may succeed or fail.

• The probability of success is 0.9 for each battery.

Graphing Calculator Hint

$_nC_r = \dfrac{n!}{r!(n-r)!}$

On a graphing calculator, use **MATH** and $_nC_r$ in the PRB menu.

Define Let $n = 4$.   Let $x = 4$.
Let $p = 0.9$.   Let $q = 0.1$.

Write $_nC_x p^x q^{n-x} = {_4}C_4(0.9)^4(0.1)^0$ **Substitute.**

$= (1)(0.9)^4(1)$ **Simplify.**

$= 0.6561$ **Simplify.**

```
(4 nCr 4) *0.9^4*0.1^0
                 .6561
```

The probability that all four batteries will last one year is about 66%.

 CA Standards Check **3** Find the probability of x successes in n trials for the given probability of success p on each trial.

a. $x = 2, n = 5, p = 0.25$ **b.** $x = 8, n = 10, p = 0.7$

2 Using a Binomial Distribution

Online **active math**

For: Probability Activity
Use: Interactive Textbook, 12-6

To find the full probability distribution for a binomial experiment, expand the binomial $(p + q)^n$. For example, suppose you guess on four questions of a five-choice multiple choice test. For four questions, $n = 4, p = 0.2,$ and $q = 0.8$.

	4 correct	3 correct	2 correct	1 correct	0 correct
$(p + q)^4 =$	$1p^4$ +	$4p^3q$ +	$6p^2q^2$ +	$4pq^3$ +	$1q^4$
$=$	$(0.2)^4$ +	$4(0.2)^3(0.8)$ +	$6(0.2)^2(0.8)^2$ +	$4(0.2)(0.8)^3$ +	$(0.8)^4$
$=$	0.0016 +	0.0256 +	0.1536 +	0.4096 +	0.4096

Of course, you can display a binomial distribution as a graph.

Guessing on a Multiple-Choice Test

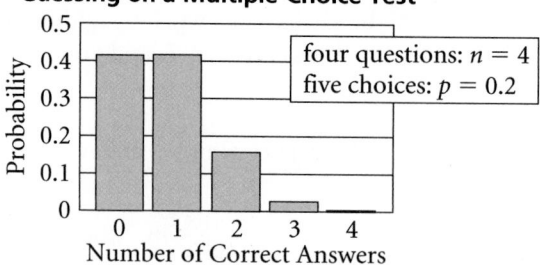

four questions: $n = 4$
five choices: $p = 0.2$

4 EXAMPLE Real-World Connection

Weather A scientist hopes to launch a weather balloon on one of the next three mornings. For each morning, there is a 40% chance of suitable weather. What is the probability that there will be at least one morning with suitable weather?

Use the expansion for $(p + q)^n$, with $n = 3$, $p = 0.4$, and $q = 0.6$.

$$
\begin{array}{ccccccc}
& \text{3 successes} & \text{2 successes} & & \text{1 success} & \text{0 successes} \\
(p + q)^3 = & 1p^3 & + & 3p^2q & + & 3pq^2 & + & 1q^3 \\
= & (0.4)^3 & + & 3(0.4)^2(0.6) & + & 3(0.4)(0.6)^2 & + & (0.6)^3 \\
= & 0.064 & + & 0.288 & + & 0.432 & + & 0.216
\end{array}
$$

$P(\text{at least 1 success}) = P(1 \text{ success}) + P(2 \text{ successes}) + P(3 \text{ successes})$
$= 0.432 + 0.288 + 0.064$
$= 0.784$

● The probability of at least one morning with suitable weather is about 78%.

Real-World Connection

Teardrop-shaped balloons collect weather data.

CA Standards Check **4** One survey found that 80% of respondents eat corn on the cob in circles rather than from side to side. Assume that this sample accurately represents the population. What is the probability that, out of five people you know, at least two of them eat corn on the cob in circles?

EXERCISES For more exercises, see *Extra Skill and Word Problem Practice*.

Standards Practice PS 3.0, 4.0, ALG2 18.0, 19.0

A Practice by Example

Example 1
(page 698)

GO for Help

For each situation, describe a trial and a success. Then design and run a simulation to find the probability.

1. On a true-or-false test, you guess the answers to five questions. Find the probability of guessing the correct answers to exactly three of the five questions.

2. A poll shows that 40% of the voters in a city favor passage of a bond issue to finance park improvements. If ten voters are selected at random, find the probability that exactly four of them will vote in favor of it.

3. A plant production line has a 90% probability of not experiencing a breakdown during an eight-hour shift. Find the probability that three successive shifts will not have a breakdown.

Example 2
(page 698)

Suppose you guess on a true-or-false test. Use a tree diagram to find each probability.

4. P(4 correct in 4 guesses)   **5.** P(1 correct in 4 guesses)

6. P(3 correct in 4 guesses)   **7.** P(6 correct in 4 guesses)

Example 3
(page 699)

Find the probability of x successes in n trials for the given probability of success p on each trial.

8. $x = 3, n = 8, p = 0.3$ **9.** $x = 4, n = 8, p = 0.3$

10. $x = 5, n = 10, p = 0.5$ **11.** $x = 5, n = 10, p = 0.1$

Example 4
(page 700)

Use the binomial expansion of $(p + q)^n$ to calculate and graph each binomial distribution.

12. $n = 6, p = 0.3$ **13.** $n = 6, p = 0.5$ **14.** $n = 6, p = 0.9$

 Apply Your Skills

Marketing **A fruit company guarantees that 90% of the pineapples it ships will be ripe within four days. Find each probability for a case containing 12 pineapples.**

15. All 12 are ripe within four days.   **16.** At least 10 are ripe within four days.

17. No more than 9 are ripe within four days.

Sociology **A study shows that 50% of the families in a community watch television during dinner. Suppose you select 10 families at random from this population. Find each probability.**

18. P(5 of the 10 families watch television during dinner)

19. P(6 of the 10 families watch television during dinner)

20. P(at least 5 of the 10 families watch television during dinner)

 21. Writing Explain how a binomial experiment is related to a binomial expansion.

22. Quality Control A company claims that 99% of its cereal boxes have at least as much cereal by weight as the amount stated on the box.
a. At a quality control checkpoint, one box out of a random sample of ten boxes falls short of its stated weight. What is the probability of this happening due to chance variation in box weights?
b. Suppose three of ten boxes fail to have the claimed weight. What would you conclude? Explain why.

23. Data Collection Use the current winning percentage of a local sports team as its probability of success. Find the team's probability of winning at least three of any five games.

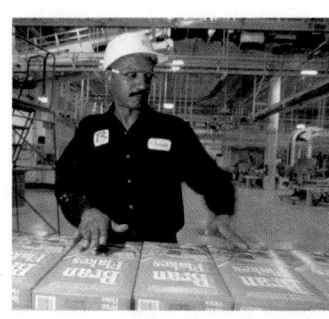

Real-World Connection

Manufacturers ensure the quality of their products by inspecting raw materials, machinery, and procedures, as well as finished products.

24. Genetics About 11% of the general population is left-handed. At a school with an average class size of 30, each classroom contains four left-handed desks. Does this seem adequate? Justify your answer.

25. For a group of 40 people, what is the probability that exactly three people in the group will celebrate their birthdays on a Wednesday this year?
a. Find the probability by using the binomial probability formula.
b. Find the probability by designing and running a simulation.
c. Compare your results for parts (a) and (b). Explain any discrepancy.

Homework Video Tutor

Visit: PHSchool.com
Web Code: bbe-1206

26. Open-Ended Describe a binomial experiment that can be solved using the expression $_7C_2(0.6)^2(0.4)^5$.

Statistics A multiple-choice test has ten questions. Each question has five choices, with only one correct.

27. Statisticians consider a "rare" event to have less than a 5% chance of occurring. According to this standard, what grades would be rare on this test if you guess? Justify your answer.

28. Design and conduct a simulation to model this situation. Gather results of simulations from your classmates. Do these results confirm the grades you identified as rare in Exercise 27? Explain.

29. Enter the binomial probability formula as shown. Set the window and table shown. (To get integer values of x, you may need to adjust your window.)

```
Plot1  Plot2  Plot3
\Y₁ (7 nCr X) * 0.5^X*
0.5^(7-X)
\Y₂ =
\Y₃ =
\Y₄ =
\Y₅ =
\Y₆ =
```

```
WINDOW
Xmin = -1.7
Xmax = 7.7
Xscl = 1
Ymin = -.2
Ymax = .5
Yscl = .1
Xres = 1
```

```
TABLE SETUP
TblStart = 0
ΔTbl = 1
Indpnt:  Auto  Ask
Depend:  Auto  Ask
```

a. Examine the graph of $y = {}_7C_x(0.5)^x(0.5)^{7-x}$. Describe any symmetry you see in the graph.

b. Verify the symmetry by displaying values of the function in table form.

c. Change the graph to $y = {}_7C_x(0.6)^x(0.4)^{7-x}$. Does this graph have any symmetry? Explain.

Multiple Choice Practice

For California Standards and CAHSEE Tutorials, visit PHSchool.com. Web Code: bbq-9045

PS 3.0 **30.** A survey shows that 60% of adults floss their teeth every day. In a random sample of ten adults, what is the probability that exactly six floss every day?

(A) 11% (C) 60%

(B) 25% (D) 100%

PS 4.0 **31.** A multiple choice quiz contains five questions, each with three answer choices. You select all five answer choices at random. What is the best estimate of the probability that you will get at least four answers correct?

(A) 4.1% (C) 13.2%

(B) 4.5% (D) 46.1%

ALG2 16.0 **32.** Which equation represents an ellipse with a center at $(-1, 3)$ and a horizontal major axis?

(A) $\dfrac{(x+1)^2}{3^2} + \dfrac{(y-3)^2}{12} = 1$

(B) $\dfrac{(x-1)^2}{3^2} + \dfrac{(y+3)^2}{12} = 1$

(C) $\dfrac{(x+1)^2}{12} + \dfrac{(y-3)^2}{3^2} = 1$

(D) $\dfrac{(x-1)^2}{12} + \dfrac{(y+3)^2}{3^2} = 1$

GO for Help

Lesson 12-5

33. The table contains information from a study of the prices of comparable airline tickets. Which sample most likely was greater in size, A or B? Explain.

Sample	Standard Deviation
A	$10.81
B	$3.97

Lesson 11-5

Find the sum of each geometric series to the given term.

34. $8 + 12 + 18 + \ldots; n = 8$

35. $20 + (-2) + 0.2 + \ldots; n = 12$

36. $729 + 243 + 81 + \ldots; n = 9$

37. $\frac{1}{16} + \frac{1}{4} + 1 + \ldots; n = 6$

Lesson 10-5

Find the equation of a hyperbola with horizontal transverse axis, centered at the origin, for the given a and c values.

38. $a = 897$ units, $c = 1024$ units

39. $a = 20$ units, $c = 29$ units

Lesson 5-4

Factor each expression.

40. $x^2 + 6x + 9$

41. $x^2 + x - 6$

42. $x^2 - 7x + 10$

43. $3x^2 + 12x + 9$

44. $2x^2 - x - 6$

45. $5x^2 + 5x - 10$

✓ Checkpoint Quiz 2   Lessons 12-4 through 12-6

Calculate the mean, range, and standard deviation for each set of data.

1. 34 36 29 45 34 25

2. 12 9 10 11 14 10

3. 1 5 2 1 4 1 3 2

4. A set of values has a mean of 300 and a standard deviation of 60. What value has a z-score of -1.2?

5. A survey on the Web site of an online CD store includes the question, "Who is your favorite singer?"

  a. Explain why the results of the survey may be biased.

  b. Open-Ended Suggest a way to make the survey an unbiased representation of the population of your high school.

6. Consumer Spending In a survey of 683 car owners selected at random, 235 reported paying cash for their first car.

  a. Find the sample proportion.

  b. Find the margin of error.

  c. Find an interval likely to contain the true population proportion.

7. Determine the sample size that produces a margin of error of $\pm 20\%$.

8. Seventy percent of the time, a friend of yours is more than 10 minutes late to meet you for a movie. What is the probability that your friend will be more than 10 minutes late to meet you for all of the next three movies you see?

Each trial of an experiment has a probability of success p. Find the probability of x successes in n trials.

9. $p = 0.8, x = 4, n = 5$

10. $p = 0.4, x = 4, n = 5$

Normal Distributions

 California Content Standards

PS 4.0 Students are familiar with normal distribution and can use it to solve for events in problems.
PS 5.0 Students determine the mean and the standard deviation of a normally distributed random variable.

What You'll Learn

• To use a normal distribution

• To use the standard normal curve

. . . And Why

To describe the jaws of great white sharks, as in Example 2

 Check Skills You'll Need

 for Help Lesson 12-4

Find the numbers that are one and two standard deviations above and below each given mean. Write these numbers from least to greatest.

1. $\bar{x} = 12, \sigma = 2$ **2.** $\bar{x} = 16.7, \sigma = 1$ **3.** $\bar{x} = 7, \sigma = 1.5$

4. $\bar{x} = 22, \sigma = 1.7$ **5.** $\bar{x} = 17.5, \sigma = 0.9$ **6.** $\bar{x} = 33.1, \sigma = 1.2$

◀)) **New Vocabulary** • normal distribution • standard normal curve

1 Using a Normal Distribution

A **normal distribution** shows data that vary randomly from the mean. The pattern the data form is a bell-shaped curve called a normal curve.

1 EXAMPLE Real-World Connection

Real-World Connection

Most newborns with a low birth rate (less than 2500 grams—or 5 pounds, 8 ounces) are treated in a neonatal intensive care unit.

Medicine The bar graph below gives the birth weights of a population of 100 babies. The red curve shows how the weights are normally distributed about the mean, 3250 g. Estimate the percent of babies weighing 2500–3999 g.

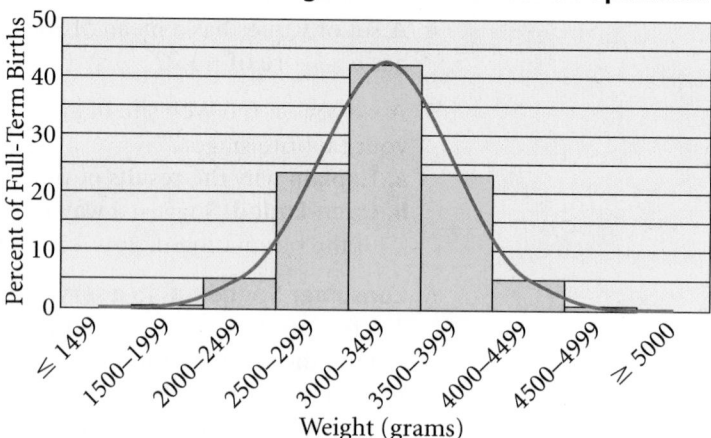

Full-Term Birth Weight Distribution for a Population

Estimate and add the percents for 2500–2999, 3000–3499, and 3500–3999.

$23\% + 42\% + 23\% = 88\%$

● About 88% of the babies weigh 2500–3999 g.

✓ **CA Standards Check** **1 a.** Estimate the percent of babies weighing less than 3500 g.
b. The standard deviation in birth weights is about 500 g. Estimate the percent of babies whose birth weights are within 1.5 standard deviations of the mean.

Every normal curve has a symmetric bell shape. When outcomes are normally distributed, you can sketch the graph of the distribution.

2 EXAMPLE   Real-World 🌐 Connection

Biology Refer to the photo. For the given population of sharks, the standard deviation of the jaw widths is 2.8 inches. Sketch a normal curve showing the jaw widths at one, two, and three standard deviations from the mean.

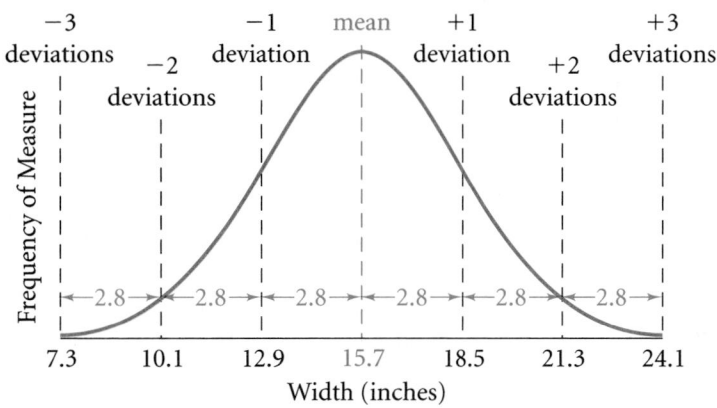

Distribution of Jaw Widths for Great White Sharks

Real-World 🌐 Connection

The jaw widths of a population of great white sharks are normally distributed about a mean of 15.7 inches.

✔ **CA Standards Check ②** Suppose the mean in Example 2 is 15.4 inches and the standard deviation is 3.1 inches. Sketch a normal curve showing the jaw widths at one, two, and three standard deviations from the mean.

---

2   Using the Standard Normal Curve

When you show a probability distribution as a bar graph, the height of the bar for each outcome indicates the probability. For a normal curve, however, the area between the curve and the *x*-axis represents the probability.

The **standard normal curve** is a normal distribution centered on the *y*-axis. The mean of the standard normal curve is 0. The standard deviation is 1.

The Standard Normal Curve

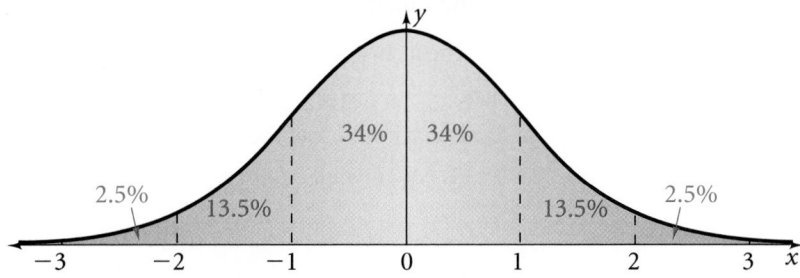

Vocabulary Tip

The z-score of a value is the number of standard deviations that the value is from the mean.

Every normal curve contains the same probability distribution. When a data set is normally distributed, about 68% of the data fall within one standard deviation of the mean. About 95% of the data fall within two standard deviations of the mean. To find the values that are two standard deviations away from the mean, find the values that have *z*-scores of −2 and 2.

3 EXAMPLE   Using the Standard Normal Curve

In a survey, the responses to the question "How much time do you spend at meals in one week?" were normally distributed. The mean was 13 h; the standard deviation was 3 h.

a. What values are one standard deviation from the mean?

Values that are one standard deviation from the mean have z-scores of -1 and 1.

$$z\text{-score} = \frac{\text{value} - \text{mean}}{\text{standard deviation}}$$

$$-1 = \frac{v - 13}{3} \qquad\qquad 1 = \frac{u - 13}{3}$$
$$v = 10 \qquad\qquad\qquad u = 16$$

The values 10 h and 16 h are one standard deviation away from the mean.

b. What percent of the responses would you expect to find from 10 h to 16 h?

The responses are normally distributed, and 10 h and 16 h are the values that are one standard deviation from the mean. Since 68% of the data are within one standard deviation of the mean, 68% should be values from 10 h to 16 h.

✅ **CA Standards Check ③ a.** Suppose there were 100 responses to the survey question. How many responses would you expect to be values from 10 h to 16 h?

b. Of 100 responses, how many would you expect to be values from 16 h to 19 h?

4 EXAMPLE   Real-World 🌐 Connection

Education In a university lecture class with 174 students, the final exam scores have a mean of 68.5 and a standard deviation of 7.3. The grades on the exams are all whole numbers, and the grade pattern follows a normal curve.

a. About how many students receive grades from one to two standard deviations above the mean.

Use the normal curve. About 13.5% of the students receive grades from one to two standard deviations above the mean.

Distribution of Final Exam Scores

$0.135(174) = 23.49$ **Find the number of students that corresponds to 13.5%.**

About 23 students receive grades from one to two standard deviations above the mean.

b. About how many students receive grades of 61 or below.

Use the normal curve from part (a). A grade of 61 is about one standard deviation below the mean.

$13.5\% + 2.5\% = 16\%$ **Find the % at least 1 standard deviation below the mean.**

$0.16(174) = 27.84$ **Find the number of students.**

About 28 students receive grades of 61 or below.

✅ **CA Standards Check ④ a.** Suppose there are 140 students in the class in Example 4. About how many would receive grades from 69 to 75?

b. Writing How do you know that in a class of 140 students, about 22 students receive grades of 76 or higher?

EXERCISES

Standards Practice

For more exercises, see *Extra Skill and Word Problem Practice*.

PS 4.0, 5.0

A Practice by Example

Example 1
(page 704)

GO for Help

Biology The heights of men in a survey are distributed normally about the mean. Use the graph for Exercises 1–4.

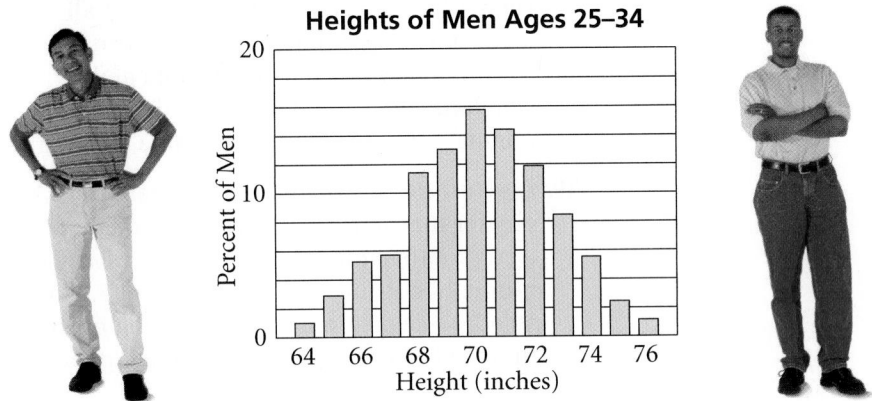

Heights of Men Ages 25–34

1. About what percent of men aged 25 to 34 are 69–71 inches tall?

2. About what percent of men aged 25 to 34 are less than 70 inches tall?

3. Suppose the survey included data on 100 men. About how many would you expect to be 69–71 inches tall?

4. The mean of the data is 70, and the standard deviation is 2.5. About what percent of men are within one standard deviation of the mean in height?

Example 2
(page 705)

Sketch a normal curve for each distribution. Label the *x*-axis values at one, two, and three standard deviations from the mean.

5. mean = 45, standard deviation = 5

6. mean = 45, standard deviation = 10

7. mean = 45, standard deviation = 2

8. mean = 45, standard deviation = 3.5

Examples 3 and 4
(page 706)

A set of data with a mean of 62 and a standard deviation of 5.7 is normally distributed. Find each value, given its distance from the mean.

9. +3 standard deviations

10. −1 standard deviation

A set of data has a normal distribution with a mean of 50 and a standard deviation of 8. Find the percent of data within each interval.

11. from 42 to 58

12. greater than 34

13. less than 50

14. **Test Scores** The scores on an exam are normally distributed, with a mean of 85 and a standard deviation of 5. What percent of the scores are from 85 to 95?

B Apply Your Skills

15. The numbers of paper clips in a truckload of boxes are normally distributed, with a mean of 100 and a standard deviation of 5. Find the probability that a box will *not* contain from 95 to 105 clips.

16. **Writing** In a class of 25, one student receives a grade of 100 on a test. The grades are distributed approximately normally, with a mean of 78 and a standard deviation of 5. Do you think the student's grade is an outlier? Explain.

17. a. From the table at the right, select the set of values that appears to be distributed normally.
   b. Using the set you chose in part (a), make a histogram of the values.
   c. Sketch a normal curve over your graph.

Set 1	Set 2	Set 3
1	5	5
10	7	6
5	7	9
19	7	1
2	4	1
7	11	5
1	7	11
7	7	1
2	7	10
10	9	4
6	7	2
9	7	8

18. Track To qualify as a contestant in a race, a runner has to be in the fastest 16% of all applicants. The running times are normally distributed, with a mean of 63 min and a standard deviation of 4 min. To the nearest minute, what is the qualifying time for the race?

19. Agriculture To win a prize, a tomato must be greater than 4 in. in diameter. The diameters of a crop of tomatoes grown in a special soil are normally distributed, with a mean of 3.2 in. and a standard deviation of 0.4 in. Find the probability that the crop will contain a winning tomato.

A normal distribution has a mean of 100 and a standard deviation of 10. Find the probability that a value selected at random is in the given interval.

20. from 80 to 100   **21.** from 70 to 130   **22.** from 90 to 120

23. at least 100   **24.** at most 110   **25.** at least 80

26. Two tomato plants were chosen from two groups of plants grown in different soils. Each sample plant produced 23 tomatoes. The mean number of tomatoes for plants in the first soil was 17, with a standard deviation of 5. The mean number of tomatoes for plants in the second soil was 18, with a standard deviation of 6. Determine which plant, if either, is in the top 16% of its group.

27. In a set of data, the value that is −3 standard deviations from the mean is 86. The value that is +1 standard deviation from the mean is 250.
   a. Find the mean.
   b. Find the standard deviation.
   c. Find an interval with an end value of 250 that contains about 81.5% of the data.

28. Seismology The table below shows the number of earthquakes worldwide in 2000.
   a. Draw a histogram to represent the data.
   b. Does the histogram approximate a normal curve? Explain.

Worldwide Earthquakes in 2000

Magnitude	Number	Magnitude	Number
0.1–0.9	6	5.0–5.9	1318
1.0–1.9	1028	6.0–6.9	157
2.0–2.9	3728	7.0–7.9	14
3.0–3.9	4741	8.0–8.9	4
4.0–4.9	8114	≥9.0	0

SOURCE: U.S. Geological Survey

Homework Video Tutor

Visit: PHSchool.com
Web Code: bbe-1207

29. Critical Thinking Jake and Elena took the same standardized test, but with different groups of students. They both received a score of 87. In Jake's group, the mean was 80 and the standard deviation was 6. In Elena's group, the mean was 76 and the standard deviation was 4. Did either student score in the top 10% of his or her group? Explain.

 Challenge

30. Quality Control Tubs of Better Butter weigh 1.0 lb each, with a standard deviation of 0.06 lb. At a quality control checkpoint, 12 of the tubs taken as samples weighed less than 0.88 lb. Assume that the weights of the samples were normally distributed. How many tubs of butter were taken as samples?

31. Games In the Japanese game pachinko, a player launches small steel balls from the bottom of a playing frame to the top. The balls then fall through pins and bounce around haphazardly. They land in slots at the bottom of the game and form a normal distribution. If a ball falls into a specially marked slot, the player wins additional balls with which to play again in the next round. If a ball does not fall into a marked slot, the player loses that ball.

a. Suppose that all slots between one and two standard deviations from the center are marked. When a ball lands in one of the marked slots, you win the ball back along with two others. If you begin with 200 balls, how many balls should you have after one round?

b. Suppose that there are two sets of marked slots. One set is within one standard deviation of the center and the other set is more than two standard deviations from the center. When a ball lands in one of the slots in the first set, you win the ball back. When a ball lands in one of the slots in the second set, you win the ball back, along with four others. If you begin with 1000 balls, how many balls should you have after one round?

c. Open-Ended Using your knowledge of normal distributions, design a pachinko game with both winning and losing slots in which you would theoretically have the same number of balls after each round as when you started. You can adjust the number of balls at the beginning of the game, the placement of the winning slots, and the number balls won per slot.

Multiple Choice Practice

For California Standards and CAHSEE Tutorials, visit PHSchool.com. Web Code: bbq-9045

PS 5.0

32. A set of data is normally distributed with a mean of 44 and standard deviation of 3.2. Which statements are NOT true?
I. 68% of the values are between 37.6 and 50.4
II. 13.5% of the values are less than 40.8
III. 5% of the values are lower than 37.6 or higher than 50.4

   Ⓐ I and II only   Ⓒ II and III only
   Ⓑ I and III only   Ⓓ I, II, and III

PS 8.0

33. What are the quartiles of these data?
   18   19   20   20   22   23   25   28   32

   Ⓐ $Q_1 = 19.5, Q_2 = 22, Q_3 = 26.5$
   Ⓑ $Q_1 = 20, Q_2 = 21, Q_3 = 26.5$
   Ⓒ $Q_1 = 20, Q_2 = 22, Q_3 = 25$
   Ⓓ $Q_1 = 19, Q_2 = 22.5, Q_3 = 28$

ALG2 10.0 **34.** For the parabola shown below, which conclusion is accurate?

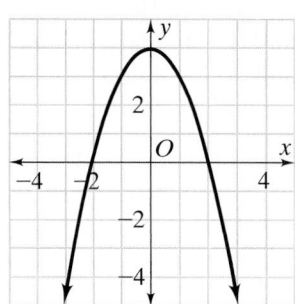

     A   The minimum value is at $(-2, 0)$.

     B   The maximum value is at $(0, 4)$.

     C   The vertex is at $(2, 0)$.

     D   The axis of symmetry is the x-axis.

ALG2 3.0 **35.** The area of a rectangular piece of land is described by the expression $2x^2 + x - 1$. Which pair of expressions could describe the dimensions of the piece of land?

     A $2x - 1$ and $x + 1$

     B $2x - 1$ and $x + 2$

     C $2x + 1$ and $x - 1$

     D $2x + 1$ and x

Mixed Review

Lesson 12-6

36. Production A plant production line has a 95% probability of not experiencing a breakdown during a six-hour shift. The plant managers want to know the probability that four successive shifts will not have a breakdown. Design and run a simulation to find the probability. Include an explanation of what constitutes a trial and a success.

Lesson 11-6   **For each set of axes, what does the area under the curve represent?**

37. y-axis: tons of garbage generated per year, x-axis: years

38. y-axis: bus passengers per hour, x-axis: hours

Lesson 10-6   **39. Coordinate Geometry** Write the equation of a circle centered at $(4, -5)$ with radius 7.

Open-Ended Write the equation of a conic section with the given characteristics.

40. an ellipse with a major axis 8 units long

41. a hyperbola with an asymptote at $y = -x$

Lesson 9-1   **Suppose that x and y vary inversely. Write a function to model inverse variation.**

42. $x = 1$ when $y = 5$ **43.** $x = -1$ when $y = 10$ **44.** $x = -3$ when $y = 3$

45. $x = 25$ when $y = -5$ **46.** $x = 1.8$ when $y = -6$ **47.** $x = 7.5$ when $y = 50$

Area Under a Curve

Statisticians use the function $f(x) = \frac{1}{\sqrt{2\pi}} e^{-\frac{x^2}{2}}$ to model data such as height or birth weight. You can use the area under the graph of the function to find probabilities.

ACTIVITY

In a given population, the weights of babies are normally distributed about the mean, 3250 g. The standard deviation is 500 g. Find the probability that a baby chosen at random weighs from 2250 g to 4250 g.

Step 1 Find the z-scores of the lower and upper limits.

$$z\text{-score} = \frac{\text{value} - \text{mean}}{\text{standard deviation}}$$

$$z_1 = \frac{2250 - 3250}{500} = \frac{-1000}{500} = -2$$

$$z_2 = \frac{4250 - 3250}{500} = \frac{1000}{500} = 2$$

Step 2 Enter $f(x) = \frac{1}{\sqrt{2\pi}} e^{-\frac{x^2}{2}}$ as Y_1. Adjust the window values.

```
WINDOW
 Xmin = -4.7
 Xmax = 4.7
 Xscl = 1
 Ymin = -.2
 Ymax = .5
 Yscl = .1
 Xres = 1
```

Step 3 Use the CALC feature and press 7 to access the $\int f(x)dx$ feature. Move the cursor until the lower limit is $x = -2$. Press ENTER . Move the cursor until the upper limit is $x = 2$. Press ENTER .

The area under the curve from $x = -2$ to $x = 2$ is about 0.95. So the probability that a baby weighs from 2250 g to 4250 g is about 95%.

EXERCISES

Use the data and the function in the example. Find the probability that the weight of a baby chosen at random falls within each interval.

1. 3150–4150 g
2. 4300–4500 g
3. less than 1800 g
4. more than 4550 g

5. For Exercises 1–4, estimate the number of babies within each interval from a population of 2400 babies.

6. **Manufacturing** A battery company manufactures batteries having life spans that are normally distributed, with a mean of 45 months and a standard deviation of 5 months. Find the probability that a battery chosen at random will have each life span.
   a. 45–52 months
   b. 48–50 months

When answering a question, be sure to answer the question that is asked. Read the question carefully and identify the quantity that you are asked to find. Some answer choices are answers to related questions, so you have to be careful that you are answering the right question.

EXAMPLE

There are five puppies in a litter. If the probability that a puppy is male is 0.5, what is the probability that at most one puppy in the litter is male?

   (A) 0.15625   (B) 0.1875   (C) 0.5   (D) 0.8125   (E) 0.96875

The problem is asking for the probability of "at most" one male puppy. Do not confuse this with "exactly" or "at least" one male puppy.

$$P(\text{at most one male puppy}) = P(\text{no male puppies}) + P(\text{exactly 1 male puppy})$$
$$= {}_5C_0(0.5)^0(0.5)^5 + {}_5C_1(0.5)^1(0.5)^4$$
$$= 0.03125 + 0.15625 = 0.1875$$

The correct answer is B.

Choices A and E are answers to related, but different, questions.

$$P(\text{exactly one male puppy}) = {}_5C_1(0.5)^1(0.5)^4 = 0.15625$$
$$P(\text{at least one male puppy}) = P(\text{exactly 1 male}) + \ldots + P(\text{exactly 5 males})$$
$$= {}_5C_1(0.5)^1(0.5)^4 + \ldots + {}_5C_5(0.5)^5(0.5)^0$$
$$= 0.15625 + \ldots + 0.03125$$
$$= 0.96875$$

EXERCISES

Identify the quantity that is being asked for. Then answer the question.

1. A box contains four quarters. Exactly two of the quarters have the American eagle on the back. Suppose you draw two quarters with replacement at random from the box.
   a. What is the probability that both have the American eagle on the back?
   b. What is the probability that neither has the American eagle on the back?
   c. What is the probability that at least one has the American eagle on the back?

2. In a survey, 28% of respondents say they are left-handed, 64% say they are right-handed, and 8% say they are ambidextrous. If the ambidextrous people are omitted, about what percent of those remaining are left-handed?

   (A) 28%   (B) 30%   (C) 32%   (D) 34%   (E) 36%

3. A student conducted a survey at school and found that 75% of the boys and 65% of the girls like to watch hockey games. There are an equal number of boys and girls in the school. If someone does not like to watch hockey games, what is the approximate probability that the person is a boy?

   (A) 25%   (B) 42%   (C) 48%   (D) 55%   (E) 75%

Chapter 12 Review

Vocabulary Review

◀》 English and Spanish Audio Online

bimodal (p. 672)
binomial experiment (p. 697)
binomial probability (p. 699)
box-and-whisker plot (p. 674)
conditional probability (p. 666)
cumulative probability (p. 660)
frequency table (p. 660)
interquartile range (p. 681)
margin of error (p. 691)

mean (p. 672)
measures of central tendency (p. 672)
measures of variation (p. 681)
median (p. 672)
mode (p. 672)
normal distribution (p. 704)
outlier (p. 676)
percentile (p. 675)
probability distribution (p. 661)

quartiles (p. 674)
random sample (p. 689)
range of a set of data (p. 681)
sample (p. 689)
sample proportion (p. 689)
standard deviation (p. 681)
standard normal curve (p. 705)
z-score (p. 683)

For: Vocabulary quiz
Web Code: bbj-1251

Choose the correct term to complete each sentence.

1. A(n) _?_ is part of a population.

2. A(n) _?_ has a value substantially different from other data in a set.

3. A function that gives the probability of each event in a sample space is a(n) _?_.

4. A(n) _?_ involves repeated trials, each of which has two possible outcomes whose probabilities are constant throughout the trials.

5. Dispersion of data in a data set can be described by _?_.

Skills and Concepts

Lessons 12-1 and 12-2

- To make a probability distribution (p. 660)
- To use a probability distribution in conducting a simulation (p. 662)
- To find conditional probabilities (p. 666)
- To use formulas and tree diagrams (p. 667)

PS 8.0, 2.0

A **probability distribution** is a function that gives the probability of each event in a sample space. A **frequency table** lists outcomes and the number of times each occurs. A frequency table can be used to find **cumulative probability**, which is the probability of a range of events.

A **conditional probability** limits the sample space to a given event. The probability of event A, given event B, is written $P(A|B)$. You can find a conditional probability from a table, a tree diagram, or by the conditional probability formula.

$$P(A|B) = \frac{P(A \text{ and } B)}{P(B)}$$

6. Use the results in the table below for the Rock-Paper-Scissors game.
   a. Make a frequency table for the winner: Player 1, Player 2, or tie.
   b. Find $P(\text{Player 2 wins})$.

Rock-Paper-Scissors

Player 1	S	P	P	R	R	P	P	P	P	S	R	S	P	S	R
Player 2	P	R	S	S	P	S	R	R	P	P	R	S	R	P	P

R = Rock   P = Paper   S = Scissors   **Bold** = Winner

7. Two number cubes are rolled. Use a table to show the probability distribution for the product of the two numbers.

8. At a bank, the number of customers c who arrive at the teller counters each minute varies according to the distribution below. Simulate the number of customers over a ten-minute period.

Number of Customers Each Minute

c	0	1	2	3	4	5	6	7
$P(c)$	0.16	0.28	0.25	0.18	0.09	0.02	0.01	0.01

Use the frequency table below for Exercises 9 and 10.

Birthday Months of Respondents to a Survey

Month	J	F	M	A	M	J	J	A	S	O	N	D
Male	0	1	2	1	1	3	2	0	1	1	0	2
Female	0	1	0	1	0	2	1	3	1	0	4	1

9. Find P(birthday in August | female respondent).

10. Find P(male respondent | birthday in June).

Use these survey results for Exercises 11–13.

- Of all respondents, 60% have 1 sibling and 20% have 2 or more siblings.
- Of the respondents with 0 siblings, 90% have their own room.
- Of the respondents with 1 sibling, 20% do not have their own room.
- Of the respondents with 2 or more siblings, 50% have their own room.

11. Make a tree diagram that reflects the results of the survey.

12. Find P(own room | 0 siblings).   **13.** Find P(share room | 1 sibling).

Lesson 12-3

- To calculate measures of central tendency (p. 672)
- To draw and interpret box-and-whisker plots (p. 674)

 PS 6.0, 8.0

You can use **measures of central tendency** to analyze data. The **mean** $\bar{x}$ equals the sum of the values divided by the number of values. The **median** is the middle value of a data set in numerical order. If the set has an even number of values, then the median is the mean of the middle two values. The **mode** is the most frequently occurring value. There can be more than one mode or no mode. A **bimodal** distribution has 2 modes. The second quartile is the median of the whole set. The first and third **quartiles** are, respectively, the medians of the values less than and greater than the median. A **box-and-whisker plot** displays data by using the quartiles to form a box and the minimum and maximum values to form whiskers. A **percentile** divides the range of a data set into two parts such that the part lying below the value contains a given percentage of the data. An **outlier** is a data value substantially different from the rest of the data.

Use the following set of values for Exercises 14–19.

13 12 15 18 14 16 18 12 13 14 14 17 15   8 17
16 12 16 14 15 13 13 17 15 14 18 16 12 12 13

14. Find the mean, median, and mode.   **15.** Make a box-and-whisker plot.

16. Find the 20th and 90th percentiles.   **17.** At what percentile is 15?

18. Identify the outlier.   **19.** Find the range without the outlier.

Lesson 12-4

- To find the standard deviation of a set of values (p. 680)
- To use standard deviation in real-world situations (p. 683)

 PS 7.0

You can use **measures of variation** to describe the spread of data. The **range of a set of data** is the difference between the maximum and minimum values. The **interquartile range** is the difference between the third and first quartiles. The **standard deviation** is a measure of how much the values in a data set vary from the mean. To find the standard deviation, (1) find the mean, (2) find the difference between each data value and the mean, (3) square each difference, (4) find the mean of the squares, and (5) take the square root of this mean. The **z-score** of a value is the number of standard deviations that value is from the mean.

Use the following set of values for Exercises 20–22.

$1.95 $1.27 $1.81 $1.33 $1.30 $.99 $1.63 $1.49 $1.39 $1.25 $1.50

20. Find the standard deviation.

21. Within how many standard deviations of the mean do all of the values fall?

22. Find the z-score of the value $1.85, to the nearest hundredth.

Lesson 12-5

- To find sample proportions (p. 689)
- To find the margin of error (p. 690)

A **sample** is part of a population. For a **random sample**, all members of the population are equally likely to be chosen for the sample. When an event occurs x times in a sample of size n, the **sample proportion** is the ratio $\frac{x}{n}$. When a random sample of size n is taken from a large population, the sample proportion has a **margin of error** of approximately $\pm \frac{1}{\sqrt{n}}$.

23. Of 50 people who rented clubs at a golf course, 38 were right-handed.
   a. Find the sample proportion as a percent.
   b. Find the margin of error.
   c. Find an interval likely to contain the true population proportion.

Lessons 12-6 and 12-7

- To find binomial probabilities (p. 697)
- To use binomial distributions (p. 699)
- To use a normal distribution (p. 704)
- To use the standard normal curve (p. 705)

 PS 3.0, 4.0, 5.0, ALG2 18.0, 19.0

A **binomial experiment** has repeated independent trials, each trial having two possible outcomes. In a binomial experiment with probability of success p and of failure q (so $p + q = 1$), the probability of x successes in n trials is ${}_nC_x p^x q^{n-x}$. This value is the **binomial probability**.

A **normal distribution** shows data that vary from the mean in a random manner. The pattern they form is a bell-shaped curve called a normal curve. The **standard normal curve** is a normal distribution centered on the y-axis. The mean is 0 and the standard deviation is 1. When a data set follows the normal curve, about 68% of the data fall within one standard deviation of the mean. About 95% of the data fall within two standard deviations of the mean.

24. A true-or-false quiz contains four questions. Design and describe a simulation you could use to find the probability of guessing three questions correctly.

25. Find the probability of 13 successes in 24 trials, given that the probability of success is 0.6 for each trial.

26. Use the binomial expansion of $(p + q)^n$ to write the binomial distribution for $n = 5$ and $p = 0.7$.

27. Sketch a curve for a normal distribution with mean 10 and standard deviation 4. Label the x-axis at one, two, and three standard deviations from the mean.

Graph the probability distribution for each sample space when two number cubes are rolled.

1. {both cubes the same number, each cube a different number}

2. {prime sum, composite sum}

 3. **Writing** Describe how a situation can have more than one sample space. Include an example.

Use the table below for Exercises 4–8.

How Many Current Music Groups Can You Name?

Age of Respondent	Number of Groups	
	0 – 4	5 or more
< 30	7	18
≥ 30	13	12

4. Make a frequency table for the ages of the respondents.

5. Make a frequency table for the number of groups named.

6. Find P(5 or more).

7. Find P(5 or more | age < 30).

8. Find P(age ≥ 30 | 0–4).

9. Find the mean, median, and mode for this set of values: 8, 9, 11, 12, 13, 15, 16, 18, 20.

10. Make a box-and-whisker plot for this set of values: 36, 36, 48, 65, 75, 82, 92, 101.

11. Find the 20th and 60th percentiles for this set of values: 36, 38, 42, 47, 51, 56, 62, 69, 70, 74.

12. Given the set of values below, at what percentiles are 78 and 81?
    43 58 64 78 78 81 89 89 91 93

13. Identify the outlier of this set of values: 17, 15, 16, 15, 9, 18, 16.

14. **Open-Ended** Write a set of values that has a range of 10, a mean of 86, and a mode of 85.

15. Find the mean and the standard deviation for this set of values: 15, 17, 19, 20, 14, 23, 12.

16. A data set has a mean 30 and a standard deviation of 3. Find the z-score of the value 38.

Find the margin of error for each sample. Then find an interval likely to contain the true population proportion.

17. 15% of 457 teachers

18. 47% of 296 teens

19. 56% of 87 musicians

20. 23% of 100 bakers

A newspaper wants to take a poll about which candidate voters prefer for President. Identify any bias in each sampling method.

21. The newspaper interviews people at a political debate.

22. The newspaper publishes a number for people to call and express their opinion.

23. The newspaper calls people selected at random from the local telephone book.

Find the probability of x successes in n trials for the given probability of success p on each trial.

24. $x = 4, n = 10, p = 0.2$

25. $x = 3, n = 8, p = 0.6$

26. At a high school, 30% of the students buy class rings. You select five students at random. Find P(exactly two buy rings) and P(at least two buy rings).

27. A student guesses the answers to three questions on a true-or-false test. Design and describe a simulation to find the probability that the student guesses at least one of the questions correctly.

A set of data has a normal distribution with a mean of 29 and a standard deviation of 4. Find the percent of data within each interval.

28. from 25 to 33

29. from 21 to 25

30. greater than 29

31. less than 21

32. A data set is normally distributed with a mean of 37 and a standard deviation of 8.1. Sketch a normal curve for the distribution. Label the x-axis values at one, two, and three standard deviations from the mean.

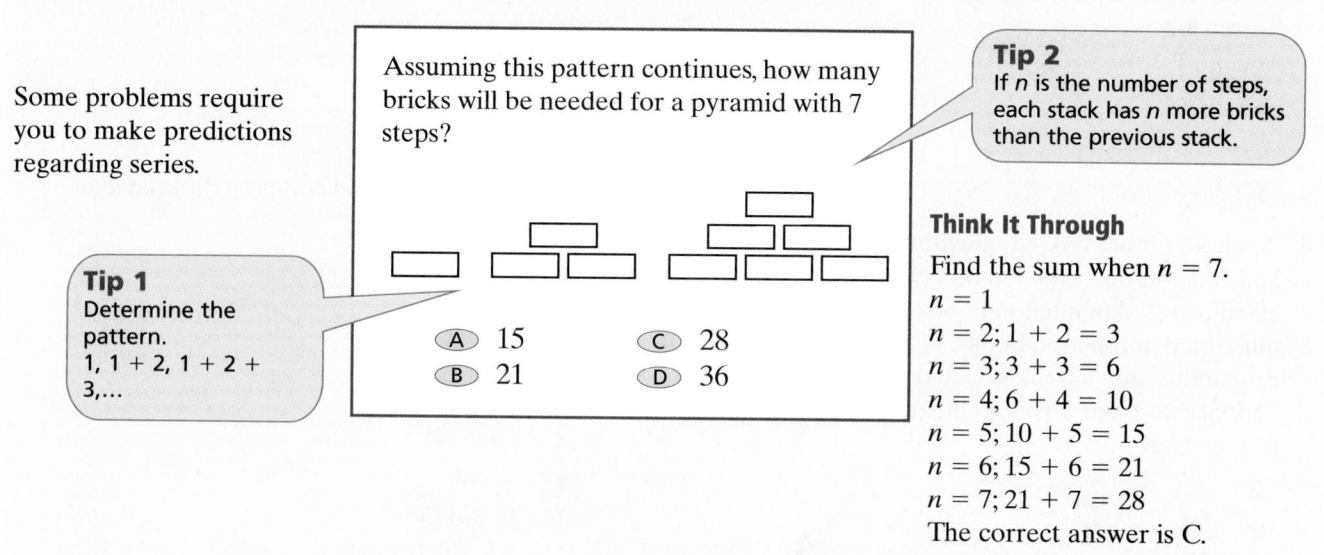

Some problems require you to make predictions regarding series.

Assuming this pattern continues, how many bricks will be needed for a pyramid with 7 steps?

Tip 1
Determine the pattern.
1, 1 + 2, 1 + 2 + 3,...

A 15   C 28
B 21   D 36

Tip 2
If n is the number of steps, each stack has n more bricks than the previous stack.

Think It Through
Find the sum when $n = 7$.
$n = 1$
$n = 2; 1 + 2 = 3$
$n = 3; 3 + 3 = 6$
$n = 4; 6 + 4 = 10$
$n = 5; 10 + 5 = 15$
$n = 6; 15 + 6 = 21$
$n = 7; 21 + 7 = 28$
The correct answer is C.

Vocabulary Review

As you solve problems, you must understand the meanings of mathematical terms. Choose the correct term for each sentence.

1. The (normal distribution, binomial distribution) shows data that vary randomly from the mean in a bell-shaped curve.

2. The (mean, median) is the middle value (or average of middle values) in a set of data.

3. The sections of a box-and-whisker plot are usually referred to as (quartiles, measures of variation).

4. A measure of how much the values in a data set vary from the mean is the (sample proportion, standard deviation).

5. A (cumulative probability, probability distribution) is a function that gives the probability of each event in a sample space.

6. A (frequency table, box-and-whisker plot) is a list of the outcomes in a sample space and the number of times each outcome occurs.

Multiple Choice

Read each question. Then write the letter of the correct answer on your paper.

1. A and B are mutually exclusive events. $P(A) = \frac{1}{3}$ and $P(B) = \frac{1}{2}$. What is $P(A \text{ or } B)$? **(Lesson 9-7)**

   A $\frac{1}{6}$ C $\frac{5}{6}$
   B $\frac{2}{3}$ D 1

2. On a certain day, the guides took 9 different groups of people on tours of Mercer Caverns just outside Murphys, California. The data show the number of people in each group. What are the quartiles of the data? **(Lesson 12-3)**

   12   14   14   17   19   20   21   21   22

   A $Q_1 = 12, Q_2 = 19, Q_3 = 21.5$
   B $Q_1 = 14, Q_2 = 19, Q_3 = 21$
   C $Q_1 = 14, Q_2 = 19.5, Q_3 = 22$
   D $Q_1 = 17, Q_2 = 20, Q_3 = 22$

Cumulative Practice (continued)

3. Hanson brought home a bag of books from school. In the bag, there are 2 novels, 5 textbooks, and 1 dictionary. What is the probability that a book pulled randomly out of the bag is fiction? **(Lesson 9-7)**

- (A) 0.15
- (B) 0.25
- (C) 0.50
- (D) 0.85

4. A school library has 420 illustrated fiction books and 780 non-illustrated fiction books. It also has 590 illustrated nonfiction books and 250 non-illustrated non-fiction books. What is the probability that a book selected at random is fiction, given that it is non-illustrated? **(Lesson 12-2)**

- (A) $\frac{780}{1030}$
- (B) $\frac{780}{2040}$
- (C) $\frac{1030}{2040}$
- (D) $\frac{250}{1030}$

5. The figure below shows the first three stages of a fractal.

  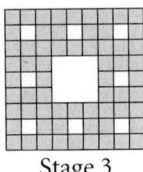

Stage 1   Stage 2   Stage 3

How many shaded squares will the nth stage of this fractal contain? **(Lesson 11-1)**

- (A) $8n$
- (B) 8^n
- (C) $8^n - 1$
- (D) 8^{n-1}

6. What is the sum of the infinite geometric series, $1 - 0.2 + 0.04 - \ldots$, as a fraction? **(Lesson 11-5)**

- (A) $\frac{1}{25}$
- (B) $\frac{1}{6}$
- (C) $\frac{1}{5}$
- (D) $\frac{5}{6}$

7. In six basketball games, Roberto scored the following points per game. What is the approximate standard deviation of points scored? **(Lesson 12-4)**

$$8 \quad 11 \quad 14 \quad 7 \quad 12 \quad 18$$

- (A) 1.0
- (B) 2.0
- (C) 4.0
- (D) 5.0

8. Which sequence has a common difference of 3? **(Lesson 11-2)**

I. $a_n = a_{n-1} - 3, a_1 = 2$
II. $a_n = 3$
III. $a_n = a_{n-1} + 3, a_1 = -7$
IV. $a_n = n^2 + 3$

- (A) I only
- (B) I and III
- (C) II only
- (D) II and IV

9. Which number completes the square for $x^2 - 3x$? **(Lesson 5-7)**

- (A) 9
- (B) $-\frac{3}{2}$
- (C) $-\frac{9}{2}$
- (D) $\frac{9}{4}$

10. What are the solutions to $9x^2 + 4 = 0$? **(Lesson 5-8)**

- (A) ± 2
- (B) $\pm\frac{2}{3}i$
- (C) $\pm\frac{2}{3}$
- (D) $\pm\sqrt{\frac{2}{3}}$

11. If $f(x) = x^2 - 1$ and $g(x) = |2x + 3|$, which has the greatest value? **(Lesson 7-6)**

- (A) $f(g(3))$
- (B) $g(f(2))$
- (C) $g(f(-1))$
- (D) $f(g(10))$

12. If $f(x) = 2x^2$ and $g(x) = 3(x + 1)$, which is an equivalent form of $f(x) + g(x)$? **(Lesson 7-6)**

- (A) $2x^2 + 3x + 1$
- (B) $2x^2 + 3x + 3$
- (C) $2x^2 + 3x - 3$
- (D) $5x^3 + 3$

13. Jacques is randomly distributing flyers for his band's next concert. There are 30 blue flyers and 46 red flyers. What is the probability that the first flyer he hands out will be blue and the second flyer will be red? (Lesson 9-7)

- Ⓐ $\frac{23}{95}$
- Ⓑ $\frac{76}{151}$
- Ⓒ $\frac{69}{285}$
- Ⓓ $\frac{61}{151}$

14. Students were asked in a survey whether they had been to a movie theater in the last month. The table below shows the results.

Have you been to a movie recently?

	Yes	No
Male	35	17
Female	28	20

What is the probability that a student has not gone to the movies recently given that the student is a male? (Lesson 12-2)

- Ⓐ $\frac{17}{52}$
- Ⓑ $\frac{37}{52}$
- Ⓒ $\frac{52}{37}$
- Ⓓ $\frac{17}{37}$

15. A jar contains 13 round mint candies, 7 round chocolate candies, 9 square mint candies, and 11 square chocolate candies. If a candy is chosen at random, what is the probability that it is mint, given that it is square? (Lesson 12-2)

- Ⓐ $\frac{1}{2}$
- Ⓒ $\frac{11}{20}$
- Ⓑ $\frac{9}{20}$
- Ⓓ $\frac{13}{40}$

16. Jason was asked to analyze rainfall for a town by his high school science teacher. The data shows the annual rainfall in inches for 9 consecutive years. What are the quartiles of the data?
(Lesson 12-3)

41 66 53 49 54 43 50 27 50

- Ⓐ $Q_1 = 42, Q_2 = 50, Q_3 = 53.5$
- Ⓑ $Q_1 = 43, Q_2 = 49, Q_3 = 53.5$
- Ⓒ $Q_1 = 43, Q_2 = 50, Q_3 = 53$
- Ⓓ $Q_1 = 41, Q_2 = 50.5, Q_3 = 54$

17. Meng has a spinner with 18 equal sections colored either yellow or green. If the spinner lands on green on 36 out of 50 spins, which is most likely the number of green sections on the spinner?
(Lesson 9-7)

- Ⓐ 5
- Ⓑ 9
- Ⓒ 13
- Ⓓ 17

18. For a school play, 6 boys and 6 girls volunteer to be ushers. If two ushers are chosen at random by drawing names from a bowl, what is the probability that both ushers will be girls? (Lesson 6-7)

- Ⓐ $\frac{5}{24}$
- Ⓑ $\frac{5}{22}$
- Ⓒ $\frac{1}{4}$
- Ⓓ $\frac{1}{2}$

Standards Reference Guide

California Content Standard	Item Number(s)
PS 1.0	1, 3, 13, 17
PS 2.0	4, 14–15
PS 7.0	7
PS 8.0	2, 16
ALG2 8.0	9–10
ALG2 19.0	18
ALG2 22.0	5–6, 8
ALG2 25.0	11–12

For additional review and practice, see the *California Standards Review and Practice Workbook* or go online to use the

California Standards Tutorials

Visit: PHSchool.com, **Web Code:** bbq-9045

CHAPTER 13
Periodic Functions and Trigonometry

 What You've Learned

California Content Standards

10.0 Students graph quadratic functions and determine the maxima, minima, and zeros of the function.

12.0 Students know the laws of fractional exponents, understand exponential functions, and use these functions in problems involving exponential growth and decay.

24.0 Students solve problems involving functional concepts.

✓ **Check Your Readiness**   **GO** **for Help** to the Lesson in green.

Analyzing Graphs of Rational Functions (Lesson 9-3)

Describe the vertical asymptotes and holes for each rational function.

1. $y = \dfrac{2}{x - 3}$

2. $y = \dfrac{(x - 5)(x - 1)}{x - 1}$

3. $y = \dfrac{x + 2}{(2x + 1)(x - 4)}$

Simplifying Complex Fractions (Lesson 9-5)

Simplify each complex fraction.

4. $\dfrac{\frac{2}{a}}{\frac{1}{b}}$

5. $\dfrac{5 + \frac{1}{2}}{2 - \frac{1}{5}}$

6. $\dfrac{\frac{3}{c + d}}{2}$

7. $\dfrac{\frac{1}{4}}{\frac{4}{c}}$

8. $\dfrac{\frac{2}{3}}{\frac{6}{c + 4}}$

9. $\dfrac{\frac{4}{x}}{\frac{2}{8}}$

10. $\dfrac{3 - \frac{1}{2}}{\frac{7}{6}}$

11. $\dfrac{\frac{9}{m - n}}{\frac{3}{2m - 2n}}$

Translating Conic Sections (Lesson 10-6)

Write an equation for each conic section. Then sketch the graph.

12. circle with center at $(1, -4)$ and radius 4

13. ellipse with center at $(2, 5)$, vertices at $(5, 5)$ and $(-1, 5)$, and co-vertices at $(2, 3)$ and $(2, 7)$

14. parabola with vertex at $(0, -3)$ and focus at $(0, 5)$

15. hyperbola with center at $(6, 1)$, one focus at $(6, 6)$, and one vertex at $(6, -2)$

Writing Formulas for Sequences (Lesson 11-1)

Find the next two terms in each sequence. Write a formula for the nth term. Identify each formula as *explicit* or *recursive*.

16. $16, 13, 10, 7, \ldots$

17. $-1, -8, -27, -64, -125, \ldots$

18. $9, 3, 1, \frac{1}{3}, \ldots$

What You'll Learn Next

California Content Standards

5.0 Students know the definitions of the tangent and cotangent functions and can graph them. *Trigonometry*

6.0 Students know the definitions of the secant and cosecant functions and can graph them. *Trigonometry*

7.0 Students know the tangent of the angle that a line makes with the *x*-axis is equal to the slope of the line. *Trigonometry*

▲ The circular path of these swings after one complete revolution measures 2π radians.

New Vocabulary
🔊 **English and Spanish Audio Online**

- **amplitude** (p. 724)
- **central angle** (p. 738)
- **cosecant** (p. 775)
- **cosine function** (p. 755)
- **cosine of** θ (p. 732)
- **cotangent** (p. 775)
- **coterminal angles** (p. 731)
- **cycle** (p. 723)
- **initial side** (p. 730)
- **intercepted arc** (p. 738)
- **period** (p. 723)
- **periodic function** (p. 723)
- **phase shift** (p. 768)
- **radian** (p. 738)
- **secant** (p. 775)
- **sine curve** (p. 747)
- **sine function** (p. 746)
- **sine of** θ (p. 732)
- **standard position** (p. 730)
- **tangent function** (p. 761)
- **tangent of** θ (p. 761)
- **terminal side** (p. 730)
- **unit circle** (p. 732)

13-1 Exploring Periodic Data

What You'll Learn

- To identify cycles and periods of periodic functions
- To find the amplitude of periodic functions

. . . And Why

To make predictions about sound waves, as in Example 4

✓ **Check Skills You'll Need**

GO for Help Lesson 2-1

Determine whether each relation is a function.

1. $\{(2, 4), (1, 3), (-3, -1), (4, 6)\}$

2. $\{(2, 6), (-3, 1), (-2, 2)\}$

3. $\{(x, y) \mid x = 3\}$

4. $\{(x, y) \mid y = 8\}$

5. $\{(x, y) \mid x = y^2\}$

6. $\{(x, y) \mid x^2 + y^2 = 36\}$

7. $\{(a, b) \mid a = b^3\}$

8. $\{(w, z) \mid w = z - 36\}$

◄))) **New Vocabulary** • periodic function • cycle • period • amplitude

---

1 Identifying Periodic Functions

Activity: Periodic Cycles

Use the diagram below. Suppose you and a friend are the last two people seated on a Ferris wheel. Once the ride begins, the wheel moves at a constant speed. It takes 36 seconds to complete one revolution.

40 ft

5 ft

1. a. At 0 seconds, when the ride starts, how high above the ground are you?
 b. At what height are you at 9 seconds? At 18 seconds? At 27 seconds?
 c. At what height are you at 126 seconds? How many revolutions have you made?
 d. Predict where you will be at 3 minutes.

2. Sketch a graph showing the relationship between your height above the ground and the time since the ride began. Use $0 \le t \le 144$ for the domain, where $t = 0$ is the time at which the ride starts.

3. Critical Thinking How far (in feet) have you traveled after one revolution of the wheel? How far have you traveled at 144 seconds?

A **periodic function** repeats a pattern of *y*-values (outputs) at regular intervals. One complete pattern is a **cycle.** A cycle may begin at any point on the graph of the function. The **period** of a function is the horizontal length of one cycle.

1 EXAMPLE Identifying Cycles and Periods

Analyze the periodic function below. Identify one cycle in two different ways. Then determine the period of the function.

Begin at any point on the graph. Trace one complete pattern.

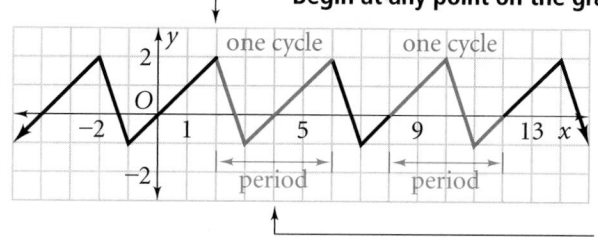

The beginning and ending *x*-values of each cycle determine the period of the function.

● Each cycle is 4 units long. The period of the function is 4.

✓ CA Standards Check 1 For each function, identify one cycle in two different ways. Then determine the period of the function.

a.
b.

You can determine whether a function is periodic by analyzing its graph.

2 EXAMPLE Identifying Periodic Functions

Determine whether each function *is* or *is not* periodic. If it is, find the period.

a.

Although the graph shows similar curves, the *y*-values from one section do not repeat in other sections. The function *is not* periodic.

b.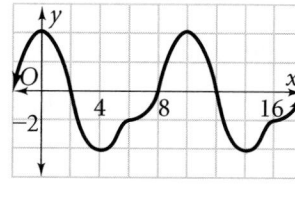

The pattern of *y*-values in one section repeats exactly in other sections. The function *is* periodic.

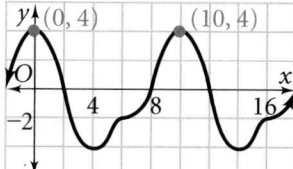

Find points at the beginning and end of one cycle. Subtract the *x*-values of the points: $10 - 0 = 10$. The pattern in the graph repeats every 10 units, so the period is 10.

✅ **CA Standards Check** ② Determine whether each function *is* or *is not* periodic. If it is, find the period.

a.

b.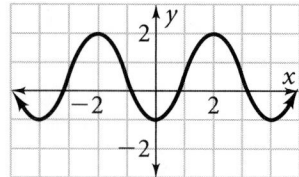

2 Finding the Amplitude of a Periodic Function

Vocabulary Tip

Amplitude modulation (AM) radio works by varying the amplitude of radio waves.

The amplitude of a periodic function measures the amount of variation in the function values.

🔑 **Key Concepts**

Definition	**Amplitude of a Periodic Function**

The **amplitude** of a periodic function is half the difference between the maximum and minimum values of the function.

3 EXAMPLE Finding Amplitude of a Periodic Function

Find the amplitude of the periodic function at the right.

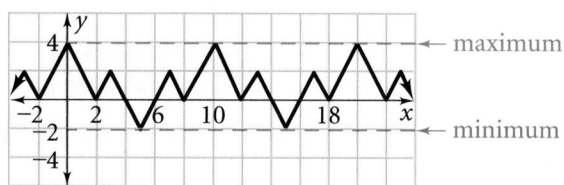

amplitude $= \frac{1}{2}$(maximum value $-$ minimum value)   **Use the definition of amplitude.**

$= \frac{1}{2}[4 - (-2)]$ **Substitute.**

$= \frac{1}{2}(6) = 3$ **Subtract within parentheses and simplify.**

● The amplitude of the function is 3.

✅ **CA Standards Check** ③ Find the amplitude of each function.

a.

b.

You can model some data with periodic functions. The rotation of a Ferris wheel, the beating of a heart, and the movement of sound waves are all examples of real-world events that generate periodic data.

4 EXAMPLE **Real-World Connection**

Sound Waves Sound is produced by periodic changes in air pressure called sound waves. The oscilloscope at the right shows the graph of a pure tone from a tuning fork. Find the period and the amplitude of the sound wave.

1 unit on the *t*-axis = 0.001 s

One cycle of the sound wave occurs from 0.003 s to 0.0075 s. The maximum value of the function is 4, and the minimum value is −4.

period = 0.0075 − 0.003   **Use the definitions.**   amplitude = $\frac{1}{2}[4 - (-4)]$

= 0.0045   **Simplify.**   = $\frac{1}{2}(8) = 4$

● The period of the sound wave is 0.0045 s. The amplitude is 4.

✓ **CA Standards Check** ④ Sketch the graph of a sound wave with a period of 0.004 s and an amplitude of 2.

EXERCISES   For more exercises, see *Extra Skill and Word Problem Practice.*

Standards Practice

A **Practice by Example**

Example 1
(page 723)

Identify one cycle in two different ways. Then determine the period of the function.

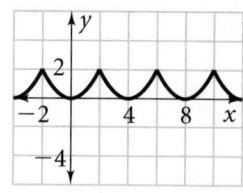

Example 2
(page 723)

Determine whether each function *is* or *is not* periodic. If it is, find the period.

Find the amplitude of each periodic function.

10.

11.

12.

13.

B **Apply Your Skills**

Sketch the graph of a sound wave with the given period and amplitude.

14. period 0.02, amplitude 4   **15.** period 0.005, amplitude 9

16. Complete each statement with x or y.
   a. You use ■-values to compute the amplitude of a function.
   b. You use ■-values to compute the period of a function.

✎ **Writing** **Could you use a periodic function to represent each situation described below? Explain.**

17. the average monthly temperature in your community, recorded every month for three years

18. the population in your community, recorded every year for the last 50 years

19. the number of cars per hour that pass through an intersection near where you live, recorded for two consecutive work days

Health **Use the graph below for Exercises 20 and 21.**

20. A person's pulse rate is the number of times his or her heart beats in one minute. Each cycle in the graph represents one heartbeat. Find the pulse rate.

21. An electrocardiogram (EKG or ECG) measures the electrical activity of a person's heart in millivolts over time.
   a. What is the period of the EKG shown above?
   b. What is the amplitude of the EKG?

22. Open-Ended Sketch a graph of a periodic function that has a period of 3 and an amplitude of 2.

Find the maximum, minimum, and period of each periodic function. Then copy the graph and sketch two more cycles.

23.

24.

25.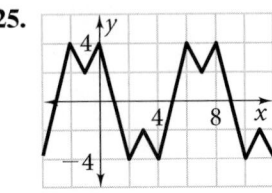

Language Arts Functions that repeat over time are common in everyday life. The English language has many words that stand for common periods of time. State the period of time from which each term derives.

26. annual   **27.** biweekly   **28.** quarterly   **29.** hourly   **30.** circadian

 Challenge

31. Suppose f is a periodic function. The period of f is 5 and $f(1) = 2$. Find $f(6)$, $f(11)$, and $f(-4)$.

32. Suppose g is a periodic function. The period of g is 24, $g(3) = 67$, and $g(8) = 70$. Find each function value.
    a. $g(27)$ **b.** $g(80)$ **c.** $g(-16)$ **d.** $g(51)$

Visit: PHSchool.com
Web Code: bbe-1301

33. Motion You are sitting on a pier watching the waves when you notice a bottle in the water. The bottle bobs so that it is between 2.5 ft and 4.5 ft below the pier. You know you can reach 3 ft below the pier. Suppose the bottle reaches its highest point every 5 s.
    a. Sketch a graph of the bottle's distance below the pier for 15 s. Assume that at $t = 0$, the bottle is closest to the pier.
    b. Find the period and the amplitude of the function.
    c. Estimation Use your graph to estimate the length of time the bottle is within reach during each cycle.

34. Calendar A day—the time Earth takes to rotate from one noon to the next— is a basic measure of time. A solar year is about 365.2422 days. We try to keep our calendar in step with the solar year.
    a. If every calendar year has 365 days, by how many days would the calendar year and the solar year differ after 100 years?
    b. If every fourth year has an extra "leap" day added, by how many days would the two systems differ after 100 years?
    c. If every hundred years the "leap" day is omitted, by how many days would the two systems differ after 100 years?
    d. Critical Thinking Why is it important for the difference between the calendar year and the solar year to be zero?

Multiple Choice Practice

For California Standards and CAHSEE Tutorials, visit PHSchool.com. Web Code: bbq-9045

ALG2 19.0   **35.** Whitney, Sophia, and Greg are among 13 students who have applied for a college scholarship. Only three of the applicants will be selected at random for the scholarship. What is the probability that Whitney, Sophia, and Greg will be the 3 students selected?
    Ⓐ $\frac{1}{143}$ Ⓑ $\frac{1}{286}$ Ⓒ $\frac{1}{858}$ Ⓓ $\frac{1}{1716}$

ALG2 10.0   **36.** With 8 seconds left, Carlo tried to kick a field goal to win the football game. The graph at the right shows the height h of the football in feet as a function of time t in seconds. What is the range of this function?
    Ⓐ $0 < h < 64$
    Ⓑ $0 < t < 4$
    Ⓒ $0 \le h \le 64$
    Ⓓ $0 \le t \le 4$

Height of the Football

ALG2 17.0

37. Which conic section is an ellipse?

Ⓐ $(x - 1)^2 + (y - 2)^2 = 4$

Ⓑ $(x + 4)^2 - (y - 3)^2 = 25$

Ⓒ $\frac{x^2}{36} + \frac{y^2}{81} = 100$

Ⓓ $\frac{x^2}{9} - \frac{y^2}{49} = 121$

PS 1.0

38. Kyle has a red and a green number cube. The sides of each cube are numbered from 1 to 6. If Kyle tosses both cubes, what is the probability that there will be an even number on the red cube and a multiple of 3 on the green cube?

Ⓐ $\frac{1}{8}$ Ⓑ $\frac{1}{6}$ Ⓒ $\frac{1}{5}$ Ⓓ $\frac{1}{4}$

Mixed Review

GO for Help

Lesson 12-7

39. Sketch a normal curve for a distribution that has mean 57 and standard deviation 12. Label the *x*-axis values at one, two, and three standard deviations from the mean.

Lesson 11-1

Find the next two terms in each sequence. Write a formula for the *n*th term. Identify each formula as *explicit* or *recursive*.

40. $1, 3, 5, 7, 9, \ldots$ **41.** $4, 6, 8, 10, 12, \ldots$ **42.** $3, 6, 11, 18, 27, \ldots$

Lesson 10-6

Write an equation for each conic section. Then sketch the graph.

43. parabola with vertex $(-3, 2)$ and focus $(-3, 7)$

44. hyperbola with center $(5, -3)$, one focus at $(5, 0)$, and one vertex at $(5, -1)$

45. ellipse with center $(-2, 1)$, vertices at $(-6, 1)$ and $(2, 1)$, and co-vertices at $(-2, 3)$ and $(-2, -1)$

A P•int in Time

1500 1600 1700 1800 1900 2000

To human beings, the most important periodic function is the rhythm of the heart. About once per second, a nerve in the heart generates an electrical signal. This causes the heart to contract and force blood through the body.

In 1958, doctors placed the first pacemaker in a patient with a malfunctioning nerve. The creator of the device's control unit was Otis Boykin, an inventor from Dallas, Texas. He began his career testing automatic airplane controls. Today, more than a million pacemakers are helping people worldwide enjoy the normal rhythms of the human heart.

Go Online
PHSchool.com

For: Information about pacemakers
Web Code: bbe-2032

Special Right Triangles

FOR USE WITH LESSON 13-2

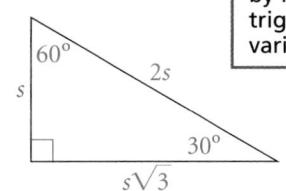

Prepares for TRIG 9.0 Students compute, by hand, the values of trigonometric functions at various standard points.

In Geometry you learned about two special right triangles, the 45°-45°-90° triangle and the 30°-60°-90° triangle. The figures at the right summarize the relationships among the lengths of the sides of each triangle.

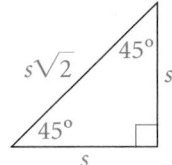

---

1 EXAMPLE Finding Side Lengths in a 45°-45°-90° Triangle

Find the missing side lengths in each figure.

a.

$h = \sqrt{2} \cdot 5$ **hypotenuse = $\sqrt{2} \cdot$ leg**

$h = 5\sqrt{2}$ **Simplify.**

b.

$5 = \sqrt{2} \cdot s$

$s = \dfrac{5}{\sqrt{2}}$

$s = \dfrac{5\sqrt{2}}{2}$

---

2 EXAMPLE Finding Side Lengths in a 30°-60°-90° Triangle

Find the missing side lengths in the triangle at the right.

$4 = \sqrt{3} \cdot s$ **longer leg = $\sqrt{3} \cdot$ shorter leg**

$s = \dfrac{4}{\sqrt{3}} = \dfrac{4\sqrt{3}}{3}$ **Divide and simplify.**

$h = 2s$ **hypotenuse = 2 · shorter leg**

$= 2 \cdot \dfrac{4\sqrt{3}}{3} = \dfrac{8\sqrt{3}}{3}$ **Substitute $\dfrac{4\sqrt{3}}{3}$ for s and simplify.**

EXERCISES

Use the given information to find the missing side length(s) in each 45°-45°-90° triangle. Rationalize any denominators.

1. hypotenuse 1 in.   **2.** leg 2 cm   **3.** hypotenuse $\sqrt{3}$ ft   **4.** leg $2\sqrt{5}$ m

Use the given information to find the missing side lengths in each 30°-60°-90° triangle. Rationalize any denominators.

5. shorter leg 3 in.   **6.** longer leg 1 cm   **7.** hypotenuse 1 ft

8. shorter leg $\sqrt{3}$ cm   **9.** hypotenuse $2\sqrt{2}$ ft   **10.** longer leg $2\sqrt{3}$ in.

11. hypotenuse $3\sqrt{2}$ m   **12.** longer leg $\sqrt{5}$ cm   **13.** shorter leg $\sqrt{13}$ mm

14. What is the ratio of the length to the width of a rectangle whose diagonals form a 90° angle? A 60° angle?

13-2 # Angles and the Unit Circle

 California Content Standards
TRIG 1.0 Students understand the notion of angle and how to measure it.
TRIG 2.0 Students know the definition of sine and cosine as *y*- and *x*- coordinates of points on the unit circle.
TRIG 9.0 Students compute, by hand, the values of trigonometric functions at various standard points.

What You'll Learn

- To work with angles in standard position
- To find coordinates of points on the unit circle

. . . And Why

To use an ancient calendar, as in Example 3

 Check Skills You'll Need

GO for Help pages 54 and 888

For each measure, draw an angle with its vertex at the origin of the coordinate plane. Use the positive *x*-axis as one ray of the angle.

1. 90°   **2.** 45°   **3.** 30°

4. 150°   **5.** 135°   **6.** 120°

New Vocabulary • standard position • initial side • terminal side • coterminal angles • unit circle • cosine of θ • sine of θ

 Working With Angles in Standard Position

Vocabulary Tip

Terminal means "at an end" or "forming a boundary."

An angle is in **standard position** when the vertex is at the origin and one ray is on the positive *x*-axis. The ray on the *x*-axis is the **initial side** of the angle; the other ray is the **terminal side** of the angle.

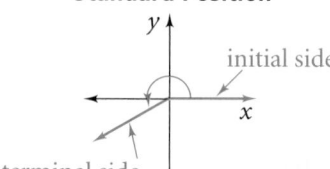

To measure an angle in standard position, find the amount of rotation from the initial side to the terminal side.

1 EXAMPLE **Measuring an Angle in Standard Position**

Find the measure of the angle at the right.

The angle measures 20° more than a straight angle of 180°.

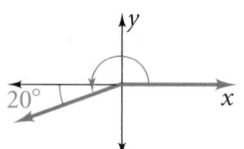

Since 180 + 20 = 200, the measure of the angle is 200°.

CA Standards Check **1** One full rotation contains 360 degrees. How many degrees are in one quarter of a rotation? In one half of a rotation? In three quarters of a rotation?

The measure of an angle is positive when the rotation from the initial side to the terminal side is in the counterclockwise direction. The measure is negative when the rotation is clockwise.

  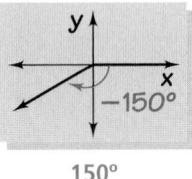

2 EXAMPLE Sketching an Angle in Standard Position

Sketch each angle in standard position.

a. 36°   **b.** 315°   **c.** −150°

36°
Counterclockwise

315°
Counterclockwise

150°
Clockwise

✓ **CA Standards Check** **2** Sketch each angle in standard position.

a. 85°   **b.** −320°   **c.** 180°

Two angles in standard position are **coterminal angles** if they have the same terminal side.

Angles that have measures 135° and −225° are coterminal.

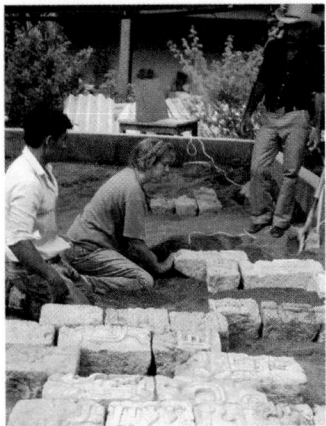

3 EXAMPLE Real-World 🌎 Connection

History The Aztec calendar stone has 20 divisions for the 20 days in each month of the Aztec year. The yellow angle marks the passage of 11 days. Find the measures of two coterminal angles that coincide with the angle.

The terminal side of the angle is $\frac{11}{20}$ of a full rotation from the initial side.

$$\frac{11}{20} \cdot 360° = 198°$$

To find a coterminal angle, subtract one full rotation.

$$198° - 360° = -162°$$

Two coterminal angle measures for the angle in the photograph are 198° and −162°.

✓ **CA Standards Check** **3** **a.** Find another angle coterminal with 198° by adding one full rotation.

   b. **Reasoning** Are angles with measures of 40° and 680° coterminal? Explain.

   c. **Make a Conjecture** Generalize how the measures of two coterminal angles are related.

Activity: Angles in a Circle

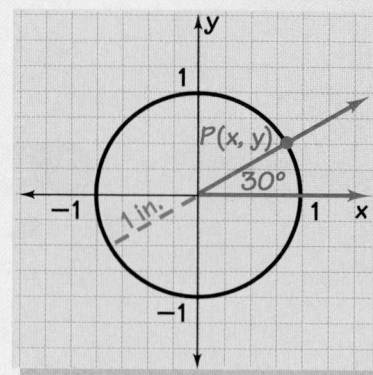

- Use a compass. Construct a circle with a radius of 1 in. on the coordinate plane. Place the center of the circle at the origin.

- Use a protractor. Draw an angle of 30°. Place one ray along the positive *x*-axis. Place the other ray in Quadrant I. Label the point where the second ray intersects the circle *P*(*x*, *y*).

1. Identify the methods you could use to find the coordinates of *P*.

2. Choose one method and find the values of *x* and *y*. Express the coordinates in decimal form.

3. Use a calculator to find the values of cos 30° (read "cosine of 30 degrees") and sin 30° (read "sine of 30 degrees"). Compare these values to the values you found in Question 2.

4. **a.** Repeat the steps above using an angle of 45°. What are the coordinates of the new point *P*?
   b. Find cos 45° and sin 45° using your calculator. How do these values compare to those you found in part (a)?
   c. **Make a Conjecture** What is the relationship between the coordinates of a point *P* on the circle and the values of the sine and cosine of the angle containing *P*?

The **unit circle** has a radius of 1 unit and its center at the origin of the coordinate plane. Points on the unit circle are related to periodic functions.

You can use the symbol θ for the measure of an angle in standard position.

 Key Concepts

Definition	**Cosine and Sine of an Angle**

Suppose an angle in standard position has measure θ. The **cosine of** θ (cos θ) is the *x*-coordinate of the point at which the terminal side of the angle intersects the unit circle. The **sine of** θ (sin θ) is the *y*-coordinate.

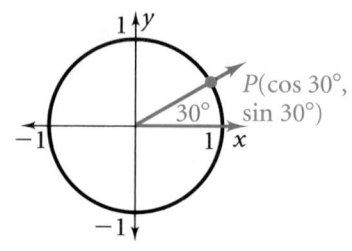

4 EXAMPLE Finding the Cosine and Sine of an Angle

Find the cosine and sine of 60°.

As the figure suggests, the *x*-coordinate of point *A* is $\frac{1}{2}$, so cos 60° = $\frac{1}{2}$, or 0.5.

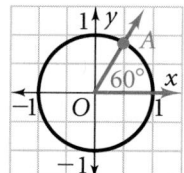

Use a 30°-60°-90° right triangle to find sin 60°.

$$\text{longer leg} = \sqrt{3} \cdot \text{shorter leg}$$
$$= \sqrt{3} \cdot \frac{1}{2} \qquad \textbf{Substitute.}$$
$$= \frac{\sqrt{3}}{2} \qquad \textbf{Multiply.}$$
$$\approx 0.87 \qquad \textbf{Simplify.}$$

The coordinates of the point at which the terminal side of a 60° angle intersects the unit circle are $(\frac{1}{2}, \frac{\sqrt{3}}{2})$, so cos 60° = 0.5 and sin 60° = $\frac{\sqrt{3}}{2} \approx 0.87$.

Problem Solving Hint

✓ **CA Standards Check** **4** Draw each angle in a unit circle. Then find the cosine and sine of each angle.
a. 45° **b.** 30° **c.** 120°

You can use right triangles to find the *exact* cosine and sine of an angle whose terminal side is not in Quadrant I.

5 EXAMPLE Finding Exact Values of Cosine and Sine

Find the exact values of cos (−120°) and sin (−120°).

Step 1 Sketch an angle of −120° in standard position. Sketch a unit circle.

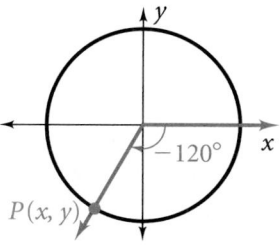

x-coordinate = cos (−120°)
y-coordinate = sin (−120°)

Step 2 Sketch a right triangle. Place the hypotenuse on the terminal side of the angle. Place one leg on the *x*-axis. (The other leg will be parallel to the *y*-axis.)

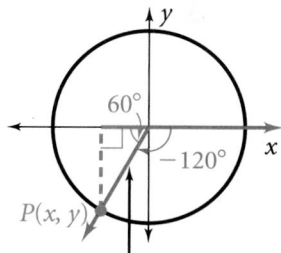

The triangle contains angles of 30°, 60°, and 90°.

Step 3 Find the length of each side of the triangle.

$$\text{hypotenuse} = 1 \qquad \textbf{The hypotenuse is a radius of the unit circle.}$$
$$\text{shorter leg} = \frac{1}{2} \qquad \textbf{The shorter leg is half the hypotenuse.}$$
$$\text{longer leg} = \frac{1}{2}\sqrt{3} \qquad \textbf{The longer leg is } \sqrt{3} \textbf{ times the short leg.}$$
$$= \frac{\sqrt{3}}{2}$$

Since the point lies in Quadrant III, both coordinates are negative. The shorter leg lies along the *x*-axis, so cos (−120°) = $-\frac{1}{2}$, and sin (−120°) = $-\frac{\sqrt{3}}{2}$.

✓ **CA Standards Check** ➎ **a.** Use a calculator to find cos (−120°) and sin (−120°). How do these values compare to the exact values found in Example 5?

b. Find the exact values of cos 135° and sin 135°. Use properties of a 45°-45°-90° triangle. Use a calculator to find the decimal equivalents.

c. Find the exact values of cos 150° and sin 150°.

EXERCISES

For more exercises, see *Extra Skill and Word Problem Practice.*

Standards Practice

TRIG 1.0, 2.0, 9.0

 Practice by Example

Example 1
(page 730)

Find the measure of each angle in standard position.

1.

2.

3.

4.

5.

6.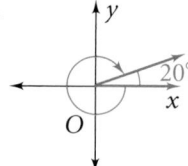

Example 2
(page 731)

Sketch each angle in standard position.

7. 40°   **8.** −130°   **9.** −270°   **10.** 120°   **11.** 95°

Example 3
(page 731)

Find the measure of an angle between 0° and 360° coterminal with each given angle.

12. 385°   **13.** 575°   **14.** −405°   **15.** −356°

16. 500°   **17.** −210°   **18.** 415°   **19.** −180°

20. Telephones Rotary telephones were widely used until the 1980s. Dialing a higher number (or 0) took longer because the dial moved through a larger central angle. Estimate the measures of two coterminal angles that coincide with the angle at the right.

Examples 4 and 5
(page 733)

Find the exact values of the cosine and sine of each angle. Then find the decimal values. Round your answers to the nearest hundredth.

21.

22.

23.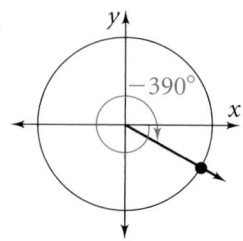

24. −240°   **25.** 390°   **26.** 315°   **27.** −30°   **28.** 135°

For each angle θ, find the values of $\cos \theta$ and $\sin \theta$. Round your answers to the nearest hundredth.

29. $0°$ **30.** $32°$ **31.** $-45°$ **32.** $-210°$

33. $-95°$ **34.** $-10°$ **35.** $154°$ **36.** $90°$

Open-Ended Find a positive and a negative coterminal angle for the given angle.

37. $45°$ **38.** $-125°$ **39.** $-675°$ **40.** $400°$

41. $-85°$ **42.** $-425°$ **43.** $213°$ **44.** $-57°$

In which quadrant, or on which axis, does the terminal side of each angle lie?

45. $150°$ **46.** $210°$ **47.** $540°$ **48.** $-60°$ **49.** $0°$

50. a. Copy and complete the chart at the right.
   b. Suppose you know that $\cos \theta$ is negative and $\sin \theta$ is positive. In which quadrant does the terminal side of the angle lie?
    c. Writing Summarize how the quadrant in which the terminal side of an angle lies affects the sign of the sine and cosine of that angle.

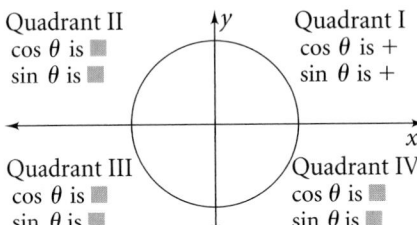

51. a. Use a calculator to find the value of each expression: $\cos 40°$, $\cos 400°$, and $\cos (-320°)$.
   b. Critical Thinking What do you notice about the values you found in part (a)? Explain.

 52. Writing Explain how to find the sine and cosine of angles with measures of $0°, 90°, 180°, 270°,$ and $360°$ without using a calculator.

C Challenge

Sketch each angle in standard position. Use the unit circle and a right triangle to find exact values of the cosine and the sine of the angle.

53. $-300°$ **54.** $120°$ **55.** $225°$

56. $-780°$ **57.** $-405°$ **58.** $1020°$

59. Design Navajo sand paintings like the one at the right have many lines of symmetry. Suppose point A is on a unit circle. Find the coordinates of A.

60. Open-Ended Find the measures of four angles in standard position that have a sine of 0.5. (*Hint:* Use the unit circle and right triangles.)

61. Critical Thinking Suppose θ is an angle in standard position and $\cos \theta = -\frac{1}{2}$ and $\sin \theta = -\frac{\sqrt{3}}{2}$. Can the value of θ be $60°$? Can it be $-120°$? Draw a diagram and justify your reasoning.

62. Navigation When navigators locate an object, they measure in a clockwise direction from due north. The measure of the angle is called the bearing. Suppose a lighthouse's bearing is 110° from a ship.

    a. Sketch the diagram at the right on a coordinate plane. Place north along the positive *y*-axis.

    b. Express the location of the lighthouse in terms of an angle in standard position.

Multiple Choice Practice

For California Standards and CAHSEE Tutorials, visit PHSchool.com. Web Code: bbq-9045

TRIG 2.0

63. What is the exact value of the cosine of the angle in the diagram?

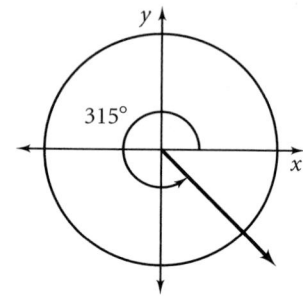

    (A) $\sqrt{2}$

    (B) $\dfrac{\sqrt{2}}{2}$

    (C) $\dfrac{\sqrt{3}}{2}$

    (D) $\dfrac{\sqrt{2}}{3}$

ALG2 5.0

64. If $i = \sqrt{-1}$, which point shows the location of $-3 + 4i$ on the plane at the right?

    (A) point *A*

    (B) point *B*

    (C) point *C*

    (D) point *D*

Mixed Review

Lesson 13-1

Determine whether each function *is* or *is not* periodic. If it is, find the period.

65.   **66.**   **67.**

Lesson 12-1

Graph the probability distribution for each sample space.

68. {two coins heads, two coins tails, one coin heads and the other tails}

69. {the sum of two number cubes a prime number, the sum a composite number}

Lesson 10-5

Find the foci of each hyperbola. Draw the graph.

70. $\dfrac{y^2}{16} - \dfrac{x^2}{4} = 1$ **71.** $\dfrac{y^2}{25} - \dfrac{x^2}{100} = 1$ **72.** $\dfrac{x^2}{36} - \dfrac{y^2}{49} = 1$ **73.** $\dfrac{x^2}{81} - \dfrac{y^2}{64} = 1$

Measuring Radians

> **TRIG 1.0** Students understand the notion of angle and how to measure it, in both degrees and radians. They can convert between degrees and radians.

In the past, you have used degrees to measure angles. When angles are used in periodic functions, they are often measured in larger units called radians.

1. Measure the diameter of a cylinder and calculate its radius. On a piece of string, mark off a "number line" with each unit equal to the radius. Mark at least seven units.

2. Wrap the string around the cylinder. How many radius units are needed to go around the cylinder one time?

3. Use the end of the cylinder to draw a circle on a sheet of paper. Keep the cylinder in place and wrap the string around it on the paper. Mark an arc of the circle equal to one radius unit of length.

4. Remove the cylinder and string. Use paper folding to locate the center of the circle. (Fold the circle onto itself and crease the paper along a diameter. Repeat to get a second diameter.) Draw a central angle that intercepts one radius unit of arc.

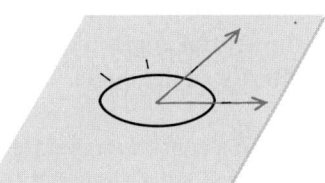

The measure of the angle you drew in Question 4 is 1 radian.

5. Use a protractor to measure the angle from Question 4 in degrees.

6. Critical Thinking The formula $C = 2\pi r$ relates the circumference of a circle C to its radius r. *Exactly* how many radians are in a 360° angle? Explain.

The diagram at the right shows that a rotation of 180° is equivalent to π radians.

7. Find the number of degrees in one radian by dividing 180 by π. How does your answer compare to the measurement you made in Question 5?

π radians $= 180°$

EXERCISES

Use the proportion $\dfrac{d°}{180°} = \dfrac{r \text{ radians}}{\pi \text{ radians}}$. Find the equivalent degree measure or radian measure.

1. 10°   **2.** 45°   **3.** 90°   **4.** 120°   **5.** 270°

6. 310°   **7.** 50°   **8.** 415°   **9.** 170°   **10.** 380°

11. $\dfrac{13\pi}{18}$ radians   **12.** $\dfrac{3\pi}{8}$ radians   **13.** $\dfrac{7\pi}{2}$ radians   **14.** $\dfrac{11\pi}{4}$ radians   **15.** $\dfrac{5\pi}{6}$ radians

Radian Measure

 California Content Standards
TRIG 1.0 Students can convert between degrees and radians.

What You'll Learn

• To use radian measure for angles

• To find the length of an arc of a circle

. . . And Why

To solve problems involving the orbits of satellites, as in Example 5

✓ **Check Skills You'll Need**

GO for Help page 910

Find the circumference of a circle with the given radius or diameter. Round your answer to the nearest tenth.

1. radius 4 in.   2. diameter 70 m

3. radius 8 mi   4. diameter 3.4 ft

5. radius 5 mm   6. diameter 6.3 cm

📢 **New Vocabulary** • central angle • intercepted arc • radian

---

1 Using Radian Measure

A **central angle** of a circle is an angle with a vertex at the center of a circle. An **intercepted arc** is the portion of the circle with endpoints on the sides of the central angle and remaining points within the interior of the angle.

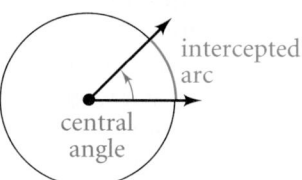

Vocabulary Tip

Radian is a shortened form of the phrase *radial angle*.

When a central angle intercepts an arc that has the same length as a radius of the circle, the measure of the angle is defined to be one **radian.** Like degrees, radians measure the amount of rotation from the initial side to the terminal side of an angle.

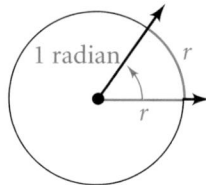

Because the circumference of a circle is $2\pi r$, there are 2π radians in any circle. Since 2π radians $= 360°$, and therefore π radians $= 180°$, you can use a proportion such as $\frac{d°}{180°} = \frac{r \text{ radians}}{\pi \text{ radians}}$ to convert between degrees and radians.

Real-World 🌐 **Connection**

Some pendulum rides travel through an arc of π radians.

1 EXAMPLE Using a Proportion

a. Find the radian measure of an angle of 60°.

$$\frac{60°}{180°} = \frac{r \text{ radians}}{\pi \text{ radians}} \qquad \textbf{Write a proportion.}$$

$$60 \cdot \pi = 180 \cdot r \qquad \textbf{Write the cross-products.}$$

$$r = \frac{60 \cdot \pi}{180} \qquad \textbf{Divide each side by 180.}$$

$$= \frac{\pi}{3} \approx 1.05 \qquad \textbf{Simplify.}$$

An angle of 60° measures about 1.05 radians.

b. Find the degree measure of $\frac{5\pi}{2}$ radians.

$$\frac{\frac{5\pi}{2}\text{ radians}}{\pi\text{ radians}} = \frac{d°}{180°} \qquad \textbf{Write a proportion.}$$

$$\frac{\frac{5\pi}{2}}{\pi} = \frac{d}{180}$$

$$\frac{5\pi}{2} \cdot 180 = \pi \cdot d \qquad \textbf{Write the cross-products.}$$

$$\frac{5\pi \cdot 180}{2 \cdot \pi} = d \qquad \textbf{Divide each side by } \boldsymbol{\pi}.$$

$$d = \frac{5\pi \cdot 180^{90}}{{}_1 2 \cdot \pi} \qquad \textbf{Simplify.}$$

$$= 450$$

An angle of $\frac{5\pi}{2}$ radians measures 450°.

CA Standards Check **1** Use a proportion for each conversion.
    a. 85° to radians   **b.** 2.5 radians to degrees

The proportion $\frac{d°}{180°} = \frac{r\text{ radians}}{\pi\text{ radians}}$ leads to the following two convenient conversion factors.

Key Concepts

Summary	Converting Between Radians and Degrees

To convert degrees to radians, multiply by $\frac{\pi\text{ radians}}{180°}$.

To convert radians to degrees, multiply by $\frac{180°}{\pi\text{ radians}}$.

You can use the conversion factors and dimensional analysis to convert between angle measurement systems.

2 **EXAMPLE** **Using Dimensional Analysis**

a. Find the degree measure of an angle of $-\frac{3\pi}{4}$ radians.

$$-\frac{3\pi}{4}\text{ radians} = -\frac{3\pi}{4}\text{ radians} \cdot \frac{180°}{\pi\text{ radians}} \qquad \textbf{Multiply by } \frac{180°}{\pi\text{ radians}}.$$

$$= -\frac{3\pi}{{}_1 4}\text{radians} \cdot \frac{{}^{45}180°}{\pi\text{ radians}} \qquad \textbf{Simplify.}$$

$$= -135°$$

An angle of $-\frac{3\pi}{4}$ radians measures $-135°$.

b. Find the radian measure of an angle of 27°.

$$27° = 27° \cdot \frac{\pi}{180°}\text{ radians} \qquad \textbf{Multiply by } \frac{\pi\text{ radians}}{180°}.$$

$$= {}^3 27° \cdot \frac{\pi}{{}_{20}180°}\text{ radians} \qquad \textbf{Simplify.}$$

$$= \frac{3\pi}{20}\text{ radians}$$

An angle of 27° measures $\frac{3\pi}{20}$ radians.

GO **nline**

Video Tutor Help
Visit: PHSchool.com
Web Code: bbe-0775

CA Standards Check **2** Use dimensional analysis to convert each degree measure from degrees to radians or from radians to degrees. (Express radian measures in terms of π.)
    a. $\frac{\pi}{2}$ radians   **b.** 225°   **c.** 2 radians   **d.** 150°

You can find the sine and cosine of angles in radian measure by first converting the radian measure to degrees and then using the unit circle.

3 EXAMPLE Finding Cosine and Sine of Radian Measures

Find the exact values of $\cos\left(\frac{\pi}{4}\text{ radians}\right)$ and $\sin\left(\frac{\pi}{4}\text{ radians}\right)$.

$\frac{\pi}{4}\text{ radians}\cdot\frac{180°}{\pi\text{ radians}}=45°$ **Convert radians to degrees.**

Draw the angle. Complete a 45°-45°-90° triangle. Since the hypotenuse has length 1, both legs have length $\frac{\sqrt{2}}{2}$.

Thus, $\cos\left(\frac{\pi}{4}\text{ radians}\right)=\frac{\sqrt{2}}{2}$ and $\sin\left(\frac{\pi}{4}\text{ radians}\right)=\frac{\sqrt{2}}{2}$.

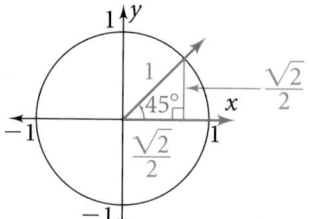

✅ **CA Standards Check** **3 a.** Use a calculator to find $\cos\left(\frac{\pi}{4}\text{ radians}\right)$ and $\sin\left(\frac{\pi}{4}\text{ radians}\right)$. How do these values compare to the coordinates found in Example 3?

b. Explain how to use mental math to convert $\frac{\pi}{4}$ radians to degrees. (*Hint:* Begin with the relationship π radians $=180°$.)

2 Finding the Length of an Arc

You can find the length of an intercepted arc by using the proportion

$$\frac{\text{arc length } s}{\text{circumference } 2\pi r}=\frac{\text{central angle measure } \theta \text{ radians}}{2\pi \text{ radians}}.$$

Simplifying this proportion results in the formula below.

 Key Concepts

Property   **Length of an Intercepted Arc**
For a circle of radius r and a central angle of measure θ (in radians), the length s of the intercepted arc is $s=r\theta$. 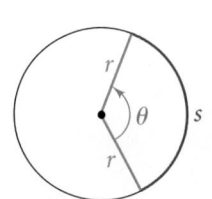

4 EXAMPLE Finding the Length of an Arc

Use the circle at the right. Find length s to the nearest tenth.

$s=r\theta$ **Use the formula.**

$=3\cdot\frac{5\pi}{6}$ **Substitute 3 for r and $\frac{5\pi}{6}$ for θ.**

$=\frac{5\pi}{2}$ **Simplify.**

≈ 7.9 **Use a calculator.**

The arc has length 7.9 in.

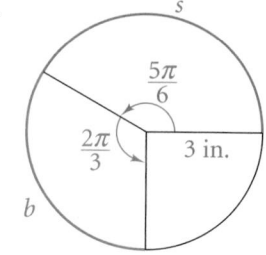

✅ **CA Standards Check** **4** Find length b in Example 4. Round your answer to the nearest tenth.

EXAMPLE **Real-World Connection**

Real-World Connection

The National Air and Space Museum in Washington, D.C., allows visitors to study satellites up close.

Weather Satellite A weather satellite in a circular orbit around Earth completes one orbit every 2 h. The radius of Earth is about 6400 km, and the satellite orbits 2600 km above Earth's surface. How far does the satellite travel in 1 h?

Since one complete revolution (orbit) takes 2 h, the satellite completes $\frac{1}{2}$ of a revolution in 1 h.

Step 1 Find the radius of the satellite's orbit.

$r = 6400 + 2600$ **Add the radius of Earth and the distance from Earth's surface to the satellite.**

$= 9000$ **Simplify.**

Step 2 Find the measure of the central angle the satellite travels through in 1 h.

$\theta = \frac{1}{2} \cdot 2\pi$ **Multiply the fraction of the revolution by the number of radians in one complete revolution.**

$= \pi$ **Simplify.**

Step 3 Find s for $\theta = \pi$.

$s = r\theta$ **Use the formula.**

$= 9000\pi$ **Substitute 9000 for r and π for θ.**

$\approx 28,274$ **Simplify.**

● The satellite travels about 28,000 km in 1 h.

 CA Standards Check ⑤ Find the length of the arc intercepted by each angle.
     a. $\angle AOB$
     b. $\angle COD$
     c. $\angle AOC$
     d. $\angle AOD$

 EXERCISES   For more exercises, see *Extra Skill and Word Problem Practice.*

Standards Practice   **TRIG 1.0**

A **Practice by Example**

Examples 1 and 2
(pages 738 and 739)

 for Help

Write each measure in radians. Express the answer in terms of π and as a decimal rounded to the nearest hundredth.

   1. $-300°$ **2.** $150°$ **3.** $-90°$

   4. $-60°$ **5.** $160°$ **6.** $20°$

Write each measure in degrees. Round your answer to the nearest degree, if necessary.

   7. 3π radians   **8.** $\frac{11\pi}{10}$ radians   **9.** $-\frac{2\pi}{3}$ radians

   10. -3 radians   **11.** 1.57 radians   **12.** 4.71 radians

13. Copy and complete the diagram at the right. Fill in the missing measures in radians or degrees.

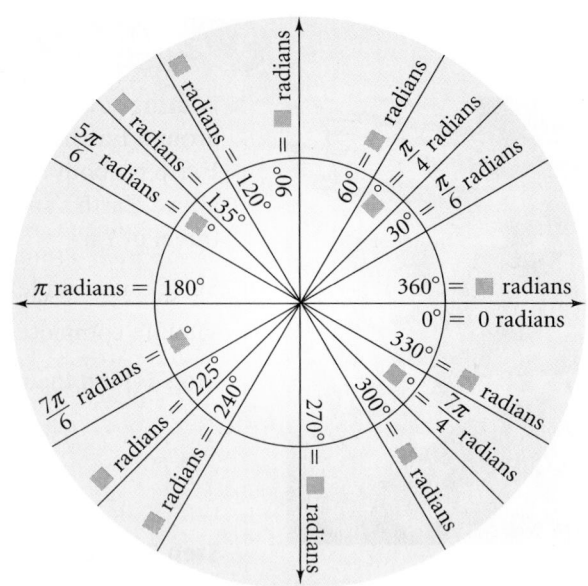

Example 3
(page 740)

The measure θ of an angle in standard position is given. Find the exact values of cos θ and sin θ for each angle measure.

14. $\frac{\pi}{6}$ radians

15. $\frac{\pi}{3}$ radians

16. $\frac{\pi}{2}$ radians

17. $\frac{2\pi}{3}$ radians

18. $\frac{5\pi}{6}$ radians

19. $-\frac{\pi}{2}$ radians

Example 4
(page 740)

Use each circle to find the length of the indicated arc. Round your answer to the nearest tenth.

20.

21.

22.

23.

24.

25.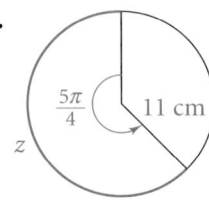

Example 5
(page 741)

Find the length of each arc.

26.

27.

28. Space A geostationary satellite is positioned 35,800 km above Earth's surface. It takes 24 h to complete one orbit. The radius of Earth is about 6400 km.
   a. What distance does the satellite travel in 1 h?
   b. What distance does the satellite travel in 3 h?
   c. What distance does the satellite travel in 2.5 h?
   d. What distance does the satellite travel in 25 h?
   e. Critical Thinking After how many hours has the satellite traveled 200,000 km?

29. Automobile Design Suppose a windshield wiper arm has a length of 22 in. and rotates through an angle of 110°. What distance does the tip of the wiper travel as it moves once across the windshield?

30. Geography The 24 lines of longitude that approximate the 24 standard time zones are equally spaced around the equator.
    a. Suppose you use 24 central angles to divide a circle into 24 equal arcs. Express the measure of each angle in degrees and in radians.
    b. The radius of the equator is about 3960 mi. About how wide is each time zone at the equator?
    c. The radius of the Arctic Circle is about 1580 mi. About how wide is each time zone at the Arctic Circle?

In which quadrant, or on which axis, does the terminal side of each angle lie?

31. $\frac{4\pi}{3}$ radians   **32.** $-\frac{5\pi}{4}$ radians   **33.** $\frac{9\pi}{2}$ radians

34. $\frac{5\pi}{6}$ radians   **35.** $-\pi$ radians   **36.** $\frac{6\pi}{5}$ radians

Draw an angle in standard position with each given measure. Then find the values of the cosine and sine of the angle to the nearest hundredth.

37. $\frac{7\pi}{4}$ radians   **38.** $-\frac{2\pi}{3}$ radians   **39.** $\frac{5\pi}{2}$ radians

40. -2π radians   **41.** $\frac{7\pi}{6}$ radians   **42.** $-\frac{\pi}{5}$ radians

 43. a. Geometry Draw a unit circle on the coordinate plane. Then draw five angles in standard position measuring $\frac{\pi}{5}$, $\frac{4\pi}{5}$, $\frac{6\pi}{5}$, $\frac{9\pi}{5}$, and $\frac{3\pi}{10}$ radians.
    b. For each angle, complete a right triangle. Place the hypotenuse along the terminal side (from the origin to the unit circle). Place one leg along the x-axis. The other leg will be parallel to the y-axis.
    c. Critical Thinking Are the five triangles congruent? Justify your answer by using the values of sin θ and cos θ for each angle.

44. Open-Ended Draw an angle in standard position. Draw a circle with its center at the vertex of the angle. Find the measure of the angle in radians and degrees.

45. Transportation Suppose the radius of a bicycle wheel is 13 in. (measured to the outside of the tire). Find the number of radians through which a point on the tire turns when the bicycle has moved forward a distance of 12 ft.

46. Error Analysis A student wanted to rewrite $\frac{9\pi}{4}$ radians in degrees. The screen shows her calculation. What error did the student make?

```
9*π/4*360/2*π
        3997.189782
```

Find the length of each arc. Also, assuming each angle to be in standard position, find the measures of two angles coterminal with the given angle.

47.

150 ft

−305°

48.

$\frac{5\pi}{6}$ radians

9 in.

49. Writing Two angles are measured in radians. Explain how to tell whether the angles are coterminal without rewriting their measures in degrees.

50. Music A CD with diameter 12 cm spins in a CD player. Calculate how much farther a point on the outside edge of the CD travels in one revolution than a point 1 cm closer to the center of the CD.

51. Geography Assume that Earth is a sphere with radius 3960 miles. A town is at latitude 32° N. Find the distance in miles from the town to the North Pole. (*Hint:* Latitude is measured north and south from the equator.)

 The given angle θ is in standard position. Find the radian measure of the angle that results after the given number of revolutions from the terminal side of θ.

52. $\theta = \frac{\pi}{2}$; 1 clockwise revolution

53. $\theta = \frac{\pi}{3}$; 2 clockwise revolutions

54. $\theta = -\frac{2\pi}{3}$; 1 counterclockwise revolution

55. $\theta = \frac{5\pi}{6}$; $2\frac{1}{2}$ counterclockwise revolutions

56. Reasoning Use the proportion $\frac{\text{measure of central angle}}{\text{measure of one complete rotation}} = \frac{\text{length of arc}}{\text{circumference}}$ to derive the formula $s = r\theta$. Use θ for the central angle measure and s for the arc length. Measure the rotation in radians.

57. a. Use the cartoon below. Use a calculator to evaluate the first three terms of Jason's expression to seven decimal places. Then evaluate the first four terms. Which is a better estimate of cos 60°?

FOX TROT by Bill Amend

b. Jason's expression will approximate the cosine of any angle if you know its radian measure. Write a general form of his expression by substituting x for $\frac{\pi}{3}$.

c. Use the general formula you wrote in part (b) to estimate $\cos\left(\frac{\pi}{10} \text{ radians}\right)$ to the nearest thousandth. What is the angle measure, in degrees?

Multiple Choice Practice

For California Standards and CAHSEE Tutorials, visit PHSchool.com. Web Code: bbq-9045

TRIG 1.0 **58.** Which pairs of measurements represent the same angle measure?

I. $240°, \frac{7\pi}{6}$ radians   II. $135°, \frac{3\pi}{4}$ radians   III. $150°, \frac{5\pi}{6}$ radians

Ⓐ I and II only

Ⓑ I and III only

Ⓒ II and III only

Ⓓ I, II, and III

ALG2 7.0

59. The area of a rectangle is $24a^5b^6$ square inches. If the width of the rectangle is $3a^2b^2$ inches, what is the length in inches?

Ⓐ $8a^3b^4$ in.   Ⓑ $21a^3b^4$ in.   Ⓒ $27a^7b^8$ in.   Ⓓ $72a^7b^8$ in.

ALG2 11.1

60. What is the solution to $x = \log_8 128$?

Ⓐ $x = \frac{4}{3}$ Ⓒ $x = 2$

Ⓑ $x = \frac{5}{2}$ Ⓓ $x = \frac{7}{3}$

ALG2 15.0

61. If t is a real number, for what values of x is the equation $\frac{t^2 - 5t}{t} = t - 5$ true?

Ⓐ all values of t Ⓒ no values of t

Ⓑ some values of t Ⓓ impossible to determine

Mixed Review

GO for Help

Lesson 13-2

Sketch each angle in standard position.

62. $15°$ **63.** $-75°$ **64.** $150°$ **65.** $-270°$ **66.** $-85°$

Lesson 12-4

Find the mean and the standard deviation for each set of values.

67. 6 1 9 12 4 15 21 7 8 8

68. 12 13 15 9 16 5 18 16 12 11 15

69. 21 29 35 26 25 28 27 51 24 34

Lesson 10-3

Write an equation of a circle with the given center and radius.

70. center $(0, 0)$, radius 8   **71.** center $(0, -5)$, radius 4

72. center $(3, 7)$, radius 6.5   **73.** center $(-8, 4)$, radius 3

Checkpoint Quiz 1   Lessons 13-1 through 13-3

Find the period and the amplitude of each periodic function.

1.   **2.**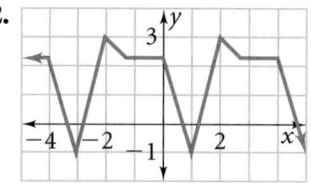

Find the exact values of $\sin \theta$ and $\cos \theta$ for an angle in standard position with each measure θ.

3. $-45°$ **4.** $210°$ **5.** π radians   **6.** $\frac{\pi}{6}$ radians

Convert each angle measure into its equivalent in radians or degrees.

7. $-180°$ **8.** $36°$ **9.** π radians   **10.** $\frac{4\pi}{3}$ radians

The Sine Function

 California Content Standards

TRIG 2.0 Students are familiar with the graph of the sine function.

What You'll Learn

- To identify properties of the sine function
- To graph sine curves

. . . And Why

To model light waves, as in Example 7

✓ **Check Skills You'll Need**

Use the graph. Find the value(s) of each of the following.

1. the period
2. the domain
3. the amplitude
4. the range

GO for Help Lesson 13-1

🔊 **New Vocabulary** • sine function • sine curve

---

1 Interpreting Sine Functions

Vocabulary Tip

<u>Sine</u> comes from the Latin word *sinus,* meaning "bay," a reference to the shape of the sine curve.

The **sine function,** $y = \sin \theta$, matches the measure θ of an angle in standard position with the y-coordinate of a point on the unit circle. This point is where the terminal side of the angle intersects the unit circle.

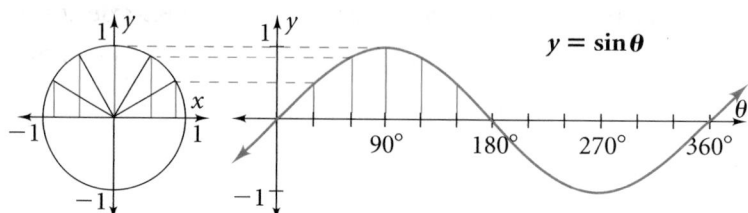

1 EXAMPLE Interpreting the Sine Function in Degrees

Use the graph of the sine function.

a. What is the value of $y = \sin \theta$ for $\theta = 270°$?

The value of the function at $\theta = 270°$ is -1.

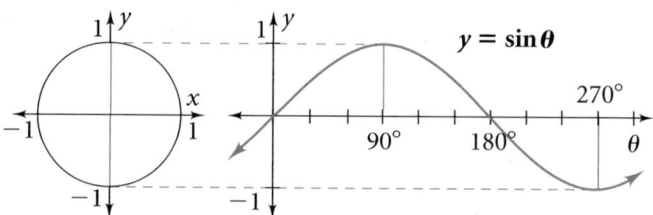

b. For what value of θ between 0° and 360° does the graph of $y = \sin \theta$ reach the maximum value of 1?

When $y = 1, \theta = 90°$.

✓ **CA Standards Check** **1 a.** Extend the graph from Example 1 to include angle measures from 270° to 720°. Will the graph reach the maximum value of 1 again, and if so, where?

b. Reasoning Is the sine function a periodic function? Explain.

Real-World Connection

If you mark a point on one of the blades of an eggbeater and plot the point's horizontal distance over time from the center of the eggbeater, the graph is a sine curve.

As you have seen, an angle measure θ can be expressed in degrees or in radians. In this book, when no unit is mentioned you should use radians.

You can graph the sine function in radians. In the unit circle, you can show radian measures along the circle as lengths of arcs. In the graphs below, the points for 1, 2, and 3 radians are marked on the unit circle and on the θ-axis.

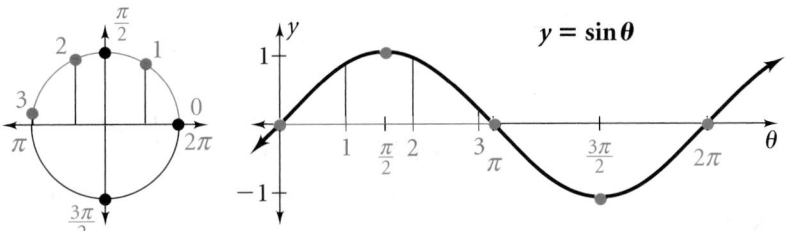

EXAMPLE 2   Estimating Sine Values in Radians

Estimate each value from the graph. Check your estimate with a calculator.

a. sin 2

The sine function reaches its maximum value of 1 at $\frac{\pi}{2} \approx 1.57$. The value of the function at 2 is slightly less than 1, or about 0.9.

$\sin 2 \approx 0.9092974268$ **Use a calculator in radian mode.**

b. $\sin \pi$

The sine function crosses the x-axis at π, so $\sin \pi = 0$.

$\sin \pi = 0$ **Use a calculator in radian mode.**

✓ **CA Standards Check**   **2** Use the graphs of $\sin \theta$ from Examples 1 and 2.
  a. Find the amplitude of the sine function.
  b. Express the period of the sine function in degrees and in radians.
  c. What are the domain and range of the sine function?

The graph of a sine function is called a **sine curve.** By varying the period, you get different sine curves.

For: Sine Function Activity
Use: Interactive Textbook, 13-4

EXAMPLE 3   Finding the Period of a Sine Curve

Use the graph of $y = \sin 4\theta$ at the right.

a. How many cycles occur in the graph at the right? How is the number of cycles related to the coefficient of θ in the equation?

Xmin=0
Xmax=2π
Xscl=π/2
Ymin=−2
Ymax=2
Yscl=1

The graph shows 4 cycles. The number of cycles is equal to the coefficient of θ.

Vocabulary Tip

The <u>period</u> of a function is the horizontal length of one cycle.

b. Find the period of $y = \sin 4\theta$.

$2\pi \div 4 = \frac{\pi}{2}$ **Divide the interval of the graph by the number of cycles.**

The period of $y = \sin 4\theta$ is $\frac{\pi}{2}$.

③ Find the period of each sine curve below. For each graph, the θ-axis shows values from 0 to 2π.

a.

b.

You can also vary the amplitude of a sine curve.

④ EXAMPLE **Finding the Amplitude of a Sine Curve**

The graphing calculator screens at the right show several graphs of $y = a \sin \theta$. Each θ-axis shows values from 0 to 2π.

a. Find the amplitude of each sine curve. How does the value of a affect the amplitude?

The amplitude of $y = \sin \theta$ is 1, and the amplitude of $y = 2 \sin \theta$ is 2. The amplitude of $y = -\sin \theta$ is 1, and the amplitude of $y = -2 \sin \theta$ is 2. In each case, the amplitude of the curve is $|a|$.

b. How does a negative value of a affect the position of the curve?

When a is negative, the graph is a reflection in the x-axis.

✓ **CA Standards Check** ④ Find the amplitude of each sine curve. Each interval on the y-axis represents one unit.

a.

b.

The summary box below lists the properties of sine functions.

🦴 **Key Concepts**

Summary	**Properties of Sine Functions**

Suppose $y = a \sin b\theta$, with $a \neq 0, b > 0$, and θ in radians.

- $|a|$ is the amplitude of the function.

- b is the number of cycles in the interval from 0 to 2π.

- $\dfrac{2\pi}{b}$ is the period of the function.

You can use five points equally spaced through one cycle to sketch a sine curve. For $a > 0$, this five-point pattern is *zero–max–zero–min–zero*.

5 EXAMPLE **Sketching a Graph**

a. Sketch one cycle of a sine curve with amplitude 2 and period 4π.

Step 1 Choose scales for the y-axis and the θ-axis that are about equal ($\pi \approx 3$ units). On the θ-axis, mark one period (4π).

Step 2 Mark equal spaces through one cycle by dividing the period into fourths.

$$\tfrac{1}{4}(4\pi) = \pi \qquad \tfrac{1}{2}(4\pi) = 2\pi \qquad \tfrac{3}{4}(4\pi) = 3\pi$$

Step 3 Since the amplitude is 2, the maximum is 2 and the minimum is -2. Plot the five points and sketch the curve.

b. Use the form $y = a \sin b\theta$. Write an equation with $a > 0$ for the sine curve in part (a).

The amplitude is 2, and $a > 0$, so $a = 2$.

The period is 4π, and $4\pi = \frac{2\pi}{b}$, so $b = \frac{1}{2}$.

An equation for the function is $y = 2 \sin \frac{1}{2}\theta$.

✓ CA Standards Check **5** **a.** Sketch one cycle of a sine curve with amplitude 3, period 4, and $a > 0$.

b. Critical Thinking Predict the five-point pattern for graphing a sine curve when $a < 0$.

c. Sketch one cycle of a sine curve with amplitude 2, period $\frac{2\pi}{3}$, and $a < 0$.

You can also graph sine functions from a given function rule.

6 EXAMPLE **Graphing From a Function Rule**

Sketch one cycle of $y = \frac{1}{2} \sin 2\theta$.

$|a| = \frac{1}{2}$, so the amplitude is $\frac{1}{2}$.

$b = 2$, so there are 2 cycles from 0 to 2π.

$\frac{2\pi}{b} = \frac{2\pi}{2} = \pi$, so the period is π.

Divide the period into fourths.

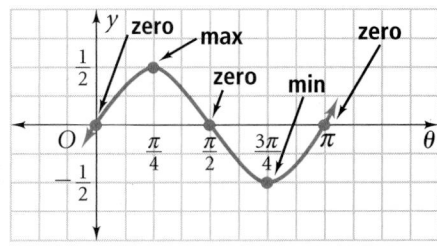

Using the values of the amplitude and period, plot the *zero–max–zero–min–zero* pattern.

Sketch the curve.

✓ CA Standards Check **6** Sketch one cycle of the graph of each sine function.

a. $y = 1.5 \sin 2\theta$ **b.** $y = 3 \sin \frac{\pi}{2}\theta$

You can use sine functions to model real-world situations.

7 EXAMPLE **Real-World Connection**

Multiple Choice The graph at the right models waves of red, blue, and yellow light. Which equation best models blue light?

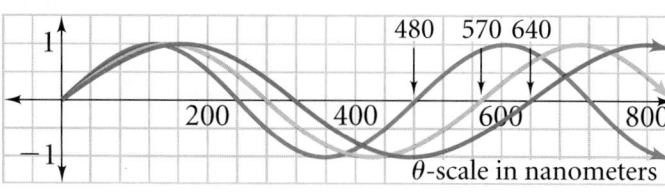
θ-scale in nanometers

Ⓐ $y = \sin 240\pi\theta$ Ⓑ $y = \sin 480\pi\theta$ Ⓒ $y = \sin \frac{\pi}{480}\theta$ Ⓓ $y = \sin \frac{\pi}{240}\theta$

According to the graph, one blue cycle takes 480 nanometers to complete, so the period is 480.

To write an equation, first find b.

$\text{period} = \frac{2\pi}{b}$ **Use the relationship between the period and b.**

$480 = \frac{2\pi}{b}$ **Substitute.**

$b = \frac{2\pi}{480}$ **Multiply each side by $\frac{b}{480}$.**

An equation for blue light is $y = \sin \frac{2\pi}{480}\theta$ or $y = \sin \frac{\pi}{240}\theta$. The correct choice is D.

Real-World Connection

Light can be modeled as waves. Changes in wavelength (period) change the color that the eye perceives. Changes in amplitude affect the intensity of the color.

✓ **CA Standards Check** **7** Write equations for the sine curves that model the red and yellow light waves in Example 7.

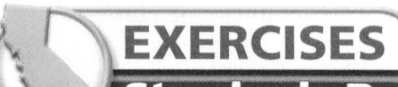

EXERCISES   For more exercises, see *Extra Skill and Word Problem Practice.*

Standards Practice   **TRIG 2.0**

A **Practice by Example**

Example 1
(page 746)

Use the graph at the right to find the value of $y = \sin \theta$ for each value of θ.

1. 30°   **2.** 45°   **3.** 120°

4. 180°   **5.** 240°   **6.** 300°

Example 2
(page 747)

Use the graph at the right to find the value of $y = \sin \theta$ for each value of θ.

7. $\frac{\pi}{2}$ radians   **8.** 3 radians

9. 4 radians   **10.** 5 radians

11. $\frac{3\pi}{2}$ radians   **12.** $\frac{7\pi}{4}$ radians

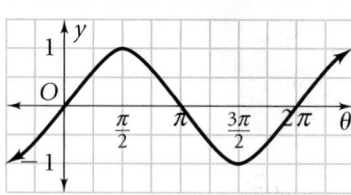

Examples 3 and 4
(pages 747 and 748)

How many cycles does each sine function have in the interval from 0 to 2π? Find the amplitude and period of each function.

13.   **14.**   **15.**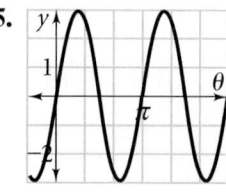

Example 5
(page 749)

Sketch one cycle of each sine curve. Assume $a > 0$. Write an equation for each graph.

16. amplitude 2, period $\frac{2\pi}{3}$

17. amplitude $\frac{1}{3}$, period π

18. amplitude 4, period 4π

19. amplitude 3, period 2π

20. amplitude 1, period 2

21. amplitude 1.5, period 3

Example 6
(page 749)

Sketch one cycle of the graph of each sine function.

22. $y = 2 \sin \theta$

23. $y = \sin 3\theta$

24. $y = -\sin \frac{\pi}{2}\theta$

25. $y = 2 \sin \pi\theta$

26. $y = 4 \sin \frac{1}{2}\theta$

27. $y = -4 \sin \frac{1}{2}\theta$

Example 7
(page 750)

Find the period of each sine curve. Then write an equation for each sine function.

28.

29.

30.

31.
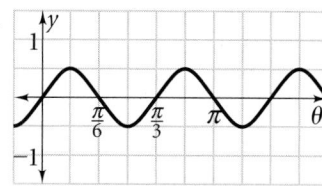

Problem Solving Hint

In a graph of a periodic function, a cycle easiest to see is often one that starts on an axis. Easiest of all is one that starts at the origin.

32.

33.
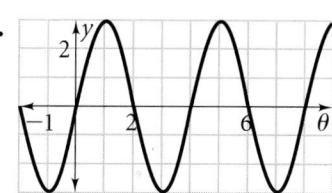

B Apply Your Skills

How many cycles does each sine function have in the interval from 0 to 2π? Find the amplitude and period of each function.

34. $y = \sin \theta$

35. $y = \sin 5\theta$

36. $y = \sin \pi\theta$

37. $y = 3 \sin \theta$

38. $y = -5 \sin \theta$

39. $y = -5 \sin 2\pi\theta$

 40. a. Graph the functions $y = \sin \theta$, $y = 2 \sin \theta$, and $y = 3 \sin \theta$ on the same screen.
  b. Critical Thinking If a is positive, how does the graph of $y = a \sin \theta$ change as the value of a changes?

 41. a. Graph the functions $y = 3 \sin \theta$ and $y = -3 \sin \theta$ on the same screen. How are the two graphs related?
  b. Graph the functions $y = \sin 3\theta$ and $y = \sin (-3\theta)$ on the same screen. How are the two graphs related?
  c. Critical Thinking How does the graph of $y = a \sin b\theta$ change when a is replaced with its opposite? How does the graph change when b is replaced with its opposite?

42. Use the formula period $= \frac{2\pi}{b}$ to find the period of each sine function.

  a. $y = 1.5 \sin 2\theta$

  b. $y = 3 \sin \frac{\pi}{2}\theta$

Homework Video Tutor

Visit: PHSchool.com
Web Code: bbe-1304

43. **Music** The sound wave for the note A above middle C can be modeled by the function $y = 0.001 \sin 880\pi\theta$.
   a. What is the period of the function?
   b. What is the amplitude of the function?
   c. How many cycles of the graph are between 0 and 2π?

44. **Writing** Suppose the independent variable θ is measured in degrees. Restate the properties of the sine function $y = a \sin b\theta$ on page 736 in terms of degrees. Which properties are affected by the conversion to degrees?

Find the period and amplitude of each sine function. Then sketch each function from 0 to 2π.

45. $y = -3.5 \sin 5\theta$

46. $y = \frac{5}{2} \sin 2\theta$

47. $y = -2 \sin 2\pi\theta$

48. $y = 0.4 \sin 3\theta$

49. $y = 0.5 \sin \frac{\pi}{3}\theta$

50. $y = -1.2 \sin \frac{5\pi}{6}\theta$

51. **Open-Ended** Write the equations of three sine functions with the same amplitude that have periods of 2, 3, and 4. Then sketch all three graphs on the same coordinate axes.

52. **Electricity** One type of electric generator consists of a rotating magnetic field surrounded by stationary coils. The voltages produced by the generator can be modeled by sine curves. Suppose three coils are placed symmetrically around a magnetic field. The graph below shows the voltage produced in each coil.

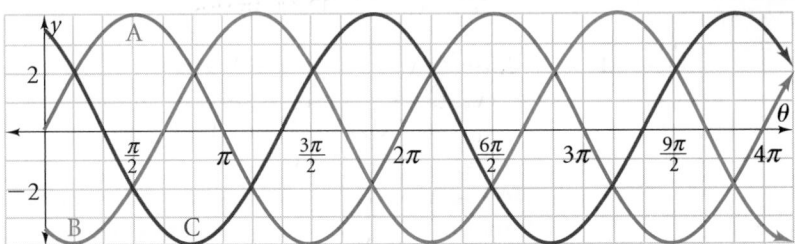

   a. Find the amplitude and period of each sine curve.
   b. Write an equation for the graph that models the voltage produced by coil A.
   c. **Critical Thinking** One of the graphs has the equation $y = 4 \sin \left(\theta - \frac{2\pi}{3}\right)$. Use your knowledge of translations in the coordinate plane to predict whether this is the equation for coil B or coil C. Check your prediction using a graphing calculator.

 Challenge

Sound For sound waves, the period and the frequency of a pitch are reciprocals of each other: period $= \frac{\text{seconds}}{\text{cycle}}$ and frequency $= \frac{\text{cycles}}{\text{second}}$. Write an equation for each pitch. Let $\theta =$ time in seconds. Use $a = 1$.

53. the lowest pitch easily heard by humans: 30 cycles per second

54. the lowest pitch heard by elephants: 15 cycles per second

55. the highest pitch heard by bats: 120,000 cycles per second

Find the period and amplitude of each function. Sketch each function from 0 to 2π.

56. $y = \sin (\theta + 2)$

57. $y = \sin (\theta - 3)$

58. $y = \sin (2\theta + 4)$

Solar Year

March 21ˢᵗ
equal day and night

June 21ˢᵗ
longest day

Dec. 21ˢᵗ
shortest day

Sept. 22ⁿᵈ
equal day and night

Not drawn to scale

59. Astronomy Sunrise and sunset are defined as the times when someone at sea level sees the uppermost edge of the sun on the horizon. In Houston, Texas, at the spring equinox (March 21), there are 12 hours and 9 minutes of sunlight. Throughout the year, the variation from 12 hours 9 minutes of sunlight can be modeled by a sine function. The longest day (June 21) has 1 hour 55 minutes more sunlight than at the equinox. The shortest day (December 21) has 1 hour 55 minutes less sunlight.

a. Define the independent and dependent variables for a function that models the variation in hours of sunlight in Houston.

b. What are the amplitude and period of the function measured in days?

c. Write a function that relates the number of days away from the spring equinox to the variation in hours of sunlight in Houston.

d. Estimation Use your function from part (c). In Houston, about how much less sunlight does February 14 have than March 21?

e. Research Find the number of hours of sunlight in your area on June 21 and on December 21. Develop a sunlight model from your data. Use your model to predict the number of hours of sunlight you will have one week from now.

Multiple Choice Practice

For California Standards and CAHSEE Tutorials, visit PHSchool.com. Web Code: bbq-9045

TRIG 2.0

60. Which answer choice describes $y = -\sin 2\theta$?

(A) amplitude -1, period 4π

(B) amplitude 2, period $-\pi$

(C) amplitude 1, period π

(D) amplitude 2π, period 1

ALG2 2.0

61. Barton has 8 more red marbles than blue marbles. He has 40 marbles in all. He wrote a system of linear equations to represent this situation. He let x represent the number of blue marbles and y represent the number of red marbles. Then he solved this system by graphing. What was the solution?

(A) $(24, 16)$ (C) $(25, 15)$

(B) $(16, 24)$ (D) $(15, 25)$

Mixed Review

GO for Help

Lesson 13-3

Write each measure in radians. Express the answer in terms of π and as a decimal rounded to the nearest hundredth.

62. $-80°$ **63.** $150°$ **64.** $-240°$ **65.** $320°$ **66.** $-450°$

Lesson 12-2

67. A poll of teenagers in one town showed that 43% play a team sport. It also showed that 21% play varsity team sports. Find the probability that a teenager plays varsity sports, given that the teenager plays a team sport.

Lesson 11-1

Write an explicit formula for each sequence. Then find a_{15}.

68. $6, 5, 4, 3, \ldots$ **69.** $15, 18, 21, 24, \ldots$ **70.** $0.6, 1.4, 2.2, 3, \ldots$

Graphing Trigonometric Functions

FOR USE WITH LESSON 13-4

TRIG 2.0 Students are familiar with the graphs of the sine and cosine functions.

You can use a graphing calculator to graph trigonometric functions in radians or degrees.

1 ACTIVITY   Comparing Graphs in Radians and Degrees

Compare the graphs of $y = \cos x$ from $-360°$ to $360°$ and from -2π to 2π radians.

Step 1 Press MODE to change the mode to degrees. Adjust the window values. Graph the function.

Step 2 Change the mode to radians. Graph the function.

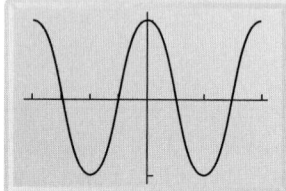

Xmin = –360   Ymin = –1.2
Xmax = 360   Ymax = 1.2
Xscl = 90   Yscl = 1

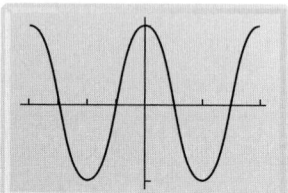

Xmin = –2π Ymin = –1.2
Xmax = 2π Ymax = 1.2
Xscl = π/2   Yscl = 1

The graphs appear to be identical, although in different windows. The function has a period of $360°$ or 2π radians.

● You can use the TRACE feature to evaluate trigonometric functions.

2 ACTIVITY   Using the Trace Feature

Graph the function $y = \sin x$. Find $\sin 30°$ and $\sin 150°$.

Step 1 Change the mode to degrees. Adjust the window values.

Step 2 Graph the function. Use the TRACE key to find the y-values when $x = 30$ and $x = 150$.

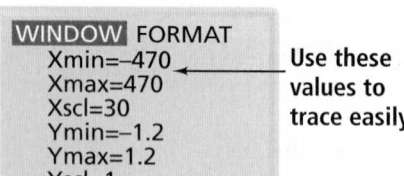

WINDOW FORMAT
Xmin=–470
Xmax=470   ← Use these
Xscl=30   values to
Ymin=–1.2   trace easily.
Ymax=1.2
Yscl=1

X=30   Y=.5

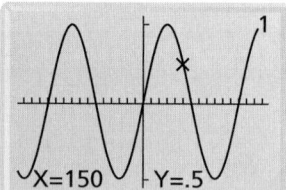

X=150   Y=.5

EXERCISES

Use appropriate window values to identify the period of each function in radians and in degrees. Then evaluate each function at 90°.

1. $y = \cos x$ **2.** $y = \sin x$ **3.** $y = \sin 3x$ **4.** $y = -3 \sin x$ **5.** $y = \cos (x + 30°)$

Writing **Graph the two functions in the same window. Compare the graphs. How are they similar? How are they different?**

6. $y = \sin x, y = \cos x$ **7.** $y = \sin x, y = \cos \left(x - \frac{\pi}{2}\right)$ **8.** $y = \sin x, y = \cos \left(x + \frac{\pi}{2}\right)$

The Cosine Function

 California Content Standards

TRIG 2.0 Students are familiar with the graph of the cosine function.

What You'll Learn

- To graph and write cosine functions
- To solve trigonometric equations

. . . And Why

To model wave motion, as in Example 3

 Check Skills You'll Need

 for Help Lesson 13-2

Find the x-coordinate of each point on the unit circle at the right.

1. A **2.** B

3. C **4.** D

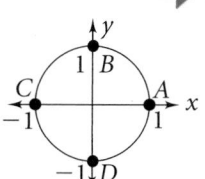

◀)) **New Vocabulary** • cosine function

---

1   Graphing and Writing Cosine Functions

The **cosine function,** $y = \cos\theta$, matches the measure θ of an angle in standard position with the x-coordinate of a point on the unit circle. This point is where the terminal side of the angle intersects the unit circle.

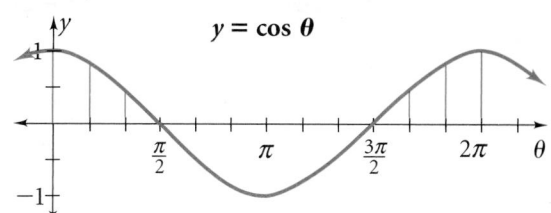

$y = \cos\theta$

---

1 EXAMPLE   **Interpreting the Graph of Cos θ**

Use the graph shown above.

a. Find the domain, period, range, and amplitude of the cosine function.

The domain of the function is all real numbers.

The function goes from its maximum value of 1 and back again in an interval from 0 to 2π. The period is 2π.

The function has a maximum value of 1 and a minimum value of -1. The range is $-1 \le y \le 1$.

$$\begin{aligned}\text{amplitude} &= \tfrac{1}{2}(\text{maximum} - \text{minimum})\\ &= \tfrac{1}{2}[1 - (-1)]\\ &= 1\end{aligned}$$

b. Examine the cycle of the cosine function in the interval from 0 to 2π. Where in the cycle does the maximum value occur? Where does the minimum occur? Where do the zeros occur?

The maximum value occurs at 0 and 2π. The minimum value occurs at π. The zeros occur at $\frac{\pi}{2}$ and $\frac{3\pi}{2}$.

Real-World **Connection**

The distance over time between the center line of a metronome and a point on the metronome's swinging arm can be modeled with a cosine function.

✓ CA Standards Check **①** Use the graphs below. How are the graphs of the sine and cosine functions alike? How are they different?

 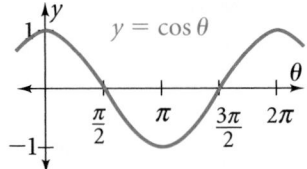

The cosine function has some of the same properties as the sine function.

 Key Concepts

Summary	Properties of Cosine Functions

Suppose $y = a \cos b\theta$, with $a \neq 0, b > 0$, and θ in radians.

- $|a|$ is the amplitude of the function.
- b is the number of cycles in the interval from 0 to 2π.
- $\frac{2\pi}{b}$ is the period of the function.

To graph a cosine function, locate five points equally spaced through one cycle. For $a > 0$, this five-point pattern is *max–zero–min–zero–max*.

② **EXAMPLE** **Sketching the Graph of a Cosine Function**

Online
active math

For: Cosine Function Activity
Use: Interactive Textbook, 13-5

Sketch the graph of $y = 1.5 \cos 2\theta$ in the interval from 0 to 2π.

$|a| = 1.5$, so the amplitude is 1.5.

$b = 2$, so the graph has two full cycles from 0 to 2π.

$\frac{2\pi}{b} = \pi$, so the period is π.

Divide the period into fourths. Plot five points for the first cycle. Use 1.5 for the maximum and -1.5 for the minimum. Repeat the pattern for the second cycle.

Sketch the curve.

Choose scales for axes that are about equal $\left(\frac{\pi}{3} \approx 1\right)$.

max zero min zero max

✓ CA Standards Check **②** **a.** Graph the equations $y = \cos x$ and $y = -\cos x$ on the same coordinate plane. Compare the graphs.
b. Critical Thinking Write the five-point pattern to graph $y = a \cos b\theta$ when $a < 0$.
c. Sketch the cosine curve $y = -\frac{1}{2} \cos \pi\theta$ in the interval from 0 to 2π.

2 **Solving Trigonometric Equations**

Waves of water show periodic motion. Away from the shore, individual water molecules move up and down, returning to their initial position after a wave passes. Their height can be modeled with a cosine function.

EXAMPLE **Real-World Connection**

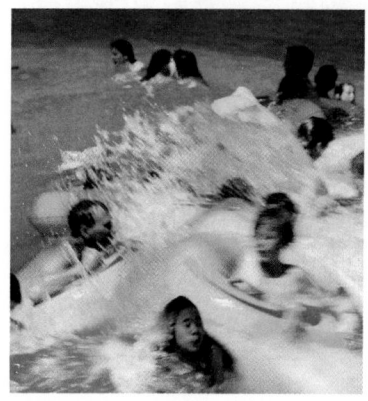

Real-World Connection

The waves generated in a wave pool can be modeled with cosine functions.

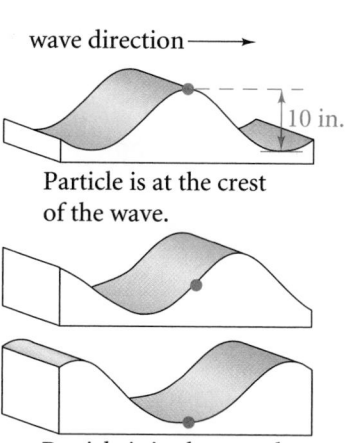

Particle is at the crest of the wave.

Particle is in the trough of the wave.

wave direction ⟶

10 in.

Wave Motion The figures at the right show the vertical motion of a particle in water as a wave moves by. Suppose 10-in. waves occur every 4 s. Write an equation that models the height of the particle as it moves from crest to crest.

The equation will have the form $y = a \cos b\theta$. Find values for a and b.

$a = \frac{10}{2}$ amplitude $= \frac{\text{maximum} - \text{minimum}}{2}$

$\quad = 5$ **Simplify.**

$\text{period} = \frac{2\pi}{b}$ **Use the formula for the period.**

$4 = \frac{2\pi}{b}$ **The period is 4. Substitute.**

$b = \frac{2\pi}{4}$ **Multiply each side by $\frac{b}{4}$.**

$\quad = \frac{\pi}{2}$ **Simplify.**

● An equation that models the height of the particle is $y = 5 \cos \frac{\pi}{2}\theta$.

CA Standards Check ③ Write a cosine function for each description. Choose $a > 0$.
  a. amplitude 4, period 6π
  b. amplitude 2.5, period 8

You can solve an equation by graphing to find an exact location along a sine or cosine curve.

EXAMPLE **Solving a Cosine Equation**

Suppose you want to find the time t in seconds when the particle from Example 3 is exactly 3 in. above the average height represented by $y = 0$. Solve $5 \cos \frac{\pi}{2}t = 3$ in the interval from 0 to 8.

Step 1 Use two equations. Graph the equations $y = 3$ and $y = 5 \cos \frac{\pi}{2}t$ on the same screen.

Step 2 Use the **Intersect** feature to find the points at which the two graphs intersect.

The graph shows four solutions in the interval. They are $t \approx 0.6$, 3.4, 4.6, and 7.4.

Intersection
X=.59033447   Y=3

Xmin=0
Xmax=8
Xscl=1
Ymin=-8
Ymax=8
Yscl=1

Graphing Calculator Hint

When you use the **Intersect** feature, move the cursor close to the desired point after the **Guess?** prompt appears.

● The particle is 3 in. above the average height at about 0.6, 3.4, 4.6, and 7.4 s.

CA Standards Check ④ Find all solutions in the interval from 0 to 2π.
  a. $3 \cos 2t = -2$
  b. $-2 \cos \theta = 1.2$
  c. **Critical Thinking** In the interval from 0 to 2π, when is $-2 \cos \theta$ less than 1.2? Greater than 1.2?

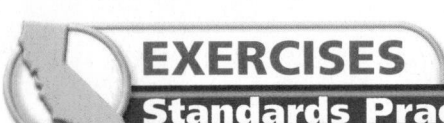
EXERCISES

Standards Practice

For more exercises, see *Extra Skill and Word Problem Practice*.

TRIG 2.0

A Practice by Example

Example 1
(page 755)

GO for Help

Find the period and amplitude of each cosine function. At what values of x for $0 \le x \le 2\pi$ do the maximum value(s), minimum value(s), and zeros occur?

1.
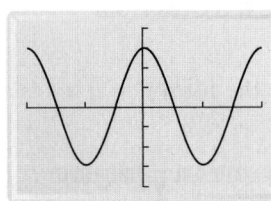
Xmin=-2π
Xmax=2π
Xscl=π
Ymin=-4
Ymax=4
Yscl=1

2.
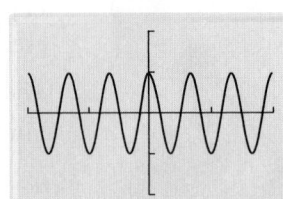
Xmin=-2π
Xmax=2π
Xscl=π
Ymin=-2
Ymax=2
Yscl=1

3.
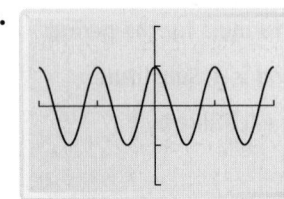
Xmin=-2π
Xmax=2π
Xscl=π
Ymin=-2
Ymax=2
Yscl=1

4.
Xmin=-2π
Xmax=2π
Xscl=π
Ymin=-4
Ymax=4
Yscl=1

Example 2
(page 756)

Sketch the graph of each function in the interval from 0 to 2π.

5. $y = \cos 2\theta$ **6.** $y = -3 \cos \theta$ **7.** $y = -\cos 3t$ **8.** $y = \cos \frac{\pi}{2}\theta$ **9.** $y = -\cos \pi\theta$

Example 3
(page 757)

Write a cosine function for each description. Assume that $a > 0$.

10. amplitude 2, period π **11.** amplitude $\frac{\pi}{2}$, period 3   **12.** amplitude π, period 2

Write an equation of a cosine function for each graph.

13.

14.
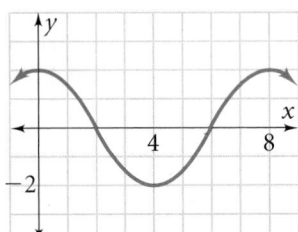

15. Wave Motion Suppose 8-in. waves pass every 3 s. Write an equation that models the height of a water molecule as it moves from crest to crest.

Example 4
(page 757)

Solve each equation in the interval from 0 to 2π. Round to the nearest hundredth.

16. $\cos 2t = \frac{1}{2}$ **17.** $20 \cos t = -8$ **18.** $-2 \cos \pi\theta = 0.3$

19. $3 \cos \frac{t}{3} = 2$ **20.** $\cos \frac{1}{4}\theta = 1$ **21.** $8 \cos \frac{\pi}{3}t = 5$

B Apply Your Skills

Identify the period, range, and amplitude of each function.

22. $y = 3 \cos \theta$ **23.** $y = -\cos 2t$ **24.** $y = 2 \cos \frac{1}{2}t$ **25.** $y = \frac{1}{3} \cos \frac{\theta}{2}$

26. $y = 3 \cos \left(-\frac{\theta}{3}\right)$ **27.** $y = -\frac{1}{2} \cos 3\theta$ **28.** $y = 16 \cos \frac{3\pi}{2}t$ **29.** $y = 0.7 \cos \pi t$

Solve each equation in the interval from 0 to 2π. Round your answers to the nearest hundredth.

30. $\sin \theta = 0.6$ **31.** $-3 \sin 2\theta = 1.5$ **32.** $\sin \pi\theta = 1$

33. a. Solve $-2 \sin \theta = 1.2$ in the interval from 0 to 2π.
  b. Solve $-2 \sin \theta = 1.2$ in the interval $2\pi \leq \theta \leq 4\pi$. How are these solutions related to the solutions in part (a)?

34. a. Graph the equation $y = 5 \cos \frac{\pi}{2}\theta$ from Example 3.
  b. The independent variable θ represents time (in seconds). Find four times at which the particle is at the crest of a wave.
  c. For how many seconds during each cycle is the particle above the line $y = 0$? Below $y = 0$?

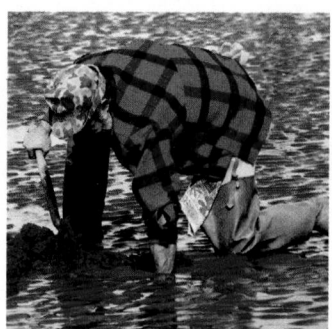
35. Tides The table at the right shows the times for high tide and low tide. The markings on the side of a local pier showed a high tide of 7 ft and a low tide of 4 ft on the previous day.

Tide Table	
High tide	4:03 A.M.
Low tide	10:14 A.M.
High tide	4:25 P.M.
Low tide	10:36 P.M.

  a. What is the average depth of water at the pier? What is the amplitude of the variation from the average depth?
  b. How long is one cycle of the tide?
  c. Write a cosine function that models the relationship between the depth of water and the time of day. Use $y = 0$ to represent the average depth of water. Use $t = 0$ to represent the time 4:03 A.M.
  d. Critical Thinking Suppose your boat needs at least 5 ft of water to approach or leave the pier. Between what times could you come and go?

36. Ferris Wheel A Ferris wheel ride (see the Activity on page 722) lets you, in a sense, ride the sine and cosine waves.

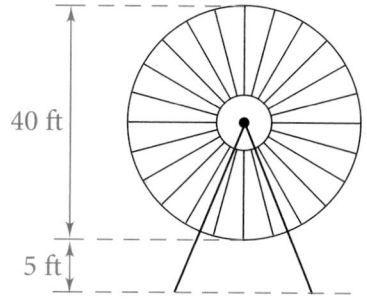

40 ft

5 ft

  a. Recall the unit circle definitions of sine and cosine (pages 746, 755). Which function, sine or cosine, might serve as a better model for a Ferris wheel ride in the sense of riding a wave? Explain. (*Hint:* For a point on the unit circle, which function suggests vertical position?)
  b. Assume the Ferris wheel pictured turns counterclockwise. For a ride on the unit-circle sine wave, it would be ideal to begin your sine wave ride halfway up on the right side. On a Ferris wheel, however, you begin your ride at the bottom where you board your car. This means that your ride will be $\frac{\pi}{2}$ radians "out of phase" with $\sin x$. Graph Y1 = sin X and Y2 = $\sin\left(X - \frac{\pi}{2}\right)$. Explain the meaning of "out of phase."
  c. How does the amplitude of your sine wave ride compare with the amplitude of a unit-circle (1 ft radius) sine wave?
  d. How does the center of your Ferris wheel compare with the center of the unit circle?
  e. Write a sine function that models your sine-wave Ferris wheel ride.
  f. Graph your function using screen dimensions $0 \leq x \leq 2\pi$ and $0 \leq y \leq 50$.
  g. How could you build the speed of the Ferris wheel into your model?
  h. How could you build the speed of the Ferris wheel into your graphical display? (*Hint:* Use parametric mode.)
  i. How can you relate the cosine function to a ride on the Ferris wheel?

Homework Video Tutor

Visit: PHSchool.com
Web Code: bbe-1305

 Challenge

37. a. Graph $y = \cos \theta$ and $y = \cos\left(\theta - \frac{\pi}{2}\right)$ in the interval from 0 to 2π. What translation of the graph of $y = \cos \theta$ produces the graph of $y = \cos\left(\theta - \frac{\pi}{2}\right)$?
  b. Graph $y = \cos\left(\theta - \frac{\pi}{2}\right)$ and $y = \sin \theta$ in the interval from 0 to 2π. What do you notice?
  c. Critical Thinking Explain how you could rewrite a sine function as a cosine function.

38. Biology A helix is a three-dimensional spiral. The coiled strands of DNA and the edges of twisted crepe paper are examples of helixes. In the diagram, the *y*-coordinate of each edge illustrates a cosine function. Write an equation for the *y*-coordinate of one edge.

39. Graph one cycle of $y = \cos \theta$, one cycle of $y = -\cos \theta$, and one cycle of $y = \cos (-\theta)$ on the same set of axes. Use the unit circle to explain any relationships you see among these graphs.

Multiple Choice Practice

For California Standards and CAHSEE Tutorials, visit PHSchool.com. Web Code: bbq-9045

TRIG 2.0

40. Which equation corresponds to the graph shown below? The screen dimensions are $-4\pi \leq x \leq 4\pi$ and $-2 \leq y \leq 2$.

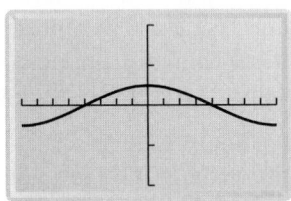

Ⓐ $y = \frac{1}{2} \cos \frac{x}{4}$ Ⓒ $y = 2 \cos \frac{x}{4}$

Ⓑ $y = \frac{1}{2} \cos 4x$ Ⓓ $y = 2 \cos 4x$

ALG2 2.0

41. Alex and Elena went to the pet store. Alex bought 4 guppies and 2 goldfish for a total of $16.50. Elena bought 3 guppies and 7 goldfish for a total of $19.25. Which system of equations could be used to determine the cost of one guppy, *p*, and one goldfish, *f*?

Ⓐ $4p + 2f = 19.25$
$3p + 7f = 16.50$

Ⓑ $4p + 2f = 16.50$
$7p + 3f = 19.25$

Ⓒ $4p + 3f = 16.50$
$2p + 7f = 19.25$

Ⓓ $4p + 2f = 16.50$
$3p + 7f = 19.25$

Mixed Review

GO for Help

Lesson 13-4

Sketch one cycle of each sine curve. Assume that $a > 0$. Then write an equation for each graph.

42. amplitude 1, period $\frac{\pi}{3}$ **43.** amplitude 2.5, period π **44.** amplitude 4, period 1

Lesson 12-5

Find the sample size that produces each margin of error.

45. $\pm 3\%$ **46.** $\pm 7\%$ **47.** $\pm 11\%$

Lesson 11-3

Write the explicit formula for each sequence. Then generate the first five terms.

48. $a_1 = 10, r = 3$ **49.** $a_1 = 12, r = -0.3$ **50.** $a_1 = 900, r = -\frac{1}{3}$

The Tangent Function

 California Content Standards

TRIG 5.0 Students know the definition of the tangent function and can graph it.

What You'll Learn

• To graph the tangent function

... And Why

To model the facade of a building, as in Example 3

✓ Check Skills You'll Need

GO for Help Lesson 13-3

Use a calculator to find the sine and cosine of each value of θ. Then calculate the ratio $\frac{\sin \theta}{\cos \theta}$.

1. $\frac{\pi}{3}$ radians
2. 30 degrees
3. 90 degrees
4. $\frac{5\pi}{6}$ radians
5. $\frac{5\pi}{2}$ radians
6. 0 degrees

🔊 **New Vocabulary** • tangent of θ • tangent function

---

1 Graphing the Tangent Function

Vocabulary Tip

A line <u>tangent</u> to a circle intersects the circle at exactly one point.

The sine and cosine of an angle derive from the coordinates of a point on the unit circle. The tangent of an angle derives from the coordinates of a point on a line *tangent* to the unit circle.

For an angle θ in standard position, the **tangent of θ** is the y-coordinate of the point where the line containing the terminal side of the angle intersects the tangent line $x = 1$.

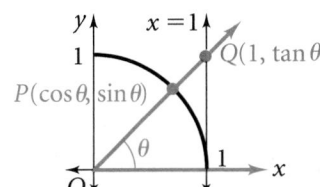

The line containing the terminal side of θ intersects the line $x = 1$ at Q.

The graph below shows one cycle of the **tangent function,** $y = \tan \theta$. Since the period is π, the asymptote that occurs at $\theta = \frac{\pi}{2}$ repeats every π units.

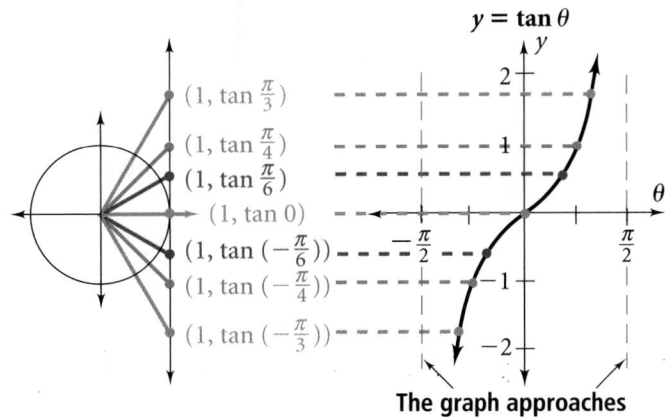

The graph approaches two vertical asymptotes.

You can estimate function values from the graph of the tangent function.

Online
active math

For: Tangent Function Activity
Use: Interactive Textbook, 13-6

 CA Standards Check

1 **EXAMPLE** **Finding Tangent Values From a Graph**

Use the graph of $y = \tan \theta$ at the right to find each value.

a. $\tan \left(-\frac{\pi}{4}\right)$ $\tan \left(-\frac{\pi}{4}\right) = -1$

b. $\tan 0$ $\tan 0 = 0$

c. $\tan \frac{\pi}{4}$ $\tan \frac{\pi}{4} = 1$

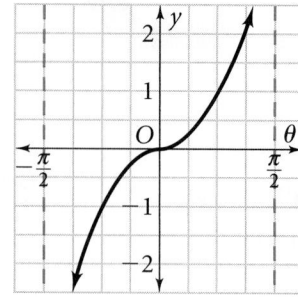

1 **a.** Use the graph in Example 1 to find $\tan \frac{\pi}{8}$ and $\tan \left(-\frac{\pi}{8}\right)$.

b. **Critical Thinking** Explain why the terminal side of an angle with measure $\frac{\pi}{2}$ *does not intersect* the tangent line.

The graph in Example 1 shows one cycle of the tangent function, $y = \tan \theta$. Since the period is π, the asymptote that occurs at $\theta = \frac{\pi}{2}$ is repeated every π units.

Key Concepts

Summary	**Properties of Tangent Functions**

Suppose $y = a \tan b\theta$, with $b > 0$ and θ in radians.

- $\frac{\pi}{b}$ is the period of the function.
- One cycle occurs in the interval from $-\frac{\pi}{2b}$ to $\frac{\pi}{2b}$.
- There are vertical asymptotes at each end of the cycle.

You can use asymptotes and three points to sketch one cycle of a tangent curve. As with sine and cosine, the five elements are equally spaced through one cycle. Use the pattern *asymptote–(–a)–zero–(a)–asymptote*. In the graph at the right, $a = b = 1$.

The next example shows how to use the period, asymptotes, and points to graph a tangent function.

2 **EXAMPLE** **Graphing a Tangent Function**

Sketch two cycles of the graph of $y = \tan \pi\theta$.

period $= \frac{\pi}{b}$ **Use the formula for the period.**

$= \frac{\pi}{\pi} = 1$ **Substitute π for b and simplify.**

One cycle occurs in the interval from $-\frac{1}{2}$ to $\frac{1}{2}$.

Asymptotes occur every 1 unit, at $\theta = -\frac{1}{2}, \frac{1}{2}$, and $\frac{3}{2}$.

Since $a = 1, \left(-\frac{1}{4}, -1\right)$ and $\left(\frac{1}{4}, 1\right)$ are on the graph.

Plot three points in each cycle. Sketch the curve.

✓ CA Standards Check ➋ Sketch the graph of each tangent curve.

a. $y = \tan 3\theta, 0 \le \theta \le \pi$ **b.** $y = \tan \frac{\pi}{2}\theta, 0 \le \theta < 3$

You can use the tangent function and a graphing calculator to solve problems involving angles.

3 EXAMPLE   **Real-World** 🌐 **Connection**

Design An architect is designing the front facade of a building to include a triangle, as shown in the figure. The base of the triangle is 200 ft wide. The function $y = 100 \tan \theta$ models the height of the triangle, where θ is the angle indicated. Graph the function in degree mode. What is the height of the triangle when $\theta = 16°$? What is the height when $\theta = 22°$?

Not drawn to scale

Step 1 Graph the function.

Xmin=0
Xmax=470
Xscl=50
Ymin=–300
Ymax=300
Yscl=90

Step 2 Use the TABLE feature.

X	Y₁
16	28.675
17	30.573
18	32.492
19	34.433
20	36.397
21	38.386
22	40.403

X=16

When $\theta = 16°$, the height of the triangle is about 28.7 ft. When $\theta = 22°$, the height of the triangle is about 40.4 ft.

✓ CA Standards Check ➌ **a.** What is the height of the triangle when $\theta = 25°$?

     b. Reasoning The architect wants the triangle to be at least one story tall. The average height of a story is 14 ft. What must the measure of θ be for the height of the triangle to be at least 14 ft?

EXERCISES

For more exercises, see *Extra Skill and Word Problem Practice.*

Standards Practice

TRIG 5.0

Ⓐ Practice by Example

Example 1
(page 762)

for Help

Use the graph of $y = \tan \theta$ to find each value. If the tangent is undefined at that point, write *undefined.*

1. $\tan(-\pi)$ **2.** $\tan \pi$

3. $\tan \frac{3\pi}{4}$ **4.** $\tan \frac{\pi}{2}$

5. $\tan\left(-\frac{7\pi}{4}\right)$ **6.** $\tan 2\pi$

7. $\tan\left(-\frac{3\pi}{4}\right)$ **8.** $\tan \frac{3\pi}{2}$

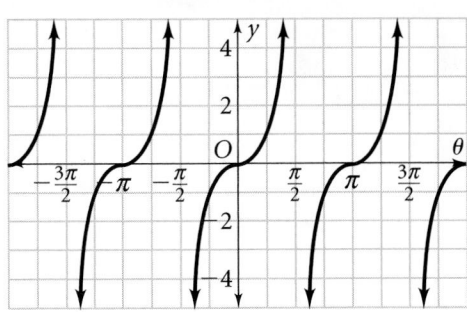

Example 2
(page 762)

Each graphing calculator screen shows the interval 0 to 2π. What is the period of each graph?

9.

10.

Identify the period and tell where two asymptotes occur for each function.

11. $y = \tan 5\theta$
12. $y = \tan \frac{3\theta}{2}$
13. $y = \tan 4\theta$
14. $y = \tan \frac{2}{3\pi}\theta$

Sketch the graph of each tangent curve in the interval from 0 to 2π.

15. $y = \tan \theta$
16. $y = \tan 2\theta$
17. $y = \tan \frac{2\pi}{3}\theta$
18. $y = \tan(-\theta)$

Example 3
(page 763)

 Graph each function on the interval $0° < x < 470°$ and $-300 < y < 300$. Evaluate the function at $x = 45°, 90°$, and $135°$.

19. $y = 50 \tan x$
20. $y = -100 \tan x$
21. $y = 125 \tan \left(\frac{1}{2}x\right)$

 22. Suppose the architect in Example 3 reduces the length of the base of the triangle to 100 ft. The function that models the height of the triangle becomes $y = 50 \tan \theta$.
 a. Graph the function on a graphing calculator.
 b. What is the height of the triangle when $\theta = 16°$?
 c. What is the height of the triangle when $\theta = 22°$?

B **Apply Your Skills**

Identify the period for each tangent function. Then graph each function in the interval from -2π to 2π.

23. $y = \tan \frac{\pi}{6}\theta$
24. $y = \tan 2.5\theta$
25. $y = \tan \left(-\frac{3}{2\pi}\theta\right)$

 Solve each equation in the interval from 0 to 2π. Round your answers to the nearest hundredth.

26. $\tan \theta = 2$
27. $\tan \theta = -2$
28. $6 \tan 2\theta = 1$

29. a. Set your graphing calculator to Degree mode. Use window values $0 \le x \le 141$ and $-500 \le y \le 500$. Graph the functions $y = 100 \tan 2x$, $y = 200 \tan 2x$, and $y = 400 \tan 2x$ on the same set of axes. Sketch the graphs.
 b. Choose five values for x. Compare the y values. Explain how doubling the coefficient of the tangent function affects the output.
 c. Without graphing, make a prediction about the difference between the y-values of $y = 200 \tan x$ and $y = 600 \tan x$. Check your prediction on your graphing calculator.

30. **Ceramics** An artist is creating triangular ceramic tiles for a triangular patio. The patio will be an equilateral triangle with base 18 ft and height 15.6 ft.
 a. Find the area of the patio in square feet.
 b. The artist uses tiles that are isosceles triangles with base 6 in. The function $y = 3 \tan \theta$ models the height of the tiles, where θ is the measure of one of the base angles. Graph the function. Find the height of the tile when $\theta = 30°$ and when $\theta = 60°$.
 c. Find the area of one tile in square inches when $\theta = 30°$ and when $\theta = 60°$.
 d. Find the number of tiles the patio will require if $\theta = 30°$ and if $\theta = 60°$.

Visit: PHSchool.com
Web Code: bbe-1306

31. a. Open-Ended Write a tangent function.
   b. Graph the function on the interval -2π to 2π.
   c. Identify the period and the asymptotes of the function.

32. Writing Explain how you can find the equations of the asymptotes of
   $y = \tan b\theta$.

**Use the function $y = 200 \tan x$ on the interval $0° \le x \le 141°$. Complete each
ordered pair. Round your answers to the nearest whole number.**

33. $(45°, \blacksquare)$ **34.** $(\blacksquare°, 0)$ **35.** $(\blacksquare°, -200)$ **36.** $(141°, \blacksquare)$ **37.** $(\blacksquare°, 550)$

Write an equation of a tangent function for each graph.

For a guide to solving
Exercise 38, see p. 767.

38.

39.

40.

41.
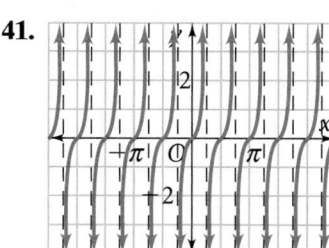

42. Construction An architect is designing a hexagonal gazebo. The floor is a
   hexagon made up of six isosceles triangles. The function $y = 4 \tan \theta$ models the
   height of one triangle, where θ is the measure of one of the base angles and the
   base of the triangle is 8 ft long.
   a. Graph the function. Find the height of one triangle when $\theta = 60°$.
   b. Find the area of one triangle in square feet when $\theta = 60°$.
   c. Find the area in square feet covered by the gazebo when the triangles
      forming the hexagon are equilateral.

C **Challenge** **43. Geometry** The base of a square pyramid has
   side length 150 ft. The function $\ell = 75 \tan \theta$
   models the slant height ℓ of the pyramid, where
   θ is the angle indicated in the figure.
   a. Graph the function $\ell = 75 \tan \theta$ as $Y_1 = 75 \tan X$
      on a graphing calculator. Sketch the graph.
   b. Find the slant height of the pyramid when
      $\theta = 60°$.
   c. Find the surface area of the pyramid.
      (*Hint:* Don't forget to include the base
      of the pyramid.)

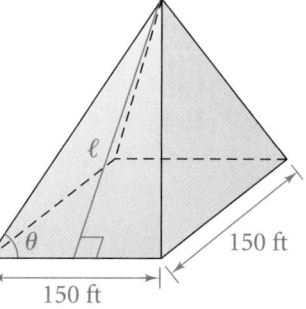

44. a. Graph $y = \tan x$, $y = a \tan x$ (with $a > 0$), and $y = a \tan x$ (with $a < 0$) on
      the same coordinate plane.
   b. Critical Thinking Recall the pattern of five elements for graphing a tangent
      function: *asymptote−(−1)−zero−(1)−asymptote*. How does the value of a
      affect this pattern?

45. Geometry Use the drawing at the right and similar triangles. Justify the statement that $\tan \theta = \frac{\sin \theta}{\cos \theta}$.

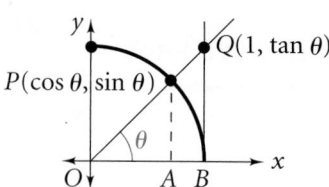

46. How many solutions does the equation $x = \tan x$ have for $0 \le x < 2\pi$? Explain.

Multiple Choice Practice

For California Standards and CAHSEE Tutorials, visit PHSchool.com. Web Code: bbq-9045

TRIG 5.0

47. Which pair of values are NOT equal?

  Ⓐ $\tan \frac{\pi}{4}, -\tan \frac{3\pi}{4}$ Ⓒ $\tan \frac{\pi}{4}, \tan \frac{5\pi}{4}$

  Ⓑ $\tan \theta, -\tan (-\theta)$ Ⓓ $\tan \theta, \tan (\pi - \theta)$

TRIG 5.0

48. Which equation does NOT represent a vertical asymptote of the graph of $y = \tan \theta$?

  Ⓐ $\theta = -\frac{\pi}{2}$ Ⓑ $\theta = 0$ Ⓒ $\theta = \frac{\pi}{2}$ Ⓓ $\theta = \frac{3\pi}{2}$

ALG2 24.0

49. Which of the following best represents the function $y = 1 - 3x + x^2$ when the replacement set for x is $\{-1, 1, 5\}$?

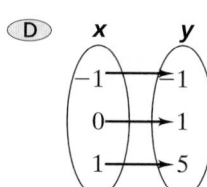

Mixed Review

Lesson 13-5

Solve each equation in the interval from 0 to 2π. Round your answer to the nearest hundredth.

50. $\cos t = \frac{1}{4}$ **51.** $10 \cos t = -2$ **52.** $-2 \cos \theta = 0.7$

53. $3 \cos \frac{t}{5} = 1$ **54.** $\cos \frac{3}{4}\theta = -0.6$ **55.** $5 \cos \pi t = 0.9$

Lesson 12-3

Find the mean, median, and mode for each set of values.

56. 9 6 8 1 3 4 5 2 6 8 4 9 12 3 4 10 7 6

57. 45 42 39 35 41 45 49 42 43 48 32 51 42

58. 7.1 8.5 7.0 7.6 8.5 8.1 7.9 8.2 7.3 9.1 8.7 7.9

Lesson 11-2

Find the 27th term of each sequence.

59. 5, 8, 11, . . .   **60.** 59, 48, 37, . . .   **61.** 1, 3.5, 6, 8.5, . . .

62. 2.1, 1.7, 1.3, . . .   **63.** −11, −5, 1, . . .   **64.** 6, −7, −20, . . .

Understanding Math Problems Read the problem below. Let the explanation guide you through reading a graph. Check your understanding with the exercises at the bottom of the page.

Write an equation of a tangent function for the graph.

A graph shows data points of a function on a coordinate grid. When you read a graph, you identify information from the graph to help you solve the problem. As you look at a graph, ask yourself the following questions.

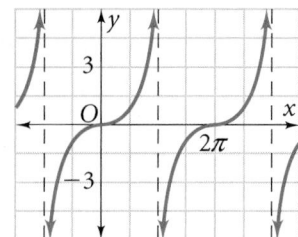

What relationship is shown in the graph?

The problem states that the graph shows a tangent function.

What information can I obtain from the graph?

Scale The scale on the y-axis shows that two grid lines represent 3 units. The scale on the x-axis shows that four grid lines represent 2π units, which means two grid lines represent π units. Redraw the graph and add labels to the x-axis.

Asymptotes A tangent function has vertical asymptotes. Now that you've added labels, you can see that asymptotes occur at x-values of $-\pi, \pi$, and 3π.

Period The period is the horizontal distance between asymptotes.

$$\text{period} = \text{distance between asymptotes} = \pi - (-\pi) = 2\pi$$

Now you can use the information you've obtained from the graph to write an equation for the tangent function shown. The standard form for the equation of a tangent function is $y = \tan bx$. Since you know the period, you can find b.

$\text{period} = \frac{\pi}{b}$, so $b = \frac{\pi}{\text{period}} = \frac{\pi}{2\pi} = \frac{1}{2}$

Since $\left(-\frac{\pi}{2}, -1\right)$ is on the graph, $a = 1$.

An equation for the tangent function is $y = \tan \frac{1}{2}x$.

EXERCISES

For each graph below (a) identify the asymptotes; (b) identify the period; (c) write an equation for the function, and (d) find the zeros of the function.

1.

2.

3.

Translating Sine and Cosine Functions

California Content Standards

TRIG 4.0 Students graph functions of the form $f(t) = A \sin(Bt + C)$ or $f(t) = A \cos(Bt + C)$ and interpret A, B, and C in terms of amplitude, frequency, period, and phase shift.

What You'll Learn

- To graph translations of trigonometric functions
- To write equations of translations

. . . And Why

To analyze temperature data, as in Example 6

 Check Skills You'll Need

GO for Help Lesson 2-6

Graph each pair of equations on the same coordinate plane. Identify each translation as *horizontal*, *vertical*, or *diagonal*.

1. $y = 2x, y = 2x + 5$ **2.** $g(x) = |x|, f(x) = |x + 3|$

3. $y = -x, y = -x - 1$ **4.** $g(x) = |x|, h(x) = |x| - 4$

5. $y = -|x|, y = -|x - 2| + 1$ **6.** $y = x^2, y = (x + 3)^2 - 2$

New Vocabulary • phase shift

---

1 Graphing Translations of Trigonometric Functions

Real-World Connection

A modem (modulator-demodulator) uses phase shifts to convert data between digital signals, which use binary digits, and analog signals, which use waves.

You can translate periodic functions horizontally and vertically using the methods you have used for other functions.

 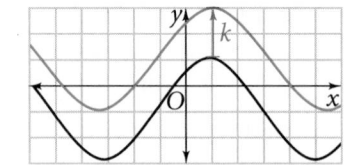

$g(x)$: horizontal translation of $f(x)$ $h(x)$: vertical translation of $f(x)$
$g(x) = f(x - h)$ $h(x) = f(x) + k$

Each horizontal translation of certain periodic functions is a **phase shift.**

When $g(x) = f(x - h)$, the value of h is the amount of the shift left or right. If $h > 0$, the shift is to the right. If $h < 0$, the shift is to the left.

1 EXAMPLE Identifying Phase Shifts

What is the value of h in each translation? Describe each phase shift (use a phrase such as *3 units to the left*).

a. $g(x) = f(x - 2)$

     $h = 2$; the phase shift is 2 units to the right.

b. $y = \cos(x + 4)$
     $= \cos(x - (-4))$
     $h = -4$; the phase shift is 4 units to the left.

CA Standards Check **1** What is the value of h in each translation? Describe each phase shift (use a phrase such as *3 units to the left*).
     a. $g(t) = f(t - 5)$
     b. $y = \sin(x + 3)$

You can analyze a translation to determine how it relates to the parent function.

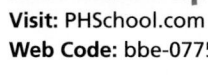

2 EXAMPLE Graphing Translations

Use the graph of the parent function $y = \sin x$ at the left. Sketch each translation of the graph in the interval $0 \leq x \leq 2\pi$.

a. $y = \sin x + 3$

Translate the graph of $y = \sin x$
3 units up.

b. $y = \sin \left(x - \frac{\pi}{2} \right)$

Translate the graph of $y = \sin x$
$\frac{\pi}{2}$ units to the right.

Video Tutor Help
Visit: PHSchool.com
Web Code: bbe-0775

✓ **CA Standards Check** **2** Use the graph of $y = \sin x$ from Example 2. Sketch each translation of the graph in the interval $0 \leq x \leq 2\pi$. Which translation is a phase shift?
a. $y = \sin x - 2$ **b.** $y = \sin (x - 2)$

You can translate both vertically and horizontally to produce combined translations.

3 EXAMPLE Graphing a Combined Translation

Use the graph of the parent function $y = \sin x$ in Example 2. Sketch the translation $y = \sin (x + \pi) - 2$ in the interval $0 \leq x \leq 2\pi$.

Translate the parent function π units to the left and 2 units down.

✓ **CA Standards Check** **3** The graph at the right shows $y = \cos x$.
Use it to graph each combined translation.
a. $y = \cos (x - 2) + 5$
b. $y = \cos (x + 1) + 3$

The translations graphed in Examples 2 and 3 belong to the families of the sine and cosine functions.

Summary   **Families of Sine and Cosine Functions**

Parent Function
$$y = \sin x$$
$$y = \cos x$$

Transformed Function
$$y = a \sin b(x - h) + k$$
$$y = a \cos b(x - h) + k$$

- $|a|$ = amplitude (vertical stretch or shrink)
- $\frac{2\pi}{b}$ = period (when x is in radians and $b > 0$)
- h = phase shift, or horizontal shift
- k = vertical shift

You can use a simpler member of the sine or cosine families to help you graph a more complicated member.

4 EXAMPLE   **Graphing a Translation of y = sin 2x**

Sketch the graph of $y = \sin 2\left(x - \frac{\pi}{3}\right) - \frac{3}{2}$ in the interval from 0 to 2π.

Since $a = 1$ and $b = 2$, the graph is a translation of $y = \sin 2x$.

Step 1   Sketch one cycle of $y = \sin 2x$. Use five points in the pattern *zero–max–zero–min–zero*.

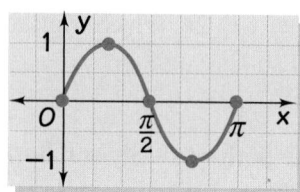

Step 2   Since $h = \frac{\pi}{3}$ and $k = -\frac{3}{2}$, translate the graph $\frac{\pi}{3}$ units to the right and $\frac{3}{2}$ units down. Extend the periodic pattern from 0 to 2π. Sketch the graph.

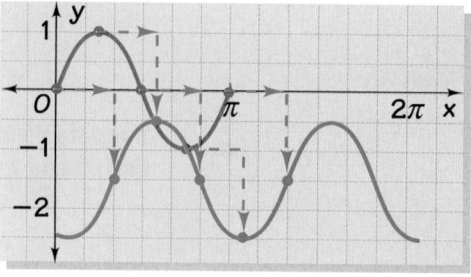

● The blue curve above is the graph of $y = \sin 2\left(x - \frac{\pi}{3}\right) - \frac{3}{2}$.

✅ **CA Standards Check**   **4** Sketch each graph in the interval from 0 to 2π.
   a. $y = -3 \sin 2\left(x - \frac{\pi}{3}\right) - \frac{3}{2}$
   b. $y = 2 \cos \frac{\pi}{2}(x + 1) - 3$

You can write an equation to describe a translation.

5 **EXAMPLE** **Writing a Translation**

Write an equation for each translation.

a. $y = \sin x$, π units down

    π units down means $k = -\pi$.

    An equation is $y = \sin x - \pi$.

b. $y = -\cos x$, 2 units to the left

    2 units to the left means $h = -2$.

    An equation is $y = -\cos (x - (-2))$.

☑ **CA Standards Check** **5** Write an equation for each translation.

a. $y = \cos x$, $\frac{\pi}{2}$ units up

b. $y = 2 \sin x$, $\frac{\pi}{4}$ units to the right

6 **EXAMPLE** **Real-World** 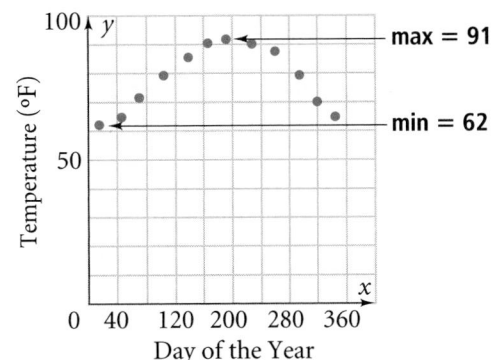 **Connection**

Temperature Cycles The table at the left gives the typical high temperature in New Orleans, Louisiana, on several days of the year (January 1 = 1, February 1 = 32, and so on). Plot the data in the table. Write a cosine model for the data.

Day of Year	Temperature (°F)
16	62
47	65
75	71
106	79
136	85
167	90
197	91
228	90
259	87
289	79
320	70
350	64

Plot the data.

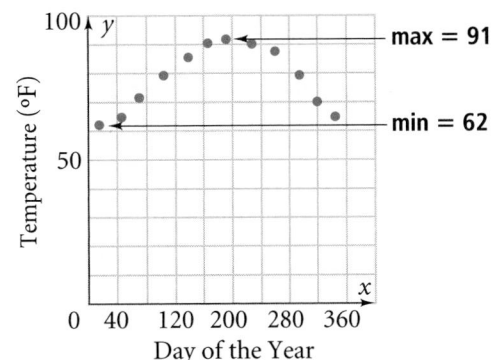

Use the form $y = a \cos b(x - h) + k$. Find values $a, b, h,$ and k.

amplitude $= \frac{1}{2}(\text{max} - \text{min})$

    $= \frac{1}{2}(91 - 62)$

    $= 14.5$

period $= \frac{2\pi}{b}$

    $365 = \frac{2\pi}{b}$ **One complete cycle takes 365 days.**

    $b = \frac{2\pi}{365}$

So (choosing $a > 0$), $a = 14.5$.

To find the values h and k, compare $y = 14.5 \cos \frac{2\pi}{365} x$ with the plot of the data.

    phase shift: $h = 197 - 0$

        $= 197$

    vertical shift: $k = 91 - 14.5$

        $= 76.5$

A model for the data is

$y = 14.5 \cos \frac{2\pi}{365}(x - 197) + 76.5$.

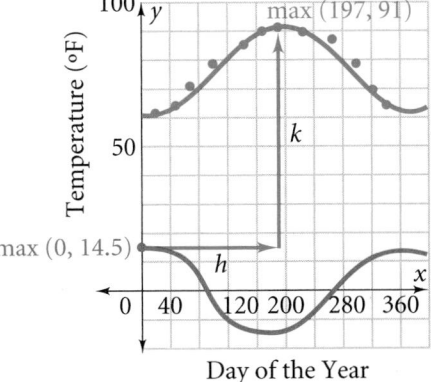

✓ CA Standards Check **6 a. Estimation** Use the model from Example 6. Estimate the high temperature in New Orleans on September 1 (day 244).

b. Graphing Calculator Graph the model on your calculator. Use it to estimate the first day of the year that the high temperature is likely to reach 75°F.

EXERCISES

For more exercises, see *Extra Skill and Word Problem Practice.*

Standards Practice

TRIG 4.0

A **Practice by Example**

Example 1
(page 768)

GO for Help

What is the value of *h* in each translation? Describe each phase shift (use a phrase like *3 units to the left*).

1. $g(x) = f(x + 1)$

2. $g(t) = f(t + 2)$

3. $h(z) = g(z - 1.6)$

4. $h(x) = f(x - 3)$

5. $y = \sin(x + \pi)$

6. $y = \cos\left(x - \frac{5\pi}{7}\right)$

Example 2
(page 769)

Use the function $f(x)$ at the right. Graph each translation.

7. $f(x) + 1$

8. $f(x) - 3$

9. $f(x + 2)$

10. $f(x - 1)$

Graph each translation of $y = \cos x$ in the interval from 0 to 2π.

11. $y = \cos(x + 3)$

12. $y = \cos x + 3$

13. $y = \cos x - 4$

14. $y = \cos(x - 4)$

15. $y = \cos x + \pi$

16. $y = \cos(x - \pi)$

Example 3
(page 769)

Describe any phase shift and vertical shift in the graph.

17. $y = 3\sin x + 1$

18. $y = 4\cos(x + 1) - 2$

19. $y = \sin\left(x + \frac{\pi}{2}\right) + 2$

20. $y = \cos(x - 3) + 2$

Graph each function in the interval from 0 to 2π.

21. $y = 2\sin\left(x + \frac{\pi}{4}\right) - 1$

22. $y = \sin\left(x + \frac{\pi}{3}\right) + 1$

23. $y = \cos(x - \pi) - 3$

24. $y = 2\sin\left(x - \frac{\pi}{6}\right) + 2$

Example 4
(page 770)

Graph each function in the interval from 0 to 2π.

25. $y = 3\sin\frac{1}{2}x$

26. $y = \cos 2\left(x + \frac{\pi}{2}\right) - 2$

27. $y = \frac{1}{2}\sin 2x - 1$

28. $y = \sin 3\left(x + \frac{\pi}{3}\right)$

29. $y = \sin 2(x + 3) - 2$

30. $y = 3\sin\frac{\pi}{2}(x - 2)$

Example 5
(page 771)

Write an equation for each translation.

31. $y = \sin x$, π units to the left

32. $y = \cos x$, $\frac{\pi}{2}$ units down

33. $y = \sin x$, 3 units up

34. $y = \cos x$, 1.5 units to the right

35. $y = \cos x$, $\frac{3}{2\pi}$ units to the left

36. $y = \sin x$, 3π units down

Example 6
(page 771)

37. Temperature The table below shows water temperatures at a buoy in the Gulf of Mexico on several days of the year.

Water Temperatures in the Gulf of Mexico

Day of the Year	16	47	75	106	136	167	197	228	259	289	320	350
Temperature (°F)	71	69	70	73	77	82	85	86	84	82	78	74

Source: *The USA Today Weather Almanac*

a. Plot the data.   **b.** Write a cosine model for the data.

B Apply Your Skills

Write an equation for each translation.

38. $y = \sin x$, 2 units to the right and 4 units down

39. $y = \cos x$, 3 units to the left and π units up

40. $y = \sin x$, $\frac{\pi}{2}$ units to the right and 3.5 units up

Write a cosine function for each graph. Then write a sine function for each graph.

41.

42.

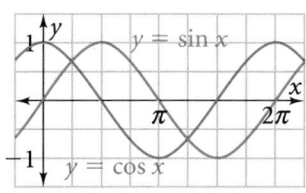

43. The graphs of $y = \sin x$ and $y = \cos x$ are shown at the left.
  a. What phase shift will translate the cosine graph onto the sine graph? Write your answer as an equation in the form $\sin x = \cos (x - h)$.
  b. What phase shift will translate the sine graph onto the cosine graph? Write your answer as an equation in the form $\cos x = \sin (x - h)$.

44. a. Critical Thinking Use a sine function to model the normal daily high temperature in New Orleans. Use the data given in Example 6 on page 771.
  b. Writing How do the sine and cosine models differ?
  c. Estimation Use your sine model to estimate the high temperature in New Orleans on December 1 (day 334).
  d. Graph your model. Use it to estimate the first day of the year that the high temperature is likely to reach 70°F.

45. a. Open-Ended Draw a periodic function. Find its amplitude and period. Then sketch a translation of your function 3 units down and 4 units to the left.
  b. Critical Thinking Suppose your original function is $f(x)$. Describe your translation using the form $g(x) = f(x - h) + k$.

46. a. Write $y = 3 \sin (2x - 4) + 1$ in the form $y = a \sin b(x - h) + k$. (*Hint:* Factor where possible.)
  b. Find the amplitude and period. Describe any translations.

Homework Video Tutor

Visit: PHSchool.com
Web Code: bbe-1307

C Challenge   **Use a graphing calculator to graph each function in the interval from 0 to 2π. Then sketch each graph.**

47. $y = \sin x + x$ **48.** $y = \sin x + 2x$

49. $y = \sin x - 0.5x$ **50.** $y = \cos x - x$

51. $y = \cos x - 2x$ **52.** $y = \cos x + x$

53. $y = \sin (x + \cos x)$ **54.** $y = \sin (x + 2 \cos x)$

Graphing Calculator Hint

Change window values between exercises to see each graph clearly.

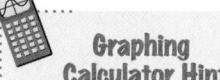

For California Standards and CAHSEE Tutorials, visit PHSchool.com. Web Code: bbq-9045

TRIG 4.0

55. Which function is a phase shift of $y = \sin \theta$ by 5 units to the left?

Ⓐ $y = 5 \sin \theta$

Ⓑ $y = \sin \theta + 5$

Ⓒ $y = \sin (\theta + 5)$

Ⓓ $y = \sin 5\theta$

ALG2 11.2

56. Which is the first *incorrect* step in simplifying $3 \log x - 2 \log 2x$?

Step 1: $3 \log x - 2 \log 2x$

Step 2: $\log x^3 - \log (2x)^2$

Step 3: $\log \dfrac{x^3}{(2x)^2}$

Step 4: $\log \dfrac{x}{2x}$

Step 5: $\log \dfrac{1}{2}$

Ⓐ Step 2   Ⓒ Step 4

Ⓑ Step 3   Ⓓ Step 5

Mixed Review

Lesson 13-6

Identify the period of each function. Then tell where two asymptotes occur for each function.

57. $y = \tan 6\theta$ **58.** $y = \tan \dfrac{\theta}{4}$ **59.** $y = \tan 1.5\theta$ **60.** $y = \tan \dfrac{\theta}{6}$

Lesson 12-6

For the given probability of success p on each trial, find the probability of x successes in n trials.

61. $x = 4, n = 5, p = 0.2$ **62.** $x = 3, n = 5, p = 0.6$

63. $x = 4, n = 8, p = 0.7$ **64.** $x = 7, n = 8, p = 0.7$

Lesson 11-5

Evaluate the finite series for the specified number of terms.

65. $2 + 4 + 8 + \dots; n = 5$ **66.** $3 + 12 + 48 + \dots; n = 7$

67. $-1 - 6 - 36 + \dots; n = 8$ **68.** $120 - 30 + 7.5 - \dots; n = 5$

✓ Checkpoint Quiz 2   Lessons 13-4 through 13-7

Graph each function in the interval from -2π to 2π.

1. $y = \sin 4x$ **2.** $y = 3 \cos x$ **3.** $y = -2 \sin \pi x$

4. $y = 2 \cos \dfrac{\pi}{2}x$ **5.** $y = \tan 2x$ **6.** $y = -\tan x$

7. $y = \cos (x - 2)$ **8.** $y = \sin x + 4$ **9.** $y = 3 \tan \dfrac{\pi}{4}x$

10. Sketch the graph of $y = \sin 3x$ after a translation of 2 units to the right and π units down.

13-8 Reciprocal Trigonometric Functions

 California Content Standards

TRIG 5.0 Students know the definition of the cotangent function and can graph it.
TRIG 6.0 Students know the definition of the secant and cosecant functions and can graph them.

What You'll Learn

- To evaluate reciprocal trigonometric functions
- To graph reciprocal trigonometric functions

. . . And Why

To find indirect measurements, as in Example 6

 Check Skills You'll Need

GO for Help Lesson 7-8 and page 891

Find the reciprocal of each fraction.

1. $\frac{9}{13}$ **2.** $\frac{-5}{8}$ **3.** $\frac{1}{2\pi}$ **4.** $\frac{4m}{15}$ **5.** $\frac{14}{-t}$

Graph each pair of relations on the same coordinate plane.

6. $y = x, y = -x$ **7.** $y = x^2, y = \pm\sqrt{x}$

8. $y = |2x|, y = -|2x|$ **9.** $y = -6x^2, y = \pm\sqrt{\frac{x}{6}}$

New Vocabulary • cosecant • secant • cotangent

---

1 Evaluating Reciprocal Trigonometric Functions

In earlier lessons in this chapter, you studied three trigonometric functions—sine, cosine, and tangent. Three other functions—cosecant, secant, and cotangent—are related to reciprocals of the three you have used.

 Key Concepts

Definition **Cosecant, Secant, and Cotangent Functions**

The cosecant (csc), secant (sec), and cotangent (cot) functions are defined as reciprocals. Their domains include all real numbers θ except those that make a denominator zero.

$$\csc \theta = \frac{1}{\sin \theta} \qquad \sec \theta = \frac{1}{\cos \theta} \qquad \cot \theta = \frac{1}{\tan \theta}$$

You can evaluate reciprocal trigonometric functions by using the definitions.

Graphing Calculator Hint

Caution! The keys for $\sin^{-1}$, $\cos^{-1}$, and $\tan^{-1}$ do not give reciprocals. They represent inverse trigonometric functions, which you will study in Chapter 14.

1 EXAMPLE Using Reciprocals

a. Find csc 60°.

Use a calculator in degree mode.

1/sin (60)
1.154700538

Use the definition.
$\csc 60° = \frac{1}{\sin 60°}$

b. Suppose $\cos \theta = \frac{5}{13}$. Find sec θ.

$\sec \theta = \frac{1}{\cos \theta}$ **Use the definition.**

$= \frac{1}{\frac{5}{13}}$ **Substitute.**

$= \frac{13}{5}$ **Simplify.**

 CA Standards Check **1 a.** Suppose $\sin \theta = \frac{15}{8}$. Find csc θ.

b. Find cot 55° to the nearest hundredth.

You can use what you know about the unit circle to find exact values for reciprocal trigonometric functions.

2 EXAMPLE Finding Exact Values

Multiple Choice Which expression represents the exact value of csc 60°?

Ⓐ $\frac{\sqrt{3}}{3}$ Ⓑ $\frac{\sqrt{3}}{2}$ Ⓒ $\frac{2\sqrt{3}}{3}$ Ⓓ $\sqrt{3}$

Use the unit circle to find the exact value of sin 60°. Then write the reciprocal.

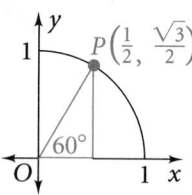

The *y*-coordinate of point *P* is $\frac{\sqrt{3}}{2}$.

$$\csc 60° = \frac{1}{\sin 60°} \quad \textbf{Use the definition.}$$

$$= \frac{1}{\frac{\sqrt{3}}{2}} \quad \textbf{Substitute.}$$

$$= \frac{2}{\sqrt{3}} \quad \textbf{Simplify.}$$

$$= \frac{2\sqrt{3}}{3} \quad \textbf{Rationalize the denominator.}$$

● The correct choice is C.

 CA Standards Check ❷ Find each exact value.

a. sec 60° **b.** cot 45° **c.** csc 30°

You can also evaluate the reciprocal functions in radians.

3 EXAMPLE Using Radians

Evaluate each expression. Use your calculator's radian mode. Round to the nearest thousandth.

a. $\cot \frac{\pi}{3}$

$$\cot \frac{\pi}{3} = \frac{1}{\tan \frac{\pi}{3}}$$

1/tan (π/3)
.5773502692

b. sec (−1)

$$\sec(-1) = \frac{1}{\cos(-1)}$$

1/cos (−1)
1.850815718

● $\cot \frac{\pi}{3} \approx 0.577$ sec (−1) ≈ 1.851

 CA Standards Check ❸ Use a calculator to evaluate each expression. Each angle is given in radians. Round to the nearest thousandth.

a. csc (−1.5) **b.** sec 2 **c.** cot π

The graphs of reciprocal trigonometric functions have asymptotes where their denominators are zero.

4 EXAMPLE Sketching a Graph

Sketch the graphs of $y = \sin x$ and $y = \csc x$ in the interval from 0 to 2π.

Step 1 Make a table of values.

x	0	$\frac{\pi}{6}$	$\frac{\pi}{3}$	$\frac{\pi}{2}$	$\frac{2\pi}{3}$	$\frac{5\pi}{6}$	π	$\frac{7\pi}{6}$	$\frac{4\pi}{3}$	$\frac{3\pi}{2}$	$\frac{5\pi}{3}$	$\frac{11\pi}{6}$	2π
sin x	0	0.5	0.9	1	0.9	0.5	0	−0.5	−0.9	−1	−0.9	−0.5	0
csc x	■	2	1.2	1	1.2	2	■	−2	−1.2	−1	−1.2	−2	■

Step 2 Plot the points and sketch the graphs.

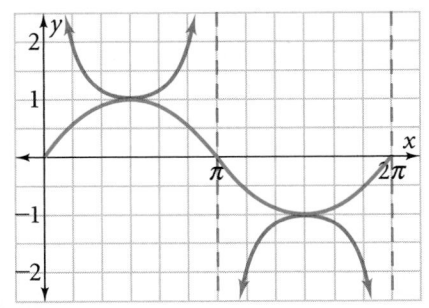

$y = \csc x$ will have a vertical asymptote wherever its denominator ($\sin x$) is 0.

To draw a smooth curve, you should first plot several points as a guide.

CA Standards Check 4 Graph $y = \tan x$ and $y = \cot x$ in the interval from 0 to 2π.

You can use a graphing calculator to graph trigonometric functions quickly.

5 EXAMPLE Using Technology to Graph Reciprocals

Graph $y = \sec x$. Find the value of sec 20°.

Step 1 Use degree mode.
Graph $y = \frac{1}{\cos x}$.

Xmin=−360
Xmax=360
Xscl=30
Ymin=−5
Ymax=5
Yscl=1

Step 2 Use the TABLE feature.

X	Y1
20	1.0642
21	1.0711
22	1.0785
23	1.0864
24	1.0946
25	1.1034
26	1.1126

X=20

sec 20° ≈ 1.0642

CA Standards Check 5 Use the graph of the reciprocal trigonometric function to find csc 45°.

You can use a reciprocal trigonometric function to solve a real-world problem.

6 EXAMPLE <u>Real-World</u> Connection

Indirect Measurement A handler of a parade balloon holds a line of length y. The length is modeled by the function $y = d \sec \theta$, where d is the distance from the handler of the balloon to the point on the ground just below the balloon, and θ is the angle formed by the line and the ground. Graph the function for $d = 6$. Find the length of line needed to form an angle of $60°$.

$$y = 6 \sec \theta = 6\left(\frac{1}{\cos \theta}\right) = \frac{6}{\cos \theta} \qquad \textbf{Use the definition of secant. Simplify.}$$

Graph the function. Use the **value** feature.

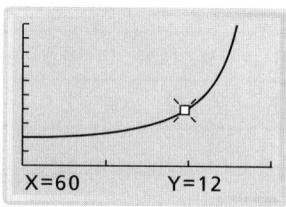

Xmin=0
Xmax=90
Xscl=30
Ymin=0
Ymax=30
Yscl=3

X=60   Y=12

● To form an angle of $60°$, the line must be 12 ft long.

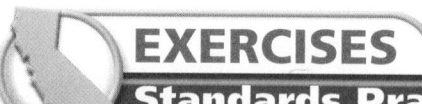 **CA Standards Check** **6** How long must the line be to form an angle of $30°$? Of $45°$? Of $85°$?

EXERCISES

For more exercises, see *Extra Skill and Word Problem Practice.*

Standards Practice

TRIG 5.0, 6.0

A Practice by Example

Example 1
(page 775)

GO for Help

Evaluate each expression. Give your answer as a decimal rounded to the nearest hundredth.

1. csc $100°$ **2.** csc $80°$ **3.** cot $(-55°)$ **4.** sec $200°$

Evaluate each expression. Write your answer in exact form.

5. Suppose $\tan \theta = \frac{20}{15}$. Find $\cot \theta$.   **6.** Suppose $\sin \theta = \frac{13}{18}$. Find $\csc \theta$.

7. Suppose $\cos \theta = -\frac{21}{35}$. Find $\sec \theta$.   **8.** Suppose $\tan \theta = -\frac{4}{3}$. Find $\cot \theta$.

Example 2
(page 776)

Find the exact value of each expression. If the expression is undefined, write *undefined*.

9. sec $45°$ **10.** cot $60°$ **11.** cot $90°$ **12.** sec $180°$

13. csc $0°$ **14.** csc $60°$ **15.** cot $0°$ **16.** cot $30°$

17. sec $90°$ **18.** csc $30°$ **19.** sec $60°$ **20.** csc $45°$

Example 3
(page 776)

Evaluate each expression to the nearest hundredth. Each angle is given in radians.

21. cot 3 **22.** sec π **23.** csc $\frac{\pi}{2}$ **24.** sec $(-\pi)$

25. sec 2.5 **26.** csc (-3.2) **27.** cot $\frac{\pi}{6}$ **28.** csc (-4.5)

Example 4
(page 777)

Graph each function in the interval from 0 to 2π.

29. $y = \sec 2\theta$ **30.** $y = \cot \theta$ **31.** $y = \csc 2\theta - 1$ **32.** $y = \csc 2\theta$

Example 5
(page 777)

Use the graph of the appropriate reciprocal trigonometric function to find each value. Round to four decimal places.

33. sec 30°   **34.** sec 80°   **35.** sec 110°   **36.** csc 30°

37. csc 70°   **38.** csc 130°   **39.** cot 30°   **40.** cot 60°

Example 6
(page 778)

41. Indirect Measurement A communications tower has wires anchoring it to the ground. Each wire is attached to the tower at a height 20 ft above the ground. The length y of the wire is modeled with the function $y = 20 \csc \theta$, where θ is the measure of the angle formed by the wire and the ground.
a. Graph the function.
b. Find the length of wire needed to form an angle of 45°.
c. Find the length of wire needed to form an angle of 60°.
d. Find the length of wire needed to form an angle of 75°.

Evaluate each expression. Write your answer in exact form. If appropriate, also state it as a decimal rounded to the nearest hundredth. If the expression is undefined, write *undefined*.

42. $\cot(-45°)$ **43.** $\sec(-30°)$

44. $\csc(-90°)$ **45.** $\sec(-180°)$

Graph each function in the interval from 0 to 2π.

46. $y = \csc \theta - \frac{\pi}{2}$ **47.** $y = \sec \frac{1}{4}\theta$

48. $y = -\sec \pi\theta$ **49.** $y = \cot \frac{\theta}{3}$

Match each function with its graph.

50. $y = \dfrac{1}{\sin x}$ **51.** $y = \dfrac{1}{\cos x}$

52. $y = -\dfrac{1}{\sin x}$ **53.** $y = \dfrac{1}{\tan x}$

A.   **B.**

C.   **D.**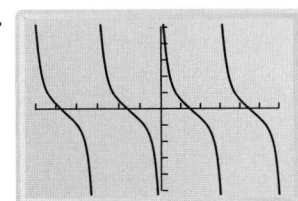

54. a. What are the domain, range, and period of $y = \csc x$?
b. What is the relative minimum in the interval $0 \le x \le \pi$?
c. What is the relative maximum in the interval $\pi \le x \le 2\pi$?

55. Reasoning Use the relationship $\csc x = \frac{1}{\sin x}$ to explain why each statement is true.
a. When the graph of $y = \sin x$ is positive, so is the graph of $y = \csc x$.
b. When the graph of $y = \sin x$ is near a y-value of -1, so is the graph of $y = \csc x$.

Explain why each expression is undefined.

56. csc 180°   **57.** sec 90°   **58.** cot 0°

59. Indirect Measurement The
function $y = 60 \sec \theta$ models
the length y of a fire ladder as
a function of the measure of
the angle θ formed by the
ladder and the horizontal
when the hinge of the ladder
is 60 ft from the building.
  a. Graph the function.
  b. In the photo, $\theta = 20°$. How
  far is the ladder extended?
  c. How far is the ladder
  extended when it forms an
  angle of 30°?

  d. Suppose the ladder is extended to its full length of 80 ft. What angle does it
  form with the horizontal? How far up a building can the ladder reach when
  fully extended? (*Hint:* Use the information in the photo.)

60. a. Graph $y = \tan x$ and $y = \cot x$ on the same axes.
  ✎ **b.** State the domain, the range, and the asymptotes of each function.
  ✎ **c. Writing** Compare the two graphs. How are they alike? How are
  they different?
  ⬦ **d. Geometry** The graph of the cotangent function can be reflected about
  a line to graph the tangent function. Name at least two lines that have
  this property.

🖩 **Graph each function in the interval from 0 to 2π. Describe any phase shift and
vertical shift in the graph.**

61. $y = \sec 2\theta + 3$ **62.** $y = \sec 2\left(\theta + \frac{\pi}{2}\right)$

63. $y = \csc 2\theta - 1$ **64.** $y = \csc 2\left(\theta - \frac{\pi}{2}\right)$

65. $y = -2 \sec (x - 4)$ **66.** $f(x) = 3 \csc (x + 2) - 1$

67. $y = \cot 2(x + \pi) + 3$ **68.** $g(x) = 2 \sec \left(3\left(x - \frac{\pi}{6}\right)\right) - 2$

69. a. Graph $y = -\cos x$ and $y = -\sec x$ on the same axes.
  b. State the domain, the range, and the period of each function.
  ✎ **c.** For which values of x does $-\cos x = -\sec x$? Justify your answer.
  ✎ **d. Writing** Compare the two graphs. How are they alike? How are
  they different?
  e. Reasoning Is the value of $-\sec x$ positive when $-\cos x$ is positive and
  negative when $-\cos x$ is negative? Justify your answer.

70. a. Critical Thinking Which expression gives the correct value of csc 60°?
  I. $\sin ((60^{-1})°)$ **II.** $(\sin 60°)^{-1}$ **III.** $(\cos 60°)^{-1}$
  b. Which expression in part (a) represents $\sin \left(\frac{1}{60}\right)°$?

Ⓒ **Challenge**

71. Reasoning Each branch of $y = \sec x$ and $y = \csc x$ is a curve.
Explain why these curves cannot be parabolas. (*Hint:* Do
parabolas have asymptotes?)

72. Reasoning Consider the relationship between the graphs of $y = \cos x$ and $y = \cos 3x$. Use the relationship to explain the distance between successive branches of the graphs of $y = \sec x$ and $y = \sec 3x$.

73. a. Graph $y = \cot x$, $y = \cot 2x$, $y = \cot(-2x)$, and $y = \cot \frac{1}{2}x$ on the same axes.
   b. Make a Conjecture Describe how the graph of $y = \cot bx$ changes as the value of b changes.

74. a. Graph $y = \sec x$, $y = 2 \sec x$, $y = -3 \sec x$, and $y = \frac{1}{2} \sec x$ on the same axes.
   b. Make a Conjecture Describe how the graph of $y = b \sec x$ changes as the value of b changes.

Multiple Choice Practice

For California Standards and CAHSEE Tutorials, visit PHSchool.com. Web Code: bbq-9045

TRIG 6.0

75. Which of the following equations best represents the graph at the right?

  Ⓐ $y = \dfrac{1}{\cos x}$

  Ⓑ $y = \dfrac{1}{\sin x}$

  Ⓒ $y = -\dfrac{1}{\cos x}$

  Ⓓ $y = -\dfrac{1}{\sin x}$

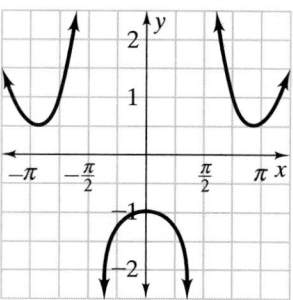

ALG2 13.0

76. Which expression is equivalent to $\log_5 18$?

  Ⓐ $\log_{10} 5 + \log_{10} 18$ Ⓒ $(\log_{10} 5)(\log_{10} 18)$

  Ⓑ $\log_{10} 5 - \log_{10} 18$ Ⓓ $\dfrac{\log_{10} 18}{\log_{10} 5}$

Mixed Review

Lesson 13-7

Find the amplitude and period of each function. Describe any phase shift and vertical shift in the graph.

77. $y = 2 \sin x - 5$ **78.** $y = -\cos(x + 4) - 7$

79. $y = -3 \sin\left(x + \frac{\pi}{6}\right) + 4$ **80.** $y = 5 \cos \pi(x - 1.5) - 8$

Lesson 12-7

Sketch a normal curve for each distribution. Label the x-axis values at one, two, and three standard deviations from the mean.

81. mean = 25, standard deviation = 5

82. mean = 25, standard deviation = 10

Lesson 11-6

Write and evaluate a sum to approximate the area under each curve for the domain $-1 \le x \le 2$.
a. Use inscribed rectangles 1 unit wide.
b. Use circumscribed rectangles 1 unit wide.

83. $f(x) = 3x^2$ **84.** $y = x^2 + 4$

85. $g(x) = -x^2 + 4$ **86.** $g(x) = -x^2 + 8$

You can solve many problems quickly when you know the sine and cosine of special angles and the pattern of the y-values of the periodic function.

θ	0° or 0 radians	30° or $\frac{\pi}{6}$ radians	45° or $\frac{\pi}{4}$ radians	60° or $\frac{\pi}{3}$ radians	90° or $\frac{\pi}{2}$ radians
sin θ	0	$\frac{1}{2}$	$\frac{\sqrt{2}}{2}$	$\frac{\sqrt{3}}{2}$	1
cos θ	1	$\frac{\sqrt{3}}{2}$	$\frac{\sqrt{2}}{2}$	$\frac{1}{2}$	0

1 EXAMPLE

Find each exact value.

a. $\sin 150°$

The terminal side of the angle lies in Quadrant II and forms an angle of 30° with the x-axis.

$\sin 150° = \sin 30° = \frac{1}{2}$

b. $\cos\left(-\frac{\pi}{4}\right)$

The terminal side of the angle lies in Quadrant IV and forms an angle of $\frac{\pi}{4}$ radians with the x-axis.

$\cos\left(-\frac{\pi}{4}\right) = \cos\frac{\pi}{4} = \frac{\sqrt{2}}{2}$

2 EXAMPLE

Solve each equation in the interval from 0° to 360°. Give exact answers.

a. $\sin\theta = -\frac{\sqrt{2}}{2}$

The sine is negative, so the terminal side of the angle must lie in Quadrant III or IV. It forms an angle of 45° with the x-axis.

$\theta = 180° + 45° = 225°$

$\theta = 360° - 45° = 315°$

The solutions are 225° and 315°.

b. $\cos\left(\frac{\theta}{2}\right) = 0$

The cosine is 0, so the terminal side of the angle must lie on the y-axis. The angle must be 90° or 270°.

If $\frac{\theta}{2} = 90°$, then $\theta = 180°$.

If $\frac{\theta}{2} = 270°$, then $\theta = 540°$.

Since 540° > 360°, the only solution is 180°.

EXERCISES

Each angle extends outside Quadrant I. Find the exact value of each expression.

1. $\cos 150°$

2. $\sin -120°$

3. $\sin\left(\frac{5\pi}{6}\right)$

4. $\cos\left(\frac{2\pi}{3}\right)$

5. $\sin\left(-\frac{4\pi}{3}\right)$

6. $\cos\left(-\frac{5\pi}{4}\right)$

7. $\tan\left(\frac{2\pi}{3}\right)$

8. $\tan(-150°)$

Solve each equation in the interval from 0° to 360°. Give exact answers.

9. $\cos\theta = \frac{1}{2}$

10. $\sin\theta = \frac{\sqrt{2}}{2}$

11. $\sin\theta = 1$

12. $\cos\left(\frac{\theta}{4}\right) = \frac{1}{2}$

Chapter 13 Review

Vocabulary Review

🔊 **English and Spanish Audio Online**

amplitude (p. 724)
central angle (p. 738)
cosecant (p. 775)
cosine function (p. 755)
cosine of θ (p. 732)
cotangent (p. 775)
coterminal angles (p. 731)
cycle (p. 723)

initial side (p. 730)
intercepted arc (p. 738)
period (p. 723)
periodic function (p. 723)
phase shift (p. 768)
radian (p. 738)
secant (p. 775)
sine curve (p. 747)

sine function (p. 746)
sine of θ (p. 732)
standard position (p. 730)
tangent function (p. 761)
tangent of θ (p. 761)
terminal side (p. 730)
unit circle (p. 732)

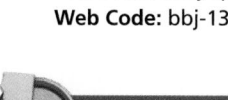

Go Online
PHSchool.com
For: Vocabulary quiz
Web Code: bbj-1351

Choose the correct term to complete each sentence.

1. The __?__ of a function is the length of one cycle.

2. Centered at the origin of the coordinate plane, the __?__ has a radius of 1 unit.

3. The asymptote of the __?__ occurs at $\theta = \frac{\pi}{2}$ and repeats every π units.

4. A horizontal translation of a periodic function is a(n) __?__.

5. The __?__ is the reciprocal of the cosine function.

Skills and Concepts

Lesson 13-1

- To identify cycles and periods of periodic functions (p. 722)
- To find the amplitude of periodic functions (p. 724)

A **periodic function** repeats a pattern of *y*-values at regular intervals. One complete pattern is called a **cycle**. A cycle may begin at any point on the graph. The **period** of a function is the length of one cycle. The **amplitude** of a periodic function is half the difference between its maximum and minimum values.

6. Determine whether the function at the right *is* or *is not* periodic. If it is, identify one cycle in two different ways. Then determine the period and amplitude.

7. Sketch the graph of a wave with a period of 0.5 and an amplitude of 3.

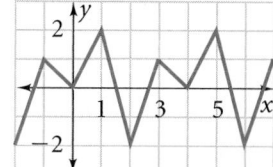

Lesson 13-2

- To work with angles in standard position (p. 730)
- To find coordinates of points on the unit circle (p. 732)

 TRIG 1.0, 2.0, 9.0

An angle is in **standard position** if the vertex is at the origin and one ray, the **initial side**, is on the positive *x*-axis. The other ray is the **terminal side** of the angle. Two angles in standard position are **coterminal** if they have the same terminal side.

The **unit circle** has a radius of 1 unit and its center at the origin. The **cosine of θ** (cos θ) is the *x*-coordinate of the point where the terminal side of the angle intersects the unit circle. The **sine of θ** (sin θ) is the *y*-coordinate.

8. Find the measure of the angle in standard position at the right.

9. Sketch a −30° angle in standard position.

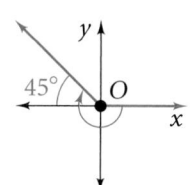

10. Find the measure of an angle between 0° and 360° coterminal with a −120° angle.

11. Find the exact coordinates of the point at which the terminal side of a 315° angle intersects the unit circle. Then find the decimal equivalents. Round your answers to the nearest hundredth.

Lesson 13-3

- To use radian measure for angles (p. 738)
- To find the length of an arc of a circle (p. 740)

 TRIG 1.0

A **central angle** of a circle is an angle whose vertex is at the center of a circle. An **intercepted arc** is the portion of the circle whose endpoints are on the sides of the angle and whose remaining points lie in the interior of the angle. A **radian** is the measure of a central angle that intercepts an arc equal in length to a radius of the circle.

To convert degrees to radians, multiply by $\frac{\pi \text{ radians}}{180°}$. To convert radians to degrees, multiply by $\frac{180°}{\pi \text{ radians}}$. When the measure of an angle θ is in radians and r is the radius, the length s of the intercepted arc is $s = r\theta$.

The measure θ of an angle in standard position is given.
a. Write each degree measure in radians and each radian measure in degrees rounded to the nearest degree.
b. Find the exact values of cos θ and sin θ for each angle measure.

12. 60°   **13.** −45°   **14.** 180°

15. 2π radians   **16.** $\frac{5\pi}{6}$ radians   **17.** $-\frac{3\pi}{4}$ radians

18. Use the circle to find the length of the indicated arc. Round your answer to the nearest tenth.

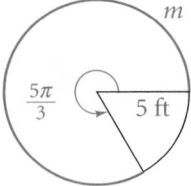

Lessons 13-4 and 13-5

- To identify properties of the sine function (p. 746)
- To graph sine curves (p. 749)
- To graph and write cosine functions (p. 755)
- To solve trigonometric equations (p. 756)

 TRIG 2.0

The **sine function** $y = \sin \theta$ matches the measure θ of an angle in standard position with the y-coordinate of a point on the unit circle. This point is where the terminal side of the angle intersects the unit circle. The graph of a sine function is called a **sine curve**.

The **cosine function** $y = \cos \theta$ matches the measure θ of an angle in standard position with the x-coordinate of a point on the unit circle. This point is where the terminal side of the angle intersects the unit circle.

For the sine function $y = a \sin b\theta$ and the cosine function $y = a \cos b\theta$, the amplitude equals $|a|$, there are b cycles from 0 to 2π, and the period is $\frac{2\pi}{b}$.

Sketch the graph of each function in the interval from 0 to 2π.

19. $y = 3 \sin \theta$ **20.** $y = 2 \cos \left(\frac{\pi}{2}\right)t$ **21.** $y = -\cos 2\theta$

22. For the graph at the right, how many cycles does the sine function have in the interval from 0 to 2π? Find the amplitude and period of the function. Then write an equation for the sine function.

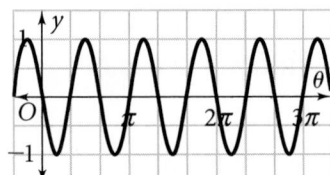

Write an equation of the function for each description or graph.

23. sine function, $a > 0$, amplitude 4, period 0.5π

24. cosine function, $a > 0$, amplitude 3, period π

25.

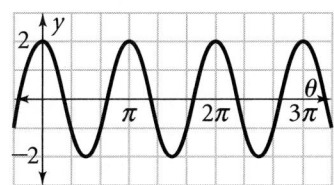

Solve each equation in the interval from 0 to 2π. Round to the nearest hundredth.

26. $\sin \theta = -0.7$ **27.** $\sin \left(\frac{\pi}{2}\right) \theta = 0.25$ **28.** $3 \cos 4\theta = -2$

Lesson 13-6

• To graph the tangent function (p. 761)

 TRIG 5.0

The **tangent** of an angle θ in standard position is the y-coordinate of the point where the terminal side of the angle intersects the tangent line $x = 1$. A **tangent function** in the form $y = a \tan b\theta$ has a period of $\frac{\pi}{b}$.

Graph each function in the interval from 0 to 2π. Then evaluate the function at $t = \frac{\pi}{4}$ and $t = \frac{\pi}{2}$. If the tangent is undefined at that point, write *undefined*.

29. $y = \tan \left(\frac{1}{2}\right) t$ **30.** $y = \tan 3t$ **31.** $y = 2 \tan t$

Lesson 13-7

• To graph translations of trigonometric functions (p. 768)

• To write equations of translations (p. 771)

 TRIG 4.0

Each horizontal translation of certain periodic functions is a **phase shift.** When $g(x) = f(x - h) + k$, the value of h is the amount of the horizontal shift and the value of k is the amount of the vertical shift.

Graph each function in the interval from 0 to 2π.

32. $y = \cos \left(x + \frac{\pi}{2}\right)$ **33.** $y = 2 \sin x - 4$ **34.** $y = \sin (x - \pi) + 3$

Write an equation for each translation.

35. $y = \sin x, \frac{\pi}{4}$ units to the right   **36.** $y = \cos x, 2$ units down

---

Lesson 13-8

• To evaluate reciprocal trigonometric functions (p. 775)

• To graph reciprocal trigonometric functions (p. 777)

 TRIG 5.0, 6.0

The **cosecant** (csc), **secant** (sec), and **cotangent** (cot) functions are defined using reciprocals for all real numbers θ (except those that make a denominator zero).

$$\csc \theta = \frac{1}{\sin \theta} \qquad \sec \theta = \frac{1}{\cos \theta} \qquad \cot \theta = \frac{1}{\tan \theta}$$

Evaluate each expression. Write your answer in exact form.

37. $\sec (-45°)$ **38.** $\cot 120°$ **39.** $\csc 150°$

Graph each function in the interval from 0 to 2π.

40. $y = 2 \csc \theta$ **41.** $y = \sec \theta - 1$ **42.** $y = \cot \left(\frac{1}{4}\right) \theta$

Determine whether each function *is* or *is not* periodic. If it is periodic, find the period and amplitude.

1.

2.
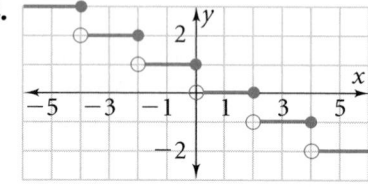

Find the measure of an angle between 0° and 360° coterminal with the given angle.

3. $-32°$ **4.** $-229°$ **5.** $375°$

Write each measure in radians. Express the answer in terms of π and also as a decimal rounded to the nearest hundredth.

6. $-225°$ **7.** $120°$ **8.** $600°$

Write each measure in degrees. If necessary, round your answer to the nearest degree.

9. $\frac{5\pi}{6}$ **10.** -2.5π **11.** 0.8

How many cycles does each sine function have in the interval from 0 to 2π? Find the amplitude and period of each function.

12.

13.
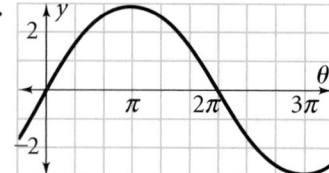

14. Open-Ended Sketch a function with period 7.

15. Writing Explain how to convert an angle measure in radians to an angle measure in degrees. Include an example.

16. Physics On each swing, a pendulum 18 inches long travels through an angle of $\frac{3\pi}{4}$ radians. How far does the tip of the pendulum travel in one swing? Round your answer to the nearest inch.

Find the amplitude and period of each function. Then sketch one cycle of the graph of each function.

17. $y = 4 \sin (2x)$ **18.** $y = 2 \sin (4x)$

Solve each equation in the interval from 0 to 2π. Give an exact answer and an answer rounded to the nearest hundredth.

19. $\cos t = \frac{1}{2}$ **20.** $2 \sin t = \sqrt{3}$

21. $3 \tan 2t = \sqrt{3}$ **22.** $\cos \frac{t\pi}{4} = 1$

Graph each function in the interval from 0 to 2π.

23. $y = 2 \cos x$ **24.** $y = -\cos \frac{\theta}{\pi}$

25. $y = 4 \sin x - 2$ **26.** $y = \cos (x + \pi)$

27. $y = \tan \frac{\theta}{3}$ **28.** $y = \tan \frac{\pi}{3}\theta$

Write an equation for each translation.

29. $y = \sin x$, 1 unit down

30. $y = \cos x$, 7.5 units to the right

31. $y = \sin x$, 3 units to the left, 1.5 units down

32. $y = \cos x$, $\frac{\pi}{2}$ units to the right, 8 units up

Evaluate each expression. Write your answer in exact form. If the expression is undefined, write *undefined*.

33. $\sin 30°$ **34.** $\cos 60°$

35. $\sin (-330°)$ **36.** $\csc (-330°)$

37. $\sec 270°$ **38.** $\tan 60°$

39. $\cos 45°$ **40.** $\cot (-60°)$

Graph each function in the interval from 0 to 2π.

41. $y = \cot \theta$ **42.** $y = \sec \theta + 1$

43. $y = \csc \frac{\theta}{2}$ **44.** $y = \csc (\theta + 1)$

Some problems ask you to use given results to find the probability of independent events.

Tip 2
Find the number of times the event "landing on orange" and "landing on blue" occurs.

The table below shows the results of spinning a spinner.

Outcome	Frequency
Orange	8
Green	7
Blue	5

What is the probability of landing on orange and then blue?

(A) $\frac{1}{10}$ (C) $\frac{2}{5}$

(B) $\frac{7}{20}$ (D) $\frac{13}{20}$

Tip 1
Find the total number of trials for the experiment.

Think It Through
The number of trials for the experiment is $8 + 7 + 5 = 20$. Of those, 8 are orange.

$$\frac{8}{20} = \frac{2}{5}$$

The probability of spinning blue is $\frac{5}{20} = \frac{1}{4}$. The probability of spinning orange, then blue is $\frac{2}{5} \cdot \frac{1}{4} = \frac{2}{20} = \frac{1}{10}$.
The correct answer is A.

Vocabulary Review

As you solve problems, you must understand the meanings of mathematical terms. Match each term with its mathematical meaning.

A. amplitude

B. initial side

C. radian

D. terminal side

E. phase shift

I. the measure of a central angle that intercepts an arc equal in length to a radius of the circle

II. the ray not on the *x*-axis of an angle in standard position

III. a horizontal translation of certain periodic functions

IV. the ray on the *x*-axis of an angle in standard position

V. half the difference between the minimum and maximum values of a periodic function

Multiple Choice

Read each question. Then write the letter of the correct answer on your paper.

1. Which statement best describes the data below?
   15, 20, 25, 25, 35, 60, 65 (Lesson 12-3)
   (A) The mean and the mode have the same value.
   (B) The median and the mode have the same value.
   (C) The range of the data is 65.
   (D) Only the median is 25.

2. Tim earned the following scores on his geography tests: 83, 83, 87, and 95. If Tim scores 82 on his one remaining test, which measure of central tendency will give him the highest grade? (Lesson 12-3)
   (A) Mode
   (B) Median
   (C) Range
   (D) Mean

3. The student council conducted a survey about outdoor activities that students prefer. The results of the survey were displayed using a bar graph. Which of the following measures of central tendency does the longest bar of the graph represent? (Lesson 12-3)
   (A) Mode
   (B) Median
   (C) Range
   (D) Mean

4. The school's basketball team scored 79, 80, 82, 84, and 89 points in the first five games of the season. If the team scored 54 points in its sixth game, which measure of data changed the most? (Lesson 12-3)
   (A) Mean
   (B) Mode
   (C) Median
   (D) All measures were affected equally.

5. The table below shows the results of spinning a spinner. Based on these results, what is the probability of the spinner landing on white, then red? (Lesson 9-7)

Outcome	Frequency
Red	7
Blue	3
White	5

Ⓐ $\frac{1}{9}$ Ⓒ $\frac{7}{18}$

Ⓑ $\frac{7}{45}$ Ⓓ $\frac{36}{45}$

6. There are 2 rainbow fish and 3 angelfish in a pet store fish tank holding 16 fish. The remaining fish are guppies. What is the probability that a customer who randomly selects two fish will choose a rainbow fish and an angelfish? (Lesson 6-7)

Ⓐ $\frac{1}{120}$ Ⓒ $\frac{5}{11}$

Ⓑ $\frac{1}{20}$ Ⓓ $\frac{2}{55}$

7. Carlos and Margaret are standing in line for concert tickets with 25 other people. If two people are chosen at random from the line to get front row seats, what is the probability that Carlos and Margaret will be picked? (Lesson 6-7)

Ⓐ $\frac{1}{351}$ Ⓒ $\frac{1}{27}$

Ⓑ $\frac{1}{54}$ Ⓓ $\frac{2}{27}$

8. Monique has 3 brown belts, 2 black belts and 4 multi-colored belts. She is packing for a trip and picks three belts at random to take with her. What is the probability that she will choose all three brown belts? (Lesson 6-7)

Ⓐ $\frac{1}{3}$ Ⓒ $\frac{1}{84}$

Ⓑ $\frac{1}{9}$ Ⓓ $\frac{1}{252}$

9. During a promotional event, two customers at a clothing store between 9 and 10 A.M. will be randomly selected to win a gift certificate. Suppose you and a friend visit the store and there are 19 other customers between 9 and 10 A.M. What is the probability you and your friend will NOT both win the gift certificate? (Lesson 6-7)

Ⓐ $\frac{1}{210}$ Ⓒ $\frac{2}{21}$

Ⓑ $\frac{2}{19}$ Ⓓ $\frac{209}{210}$

10. Using Pascal's Triangle, what is the expansion of $(r-3)^4$? (Lesson 6-8)

$$1$$
$$1 \quad 1$$
$$1 \quad 2 \quad 1$$
$$1 \quad 3 \quad 3 \quad 1$$
$$1 \quad 4 \quad 6 \quad 4 \quad 1$$
$$1 \quad 5 \quad 10 \quad 10 \quad 5 \quad 1$$

Ⓐ $r^4 + 4r^3 + 6r^2 + 4r^3 + 1$

Ⓑ $r^4 + 12r^3 + 54r^2 + 108r^3 + 81$

Ⓒ $r^4 - 12r^3 + 54r^2 - 108r^3 + 81$

Ⓓ $r^4 - 12r^3 + 12r^2 - 12r^3 + 81$

11. What is the coefficient of the third term in the expansion of $(2a - b)^5$? (Lesson 6-8)

Ⓐ -80 Ⓒ 40

Ⓑ 32 Ⓓ 80

12. What is the sixth term in the expansion of $(2x - 3y)^7$? (Lesson 6-8)

Ⓐ $21x^2y^5$

Ⓑ $-126x^2y^5$

Ⓒ $-20{,}412x^2y^5$

Ⓓ $20{,}412x^2y^5$

13. What is the directrix of the graph of $6x = x^2 + 8y + 9$? (Lesson 10-2)

Ⓐ $x = 2$

Ⓑ $y = 2$

Ⓒ $x = -4$

Ⓓ $y = -4$

14. Which equation represents a circle with center $(-3, 8)$ and radius 12? (Lesson 10-3)

Ⓐ $(x - 8)^2 + (y + 3)^2 = 144$

Ⓑ $(x - 8)^2 - (y + 3)^2 = 144$

Ⓒ $(x + 3)^2 + (y - 8)^2 = 144$

Ⓓ $(x - 3)^2 - (y - 8)^2 = 144$

15. Which is equivalent to i^6? (Lesson 5-6)

Ⓐ i Ⓒ 1

Ⓑ $-i$ Ⓓ -1

16. Which of the following expressions is represented by point A on the coordinate plane below? (Lesson 5-6)

Ⓐ $1 + 3i$

Ⓑ $3 + i$

Ⓒ $1 - 3i$

Ⓓ $3i - 1$

17. What is the distance of $4 - 5i$ from the origin? (Lesson 5-6)

Ⓐ 9 units

Ⓑ $\sqrt{41}$ units

Ⓒ 3 units

Ⓓ 1 unit

18. What is the number $\sqrt{-225} + 36$ when written in the form $a + bi$? (Lesson 5-6)

Ⓐ $-15 + 6i$

Ⓑ $6 + 15i$

Ⓒ $6 - 15i$

Ⓓ $36 + 15i$

19. What is the solution to the equation $7^{2x} = 75$ to the nearest hundredth? (Lesson 8-5)

Ⓐ 1.11 Ⓒ 8.66

Ⓑ 5.36 Ⓓ 10.71

20. Which is equivalent to $2^9 = 512$? (Lesson 8-3)

Ⓐ $\log_{512} 2 = 9$

Ⓑ $\log_2 512 = 9$

Ⓒ $\log_2 9 = 512$

Ⓓ $\log_9 512 = 2$

21. What is the logarithmic form of the exponential equation $2^4 = 16$? (Lesson 8-3)

Ⓐ $\log_{16} 2 = 4$

Ⓑ $\log_{16} 4 = 2$

Ⓒ $\log_4 16 = 2$

Ⓓ $\log_2 16 = 4$

Standards Reference Guide

California Content Standard	Item Number(s)
PS 6.0	1–4
PS 1.0	5
ALG2 19.0	6–9
ALG2 20.0	10–12
ALG2 16.0	13–14
ALG2 5.0	15–18
ALG2 11.1	19–21

For additional review and practice, see the *California Standards Review and Practice Workbook* or go online to use the

California Standards Tutorials

Visit: PHSchool.com, **Web Code:** bbq-9045

Trigonometric Identities and Equations

 What You've Learned

California Content Standards

1.0 Students understand the notion of angle and how to measure it, in both degrees and radians. They can convert between degrees and radians. *Trigonometry*

5.0 Students know the definitions of the tangent and cotangent functions and can graph them. *Trigonometry*

6.0 Students know the definitions of the secant and cosecant functions and can graph them. *Trigonometry*

✔ Check Your Readiness

 for Help to the Lesson in green.

Solving Quadratic Equations (Lesson 5-5)

Solve each equation.

1. $4x^2 = 25$ **2.** $x^2 - 23 = 0$ **3.** $3x^2 = 80$

4. $8x^2 - 44 = 0$ **5.** $0.5x^2 = 15$ **6.** $6x^2 - 13 = 11$

Finding the Inverse of a Function (Lesson 7-7)

For each function f, find f^{-1} and the domain and range of f and f^{-1}. Determine whether f^{-1} is a function.

7. $f(x) = 5x + 2$ **8.** $f(x) = \sqrt{x + 3}$ **9.** $f(x) = \sqrt{3x - 4}$

10. $f(x) = \frac{5}{x}$ **11.** $f(x) = \frac{10}{x - 1}$ **12.** $f(x) = \frac{10}{x} - 1$

Solving Exponential and Logarithmic Equations (Lesson 8-5)

Solve each equation.

13. $4^x = \frac{1}{8}$ **14.** $\log 5x + 1 = -1$ **15.** $7^{3x} = 500$

16. $\log 3x + \log x = 9$ **17.** $\log (4x + 3) - \log x = 5$ **18.** $3^x = 243$

Evaluating Trigonometric Functions (Lessons 13-2 and 13-6)

For each value of θ, find the values of $\cos \theta$, $\sin \theta$, and $\tan \theta$. Round your answers to the nearest hundredth.

19. $48°$ **20.** $-105°$ **21.** $16°$ **22.** $\frac{5\pi}{6}$

What You'll Learn Next

▲ In Lesson 14-1, you will solve a problem involving the refraction of a ray of light passing from one medium (air) into another (water).

California Content Standards

8.0 Students know the definitions of the inverse trigonometric functions and can graph the functions. *Trigonometry*

13.0 Students know the law of sines and the law of cosines and apply those laws to solve problems. *Trigonometry*

19.0 Students are adept at using trigonometry in a variety of applications and word problems. *Trigonometry*

New Vocabulary

🔊 **English and Spanish Audio Online**

- **Law of Cosines** (p. 822)
- **Law of Sines** (p. 815)
- **trigonometric identity** (p. 792)
- **trigonometric ratios for a right triangle** (p. 806)

14-1 Trigonometric Identities

 California Content Standards

TRIG 3.0 Students know the identity $\cos^2(x) + \sin^2(x) = 1$.
TRIG 3.2 Students prove other trigonometric identities and simplify others by using the identity $\cos^2(x) + \sin^2(x) = 1$.
TRIG 7.0 Students know that the tangent of the angle that a line makes with the x-axis is equal to the slope of the line.

What You'll Learn

- To verify trigonometric identities

. . . And Why

To use trigonometric identities in simplifying expressions

 Check Skills You'll Need

 for Help Lessons 1-1, 1-2, and 9-4

Determine whether each equation is true for all real numbers x. Explain your reasoning.

1. $2x + 3x = 5x$

2. $-(4x - 10) = 10 - 4x$

3. $\dfrac{4x^2}{x} = 4x$

4. $\dfrac{x^2 + 1}{x - 1} = x + 1$

 New Vocabulary • trigonometric identity

---

1 Verifying Trigonometric Identities

> **Technology Activity:** Trigonometric Identities
>
> **1.** Use a graphing calculator to graph $y_1 = \tan x$ and $y_2 = \dfrac{\sin x}{\cos x}$. If your calculator has the "animate" graph style, use it for y_2.
>
> **2.** Graph $y_1 = (\cos x)^2 + (\sin x)^2$ and $y_2 = 1$.
>
> **3.** **Make a Conjecture** In each Question 1 and 2, make a conjecture about the relationship between y_1 and y_2.

Real-World **Connection**

Astronomers use trigonometry to determine the angles that locate an object in the celestial coordinate system. This system is similar to the system of latitude and longitude used on Earth.

A trigonometric equation such as $\csc \theta = \dfrac{1}{\sin \theta}$ is true for all values of θ except those for which $\sin \theta = 0$. A **trigonometric identity** is a trigonometric equation that is true for all values except those for which the expressions on either side of the equal sign are undefined. The three equations $\csc \theta = \dfrac{1}{\sin \theta}$, $\sec \theta = \dfrac{1}{\cos \theta}$, and $\tan \theta = \dfrac{1}{\cot \theta}$ are known as the reciprocal identities.

You can derive some other identities from the unit circle definitions of sine, cosine, and tangent. In the diagram below, $\cos \theta$, $\sin \theta$, and $\tan \theta$ are the coordinates of points P and Q. You can use the slope of $\overleftrightarrow{PQ}$ to show that $\tan \theta = \dfrac{\sin \theta}{\cos \theta}$.

slope $\overleftrightarrow{PQ} = \dfrac{\sin \theta - 0}{\cos \theta - 0}$ slope $= \dfrac{y_2 - y_1}{x_2 - x_1}$

$\qquad\qquad = \dfrac{\sin \theta}{\cos \theta}$

slope $\overleftrightarrow{PQ} = \dfrac{\tan \theta - 0}{1 - 0}$ slope $= \dfrac{y_2 - y_1}{x_2 - x_1}$

$\qquad\qquad = \tan \theta$

So, $\tan \theta = \dfrac{\sin \theta}{\cos \theta}$.   **Transitive Property of Equality**

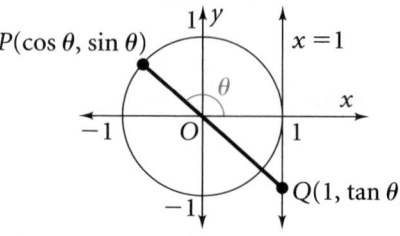

Using the reciprocal identity $\cot \theta = \frac{1}{\tan \theta}$ and the Tangent Identity $\tan \theta = \frac{\sin \theta}{\cos \theta}$, you can derive the Cotangent Identity $\cot \theta = \frac{\cos \theta}{\sin \theta}$.

$$\cot \theta = \frac{1}{\tan \theta} \qquad \textbf{Reciprocal identity}$$

$$= \frac{1}{\frac{\sin \theta}{\cos \theta}} \qquad \textbf{Substitute using the Tangent Identity.}$$

$$= \frac{\cos \theta}{\sin \theta} \qquad \textbf{Divide.}$$

Vocabulary Tip

The expression $\cos^2 \theta$ is equivalent to $(\cos \theta)^2$. The meaning of the phrase "cosine theta squared," when spoken, is not clear.

You can derive another identity from the definitions of $\cos \theta$ and $\sin \theta$. The ordered pair $(\cos \theta, \sin \theta)$ is a point on the unit circle, and for any point (x, y) on the unit circle, $x^2 + y^2 = 1$. So $\cos^2 \theta + \sin^2 \theta = 1$. This is one of the three Pythagorean identities.

To verify an identity, you should transform one side of the equation until it is the same as the other side. This eliminates the possibility of introducing errors that can be caused by squaring both sides of an equation or multiplying both sides of an equation by an expression that equals 0. These are the errors that can introduce extraneous roots when solving equations.

It is sometimes helpful to write all the functions in terms of sine and cosine.

For: Trig. Identity Activity
Use: Interactive Textbook, 14-1

1 EXAMPLE Verifying Identities

Verify the Pythagorean identity $1 + \tan^2 \theta = \sec^2 \theta$.

$$1 + \tan^2 \theta = 1 + \left(\frac{\sin \theta}{\cos \theta}\right)^2 \qquad \textbf{Tangent Identity}$$

$$= 1 + \frac{\sin^2 \theta}{\cos^2 \theta} \qquad \textbf{Simplify.}$$

$$= \frac{\cos^2 \theta}{\cos^2 \theta} + \frac{\sin^2 \theta}{\cos^2 \theta} \qquad \textbf{Write the fractions with common denominators.}$$

$$= \frac{\cos^2 \theta + \sin^2 \theta}{\cos^2 \theta} \qquad \textbf{Add.}$$

$$= \frac{1}{\cos^2 \theta} \qquad \textbf{Pythagorean identity}$$

$$= \sec^2 \theta \qquad \textbf{Reciprocal identity}$$

The left side of the equation has been transformed into the right side. Therefore the equation is an identity.

 CA Standards Check **1** Verify the third Pythagorean identity, $1 + \cot^2 \theta = \csc^2 \theta$.

Key Concepts

Properties	Trigonometric Identities

Reciprocal identities

$$\csc \theta = \frac{1}{\sin \theta} \qquad\qquad \sec \theta = \frac{1}{\cos \theta} \qquad\qquad \cot \theta = \frac{1}{\tan \theta}$$

Tangent and cotangent identities

$$\tan \theta = \frac{\sin \theta}{\cos \theta} \qquad\qquad \cot \theta = \frac{\cos \theta}{\sin \theta}$$

Pythagorean identities

$$\cos^2 \theta + \sin^2 \theta = 1 \qquad 1 + \tan^2 \theta = \sec^2 \theta \qquad 1 + \cot^2 \theta = \csc^2 \theta$$

There are many trigonometric identities in addition to the identities named in the summary above.

EXAMPLE **Verifying Identities**

Verify the identity $\tan^2 \theta - \sin^2 \theta = \tan^2 \theta \sin^2 \theta$.

$\tan^2 \theta - \sin^2 \theta = \left(\dfrac{\sin \theta}{\cos \theta}\right)^2 - \sin^2 \theta$	**Tangent Identity**
$= \dfrac{\sin^2 \theta}{\cos^2 \theta} - \sin^2 \theta$	**Simplify.**
$= \dfrac{\sin^2 \theta}{\cos^2 \theta} - \dfrac{\sin^2 \theta \cos^2 \theta}{\cos^2 \theta}$	**Write fractions with common denominators.**
$= \dfrac{\sin^2 \theta - \sin^2 \theta \cos^2 \theta}{\cos^2 \theta}$	**Subtract.**
$= \dfrac{\sin^2 \theta(1 - \cos^2 \theta)}{\cos^2 \theta}$	**Factor.**
$= \dfrac{\sin^2 \theta (\sin^2 \theta)}{\cos^2 \theta}$	**Pythagorean identity**
$= \dfrac{\sin^2 \theta}{\cos^2 \theta} \sin^2 \theta$	**Rewrite the fraction.**
$= \tan^2 \theta \sin^2 \theta$	**Tangent Identity**

✓ **CA Standards Check** ② Verify the identity $\sec^2 \theta - \sec^2 \theta \cos^2 \theta = \tan^2 \theta$.

You can use the trigonometric identities to simplify trigonometric expressions. Again, it is often helpful to write all the functions in terms of sines and cosines.

③ **EXAMPLE** **Simplifying Expressions**

Simplify the trigonometric expression $\csc \theta \tan \theta$.

$\csc \theta \tan \theta = \dfrac{1}{\sin \theta} \cdot \tan \theta$	**Reciprocal Identity**
$= \dfrac{1}{\sin \theta} \cdot \dfrac{\sin \theta}{\cos \theta}$	**Tangent Identity**
$= \dfrac{\sin \theta}{\sin \theta \cos \theta}$	**Multiply.**
$= \dfrac{1}{\cos \theta}$	**Simplify.**
$= \sec \theta$	**Reciprocal identity**

So $\csc \theta \tan \theta = \sec \theta$.

✓ **CA Standards Check** ③ Simplify the trigonometric expression $\sec \theta \cot \theta$.

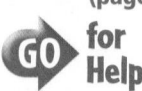

EXERCISES

For more exercises, see *Extra Skill and Word Problem Practice.*

Standards Practice

TRIG 3.0, 3.2, 7.0

A **Practice by Example**

Examples 1 and 2
(pages 793 and 794)

GO for Help

Verify each identity.

1. $\cos \theta \cot \theta = \dfrac{1}{\sin \theta} - \sin \theta$

2. $\sin \theta \cot \theta = \cos \theta$

3. $\cos \theta \tan \theta = \sin \theta$

4. $\sin \theta \sec \theta = \tan \theta$

5. $\cos \theta \sec \theta = 1$

6. $\tan \theta \cot \theta = 1$

7. $\sin \theta \csc \theta = 1$

8. $\cot \theta = \dfrac{\csc \theta}{\sec \theta}$

Example 3
(page 794)

Simplify each trigonometric expression.

9. $\tan \theta \cot \theta$

10. $1 - \cos^2 \theta$

11. $\sec^2 \theta - 1$

12. $1 - \csc^2 \theta$

13. $\sec \theta \cot \theta$

14. $\cos \theta \tan \theta$

15. $\sin \theta \cot \theta$

16. $\sin \theta \csc \theta$

17. $\sec \theta \cos \theta \sin \theta$

18. $\sin \theta \sec \theta \cot \theta$

19. $\sec^2 \theta - \tan^2 \theta$

20. $\dfrac{\sin \theta}{\cos \theta \tan \theta}$

B **Apply Your Skills**

Simplify each trigonometric expression.

21. $\cos \theta + \sin \theta \tan \theta$

22. $\csc \theta \cos \theta \tan \theta$

23. $\tan \theta (\cot \theta + \tan \theta)$

24. $\sin^2 \theta + \cos^2 \theta + \tan^2 \theta$

25. $\cos^2 \theta \sec \theta \csc \theta$

26. $\sin \theta (1 + \cot^2 \theta)$

27. $\cot \theta \tan \theta - \sec^2 \theta$

28. $\sin^2 \theta \csc \theta \sec \theta$

29. $\cos \theta (1 + \tan^2 \theta)$

30. $\dfrac{\tan \theta}{\sec \theta - \cos \theta}$

31. $\sec \theta \cos \theta - \cos^2 \theta$

32. $\sin \theta \csc \theta - \cos^2 \theta$

33. $\csc \theta - \cos \theta \cot \theta$

34. $\cos \theta + \sin \theta \tan \theta$

35. $\sec \theta (1 + \cot^2 \theta)$

36. $\csc^2 \theta (1 - \cos^2 \theta)$

37. $\dfrac{\cos \theta \csc \theta}{\cot \theta}$

38. $\dfrac{\sin^2 \theta \csc \theta \sec \theta}{\tan \theta}$

Express the first trigonometric function in terms of the second.

39. $\sin \theta, \cos \theta$

40. $\tan \theta, \cos \theta$

41. $\cot \theta, \sin \theta$

42. $\csc \theta, \cot \theta$

43. $\cot \theta, \csc \theta$

44. $\sec \theta, \tan \theta$

Verify each identity.

45. $\sin^2 \theta \tan^2 \theta = \tan^2 \theta - \sin^2 \theta$

46. $\sec \theta - \sin \theta \tan \theta = \cos \theta$

47. $\sin \theta \cos \theta (\tan \theta + \cot \theta) = 1$

48. $\dfrac{1 - \sin \theta}{\cos \theta} = \dfrac{\cos \theta}{1 + \sin \theta}$

49. $\dfrac{\sec \theta}{\cot \theta + \tan \theta} = \sin \theta$

50. $(\cot \theta + 1)^2 = \csc^2 \theta + 2 \cot \theta$

51. Express $\cos \theta \csc \theta \cot \theta$ in terms of $\sin \theta$.

52. Express $\dfrac{\cos \theta}{\sec \theta + \tan \theta}$ in terms of $\sin \theta$.

53. **Open-Ended** Create a trigonometric identity. (*Hint:* Start with a simple trigonometric expression and work backward.)

 54. **Writing** Describe the similarities and differences in solving an equation and in verifying an identity.

C **Challenge**

Verify each identity.

55. $1 + \sec \theta = \dfrac{1 + \cos \theta}{\cos \theta}$

56. $\dfrac{1 + \tan \theta}{\tan \theta} = \cot \theta + 1$

57. $\dfrac{\cot \theta \sin \theta}{\sec \theta} + \dfrac{\tan \theta \cos \theta}{\csc \theta} = 1$

58. $\sin^2 \theta \tan^2 \theta + \cos^2 \theta \tan^2 \theta = \sec^2 \theta - 1$

Simplify each trigonometric expression.

59. $\dfrac{\cot^2 \theta - \csc^2 \theta}{\tan^2 \theta - \sec^2 \theta}$

60. $(1 - \sin \theta)(1 + \sin \theta) \csc^2 \theta + 1$

Homework Video Tutor

Visit: PHSchool.com
Web Code: bbe-1401

61. Physics When a ray of light passes from one medium into a second, the angle of incidence θ_1 and the angle of refraction θ_2 are related by Snell's law: $n_1 \sin \theta_1 = n_2 \sin \theta_2$, where n_1 is the index of refraction of the first medium and n_2 is the index of refraction of the second medium. How are θ_1 and θ_2 related if $n_2 > n_1$? If $n_2 < n_1$? If $n_2 = n_1$?

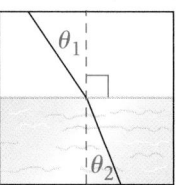

Multiple Choice Practice

For California Standards and CAHSEE Tutorials, visit PHSchool.com. Web Code: bbq-9045

TRIG 3.0

62. Which equation is NOT true?

Ⓐ $\cos^2 \theta = 1 - \sin^2 \theta$

Ⓑ $\sin^2 \theta = \cos^2 \theta - 1$

Ⓒ $\cot^2 \theta = \csc^2 \theta - 1$

Ⓓ $\tan^2 \theta = \sec^2 \theta - 1$

ALG2 11.1

63. Which equation represents the *inverse* of the graph shown below?

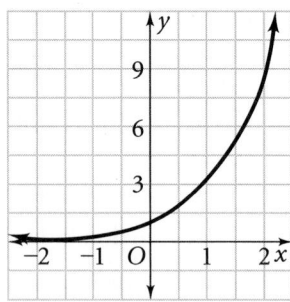

Ⓐ $y = 3^x$ Ⓒ $x = \log_3 y$

Ⓑ $y = \log_x 3$ Ⓓ $y = \log_3 x$

Mixed Review

Lesson 13-8

Graph each function in the interval from 0 to 2π.

64. $y = \csc(-\theta)$ **65.** $y = -\cot \theta$ **66.** $y = -\sec 0.5\theta$

67. $y = -\sec(0.5\theta + 2)$ **68.** $y = \cot \frac{\theta}{5}$ **69.** $y = \pi \sec \theta$

Lesson 13-2

Find the measure of an angle between 0° and 360° that is coterminal with the given angle.

70. 395° **71.** 405° **72.** $-225°$ **73.** $-149°$

74. 627° **75.** $-281°$ **76.** 493° **77.** $-609°$

Lesson 12-3

Make a box-and-whisker plot for each set of values.

78. 300 345 333 295 302 321

79. 32 48 87 43 62 15 49 51 47 36 50 109 64

Solving Trigonometric Equations Using Inverses

 California Content Standards

TRIG 8.0 Students know the definitions of the inverse trigonometric functions and can graph the functions.
TRIG 9.0 Students compute, by hand, the values of the inverse trigonometric functions at various standard points.

What You'll Learn

- To evaluate inverses of trigonometric functions
- To solve trigonometric equations

. . . And Why

To solve problems involving springs, as in Example 7

✓ Check Skills You'll Need

 GO for Help Lessons 7-7, 13-2, and 13-6

For each function f, find f^{-1}.

1. $f(x) = x + 1$ **2.** $f(x) = 2x - 3$ **3.** $f(x) = x^2 + 4$

Find each value.

4. $\sin 30°$ **5.** $\cos \frac{\pi}{4}$ **6.** $\cos 135°$

7. $\tan(-\pi)$ **8.** $\tan 315°$ **9.** $\sin\left(-\frac{7\pi}{3}\right)$

---

 1   **Inverses of Trigonometric Functions**

The cosine function $y = \cos \theta$ is periodic, so a horizontal line, such as the x-axis, can intersect the graph of $y = \cos \theta$ in infinitely many points. Therefore a vertical line can intersect the graph of the inverse of $y = \cos \theta$ in infinitely many points. The inverse of $y = \cos \theta$ is a relation that is not a function.

You can use a graph of an inverse function to find the measures of angles that have a given value of the function.

1 **EXAMPLE**   **Using a Graph to Find Angles With a Given Cosine**

Use the graph of the inverse of $y = \cos \theta$ at the right.

a. Find the radian measures of the angles whose cosine is -1.

The line $x = -1$ intersects the graph at $(-1, \pi)$ and $(-1, -\pi)$. So the measures of two angles whose cosine is -1 are π and $-\pi$.

Other points of intersection are $(-1, \pm3\pi)$, $(-1, \pm5\pi)$, and so on. The measures of all the angles whose cosine is -1 can be written as $\pi + 2\pi n$, where n is any integer.

b. Find the radian measures of the angles θ whose cosine is 2.

The line $x = 2$ does not intersect the graph. 2 is not in the domain of the inverse of $y = \cos \theta$. There is no angle whose cosine is 2.

Inverse of $y = \cos \theta$

✓ CA Standards Check **1** What are the radian measures of the angles whose cosine is 1.1? Whose cosine is 0? Whose cosine is -1.1?

You can use a unit circle to find angle measures for given sine or cosine values.

2 EXAMPLE Using a Unit Circle

Multiple Choice Find the degree measures of the angles whose cosine is $\frac{1}{2}$.

Ⓐ $30° + n \cdot 360°$ and $330° + n \cdot 360°$ Ⓒ $30° + n \cdot 360°$ and $210° + n \cdot 360°$

Ⓑ $60° + n \cdot 360°$ and $300° + n \cdot 360°$ Ⓓ $60° + n \cdot 360°$ and $120° + n \cdot 360°$

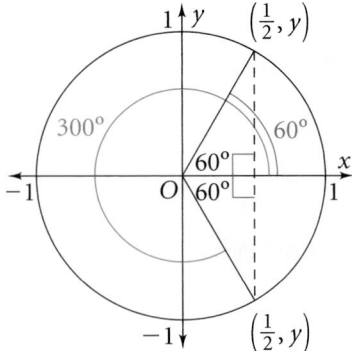

Draw a unit circle and mark the points on the circle that have x-coordinates of $\frac{1}{2}$. These points and the origin form 30°-60°-90° triangles. 60° and 300° are the measures of two angles whose cosine is $\frac{1}{2}$. All their coterminal angles also have a cosine of $\frac{1}{2}$.

The measures of all the angles whose cosine is $\frac{1}{2}$ can be written as $60° + n \cdot 360°$ and $300° + n \cdot 360°$.

The correct choice is B.

✓ **CA Standards Check** ② Use a unit circle. Find the degree measures of all angles with the given cosine.

a. $-\frac{1}{2}$ **b.** $-\frac{\sqrt{3}}{2}$ **c.** $\frac{\sqrt{2}}{2}$

The domain of the cosine function can be restricted to $0 \le \theta \le \pi$ so that its inverse is a function. The inverse function is written $\theta = \cos^{-1} x$ and is read as "θ is the angle whose cosine is x."

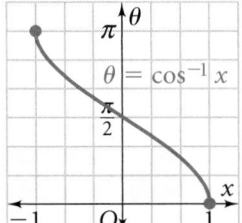

The domains are similarly restricted for $y = \sin \theta \left(-\frac{\pi}{2} \le \theta \le \frac{\pi}{2} \right)$ and $y = \tan \theta \left(-\frac{\pi}{2} < \theta < \frac{\pi}{2} \right)$ to obtain the inverse functions $\theta = \sin^{-1} x$ and $\theta = \tan^{-1} x$.

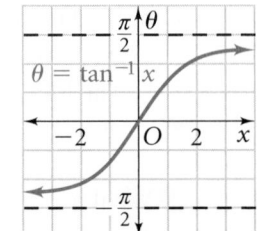

3 EXAMPLE Using a Calculator to Find the Inverse of Sine

Use a calculator and an inverse function to find the radian measures of all the angles whose sine is -0.9.

$\sin^{-1}(-0.9) \approx -1.12$ **Use a calculator.**

This angle is in Quadrant IV. The sine function is also negative in Quadrant III, as shown in the figure at the right. So $\pi + 1.12 \approx 4.26$ is another solution.

The radian measures of all the angles whose sine is -0.9 can be written as

● $-1.12 + 2\pi n$ and $4.26 + 2\pi n$.

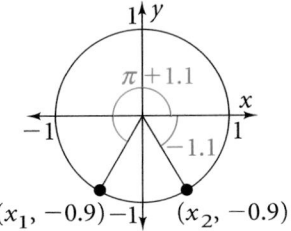

☑ **CA Standards Check** ③ Find the radian measures of the angles.
    a. angles whose sine is 0.44 **b.** angles whose sine is -0.73

4 EXAMPLE Using a Calculator to Find the Inverse of Tangent

Use a calculator and an inverse function to find the measure in radians of all the angles whose tangent is -0.84.

$\tan^{-1}(-0.84) \approx -0.70$ **Use a calculator.**

The tangent function is also negative in Quadrant II, as shown in the figure at the right. So $\pi - 0.70 \approx 2.44$ is another solution.

The radian measures of all the angles whose tangent is -0.84 can be written as

● $-0.70 + 2\pi n$ and $2.44 + 2\pi n$.

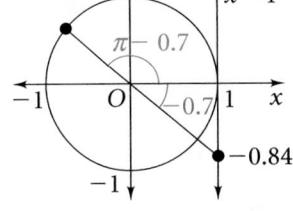

☑ **CA Standards Check** ④ Find the radian measures of the angles.

    a. angles whose tangent is 0.44 **b.** angles whose tangent is -0.73

---

2   Solving Trigonometric Equations

In contrast to trigonometric identities, most trigonometric equations are true for only certain values of the variable.

5 EXAMPLE Solving Trigonometric Equations

Solve $4\cos\theta - 1 = \cos\theta$ for $0 \le \theta < 2\pi$.

$4\cos\theta - 1 = \cos\theta$

$\qquad 3\cos\theta = 1$ **Add $1 - \cos\theta$ to each side.**

$\qquad \cos\theta = \frac{1}{3}$ **Divide each side by 3.**

$\qquad \cos^{-1}\frac{1}{3} \approx 1.23$ **Use the inverse function to find one value of θ.**

The cosine function is also positive in Quadrant IV. So another value of θ is $2\pi - 1.23 \approx 5.05$. The two solutions between 0 and 2π are approximately 1.23
● and 5.05.

Sometimes you can solve trigonometric equations by factoring.

6 EXAMPLE **Solving by Factoring**

Solve $2 \cos \theta \sin \theta + \sin \theta = 0$ for $0 \le \theta < 2\pi$.

$2 \cos \theta \sin \theta + \sin \theta = 0$

$\quad \sin \theta \, (2 \cos \theta + 1) = 0$ **Factor.**

$\sin \theta = 0 \quad$ or $\quad 2 \cos \theta + 1 = 0$ **Zero-Product Property**

$\sin \theta = 0 \qquad\qquad\qquad \cos \theta = -\frac{1}{2}$ **Solve for cos θ.**

$\quad \theta = 0$ and $\pi \qquad\qquad \theta = \frac{2\pi}{3}$ and $\frac{4\pi}{3}$ **Use the unit circle.**

● The four values of θ are $0, \pi, \frac{2\pi}{3}$, and $\frac{4\pi}{3}$.

✓ **CA Standards Check** ⑥ Solve $\sin \theta \cos \theta - \cos \theta = 0$ for $0 \le \theta < 2\pi$.

You can use trigonometric equations to solve problems involving repetitive events.

7 EXAMPLE **Real-World** **Connection**

Real-World **Connection**

The motion of an oscillating spring is called simple harmonic motion.

Physics The spring at the left is stretched and released. The equation $h = -4 \cos \frac{2\pi}{3}t$ models the toy's height h in inches above or below the rest position as a function of time t in seconds. When will the toy first be 2 in. above the rest position?

$h = -4 \cos \frac{2\pi}{3}t$

$2 = -4 \cos \frac{2\pi}{3}t$ **Substitute 2 for h.**

$-\frac{2}{4} = \cos \frac{2\pi}{3}t$ **Divide each side by -4.**

$-\frac{1}{2} = \cos \frac{2\pi}{3}t$ **Simplify.**

$\cos^{-1}\left(-\frac{1}{2}\right) = \frac{2\pi}{3}t$ **Use the inverse of the cosine to solve for t.**

$\frac{2\pi}{3} = \frac{2\pi}{3}t$ **Evaluate the inverse. Use the unit circle.**

$1 = t$ **Multiply each side by $\frac{3}{2\pi}$.**

● The toy is 2 in. above the rest position at 1 s.

✓ **CA Standards Check** ⑦ **a.** When will the toy in Example 7 first be 2 in. below the rest position? When will the toy next be 4 in. below the rest position?

b. You found that the toy in Example 7 is 2 in. above the rest position after 1 s. Will it ever be at that same position again? Explain.

c. How could you use a graphing calculator to solve Example 7?

EXERCISES

For more exercises, see *Extra Skill and Word Problem Practice*.

Standards Practice

TRIG 8.0, 9.0

A Practice by Example

Example 1
(page 797)

for Help

Use the graph of the inverse of $y = \sin \theta$ at the right.

1. Find the measures of the angles whose sine is -1.

2. Find the measures of the angles whose sine is 0.

3. Find the measures of the angles whose sine is 1.

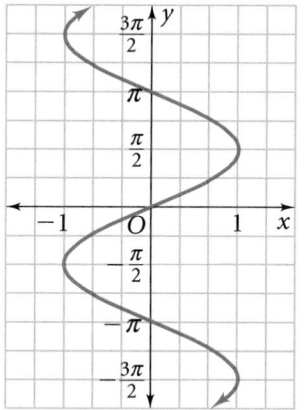

Example 2
(page 798)

Use a unit circle and 30°-60°-90° triangles to find the degree measures of the angles.

4. angles whose sine is $\frac{1}{2}$

5. angles whose tangent is $\frac{\sqrt{3}}{3}$

6. angles whose sine is $-\frac{1}{2}$

7. angles whose tangent is $-\sqrt{3}$

Examples 3 and 4
(page 799)

Use a calculator and inverse functions to find the radian measures of the angles.

8. angles whose tangent is 1

9. angles whose sine is 0.37

10. angles whose sine is (-0.78)

11. angles whose tangent is (-3)

12. angles whose cosine is (-0.89)

13. angles whose sine is (-1.1)

14. angles whose tangent is 5

15. angles whose cosine is 0.58

Example 5
(page 799)

Solve each equation for $0 \le \theta < 2\pi$.

16. $2 \sin \theta = 1$

17. $2 \cos \theta - \sqrt{3} = 0$

18. $4 \tan \theta = 3 + \tan \theta$

19. $2 \sin \theta - \sqrt{2} = 0$

20. $3 \cos \theta = 2$

21. $3 \tan \theta - 1 = \tan \theta$

22. $\sqrt{2} \cos \theta - \sqrt{2} = 0$

23. $3 \tan \theta + 5 = 0$

24. $2 \sin \theta = 3$

25. $2 \sin \theta = -\sqrt{3}$

Example 6
(page 800)

26. $(\cos \theta)(\cos \theta + 1) = 0$

27. $(\sin \theta - 1)(\sin \theta + 1) = 0$

28. $\tan^2 \theta + \tan \theta = 0$

29. $2 \sin^2 \theta - 1 = 0$

30. $\tan \theta = \tan^2 \theta$

31. $\sin^2 \theta + 3 \sin \theta = 0$

32. $\sin \theta = -\sin \theta \cos \theta$

33. $2 \sin^2 \theta - 3 \sin \theta = 2$

Example 7
(page 800)

34. Physics Two students set up a spring experiment similar to the one in Example 7. In their experiment, a weight was released 4 cm below the rest position. It rose to 4 cm above the rest position and returned to 4 cm below the rest position once every 4 seconds. The equation $h = -4 \cos\left(\frac{\pi}{2}t\right)$ models the height above and below the rest position at t seconds.
   a. Solve the equation for t.
   b. Find the times at which the weight is first at a height of 1 cm, 2 cm, and 3 cm above the rest position.
   c. Find the times at which the weight is at a height of 1 cm, 2 cm, and 3 cm below the rest position for the second time.

Each diagram shows one solution to the equation below it. Find the complete solution of each equation.

35.
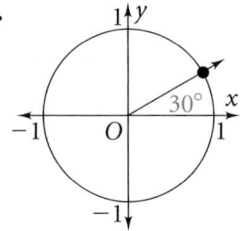

$$5 \sin \theta = 1 + 3 \sin \theta$$

36.
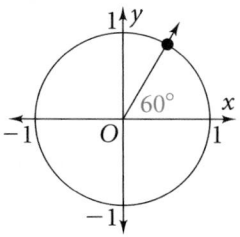

$$6 \cos \theta - 5 = -2$$

37.
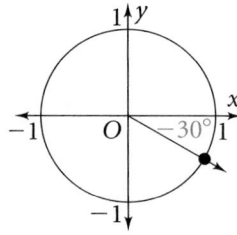

$$4 \sin \theta + 3 = 1$$

Solve each equation for $0 \le \theta < 2\pi$.

38. $\sec \theta = 2$ **39.** $\csc \theta = -1$

40. $\cot \theta = 10$ **41.** $\csc \theta = 3$

42. $\cot \theta = -10$ **43.** $\sec \theta = 1$

Real-World Connection

Electric generators convert mechanical energy into electricity.

44. Electricity The function $I = 40 \sin 60\pi t$ models the current I in amps that the electric generator shown at the left is producing after t seconds. When is the first time that the current will reach 20 amps? -20 amps?

45. Critical Thinking The graphing calculator screen below shows a portion of the graphs of $y = \sin \theta$ and $y = 0.5$.

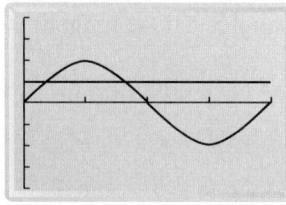

```
Xmin=0
Xmax=360
Xscl=90
Ymin=-2
Ymax=2
Yscl=0.5
```

  a. Write the complete solution of $\sin \theta \ge 0.5$.
  b. Write the complete solution of $\sin \theta \le 0.5$.
  c. Writing Explain how you can solve inequalities involving trigonometric functions.

Find the complete solution in radians of each equation.

46. $2 \sin^2 \theta + \cos \theta - 1 = 0$ **47.** $\sin^2 \theta - 1 = \cos^2 \theta$

48. $2 \sin \theta + 1 = \csc \theta$ **49.** $3 \tan^2 \theta - 1 = \sec^2 \theta$

50. $\sin \theta \cos \theta = \frac{1}{2} \cos \theta$ **51.** $\tan \theta \sin \theta = 3 \sin \theta$

52. $2 \cos^2 \theta + \sin \theta = 1$ **53.** $\sin \theta \cot^2 \theta - 3 \sin \theta = 0$

54. $4 \sin^2 \theta + 1 = 4 \sin \theta$ **55.** $\tan \theta \cot \theta - \tan \theta + 2 \cot \theta = 0$

56. Error Analysis A student solved an equation as shown below. What error did the student make?

$$\theta = \cos^{-1} 0.5$$
$$= \frac{1}{\cos 0.5}$$
$$\approx \frac{1}{0.88}$$
$$\approx 1.14$$

Homework Video Tutor

Visit: PHSchool.com
Web Code: bbe-1402

57. Error Analysis A student solved the equation $\sin^2 \theta = \frac{1}{2} \sin \theta$, $0 \le \theta < 2\pi$, as shown below. What error did the student make?

$$\sin^2 \theta = \tfrac{1}{2} \sin \theta$$

$$\sin \theta = \tfrac{1}{2}$$

$$\theta = \tfrac{\pi}{6} \text{ and } \tfrac{5\pi}{6}$$

Find the x-intercepts of the graph of each function.

58. $y = 2 \cos \theta + 1$ **59.** $y = 2 \sin^2 \theta - 1$

60. $y = \cos^2 \theta - 1$ **61.** $y = \tan^2 \theta - 1$

62. $y = 2 \sin^4 \theta - \sin^2 \theta$ **63.** $y = 2 \cos^2 \theta - 3 \cos \theta - 2$

 64. Writing Describe the similarities and differences in solving the equations $4x + 1 = 3$ and $4 \sin \theta + 1 = 3$.

65. Find the complete solution of $\sin^2 \theta + 2 \sin \theta + 1 = 0$. (*Hint:* How would you solve $x^2 + 2x + 1 = 0$?)

66. a. Open-Ended Write three trigonometric equations whose complete solution is $\pi + 2\pi n$.
    b. Describe how you found the equations in part (a).

C Challenge

Solve each trigonometric equation for θ in terms of y.

Sample $y = 2 \sin 3\theta + 4$

$$\sin 3\theta = \frac{y - 4}{2}$$

$$3\theta = \sin^{-1} \left(\frac{y - 4}{2} \right)$$

$$\theta = \tfrac{1}{3} \sin^{-1} \left(\frac{y - 4}{2} \right)$$

67. $y = 2 \sin \theta$ **68.** $y = \cos 2\theta$

69. $y = 3 \sin (\theta + 2)$ **70.** $y = -4 \cos 2\pi\theta$

71. $y = \cos \theta + 1$ **72.** $y = 2 \cos \pi\theta + 1$

73. Parks A segment of a circle is the region formed by an arc of a circle and the line segment joining the endpoints of the arc. (The measure of the arc must be between 0 and 2π.) The expression below gives the area K in square feet of a segment in terms of the radius of the circle r in feet and the radian measure θ of the arc.

50 ft

$$K = \frac{r^2}{2}(\theta - \sin \theta)$$

    a. Suppose a circular park has a radius of 50 ft. Write an equation for the area of any segment of the park using $r = 50$.
    b. Use trial and error to approximate the measure of θ that makes the area of the segment 1500 ft^2.

74. Tides One day the tides at a point in Maine could be modeled by $h = 5 \cos \frac{2\pi}{13} t$, where h is the height of the tide in feet above the mean water level and t is the number of hours past midnight.

a. At what times that day will the tide be 3 ft above the mean water level?

b. At what times that day will the tide be *at least* 3 ft above the mean water level?

Multiple Choice Practice

For California Standards and CAHSEE Tutorials, visit PHSchool.com. Web Code: bbq-9045

TRIG 9.0

75. Which of these angles have a sine of about -0.6?

I. $143.1°$ II. $216.9°$ III. $323.1°$

  (A) I and II only

  (B) I and III only

  (C) II and III only

  (D) I, II, and III

ALG2 10.0

76. On the short eighth hole of the golf course, the tee sits on a hillside above the green. Anita used a golf club known as a 7-iron on her shot from the tee. The graph at the right shows h, the height in meters of the golf ball above the green, versus t, the time in seconds after Anita hit the ball. From the graph, what conclusion can be made about the flight of the golf ball?

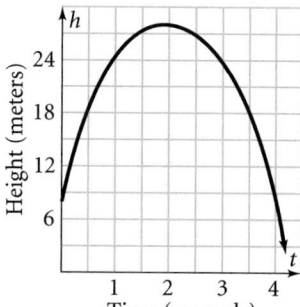

  (A) At 0 seconds the golf ball was 8 meters higher than the green.

  (B) The maximum height of the golf ball above the green was 24 m.

  (C) The golf ball was in flight for 5 seconds.

  (D) The golf ball reached its maximum height after 2.5 seconds.

Mixed Review

Lesson 14-1

Simplify each expression.

77. $\cos^2 \theta \sec \theta \csc \theta$

78. $\sin \theta \sec \theta \tan \theta$

79. $\csc^2 \theta (1 - \cos^2 \theta)$

80. $\frac{\cos \theta \csc \theta}{\cot \theta}$

81. $\frac{\sec \theta}{\cot \theta + \tan \theta}$

82. $\frac{\sin \theta + \tan \theta}{1 + \cos \theta}$

Lesson 13-5

Write a cosine function for each description.

83. amplitude 4, period 8

84. amplitude 3, period 2π

85. amplitude 3π, period 1

86. amplitude $\frac{\pi}{4}$, period 3π

Lesson 12-2

87. Transportation Ninety-eight percent of a railroad's trains depart on schedule. Eighty-nine percent of its trains depart and arrive on schedule. Find the probability that a train that departs on time also arrives on time.

Lissajous Figures

> **MA 7.0** Students demonstrate an understanding of functions and equations defined parametrically and can graph them.

A clock pendulum swings in only one plane. Its oscillating path projected on a sheet of paper below it would be a segment. A pendulum supported by a string can move so that its path is a circle, ellipse, or other complicated curve. These curves are called Lissajous (lee suh zhoo) figures.

Lissajous figures can be described by parametric equations of this form.

$$x = a_1 \sin b_1(t - h_1)$$
$$y = a_2 \sin b_2(t - h_2)$$

x represents the oscillating motion in one direction and y represents the oscillating motion in the perpendicular direction. t is time, $|a_1|$ and $|a_2|$ are amplitudes of the oscillations, $\frac{b_1}{2\pi}$ and $\frac{b_2}{2\pi}$ are cycles per second, and h_1 and h_2 are phase shifts.

The parametric equations can be graphed with a graphing calculator. See page 126.

ACTIVITY

Set the calculator to radian and parametric mode. Set the window values as shown.

```
WINDOW
  Tmin=0
  Tmax=7
  Tstep=.05
  Xmin=-3
  Xmax=3
  Xscl=1
↓Ymin=-2
```

```
WINDOW
↑Tstep=.05
  Xmin=-3
  Xmax=3
  Xscl=1
  Ymin=-2
  Ymax=2
  Yscl=1
```

Graph each pair of parametric equations.

a. $x = 3 \sin 2(t - \pi)$
$y = 2 \sin 4(t - \pi)$

b. $x = 3 \sin 2\left(t - \frac{\pi}{3}\right)$
$y = 2 \sin 4(t - \pi)$

c. $x = 3 \sin 2(t - 1)$
$y = 2 \sin 3(t - 1)$

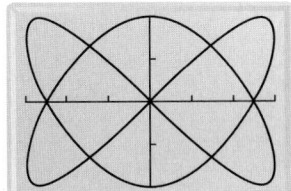

EXERCISES

Use your calculator to graph each pair of parametric equations. Sketch each graph.

1. $x = 2.1 \sin (t - 1)$
$y = 1.8 \sin (t - 2)$

2. $x = 3 \sin 2\left(t - \frac{3}{2}\right)$
$y = 2 \sin 3\left(t - \frac{2}{3}\right)$

3. $x = 3 \sin 3(t - 1)$
$y = 2 \sin 2(t - 1)$

4. Open-Ended Graph other Lissajous figures by changing the numbers in the equations. Sketch the interesting graphs and record their equations.

Right Triangles and Trigonometric Ratios

 California Content Standards

TRIG 12.0 Students use trigonometry to determine unknown sides or angles in right triangles.

TRIG 19.0 Students are adept at using trigonometry in a variety of applications and word problems.

What You'll Learn

- To find lengths of sides in a right triangle
- To find measures of angles in a right triangle

...And Why

To design bridges, as in Example 3

✓ Check Skills You'll Need

△*ABC* is similar to △*RST*. Complete the following proportions.

1. $\frac{a}{b} = \frac{r}{\blacksquare}$

2. $\frac{a}{c} = \frac{\blacksquare}{t}$

3. $\frac{t}{r} = \frac{c}{\blacksquare}$

4. $\frac{c}{b} = \frac{\blacksquare}{s}$

GO for Help Skills Handbook page 884

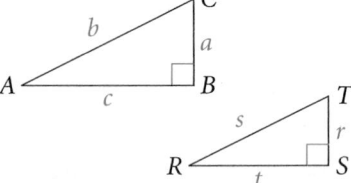

◀)) New Vocabulary • trigonometric ratios for a right triangle

---

1 **Finding the Lengths of Sides in a Right Triangle**

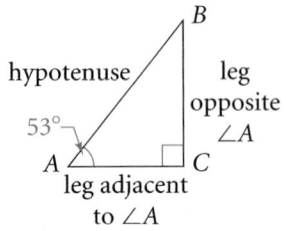

Activity: Right Triangle Ratios

Draw three right triangles, each one having an acute angle of 53°. Make the hypotenuse of the first triangle 10 cm long, and make the other two hypotenuses differ by at least 5 cm. Label the triangles 1, 2, and 3.

1. In each triangle, measure the lengths of the hypotenuse, the leg opposite the 53° angle, and the leg adjacent to the 53° angle. Copy the table below and record your measurements. Then calculate the three ratios for each triangle.

Triangle	Hyp. (cm)	Leg opp. ∠A (cm)	Leg adj. to ∠A (cm)	opp./hyp.	adj./hyp.	opp./adj.
1	10	8.0	6.0	0.80	0.60	1.33
2	■	■	■	■	■	■
3	■	■	■	■	■	■

2. Reasoning What patterns do you see in the last three columns of the table? Check your results with others.

3. Make a Conjecture What is true about these ratios for all right triangles that have an acute angle of 53°?

The **trigonometric ratios for a right triangle** are the six different ratios of the sides of a right triangle. These ratios do not depend on the size of the right triangle. They depend only on the measures of the acute angles in the triangle.

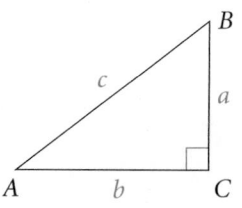

In a right triangle that has an acute $\angle A$, the ratios are defined as follows.

$$\sin A = \frac{\text{length of leg opposite } \angle A}{\text{length of hypotenuse}} = \frac{a}{c}$$

$$\cos A = \frac{\text{length of leg adjacent to } \angle A}{\text{length of hypotenuse}} = \frac{b}{c}$$

$$\tan A = \frac{\text{length of leg opposite } \angle A}{\text{length of leg adjacent to } \angle A} = \frac{a}{b}$$

$$\csc A = \frac{1}{\sin A} = \frac{\text{length of hypotenuse}}{\text{length of leg opposite } \angle A} = \frac{c}{a}$$

$$\sec A = \frac{1}{\cos A} = \frac{\text{length of hypotenuse}}{\text{length of leg adjacent to } \angle A} = \frac{c}{b}$$

$$\cot A = \frac{1}{\tan A} = \frac{\text{length of leg adjacent to } \angle A}{\text{length of leg opposite } \angle A} = \frac{b}{a}$$

1 EXAMPLE **Real-World Connection**

In the pyramid of Khafre, $AC \approx 108$ m and $m\angle A \approx 53°$.

Egyptology Given that $\sin 53° \approx 0.80$, $\cos 53° \approx 0.60$, and $\tan 53° \approx 1.33$, find the height BC of the pyramid.

$\tan A = \dfrac{BC}{AC}$ **definition of tan**

$1.33 \approx \dfrac{BC}{108}$ **Substitute.**

$BC \approx 108 \, (1.33) \approx 144$

The height of the pyramid of Khafre is about 144 m.

✓ **CA Standards Check** **1** Find the length of a lateral edge of the pyramid.

For acute angles, the unit circle definition of sine is equivalent to the definition of sine for right triangles.

$\sin \theta$ using the unit circle

$\sin \theta = y$-coordinate of P

$\quad = PQ$

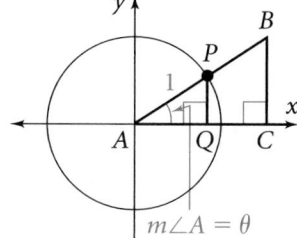

$\sin A$ using a right triangle

$\sin A = \dfrac{\text{length of leg opposite } \angle A}{\text{length of hypotenuse}}$

$\quad = \dfrac{BC}{AB}$

Since $\triangle APQ$ and $\triangle ABC$ are similar triangles, $\dfrac{PQ}{PA} = \dfrac{BC}{AB}$.

So $\sin \theta = PQ = \dfrac{PQ}{1} = \dfrac{PQ}{PA} = \dfrac{BC}{AB} = \sin A$.

You can use a similar argument for each of the other five ratios. In each case, the definition based on a right triangle is equivalent to the corresponding unit circle definition for an acute angle.

2 EXAMPLE Using a Right Triangle to Find Ratios

In $\triangle ABC$, $\angle C$ is a right angle and $\sin A = \frac{5}{13}$. Find $\cos A$, $\cot A$, and $\sin B$ in fraction and in decimal form.

Step 1 Draw a diagram.

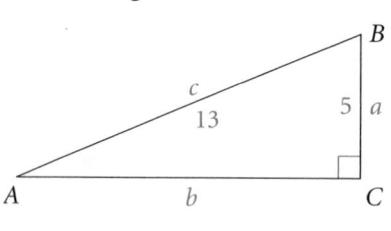

Step 2 Use the Pythagorean Theorem to find b.

$$c^2 = a^2 + b^2$$
$$13^2 = 5^2 + b^2$$
$$169 = 25 + b^2$$
$$144 = b^2$$
$$12 = b$$

Step 3 Calculate the ratios.

$$\cos A = \frac{\text{length of leg adjacent to } \angle A}{\text{length of hypotenuse}} = \frac{b}{c} = \frac{12}{13} \approx 0.9231$$

$$\cot A = \frac{\text{length of leg adjacent to } \angle A}{\text{length of leg opposite } \angle A} = \frac{b}{a} = \frac{12}{5} = 2.4$$

$$\sin B = \frac{\text{length of leg opposite } \angle B}{\text{length of hypotenuse}} = \frac{b}{c} = \frac{12}{13} \approx 0.9231$$

✓ **CA Standards Check** **2** In $\triangle DEF$, $\angle D$ is a right angle and $\tan E = \frac{3}{4}$. Draw a diagram and find $\sin E$ and $\sec F$ in fraction and in decimal form.

If you are given the measures of an acute angle and a side of a right triangle, you can find the length of another side of the triangle.

3 EXAMPLE Real-World Connection

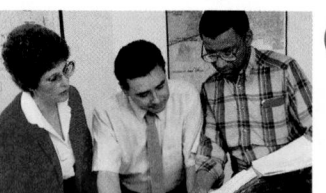

Real-World Connection

Park planners must consider the width of a creek when deciding where to build a bridge.

Planning Park planners would like to build a bridge across a creek. Surveyors have determined that from 5 ft above the ground, the angle of elevation to the top of an 8-ft pole on the opposite side of the creek is 5°. Find the length of the bridge to the nearest foot.

In the right triangle, the length of the leg opposite the 5° angle is $8 - 5$, or 3 ft. You need to find the length of the leg adjacent to the 5° angle. Use the tangent ratio.

$$\tan 5° = \frac{3}{x}$$

$x = \dfrac{3}{\tan 5°}$ **Solve for x.**

≈ 34.29 **Use a calculator in degree mode.**

The bridge will be about 34 ft long.

✓ **CA Standards Check** **3 a. Critical Thinking** What are the advantages and disadvantages of using cot 5° instead of tan 5° in solving Example 3?

    b. Find the length of the bridge in Example 3 by using the 85° angle in the right triangle instead of the 5° angle.

To find the measure of an acute angle in a right triangle, you can use the inverses of the trigonometric functions.

4 **EXAMPLE** **Finding Angle Measures**

In $\triangle DEF$, $\angle F$ is a right angle, $f = 13$, and $e = 5$. Find $m\angle D$ to the nearest tenth of a degree.

Step 1 Draw a diagram.

E
13 ← **Side _f_ is opposite ∠F.**
F ⌐ D
5 ← **Side _e_ is opposite ∠E.**

Step 2 Use a cosine ratio.

$$\cos D = \frac{5}{13}$$
$$m\angle D = \cos^{-1}\frac{5}{13}$$
$$\approx 67.38° \qquad \textbf{Use a calculator.}$$

To the nearest tenth of a degree, $m\angle D$ is 67.4°.

✓ CA Standards Check **4** Use a trigonometric ratio to find $m\angle A$ in each triangle.

a.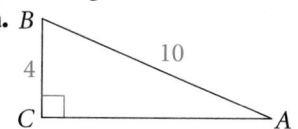

B
4   10
C ⌐   A

b.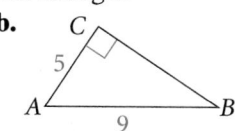

C
5
A   B
9

5 **EXAMPLE** **Real-World Connection**

Construction A wheelchair ramp must be constructed so the slope is not more than 1 in. of rise for every 1 ft of run. What is the maximum angle that the ramp can make with the ground, to the nearest tenth of a degree?

Surface of ramp
θ   1 in. **Rise**
1 ft
Horizontal projection or run

Not drawn to scale

Let θ = the measure of the angle the ramp makes with the ground.

You know the length of the leg opposite the angle you need to find. You know the length of the leg adjacent to the angle you need to find. So, use the tangent ratio.

$$\tan\theta = \frac{1}{12} \qquad \textbf{Rewrite 1 ft as 12 in.}$$
$$\theta = \tan^{-1}\frac{1}{12} \qquad \textbf{Use the inverse of the tangent function.}$$
$$\theta \approx 4.8 \qquad \textbf{Use a calculator.}$$

The angle between the ramp and the ground will be about 4.8°.

Real-World Connection

Federal regulations define allowable slopes for handicap-accessible facilities.

✓ CA Standards Check **5** In $\triangle DEF$, $\angle F$ is a right angle, $d = 7$, and $f = 10$. Draw a diagram and find the remaining side length and angle degree measures. Round to the nearest tenth.

A Practice by Example

Example 1
(page 807)

GO for Help

1. **Ballooning** From a hot-air balloon 3000 ft above the ground, you see a clearing whose angle of depression is 20°. Given that sin 20° ≈ 0.34, cos 20° ≈ 0.94, and tan 20° ≈ 0.36, find each distance to the nearest foot.
   a. your horizontal distance from the clearing
   b. your direct distance from the clearing

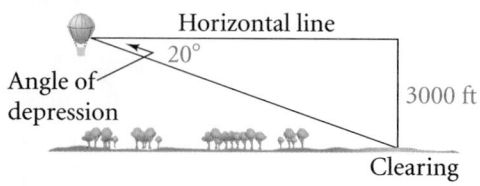

Example 2
(page 808)

2. In △ABC, find each value as a fraction and as a decimal. Round to the nearest hundredth.
   a. sin A
   b. sec A
   c. cot A
   d. csc B
   e. sec B
   f. tan B

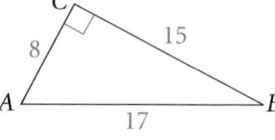

3. In △GHI, ∠H is a right angle, GH = 40, and cos G = $\frac{40}{41}$. Draw a diagram and find each value in fraction and in decimal form.
   a. sin G
   b. sin I
   c. cot G
   d. csc G
   e. cos I
   f. sec H

4. In △PQR, ∠R is a right angle and cot P = $\frac{5}{12}$. Draw a diagram. Find the values of the other five trigonometric functions of ∠P in fraction and in decimal form.

Example 3
(page 808)

Find each length x. Round to the nearest tenth.

5.

6.

7.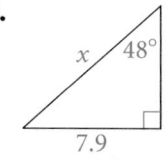

8. **Indirect Measurement** In 1915, the tallest flagpole in the world was in San Francisco.
   a. When the angle of elevation of the sun was 55°, the length of the shadow cast by this flagpole was 210 ft. Find the height of the flagpole to the nearest foot.
   b. What was the length of the shadow when the angle of elevation of the sun was 34°?
   c. What do you need to assume about the flagpole and the shadow to solve these problems? Explain why.

Examples 4 and 5
(page 809)

Find each angle measure to the nearest tenth of a degree.

9. $\cos^{-1} \frac{\sqrt{2}}{2}$

10. $\tan^{-1} 0.3333$

11. $\sin^{-1} \frac{3}{4}$

12. $\tan^{-1} \sqrt{3}$

13. $\sin^{-1} 0.335$

14. $\cos^{-1} 0.992$

15. $\tan^{-1} 3.552$

16. $\sin^{-1} 0.052$

17. $\cos^{-1} \frac{3}{8}$

In △ABC, ∠C is a right angle. Find the remaining sides and angles. Round your answers to the nearest tenth.

18. $b = 5, c = 10$ **19.** $a = 5, b = 6$ **20.** $b = 12, c = 15$

21. $a = 8.1, b = 6.2$ **22.** $b = 4.3, c = 9.1$ **23.** $a = 17, c = 22$

24. Rocketry An observer on the ground at point A watches a rocket ascend. The observer is 1200 ft from the launch point B. As the rocket rises, the distance d from the observer to the rocket increases.
  a. Write a model for $m\angle A$.
  b. Find $m\angle A$ if $d = 1500$ ft. Round your answer to the nearest degree.
  c. Find $m\angle A$ if $d = 2000$ ft. Round your answer to the nearest degree.

 Apply Your Skills

Sketch a right triangle with θ as the measure of one acute angle. Find the other five trigonometric ratios of θ.

25. $\sin \theta = \frac{3}{8}$ **26.** $\cos \theta = \frac{7}{20}$ **27.** $\cos \theta = \frac{1}{5}$

28. $\tan \theta = \frac{24}{7}$ **29.** $\csc \theta = \frac{21}{12}$ **30.** $\sec \theta = \frac{16}{9}$

31. $\cot \theta = \frac{5}{4}$ **32.** $\sin \theta = 0.35$ **33.** $\csc \theta = 5.2$

34. a. Engineering A radio tower has supporting cables attached to it at points 100 ft above the ground. Write a model for the length d of each supporting cable as a function of the angle θ that it makes with the ground.
  b. Find d when $\theta = 60°$ and when $\theta = 50°$.

In △ABC, ∠C is a right angle. Two measures are given. Find the remaining sides and angles. Round your answers to the nearest tenth.

35. $b = 8, c = 17$ **36.** $a = 7, b = 10$

37. $m\angle A = 52°, c = 10$ **38.** $m\angle A = 34.2°, b = 5.7$

39. $m\angle B = 17.2°, b = 8.3$ **40.** $m\angle B = 8.3°, c = 20$

100 ft d θ

41. A 150-ft pole casts a shadow 210 ft long. Find the measure of the angle of elevation of the sun.

 for Help

For a guide to solving Exercise 42, see p. 814.

42. Indirect Measurement A transit is 330 ft from the base of a building. The angles of elevation of the top and bottom of a flagpole situated on top of the building are 55° and 53°. Find the height of the flagpole.

43. Geometry An altitude inside a triangle forms angles of 36° and 42° with two of the sides. The altitude is 5 m long. Find the area of the triangle.

44. Construction When a crane's boom is at an angle of 70°, the top is 128 ft high. (See the diagram at the right.) How long is the boom? How far is the crane's cab from the bottom of the free-fall path of something dropped from the top of the boom?

128 ft

70°

d

45. a. In Example 4, use the Pythagorean Theorem to find EF.
  b. Use a trigonometric ratio to find EF.

46. Open-Ended If $\sin \theta = \frac{1}{2}$, describe a method you could use to find all the angles between 0° and 360° that satisfy this equation.

 Homework Video Tutor

Visit: PHSchool.com
Web Code: bbe-1403

47. Reasoning Show that $\cos A$ defined as a ratio equals $\cos \theta$ using the unit circle.

48. Baseball The bases on a baseball diamond form a square 90 ft on a side. The pitcher's plate is 60 ft 6 in. from the back corner of home plate.

  a. About how far is the pitcher's plate from second base?
  b. A line drive is 10 ft high when it passes over the third baseman, who is 100 ft from home plate. At what angle did the ball leave the bat? (Assume the ball is 4 ft above the ground when it is hit.)

 Challenge

Use the definitions of trigonometric ratios in right $\triangle ABC$ to verify each identity.

49. $\sec A = \dfrac{1}{\cos A}$ **50.** $\tan A = \dfrac{\sin A}{\cos A}$ **51.** $\cos^2 A + \sin^2 A = 1$

52. a. In $\triangle DEF$ below, h is the length of an altitude. Find h to the nearest tenth.
  b. For $DF = 10.8$, find the area of $\triangle DEF$ to the nearest tenth.
  c. Find the area of $\triangle RST$ to the nearest tenth.

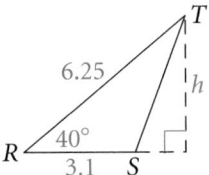

Vocabulary Tip

A regular polygon has congruent sides and congruent angles.

 53. Geometry A regular pentagon is inscribed in a circle of radius 10 cm.
  a. Find the measure of $\angle C$.
  b. Find the length of the diagonal PS. (*Hint:* First find RS.)

 Multiple Choice Practice

For California Standards and CAHSEE Tutorials, visit PHSchool.com. Web Code: bbq-9045

TRIG 19.0 **54.** A ladder rests against a vertical building, as shown at the right. The ladder is 14 ft long and forms an angle of 76.5° with the ground. Which statement is NOT true?

  (A) The bottom of the ladder is 13.6 ft from the base of the building.

  (B) The bottom of the ladder is 3.3 ft from the base of the building.

  (C) The top of the ladder is 13.6 ft from the ground.

  (D) The ladder forms an angle of 13.5° with the building.

ALG2 18.0 **55.** There are 13 DVDs on a shelf. How many ways can you randomly select 6 DVDs?

  (A) 36   (B) 78   (C) 169   (D) 1,716

56. The figure below is a rectangle. What is the value of x?

30 cm

18 cm

x°

A) 31.0

B) 53.1

C) 36.9

D) 59.0

57. If $f(x) = 2x + 1$ and $g(x) = 3 - x^2$, which is an equivalent form of $(g \circ f)(x)$?

A) $-2x^2 + 1$

B) $-4x^2 + 4x + 5$

C) $-4x^2 - 4x + 2$

D) $-4x^2 - 4x + 1$

Mixed Review

Lesson 14-2

Find the complete solution of each equation. Express your answer in degrees.

58. $\sec^2 \theta + \sec \theta = 0$

59. $2 \cos^2 \theta + 1 = 0$

60. $\cot \theta = \cot^2 \theta$

61. $\sin^2 \theta + 5 \sin \theta = 0$

Lesson 13-7

Graph each function in the interval from 0 to 2π.

62. $y = \sin(x - \pi) + 4$

63. $y = 3 \sin 2\left(x + \frac{\pi}{2}\right) - 5$

64. $y = \cos(x + \pi) - 3$

65. $y = -2 \cos\left(x - \frac{\pi}{3}\right) - 4$

Lesson 12-6

Use the binomial expansion of $(p + q)^n$ to calculate and graph each binomial distribution.

66. $n = 8, p = 0.2$

67. $n = 8, p = 0.4$

68. $n = 8, p = 0.8$

✓ Checkpoint Quiz 1   Lessons 14-1 through 14-3

Simplify each trigonometric expression.

1. $\sec \theta \cot \theta$

2. $\sec^2 \theta - 1$

3. $-1 - \cot^2 \theta$

Find the value of each expression to the nearest thousandth.

4. $\cos^{-1}\left(-\frac{\pi}{5}\right)$

5. $\sin^{-1} \frac{\pi}{10}$

6. $\tan^{-1} 4.35$

In $\triangle ABC$, $\angle C$ is a right angle. Find the remaining sides and angles. Round your answers to the nearest tenth.

7. $b = 14, c = 16$

8. $a = 7.9, b = 6.2$

9. $b = 29, c = 35$

10. Open-Ended Draw a right triangle. Measure the lengths of two sides, and then find the remaining sides and angles without measuring.

Understanding Word Problems Read the problem below. Then follow along with what Christiana thinks and writes. Check your understanding by solving the exercises at the bottom of the page.

Indirect Measurement A transit is 330 ft from the base of a building. The angles of elevation of the top and bottom of a flagpole situated on top of the building are 55° and 53°. Find the height of the flagpole.

What Christiana Thinks

A diagram will help me solve the problem.

I need the building, the flagpole on top, and two angles on the ground. One goes to the top of the pole and the other to the bottom. I'll use x and y for heights.

Aha! The height of the flagpole is $x - y$!

x is opposite the 55° angle.

330 is adjacent to the 55° angle.

I can use the tangent ratio to find x.

y is opposite the 53° angle and 330 is still the adjacent side. I can use tangent again to find y.

The height of the flagpole is $x - y$.

What Christiana Writes

Flagpole

55°
53°
330 ft

$$\frac{x}{330} = \tan 55°$$
$$x = 330 \tan 55°$$
$$x \approx 471.3$$

$$\frac{y}{330} = \tan 53°$$
$$y = 330 \tan 53°$$
$$y \approx 437.9$$

$$\text{Height} = x - y$$
$$\approx 471.3 - 437.9$$
$$= 33.4$$

The height of the flagpole is 33.4 ft.

EXERCISES

1. A monument has a cylindrical base and a tall spire. You are standing 50 ft from the center of the base. The top and the bottom of the spire have elevation angles of 62° and 42°, respectively. How tall is the spire to the nearest foot?

2. You are standing 250 ft from the town water tower. The top and the bottom of the tank at the top of the tower have angles of elevation of 22° and 15° respectively. What is the height of the water tank to the nearest foot?

14-4

Area and the Law of Sines

 California Content Standards

TRIG 13.0 Students know the law of sines and apply the law to solve problems.
TRIG 14.0 Students determine the area of a triangle, given one angle and the two adjacent sides.

What You'll Learn

- To find the area of any triangle and to use the Law of Sines

. . . And Why

To measure heights, as in Example 4

✓ **Check Skills You'll Need**

GO for Help Lesson 13-4

Simplify each expression.

1. $\dfrac{\sin 30°}{6}$

2. $\dfrac{\sin 45°}{4}$

3. $\dfrac{\sin 60°}{10}$

4. $\dfrac{\sin 30°}{12}$

5. $\dfrac{\sin 45°}{8}$

6. $\dfrac{\sin 60°}{9}$

Find the area of a triangle with the given base b and height h.

7. $b = 3$ cm, $h = 4$ cm

8. $b = 6$ in., $h = 15$ in.

9. $b = 5.2$ mm, $h = 12.6$ mm

10. $b = 6.17$ ft, $h = 3.25$ ft

🔊 **New Vocabulary** • Law of Sines

---

1 Area and the Law of Sines

Vocabulary Tip

An <u>oblique</u> <u>triangle</u> is a triangle that does not contain a right angle.

The formula for the area K of a triangle is $K = \frac{1}{2}bh$.

In any oblique $\triangle ABC$ with side lengths $a, b,$ and $c, h = c \sin A$. Therefore $K = \frac{1}{2}bh = \frac{1}{2}bc \sin A$. Similarly, $K = \frac{1}{2}ac \sin B$ and $K = \frac{1}{2}ab \sin C$.

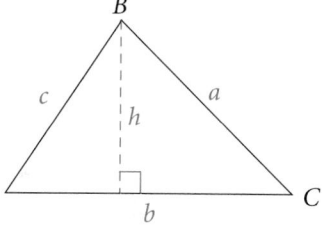

1 EXAMPLE Finding the Area of a Triangle

Find the area of the triangle at the right.

In the triangle, $b = 5, c = 10,$ and $m\angle A = 31°$.

$$K = \tfrac{1}{2}bc \sin A = \tfrac{1}{2}(5)(10) \sin 31°$$

$$\approx 12.9$$

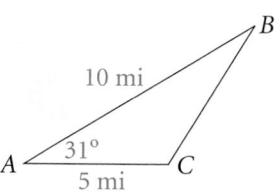

● The area is about 12.9 mi².

✓ **CA Standards Check** **1** A triangle has sides of lengths 12 in. and 15 in., and the measure of the angle between them is 24°. Find the area of the triangle.

Combining the three equations for the area of $\triangle ABC$ yields a useful formula.

$\frac{1}{2}bc \sin A = \frac{1}{2}ac \sin B = \frac{1}{2}ab \sin C$ **Transitive Property of Equality**

$\dfrac{\sin A}{a} = \dfrac{\sin B}{b} = \dfrac{\sin C}{c}$ **Divide by $\frac{1}{2}abc$.**

This relationship of the lengths of the sides of any triangle to the sines of the angles opposite them is known as the **Law of Sines.**

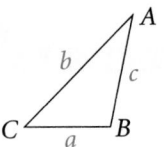

Key Concepts

Theorem	Law of Sines

In $\triangle ABC$, let a, b, and c represent the lengths of the sides opposite $\angle A$, $\angle B$, and $\angle C$, respectively.

Then $\dfrac{\sin A}{a} = \dfrac{\sin B}{b} = \dfrac{\sin C}{c}$.

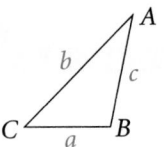

Vocabulary Tip

In math, <u>law</u> refers to a general property. The Law of Sines could have been named the Property of Sines.

You can use the Law of Sines to find missing measures of any triangle when you know the measures of

- two angles and any side, or
- two sides and the angle opposite one of them.

In Example 2, you are given the measures of two angles and a side.

2 EXAMPLE **Finding a Side of a Triangle**

In $\triangle PQR$, $m\angle R = 39°$, $m\angle Q = 32°$, and $PQ = 40$ cm. Find RQ.

Step 1 Draw and label a diagram.

Step 2 Find the measure of the angle opposite $\overline{RQ}$.

$$m\angle P = 180° - 39° - 32° = 109°$$

Step 3 Find RQ.

$$\frac{\sin 109°}{RQ} = \frac{\sin 39°}{40} \qquad \text{Law of Sines}$$

$$RQ = \frac{40 \sin 109°}{\sin 39°} \qquad \text{Solve for } RQ.$$

$$RQ \approx 60.1 \text{ cm} \qquad \text{Use a calculator.}$$

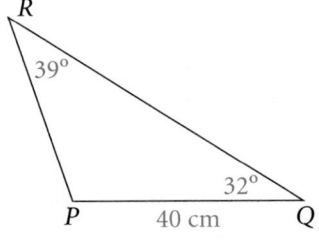

✓ CA Standards Check **2** In $\triangle KLM$, $m\angle K = 120°$, $m\angle M = 50°$, and $ML = 35$ yd. Find KL.

In Example 3, you are given the measures of two sides and an angle opposite one of the sides.

3 EXAMPLE **Finding an Angle of a Triangle**

In $\triangle RST$, $t = 7$, $r = 9$, and $m\angle R = 110°$. Find $m\angle S$.

Step 1 Draw and label a diagram.

Step 2 Find the measure of the angle opposite t.

$$\frac{\sin T}{7} = \frac{\sin 110°}{9} \qquad \text{Law of Sines.}$$

$$\sin T = \frac{7 \sin 110°}{9} \qquad \text{Solve for } \sin T.$$

$$m\angle T = \sin^{-1}\left(\frac{7 \sin 110°}{9}\right) \qquad \text{Solve for } m\angle T.$$

$$m\angle T \approx 47° \qquad \text{Use a calculator.}$$

Step 3 Find the measure of $\angle S$.

$$m\angle S \approx 180° - 110° - 47° = 23°$$

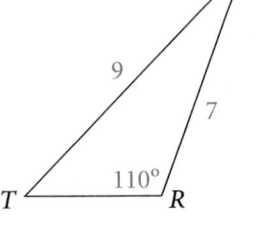

✓ CA Standards Check **3** In $\triangle PQR$, $m\angle R = 97.5°$, $r = 80$, and $p = 75$. Find $m\angle P$.

Surveyors can use the Law of Sines to indirectly measure the height of a mountain.

4 EXAMPLE Real-World Connection

Surveying A surveyor locates points *A* and *B* at the same elevation and 3950 ft apart. At *A*, the angle of elevation to the summit of the mountain is 18°. At *B*, the angle of elevation is 31°.

a. Find *BC*, the distance from *B* to the summit.

First find $m\angle ABC$ and $m\angle ACB$.

$m\angle ABC = 180° - 31° = 149°$
$m\angle ACB = 180° - 18° - 149° = 13°$

Now use the Law of Sines in $\triangle ABC$. Write a proportion that includes the side you know, *AB*, and the side you want, *BC*.

$\dfrac{\sin A}{BC} = \dfrac{\sin C}{AB}$	**Law of Sines**
$\dfrac{\sin 18°}{BC} = \dfrac{\sin 13°}{3950}$	**Substitute.**
$BC = \dfrac{3950 \sin 18°}{\sin 13°}$	**Solve for BC.**
$BC \approx 5426$	**Simplify.**

The distance from *B* to the summit is about 5426 ft.

b. Find *CD*, the height of the mountain.

In right $\triangle BCD$, you know *BC* and $m\angle B$. Use the sine ratio.

$\sin 31° \approx \dfrac{CD}{5426}$	**Definition of Sine**
$CD \approx 5426 \sin 31°$	**Solve for CD.**
$CD \approx 2795$	**Use a calculator.**

The summit is about 2795 ft higher than points *A* and *B*.

Real-World Connection

Surveyors use modern transits that measure distances with a laser beam and store data electronically.

✓ CA Standards Check ④ In $\triangle MNP$, $m\angle M = 35°$, $m\angle N = 120°$, and $MN = 48$. Find the length of the altitude of $\triangle MNP$ from vertex *P*.

EXERCISES For more exercises, see *Extra Skill and Word Problem Practice.*

Standards Practice **TRIG 13.0, 14.0**

A Practice by Example

Example 1 (page 815)

 GO for Help

Find the area of each triangle. Round your answer to the nearest tenth.

1.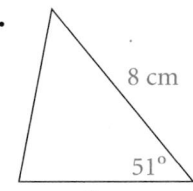
8 cm
51°
6 cm

2.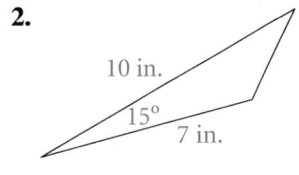
10 in.
15°
7 in.

3.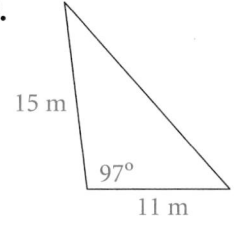
15 m
97°
11 m

4. A triangle has sides of lengths 10 cm and 16 cm, and the measure of the angle between them is 130°. Find the area of the triangle.

Example 2
(page 816)

Use the Law of Sines. Find the measure x to the nearest tenth.

5.

6.

7.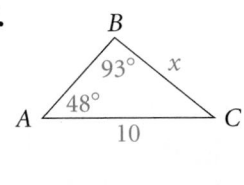

8. In $\triangle RST, m\angle R = 78°, m\angle T = 39°$, and $TS = 19$ in. Find RS.

9. In $\triangle JKL, m\angle L = 64°, j = 18$ m, and $m\angle K = 36°$. Find k.

10. In $\triangle RNP, m\angle N = 58°, n = 20$ in., and $m\angle R = 42°$. Find r.

Example 3
(page 816)

Use the Law of Sines. Find the measure x to the nearest tenth.

11.

12.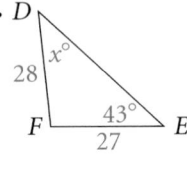

13. In $\triangle DEF, m\angle F = 43°, d = 16$ mm, and $f = 24$ mm. Find $m\angle D$.

14. In $\triangle ABC, m\angle A = 52°, c = 10$ ft, and $a = 15$ ft. Find $m\angle C$.

15. In $\triangle XYZ, m\angle Z = 33°, z = 35$ cm, and $x = 31$ cm. Find $m\angle X$.

Example 4
(page 817)

16. Surveying The distance from point A to the top of the hill is 2760 ft. The angle of elevation from A to the base of the tower is 28° and the angle of elevation from A to the top of the tower is 32°.

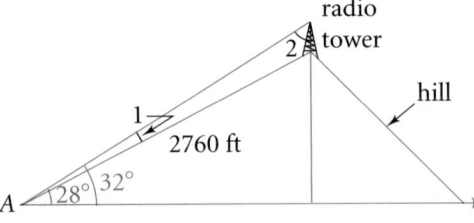

a. Find the measures of $\angle 1$ and $\angle 2$.
b. Find to the nearest foot the height of the tower above the top of the hill.

B **Apply Your Skills**

Find the remaining sides and angles in each triangle. Round your answers to the nearest tenth.

17.

18.

19.

20.

21.

22.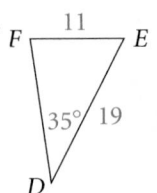

23. In $\triangle DEF, m\angle D = 54°, m\angle E = 54°$, and $d = 20$ in.

24. In $\triangle DEF, m\angle D = 54°, e = 8$ m, and $d = 10$ m.

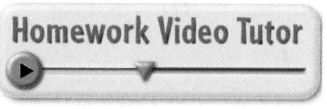
25. Critical Thinking In $\triangle ABC$, $a = 10$ and $b = 15$.
   a. Does the triangle have a greater area when $m\angle C = 1°$ or when $m\angle C = 50°$?
   b. Does the triangle have a greater area when $m\angle C = 50°$ or when $m\angle C = 179°$?
   c. For what measure of $\angle C$ does $\triangle ABC$ have the greatest area? Explain.

26. a. Open-Ended Sketch a triangle. Specify three of its measures so that you can use the Law of Sines to find the remaining measures.
   b. Solve for the remaining measures of the triangle.

27. Forestry A forest ranger in an observation tower sights a fire 39° east of north. A ranger in a tower 10 miles due east of the first tower sights the fire at 42° west of north. How far is the fire from each tower?

28. Geometry One of the congruent sides of an isosceles triangle is 10 cm long. One of the congruent angles has a measure of 54°. Find the perimeter of the triangle. Round your answer to the nearest centimeter.

29. Geometry The sides of a triangle are 15 in., 17 in., and 16 in. long. The smallest angle has a measure of 54°. Find the measure of the largest angle. Round your answer to the nearest degree.

Find the area of $\triangle ABC$. Round your answer to the nearest tenth.

30. $m\angle C = 68°, b = 12.9, c = 15.2$ **31.** $m\angle A = 52°, a = 9.71, c = 9.33$

32. $m\angle A = 23°, m\angle C = 39°, b = 14.6$ **33.** $m\angle B = 87°, a = 10.1, c = 9.8$

34. $m\angle A = 96°, m\angle C = 18°, a = 43.4$ **35.** $m\angle C = 33°, a = 1.2, b = 0.9$

36. $m\angle B = 40°, m\angle C = 80°, c = 5.5$ **37.** $m\angle A = 20°, b = 1, c = 5$

In $\triangle ABC$, $m\angle A = 40°$ and $m\angle B = 30°$. Find each value to the nearest tenth.

38. Find AC for $BC = 10.5$ m.   **39.** Find BC for $AC = 21.8$ ft.

40. Find AC for $AB = 81.2$ yd.   **41.** Find BC for $AB = 5.9$ cm.

42. Measurement A vacant lot is in the shape of an isosceles triangle. It is between two streets that intersect at an 85.9° angle. Each of the sides of the lot that face these streets is 150 ft long. Find the length of the third side, to the nearest foot.

C **Challenge**

43. Sailing Buoys are located in the sea at points A, B, and C. $\angle ACB$ is a right angle. $AC = 3.0$ mi, $BC = 4.0$ mi, and $AB = 5.0$ mi. A ship is located at point D on $\overline{AB}$ so that $m\angle ACD = 30°$. How far is the ship from the buoy at point C? Round your answer to the nearest tenth of a mile.

44. Writing Suppose you know the measures of all three angles of a triangle. Can you use the Law of Sines to find the lengths of the sides? Explain.

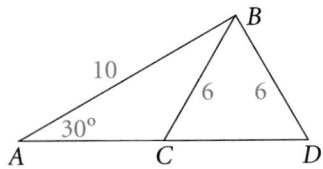

45. a. In the diagram at the left, $m\angle A = 30°$, $AB = 10$, and $BC = BD = 6$. Use the Law of Sines to find $m\angle D$.
  b. Find $m\angle ABD$ and $m\angle ABC$.
  c. Reasoning Notice that two sides and a nonincluded angle of $\triangle ABC$ are congruent to the corresponding parts of $\triangle ABD$, but the triangles are not congruent. Must $\triangle EFG$ be congruent to $\triangle ABD$ if $EF = 10$, $FG = 6$, and $\angle E \cong \angle A$? Explain.

Multiple Choice Practice

For California Standards and CAHSEE Tutorials, visit PHSchool.com. Web Code: bbq-9045

TRIG 14.0

46. For which set of given information can you compute the area of the triangle?
  - Ⓐ Given: the length of one side and the measure of the angle opposite it
  - Ⓑ Given: the length of one side and the measure of an angle adjacent to it
  - Ⓒ Given: the lengths of two sides and the measure of a nonincluded angle
  - Ⓓ Given: the lengths of two sides and the measure of the included angle

ALG2 20.0

47. What is the coefficient of a^2b^3 in the expansion of $(a + b)^5$?
  - Ⓐ 3
  - Ⓑ 5
  - Ⓒ 10
  - Ⓓ 25

ALG2 8.0

48. What can you tell about the roots of $3x^2 + 4x - 1 = 0$ from the discriminant?
  - Ⓐ There are two real roots.
  - Ⓑ There are two imaginary roots.
  - Ⓒ There is one real and one imaginary root.
  - Ⓓ There are no roots.

Mixed Review

Lesson 14-3 **Find each angle measure to the nearest tenth of a degree.**

49. $\cos^{-1} \frac{3}{5}$ **50.** $\tan^{-1} 0.4569$ **51.** $\sin^{-1} \frac{5}{8}$ **52.** $\tan^{-1} \sqrt{2}$

In $\triangle ABC$, $\angle B$ is a right angle. Find the remaining sides and angles. Round your answers to the nearest tenth.

53. $b = 5, c = 4$ **54.** $a = 3, c = 3$ **55.** $a = 10, b = 15$

56. $a = 1.6, c = 8.1$ **57.** $a = 4.1, b = 9.4$ **58.** $b = 100, c = 45$

Lesson 13-4 **Sketch one cycle of the graph of each sine function.**

59. $y = 4 \sin \theta$ **60.** $y = 4 \sin \pi\theta$ **61.** $y = \sin 4\theta$

Lesson 12-4 **62.** A set of values has a mean of 36 and a standard deviation of 5. Find the z-score of the value 43.

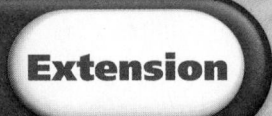

Extension The Ambiguous Case

The triangles at the right have one pair of congruent angles and two pairs of congruent sides. But the triangles are not congruent. Notice that each of the congruent angles is opposite one of the congruent sides.

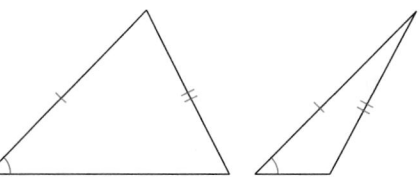

When you know the measures of two sides of a triangle and one of the opposite angles, there may be two triangles with those measurements. You can use the Law of Sines to find the other measures for both triangles.

EXAMPLE

In each $\triangle ABC$ at the right, $m\angle A = 35°$, $a = 11$, and $b = 15$. Find $m\angle B$.

$\dfrac{\sin A}{a} = \dfrac{\sin B}{b}$ **Law of Sines**

$\dfrac{\sin 35°}{11} = \dfrac{\sin B}{15}$ **Substitute.**

$\sin B = \dfrac{15 \sin 35°}{11}$ **Solve for sin B.**

$m\angle B \approx \sin^{-1}\left(\dfrac{15 \sin 35°}{11}\right)$ **Find one value of $m\angle B$.**

$m\angle B \approx 51°$ **Use a calculator.**

The sine function is also positive in Quadrant II. So another value of $m\angle B$ is about $180° - 51° = 129°$.

Because there are two possible angle measures for $\angle B$, there are two triangles that satisfy the given conditions. In one triangle, the angle measures are about 35°, 51°, and 94°. In the other, the angle measures are about 35°, 129°, and 16°.

EXERCISES

In each $\triangle ABC$, find the measures for $\angle B$ and $\angle C$ that satisfy the given conditions. Draw diagrams to help you decide whether two triangles are possible. Remember that a triangle can have only one obtuse angle.

1. $m\angle A = 62°$, $a = 30$, and $b = 32$ **2.** $m\angle A = 16°$, $a = 12$, and $b = 37.5$

3. $m\angle A = 48°$, $a = 93$, and $b = 125$ **4.** $m\angle A = 112°$, $a = 16.5$, and $b = 5.4$

5. $m\angle A = 23.6°$, $a = 9.8$, and $b = 17$ **6.** $m\angle A = 155°$, $a = 12.5$, and $b = 8.4$

7. Multiple Choice You can construct a triangle with a compass and straightedge when given three parts of the triangle (except for three angles). Which of the following given sets could result in the ambiguous case?

   A Given: three sides

   B Given: two sides and an included angle

   C Given: two sides and a nonincluded angle

   D Given: two angles and a nonincluded side

The Law of Cosines

 California Content Standards

TRIG 13.0 Students know the law of cosines and apply the law to solve problems.

What You'll Learn

• To use the Law of Cosines in finding the measures of sides and angles of a triangle

. . . And Why

To find the length of a sailing course, as in Example 1

 Check Skills You'll Need

GO for Help Lesson 14-4

Use the Law of Sines.

1. In $\triangle ABC$, $m\angle C = 33°$, $a = 17$, and $c = 21$. Find $m\angle A$.
2. In $\triangle RST$, $m\angle R = 59°$, $m\angle S = 45°$, and $r = 16$. Find t.
3. In $\triangle DEF$, $m\angle D = 55°$, $d = 18$, and $e = 21$. Find $m\angle F$.

New Vocabulary • Law of Cosines

---

1 The Law of Cosines

Since you can't use the Law of Sines to find the missing measures in the triangles at the right, another formula is needed.

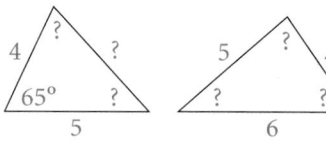

In this oblique $\triangle ABC$ with altitude h, let $AD = x$.

Then $DB = c - x$.

In $\triangle ADC$,
$b^2 = x^2 + h^2$ and
$\cos A = \frac{x}{b}$ or $x = b \cos A$.

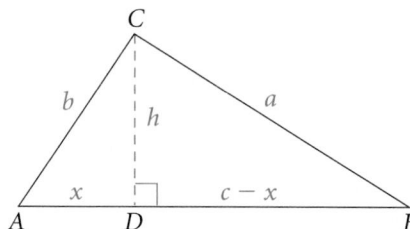

In $\triangle CBD$,

$a^2 = (c - x)^2 + h^2$	**Pythagorean Theorem**
$= c^2 - 2cx + x^2 + h^2$	**Square the binomial.**
$= c^2 - 2cx + b^2$	**Substitute b^2 for $x^2 + h^2$.**
$= c^2 - 2cb \cos A + b^2$	**Substitute $b \cos A$ for x.**
$= b^2 + c^2 - 2bc \cos A$	**Commutative Property of Addition**

The last equation relates the length of a side of any triangle to the measure of the opposite angle. It applies to any of the three sides and is called the **Law of Cosines.**

 Key Concepts

Theorem	**Law of Cosines**

In $\triangle ABC$, let a, b, and c represent the lengths of the sides opposite $\angle A$, $\angle B$, and $\angle C$, respectively.

$$a^2 = b^2 + c^2 - 2bc \cos A$$

$$b^2 = a^2 + c^2 - 2ac \cos B$$

$$c^2 = a^2 + b^2 - 2ab \cos C$$

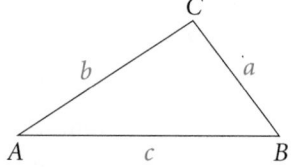

You can use the Law of Cosines to find missing measures in any triangle when you know the measures of

- two sides and the angle between them, or
- all three sides.

In this example, you are given the measures of two sides and the included angle.

1 EXAMPLE Real-World 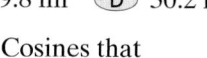 Connection

Multiple Choice A racing committee wants to lay out a triangular course with a 40° angle between two sides of 3.5 mi and 2.5 mi. What will be the length of the third side?

(A) 2.0 mi (B) 2.3 mi (C) 9.8 mi (D) 30.2 mi

Choose the form of the Law of Cosines that has a^2 on one side.

$a^2 = b^2 + c^2 - 2bc \cos A$

$a^2 = 2.5^2 + 3.5^2 - 2(2.5)(3.5) \cos 40°$ **Substitute.**

   ≈ 5.094 **Use a calculator.**

$a \approx 2.3$ **Use a calculator.**

The third side of the triangular course will be about 2.3 mi long. The correct choice is B.

CA Standards Check ① The lengths of two sides of a triangle are 8 and 10, and the measure of the angle between them is 40°. Find the length of the third side.

In this example, you are given the measures of three sides.

2 EXAMPLE Finding an Angle Measure

Find the measure of $\angle C$ in the triangle below. Round your answer to the nearest tenth of a degree.

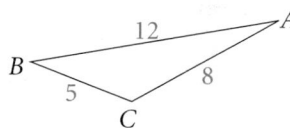

Choose the form of the Law of Cosines that contains $\angle C$.

$c^2 = a^2 + b^2 - 2ab \cos C$

$12^2 = 5^2 + 8^2 - 2(5)(8) \cos C$ **Substitute.**

$144 = 25 + 64 - 80 \cos C$ **Simplify.**

$55 = -80 \cos C$ **Combine like terms.**

$-\dfrac{55}{80} = \cos C$ **Solve for cos C.**

$\cos^{-1}\left(-\dfrac{55}{80}\right) = m\angle C$ **Solve for m∠C.**

$m\angle C \approx 133.4°$ **Use a calculator.**

CA Standards Check ② The lengths of the sides of a triangle are 10, 14, and 15. Find the measure of the angle opposite the longest side.

Sometimes you need to use the Law of Cosines followed by the Law of Cosines again or by the Law of Sines.

 3 EXAMPLE Finding an Angle Measure

In $\triangle ABC$, $b = 6.2$, $c = 7.8$, and $m\angle A = 45°$. Find $m\angle B$.

Step 1 Draw a diagram.

Step 2 Find a. Since you cannot find $m\angle B$ directly, use the Law of Cosines to find a.

$a^2 = b^2 + c^2 - 2bc \cos A$

$a^2 = 6.2^2 + 7.8^2 - 2(6.2)(7.8) \cos 45°$ **Substitute.**

$ \approx 30.89$ **Simplify.**

$a \approx \sqrt{30.89}$ **Solve for a.**

$a \approx 5.56$ **Find the principal square root.**

Step 3 Now you can use the Law of Sines or the Law of Cosines to find $m\angle B$.

$\dfrac{\sin B}{6.2} \approx \dfrac{\sin 45°}{5.56}$ **Law of Sines**

$\sin B \approx \dfrac{6.2 \sin 45°}{5.56}$ **Solve for $\sin B$.**

$m\angle B \approx \sin^{-1}\left(\dfrac{6.2 \sin 45°}{5.56}\right)$ **Solve for $m\angle B$. ($\angle B$ is not obtuse because $b < c$.)**

$ \approx 52°$ **Use a calculator.**

> **Problem Solving Hint**
>
> To help remember the formulas for the Law of Cosines, notice that the first and last letters are the same and the last one is capitalized.

CA Standards Check **3** In $\triangle RST$, $s = 41$, $t = 53$, and $m\angle R = 126°$. Find $m\angle T$.

 EXERCISES   For more exercises, see *Extra Skill and Word Problem Practice.*

Standards Practice   **TRIG 13.0**

A Practice by Example

Example 1
(page 823)

 for Help

Use the Law of Cosines. Find the length of x to the nearest tenth.

1.
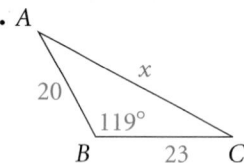

2.

3.

4. In $\triangle DEF$, $m\angle E = 54°$, $d = 14$ ft, and $f = 20$ ft. Find e.

5. In $\triangle RST$, $m\angle T = 32°$, $r = 10$ cm, and $s = 17$ cm. Find t.

6. In $\triangle ABC$, $m\angle B = 52°$, $a = 15$ in., and $c = 10$ in. Find b.

Example 2
(page 823)

Use the Law of Cosines. Find the measure of x to the nearest tenth of a degree.

7.   **8.**   **9.**

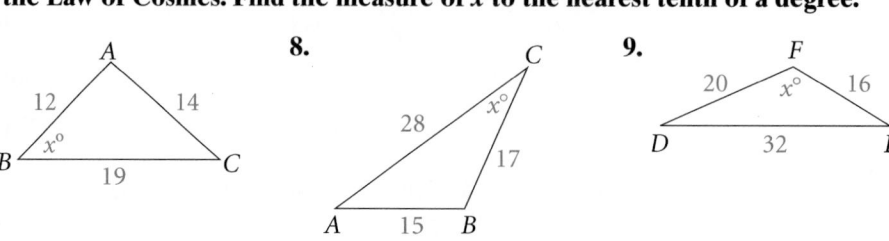

10. In $\triangle DEF$, $d = 15$ in., $e = 18$ in., and $f = 10$ in. Find $m\angle F$.

11. In $\triangle ABC$, $a = 20$ m, $b = 14$ m, and $c = 16$ m. Find $m\angle A$.

12. In $\triangle DEF$, $d = 12$ ft, $e = 10$ ft, and $f = 9$ ft. Find $m\angle F$.

Example 3
(page 824)

Use the Law of Cosines and the Law of Sines. Find x to the nearest tenth.

13.

14.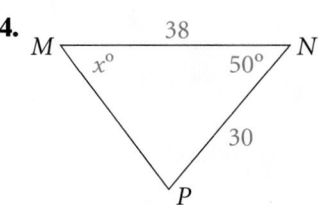

15. In $\triangle ABC$, $b = 4$ in., $c = 6$ in., and $m\angle A = 69°$. Find $m\angle C$.

16. In $\triangle RST$, $r = 17$ cm, $s = 12$ cm, and $m\angle T = 13°$. Find $m\angle S$.

17. In $\triangle DEF$, $d = 20$ ft, $e = 25$ ft, and $m\angle F = 98°$. Find $m\angle D$.

B **Apply Your Skills**

For each triangle, write the correct form of the Law of Cosines or the Law of Sines to solve for the measure in red. Use only the information given in blue.

18.

19.

20.

21.

22.

23.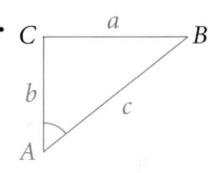

Find the remaining sides and angles in each triangle. Round your answers to the nearest tenth.

24.

25.

26.

Homework Video Tutor

Visit: PHSchool.com
Web Code: bbe-1405

27.

28.

29.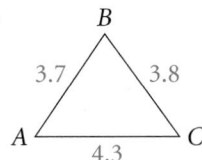

30. a. Open-Ended Sketch a triangle. Specify three of its measures so that you can use the Law of Cosines to find the remaining measures.
   b. Solve for the remaining measures of the triangle.

31. Sports A softball diamond is a square that is 65 ft on a side. The pitcher's mound is 46 ft from home plate. How far is the pitcher from third base?

32. Writing Given the measures of three angles of a triangle, explain how to find the ratio of the lengths of two sides of the triangle.

33. Geometry The lengths of the sides of a triangle are 7.6 cm, 8.2 cm, and 5.2 cm. Find the measure of the largest angle.

34. Navigation A pilot is flying from city A to city B, which is 85 mi due north. After flying 20 mi, the pilot must change course and fly 10° east of north to avoid a cloudbank.
   a. If the pilot remains on this course for 20 mi, how far will the plane be from city B?
   b. How many degrees will the pilot have to turn to the left to fly directly to city B? How many degrees from due north is this course?

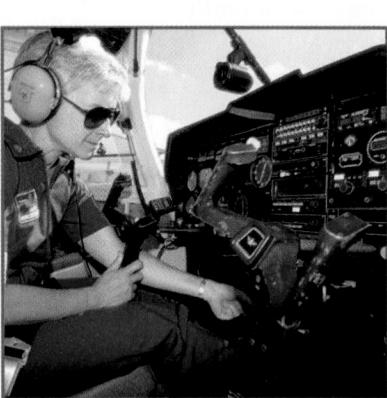

In $\triangle ABC$, $m\angle A = 53°$ and $c = 7$ cm. Find each value to the nearest tenth.

35. Find $m\angle B$ for $b = 6.2$ cm.   **36.** Find a for $b = 13.7$ cm.

37. Find a for $b = 11$ cm.   **38.** Find $m\angle C$ for $b = 15.2$ cm.

39. Find $m\angle B$ for $b = 37$ cm.   **40.** Find a for $b = 16$ cm.

In $\triangle RST$, $t = 7$ ft and $s = 13$ ft. Find each value to the nearest tenth.

41. Find $m\angle T$ for $r = 11$ ft.   **42.** Find $m\angle T$ for $r = 6.97$ ft.

43. Find $m\angle S$ for $r = 14$ ft.   **44.** Find r for $m\angle R = 35°$.

45. Find $m\angle S$ for $m\angle R = 87°$.   **46.** Find $m\angle R$ for $m\angle S = 70°$.

47. Geometry The lengths of the adjacent sides of a parallelogram are 54 cm and 78 cm. The larger angle measures 110°. What is the length of the longer diagonal? Round your answer to the nearest centimeter.

48. Geometry The lengths of the adjacent sides of a parallelogram are 21 cm and 14 cm. The smaller angle measures 58°. What is the length of the shorter diagonal? Round your answer to the nearest centimeter.

49. Critical Thinking Does the Law of Cosines apply to a right triangle? That is, does $c^2 = a^2 + b^2 - 2ab \cos C$ remain true when $\angle C$ is a right angle? Justify your answer.

Challenge

50. Physics A pendulum 36 in. long swings 30° from the vertical. How high above the lowest position is the pendulum at the end of its swing? Round your answer to the nearest tenth of an inch.

51. a. Find the length of the altitude to $\overline{PQ}$ in the triangle below.
   b. Find the area of $\triangle PQR$.

52. Find x in $\triangle ABC$.

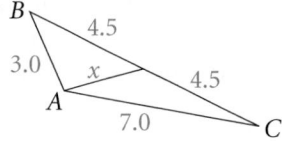

For California Standards and CAHSEE Tutorials, visit PHSchool.com. Web Code: bbq-9045

TRIG 13.0

53. Suppose $a = 23.2$, $b = 18.5$, and $m\angle C = 42°$ in the diagram below. What is c to the nearest tenth?

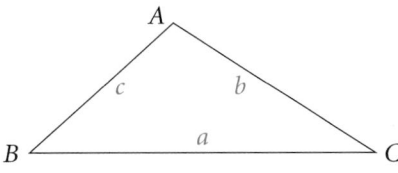

Ⓐ 11.0　　　Ⓑ 15.6　　　Ⓒ 27.1　　　Ⓓ 42.0

ALG2 7.0

54. What is the product of $\dfrac{x^2(x-2)}{x+4} \cdot \dfrac{2(2x+8)}{x^3-x^2}$?

Ⓐ $\dfrac{x^4(x-1)(x-2)-4(x+4)^2}{x^2(x-1)(x+4)}$　　　Ⓒ $\dfrac{x^4(x-1)(x-2)}{4(x+4)^2}$

Ⓑ $\dfrac{12x^4+14x^3-32x^2}{x^4+2x^3-4x^2}$　　　Ⓓ $\dfrac{4(x-2)}{x-1}$

Mixed Review

Lesson 14-4

55. In $\triangle RST$, $m\angle R = 37°$, $m\angle T = 59°$, and $TS = 12$ in. Find RS.

56. In $\triangle JKL$, $m\angle L = 71°$, $j = 11$ m, and $m\angle K = 46°$. Find k.

57. In $\triangle MNP$, $m\angle N = 42°$, $n = 21$ in., and $m\angle M = 57°$. Find m.

58. In $\triangle DEF$, $m\angle F = 91°$, $d = 17$ mm, and $f = 21$ mm. Find $m\angle D$.

Lesson 13-6

Identify the period and tell where two asymptotes occur for each function.

59. $y = \tan 0.5\theta$　　**60.** $y = \tan \dfrac{3\pi\theta}{2}$　　**61.** $y = \tan(-3\theta)$　　**62.** $y = \tan \dfrac{2\pi}{5}\theta$

Lesson 12-1

63. Use a table and a graph to show the probability distribution for the sum of two octahedral number cubes. $\{2, 3, 4, 5, 6, 7, 8, 9, 10, 11, 12, 13, 14, 15, 16\}$

Algebra at Work

Acoustical Physicist

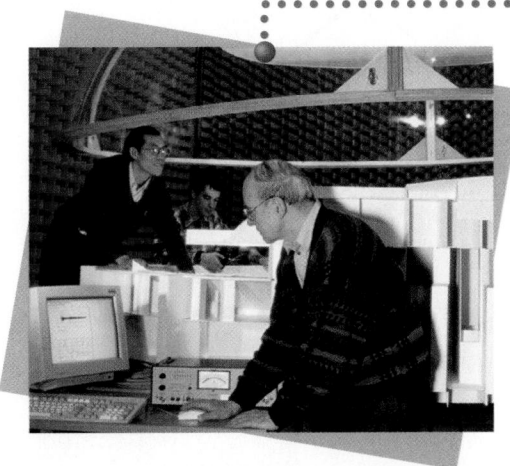

Acoustical physicists study sound to design concert halls, theaters, and auditoriums. They consider building materials, the shape of the hall, and the placement of people and equipment. Acoustical physicists ensure that sound is distributed evenly so that all of the people in the theater or auditorium hear equally well.

Go Online
PHSchool.com

For: Information about acoustical physicists
Web Code: bbb-2031

Angle Identities

 California Content Standards

TRIG 10.0 Students demonstrate an understanding of the addition formulas for sines and cosines and their proofs and can use those formulas to prove and/or simplify other trigonometric identities.

What You'll Learn

- To verify and use angle identities
- To verify and use sum and difference identities

... And Why

To simplify trigonometric expressions and find values of trigonometric functions

✓ Check Skills You'll Need

GO for Help Lesson 14-1

Complete the three reciprocal identities.

1. $\csc \theta = \dfrac{1}{\blacksquare}$ **2.** $\sec \theta = \dfrac{1}{\blacksquare}$ **3.** $\cot \theta = \dfrac{1}{\blacksquare}$

Complete the three Pythagorean identities.

4. $\cos^2 \theta + \sin^2 \theta = \blacksquare$ **5.** $1 + \tan^2 \theta = \blacksquare$ **6.** $1 + \cot^2 \theta = \blacksquare$

---

1 Angle Identities

Real-World Connection

Over 2000 years ago, the Greek astronomer Hipparchus needed a table of trigonometric ratios to calculate the positions of the stars. He had to compute the table himself and he used angle identities to make the computations easier.

In the figure at the right, angles θ and $-\theta$ have the same amount of rotation, but the rotations are in opposite directions.

Point Q is a reflection of P in the x-axis. The x-coordinates of P and Q are the same and their y-coordinates are opposites. So $\cos(-\theta) = \cos \theta$ and $\sin(-\theta) = -\sin \theta$.

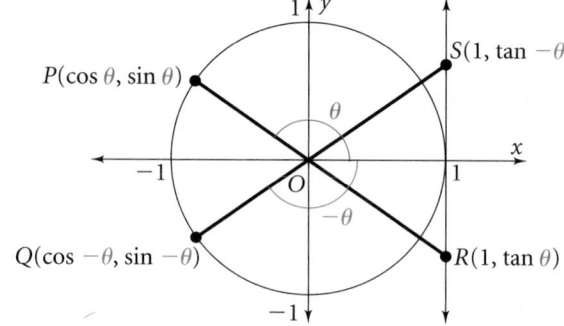

Similarly, R is the reflection of S in the x-axis. So $\tan(-\theta) = -\tan \theta$.

In the figure at the right, θ is a counterclockwise rotation from the positive x-axis and $\frac{\pi}{2} - \theta$ is the same amount of rotation clockwise from the positive y-axis.

Point Q is a reflection of P in the line $y = x$. If (x, y) are the coordinates of P, then (y, x) are the coordinates of Q. So $\cos\left(\frac{\pi}{2} - \theta\right) = \sin \theta$ and $\sin\left(\frac{\pi}{2} - \theta\right) = \cos \theta$.

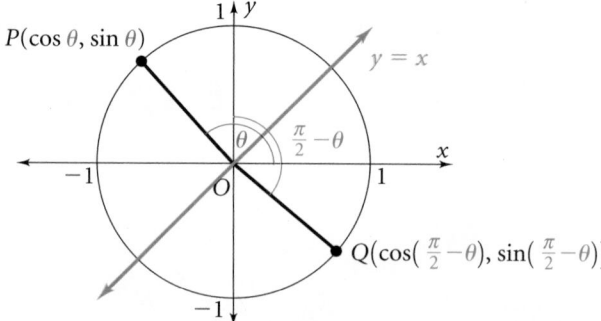

Then, by the Tangent Identity, $\tan\left(\frac{\pi}{2} - \theta\right) = \dfrac{\sin\left(\frac{\pi}{2} - \theta\right)}{\cos\left(\frac{\pi}{2} - \theta\right)} = \dfrac{\cos \theta}{\sin \theta} = \cot \theta$.

Key Concepts

Vocabulary Tip

The word <u>cofunction</u> is derived from complementary angle *function*.

Properties	Angle Identities

Negative angle identities

$$\sin(-\theta) = -\sin\theta \qquad \cos(-\theta) = \cos\theta \qquad \tan(-\theta) = -\tan\theta$$

Cofunction identities

$$\sin\left(\frac{\pi}{2} - \theta\right) = \cos\theta \qquad \cos\left(\frac{\pi}{2} - \theta\right) = \sin\theta \qquad \tan\left(\frac{\pi}{2} - \theta\right) = \cot\theta$$

1 EXAMPLE **Verifying Angle Identities**

Verify the identity $\sin\left(\theta - \frac{\pi}{2}\right) = -\cos\theta$.

$$\sin\left(\theta - \frac{\pi}{2}\right) = \sin\left(-\left(\frac{\pi}{2} - \theta\right)\right) \qquad -(a - b) = b - a$$

$$= -\sin\left(\frac{\pi}{2} - \theta\right) \qquad \sin(-\theta) = -\sin\theta$$

$$= -\cos\theta \qquad \sin\left(\frac{\pi}{2} - \theta\right) = \cos\theta$$

✓ **CA Standards Check** **1** Verify the identity $\cos\left(\theta - \frac{\pi}{2}\right) = \sin\theta$.

You can use angle identities to solve trigonometric equations.

2 EXAMPLE **Solving Trigonometric Equations**

Solve $\sin\theta = \sin\left(\frac{\pi}{2} - \theta\right)$ for $0 \le \theta < 2\pi$.

$$\sin\theta = \sin\left(\frac{\pi}{2} - \theta\right)$$

$$\sin\theta = \cos\theta \qquad \text{cofunction identity}$$

$$\frac{\sin\theta}{\cos\theta} = 1 \qquad \text{Divide by } \cos\theta.$$

$$\tan\theta = 1 \qquad \text{Tangent Identity}$$

$$\theta = \tan^{-1}1 \qquad \text{Solve for one value of } \theta.$$

$$\theta = \frac{\pi}{4}$$

Another solution is $\frac{\pi}{4} + \pi$, or $\frac{5\pi}{4}$.

✓ **CA Standards Check** **2** Solve $\sin\left(\frac{\pi}{2} - \theta\right) = \sec\theta$ for $0 \le \theta < 2\pi$.

3 EXAMPLE **Cofunction Identities in a Right Triangle**

The cofunction identities were derived using the unit circle. So they apply to an angle θ of any size. Use the definitions of the trigonometric ratios for a right triangle to derive a cofunction identity for $\sin(90° - A)$.

In a right triangle, the acute angles are complementary. So $A + B = 90°$ and $B = 90° - A$, where A and B are the measures of the acute angles.

$$\sin(90° - A) = \sin B \qquad \textbf{A and B are complementary angles.}$$

$$= \frac{b}{a} \qquad \textbf{definition of sine in a right triangle}$$

$$= \cos A \qquad \textbf{definition of cosine in a right triangle}$$

2 Sum and Difference Identities

In the cofunction identities, any angle θ is subtracted from $\frac{\pi}{2}$. There are also identities for subtracting any two angles.

It is convenient to start with an identity for finding the cosine of the difference of two angles.

In the figure below, angles A, B, and $A - B$ are shown. Use the distance formula to find the square of the distance between P and Q.

$$(PQ)^2 = (x_1 - x_2)^2 + (y_1 - y_2)^2$$
$$= (\cos A - \cos B)^2 + (\sin A - \sin B)^2$$
$$= \cos^2 A - 2 \cos A \cos B + \cos^2 B + \sin^2 A - 2 \sin A \sin B + \sin^2 B$$
$$= 2 - 2 \cos A \cos B - 2 \sin A \sin B \quad \textbf{Use the Pythagorean identity } \sin^2 \theta + \cos^2 \theta = 1.$$

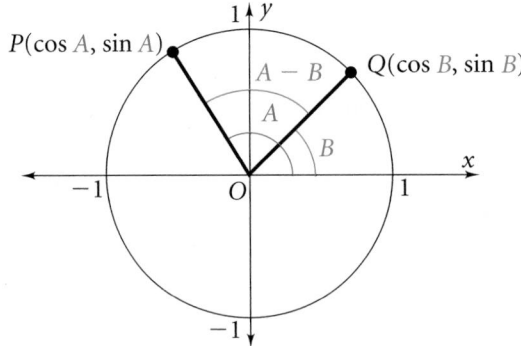

Now use the Law of Cosines to find $(PQ)^2$ in $\triangle POQ$.

$$(PQ)^2 = (PO)^2 + (QO)^2 - 2(PO)(QO) \cos (A - B)$$
$$= 1^2 + 1^2 - 2(1)(1) \cos (A - B)$$
$$= 2 - 2 \cos (A - B)$$

The Transitive Property for Equality tells you that the two expressions for $(PQ)^2$ are equal.

$$2 - 2 \cos (A - B) = 2 - 2 \cos A \cos B - 2 \sin A \sin B$$
$$-2 \cos (A - B) = -2 \cos A \cos B - 2 \sin A \sin B \quad \textbf{Subtract 2 from each side.}$$
$$\cos (A - B) = \cos A \cos B + \sin A \sin B \quad \textbf{Divide each side by } -2.$$

You can also derive an identity for $\sin (A - B)$. Then you can use the Tangent Identity to derive an identity for $\tan (A - B)$.

 Key Concepts

Properties	Angle Difference Identities
$\sin (A - B) = \sin A \cos B - \cos A \sin B$	
$\cos (A - B) = \cos A \cos B + \sin A \sin B$	
$\tan (A - B) = \frac{\tan A - \tan B}{1 + \tan A \tan B}$	

4 EXAMPLE Using Angle Difference Identities

Find the exact value of cos 15°.

You know exact values for 30°, 60°, and 45°. Use the fact that $15° = 60° - 45°$.

$$\cos(A - B) = \cos A \cos B + \sin A \sin B \quad \text{**Cosine Angle Difference Identity**}$$

$$\cos(60° - 45°) = \cos 60° \cos 45° + \sin 60° \sin 45° \quad \text{**Substitute 60° for A and 45° for B.**}$$

$$= \frac{1}{2}\left(\frac{\sqrt{2}}{2}\right) + \frac{\sqrt{3}}{2}\left(\frac{\sqrt{2}}{2}\right) \quad \text{**Replace with exact values.**}$$

$$= \frac{\sqrt{2}}{4} + \frac{\sqrt{6}}{4} \quad \text{**Simplify.**}$$

$$= \frac{\sqrt{2} + \sqrt{6}}{4}$$

● So $\cos 15° = \frac{\sqrt{2} + \sqrt{6}}{4}$.

✓ **CA Standards Check** ④ Find the exact value of sin 15°.

You can use the Negative Angle Identities and the Sine Angle Difference Identity to derive an identity for $\sin(A + B)$.

$$\sin(A + B) = \sin(A - (-B)) \quad \text{**Rewrite as subtraction.**}$$

$$= \sin A \cos(-B) - \cos A \sin(-B) \quad \text{**Sine Angle Difference Identity**}$$

$$= \sin A \cos B - \cos A (-\sin B) \quad \text{**negative angle identities**}$$

$$= \sin A \cos B + \cos A \sin B \quad \text{**Simplify.**}$$

You can similarly derive an identity for $\cos(A + B)$. You can use the Tangent Identity to derive $\tan(A + B)$.

Key Concepts

Properties	Angle Sum Identities
$\sin(A + B) = \sin A \cos B + \cos A \sin B$	
$\cos(A + B) = \cos A \cos B - \sin A \sin B$	
$\tan(A + B) = \frac{\tan A + \tan B}{1 - \tan A \tan B}$	

For: Identities Activity
Use: Interactive Textbook, 14-6

5 EXAMPLE Using Angle Sum Identities

Find the exact value of sin 105°.

Use the fact that $105° = 60° + 45°$.

$$\sin(A + B) = \sin A \cos B + \cos A \sin B \quad \text{**Sine Angle Sum Identity**}$$

$$\sin(60° + 45°) = \sin 60° \cos 45° + \cos 60° \sin 45° \quad \text{**Substitute 60° for A and 45° for B.**}$$

$$= \frac{\sqrt{3}}{2}\left(\frac{\sqrt{2}}{2}\right) + \frac{1}{2}\left(\frac{\sqrt{2}}{2}\right) \quad \text{**Replace with exact values.**}$$

$$= \frac{\sqrt{6}}{4} + \frac{\sqrt{2}}{4} \quad \text{**Simplify.**}$$

$$= \frac{\sqrt{6} + \sqrt{2}}{4}$$

So, $\sin 105° = \frac{\sqrt{6} + \sqrt{2}}{4}$.

✓ **CA Standards Check** ⑤ Find the exact value of tan 105°.

EXERCISES
Standards Practice

A Practice by Example

Example 1
(page 829)

GO for Help

Verify each identity.

1. $\csc\left(\theta - \frac{\pi}{2}\right) = -\sec\theta$

2. $\sec\left(\theta - \frac{\pi}{2}\right) = \csc\theta$

3. $\cot\left(\frac{\pi}{2} - \theta\right) = \tan\theta$

4. $\csc\left(\frac{\pi}{2} - \theta\right) = \sec\theta$

5. $\tan\left(\theta - \frac{\pi}{2}\right) = -\cot\theta$

6. $\sec\left(\frac{\pi}{2} - \theta\right) = \csc\theta$

Example 2
(page 829)

Solve each trigonometric equation for $0 \le \theta < 2\pi$.

7. $\cos\left(\frac{\pi}{2} - \theta\right) = \csc\theta$

8. $\sin\left(\frac{\pi}{2} - \theta\right) = -\cos(-\theta)$

9. $\tan\left(\frac{\pi}{2} - \theta\right) + \tan(-\theta) = 0$

10. $\sin^2\theta + \cos^2\theta = \sin\theta$

11. $\tan^2\theta - \sec^2\theta = \cos(-\theta)$

12. $2\sin\left(\frac{\pi}{2} - \theta\right) = \sin(-\theta)$

13. $\tan\left(\frac{\pi}{2} - \theta\right) = \cos(-\theta)$

14. $1 + \cot^2\theta = \csc\theta$

Example 3
(page 829)

Use the definitions of the trigonometric ratios for a right triangle to derive each cofunction identity.

15. a cofunction identity for $\csc(90° - A)$

16. a cofunction identity for $\cot(90° - A)$

Examples 4 and 5
(page 831)

Mental Math **Find the value of each trigonometric expression.**

17. $\cos 50° \cos 40° - \sin 50° \sin 40°$

18. $\sin 80° \cos 35° - \cos 80° \sin 35°$

19. $\sin 100° \cos 170° + \cos 100° \sin 170°$

20. $\cos 183° \cos 93° + \sin 183° \sin 93°$

Find each exact value. Use a sum or difference identity.

21. $\cos 105°$	**22.** $\tan 105°$	**23.** $\tan 15°$	**24.** $\sin 75°$
25. $\cos 75°$	**26.** $\tan 75°$	**27.** $\cos 135°$	**28.** $\tan 135°$
29. $\sin(-15°)$	**30.** $\cos(-15°)$	**31.** $\tan(-15°)$	**32.** $\sin 225°$
33. $\cos 240°$	**34.** $\sin 390°$	**35.** $\cos(-300°)$	**36.** $\tan 390°$

B Apply Your Skills

Verify each identity.

37. $\sin(A - B) = \sin A \cos B - \cos A \sin B$

38. $\tan(A - B) = \dfrac{\tan A - \tan B}{1 + \tan A \tan B}$

39. $\cos(A + B) = \cos A \cos B - \sin A \sin B$

40. $\tan(A + B) = \dfrac{\tan A + \tan B}{1 - \tan A \tan B}$

41. $\sin\left(x + \frac{\pi}{3}\right) + \sin\left(x - \frac{\pi}{3}\right) = \sin x$

42. $\sin\left(\frac{3\pi}{2} - x\right) = -\cos x$

Homework Video Tutor

Visit: PHSchool.com
Web Code: bbe-1406

43. Reasoning Show that the equation $\sin(A + B) = \sin A + \sin B$ is *not* an identity by finding a counterexample, values for A and B for which the equation is false.

Rewrite each expression as a trigonometric function of a single angle measure.

44. $\sin 2\theta \cos \theta + \cos 2\theta \sin \theta$

45. $\sin 3\theta \cos 2\theta + \cos 3\theta \sin 2\theta$

46. $\cos 3\theta \cos 4\theta - \sin 3\theta \sin 4\theta$

47. $\cos 2\theta \cos 3\theta - \sin 2\theta \sin 3\theta$

48. $\dfrac{\tan 5\theta + \tan 6\theta}{1 - \tan 5\theta \tan 6\theta}$

49. $\dfrac{\tan 3\theta - \tan \theta}{1 + \tan 3\theta \tan \theta}$

 50. a. Graph $y = \sin 2x$ and $y = 2 \sin x$ on the same axes.
   b. Does $\sin 2x = 2 \sin x$ for all values of x? Is $\sin 2x = 2 \sin x$ an identity? Explain.
   c. Does $\sin 2x = 2 \sin x$ for any values of x? If so, what are they?
   d. Open-Ended Find an equation of the form $a \sin b = c \sin d$ whose solutions are $2\pi n$.

51. Gears The diagram at the right shows a gear whose radius is 10 cm. Point A represents a $60°$ counterclockwise rotation of point $P(10, 0)$. Point B represents a θ-degree rotation of point A. The coordinates of B are $(10 \cos (\theta + 60°), 10 \sin (\theta + 60°))$. Write these coordinates in terms of $\cos \theta$ and $\sin \theta$.

52. a. Critical Thinking A function is even if $f(-x) = f(x)$. A function is odd if $f(-x) = -f(x)$. Which trigonometric functions are even? Which are odd?
   b. Writing Are all functions either even or odd? Explain your answer. Give a counterexample if possible.

C Challenge

Use the sum and difference formulas to verify each identity.

53. $\cos (\pi - \theta) = -\cos \theta$

54. $\sin (\pi - \theta) = \sin \theta$

55. $\sin (\pi + \theta) = -\sin \theta$

56. $\cos (\pi + \theta) = -\cos \theta$

57. Reasoning For any parallelogram, prove that the sum of the squares of the lengths of the diagonals equals twice the sum of the squares of the lengths of two adjacent sides.

Multiple Choice Practice

For California Standards and CAHSEE Tutorials, visit PHSchool.com. Web Code: bbq-9045

TRIG 10.0

58. Which expression is equal to $\cos 50°$?
   A $\sin 20° \cos 30° + \cos 20° \sin 30°$
   B $\sin 20° \cos 30° - \cos 20° \sin 30°$
   C $\cos 20° \cos 30° + \sin 20° \sin 30°$
   D $\cos 20° \cos 30° - \sin 20° \cos 30°$

ALG2 13.0

59. Which expression is equivalent to $\log_3 18$?
   A $\log_{10} 3 + \log_{10} 18$
   B $\log_{10} 3 - \log_{10} 18$
   C $(\log_{10} 3)(\log_{10} 18)$
   D $\dfrac{\log_{10} 18}{\log_{10} 3}$

ALG2 17.0   **60.** The equation $y = (x - 4)^2$ represents which conic section?

A circle

B parabola

C ellipse

D hyperbola

Mixed Review

Lesson 14-5

61. In $\triangle RST$, $m\angle S = 24°$, $r = 10$ ft, and $t = 18$ ft. Find s.

62. In $\triangle XYZ$, $m\angle Z = 51°$, $x = 13$ cm, and $y = 17$ cm. Find z.

63. In $\triangle DEF$, $m\angle F = 68°$, $d = 16$ mm, and $e = 21$ mm. Find f.

64. In $\triangle ABC$, $m\angle A = 87°$, $b = 22$ m, and $c = 19$ m. Find a.

Lesson 13-3

Write each measure in radians. Express the answer in terms of π and as a decimal rounded to the nearest hundredth.

65. $80°$ **66.** $-50°$ **67.** $-15°$

68. $70°$ **69.** $190°$ **70.** $200°$

Lesson 12-7

A set of data with a mean of 39 and a standard deviation of 6.2 is normally distributed. Find each value, given its distance from the mean.

71. $+1$ standard deviation   **72.** -2 standard deviations

73. $+3$ standard deviations   **74.** -1 standard deviation

Checkpoint Quiz 2   Lessons 14-4 through 14-6

Find the area of $\triangle ABC$.

1. $m\angle A = 37°$, $b = 10$ cm, and $c = 12$ cm.

2. $m\angle B = 18°$, $a = 20$ ft, and $c = 25$ ft.

3. $m\angle B = 104°$, $a = 8$ m, and $c = 9$ m.

4. $m\angle C = 96°$, $a = 26$ in., and $b = 31$ in.

Find the remaining sides and angles in each triangle. Round your answers to the nearest tenth.

5. In $\triangle ABC$, $m\angle A = 27°$, $b = 17$ ft, and $c = 18$ ft.

6. In $\triangle DEF$, $d = 32$ mm, $e = 30$ mm, and $f = 35$ mm.

Simplify each trigonometric expression.

7. $\cos 60° \cos 20° - \sin 60° \sin 20°$

8. $\sin 90° \cos 27° - \cos 90° \sin 27°$

9. $\sin 150° \cos 290° + \cos 150° \sin 290°$

10. $\cos 233° \cos 154° + \sin 233° \sin 154°$

Double-Angle and Half-Angle Identities

 California Content Standards

TRIG 11.0 Students demonstrate an understanding of the half-angle and double-angle formulas for sines and cosines and can use those formulas to prove and/or simplify other trigonometric formulas.

What You'll Learn

- To verify and use double-angle identities
- To verify and use half-angle identities

...And Why

To find exact values of trigonometric functions

 Check Skills You'll Need

Complete the following angle identities.

1. $\cos(A - B) = $ ■
2. $\cos(A + B) = $ ■
3. $\tan(A - B) = $ ■
4. $\sin(A - B) = $ ■
5. $\sin(A + B) = $ ■
6. $\tan(A + B) = $ ■

 for Help Lesson 14-6

---

1 Double-Angle Identities

You can use the angle sum identities to derive the double-angle identities.

Let $\theta = A = B$.

$$\cos(A + B) = \cos A \cos B - \sin A \sin B \qquad \textbf{Cosine Angle Sum Identity}$$
$$\cos(\theta + \theta) = \cos\theta \cos\theta - \sin\theta \sin\theta \qquad \textbf{Substitute } \theta \textbf{ for } A \textbf{ and } B.$$
$$\cos 2\theta = \cos^2\theta - \sin^2\theta \qquad \textbf{Simplify.}$$

You can use the Pythagorean identity $\sin^2\theta + \cos^2\theta = 1$ in the form $\sin^2\theta = 1 - \cos^2\theta$ to derive another identity for $\cos 2\theta$.

$$\cos 2\theta = \cos^2\theta - \sin^2\theta$$
$$= \cos^2\theta - (1 - \cos^2\theta) \qquad \textbf{Substitute } 1 - \cos^2\theta \textbf{ for } \sin^2\theta.$$
$$= \cos^2\theta - 1 + \cos^2\theta \qquad \textbf{Remove parentheses.}$$
$$= 2\cos^2\theta - 1 \qquad \textbf{Simplify.}$$

You can use the Pythagorean theorem in the form $\cos^2\theta = 1 - \sin^2\theta$ to derive a third identity for $\cos 2\theta$.

$$\cos 2\theta = \cos^2\theta - \sin^2\theta$$
$$= (1 - \sin^2\theta) - \sin^2\theta \qquad \textbf{Substitute } 1 - \sin^2\theta \textbf{ for } \cos^2\theta.$$
$$= 1 - 2\sin^2\theta \qquad \textbf{Simplify.}$$

You can use the other angle sum identities to derive double-angle identities for the sine and tangent.

 Key Concepts

Properties	**Double-Angle Identities**
$\cos 2\theta = \cos^2\theta - \sin^2\theta$	$\sin 2\theta = 2\sin\theta \cos\theta$
$\cos 2\theta = 2\cos^2\theta - 1$	$\tan 2\theta = \dfrac{2\tan\theta}{1 - \tan^2\theta}$
$\cos 2\theta = 1 - 2\sin^2\theta$	

1 EXAMPLE Using a Double-Angle Identity

Use a double-angle identity to find the exact value of cos 120°.

$$\cos 120° = \cos(2 \cdot 60°) \qquad \text{Rewrite 120 as } (2 \cdot 60).$$
$$= \cos^2 60° - \sin^2 60° \qquad \text{Use a cosine double-angle identity.}$$
$$= \left(\tfrac{1}{2}\right)^2 - \left(\tfrac{\sqrt{3}}{2}\right)^2 \qquad \text{Replace with exact values.}$$
$$= -\tfrac{1}{2} \qquad \text{Simplify.}$$

☑ **CA Standards Check** ❶ Use a double-angle identity to find the exact value of sin 120°.

You can use the double-angle identities to verify other identities.

2 EXAMPLE Verifying an Identity

Verify the identity $\cos 2\theta = \dfrac{1 - \tan^2 \theta}{1 + \tan^2 \theta}$.

$$\dfrac{1 - \tan^2 \theta}{1 + \tan^2 \theta} = \dfrac{1 - \tan^2 \theta}{\sec^2 \theta} \qquad \textbf{Pythagorean identity}$$

$$= \dfrac{1}{\sec^2 \theta} - \dfrac{\tan^2 \theta}{\sec^2 \theta} \qquad \textbf{Write as two fractions.}$$

$$= \dfrac{1}{\frac{1}{\cos^2 \theta}} - \dfrac{\frac{\sin^2 \theta}{\cos^2 \theta}}{\frac{1}{\cos^2 \theta}} \qquad \textbf{Express in terms of sin } \theta \textbf{ and cos } \theta.$$

$$= \cos^2 \theta - \sin^2 \theta \qquad \textbf{Simplify.}$$

$$= \cos 2\theta \qquad \textbf{double-angle identity}$$

☑ **CA Standards Check** ❷ Verify the identity $2 \cos 2\theta = 4 \cos^2 \theta - 2$.

2 Half-Angle Identities

You can use double-angle identities to derive half-angle identities.
Let $\theta = \frac{A}{2}$.

$$\cos 2\theta = 2 \cos^2 \theta - 1 \qquad \textbf{cosine double-angle identity}$$

$$\cos 2\left(\tfrac{A}{2}\right) = 2 \cos^2 \tfrac{A}{2} - 1 \qquad \textbf{Substitute } \tfrac{A}{2} \textbf{ for } \theta.$$

$$\dfrac{\cos A + 1}{2} = \cos^2 \tfrac{A}{2} \qquad \textbf{Solve for } \cos^2 \tfrac{A}{2}.$$

$$\pm\sqrt{\dfrac{\cos A + 1}{2}} = \cos \tfrac{A}{2} \qquad \textbf{Take the square root of each side.}$$

Similarly, $\sin \frac{A}{2} = \pm\sqrt{\dfrac{1 - \cos A}{2}}$ and $\tan \frac{A}{2} = \pm\sqrt{\dfrac{1 - \cos A}{1 + \cos A}}$.

🔑 **Key Concepts**

Properties	Half-Angle Identities

$$\sin \tfrac{A}{2} = \pm\sqrt{\dfrac{1 - \cos A}{2}} \qquad \cos \tfrac{A}{2} = \pm\sqrt{\dfrac{1 + \cos A}{2}} \qquad \tan \tfrac{A}{2} = \pm\sqrt{\dfrac{1 - \cos A}{1 + \cos A}}$$

Choose the positive or negative sign for each function depending on the quadrant in which $\frac{A}{2}$ lies.

3 EXAMPLE Using Half-Angle Identities

Use the half-angle identities to find each exact value.

a. sin 15°

$$\sin 15° = \sin\left(\frac{30}{2}\right)° \qquad \text{Rewrite } 15° \text{ as } \frac{30°}{2}.$$

$$= \sqrt{\frac{1 - \cos 30°}{2}} \qquad \text{Use the principal square root, since sin } 15° \text{ is positive.}$$

$$= \sqrt{\frac{1 - \frac{\sqrt{3}}{2}}{2}} \qquad \text{Substitute the exact value for cos } 30°.$$

$$= \sqrt{\frac{2 - \sqrt{3}}{4}} \qquad \text{Simplify.}$$

$$= \frac{\sqrt{2 - \sqrt{3}}}{2} \qquad \text{Simplify.}$$

b. cos 150°

$$\cos 150° = \cos\left(\frac{300}{2}\right)° \qquad \text{Rewrite 150 as } \frac{300}{2}.$$

$$= -\sqrt{\frac{1 + \cos 300°}{2}} \qquad \text{Use the negative square root, since cos } 150° \text{ is negative.}$$

$$= -\sqrt{\frac{1 + \left(\frac{1}{2}\right)}{2}} \qquad \text{Replace with an exact value.}$$

$$= -\sqrt{\frac{3}{4}} \qquad \text{Simplify.}$$

$$= -\frac{\sqrt{3}}{2} \qquad \text{Simplify.}$$

✓ **CA Standards Check** **3** Use the half-angle identities to find the exact value of each expression.
   a. sin 150°   **b.** tan 150°

4 EXAMPLE Using Half-Angle Identities

Given $\sin \theta = -\frac{24}{25}$ and $180° < \theta < 270°$, find $\sin \frac{\theta}{2}$.

First find cos θ.

$$\cos^2 \theta + \sin^2 \theta = 1 \qquad \text{Pythagorean identity}$$

$$\cos^2 \theta + \left(-\frac{24}{25}\right)^2 = 1 \qquad \text{Substitute.}$$

$$\cos^2 \theta = \frac{49}{25^2} \qquad \text{Solve for } \cos^2 \theta.$$

$$\cos \theta = -\frac{7}{25} \qquad \text{Choose the negative square root since } \theta \text{ is in Quadrant III.}$$

Now find $\sin \frac{\theta}{2}$.

Since $180° < \theta < 270°$, $90° < \frac{\theta}{2} < 135°$ and $\frac{\theta}{2}$ is in Quadrant II.

$$\sin \frac{\theta}{2} = \pm\sqrt{\frac{1 - \cos \theta}{2}} \qquad \text{half-angle identity}$$

$$= \sqrt{\frac{1 - \left(-\frac{7}{25}\right)}{2}} \qquad \text{Substitute. Choose the positive square root since } \frac{\theta}{2} \text{ is in Quadrant II.}$$

$$= \frac{4}{5} \qquad \text{Simplify.}$$

✓ **CA Standards Check** **4** Use the information in Example 4 to find the exact values of $\cos \frac{\theta}{2}$ and $\tan \frac{\theta}{2}$.

EXERCISES

Standards Practice

For more exercises, see *Extra Skill and Word Problem Practice*.

TRIG 11.0

A **Practice by Example**

Example 1
(page 836)

GO for Help

Use a double-angle identity to find the exact value of each expression.

1. $\sin 240°$ **2.** $\cos 120°$ **3.** $\tan 120°$ **4.** $\sin 90°$

5. $\cos 240°$ **6.** $\tan 240°$ **7.** $\cos 600°$ **8.** $\sin 600°$

Example 2
(page 836)

Use an angle sum identity to verify each identity.

9. $\sin 2\theta = 2 \sin \theta \cos \theta$ **10.** $\tan 2\theta = \dfrac{2 \tan \theta}{1 - \tan^2 \theta}$

Example 3
(page 837)

Use a half-angle identity to find the exact value of each expression.

11. $\cos 15°$ **12.** $\tan 15°$ **13.** $\sin 15°$ **14.** $\sin 22.5°$

15. $\cos 22.5°$ **16.** $\tan 22.5°$ **17.** $\cos 90°$ **18.** $\sin 7.5°$

Example 4
(page 837)

Given $\cos \theta = -\frac{4}{5}$ and $90° < \theta < 180°$, find the exact value of each expression.

19. $\sin \frac{\theta}{2}$ **20.** $\cos \frac{\theta}{2}$ **21.** $\tan \frac{\theta}{2}$ **22.** $\cot \frac{\theta}{2}$

Given $\cos \theta = -\frac{15}{17}$ and $180° < \theta < 270°$, find the exact value of each expression.

23. $\sin \frac{\theta}{2}$ **24.** $\cos \frac{\theta}{2}$ **25.** $\tan \frac{\theta}{2}$ **26.** $\sec \frac{\theta}{2}$

B **Apply Your Skills**

$\triangle RST$ has a right angle at $\angle T$. Use identities to show that each equation is true.

27. $\sin 2R = \dfrac{2rs}{t^2}$ **28.** $\cos 2R = \dfrac{s^2 - r^2}{t^2}$

29. $\sin 2S = \sin 2R$ **30.** $\sin^2 \frac{S}{2} = \dfrac{t - r}{2t}$

31. $\tan \frac{R}{2} = \dfrac{r}{t + s}$ **32.** $\tan^2 \frac{S}{2} = \dfrac{t - r}{t + r}$

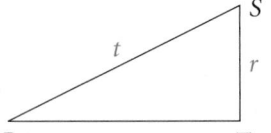

33. Critical Thinking If $\sin 2A = \sin 2B$, must $A = B$? Explain.

Given $\cos \theta = \frac{3}{5}$ and $270° < \theta < 360°$, find the exact value of each expression.

34. $\sin 2\theta$ **35.** $\cos 2\theta$ **36.** $\tan 2\theta$ **37.** $\csc 2\theta$

38. $\sin \frac{\theta}{2}$ **39.** $\cos \frac{\theta}{2}$ **40.** $\tan \frac{\theta}{2}$ **41.** $\cot \frac{\theta}{2}$

Use identities to write each equation in terms of the single angle θ. Then solve the equation for $0 \le \theta < 2\pi$.

42. $4 \sin 2\theta - 3 \cos \theta = 0$ **43.** $2 \sin 2\theta - 3 \sin \theta = 0$

44. $\sin 2\theta \sin \theta = \cos \theta$ **45.** $\cos 2\theta = -2 \cos^2 \theta$

Simplify each expression.

46. $2 \cos^2 \theta - \cos 2\theta$ **47.** $\sin^2 \frac{\theta}{2} - \cos^2 \frac{\theta}{2}$ **48.** $\dfrac{\cos 2\theta}{\sin \theta + \cos \theta}$

49. Open-Ended Choose an angle measure A.
 a. Find $\sin A$ and $\cos A$.
 b. Use an identity to find $\sin 2A$.
 c. Use an identity to find $\cos \frac{A}{2}$.

Homework Video Tutor

Visit: PHSchool.com
Web Code: bbe-1407

50. Writing Is $\frac{\tan \theta}{4} = \tan \frac{\theta}{4}$ an identity? Explain.

Challenge Use double-angle identities to write each expression, using trigonometric functions of θ instead of 4θ.

51. $\sin 4\theta$ **52.** $\cos 4\theta$ **53.** $\tan 4\theta$

Use half-angle identities to write each expression, using trigonometric functions of θ instead of $\frac{\theta}{4}$.

54. $\sin \frac{\theta}{4}$ **55.** $\cos \frac{\theta}{4}$ **56.** $\tan \frac{\theta}{4}$

57. Use the Tangent Half-Angle Identity and a Pythagorean identity to prove each identity.

     a. $\tan \frac{A}{2} = \frac{\sin A}{1 + \cos A}$ **b.** $\tan \frac{A}{2} = \frac{1 - \cos A}{\sin A}$

Multiple Choice Practice

For California Standards and CAHSEE Tutorials, visit PHSchool.com. Web Code: bbq-9045

TRIG 11.0

58. If θ is in Quadrant I and $\tan \theta = \frac{5}{12}$, what is the value of $\frac{\tan 4\theta}{5}$ to the nearest hundredth?

     Ⓐ 18.10   Ⓒ 0.32

     Ⓑ 0.33   Ⓓ −23.90

ALG2 5.0

59. A pattern exists as a result of raising i, an imaginary number, to consecutive integer powers, i^n, beginning with $n = 1$. Based on the table, what is i^n when $n = 32$?

     Ⓐ $\sqrt{-1}$ Ⓒ $-i$

     Ⓑ -1 Ⓓ 1

Powers of i

$i^n (n \geq 1)$	Solution
i^1	$\sqrt{-1}$
i^2	-1
i^3	$-i$
i^4	1
i^5	$\sqrt{-1}$
i^6	-1

ALG2 3.0

60. Which expression is equivalent to $\left(3\sqrt{6} - 3\sqrt{2}\right)\left(\sqrt{6} - 3\sqrt{2}\right)$?

     Ⓐ $36 - 24\sqrt{3}$ Ⓒ 6

     Ⓑ $6 - 12\sqrt{3}$ Ⓓ 9

Mixed Review

 for Help

Lesson 14-6   **Find each exact value. Use a sum or difference identity.**

61. $\cos 405°$ **62.** $\sin (-300°)$ **63.** $\tan (-300°)$

Lesson 13-1   **Find the period and amplitude of each periodic function.**

64.   **65.**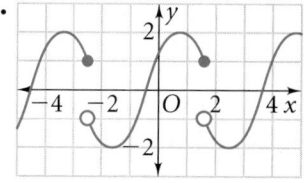

Open-ended questions ask you to create an example that satisfies certain given conditions. You may need to use your example to answer follow-up questions. As with extended-response questions, you should show all your work since you can receive partial credit.

EXAMPLE

For angles A and B, $A \neq B$ and $\sin A = \sin B$.

a. Find three pairs of values for A and B.

b. Write and prove a relation for A and B.

Here is a scoring rubric for a 4-point response.

[4] **a.** three pairs that satisfy the conditions

    b. $A + B = n\pi$, where n is an odd integer, or $A - B = 2n\pi$, or any other correct relation with a specific value of n; proves the relation.

[3] **a.** three pairs that satisfy the conditions

    b. $A + B = n\pi$, where n is an odd integer, or $A - B = 2n\pi$, or any other correct relation with a specific value of n; does not prove the relation.

[2] **a.** three pairs that satisfy the conditions

    b. no answer or incorrect answer

[1] **a.** one or two pairs that satisfy the conditions

    b. no answer or incorrect answer

The following response is worth 2 points.

a. $A = 0, B = \pi$

    $A = 0, B = 2\pi$

    $A = \frac{\pi}{6}, B = \frac{5\pi}{6}$

b. Let $A + B = 2\pi$. Then $A = 2\pi - B$.

$$\sin(2\pi - B) = \sin(2\pi)\cos(B) - \cos(2\pi)\sin(B)$$
$$= 0 - (-1)\sin(B)$$
$$= \sin(B)$$

EXERCISES

1. Explain why the response above received only 2 points.

2. Write a 4-point response for the Example.

Find three sets of values for A and B, where $A \neq B$, that make each equation true. Write and prove a relation for A and B.

3. $\cos A = \cos B$

4. $\tan A = \tan B$

5. Find three sets of values for A and B such that $\sin(A + B) = \sin A + \sin B$. Write and prove a relation for A and B.

6. Find three pairs of values for A and B such that $\cos^2 A - \sin^2 A = \sin B$. Write and prove the relation for A and B.

Chapter 14 Review

Vocabulary Review

🔊 **English and Spanish Audio Online**

Law of Cosines (p. 822)
Law of Sines (p. 815)

trigonometric identity (p. 792)

trigonometric ratios for a right
triangle (p. 806)

Choose the correct vocabulary term to complete each sentence.

1. You can find missing measures of any triangle by using the _?_ if you know the measures of two angles and a side.

2. The six ratios of the lengths of the sides of a right triangle are known as the _?_ .

3. If you know the measures of two sides and the angle between them, you can use the _?_ to find missing parts of any triangle.

4. A trigonometric equation that is true for all values except those for which the expressions on either side of the equal sign are undefined is a _?_ .

5. The _?_ can be used to find missing measures of any triangle when you know two sides and the angle opposite one of them.

Go Online
PHSchool.com

For: Vocabulary quiz
Web Code: bbj-1451

Skills and Concepts

Lesson 14-1

• To verify trigonometric identities (p. 792)

 TRIG 3.0, 3.2, 7.0

A **trigonometric identity** is a trigonometric equation that is true for all values except those for which the expressions on either side of the equal sign are undefined.

Reciprocal Identities	**Tangent and Cotangent Identities**	**Pythagorean Identities**
$\csc \theta = \frac{1}{\sin \theta}$	$\tan \theta = \frac{\sin \theta}{\cos \theta}$	$\cos^2 \theta + \sin^2 \theta = 1$
$\sec \theta = \frac{1}{\cos \theta}$	$\cot \theta = \frac{\cos \theta}{\sin \theta}$	$1 + \tan^2 \theta = \sec^2 \theta$
$\cot \theta = \frac{1}{\tan \theta}$		$1 + \cot^2 \theta = \csc^2 \theta$

Verify each identity.

6. $\sin \theta \tan \theta = \frac{1}{\cos \theta} - \cos \theta$

7. $\cos^2 \theta \cot^2 \theta = \cot^2 \theta - \cos^2 \theta$

Simplify each trigonometric expression.

8. $1 - \sin^2 \theta$

9. $\frac{\cos \theta}{\sin \theta \cot \theta}$

10. $\csc^2 \theta - \cot^2 \theta$

Lesson 14-2

• To evaluate inverses of trigonometric functions (p. 797)
• To solve trigonometric equations (p. 799)

 TRIG 8.0, 9.0

The function $\cos^{-1} x$ is the inverse of $\cos \theta$ with the restricted domain $0 \le \theta \le \pi$. The function $\sin^{-1} x$ has domain $-\frac{\pi}{2} \le \theta \le \frac{\pi}{2}$, and $\tan^{-1} x$ has domain $-\frac{\pi}{2} < \theta < \frac{\pi}{2}$.

Use a unit circle and 30°-60°-90° triangles to find the value in degrees of each expression.

11. $\sin^{-1}\left(-\frac{\sqrt{3}}{2}\right)$

12. $\tan^{-1} \sqrt{3}$

13. $\tan^{-1}\left(-\frac{\sqrt{3}}{3}\right)$

14. $\cos^{-1} \frac{\sqrt{3}}{2}$

Use a calculator to find the value in radians of each expression.

15. $\sin^{-1} 0.33$ **16.** $\tan^{-1}(-2)$ **17.** $\cos^{-1}(-0.64)$ **18.** $\cos^{-1} 0.98$

Solve each equation for $0 \le \theta < 2\pi$.

19. $2\cos\theta = 1$ **20.** $\sqrt{3}\tan\theta = 1$ **21.** $\sin\theta = \sin^2\theta$

Lesson 14-3

- To find lengths of sides in a right triangle (p. 806)
- To find measures of angles in a right triangle (p. 809)

 TRIG 12.0, 19.0

The six different ratios of the sides of a right triangle are known as the **trigonometric ratios for a right triangle**. These ratios depend on the size of the acute angles in the right triangle.

In a right triangle ABC that has an acute $\angle A$ and right $\angle C$, the ratios are defined as follows.

$$\sin A = \frac{\text{length of leg opposite } \angle A}{\text{length of hypotenuse}} = \frac{a}{c} \qquad \csc A = \frac{\text{length of hypotenuse}}{\text{length of leg opposite } \angle A} = \frac{c}{a}$$

$$\cos A = \frac{\text{length of leg adjacent to } \angle A}{\text{length of hypotenuse}} = \frac{b}{c} \qquad \sec A = \frac{\text{length of hypotenuse}}{\text{length of leg adjacent to } \angle A} = \frac{c}{b}$$

$$\tan A = \frac{\text{length of leg opposite } \angle A}{\text{length of leg adjacent to } \angle A} = \frac{a}{b} \qquad \cot A = \frac{\text{length of leg adjacent to } \angle A}{\text{length of leg opposite } \angle A} = \frac{b}{a}$$

In $\triangle ABC$, $\angle B$ is a right angle, $AB = 30$, and $\sec A = \frac{5}{3}$. Find each value in fraction and in decimal form.

22. $\cos A$ **23.** $\sin A$ **24.** $\tan C$

In $\triangle GHI$, $\angle H$ is a right angle. Find the remaining sides and angles. Round your answers to the nearest tenth.

25. $g = 3, i = 9$ **26.** $g = 12, h = 20$ **27.** $h = 55, i = 40$

Lesson 14-4

- To find the area of any triangle and to use the Law of Sines (p. 815)

 TRIG 13.0, 14.0

You can find missing measures of any triangle if you know the measures of two angles and any side or if you know the measures of two sides and the angle opposite one of them by using the **Law of Sines.**

The Law of Sines states that for $\triangle ABC$, if a, b, and c represent the lengths of the sides opposite $\angle A$, $\angle B$, and $\angle C$, respectively, then $\frac{\sin A}{a} = \frac{\sin B}{b} = \frac{\sin C}{c}$.

Find the area of each triangle. Round your answers to the nearest hundredth.

28.
$40°$ 7.3 m
5.6 m

29.
21.1 ft
18.6 ft $28°$

30.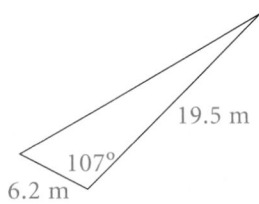
19.5 m
$107°$
6.2 m

31. In $\triangle LMN$, $m\angle L = 67°$, $m\angle N = 24°$, and $MN = 16$ in. Find LM to the nearest tenth.

32. In $\triangle XYZ$, $m\angle Z = 34°$, $x = 61$ cm, and $z = 42$ cm. Find $m\angle X$ to the nearest tenth.

Lesson 14-5

- To use the Law of Cosines to find the measures of sides and angles of a triangle (p. 822)

 TRIG 13.0

You can find missing parts of any triangle when you know the measures of two sides and the angle between them, or all three sides, by using the **Law of Cosines.** For $\triangle ABC$, the following are true.

$$a^2 = b^2 + c^2 - 2bc \cos A \quad b^2 = a^2 + c^2 - 2ac \cos B \quad c^2 = a^2 + b^2 - 2ab \cos C$$

33. In $\triangle ABC$, $m\angle B = 45°$, $a = 24$ ft, and $c = 30$ ft. Find b to the nearest tenth.

34. In $\triangle DEF$, $d = 25$ in., $e = 28$ in., and $f = 20$ in. Find $m\angle F$ to the nearest tenth.

35. In $\triangle GHI$, $h = 8$, $i = 12$, and $m\angle G = 96°$. Find $m\angle I$ to the nearest tenth.

Lesson 14-6

- To verify and use angle identities (p. 828)
- To verify and use sum and difference identities (p. 830)

 TRIG 10.0

Angle identities are used to solve trigonometric equations.

Negative angle identities
$$\sin(-\theta) = -\sin\theta \qquad \cos(-\theta) = \cos\theta \qquad \tan(-\theta) = -\tan\theta$$

Cofunction identities
$$\sin\left(\frac{\pi}{2} - \theta\right) = \cos\theta \qquad \cos\left(\frac{\pi}{2} - \theta\right) = \sin\theta \qquad \tan\left(\frac{\pi}{2} - \theta\right) = \cot\theta$$

Angle difference identities
$$\sin(A - B) = \sin A \cos B - \cos A \sin B \qquad \tan(A - B) = \frac{\tan A - \tan B}{1 + \tan A \tan B}$$
$$\cos(A - B) = \cos A \cos B + \sin A \sin B$$

Angle sum identities
$$\sin(A + B) = \sin A \cos B + \cos A \sin B \qquad \tan(A + B) = \frac{\tan A + \tan B}{1 - \tan A \tan B}$$
$$\cos(A + B) = \cos A \cos B - \sin A \sin B$$

Verify each identity.

36. $\cos\left(\theta + \frac{\pi}{2}\right) = -\sin\theta$

37. $\sin^2\left(\theta - \frac{\pi}{2}\right) = \cos^2\theta$

Solve each trigonometric equation for $0 \le \theta < 2\pi$.

38. $\tan\left(\frac{\pi}{2} - \theta\right) = \cos\theta$

39. $1 + \tan^2\theta = \cos\theta$

Lesson 14-7

- To verify and use double-angle identities (p. 835)
- To verify and use half-angle identities (p. 836)

 TRIG 11.0

You can use double-angle and half-angle identities to find exact values of trigonometric expressions. In the half-angle identities, choose the positive or negative sign for each function depending on the quadrant in which $\frac{A}{2}$ lies.

Double-angle identities
$$\cos 2\theta = \cos^2\theta - \sin^2\theta \qquad \sin 2\theta = 2\sin\theta\cos\theta \qquad \tan 2\theta = \frac{2\tan\theta}{1 - \tan^2\theta}$$
$$\cos 2\theta = 2\cos^2\theta - 1 \qquad \cos 2\theta = 1 - 2\sin^2\theta$$

Half-angle identities
$$\sin\frac{A}{2} = \pm\sqrt{\frac{1 - \cos A}{2}} \qquad \cos\frac{A}{2} = \pm\sqrt{\frac{1 + \cos A}{2}} \qquad \tan\frac{A}{2} = \pm\sqrt{\frac{1 - \cos A}{1 + \cos A}}$$

Use a double-angle identity to find the exact value of each expression.

40. $\sin 120°$ **41.** $\cos 90°$ **42.** $\tan 300°$

Use a half-angle identity to find the exact value of each expression.

43. $\cos 180°$ **44.** $\tan 60°$ **45.** $\sin 120°$

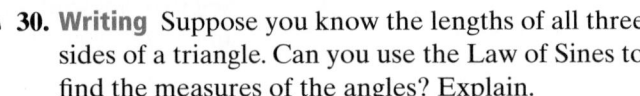
Simplify each trigonometric expression.

1. $\sin \theta + \cos \theta \cot \theta$

2. $\sec \theta \sin \theta \cot \theta$

3. $\cot \theta (\tan \theta + \cot \theta)$

Verify each identity.

4. $\csc \theta \cos \theta \tan \theta = 1$ **5.** $\csc^2 \theta - \cot^2 \theta = 1$

6. $\sec \theta \cot \theta = \csc \theta$ **7.** $\sec^2 \theta - 1 = \tan^2 \theta$

Use a unit circle and 30°-60°-90° triangles to find the values of θ in degrees for each expression.

8. $\sin \theta = \frac{\sqrt{3}}{2}$ **9.** $\cos \theta = \frac{\sqrt{3}}{2}$

10. $\cos \theta = -1$ **11.** $\tan \theta = \sqrt{3}$

Solve each equation for $0 \le \theta < 2\pi$.

12. $4 \sin \theta + 2\sqrt{3} = 0$ **13.** $2 \cos \theta = 1$

14. $\sqrt{2} \sin \theta - 1 = 0$

In $\triangle ABC$, find each value as a fraction and as a decimal. Round to the nearest hundredth.

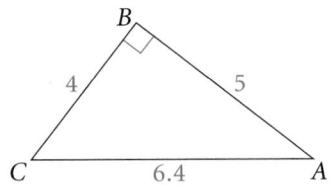

15. $\sin A$ **16.** $\sec A$ **17.** $\cot A$

18. $\csc C$ **19.** $\sec C$ **20.** $\tan C$

In $\triangle DEF$, $\angle F$ is a right angle. Find the remaining sides and angles. Round your answers to the nearest tenth.

21. $e = 6, f = 10$ **22.** $d = 10, e = 12$

23. $e = 21, f = 51$ **24.** $d = 5.5, e = 2.6$

25. Find the area of the triangle.

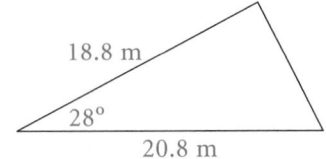

26. In $\triangle ABC$, $m\angle A = 45°$, $m\angle C = 23°$, and $BC = 25$ in. Find AB to the nearest tenth.

27. In $\triangle DEF$, $m\angle F = 56°$, $m\angle E = 34°$, and $DF = 10$ ft. Find EF to the nearest tenth.

28. In $\triangle GHI$, $m\angle I = 45°$, $g = 32$ cm, and $i = 52$ cm. Find $m\angle G$ to the nearest tenth.

29. In $\triangle JKL$, $m\angle J = 29°$, $l = 35$ m, and $j = 56$ m. Find $m\angle L$ to the nearest tenth.

30. Writing Suppose you know the lengths of all three sides of a triangle. Can you use the Law of Sines to find the measures of the angles? Explain.

31. In $\triangle MNO$, $m\angle N = 45°$, $m = 20$ cm, and $o = 41$ cm. Find n to the nearest tenth.

32. In $\triangle PQR$, $p = 51$ ft, $q = 81$ ft, and $r = 61$ ft. Find $m\angle R$ to the nearest tenth.

33. In $\triangle STU$, $m\angle S = 96°$, $t = 8$ in., and $u = 10$ in. Find $m\angle U$ to the nearest tenth.

Verify each identity.

34. $-\sin \left(\theta - \frac{\pi}{2} \right) = \cos \theta$

35. $\csc \left(\theta + \frac{\pi}{2} \right) = \sec \theta$

36. $\csc \left(\theta - \frac{\pi}{2} \right) = -\sec \theta$

37. $\cos \left(-\theta - \frac{\pi}{2} \right) = \sin (-\theta)$

Solve each trigonometric equation for $0 \le \theta < 2\pi$.

38. $\sin \left(\frac{\pi}{2} - \theta \right) = \sec \theta$ **39.** $\cos \left(\frac{\pi}{2} - \theta \right) = \csc \theta$

40. $\cot \left(\frac{\pi}{2} - \theta \right) = \sin \theta$

Use a double-angle identity to find the exact value of each expression.

41. $\sin 60°$ **42.** $\cos 60°$ **43.** $\tan 60°$

Use a half-angle identity to find the exact value of each expression.

44. $\tan 30°$ **45.** $\sin 90°$ **46.** $\cos 180°$

47. Open-Ended Choose an angle measure A. Find $\sin A$ and $\cos A$. Then use the identities to find $\cos 2A$ and $\sin \frac{A}{2}$.

Multiple Choice

Read each question. Then write the letter of the correct answer on your paper.

1. Four students—2 juniors and 2 sophomores—are seated randomly together in a row. What is the probability that the 2 sophomores are seated next to each other? **(Lesson 6-7)**

- Ⓐ $\frac{1}{6}$
- Ⓑ $\frac{1}{4}$
- Ⓒ $\frac{1}{2}$
- Ⓓ $\frac{3}{4}$

2. The graph at the right shows the height of a tennis ball from the time it is hit from the top of a building to the time it strikes the ground. How much time elapses while the tennis ball is 60 meters or more above the ground? **(Lesson 5-1)**

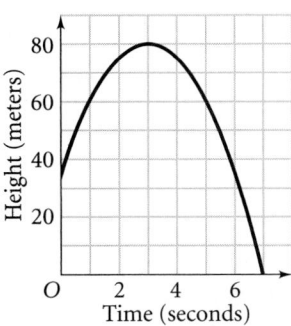

- Ⓐ 1 s
- Ⓒ 5 s
- Ⓑ 4 s
- Ⓓ 7 s

3. Steve has a game with 2 groups of cards. The first group of 26 cards is labeled with all the letters of the alphabet. The second group of 10 cards is numbered 0 through 9. If Steve draws 1 letter card and 1 number card at random, what is the probability that he will draw a letter in his name and an even number? **(Lesson 9-7)**

- Ⓐ $\frac{1}{13}$
- Ⓑ $\frac{5}{52}$
- Ⓒ $\frac{1}{4}$
- Ⓓ $\frac{7}{26}$

4. Which expression is equivalent to $\frac{3}{5}(5x - 15y) + (8y - 6x)$? **(Lesson 6-1)**

- Ⓐ $11x - 15y$
- Ⓑ $-3x - 21y$
- Ⓒ $11x - 9y$
- Ⓓ $-3x - y$

5. Which equation best represents the following graph? **(Lesson 2-7)**

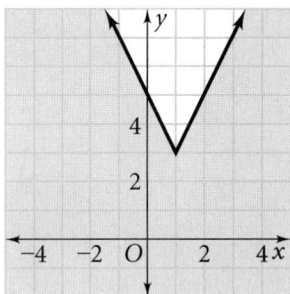

- Ⓐ $y \le 2|x - 1| + 3$
- Ⓑ $y \ge 2|x - 1| + 3$
- Ⓒ $y \le 2|x - 1| - 3$
- Ⓓ $y < 2|x + 1| + 3$

6. At a college bookstore, Carla purchased a calculus textbook and a novel that cost a total of $91, not including tax. If the price of the calculus textbook c is $6 more than 4 times the price of the novel n, which system of linear equations could be used to determine the price of each book? **(Lesson 3-2)**

- Ⓐ $c + n = 6$
     $c = 4n + 91$
- Ⓑ $c + n = 91$
     $c = 4n - 6$
- Ⓒ $c + n = 6$
     $c = 4n - 91$
- Ⓓ $c + n = 91$
     $c = 4n + 6$

7. The area of a rectangle is $256r^8 s^{12}$ square units. If the width of the rectangle is $8r^3 s^4$ units, what is the rectangle's length? **(Lesson 9-4)**

- Ⓐ $2048r^{11}s^{16}$ units
- Ⓑ $64r^{11}s^{16}$ units
- Ⓒ $32r^5 s^8$ units
- Ⓓ $24r^5 s^8$ units

8. Which ordered pair corresponds to one of the zeros of the function $f(x) = 2x^2 + x - 6$? **(Lesson 5-5)**

- Ⓐ $\left(-\frac{3}{2}, 0\right)$
- Ⓑ $(-2, 0)$
- Ⓒ $(-3, 0)$
- Ⓓ $(-6, 0)$

9. The price t of a television at Terrific TVs is $230 less than twice the price s of the same television at Super TVs. The difference in price between the two televisions is $185. Which system of linear equations can be used to determine the price of the television at each store? **(Lesson 3-2)**

Ⓐ $t - s = 185$
$t - 2s = -230$

Ⓑ $t + s = 185$
$2t - s = 230$

Ⓒ $t - s = -185$
$2t - s = 230$

Ⓓ $t - s = -185$
$2t - 4s = 460$

10. Which equation represents the graph of the conic section below? **(Lesson 10-6)**

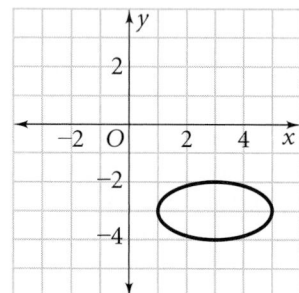

Ⓐ $x^2 + 4y^2 - 6x + 24y = 0$

Ⓑ $x^2 + 4y^2 - 6x + 24y + 41 = 0$

Ⓒ $x^2 + 4y^2 + 6x - 24y + 41 = 0$

Ⓓ $x^2 + 4y^2 - 6x + 24y = 41$

11. Which equation will produce the widest parabola when graphed in the same coordinate plane? **(Lesson 5-2)**

Ⓐ $y = 3x^2$

Ⓑ $y = -5x^2$

Ⓒ $y = -0.5x^2$

Ⓓ $y = 0.3x^2$

12. In which sequence is a_{25} the greatest? **(Lesson 11-3)**

Ⓐ $a_n = 2a_{n-1} + 7, a_1 = 5$

Ⓑ $a_n = 3n - 10$

Ⓒ $a_n = a_{n-1} + 18, a_1 = -7$

Ⓓ $a_n = n^2 - 200$

13. What is the inverse of the function $f(x) = x^3 + 4$? **(Lesson 7-7)**

Ⓐ $f^{-1}(x) = \frac{1}{3}x - 4$

Ⓑ $f^{-1}(x) = \sqrt[3]{x} - 4$

Ⓒ $f^{-1}(x) = \sqrt[3]{x - 4}$

Ⓓ $f^{-1}(x) = \sqrt[4]{x - 3}$

14. Which of the following expressions is equivalent to $3 \log x + 2 \log y - \log x$? **(Lesson 8-4)**

I. $2 \log xy$
II. $\log x^2 + \log y^2$
III. $2 \log x + 2 \log y$
IV. $4 \log x - y$

Ⓐ I and II only

Ⓑ II and III only

Ⓒ III and IV only

Ⓓ I, II, and III only

15. Which geometric sequence DOES NOT include the term 100? **(Lesson 11-3)**

Ⓐ $5, 10, 20, \ldots$

Ⓑ $337.5, 225, 150, \ldots$

Ⓒ $a_1 = 25, a_n = 2a_{n-1}$

Ⓓ $a_n = 4 \cdot 5^n$

16. Which of the following equations represents an ellipse? **(Lesson 10-4)**

Ⓐ $3y^2 - x - 6y + 5 = 0$

Ⓑ $x^2 + y^2 - 4x - 6y + 4 = 0$

Ⓒ $4x^2 + y^2 - 16x - 6y + 9 = 0$

Ⓓ $4x^2 - y^2 - 16x + 6y - 9 = 0$

17. Which function shifts $y = |x + 1| - 3$ right 4 units and down 7 units? **(Lesson 2-6)**

Ⓐ $y = |x - 6| + 1$

Ⓑ $y = |x - 3| + 4$

Ⓒ $y = |x + 5| - 10$

Ⓓ $y = |x - 3| - 10$

18. What is the quotient of $2x^4 + 4x^3 + 5x^2 + 9x - 2$ and $x + 2$? **(Lesson 6-3)**

Ⓐ $x^3 + 2x^2 + 5x - 1$

Ⓑ $2x^3 + 5x - 1$

Ⓒ $2x^3 - 5x - 1$

Ⓓ $2x^3 + 5x + 1$

19. Which of the following is an equation of a parabola? **(Lesson 10-2)**

Ⓐ $2x^2 - 5y^2 + 4x - 36 = 0$

Ⓑ $2x^2 - 5y + 4x - 36 = 0$

Ⓒ $2x^2 + 2y^2 + 4x - 12y - 36 = 0$

Ⓓ $2x^2 + 5y^2 - 36 = 0$

20. Which equation is the parent function of the function whose graph is shown below? (Lesson 5-2)

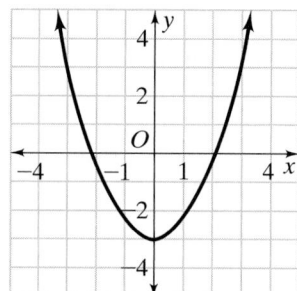

- Ⓐ $y = |x|$
- Ⓑ $y = x$
- Ⓒ $y = x^2$
- Ⓓ $y = \sqrt{x}$

21. Which expression is equivalent to $(5 + 2i)(-3 + i)$? (Lesson 5-6)

- Ⓐ $-17 - i$
- Ⓑ $17 + i$
- Ⓒ $8 + i$
- Ⓓ $-15 - 2i$

22. You put $600 in an account earning 5% annual interest, compounded continuously. How much will you have after 18 months? (Lesson 8-2)

- Ⓐ $631.38
- Ⓑ $633.33
- Ⓒ $646.73
- Ⓓ $1475.76

23. You roll three number cubes. What is P (all three show the same number)? (Lesson 9-7)

- Ⓐ $\frac{1}{27}$
- Ⓑ $\frac{1}{36}$
- Ⓒ $\frac{1}{6}$
- Ⓓ $\frac{1}{3}$

24. Which of the following is a simplification of $\frac{x^2y^3z}{4x} \div \frac{3xy^4z^2}{2z}$? (Lesson 9-4)

- Ⓐ $\frac{3x^3y^7z^3}{8xz}$
- Ⓒ $\frac{2x^2y^3z^2}{12x^2y^4z^2}$
- Ⓑ $\frac{3x^2y^7z^2}{8}$
- Ⓓ $\frac{1}{6y}$

25. The graph of the equation $y = \frac{5}{2}x - 2$ is shown below. If the equation $y = x + 1$ was also graphed, what would be the solution to the resulting system of equations? (Lesson 3-1)

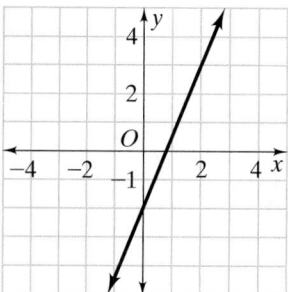

- Ⓐ $(0, 1)$
- Ⓑ $(2, 3)$
- Ⓒ $(3, 4)$
- Ⓓ No solution

26. What is the complete solution of $\log (6x - 9) = 2 \log x$? (Lesson 8-5)

- Ⓐ 3
- Ⓑ -3
- Ⓒ $-3, 3$
- Ⓓ $1, 3$

27. Suppose you receive $350 for your birthday. You can put the money into Account A earning 4.5% annual interest compounded continuously, or into Account B earning 5% annual interest compounded monthly. Which statement is NOT true? (Lesson 8-2)

- Ⓐ The balance of Account A after 1 year would be about $366.11.
- Ⓑ The balance of Account B after 1 year would be about $367.91.
- Ⓒ The balance of Account A after 5 years would be about $438.31.
- Ⓓ The balance of Account B after 5 years would be about $429.18.

28. Solve $10 - |4x + 1| < 7$. (Lesson 1-5)

- Ⓐ $x > \frac{1}{2}$
- Ⓑ $x < -\frac{1}{2}$ or $x > 1$
- Ⓒ $x < -1$ or $x > \frac{1}{2}$
- Ⓓ $-1 < x < \frac{1}{2}$

Cumulative Practice (continued)

29. Jeremy bought sandwiches for his computer class and put them all in a big bag. He bought 7 ham sandwiches, 6 turkey sandwiches, 4 roast beef sandwiches, and 3 cheese sandwiches. What is the probability that a sandwich pulled randomly out of the bag does NOT contain meat? **(Lesson 6-7)**

    (A) 0.15   (C) 0.50

    (B) 0.25   (D) 0.85

30. Which graph represents the equation $y = (x + 2)^2 - 3$? **(Lesson 5-3)**

    (A)   (C)

    (B)   (D)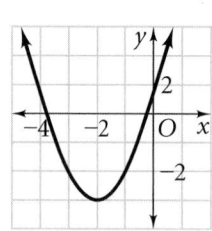

31. Suzanne's economics teacher gave her four functions that show the growth of four different businesses. Which function has an exponential growth factor of 25%? **(Lesson 8-1)**

    (A) $y = 0.25^x$

    (B) $y = 5(0.25)^x$

    (C) $y = 4.1(1.25)^x$

    (D) $y = 1.25(0.9)^x$

32. Heidi applied to five different colleges. Two of the colleges are in California. If she is accepted by all of the colleges, what is the probability that Heidi will attend school in California? **(Lesson 1-6)**

    (A) $\frac{1}{5}$ (C) $\frac{3}{5}$

    (B) $\frac{2}{5}$ (D) $\frac{5}{2}$

33. Which expression is equivalent to $(x + \sqrt{3})(x - \sqrt{2})$? **(Lesson 7-2)**

    (A) $x^2 - 5$

    (B) $x^2 + x - \sqrt{5}$

    (C) $x^2 + (\sqrt{3} - \sqrt{2})x - \sqrt{6}$

    (D) $x^2 - (\sqrt{3} + \sqrt{2})x - \sqrt{6}$

34. How many solutions does the system $\begin{cases} y = \frac{1}{2}x^3 - 1 \\ y = -x^2 + 4 \end{cases}$ have? **(Lesson 3-2)**

    (A) 0

    (B) 1

    (C) 2

    (D) 3

35. Organisms in a culture are growing exponentially with time, as shown in the table below.

Day	Organisms
0	75
1	225
2	675

    Which of the following equations expresses the number of organisms, n, present at any time, t? **(Lesson 8-1)**

    (A) $n = 75^t$

    (B) $n = 75 + (3)^t$

    (C) $n = 75 \cdot (3)^t$

    (D) $n = 225 \cdot (3)^t$

36. Which arithmetic sequence includes the term 27? **(Lesson 11-2)**

    I. $a_1 = 7, a_n = a_{n-1} + 5$
    II. $a_n = 3 + (n - 1)4$
    III. $a_n = 57 - 6n$

    (A) I only

    (B) I and II only

    (C) II and III only

    (D) I, II, and III

37. An ellipse with center $(-4, -2)$ has a horizontal major axis of length 6 and a minor axis of length 4. Which equation represents the ellipse? **(Lesson 10-6)**

    (A) $\frac{(x - 4)^2}{4} - \frac{(y - 2)^2}{9} = 1$

    (B) $\frac{(x + 2)^2}{9} - \frac{(y + 4)^2}{4} = 1$

    (C) $\frac{(x + 4)^2}{9} + \frac{(y + 2)^2}{4} = 1$

    (D) $\frac{(x + 4)^2}{4} + \frac{(y + 2)^2}{9} = 1$

38. Which expressions are equivalent to $\log a - 3 \log b$? **(Lesson 8-4)**

I. $\log ab^3$

II. $\log \frac{a}{b^3}$

III. $\log a - \log b^3$

IV. $\log (ab)^3$

Ⓐ I and II   Ⓒ III and IV

Ⓑ II and III   Ⓓ I and IV

39. What is the solution of the following system? **(Lesson 3-6)**

$$\begin{cases} -3x + 2y - z = 6 \\ 3x + y + 2z = 5 \\ 2x - 2y - z = -5 \end{cases}$$

Ⓐ $(1, 4, -1)$

Ⓑ $(6, 5, -3)$

Ⓒ $(0, \frac{17}{5}, \frac{4}{5})$

Ⓓ no solution

40. If $f(x) = 2x + 9$ and $g(x) = x - 6$, what is $(f \circ g)(-1)$? **(Lesson 7-6)**

Ⓐ 0

Ⓑ 1

Ⓒ 7

Ⓓ -5

41. What is an equivalent form of $\frac{4}{5 - i}$? **(Lesson 5-6)**

Ⓐ $\frac{5 - i}{6}$

Ⓑ $\frac{5 + i}{6}$

Ⓒ $\frac{10 + 2i}{13}$

Ⓓ $\frac{10 - 2i}{13}$

42. Which expression describes the area in square units of a rectangle that has a width of $3a^3b^4 + 1$ and a length of $4a^2b^5$ **(Lesson 6-1)**

Ⓐ $7a^5b^9 + 4a^2b^5$ Ⓒ $12a^6b^{20}$

Ⓑ $8a^6b^{20}$ Ⓓ $12a^5b^9 + 4a^2b^5$

43. The volume of a rectangular prism is $72r^9t^{10}$ cubic units. The length is $4r^2t^3$ units and the width is $6r^3t^2$ units. What is the height of the prism? **(Lesson 9-4)**

Ⓐ $3r^4t^5$ units   Ⓒ $62r^4t^5$ units

Ⓑ $3r^{14}y^{15}$ units   Ⓓ $62r^{14}t^{15}$ units

Standards Reference Guide

California Content Standard	Item Number(s)
ALG2 19.0	1, 29
ALG2 10.0	2, 8
PS 1.0	3, 23, 32
ALG2 3.0	4, 18, 33, 42
ALG2 1.0	5, 17, 28
ALG2 2.0	6, 9, 25, 34, 39
ALG2 7.0	7, 24, 43
ALG2 9.0	11, 20, 30
ALG2 22.0	12, 15, 36
ALG2 24.0	13, 40
ALG2 14.0	14, 26, 38
ALG2 17.0	10, 16, 19, 37
ALG2 6.0	21, 41
ALG2 12.0	22, 27, 31, 35

For additional review and practice, see the *California Standards Review and Practice Workbook* or go online to use the

Visit: PHSchool.com, **Web Code:** bbq-9045

Chapter 1

Extra Practice: Skills and Word Problems

● **Lesson 1-1** Replace each ■ with the symbol $<$, $>$, or $=$ to make the sentence true.

1. -5 ■ -8 **2.** 7 ■ 7 **3.** 0.1 ■ 0.01 **4.** 12 ■ $\sqrt{12}$

5. $\frac{3}{8}$ ■ 0.375 **6.** $\frac{1}{5}$ ■ $\frac{1}{4}$ **7.** $\frac{1}{3}$ ■ 0.333 **8.** $\sqrt{6}$ ■ 3

● **Lesson 1-1** Find the opposite and the reciprocal of each number.

9. 102 **10.** -3.7 **11.** $2\frac{3}{4}$ **12.** -0.04 **13.** $\sqrt{2}$ **14.** $\pi - 4$

15. $-\frac{8}{5}$ **16.** 1.5 **17.** $\frac{6}{7}$ **18.** $\frac{3\pi}{2}$ **19.** 0.0001 **20.** $5\sqrt{7}$

● **Lesson 1-2** Evaluate each expression for the given values of the variables.

21. $6c + 5d - 4c - 3d + 3c - 6d$; $c = 4$ and $d = -2$

22. $10a + 3b - 5a + 4b + 1a + 5b$; $a = -3$ and $b = 5$

23. $3m + 9n + 6m - 7n - 4m + 2n$; $m = 6$ and $n = -4$

● **Lesson 1-3** Solve each equation. Check your answers.

24. $5 - w = 2w - 1$ **25.** $-2s = 3s - 10$ **26.** $2(x + 3) + 2(x + 4) = 24$

27. $8z + 12 = 5z - 21$ **28.** $7b - 6(11 - 2b) = 10$ **29.** $10k - 7 = 2(13 - 5k)$

● **Lesson 1-4** Solve each inequality. Graph the solution.

30. $3x - 8 \geq 1$ **31.** $7t + 4 \leq 3t$ **32.** $3v \leq 5v + 18$

33. $4a < 2a - 7$ **34.** $7 - x \geq 24$ **35.** $2(y - 3) + 7 < 21$

● **Lesson 1-4** Solve each compound inequality. Graph the solution.

36. $4r > -12$ and $2r < 10$ **37.** $5z \geq -10$ and $3z < 3$ **38.** $7x \geq 21$ and $8x \leq 56$

39. $3x < -6$ or $7x > 56$ **40.** $9b > 27$ and $4b \leq 44$ **41.** $5p \geq 10$ or $-2p < 10$

● **Lesson 1-5** Solve each equation. Check your answers.

42. $|4m + 2| = 10$ **43.** $|9 - 4z| = 53$ **44.** $|5x| = 30$

45. $|3x - 6| - 7 = 14$ **46.** $3|2d - 1| = 21$ **47.** $|2v + 3| - 6 = 14$

● **Lesson 1-5** Solve each inequality. Graph the solution.

48. $|3 - k| < 7$ **49.** $|2t + 7| \geq 4$ **50.** $|x - 2| < 6$

51. $2|w + 6| \leq 10$ **52.** $|3y - 5| + 6 > 15$ **53.** $3|2z + 5| + 2 \leq 8$

● **Lesson 1-6** Suppose you select a number at random from the sample space
$\{1, 2, 3, 4, 5, 6, 7, 8, 9\}$. Find each theoretical probability.

54. P(a number that is a multiple of 5) **55.** P(a number that is an integer)

56. P(a number that is a factor of twelve) **57.** P(a number that is less than or equal to 4)

58. P(a number that is greater than 6) **59.** P(a number that is a composite number)

● **Lessons 1-1, 1-2, and 1-3**

60. You can use the equation $T = 0.6(205 - \frac{a}{2} - r) + r$ to determine the target heart rate, T, for a cardiovascular workout for an athletic male a years old. His rest heart rate is r heartbeats per minute. What is the rest heart rate of an athletic 18-year-old male whose target heart rate is 144 heartbeats per minute?

61. A desktop computer now sells for 15% less than it did last year. The current price is $425. What was the price of the computer last year?

62. Mrs. Chavez invested $6000. She invested the money in two accounts—one with a 4% simple interest and the other with a 6% simple interest. At the end of the year, the total amount she earned in interest was $320. How much did Mrs. Chavez invest in each account?

63. A plane travels from New York City to San Francisco with an average speed of 550 mi/h. Another plane leaves from the same airport a half-hour later and travels the same route with an average speed of 625 mi/h. How many hours later will the second plane pass the first?

64. Mehmed and Colin run around a 450-meter track in opposite directions. They start at the same point and at the same time. Mehmed's speed is 2.0 m/s. Colin's speed is 2.5 m/s. How far will Colin have run when they meet again?

65. Angela is considering two job offers. Job A would pay a salary of $2500 plus a 4% commission on her total sales per month. Job B would pay $2200 plus an 8% commission on all sales over $2000 per month. What is the least amount Angela would have to sell each month for Job B to pay more than Job A?

66. Amando has $625 in his savings account. He wants to take a vacation that he estimates will cost $1300. If possible, he would like to have extra money to buy souvenirs for friends. Amando works 40 hours per week, earns $15 per hour, and saves 6% of each week's earnings. How many whole weeks must he work before he earns enough money to take the vacation?

67. A homeowner needs to rent some cleaning equipment. Company A will rent the machine he needs for $28 plus $4 per hour. Company B will charge $22 plus $4.75 per hour. For what range of hours will Company B charge less than Company A?

● **Lessons 1-4 and 1-5**

68. A metal part for a machine is now 5.85 inches long. The specifications call for it to be 5.72 inches long, with a tolerance of ±0.02 inch. By how much can a machinist decrease the length of the part?

● **Lesson 1-6**

69. In a group of 38 students, 15 take chemistry, 28 take Spanish, and 8 take both chemistry and Spanish. One student is selected at random from the group. What is the probability that the student takes neither chemistry nor Spanish?

70. A bag contains marbles of three different colors. You draw a marble, record its color, then put it back in the bag. The table shows the results of the 150 trials. What is the experimental probability of drawing a red marble?

71. Charles is one of a group of five students who have volunteered to work at the ticket table for a school band concert. If two students are selected at random to work at the ticket table, what is the probability that Charles will be one of the two?

72. Within a 10-by-10 grid of squares, two overlapping 6-by-6 squares are drawn. The area of overlap is 9 square units. If a dart hits the 10-by-10 square at a random point, what is the probability that it lands in one or both of the 6-by-6 squares?

Color	Frequency
Red	45
Blue	58
Yellow	47

● **Lesson 2-1** Determine whether each relation is a function. Justify your answer.

1. $\{(0,1),(1,0),(2,1),(3,1),(4,2)\}$

2. $\{(7,4),(4,9),(-3,1),(1,7),(2,8)\}$

3. $\{(1,4),(3,2),(5,2),(1,-8),(6,7)\}$

4. $\{(-5,1),(0,-3),(-2,1),(10,11),(7,1)\}$

5. $\{(9,3),(6,2),(3,2),(3,1),(6,-2)\}$

6. $\{(4,9),(5,3),(-2,0),(5,4),(8,1)\}$

● **Lesson 2-2** Graph each equation.

7. $y = x - 7$

8. $4x - y = 8$

9. $y = -x + 4$

10. $2x + 5y = 10$

11. $y = -4x + 3$

12. $-6x - 2y = 7$

13. $-2y = x - 2$

14. $3x - 8y = 9$

● **Lesson 2-2** Write in standard form the equation of each line.

15. slope $= 3; (-1, 4)$

16. slope $= -1; (0, 7)$

17. slope $= \frac{3}{4}; (2, 8)$

18. slope $= -\frac{2}{5}; (3, -9)$

19. slope $= \frac{8}{3}; (-2, 0)$

20. slope $= -5; (-3, -12)$

● **Lesson 2-2** Write in point-slope form the equation of the line through each pair of points.

21. $(0, 2)$ and $(-1, 3)$

22. $(1, 2)$ and $(-2, -4)$

23. $(11, 4)$ and $(3, 0)$

24. $(-4, -5)$ and $(-1, -8)$

25. $(-5, 6)$ and $(3, -10)$

26. $(12, 10)$ and $(0, 0)$

● **Lesson 2-2** Find the slope, y-intercept, and x-intercept of each line.

27. $y = 2x - 5$

28. $y = -x + 1$

29. $y = 4$

30. $y = 5x + 10$

31. $y = \frac{1}{3}x - 15$

32. $x = -7$

33. $y = -6x$

34. $y = -\frac{2}{5}x + 20$

● **Lesson 2-2** Write each equation in standard form.

35. $y = 3x + 9$

36. $4x = 6y - 9$

37. $2y = 8x - 7$

38. $y = -x + 1$

39. $0.3x + 1.2y = 2.4$

40. $y = \frac{2}{3}x + 15$

41. $x = 8 - y$

42. $\frac{1}{2}x - \frac{3}{4}y = 1$

● **Lesson 2-3** Write an equation of a direct variation that passes through each point.

43. $(3, 7)$

44. $(5, -8)$

45. $(-4, -10)$

46. $(-2, 9)$

47. $(-6, 6)$

48. $(6, -3)$

49. $(12, 8)$

50. $(-15, -1)$

● **Lesson 2-5** Graph each equation by writing two linear equations.

51. $y = |x - 2|$

52. $y = \left|x + \frac{1}{2}\right|$

53. $y = |4x + 3|$

54. $y = |4x - 3|$

55. $y = -|x + 4|$

56. $y = 2|x - 3|$

57. $y = |x + 4| - 2$

58. $y = \frac{4}{3}|2x - 1|$

● **Lesson 2-7** Graph each inequality.

59. $y < -x + 5$

60. $0.1x + 0.6y \geq 2$

61. $y \leq 3x - 1$

62. $x + 3y > 12$

63. $y \geq 5x - 3$

64. $6x + 2y \geq 7$

65. $y + 1 > \frac{1}{3}x + 2$

66. $5x - 4y \leq -3$

Lesson 2-1

67. A garden has the shape of an isosceles triangle. The base of the triangle is 42 ft long, with an altitude of h ft. Write an equation that describes the area A of the garden as a function of h. What is the area of the garden for $h = 38$ ft?

68. To avoid air turbulence, a plane climbs from an altitude of 20,700 feet to a higher altitude at the rate of 325 feet per minute. Write a function that describes the altitude, y, of the plane x minutes after it begins its climb. Then find the altitude of the plane for $x = 5$.

Lesson 2-2

69. The blueprint for a toy, shown at the right, identifies two perpendicular rods, each 5 in. long. Suppose each square in the coordinate grid measures 1 in.^{2} and the origin is O. Rods I and II are connected at point $A(4, 3)$.
  a. Write an equation in slope-intercept form for the line containing Rod I.
  b. Write an equation in point-slope form for the line containing Rod II.

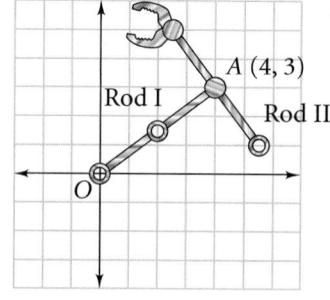

Lesson 2-3

70. When a pump is turned on, it pumps water at a rate of 12 gal/min. What information do you need to know to decide if the volume of water in the tank varies directly with the time the pump is on? Explain.

71. Williamsville has streets that form a square grid. Adams Street forms the x-axis and Calvin Avenue forms the y-axis. A bank is located at $(100, 0)$, a bus stop at $(300, 0)$, and a post office at $(300, 200)$. Suppose a car departs somewhere on Adams Street, as shown at the right.
  a. The minimum distance the car has to drive to get to the bank is an absolute value function $f(x)$, where x is the x-coordinate of the location of the car. Write an equation and draw the graph for $f(x)$.
  b. Let $g(x)$ be the absolute value function that describes the minimum distance the car has to drive to get to the bus stop. Write an equation and draw the graph for this function.
  c. Let $h(x)$ be the function that describes the minimum distance the car has to drive to get to the post office. Write an equation and draw the graph for this function.
  d. Describe how the graphs in parts (a)–(c) are related.

Legend
B – Bank
S – Bus Stop
P – Post Office

Lessons 2-4, 2-5, and 2-6

72. The table shows the winning times in the men's Olympic 100-meter freestyle swimming event for the years 1960–2004. Use a graphing calculator.
  a. Make a scatter plot of the data.
  b. Find a line of best fit for the data. Round the coefficients to the nearest hundredth.
  c. Use the equation for the line of best fit to predict the winning time for the event in the year 2012.

73. A truck rental company purchased a used truck for $18,000. It plans to rent the truck for $75 per day. Write an equation that describes how the profit, y, on the truck is related to the number of days, x, the truck earns rental income. Explain what the intercepts and slope of the graph of this function represent.

Years Since 1960	Winning Time
0	55.20
4	53.40
8	52.20
12	51.22
16	49.99
20	50.40
24	49.80
28	48.63
32	49.02
36	48.74
40	48.30
44	48.17

Lesson 2-7

74. Andrea is going to buy x lbs of pasta salad and y lbs of chicken salad for a party. The pasta salad costs $4 per pound and the chicken salad costs $6 per pound. Andrea has at most $28 to spend. Write and graph an inequality that describes the relationship between x and y.

Chapter 3

Extra Practice: Skills and Word Problems

● **Lesson 3-1** Solve each system by graphing.

1. $\begin{cases} y = 2x + 1 \\ y = 4x - 5 \end{cases}$

2. $\begin{cases} x + y = 2 \\ y = 2x - 1 \end{cases}$

3. $\begin{cases} y = x + 4 \\ y = -2x + 3 \end{cases}$

4. $\begin{cases} 3x - 4y = 13 \\ 2x + y = 5 \end{cases}$

5. $\begin{cases} 2x = y - 7 \\ 4x - 2y = 14 \end{cases}$

6. $\begin{cases} x = 8 \\ x - y = 2 \end{cases}$

● **Lesson 3-2** Solve each system of equations.

7. $\begin{cases} x + y = 5 \\ x - y = -3 \end{cases}$

8. $\begin{cases} y = 3x - 1 \\ 2x + y = 14 \end{cases}$

9. $\begin{cases} 3x + 2y = 12 \\ x + y = 3 \end{cases}$

10. $\begin{cases} x - 4y = 16 \\ x + 2y = 4 \end{cases}$

11. $\begin{cases} y = 2x + 5 \\ y = 4 - x \end{cases}$

12. $\begin{cases} y = 5x - 1 \\ y = 14 \end{cases}$

● **Lesson 3-3** Solve each system of inequalities by graphing.

13. $\begin{cases} y \geq x - 3 \\ y \leq 3x + 7 \end{cases}$

14. $\begin{cases} 3x + 4y > 8 \\ y < 5x \end{cases}$

15. $\begin{cases} -x - 2y \geq -5 \\ y < 3 \end{cases}$

● **Lesson 3-4** Find the values of x and y that maximize or minimize the objective function.

16. $\begin{cases} x \leq 4 \\ y \leq 3 \\ x \geq 0 \\ y \geq 0 \end{cases}$

maximum for
$P = 2x + y$

17. $\begin{cases} x + y \leq 5 \\ y \geq x \\ x \geq 0 \end{cases}$

minimum for
$C = x + y$

18. $\begin{cases} 1 \leq x \leq 6 \\ 2 \leq y \leq 4 \\ x + y \geq 4 \end{cases}$

maximum for
$P = 3x + 2y$

19. A lunch stand makes $.75 in profit on each chef's salad and $1.20 in profit on each Caesar salad. On a typical weekday, it sells between 40 and 60 chef's salads and between 35 and 50 Caesar salads. The total number sold has never exceeded 100 salads. How many of each type of salad should be prepared to maximize profit?

● **Lesson 3-5** Graph each point in coordinate space.

20. $(0, 3, 0)$

21. $(4, 0, -2)$

22. $(0, 0, 5)$

23. $(1, 1, 0)$

24. $(0, 4, 2)$

25. $(-1, 2, 2)$

26. $(3, 0, 1)$

27. $(6, 1, 3)$

28. $(3, -1, 4)$

● **Lesson 3-5** Sketch the graph of each equation.

29. $x - y + z = 4$

30. $2x - y - z = 6$

31. $-x + y + 3z = 9$

32. $x + y + z = 5$

33. $-5x + 2y + 2z = 10$

34. $x - y + 3z = 3$

● **Lesson 3-6** Solve each system of equations.

35. $\begin{cases} x + y + z = 6 \\ x = 2y \\ z = x + 1 \end{cases}$

36. $\begin{cases} x - 2y + z = 8 \\ y - z = 4 \\ z = 3 \end{cases}$

37. $\begin{cases} 3x + y - z = 15 \\ x - y + 3z = -19 \\ 2x + 2y + z = 4 \end{cases}$

● **Lessons 3-1 and 3-2**

38. Carla has $2.40 in nickels and dimes. Deron has $5.50 in dimes and quarters. Deron has as many dimes as Carla has nickels and as many quarters as Carla has dimes. How many of each kind of coin does Carla have?

39. A kayaker can paddle 12 mi in 2 h moving with the river current. Paddling at the same pace, the trip back against the current takes 4 h. Assume that the river current is constant. Find what the kayaker's speed would be in still water.

40. Mrs. Mitchell put a total of $10,000 into two accounts. One account earns 6% simple annual interest. The other account earns 6.5% simple interest. After 1 year, the two accounts earned $632.50 interest. Find how much money was invested in each account.

41. Mr. Chandra bought 2 lbs of cheddar cheese and 3 lbs of chicken loaf. He paid $26.35. Mrs. Hsing paid $18.35 for 1.5 lbs of cheese and 2 lbs of chicken loaf. What was the price per pound of each item?

● **Lesson 3-3**

42. Leyla wants to buy fish, chicken, or some of each for weekend meals. The fish costs $4 per pound and the chicken costs $3 per pound. She will spend at least $11 but no more than $15.
a. Write a system of inequalities to model the situation.
b. Graph the system to show the possible amounts Layla could buy.

43. A furniture company makes desks and chairs. A carpenter can make a chair in 5 h and a desk in 8 h. Finishers take 2.5 h to paint a chair and 2 h to paint a desk. The carpentry department has enough people to work up to 400 h per week, and the finishing department can put in 120 h per week.
a. Write a system of inequalities to model the situation.
b. Graph the system to show the possible numbers of desks and chairs the company can produce in a week.

● **Lesson 3-4**

44. There are 20 true/false and 20 multiple choice questions on a test. A correct answer to a true/false question earns 10 points. A correct answer to a multiple choice question earns 12 points. The test makers determined that it takes, on average, 3 minutes to answer a true/false question and 4 minutes to answer a multiple choice question. Students have 1 hour to answer at most 18 questions of their choice. How many of each kind of question should a student answer correctly to get the greatest possible score?

45. A caterer must make at least 50 gal of potato soup and at least 120 gal of tomato soup. One chef can make 5 gal of potato soup and 6 gal of tomato soup in 1 h. Another chef can make 4 gal of potato soup and 12 gal of tomato soup in 1 h. The first chef earns $20/h. The second chef earns $22/h. How many hours should the company ask each chef to work to minimize the cost?

● **Lessons 3-5 and 3-6**

46. Three pumps can transfer 4150 gal of water per day when working at the same time. Pumps A and B together can transfer 3200 gal per day. Pumps A and C together can transfer 2900 gal per day. How many gallons can each pump transfer working alone?

47. For the school play, the Chavez family bought 2 student tickets, 1 adult ticket, and 2 senior tickets for $43. The Martinez family bought 3 student tickets and 2 adult tickets for $48. The Lynn family bought 4 student tickets, 2 adult tickets, and 1 senior ticket for $62. What was the price of each kind of ticket?

Extra Practice: Skills and Word Problems

Lesson 4-1 State the dimensions of each matrix. Identify the indicated element.

1. $\begin{bmatrix} 3 & 1 & -5 \\ 6 & 9 & 10 \end{bmatrix}; a_{21}$

2. $\begin{bmatrix} 0.5 & 6.1 \\ -9.2 & 4.7 \end{bmatrix}; a_{11}$

3. $\begin{bmatrix} 56 & -83 & 12 \\ 101 & -71 & 49 \end{bmatrix}; a_{12}$

4. $\begin{bmatrix} 5 & 8 \\ -2 & 3 \\ 3 & 4 \end{bmatrix}; a_{21}$

5. $\begin{bmatrix} \frac{1}{4} & \frac{3}{8} \end{bmatrix}; a_{12}$

6. $\begin{bmatrix} 17 & -23 & 79 \\ 47 & 61 & 5 \end{bmatrix}; a_{22}$

Lesson 4-2 Find each sum or difference.

7. $\begin{bmatrix} -8 & 3 \\ 19 & -45 \end{bmatrix} + \begin{bmatrix} 12 & 64 \\ -7 & 63 \end{bmatrix}$

8. $\begin{bmatrix} 3.6 & -9.8 \\ 4.0 & -1.7 \end{bmatrix} - \begin{bmatrix} 0.8 & 3.4 \\ -6.1 & 7.9 \end{bmatrix}$

9. $\begin{bmatrix} 4 & 6 & -3 \\ 8 & -9 & -1 \end{bmatrix} - \begin{bmatrix} 10 & 7 & -3 \\ -9 & 2 & 7 \end{bmatrix}$

10. $\begin{bmatrix} -308 & 651 \\ 912 & -347 \end{bmatrix} + \begin{bmatrix} 105 & 318 \\ -762 & -438 \end{bmatrix}$

Lesson 4-3 Solve each matrix equation.

11. $\begin{bmatrix} 25 & -60 \\ 42 & 91 \end{bmatrix} + X = \begin{bmatrix} -37 & 61 \\ 85 & 37 \end{bmatrix}$

12. $\begin{bmatrix} -8 & 3 & 1 \\ -9 & 6 & 7 \end{bmatrix} - X = \begin{bmatrix} 5 & 8 & 3 \\ 4 & 2 & 6 \end{bmatrix}$

13. $X + \begin{bmatrix} 6 & 2 & 9 \\ 1 & 5 & 10 \end{bmatrix} = \begin{bmatrix} 11 & -5 & 16 \\ 3 & 6 & 8 \end{bmatrix}$

14. $X - \begin{bmatrix} 2.3 & 6.5 \\ 9.4 & -8.2 \end{bmatrix} = \begin{bmatrix} -4.7 & 3.6 \\ 9.4 & -5.8 \end{bmatrix}$

Lesson 4-3 For exercises 15–26, use matrices A, B, C, and D shown below. Perform the indicated operations if they are defined. If an operation is not defined, label it *undefined*.

$$A = \begin{bmatrix} 8 & 1 \\ -2 & 5 \end{bmatrix} \qquad B = \begin{bmatrix} -3 & 1 & 0 \\ -2 & -1 & 5 \end{bmatrix} \qquad C = \begin{bmatrix} 9 & 4 \\ 5 & 1 \\ 2 & 0 \end{bmatrix} \qquad D = \begin{bmatrix} 1 & 7 & 3 \\ 8 & 10 & -2 \end{bmatrix}$$

15. AB

16. BD

17. $2A$

18. CD

19. DA

20. $-3B$

21. $0.2A$

22. BA

23. $5C$

24. CB

25. $\frac{1}{2}D$

26. BC

Lesson 4-4 Use $\triangle ABC$ with coordinates $A(1, 5)$, $B(2, -1)$, and $C(4, 3)$. Write the coordinates of each image in matrix form.

27. a dilation 5 times the size

28. a translation 3 units left and 1 unit up

29. a translation 2 units right and 7 units down

30. a dilation one third the size

Lesson 4-5 Solve each matrix equation. If an equation cannot be solved, explain why.

31. $\begin{bmatrix} 2 & 1 \\ -1 & 7 \end{bmatrix} X = \begin{bmatrix} 8 & 1 \\ -12 & 41 \end{bmatrix}$

32. $\begin{bmatrix} -1 & 0 \\ 6 & 3 \end{bmatrix} X = \begin{bmatrix} -9 \\ -3 \end{bmatrix}$

33. $\begin{bmatrix} -3 & 5 \\ 1 & 8 \end{bmatrix} X = \begin{bmatrix} 29 \\ 58 \end{bmatrix}$

Lesson 4-7 Solve each system of equations. Check your answers.

34. $\begin{cases} x - y = 3 \\ x + y = 5 \end{cases}$

35. $\begin{cases} x - 2y = 7 \\ x + 3y = 12 \end{cases}$

36. $\begin{cases} 2x + 5y = 10 \\ x + y = 2 \end{cases}$

Lessons 4-1, 4-2, and 4-3

37. A frozen yogurt supplier uses two machines to make chocolate and vanilla frozen yogurt. Both machines can be used in the morning and afternoon. Matrix A show the maximum hourly output of each machine. Matrix B shows how long the machines are used for production of each flavor.

Matrix A: **Output (gal/h)**

	Chocolate	Vanilla
Machine 1	4	5
Machine 2	7	8

Matrix B: **Time (h)**

	A.M.	P.M.
Chocolate	2	3
Vanilla	1	2

a. Compute the product AB of these matrices.
b. Describe what this product represents.

38. A distributor has orders for desk lamps and floor lamps from two motels. Matrix A shows the number of lamps each motel will purchase. Matrix B shows the cost of each type of lamp.

Matrix A:

	Desk	Floor
Motel 1	20	7
Motel 2	25	6

Matrix B:

	Cost
Desk	85
Floor	130

a. Compute the product AB of these matrices.
b. Describe what this product represents.

Lesson 4-4

39. The matrix $\begin{bmatrix} \frac{\sqrt{3}}{2} & -\frac{1}{2} \\ \frac{1}{2} & \frac{\sqrt{3}}{2} \end{bmatrix}$ represents a 30° counterclockwise rotation. The preimage is $\triangle ABC$ with the vertices $A(1, 1)$, $B(1, 2)$, and $C(5, 4)$. Write a matrix for the vertices of the image.

Lessons 4-5 and 4-6

40. County economists calculated that, in an average year, 9% of employed people lose their jobs and 86% of the unemployed find new jobs. The remaining people remain employed or unemployed, depending on their previous status. On January 1, the county has an unemployment rate of 7%. Calculate the expected unemployment rate for the next two years to the nearest tenth of a percent.

Lessons 4-7 and 4-8

41. Margery got a total of 249 points on three tests. The combined scores on the first two tests were 95 more than the score on the third test. The score on the second test was 6 points more than the score on the first test. Write and solve a matrix equation to find the score on each test.

42. Leona's Diner offers 8-piece, 12-piece, and 16-piece family chicken meals. The table at the right lists the costs of three different orders. What is the price of each kind of meal?

8-piece meals	12-piece meals	16-piece meals	Total Cost
2	3	1	$96
4	5	0	$133
2	4	2	$134

43. At a diner, two hot dogs and one hamburger cost $10, while three hot dogs and two hamburgers cost $17.25. Write and solve a matrix equation to find the cost of a hot dog and a hamburger.

● **Lesson 5-1** Determine whether each function is *linear* or *quadratic*. Identify the quadratic, linear, and constant terms.

1. $y = 3x + 4$

2. $y = x^2 + 1$

3. $3x + 2y = 1$

4. $y = (x + 1)(x - 1)$

5. $y = 3 - x^2$

6. $y = 5x(x + 2)$

● **Lessons 5-2 and 5-3** Graph each function.

7. $y = 3x^2$

8. $y = (x + 3)^2 + 1$

9. $y = 2x^2 + 4$

10. $y = \frac{1}{2}(x - 3)^2$

11. $y = x^2 - 9$

12. $y = 2(x + 1)^2 - 5$

13. $y = (x + 1)^2 - 3$

14. $y = (x - 2)^2$

● **Lesson 5-4** Factor each expression.

15. $x^2 + 3x - 54$

16. $x^2 + 10x + 24$

17. $x^2 - 36$

18. $x^2 - 9x - 36$

19. $x^2 - 15x + 56$

20. $25x^2 + 70x + 49$

21. $7x^2 - 20x - 3$

22. $5x^2 + 23x - 10$

23. $\frac{1}{4}x^2 - 4$

24. $x^2 - 6x - 16$

25. $4x^2 + 12x + 40$

26. $4x^2 - 6x + 9$

● **Lesson 5-5** Solve each equation by factoring, by taking square roots, or by graphing. When necessary, round your answer to the nearest hundredth.

27. $x^2 + 4x - 1 = 0$

28. $4x^2 - 100 = 0$

29. $x^2 = -2x + 1$

30. $x^2 - 9 = 0$

31. $2x^2 + 4x = 70$

32. $x^2 - 30 = 10$

33. $x^2 + 4x = 0$

34. $x^2 + 3x + 2 = 0$

● **Lesson 5-6** Simplify each expression.

35. $(3 - i) + (5 - 2i)$

36. $(4 + 2i)(1 - i)$

37. $(4 + 2i) - (3 + 5i)$

38. $(8 - 3i)(6 + 9i)$

39. $(2 + 5i) - (-6 + i)$

40. $(-2 - 3i)(7 - i)$

● **Lesson 5-6** Solve each equation. Check your answers.

41. $x^2 + 16 = 0$

42. $4x^2 = -1$

43. $x^2 = -10$

44. $4x^2 + 48 = 0$

45. $-2x^2 = 5$

46. $x^2 + 3 = 0$

● **Lesson 5-6** Find the first three output values of each fractal-generating function. Use $z = 0$ as the first input value.

47. $f(z) = z^2 - i$

48. $f(z) = z^2 + 2 + i$

● **Lessons 5-7 and 5-8** Solve each equation by completing the square or using the Quadratic Formula.

49. $x^2 + 5x + 8 = 4$

50. $8x^2 + 64 = 0$

51. $2x^2 - 5x + 1 = 0$

52. $3x^2 = x - 9$

53. $x^2 + 10 = 4x - 2$

54. $x^2 - 7x = 0$

55. $x^2 + 4x + 4 = 0$

56. $x^2 - 7 = 0$

57. $x^2 + 8x - 17 = 0$

● **Lesson 5-8** Evaluate the discriminant of each equation. Tell how many solutions each equation has and whether the solutions are real or imaginary.

58. $x^2 + 4x = 17$

59. $2x^2 + x = -1$

60. $x^2 - 4x + 5 = 0$

61. $2x^2 + 5x = 0$

62. $x^2 - 19 = 1$

63. $3x^2 = 8x - 4$

64. $-2x^2 + 1 = 7x$

65. $4x^2 + 4x = -1$

Lesson 5-1

66. The table shows the relation between the speed of a car and its stopping distance.

Speed (mi/h)		35	45	50	60
Stopping Distance (ft)		96	140	165	221

    a. Use a quadratic function to model the data.
    b. Predict the stopping distance for a car traveling at 65 mi/h.

Lessons 5-2 and 5-3

67. Martin has 120 feet of fencing to enclose two rectangular play areas for children. He plans to enclose a rectangular area and then divide it into two equal sections, as shown in the figure.
    a. Find the dimensions of the largest total area Martin can enclose.
    b. Find the area of each of the small play areas.

68. Marnie throws a softball straight up into the air. The ball leaves her hand when it is exactly 5 ft from the ground. The height h of the ball, in feet, can be written as a function of time t, in seconds, as $h = -16t^2 + 40t + 5$.
    a. What is the maximum height the ball reaches?
    b. Marnie catches the ball 5 ft from the ground. How long was the ball in the air?

Lessons 5-4 and 5-5

69. Hal's sister is 5 years older than Hal. The product of their ages is 456. How old are Hal and his sister?

70. A toy rocket is fired upward from the ground. The relation between its height h, in feet, and the time t from launch, in seconds, can be described by the equation $h = -16t^2 + 64t$. How long does the rocket stay more than 48 feet above the ground?

71. The equation $P(x) = 2500x - 2x^2$ describes the profit of a company that customizes bulldozers when it customizes x bulldozers in a month.
    a. How many bulldozers per month must the company customize to make the maximum possible profit? What is the maximum profit?
    b. Describe a reasonable domain and range for the function $P(x)$.
    c. For what number of bulldozers per month is the profit at least $750,000?

72. Flor is designing a kite with two perpendicular crosspieces that are 26 inches and 24 inches long, as shown in the figure. How long should $\overline{AK}$ be so that $\overline{AB} \perp \overline{BC}$ and $\overline{AD} \perp \overline{DC}$?

73. The lengths of the sides of a right triangle are $x, x + 4$, and $x + 8$ inches. What is the value of x? What is the length of the hypotenuse of the triangle?

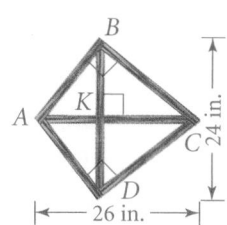

Lessons 5-6, 5-7, and 5-8

74. The height y of a parabolic arch is given by $y = -\frac{1}{16}x^2 + 40$, where x is the horizontal distance from the center of the base of the arch. All distances are in feet.
    a. What is the highest point on the arch?
    b. How wide is the arch at the base to the nearest tenth of a foot?

75. An archer's arrow follows a parabolic path. The path of the arrow can be described by the equation $y = -0.005x^2 + 2x + 5$.
    a. Describe the meaning of the y-intercept of the graph of the equation.
    b. What is the horizontal distance the arrow travels before it hits the ground? Round your answer to the nearest foot.

● **Lesson 6-1** Write each polynomial in standard form. Then classify it by degree and by number of terms.

1. $a^2 + 4a - 5a^2 - a$

2. $3x - \frac{1}{3} - 5x$

3. $3n^2 + n^3 - n - 3 - 3n^3$

4. $15 - y^2 - 10y - 8 + 8y$

5. $6c^2 - 4c + 7 - 8c^2$

6. $3x^2 - 5x - x^2 + x + 4x$

● **Lesson 6-2** Write a polynomial function in standard form with the given zeros.

7. $x = 3, 2, -1$

8. $x = 1, 1, 2$

9. $x = -2, -1, 1$

10. $x = 1, 2, 6$

11. $x = -3, -1, 5$

12. $x = 0, 0, 2, 3$

13. $x = -2, 1, 2, 2$

14. $x = 2, 4, 5, 7$

● **Lesson 6-3** Divide.

15. $(x^3 - 3x^2 + 2) \div (x - 1)$

16. $(x^3 - x^2 - 6x) \div (x - 3)$

17. $(2x^3 + 10x^2 + 8x) \div (x + 4)$

18. $(x^4 + x^2 - 6) \div (x^2 + 3)$

19. $(x^2 - 4x + 2) \div (x - 2)$

20. $(x^3 + 11x + 12) \div (x + 3)$

● **Lesson 6-4** Solve each equation.

21. $t^3 - 3t^2 - 10t = 0$

22. $4m^3 + m^2 - m + 5 = 0$

23. $t^3 - 6t^2 + 12t - 8 = 0$

24. $2c^3 - 7c^2 - 4c = 0$

25. $w^4 - 13w^2 + 36 = 0$

26. $x^3 + 2x^2 - 13x + 10 = 0$

● **Lesson 6-5** Find the roots of each polynomial equation.

27. $x^3 + 2x^2 + 3x + 6 = 0$

28. $x^3 - 3x^2 + 4x - 12 = 0$

29. $3x^4 + 11x^3 + 14x^2 + 7x + 1 = 0$

30. $3x^4 - x^3 - 22x^2 + 24x = 0$

31. $45x^3 + 93x^2 - 12 = 0$

32. $8x^4 - 66x^3 + 175x^2 - 132x - 45 = 0$

● **Lesson 6-7** Evaluate each expression.

33. $6!$

34. $3!4!$

35. $\frac{7!}{4!}$

36. $\frac{6!2!}{8!}$

37. $_8P_5$

38. $_4C_1$

39. $_6C_2$

40. $_6P_2$

41. $_7C_3$

42. $_7P_3$

43. $2(_7C_5)$

44. $\frac{_7C_5}{_5C_2}$

● **Lesson 6-7** Indicate whether each situation involves a combination or a permutation. Then answer the question.

45. How many different orders can you choose to read six of the nine books on your summer reading list?

46. How many ways are there to choose five shirts out of seven to take to camp?

47. How many ways can you choose two out of four kinds of flowers for a bouquet?

● **Lesson 6-8** Use the Binomial Theorem to expand each binomial.

48. $(x - 1)^3$

49. $(3x + 2)^4$

50. $(4x + 10)^3$

51. $(2x + 5y)^4$

52. $(x^2 + 2)^4$

53. $(x + 2y)^7$

54. $(5x - y)^5$

55. $(x - 4y^3)^4$

● **Lessons 6-1, 6-2, and 6-3**

56. Tonya wants to make a metal tray by cutting four identical square corner pieces from a rectangular metal sheet. Then she will bend the sides up to make an open tray.
   a. Let the length of each side of the removed squares be x in. Express the volume of the box as a polynomial function of x.
   b. Find the dimensions of a tray that would have a 384-in.^{3} capacity.

not to scale

57. The product of three consecutive integers is 210. Use N to represent the middle integer.
   a. Write the product as a polynomial function of $P(N)$.
   b. Find the three integers.

58. To determine safe dosage of a medication, researchers measure the concentration of the medication in a patient's bloodstream. Let the function that models the concentration in parts per million at x hours after the medication is administered be $C(x) = -\frac{2}{3}x^4 + 8x^3 - \frac{130}{3}x^2 + 116x$.
   a. How many hours does it take for the medication to be completely eliminated from a patient's bloodstream?
   b. How many hours is the concentration above 80 parts per million?

● **Lessons 6-4, 6-5, and 6-6**

59. A block of cheese is a cube whose side is x in. long. You cut off a 1-inch thick piece from the right side. Then you cut off a 3-inch thick piece from the top, as shown at the right. The volume of the remaining block is 2002 in.^{3}. What are the dimensions of the original block of cheese?

60. You can construct triangles by connecting three vertices of a convex polygon with n sides. The number of all possible such triangles can be represented as $f(n) = \frac{n^3 - 3n^2 + 2n}{6}$. Find the value of n such that you can construct 84 such triangles from the polygon.

● **Lessons 6-7 and 6-8**

61. You must answer exactly 12 out of 15 questions on a test. How many different ways can you select the questions to answer?

62. A lab assigns a three-digit identification to each subject in an experiment. No two subjects have the same identification. No digit can be repeated in an identification. What is the greatest number of subjects that can be used in the experiment?

63. To mark its eighth anniversary, Pizzeria Otto has a special coupon that offers the same price on a pizza with any combination of the 8 original toppings. Each pizza must have at least one topping. How many different kinds of pizza can be ordered with the coupon?

64. Ten friends want to take photographs of each other with exactly four of them in each picture. They want exactly one photograph with each combination. How many photographs do they need to take?

65. A total of 23 students will be coming to the end-of-the-year picnic. In how many ways can the teacher select 6 students for the clean-up crew?

66. City streets form a square grid. Each street runs one-way, either north or east. You want to take a taxi from a post office to a bank that is five blocks east and seven blocks north. How many different routes can the taxi take from the post office to the bank?

● **Lesson 7-1** Simplify each radical expression. Use absolute value symbols as needed.

1. $\sqrt{36x^4}$ **2.** $\sqrt{c^{80}d^{50}}$ **3.** $\sqrt[4]{81x^{12}}$ **4.** $\sqrt[3]{-64}$

5. $\sqrt[5]{-32k^5}$ **6.** $\sqrt[4]{\frac{1}{16}w^{12}}$ **7.** $\sqrt[4]{m^{18}n^8}$ **8.** $\sqrt[3]{27y^{15}}$

● **Lesson 7-2** Multiply or divide and simplify. Assume that all variables are positive.

9. $\sqrt{3x^4} \cdot \sqrt{24x^3}$ **10.** $\sqrt[3]{4} \cdot \sqrt[3]{18}$ **11.** $\sqrt{5a^3} \cdot \sqrt{20a}$

12. $\frac{\sqrt{80}}{\sqrt{5}}$ **13.** $\frac{\sqrt{18x^5y}}{\sqrt{2x}}$ **14.** $\frac{\sqrt[3]{640w^3z^8}}{\sqrt[3]{5wz^4}}$

● **Lesson 7-3** Simplify.

15. $2\sqrt{7} + 3\sqrt{7}$ **16.** $\sqrt{32} + \sqrt{8}$ **17.** $\sqrt{7x} + \sqrt{28x}$

18. $3\sqrt{18} + 2\sqrt{72}$ **19.** $\sqrt{27} + \sqrt{48}$ **20.** $8\sqrt{45} - 3\sqrt{80}$

● **Lesson 7-4** Write each expression in simplest form. Assume that all variables are positive.

21. $\left(x^{-\frac{4}{3}}y^{\frac{3}{5}}\right)^{15}$ **22.** $\left(x^{\frac{1}{4}}y^{-\frac{3}{8}}\right)^{16}$ **23.** $\left(8x^{15}y^{-9}\right)^{-\frac{1}{3}}$ **24.** $\left(-27x^{-9}y^6\right)^{\frac{1}{3}}$

25. $\left(-32x^{-10}y^{15}\right)^{\frac{1}{5}}$ **26.** $\left(32x^{20}y^{-10}\right)^{-\frac{1}{5}}$ **27.** $\left(\frac{81y^{16}}{16x^{12}}\right)^{\frac{1}{4}}$ **28.** $\left(\frac{16x^{14}}{81y^{18}}\right)^{\frac{1}{2}}$

● **Lesson 7-5** Solve. Check for extraneous solutions.

29. $\sqrt{13x - 10} = 3x$ **30.** $\sqrt{x + 20} = x$

31. $(4x - 12)^{\frac{1}{2}} + 3 = x$ **32.** $(7x)^{\frac{1}{3}} = (5x + 2)^{\frac{1}{3}}$

33. $\sqrt{x - 2} - \sqrt{2x + 3} = -2$ **34.** $\sqrt{10x} - 2\sqrt{5x - 25} = 0$

● **Lesson 7-6** Let $f(x) = x^2$ and $g(x) = 3x + 1$. Evaluate each expression.

35. $(f \circ g)(0)$ **36.** $(f \circ g)(2)$ **37.** $(f \circ g)(-3)$

38. $(f \circ g)(5)$ **39.** $(g \circ f)(0)$ **40.** $(g \circ f)(1)$

41. $(g \circ f)(-1)$ **42.** $(f \circ f)(3)$ **43.** $(g \circ g)(4)$

● **Lesson 7-7** For each function f, find f^{-1} and the domain and range of f and f^{-1}. Determine whether f^{-1} is a function.

44. $f(x) = 6x + 1$ **45.** $f(x) = \sqrt{x + 4}$ **46.** $f(x) = \sqrt{x - 3}$

47. $f(x) = \sqrt{-5x + 2}$ **48.** $f(x) = 3x^2 + 1$ **49.** $f(x) = 2 - x^2$

● **Lesson 7-8** Graph each function.

50. $y = \sqrt{x}$ **51.** $y = \sqrt{x} - 1$ **52.** $y = \sqrt{x} + 3$

53. $y = \sqrt{x + 3}$ **54.** $y = 4\sqrt{x}$ **55.** $y = \frac{3}{4}\sqrt{x}$

56. $y = 2\sqrt{x - 5} + 2$ **57.** $y = \sqrt[3]{x + 1}$ **58.** $y = \sqrt[3]{x - 2} - 3$

Lessons 7-1, 7-2, and 7-3

59. The time T it takes a pendulum to make a full swing in each direction and return to its original position is called the period of the pendulum. The equation $T = 2\pi\sqrt{\frac{\ell}{32}}$ relates the length of the pendulum ℓ, in feet, to its period T, in seconds. How long is a pendulum if its period is 3 seconds? Round the answer to the nearest tenth.

60. You can use the expression $D = 1.2\sqrt{h}$ to approximate the visibility range D, in miles, from a height of h feet above ground.
a. Estimate the visibility from a height of 900 feet.
b. How far above ground is an observer whose visibility range is 84 miles?

61. You can approximate the speed of a falling object as $v = 8\sqrt{d}$, where v is the speed in feet per second and d is the distance, in feet, the object has fallen. Express d in terms of v.

Lessons 7-4, 7-5, and 7-6

62. Halina works in a department store. Three times per year she is allowed to combine her employee discount with special sale prices. Let x be the retail price of a blouse.
a. Halina's employee discount is 20%. Write a function $E(x)$ that represents the cost of the blouse after the discount.
b. Due to a manufacturer's incentive, the blouse is marked down 25%. Write a function $M(x)$ that represents the sale price.
c. The sales tax on clothing is 6%. Write a function $T(x)$ that describes the cost of a clothing item with sales tax included.
d. Halina found a blouse to which the discounts apply. Use the function composition $f = T \circ E \circ M$ to write the function $f(x)$ that represents the price Halina will pay for the blouse.

63. You invest p dollars in an account that earns a simple interest of 6%. The function that represents the account balance at the end of the year is $f(p) = 1.06p$.
a. Suppose that at the end of the year you deposit $500 in the account. Write a new function $g(p)$ that shows the balance that will earn interest in the second year.
b. At the end of every year you add $500 to the account. The interest rate remains 6%. Write a composition of functions f and g to find the account balance at the end of the third year, before adding the $500. Find that balance for an initial investment of $1000.

Lessons 7-7 and 7-8

64. You can use the function $f(x) = 331.4 + 0.6x$ to approximate the speed of sound in dry air, where x is the temperature in degrees Celsius.
a. Write an algebraic expression for the inverse function $f^{-1}(x)$.
b. Evaluate $f^{-1}(x)$ for $x = 350$. Round the result to the nearest whole number. Explain what your result represents.

65. Nisha built a model rocket. The initial speed of the rocket is 64 ft/s. The equation $h(t) = -16t^2 + 64t$ describes the relationship between the height of the rocket h, in feet, as a function of time t, in seconds.
a. Write an equation for h^{-1}. (*Hint:* Use $t(h) = \ldots$.) Is this relation a function? Explain what this relation represents.
b. Write a function that can be used to find how long it takes the object to reach a given height h as it moves upward.

Chapter 8 Extra Practice: Skills and Word Problems

● **Lesson 8-1** Write an exponential equation $y = ab^x$ whose graph passes through the given points.

1. $(1, 10), (2, 25)$

2. $\left(2, 10\frac{2}{3}\right), (-1, 4.5)$

3. $(2, 6), (4, 54)$

4. $(-2, 0.05), (2, 12.8)$

5. $(2, 128), (-1, 16)$

6. $(-1, 12.25), (1, 4)$

● **Lesson 8-1** Without graphing, determine whether each equation represents exponential growth or exponential decay.

7. $y = 10^x$

8. $y = 327(0.05)^x$

9. $y = 1.023(0.98)^x$

10. $y = 0.5(1.67)^x$

11. $y = 1.14^x$

12. $y = 8(1.3)^x$

13. $y = 2\left(\frac{9}{10}\right)^x$

14. $y = 4.1(0.72)^x$

15. $y = 9.2(2.3)^x$

● **Lessons 8-1 and 8-2** Graph each equation.

16. $y = 3^x$

17. $y = 2(4)^x$

18. $y = 2^{-x}$

19. $y = \left(\frac{1}{4}\right)^x$

20. $y = 2^{3x}$

21. $y = 9^{-2x}$

22. $y = -0.1^x$

23. $y = -\left(\frac{1}{2}\right)^x$

● **Lesson 8-3** Write each equation in logarithmic form.

24. $100 = 10^2$

25. $9^3 = 729$

26. $64 = 4^3$

27. $\left(\frac{1}{2}\right)^4 = \frac{1}{16}$

28. $49^{\frac{1}{2}} = 7$

29. $\left(\frac{1}{3}\right)^{-3} = 27$

30. $625^{\frac{1}{4}} = 5$

31. $2^{-5} = \frac{1}{32}$

32. $6^2 = 36$

● **Lesson 8-3** Graph each logarithmic function.

33. $y = 2\log x$

34. $y = \log_8 x$

35. $y = \log_4 (x + 1)$

36. $y = 3 + \log x$

37. $y = -1 + \log_2 x$

38. $y = \log (x - 2)$

39. $y = \log (x + 2)$

40. $y = \log (x - 5)$

● **Lesson 8-4** Write each expression as a single logarithm.

41. $\log 8 + \log 3$

42. $4(\log_2 x + \log_2 3)$

43. $3\log x + 4\log x$

44. $\log 4 + \log 2 - \log 5$

45. $\log r - \log t + 2\log s$

46. $2\log x - 4\log y$

● **Lesson 8-4** Expand each logarithm.

47. $\log_b 2x^2y^3$

48. $\log_b 3m^3p^2$

49. $\log_b (4mn)^5$

50. $\log_b \frac{x^2}{2y}$

51. $\log_b \frac{(xy)^4}{2}$

52. $\log_b \sqrt[5]{x^3}$

● **Lessons 8-5 and 8-6** Solve each equation.

53. $\sqrt[3]{y^2} = 4$

54. $2 - 4^x = -62$

55. $\log x + \log 2 = 5$

56. $\log_3 (x + 1) = 4$

57. $e^x = 5$

58. $e^{\frac{x}{4}} = 5$

59. $\ln x - \ln 4 = 7$

60. $\log 4x = -1$

61. $\log 4 - \log x = -2$

62. $\ln 2 + \ln x = 4$

63. $4 + 5^x = 29$

64. $e^{3x} = 20$

Lessons 8-1 and 8-2

65. Mr. Andersen put $1000 into an account that earns 4.5% annual interest. The interest is compounded annually and there are no withdrawals. How much money will be in the account at the end of 30 years?

66. A manufacturer bought a new rolling press for $48,000. It has depreciated in value at an annual rate of 15%. What is its value 5 years after purchase? Round to the nearest hundred dollars.

67. You place $900 in an investment account that earns 6% interest compounded continuously. Find the balance after 5 years.

68. Bram invested $10,000 in an account that earns simple 5% interest annually.
  a. How much interest does the account earn in the first 10 years? Round to the nearest dollar.
  b. How much more would the account earn in interest in the first 10 years if the interest compounded continuously? Round to the nearest dollar.

69. Radium-226 has a half-life of 1660 years. How many years does it take a radium sample to decay to 55% of the original amount? Round your answer to the nearest year.

70. The population of Blinsk was 26,150 in 2000. In 2005, the population was 28,700. Find the growth function $P(x)$ that models the population.

Lessons 8-3 and 8-4

71. You can use the equation $N = k \log A$ to estimate the number of species N that live in a region of area A. The parameter k is determined by the conditions in the region. In a rain forest, 2700 species live in 500 km^2. How many species would remain if half of the forest area were destroyed by logging and farming?

72. The work done in joules (J) by a gas expanding from volume V_1 to volume V_2 is modeled by the equation $W = nRT \ln V_2 - nRT \ln V_1$, where n is the quantity of gas in moles (mol), T is the temperature in kelvin (K), and $R = 8.314 \frac{J}{mol \cdot K}$.
  a. Write the equation in terms of the ratio of the two volumes.
  b. Find the work done by 1 mol of gas at 300 K as it doubles its volume.

Lessons 8-5 and 8-6

73. The function $T(t) = T_r + (T_i - T_r)e^{kt}$ models Newton's Law of Cooling. It allows you to predict the temperature $T(t)$ of an object t minutes after it is placed in a constant-temperature cooling environment, such as a refrigerator. T_i is the initial temperature of the object, and T_r is the temperature inside the refrigerator. The number k is a constant for the particular object in question.
  a. A canned fruit drink takes 5 minutes to cool from 75°F to 68°F after it is placed in a refrigerator that keeps a constant temperature of 38°F. Find the value of the constant k for the fruit drink. Round to the nearest thousandth.
  b. What will be the temperature of the fruit drink after it has been in the refrigerator for 30 minutes?
  c. How long will the fruit drink have to stay in the refrigerator to have a temperature of 40°F?
  d. Will the fruit drink ever have a temperature of exactly 38°F? Explain.

74. The adult population of a city is 1,150,000. A consultant to a law firm uses the function $P(t) = 1,150,000(1 - e^{-0.03t})$ to estimate the number of people $P(t)$ who have heard about a major crime t days after the crime was first reported. About how many days does it take for 60% of the population to have been exposed to news of the crime?

● **Lesson 9-1** Suppose that x and y vary inversely. Write a function that models each inverse variation.

1. $x = 3$ when $y = 2$
2. $x = 4$ when $y = -1$
3. $x = 5$ when $y = 8$

4. $x = -6$ when $y = -2$
5. $x = -8$ when $y = 3$
6. $x = 10$ when $y = 15$

● **Lesson 9-2** Sketch the asymptotes and the graph of each equation.

7. $y = \dfrac{x + 1}{x - 2}$
8. $y = \dfrac{x - 3}{(x + 1)^2}$
9. $y = \dfrac{3x}{2x + 1}$
10. $y = \dfrac{8 - x}{x}$

11. $y = \dfrac{x - 4}{x^2}$
12. $y = \dfrac{2x + 1}{2x - 1}$
13. $y = \dfrac{x}{x + 3}$
14. $y = \dfrac{x + 2}{x - 4}$

● **Lesson 9-3** Find any points of discontinuity for each rational function.

15. $y = \dfrac{3x^2 + 2x}{x}$
16. $y = \dfrac{x^2 - 16}{x^2 + 4}$
17. $y = \dfrac{(x + 2)(x - 1)}{(x + 2)^2(x - 1)}$
18. $y = \dfrac{4}{x - 6}$

19. $y = \dfrac{9x}{3x^3 - 6x}$
20. $y = \dfrac{x^2 + 7x + 12}{x + 4}$
21. $y = \dfrac{x - 7}{x - 7}$
22. $y = \dfrac{x^2 - 3x + 2}{x - 1}$

● **Lesson 9-4** Simplify each rational expression. What are the restrictions on the variables?

23. $\dfrac{x^2 + 9x + 18}{x + 6}$

24. $\dfrac{x^2 + 3x + 2}{x - 1} \cdot \dfrac{1 - x}{x + 2}$

25. $\dfrac{x^2 - 2x - 8}{x + 3} \div \dfrac{x - 4}{x + 3}$

26. $\dfrac{2x^2 + 5x - 3}{x^2 - 4x} \cdot \dfrac{2x^3 - 8x^2}{x^2 + 6x + 9}$

27. $\dfrac{3x + 1}{x^2 - 6x - 6} \div \dfrac{6x^2 + 11x + 3}{x^2 + 4x + 4}$

28. $\dfrac{3x^4 - x^3 - 2x^2}{6x^2 - 2x - 4}$

● **Lesson 9-5** Add or subtract. Simplify where possible.

29. $\dfrac{6x + 1}{x + 2} + \dfrac{2x - 5}{2x + 4}$

30. $\dfrac{8}{x^2 - 25} + \dfrac{9}{x - 5}$

31. $\dfrac{x - 3}{x^2 + 3x} + \dfrac{7}{x + 3}$

32. $\dfrac{3x}{x^2 + 5x + 6} - \dfrac{2x}{x^2 + 8x + 16}$

33. $\dfrac{2}{x^2 - 1} - 3$

34. $\dfrac{2x}{x - 5} - \dfrac{x}{x + 7}$

● **Lesson 9-6** Solve each equation. Check your answers.

35. $\dfrac{x}{4} = \dfrac{x + 1}{3}$

36. $\dfrac{2}{x^2 - 1} = \dfrac{4}{x + 1}$

37. $\dfrac{3x}{5} + \dfrac{4}{x} = \dfrac{4x + 1}{5}$

38. $\dfrac{3x}{x - 2} = 4 + \dfrac{x}{5}$

39. $x + \dfrac{x}{4} - \dfrac{x}{5} = 21$

40. $\dfrac{3}{x + 4} + \dfrac{5}{4} = \dfrac{18}{x + 4}$

● **Lesson 9-7** Classify each pair of events as dependent or independent.

41. A main dish is selected at random; a type of salad is selected at random.

42. A department is selected at random; a class in that department is selected at random.

43. A volleyball team is selected at random from the league; one of the remaining teams is selected at random.

● **Lessons 9-1 and 9-2**

44. Sound intensity is inversely proportional to the square of the distance from the source—the farther from the source you are, the less intense the sound. Suppose the sound intensity is 30 watts per square meter (W/m^2) at 8 meters. What is the sound intensity at 4 meters?

45. The maximum load a cylindrical column can support varies directly as the fourth power of the diameter and inversely as the square of the height. A column that is 2 ft in diameter and 10 ft high can support up to 6 tons. If a column is 1 ft in diameter and 12 ft high, what is the maximum load it can support?

46. The force required to keep a car from skidding in a turn varies jointly with the mass of the car m, the square of its speed v, and the curvature k of the turn. The curvature is the reciprocal of the radius of the turn, $k = \frac{1}{r}$. Suppose it takes 2800 lb of force to keep an 1800-lb car from skidding at 45 mi/h on a curve with radius 425 ft. What force is needed to keep the car from skidding at 50 mi/h on a curve with a radius of 440 ft?

● **Lessons 9-3 and 9-4**

47. In her first 16 basketball games, Kimberlyn made 65.8% of her free throws. In the next game, she made 7 of 9 free throws. Let x be the number of free throws Kimberlyn tried in the first 16 games. Write a rational function that represents the percent of free throws made after 17 games.

48. The monthly cost $C(p)$ of removing p percent of pollutants from waste byproduct in manufacturing can be modeled by the function $C(p) = \frac{1500p}{100 - p}$. A manufacturer decides to spend $28,500 per month for removal of pollutants. What percent of the pollutant can the manufacturer expect to remove from the waste?

● **Lessons 9-5 and 9-6**

49. Michael rows downstream on a river. He then returns to the starting point. Michael traveled a total distance of 16 mi in 6.25 h. Michael's average rowing speed in still water is 4 mi/h. Assume the speed of the river current is constant. What is the speed of the river current?

50. It would take an apprentice house painter 1.5 h longer than his supervisor to paint an apartment. If they work together, they can complete the job in 4 h. About how long would it take the apprentice to complete the job working alone? Round your answer to the nearest tenth of an hour.

51. A master roofer can cover a garage in 1 h less than her new assistant. If they work together, they can complete the job in 7.75 h. How long would it take the assistant to complete the job working alone?

● **Lesson 9-7**

52. A game-show spinner has 26 equal sections labeled with the letters of the alphabet. What is the probability that on two consecutive spins you get your first and last initials, in that order?

53. The diagram at the right shows student membership in the math and science clubs. A student is selected at random. What is the probability that the student is a member of the math club *or* the science club?

54. You roll two number cubes. What is the probability that at least one of the numbers is prime *or* even?

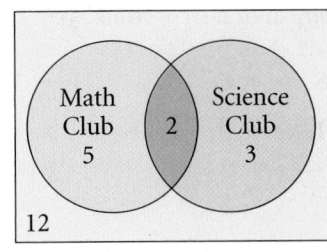

● **Lesson 10-1** Graph each equation. Identify the conic section and describe the graph and its lines of symmetry. Then find the domain and range.

1. $x^2 + y^2 = 4$

2. $x^2 - 16y^2 = 64$

3. $4x^2 + 9y^2 = 36$

4. $8x^2 - 16y^2 = 32$

5. $9x^2 + 9y^2 - 36 = 0$

6. $25x^2 + 4y^2 = 100$

● **Lesson 10-2** Write an equation of a parabola with its vertex at the origin.

7. focus at $(0, 3)$

8. directrix at $x = 4$

9. focus at $(0, -2)$

10. directrix at $y = \frac{1}{2}$

11. focus at $(0, 1)$

12. directrix at $x = 2$

13. directrix at $y = 3$

14. focus at $(0, -5)$

15. focus at $\left(\frac{3}{2}, 0\right)$

● **Lesson 10-2** Identify the focus and the directrix of the graph of each equation. Then sketch the graph.

16. $y = 4x^2$

17. $x = \frac{1}{16}y^2$

18. $-y = 10x^2$

19. $y^2 - 8x = 0$

20. $x^2 = 6y$

21. $y^2 = 20x$

22. $x^2 + 4y = 0$

23. $x^2 = -2y$

● **Lesson 10-3** Write an equation of a circle with the given center and radius.

24. center $(0, 0)$; radius 8

25. center $(-4, -6)$; radius 2

26. center $(-5, 1)$; radius 3

27. center $(1, 4)$; radius 5

28. center $(3, -2)$; radius 3.5

29. center $(0, -3)$; radius 1

● **Lesson 10-3** For each equation, find the center and radius of the circle.

30. $(x + 1)^2 + (y - 3)^2 = 4$

31. $(x + 6)^2 + (y + 9)^2 = 144$

32. $(x - 2)^2 + (y + 4)^2 = 16$

33. $(x + 8)^2 + (y - 1)^2 = 100$

34. $(x - 3)^2 + (y + 10)^2 = 25$

35. $(x - 7)^2 + (y - 2)^2 = 81$

● **Lesson 10-4** Find the foci for each equation of an ellipse. Then graph the ellipse.

36. $\frac{x^2}{9} + \frac{y^2}{25} = 1$

37. $\frac{x^2}{36} + \frac{y^2}{4} = 1$

38. $\frac{x^2}{100} + \frac{y^2}{121} = 1$

39. $\frac{x^2}{81} + \frac{y^2}{64} = 1$

40. $\frac{x^2}{49} + \frac{y^2}{144} = 1$

41. $\frac{x^2}{4} + y^2 = 1$

● **Lesson 10-5** Graph each equation.

42. $4x^2 - 25y^2 = 100$

43. $81x^2 - 16y^2 = 1296$

44. $y^2 - 4x^2 = 36$

45. $12x^2 - 3y^2 = 432$

46. $9x^2 - 121y^2 = 1089$

47. $x^2 - 64y^2 = 64$

● **Lesson 10-6** Identify the conic section represented by each equation. If it is a parabola, give the vertex. If it is a circle, give the center and radius. If it is an ellipse or a hyperbola, give the center and foci. Sketch the graph.

48. $(x + 1)^2 + (y - 2)^2 = 7$

49. $\frac{x^2}{89} + \frac{y^2}{62} = 1$

50. $\frac{x^2}{73} - \frac{y^2}{19} = 1$

51. $x + y^2 - 3y + 4 = 0$

52. $x^2 + y^2 + 16x - 6y = 11$

53. $3x^2 - 6x + y - 10 = 0$

● **Lessons 10-1 and 10-2**

54. The main mirror in the Hubble space telescope is parabolic. Its cross section is shown at the right. The focus of the parabola is 57.6 m from the vertex. Use this information and the diagram to find the equation of the parabola.

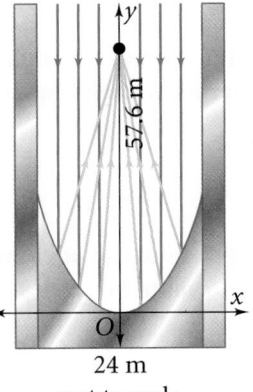

24 m

not to scale

55. Sports TV Group is designing a long-distance microphone for use at

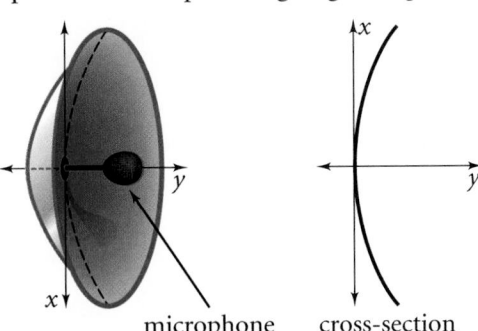

microphone   cross-section

football games. The microphone consists of a parabolic reflector and a sensor that is located at its focus. The equation for a cross section of the reflector is $y = \frac{1}{32}x^2$. All distances are measured in inches. What is the distance between the sensor and the vertex of the reflector?

● **Lessons 10-3 and 10-4**

56. A carpenter wants to cut a template for an elliptical window. He has a 10-ft by 3-ft rectangular piece of plywood. The carpenter plans to use a string to draw the top half of the ellipse, using a nail at each focus. The nails are along the bottom edge, 1 ft from each end.
  a. What length of string should the carpenter use to sketch the curve?
  b. If the x-axis is the bottom edge of the board, and $(0, 0)$ is the midpoint of that edge, what are the coordinates of the nails?
  c. Find the equation of the ellipse.

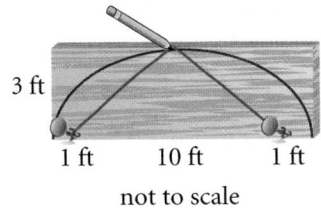

3 ft

1 ft   10 ft   1 ft

not to scale

57. A tanker truck carrying hazardous chemicals overturned on a highway, possibly spilling some of its cargo. Everyone within a 1.5-mile radius of the spill must be evacuated. The map that safety workers are using shows the spill site at coordinates $(4.5, 7)$. Each unit of measurement is 1 mi. Write an equation that describes the boundary of the evacuation region.

● **Lessons 10-5 and 10-6**

58. Some long-range navigation systems use hyperbolas to determine a ship's position. Suppose the system imposes coordinates so that the location of a ship is in the first quadrant. A ship is located at the intersection of the hyperbolas with equations $9x^2 - 4y^2 = 36$ and $16y^2 - x^2 = 25$. Find the coordinates of the ship to the nearest hundredth of a unit.

59. An engineer determines that the shape of a mirror surface in a motion sensor can be described by the equation $9x^2 - 25y^2 - 12x + 20y = 26$. Identify the conic section that represents the shape of the mirror.

60. One of the oldest known quadratic equations dates from the early Babylonian Empire about 1700 BC. An ancient mathematician posed this question:
  An area consists of two squares whose sum is 1000. The sides of one square are 10 less than $\frac{2}{3}$ of the sides of the other square. Find the sides of the squares.
  You can model the situation with a system: $x^2 + y^2 = 1000$; $y = \frac{2}{3}x - 10$.
  a. What conic section does the first equation represent?
  b. Use a graphing calculator to solve the system.
  c. Ancient Babylonians did not have graphing calculators. Use substitution to rewrite the system as a quadratic equation. Find the roots of the equation.
  d. In each of parts (b) and (c), you find two solutions. Explain why only one of them is reasonable for the situation.

Extra Practice: Skills and Word Problems

● **Lesson 11-1** Decide whether each formula is *explicit* or *recursive*. Then find the first five terms of each sequence.

1. $a_n = 3n + 2$

2. $a_1 = 4; a_n = a_{n-1} + 7$

3. $a_n = 5n(n + 2)$

4. $a_1 = 2; a_n = a_{n-1} - 3$

5. $a_n = 6n^2 - 1$

6. $a_n = 6 - 2n$

● **Lesson 11-1** Find the next three terms in each sequence. Write an explicit and a recursive formula for each sequence.

7. $3, 5, 7, \ldots$

8. $19, 15, 11, \ldots$

9. $-12, -10.5, -9, \ldots$

10. $0.2, 0.5, 0.8, \ldots$

11. $-23, -36, -49, \ldots$

12. $25, 37.5, 50, \ldots$

● **Lesson 11-2** Find the arithmetic mean a_n of the given terms.

13. $a_{n-1} = 10, a_{n+1} = 20$

14. $a_{n-1} = 7, a_{n+1} = 19$

15. $a_{n-1} = -2, a_{n+1} = -7$

● **Lesson 11-3** Write the explicit formula for each geometric sequence. Then generate the first five terms.

16. $a_1 = 6, r = 2$

17. $a_1 = -27, r = \frac{1}{3}$

18. $a_1 = 1900, r = 0.1$

19. $a_1 = -5, r = 3$

20. $a_1 = 1, r = 4$

21. $a_1 = 500, r = 0.2$

● **Lesson 11-4** Use summation notation to write each arithmetic series for the specified number of terms. Then evaluate each series.

22. $21, 19, 17, 15, \ldots; 8$ terms

23. $4, 7, 10, 13, 16, 19, \ldots; 10$ terms

24. $-35, -28, -21, -14, \ldots; 7$ terms

25. $97, 96, 95, 94, 93, \ldots; 20$ terms

● **Lesson 11-4** For each sum, find the number of terms, the first term, and the last term. Then evaluate the sum.

26. $\sum_{n=1}^{5} (2n + 3)$

27. $\sum_{n=2}^{7} (4 - n)$

28. $\sum_{n=1}^{5} (n + 1)$

29. $\sum_{n=3}^{10} (3n - 5)$

● **Lesson 11-5** Find the sum of each infinite geometric series.

30. $4 + 2 + 1 + \frac{1}{2} + \ldots$

31. $3 - 1 + \frac{1}{3} - \frac{1}{9} + \ldots$

32. $2.2 - 0.22 + 0.022 - \ldots$

33. $0.9 + 0.09 + 0.009 + \ldots$

34. $5 - \frac{5}{2} + \frac{5}{4} - \frac{5}{8} + \ldots$

35. $1 + 0.1 + 0.01 + \ldots$

● **Lesson 11-5** Determine whether each series is *arithmetic* or *geometric*. Then find the sum to the given term.

36. $3 + 6 + 9 + 12 + 15 + \ldots; 10$th term

37. $3 + 6 + 12 + 24 + 48 + \ldots; 10$th term

38. $-1000 + 500 - 250 + 125 - \ldots; 7$th term

39. $87 + 72 + 57 + 42 + \ldots; 20$th term

● **Lesson 11-6** Write and evaluate sums to approximate the area under each curve for the domain $0 \le x \le 2$. First use inscribed rectangles 1 unit wide. Then use circumscribed rectangles 1 unit wide.

40. $f(x) = 2x^2$

41. $y = x^3$

42. $g(x) = 2x + 3$

43. $h(x) = |x + 3|$

Lesson 11-1

44. A contractor must pay a penalty if work on a project is not completed on time. The penalty on the first day is $300. The penalty increases to $500 on the second day, to $700 on the third day, and so on.
 a. Write an explicit formula that describes the sequence.
 b. The contractor accumulated a penalty of $4500. How many days after the due date was the project completed?

45. Table tennis rules regulate the specific properties for the table, the ball, the net, and the paddles. According to the rules, a ball dropped from 30 cm above the table surface must bounce back to the height of 23 cm. This ratio of the drop height to the bounce height remains the same for any two consecutive bounces.
 a. Write the first five terms of a sequence that describes the bounce heights after an initial drop of 30 cm. Round your answers to the nearest tenth.
 b. Write an explicit formula that describes the sequence.

Lessons 11-2 and 11-4

46. a. Find the common difference for the arithmetic sequence that has 17 as its twelfth term and 71 as its sixth term.
 b. Write the explicit formula for the sequence.

47. The orchestra section of a theater has 25 seats in the front row, 27 seats in the second row, 29 seats in the third row, and so on. The pattern continues until the twelfth row. After that, every row has the same number of seats as row 12.
 a. How many seats are there in row 12?
 b. The orchestra section has 19 rows. How many seats are in the orchestra section?

Lessons 11-3 and 11-5

48. A fruit fly receives genetic material from two parents. Each parent also receives genetic material from 2 parents. So each fruit fly receives genes from 4 grandparents, 8 great-grandparents, and so on. How many ancestors does a fruit fly have going back 15 generations?

49. Suppose a dropped ball bounces back to $\frac{4}{5}$ of its original height. A ball falls from a height of 5 feet and keeps bouncing until someone picks it up. Estimate the total vertical distance the ball travels if no one picks it up.

50. A new company hires an executive. The company is not expected to make a profit right away, so the executive agrees to an alternative payment scheme. The first month, he receives $.01. Each successive month his salary doubles, until his annual salary exceeds $200,000. Then this salary remains as the maximum level.
 a. What is the total salary the executive receives in the first year?
 b. After how many months will the company start paying the executive the maximum salary under the contract?
 c. According to the contract, what is the maximum *annual* salary?

Lesson 11-6

51. The city park is being renovated. In the renovated part shown at the right, there are two flower beds and a grass lawn between them. The equations of the flower bed boundaries are $y = \pm\frac{1}{2}\sqrt{16 + x^2}$. The units in the coordinate system are meters. Round all answers to the nearest hundredth.
 a. Use 5 inscribed rectangles to estimate the area of each flower bed.
 b. Use 5 circumscribed rectangles to estimate the same area.
 c. Use the mean of your estimates in parts (a) and (b) to estimate the area of the lawn.

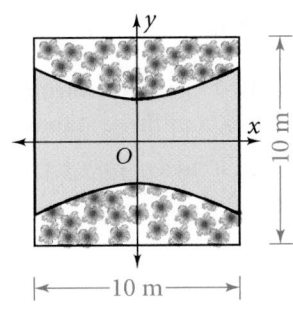

Extra Practice: Skills and Word Problems

● **Lesson 12-1** Graph the probability distribution for each sample space.

1. {the product of two number cubes an even number, the product an odd number}

2. {the sum of two number cubes a prime number, the sum a composite number}

● **Lesson 12-2** Use the data in the table to find each probability.

Characteristics of Camp Counselors

Grade Level	Male	Female
Junior	18	21
Senior	25	16

3. P(counselor a junior)

4. P(counselor female)

5. P(counselor a senior and male)

6. P(counselor a junior | counselor female)

7. P(counselor male | counselor a senior)

● **Lesson 12-3** Find the mean, median, and mode for each set of values.

8. 3 2 6 4 5 3 4 2 7 5 3

9. 16 62 24 13 21 35 24 17 20

10. 125 135 126 138 137 135 121

11. 6.1 9.5 3.8 4.6 6.1 2.3 3.7 2.1

● **Lesson 12-4** Find the mean, range, interquartile range, and standard deviation for each set of data.

12. 6 8 5 2 7 3 5 6 7

13. 25 29 21 19 30 26 28

14. 12 9 10 11 13 9 20

15. 100 98 101 100 102 97 100

● **Lesson 12-5** Find the margin of error for the sample proportion, given each sample size n.

16. $n = 90$

17. $n = 300$

18. $n = 125$

19. $n = 900$

20. $n = 1000$

21. $n = 5000$

● **Lesson 12-6** Find the probability of x successes in n trials for the given probability of success p on each trial.

22. $x = 2, n = 6, p = 0.7$

23. $x = 3, n = 8, p = \frac{2}{5}$

24. $x = 9, n = 10, p = 0.3$

25. $x = 7, n = 9, p = \frac{1}{5}$

26. $x = 4, n = 12, p = 0.8$

27. $x = 8, n = 11, p = 0.9$

● **Lesson 12-6** Use the binomial expansion of $(p + q)^n$ to calculate and graph each binomial distribution.

28. $n = 5, p = 0.2$

29. $n = 6, p = 0.4$

30. $n = 5, p = 0.7$

31. $n = 4, p = 0.2$

32. $n = 5, p = 0.4$

33. $n = 6, p = 0.8$

● **Lesson 12-7** Sketch a normal curve for each distribution. Label the x-axis values at one, two, and three standard deviations from the mean.

34. mean = 30, standard deviation = 4

35. mean = 45, standard deviation = 11

36. mean = 10, standard deviation = 2

37. mean = 60, standard deviation = 12

● **Lesson 12-1**

38. Suppose you have a spinner with five congruent sections numbered 1 through 5 and another with seven congruent sections numbered 1 through 7. Make a table and a graph to show the probability distribution for the sum obtained by spinning both spinners at the same time.

● **Lesson 12-2**

39. The probability that Luis wins the election for class president is $\frac{3}{5}$. The probability that Mac wins the election for class treasurer is $\frac{2}{3}$.
The probability that both will win the office they are running for is $\frac{1}{2}$. What is the probability that Luis wins given that Mac wins?

40. You toss two number cubes. The sum of the numbers is greater than 5. What is the probability that you tossed the same number on each cube?

● **Lesson 12-3**

41. All the scores on an Advanced Algebra final exam are shown below.

59 62 63 63 72 74 74 78 79 81
83 84 84 84 89 90 92 94 96 98

a. Find the mean, median, and mode for the data.
b. What percentile is the student who scored 89?
c. Draw a box-and-whisker plot for the data.
d. Identify any outliers in the data. Explain your choice.

● **Lesson 12-4**

42. The table shows 12 monthly averages of daily high temperatures in °F for San Antonio, Texas.

49.3 53.5 61.7 69.3 75.5 82.2 85.0 84.9 79.3 70.2 60.4 52.2

a. Find the mean and the standard deviation of the data. Round to the nearest tenth.
b. The high temperature on April 1 was 50°F. What is the z-score for that day?

● **Lesson 12-5**

43. In a survey of 380 art students 32% reported that their favorite color is red.
a. Find the margin of error for the sample.
b. Find an interval that is likely to contain the true population proportion.

● **Lesson 12-6**

44. Jean is visiting her grandparents in Houston for five days. She wants to arrange a lunch with friends. If she picks a day at random, there is a 20% chance that all of her friends will be available to meet for lunch. What is the probability that all her friends are available to meet for lunch on three different days?

● **Lesson 12-7**

45. The mean score on a quiz is 82 out of 100 possible points and the standard deviation is 4. Estimate the percent of scores that were 90 or higher.

46. A psychology professor gives a 100-item true/false test in a large college class. The mean score is 75.2 and the standard deviation is 8.1. The scores follow a normal distribution. What is the minimum score that is in the 99th percentile?

Chapter 13 Extra Practice: Skills and Word Problems

● **Lesson 13-1** Find the period and amplitude of each periodic function.

1.

2.

3.
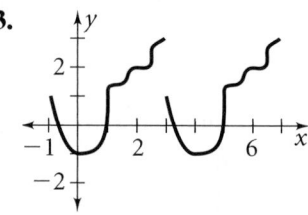

● **Lesson 13-2** Sketch each angle in standard position.

4. $15°$

5. $-230°$

6. $400°$

7. $-145°$

8. $280°$

9. $-750°$

● **Lesson 13-3** Write each measure in radians. Express the answer in terms of π and as a decimal rounded to the nearest hundredth.

10. $100°$

11. $270°$

12. $-45°$

13. $-550°$

14. $425°$

15. $10°$

● **Lesson 13-3** Write each measure in degrees. When necessary, round your answer to the nearest degree.

16. 5π radians

17. -2 radians

18. $\frac{5\pi}{6}$ radians

19. -3π radians

20. $-\frac{13\pi}{10}$ radians

21. 9 radians

● **Lessons 13-4, 13-5, and 13-6** Identify the amplitude or asymptotes, and the period for each function.

22. $y = 4 \sin 3x$

23. $y = \cos 4x$

24. $y = \frac{1}{3} \tan \pi x$

25. $y = 2 \cos \frac{x}{4}$

26. $y = 3 \tan x$

27. $y = \frac{1}{9} \sin 5x$

● **Lessons 13-4, 13-5, and 13-6** Sketch the graph of each function in the interval from 0 to 2π.

28. $y = 2 \cos x$

29. $y = 3 \sin 2x$

30. $y = \tan \frac{x}{2}$

31. $y = -\sin 3x$

32. $y = -2 \tan \pi x$

33. $y = \cos 4x$

● **Lesson 13-7** Graph each function in the interval from 0 to 2π.

34. $y = -3 \cos (x + \pi) + 3$

35. $y = 2 \sin \left(2x - \frac{\pi}{3}\right) - 2$

36. $y = -\sin \left(x - \frac{\pi}{4}\right) + 1$

37. $y = 3 \cos \left(3x + \frac{\pi}{2}\right) - 1$

● **Lesson 13-8** Evaluate each expression in radians.

38. $\cot 1$

39. $\sec 4$

40. $\csc (-0.8)$

41. $\sec (-\pi)$

42. $\cot \frac{3\pi}{2}$

43. $\csc \frac{\pi}{4}$

44. $\sec 1.1$

45. $\cot 2$

46. $\csc 2.5$

● **Lesson 14-2** Use a unit circle and 30°-60°-90° triangles to find the degree measures of the angles.

1. angles whose sine is $\frac{\sqrt{3}}{2}$

2. angles whose cosine is $-\frac{1}{2}$

3. angles whose tangent is $\sqrt{3}$

● **Lesson 14-2** Use a calculator to find the value in radians of each expression.

4. $\tan^{-1}(-1.6)$

5. $\sin^{-1}(-2.8)$

6. $\sin^{-1}1.2$

7. $\tan^{-1}3.8$

8. $\cos^{-1}0.5$

9. $\sin^{-1}(-2.1)$

10. $\tan^{-1}1.3$

11. $\cos^{-1}(-1)$

● **Lesson 14-2** Solve each equation for $0 \le \theta \le 2\pi$.

12. $4\cos\theta = 3$

13. $\sqrt{3}\sin\theta + \sqrt{3} = 0$

14. $2\tan\theta + 3 = \tan\theta$

15. $(\tan\theta)\left(\tan\theta + \frac{1}{2}\right) = 0$

16. $\cos^2\theta - \frac{1}{3}\cos\theta = 0$

17. $\sin\theta\cos\theta + \sin\theta = 0$

● **Lesson 14-3** In $\triangle ABC$, $\angle C$ is a right angle. Find the remaining sides and angles. Round your answer to the nearest tenth.

18. $m\angle A = 29°, b = 8$

19. $a = 7, c = 9$

20. $m\angle B = 52°, b = 10$

21. $a = 2, b = 4$

22. $m\angle A = 37°, c = 12$

23. $b = 5, c = 8$

● **Lesson 14-3** In $\triangle RST$, $\angle S$ is a right angle, $RS = 24$, and $\cos R = \frac{12}{13}$. Draw a diagram and find each value in fraction and decimal form.

24. $\sin R$

25. $\sin T$

26. $\cos T$

27. $\cot R$

● **Lessons 14-4 and 14-5** Use the Law of Sines or the Law of Cosines. Find the measure x to the nearest tenth.

28.

29.

30.

31.
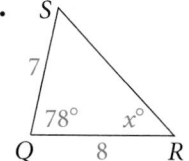

● **Lesson 14-6** Find each exact value. Use a sum or difference identity.

32. $\cos 15°$

33. $\sin 15°$

34. $\tan 315°$

35. $\cos 390°$

36. $\sin 105°$

37. $\tan 225°$

● **Lesson 14-7** Use a double-angle identity to find the exact value of each expression.

38. $\sin 120°$

39. $\cos 720°$

40. $\tan 480°$

41. $\cos 180°$

42. $\sin 180°$

43. $\cos 480°$

● **Lesson 14-7** Use a half-angle identity to find the exact value of each expression.

44. $\sin 90°$

45. $\cos 75°$

46. $\tan 75°$

47. $\sin 67.5°$

48. $\tan 67.5°$

49. $\cos 7.5°$

Skills Handbook

Problem Solving Strategies

You may find these strategies helpful when solving word problems.

STRATEGY	WHEN TO USE IT
Draw a Diagram	The problem describes a picture or diagram.
Try, Check, Revise	Solving the problem directly is too complicated.
Look for a Pattern	The problem describes a relationship.
Make a Table	The problem has data that need to be organized.
Solve a Simpler Problem	The problem is complex or has numbers that are too cumbersome to use at first.
Use Logical Reasoning	You need to reach a conclusion using given information.
Work Backward	You need to find the number that led to the result in the problem.

Problem Solving: Draw a Diagram

EXAMPLE

Two students leave school at the same time and travel in opposite directions along the same road. One walks at a rate of 3 mi/h. The other bikes at a rate of 8.5 mi/h. How far apart are the students after two hours?

Draw a Diagram:

After two hours, the students will be 6 + 17, or 23 mi apart.

EXERCISES

1. A bug starts at point $P(0, 0)$. Each time it moves, it crawls one half the distance traveled in the previous move. It travels east, north, west, south, east, north, and so on, in order. Its first move is east 16 units. Where is the bug after six moves?

2. Draw a graph to check this statement: The graph of $y = 2(x - 3) + 1$ is the graph of $y = 2x + 1$ shifted to the right 3 units.

3. Suppose you have four metal rods with lengths 2 in., 5 in., 7 in., and 9 in. How could you use all four rods to measure a length of 1 in.?

4. Two cars leave Los Angeles at the same time and follow the same route toward the Grand Canyon. The first car averages 55 mi/h. The second car averages 65 mi/h. How far apart are the two cars after five hours?

Problem Solving: Try, Check, Revise

When you are not sure how to start solving a problem, try an answer and then test it. In the process of testing, you may see a way to revise your trial answer to get closer to the actual answer.

EXAMPLE

The automatic leg-counter at the Brazinski farm counted 114 legs as the pigs and ducks swarmed through the gate at feeding time. A total of 40 animals passed through the gate. How many pigs and how many ducks passed through the gate?

Try   20 pigs   **Test** $20 \cdot 4 = $ 80 legs
          20 ducks $20 \cdot 2 = $ +40 legs
                                                          120 legs

Revise your guess. You need fewer pigs to bring the total number of legs down.

Try   18 pigs   **Test** $18 \cdot 4 = $ 72 legs
          22 ducks $22 \cdot 2 = $ +44 legs
                                                          116 legs

The number is still too high.

Try   17 pigs   **Test** $17 \cdot 4 = $ 68 legs
          23 ducks $23 \cdot 2 = $ +46 legs
                                                          114 legs

● Seventeen pigs and 23 ducks passed through the gate.

EXERCISES

1. Suppose the automatic leg-counter at the Brazinski farm counted 126 legs, but there were still a total of 40 animals. How many pigs and how many ducks passed through the gate?

2. Suppose the automatic leg-counter at the Brazinski farm counted 114 legs, but a total of 32 animals passed through the gate. How many pigs and how many ducks passed through the gate?

3. Marika biked a total of 110 mi during three days of training for a bicycle race. On the second day of her training session, she biked 15 mi more than on the first day but 5 mi less than on the third day. How many miles did she bike on the third day?

4. Use each of the integers from 1 to 9 once to fill the circles so that the sums along the spokes are equal. (Each spoke contains three numbers.)

5. Use each of the integers 2, 4, 6, 8, 12, 14, 16, 18, and 20 to fill the circles so that the sums along the spokes are equal.

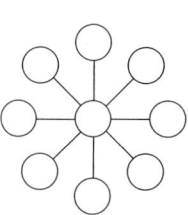

6. Find a and b such that $x^2 - x - 72 = (x + a)(x + b)$.

7. Approximate $\sqrt{385}$ to the nearest tenth.

8. Mr. Hoerner spent $45.50 last month to see 11 movies. If video rentals cost $3, movie matinees cost $4.50, and evening movies cost $7, how many of each type of movie did he see?

Problem Solving: Look for a Pattern and Make a Table

Some problems describe relationships that involve regular sequences of numbers or other things. To solve the problem you need to be able to recognize and describe the *pattern* that shows the relationship among the numbers or things. One way to organize the information is to *make a table*.

EXAMPLE

After scrounging around in the couch cushions, your father tells you he has found $2.40 in equal numbers of quarters, dimes, and nickels. He says you can have the money if you can tell him how many of each coin he has.

Make a table to help find a pattern.

Number of Nickels	1	2	3	4	5	6
Number of Dimes	1	2	3	4	5	6
Number of Quarters	1	2	3	4	5	6
Total Value	$.40	$.80	$1.20	$1.60	$2.00	$2.40

● Your father has six of each type of coin.

EXERCISES

1. Your father tells you that he has found $3.10 in equal numbers of quarters, nickels, and pennies. How many of each coin does he have?

2. **a.** A college radio station sponsors a contest once a week. One resident from a dormitory calls in and tries to answer ten questions correctly. Each correct answer earns the dorm $50, but each incorrect answer reduces the winnings by $25. Last week's contestant earned $350. How many answers were correct?

   b. The contest rules were changed so that each incorrect answer reduces the winnings by $50. A contestant earned $100. How many answers were correct?

3. **a.** Make tables to show the perimeters and areas of rectangles whose lengths are 1, 2, 3, 4, 5, 6, and 7 units and whose widths are 1, 2, 3, 4, 5, 6, and 7 units.
   b. Use the tables to find out whether there is a rectangle whose area and perimeter are numerically the same.

4. Lisa's school uniform is any combination of a white or light blue shirt, a dark blue skirt or a dark blue pair of slacks, and a plaid blazer. How many different outfits can she make?

5. How many different ways are there to make $.50 in change without using pennies?

6. How many different ways are there to make $.75 in change without using pennies?

7. How many ways can you roll two standard number cubes and get a sum of 7?

8. Suppose you have five 32¢ stamps and three 20¢ stamps. How many different amounts of postage could you make?

Problem Solving: Solve a Simpler Problem

By solving one or more simpler problems, you can often find a pattern that will help solve a more complicated problem.

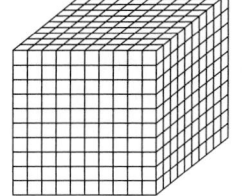

> ### EXAMPLE
>
> One thousand snap-together cubes make up a large cube measuring 10 units along each edge. The large cube is painted red and then taken apart. How many of the snap-together cubes are painted red on two sides?
>
> Begin with one snap-together cube, and then add cubes to make a larger cube. Find out whether there is a pattern.
>
> | Length of edge | 1 | 2 | 3 | 4 | 5 | . . . |
> |---|---|---|---|---|---|---|
> | Number of snap-together cubes | 1 | 8 | 27 | 64 | 125 | . . . |
> | Number of cubes with two sides painted | 0 | 0 | 12 | 24 | 36 | . . . |
> | Pattern | | | $12 \cdot 1$ | $12 \cdot 2$ | $12 \cdot 3$ | . . . |
>
> The pattern is that there are $12 \cdot (n - 2)$ snap-together cubes painted red on two sides.
>
> $12 \cdot (10 - 2) = 12 \cdot 8$ **Substitute 10 for *n*.**
> $ = 96$
>
> ● There are 96 cubes that are painted red on two sides.

EXERCISES

1. Six different cuts are made through the center of a pizza. How many slices are formed?

2. a. Find each sum at the right.
 b. Describe a relationship between the number of addends and the sum of each addition in part (a).
 c. Evaluate $1 + 3 + 5 + \ldots + 997 + 999$.

$1 + 3 = \blacksquare$
$1 + 3 + 5 = \blacksquare$
$1 + 3 + 5 + 7 = \blacksquare$
$1 + 3 + 5 + 7 + 9 = \blacksquare$

3. Find the total number of squares of all sizes on a standard checkerboard, a board with eight units on a side.

4. Suppose your heart beats 68 times per minute.
 a. How many times had your heart beaten by your 15th birthday?
 b. If you live to be 87 years old, how many times will your heart have beaten?

5. a. The Steuben County Regional Soccer League has ten teams. During a season, each team plays every other team twice, once at home and once away. How many games are played in one season?
 b. Suppose there are *s* teams in the league. How many games are played in one season?

6. First, Second, Third, and Fourth Streets run east and west. They intersect A, B, and C Boulevards, which run north and south. How many different one-way paths are there from the intersection of First Street and A Boulevard to the intersection of Fourth Street and C Boulevard?

Problem Solving: Use Logical Reasoning

Some problems can be solved without using numbers. They can be solved by *logical reasoning,* given some information.

EXAMPLE

Four pigs (Julie, Snowball, Ladybug, and Tina) and their owners (Juan, Suzanne, LaShawn, and Trevor) went home happy after winning prizes at the county fair. None of the pigs have the same first initial as their owners. Juan's pig is not Tina. LaShawn's pig got her name because she was born during a blizzard. Match the owners with their pigs.

Make a table to organize what you know.

	Julie	Snowball	Ladybug	Tina
Juan	X	X		X
Suzanne		X		
LaShawn	X	✔	X	X
Trevor		X		X

Juan's pig is not Tina, so put an X in that box.
LaShawn's pig must be Snowball.
Since the pigs and their owners have different first initials, put an X in each box along the main diagonal.

Use *logical reasoning* to complete the table.

	Julie	Snowball	Ladybug	Tina
Juan	X	X	✔	X
Suzanne	X	X	X	✔
LaShawn	X	✔	X	X
Trevor	✔	X	X	X

Juan must own Ladybug.
The only pig left for Suzanne is Tina.
The only possible pig for Trevor is Julie.

Juan owns Ladybug, Suzanne owns Tina, LaShawn owns Snowball, and Trevor owns Julie.

EXERCISES

1. The junior class is selling mugs with the school logo as part of a school-wide fundraising campaign. The top four salespeople in the class are Pat, Andy, Leon, and Shana. Pat sold more mugs than Andy but fewer than Leon. Shana also sold more than Andy, but she sold fewer than Pat. Andy sold the fewest mugs. Who sold the most mugs in the junior class?

2. Gregor has the same number of brothers as sisters. His sister Delores has twice as many brothers as sisters. How many children are in Gregor and Delores' family?

3. Ray has the same number of male classmates as female classmates. His classmate Rita has three fourths as many female classmates as male classmates. How many students are in the class?

4. Which expression(s) will be positive for all positive integers n?
   A. $2^n - n$ **B.** $n - 2^n$ **C.** $(n + 1) - 2^n$ **D.** $2^n - (n - 1)$ **E.** $2^n + n$

5. Four people, Luis, Marisa, Neil, and Ophelia, were on a bus. The florist sat next to Marisa. Luis and the surgeon are married to each other. The caterer, the editor, and Neil don't know each other. The surgeon was sitting behind Ophelia. Luis doesn't make salmon. Which person does which work?

Problem Solving: Work Backward

To solve some problems you need to start with the end result and work backward to the beginning.

EXAMPLE

A ball bounced four times, reaching one half its previous height with each bounce. After the fourth bounce, the ball reached a height of 2 ft. How high was the ball when it was dropped?

Each bounce reaches one half the previous height. So multiply by two to find the previous height. Work backward.

Bounce	4	3	2	1
Height	2 ft	4 ft	8 ft	16 ft

After the first bounce, the ball reached a height of 16 ft, so it must have been dropped from a height of 2(16) or 32 ft.

EXERCISES

1. A ball bounced four times, reaching three fourths of its previous height with each bounce. After the fourth bounce, the ball reached a height of 27 cm. How high was the ball when it was dropped?

2. On Friday, Kamiko deposited $475 in her account. On Sunday, she withdrew $150. On Tuesday she deposited $25 and withdrew $50. On Wednesday she wrote a check for $127.50. She now has $627.45 in her account. How much was in Kamiko's account before she made Friday's deposit?

3. The diagram at the right shows the final resting place of a ball on a billiard table. Suppose the ball bounced off the cushions of the table four times. Show where the ball was when it was originally set in motion. (*Hint:* The ball makes equal angles with the side when it rebounds.)

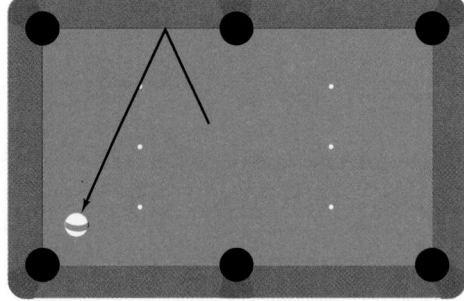

4. Suppose you start with a number. You multiply the number by 3, add 7, divide by $\frac{1}{2}$, subtract 5, and then divide by 12. The result is 5. What number did you start with?

5. Suppose you start with a number. You subtract 10, multiply by 3, add 5, multiply by $\frac{1}{4}$, and divide by $\frac{1}{3}$. The final result is 33. What number did you start with?

6. Derwood decided to sell a box of pencils. On Monday he sold half the pencils. On Tuesday he sold another 40 pencils. On Wednesday he sold half the pencils that were left. On Thursday he sold the remaining 25 pencils. How many pencils were in the box originally?

7. Tian rented a car to drive from his town to Chicago. The rental company charges $53 per day plus $.27 per mile. When Tian dropped the car off in Chicago three days later, his bill from the rental company was $453.57, which included 5% sales tax. How far from Chicago does Tian live?

Percents and Percent Applications

Percent means "per hundred." Find fraction, decimal, and percent equivalents by replacing one symbol for *hundredths* with another.

1 EXAMPLE Write each number as a percent.

a. $0.082 = 8.2\%$

Move the decimal point two places to the right and write a percent sign.

b. $1.20 = 120\%$

Move the decimal point two places to the right and write a percent sign.

c. $\frac{3}{5} = \frac{60}{100} = 60\%$

Write the fraction as hundredths. Then replace hundredths with a percent sign.

d. $1\frac{1}{6} = \frac{7}{6}$
$= 1.166\overline{6}$
$= 116.\overline{6}\%$

First, use $7 \div 6$ to write $1\frac{1}{6}$ as a decimal.

2 EXAMPLE Write each percent as a decimal.

a. $50\% = 0.50 = 0.5$

Move the decimal point two places to the left and drop the percent sign.

b. $\frac{1}{2}\% = 0.5\% = 00.5\% = 0.005$

To model a percent problem with an equation, express each percent as a decimal. There are three basic kinds of percent problems.

3 EXAMPLE Use an equation to solve each percent problem.

a. What is 30% of 12?

$n = 0.3 \times 12$
$n = 3.6$

b. 18 is 0.3% of what?

$18 = 0.003 \times n$
$\frac{18}{0.003} = \frac{0.003n}{0.003}$
$6000 = n$

c. What percent of 60 is 9?

$n \times 60 = 9$
$60n = 9$
$n = \frac{9}{60} = 0.15 = 15\%$

EXERCISES

Write each number as a percent.

1. 0.46
2. 0.3
3. 0.294
4. 1.03
5. 0.007
6. 1.506
7. $\frac{1}{4}$
8. $\frac{3}{8}$
9. $\frac{2}{3}$
10. $\frac{4}{9}$
11. $1\frac{3}{20}$
12. $\frac{1}{200}$

Write each percent as a decimal.

13. 40%
14. 8%
15. 150%
16. 0.7%
17. 103.5%
18. 3.3%

Use an equation to solve each percent problem.

19. What is 25% of 50?
20. What percent of 58 is 37?
21. 120% of what is 90?
22. 8 is what percent of 40?
23. 15 is 75% of what?
24. 80% of 58 is what?

25. In Louisiana the state sales tax is 4%. If you buy a $15,000 car in Louisiana, how much tax will you pay?

26. The Mississippi River drains about 1,247,300 mi^2, which is 13.3% of the land area of North America. Estimate the total area of North America.

Operations With Fractions

To add or subtract fractions, use a common denominator. The common denominator is the least common multiple of the denominators.

1 EXAMPLE Simplify $\frac{2}{3} + \frac{3}{5}$.

$\frac{2}{3} + \frac{3}{5} = \frac{10}{15} + \frac{9}{15}$ For 3 and 5, the least common multiple is 15.

Write $\frac{2}{3}$ and $\frac{3}{5}$ as equivalent fractions with denominators of 15.

$= \frac{19}{15}$ or $1\frac{4}{15}$ Add the numerators.

2 EXAMPLE Simplify $5\frac{1}{4} - 3\frac{2}{3}$.

$5\frac{1}{4} - 3\frac{2}{3} = 5\frac{3}{12} - 3\frac{8}{12}$ Write equivalent fractions.

$= 4\frac{15}{12} - 3\frac{8}{12}$ Write $5\frac{1}{4}$ as $4\frac{15}{12}$ so you can subtract the fractions.

$= 1\frac{7}{12}$ Subtract the fractions. Then subtract the whole numbers.

To multiply fractions, multiply the numerators and multiply the denominators. You can simplify by using a greatest common factor.

3 EXAMPLE Simplify $\frac{3}{4} \cdot \frac{8}{11}$.

Method 1 $\frac{3}{4} \cdot \frac{8}{11} = \frac{24}{44} = \frac{24 \div 4}{44 \div 4} = \frac{6}{11}$ **Method 2** $\frac{3}{{}_1 4} \cdot \frac{8^2}{11} = \frac{6}{11}$

Divide 24 and 44 by 4, their greatest common factor. Divide 4 and 8 by 4, their greatest common factor.

To divide fractions, use a reciprocal to change the problem to multiplication.

4 EXAMPLE Simplify $3\frac{1}{5} \div 1\frac{1}{2}$.

$3\frac{1}{5} \div 1\frac{1}{2} = \frac{16}{5} \div \frac{3}{2}$ Write mixed numbers as improper fractions.

$= \frac{16}{5} \cdot \frac{2}{3}$ Multiply by the reciprocal of the divisor.

$= \frac{32}{15}$ or $2\frac{2}{15}$ Simplify.

EXERCISES

Perform the indicated operation.

1. $\frac{3}{5} + \frac{4}{5}$ 2. $\frac{1}{2} + \frac{2}{3}$ 3. $4\frac{1}{2} + 2\frac{1}{3}$ 4. $6\frac{4}{5} + 1\frac{1}{9}$

5. $5\frac{3}{4} + 4\frac{2}{5}$ 6. $\frac{4}{5} - \frac{1}{5}$ 7. $\frac{2}{3} - \frac{3}{7}$ 8. $5\frac{1}{2} - 3\frac{2}{5}$

9. $8\frac{2}{5} - 1\frac{1}{10}$ 10. $7\frac{3}{4} - 4\frac{4}{5}$ 11. $\frac{3}{4} \cdot \frac{1}{2}$ 12. $\frac{9}{2} \cdot \frac{6}{7}$

13. $3\frac{4}{5} \cdot 10$ 14. $2\frac{1}{2} \cdot 3\frac{1}{5}$ 15. $6\frac{3}{4} \cdot 5\frac{2}{3}$ 16. $\frac{1}{2} \div \frac{1}{3}$

17. $\frac{6}{5} \div \frac{3}{5}$ 18. $8\frac{1}{2} \div 4\frac{1}{4}$ 19. $5\frac{5}{6} \div 2\frac{1}{3}$ 20. $3\frac{1}{6} \div 1\frac{3}{4}$

21. $7\frac{1}{2} + 3\frac{3}{4}$ 22. $3\frac{2}{3} \div \frac{1}{2}$ 23. $\frac{8}{9} - \frac{2}{3}$ 24. $7\frac{2}{7} \div 2\frac{3}{7}$

25. $\frac{7}{8} \cdot 5\frac{1}{2}$ 26. $2\frac{3}{4} \cdot \frac{5}{8}$ 27. $8 - 5\frac{5}{6}$ 28. $14\frac{1}{4} - 5\frac{2}{3}$

29. $4\frac{2}{3} + 1\frac{6}{11}$ 30. $5\frac{1}{4} \cdot 8$ 31. $3\frac{1}{2} \div 6$ 32. $8 \div 3\frac{5}{6}$

Ratios and Proportions

A *ratio* is a comparison of two quantities by division. You can write *equal ratios* by multiplying or dividing each quantity by the same nonzero number.

Ways to Write a Ratio

$a : b$ a to b $\frac{a}{b} (b \neq 0)$

1 EXAMPLE   Write $3\frac{1}{3} : \frac{1}{2}$ as a ratio in simplest form.

$$3\frac{1}{3} : \frac{1}{2} \longrightarrow \overset{\times 6}{\underset{\times 6}{\frac{3\frac{1}{3}}{\frac{1}{2}}}} = \frac{20}{3} \text{ or } 20 : 3$$

In simplest form, both terms should be integers. Multiply by the common denominator, 6.

A rate is a ratio that compares different types of quantities. In simplest form for a rate, the second quantity is one unit.

2 EXAMPLE   Write 247 mi in 5.2 h as a rate in simplest form.

$$\overset{\div\, 5.2}{\underset{\div\, 5.2}{\frac{247 \text{ mi}}{5.2 \text{ h}}}} = \frac{47.5 \text{ mi}}{1 \text{ h}} \text{ or } 47.5 \text{ mi/h}$$ **Divide by 5.2 to make the second quantity one unit.**

A proportion is a statement that two ratios are equal. You can find a missing term in a proportion by using the cross products.

Cross Products of a Proportion

$\frac{a}{b} = \frac{c}{d} \longrightarrow ad = bc$

3 EXAMPLE   Write a proportion. Then solve.

The Copy Center charges $2.52 for 63 copies. At that rate, how much will the Copy Center charge for 140 copies?

$$\begin{array}{l} \text{cost} \longrightarrow \\ \text{copies} \longrightarrow \end{array} \frac{2.52}{63} = \frac{c}{140}$$ **Write each ratio as cost : copies.**

$$2.52 \cdot 140 = 63c$$ **Use cross products.**

$$c = \frac{2.52 \cdot 140}{63}$$ **Solve for c.**

$$= 5.6 \text{ or } \$5.60$$

EXERCISES

Write each ratio or rate in simplest form.

1. 15 to 20

2. 85 : 34

3. 38 g in 4 oz

4. 375 mi in 4.3 h

5. $\frac{84}{30}$

Solve each proportion.

6. $\frac{a}{5} = \frac{12}{15}$

7. $\frac{21}{12} = \frac{14}{x}$

8. $8 : 15 = n : 25$

9. $2.4 : c = 4 : 3$

10. $\frac{17}{8} = \frac{n}{20}$

11. $\frac{13}{n} = \frac{20}{3}$

12. $5 : 7 = y : 5$

13. $\frac{0.4}{3.5} = \frac{5.2}{x}$

14. $\frac{4}{x} = \frac{7}{6}$

15. $4 : n = n : 9$

16. A canary's heart beats 130 times in 12 s. Use a proportion to find how many times its heart beats in 50 s.

17. According to the label, there are 65 calories in 4 fl oz of pineapple juice. How many calories are in 14 oz of the juice?

Simplifying Expressions With Integers

To add two numbers with the same sign, *add* their absolute values. The sum has the same sign as the numbers. To add two numbers with different signs, find the *difference* between their absolute values. The sum has the same sign as the number with the greater absolute value.

1 EXAMPLE Add.

a. $-8 + (-5) = -13$ **b.** $-8 + 5 = -3$ **c.** $8 + (-5) = 3$

To subtract a number, add its opposite.

2 EXAMPLE Subtract.

a. $4 - 7 = 4 + (-7)$ **b.** $-4 - (-7) = -4 + 7$ **c.** $-4 - 7 = -4 + (-7)$
$\quad\quad = -3$ $\quad\quad\quad\quad\quad\quad = 3$ $\quad\quad\quad\quad\quad\quad = -11$

The product or quotient of two numbers with the same sign is positive. The product or quotient of two numbers with different signs is negative.

3 EXAMPLE Multiply or divide.

a. $(-3)(-5) = 15$ **b.** $-35 \div 7 = -5$ **c.** $24 \div (-6) = -4$

4 EXAMPLE Simplify $2^2 - 3(4 - 6) - 12$.

Use the order of operations shown at the right.

$$2^2 - 3(4 - 6) - 12 = 2^2 - 3(-2) - 12$$
$$= 4 - 3(-2) - 12$$
$$= 4 - (-6) - 12$$
$$= 4 + 6 - 12$$
$$= 10 - 12 = -2$$

Order of Operations

1. Perform any operation(s) inside grouping symbols.
2. Simplify any terms with exponents.
3. Multiply and divide in order from left to right.
4. Add and subtract in order from left to right.

EXERCISES

Simplify each expression.

1. $-4 + 5$ **2.** $12 - 12$ **3.** $-15 + (-23)$ **4.** $4 - 17$ **5.** $-5 - 12$

6. $17 + (-18)$ **7.** $3 - (-5)$ **8.** $-8 - (-12)$ **9.** $-19 + 5$ **10.** $-8 + (-8)$

11. $(-7)(-4)$ **12.** $-120 \div 30$ **13.** $(-3)(4)$ **14.** $75 \div (-3)$ **15.** $(-6)(15)$

16. $(18)(-4)$ **17.** $-84 \div (-7)$ **18.** $(-13)(-3)$ **19.** $(-225) \div (-15)$ **20.** $-16 \div 8$

21. $-2(1 + 5) + (-3)(2)$ **22.** $-4(-2 - 5) + 3(1 - 4)$ **23.** $20 - (3)(12) + 4^2$

24. $\frac{-15}{-5} - \frac{36}{-12} + \frac{-12}{-4}$ **25.** $5^2 - 6(5 - 9)$ **26.** $4\left[(12)(3) - \frac{12}{3}\right]$

27. $\left(-3 + 2^3\right)\left(4 + \frac{-42}{7}\right)$ **28.** $(3 - 10)^2 + 3(-10)$ **29.** $(7 + 7)(7 - 7) - \frac{7}{-7}$

30. $5 - (-4)(-3) + 3^2$ **31.** $\left(\frac{-15}{5}\right)^2 \div (7 - 4)^2$ **32.** $[4(-3)]^2 + 4(-3)^2$

Evaluating Formulas and Solving Literal Equations

To evaluate a formula, first substitute the known values for the variables. Then perform the indicated operations.

1 EXAMPLE Find the volume of a cone that has a radius of 5 in. and a height of 10 in. Use the formula $V = \frac{1}{3}\pi r^2 h$.

$V = \frac{1}{3}\pi r^2 h$

$\approx \frac{1}{3}(3.14)(5)^2(10)$ **Replace π with 3.14, r with 5, and h with 10.**

≈ 262 in.^{3} **Round your answer.**

Sometimes you do not know values for the variables in a formula, so you cannot substitute. To solve a formula or a literal equation for one of the variables in it, use properties of equality.

2 EXAMPLE Solve $P = 2(\ell + w)$ for w.

$P = 2(\ell + w)$

$\frac{P}{2} = \ell + w$ **Divide each side by 2.**

$\frac{P}{2} - \ell = w$ **Subtract ℓ from each side.**

Thus, $w = \frac{P}{2} - \ell$.

EXERCISES

Evaluate each formula. Give decimal answers to the nearest tenth.

1. $P = 2(\ell + w); \ell = 3.2, w = 4$

2. $c = 0.5q + 0.5n; q = 3, n = 5$

3. $d = rt; r = 35, t = 2.4$

4. $y = 3.5x + 2; x = 1.5$

5. $y = (x + 2)(x - 2); x = 5$

6. $A = s^2; s = 10.5$

7. $a = \sqrt{c^2 - b^2}; c = 5.5, b = 3$

8. $d = 0.5gt^2; g = -32, t = 4.5$

9. $y = 2x^2 - 3x + 1; x = 6$

10. $A = \frac{1}{2}(b_1 + b_2)h; b_1 = 13, b_2 = 9, h = 8$

11. $V = \pi r^2 h; r = 4.3, h = 9.1$

12. $A = \frac{1}{2}bh; b = 13.7, h = 8.5$

Solve each equation for the given variable.

13. $P = 2(\ell + w); \ell$

14. $d = rt; r$

15. $2a + b = c; b$

16. $I = Prt; P$

17. $\frac{1}{2}x = y; x$

18. $2(x + a) = c; a$

19. $m + n + p = q; m$

20. $\frac{c + d}{2} = a; c$

21. $mnp = q; m$

22. $y = mx + b; m$

23. $2r + 3s = 1; r$

24. $3a = 2b; b$

25. $A = \frac{1}{2}bh; b$

26. $V = \ell wh; h$

27. $c^2 = a^2 + b^2; b$

28. $m = \frac{a + b + c}{3}; b$

29. The formula $V = \frac{1}{2}\ell(A_1 + A_2)$ relates the volume V of a log to its length ℓ and the areas of the ends A_1 and A_2. Solve the formula for ℓ and find the length of a log that has a volume of 23 ft^3 and end areas of 0.32 ft^2 and 1.58 ft^2.

30. The formula $A = \frac{1}{2}h(b_1 + b_2)$ relates the area A of a trapezoid to its height h and the lengths of its bases b_1 and b_2. Solve the formula for b_1 and find the length of a base of a trapezoid that has an area of 43 cm^2, a height of 10 cm, and one base of 5.2 cm.

Area and Volume

The *area* of a plane figure is the number of square units contained in the figure. The *volume* of a space figure is the number of cubic units contained in the figure. Formulas for area and volume are listed on page 910.

1 EXAMPLE Find the area of each figure.

a.

$A = bh$

$= 3.2 \cdot 1.8$

$= 5.76 \approx 5.8 \text{ cm}^2$

b.

$A = \pi r^2$

$\approx \frac{22}{7} \cdot \left(\frac{21}{10}\right)^2$

$= \frac{693}{50} = 13\frac{43}{50} \text{ in.}^2$

c.

19 mm
8.5 mm
23 mm

$A = \frac{1}{2}(b_1 + b_2)h$

$= \frac{1}{2}(19 + 23) \cdot 8.5$

$= 178.5 \text{ mm}^2$

2 EXAMPLE Find the volume of each figure.

a.

$V = \ell wh$

$= 7.5 \cdot 5.0 \cdot 3.3$

$= 123.75 \approx 124.8 \text{ cm}^3$

b.

$V = \frac{1}{3}Bh$

$= \frac{1}{3}(37^2) \cdot 24$

$= 10{,}952 \text{ ft}^3$

c.

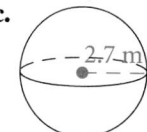

$V = \frac{4}{3}\pi r^3$

$\approx \frac{4}{3} \cdot 3.14 \cdot 2.7^3$

$= 82.40616 \approx 82.4 \text{ m}^3$

EXERCISES

Find the area of each figure.

1.

4 m
7 m

2.

$3\frac{3}{4}$ ft
$3\frac{3}{4}$ ft

3.

9 cm
5 cm
4 cm
6 cm

4.

10 in.

Find the volume of each figure.

5.

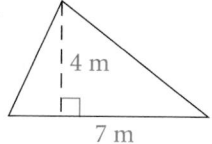

$4\frac{1}{2}$ ft
$4\frac{1}{2}$ ft
$4\frac{1}{2}$ ft

6.

8 m

7.

12 in.
5 in.

8.

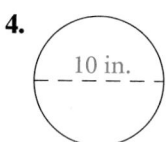

50 ft
60 ft
80 ft

9. Find the area of a triangle with a base of 17 in. and a height of 13 in.

10. Find the volume of a rectangular box 64 cm long, 48 cm wide, and 58 cm high.

11. Find the surface area of the cube in Exercise 5.

12. Find the surface area of the rectangular solid in Example 2a.

The Coordinate Plane, Slope, and Midpoint

The *coordinate plane* is formed when two number lines intersect at right angles. The ordered pair $(-2, 4)$ identifies the location of a point on the plane. From the origin, move 2 units to the left and 4 units up.

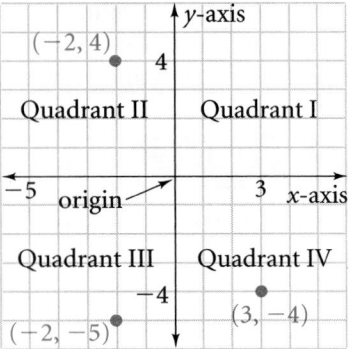

1 EXAMPLE In which quadrant would you find each point?

  a. $(3, -4)$ Move 3 units right and 4 units down. The point is in Quadrant IV.
  b. $(-2, -5)$ Move 2 units left and 5 units down. The point is in Quadrant III.

To find the slope of a line on the coordinate plane, choose two points on the line and use the slope formula.

2 EXAMPLE Find the slope of each line.

a.
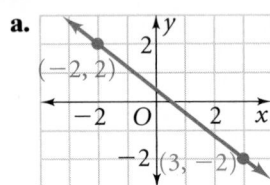

$$m = \frac{y_2 - y_1}{x_2 - x_1}$$
$$= \frac{2 - (-2)}{-2 - 3}$$
$$= \frac{4}{-5} \text{ or } -\frac{4}{5}$$

b.
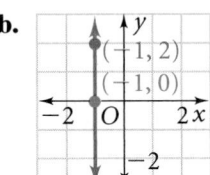

$$m = \frac{y_2 - y_1}{x_2 - x_1}$$
$$= \frac{2 - 0}{-1 - (-1)} = \frac{2}{0}$$

Since you cannot divide by zero, this line has an undefined slope.

Each coordinate of the midpoint of a segment is the mean of the corresponding coordinates of its endpoints. If (x_m, y_m) is the midpoint of the segment joining (x_1, y_1) and (x_2, y_2), then $x_m = \frac{x_1 + x_2}{2}$ and $y_m = \frac{y_1 + y_2}{2}$.

3 EXAMPLE Find the coordinates of the midpoint of the segment with endpoints $(-2, 5)$ and $(6, -3)$.

  $\frac{-2 + 6}{2} = 2$ and $\frac{5 + (-3)}{2} = 1$, so the midpoint is $(2, 1)$.

EXERCISES

In which quadrant would you find each point?

  1. $(3, 2)$ **2.** $(-4, 3)$ **3.** $(2, -3)$ **4.** $(4, -2)$ **5.** $(-4, -5)$ **6.** $(-1, -3)$

Graph each point on a coordinate plane.

  7. $(4, 0)$ **8.** $(-3, 5)$ **9.** $(4, -3)$ **10.** $(-5, -2)$ **11.** $(0, -2)$ **12.** $(-4, 5)$

Find the slope of each line.

13.

14.

15.
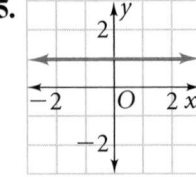

16. the line containing $(-3, 4)$ and $(2, -6)$

17. the line containing $(25, 40)$ and $(100, 55)$

Find the midpoint of the segment with the given endpoints.

  18. $(-4, 4), (2, -5)$ **19.** $(3, 3), (7, -6)$ **20.** $(-1, -8), (0, -3)$ **21.** $(3, 4), (2, -6)$

Solving Linear Equations and Inequalities

To solve a linear equation having one variable, use inverse operations and properties of equality to get the variable alone on one side of the equal sign.

1 EXAMPLE Solve each equation.

a. $3x - 11 = -5$

$3x - 11 + 11 = -5 + 11$ **Add 11 to each side.**

$3x = 6$

$\frac{3x}{3} = \frac{6}{3}$ **Divide each side by 3.**

$x = 2$

b. $\frac{2}{3}x + 1 = -5$

$\frac{2}{3}x + 1 - 1 = -5 - 1$ **Subtract 1 from each side.**

$\frac{2}{3}x = -6$

$\frac{3}{2} \cdot \frac{2}{3}x = \frac{3}{2} \cdot (-6)$ **Multiply each side by $\frac{3}{2}$.**

$x = -9$

Sometimes you can use the Distributive Property to simplify an equation.

2 EXAMPLE Solve each equation.

a. $2(x + 8) - 5 = 7$

$2x + 16 - 5 = 7$ **Distribute to remove parentheses.**

$2x = -4$

$x = -2$

b. $2x + 9 = 6x$

$2x - 2x + 9 = 6x - 2x$ **Subtract 2x from each side.**

$9 = 4x$

$\frac{9}{4} = x$ (or $x = 2.25$)

In solving an inequality, you must reverse the order of the inequality when you multiply or divide each side by a negative number.

3 EXAMPLE Solve and graph each inequality.

a. $\frac{x}{3} - 2 > -4$

$\frac{x}{3} - 2 + 2 > -4 + 2$

$\frac{x}{3} > -2$

$3 \cdot \frac{x}{3} > 3(-2)$

$x > -6$

b. $2x \geq 5x - 9$

$2x - 5x \geq 5x - 5x - 9$ **Divide each side by −3 and reverse the order of the inequality.**

$-3x \geq -9$

$\frac{-3x}{-3} \leq \frac{-9}{-3}$

$x \leq 3$

EXERCISES

Solve each equation.

1. $x + 4 = 3$

2. $3c - 7 = -13$

3. $8y - 3 + y = 51$

4. $6a = -48$

5. $\frac{1}{2}(s - 6) = 17$

6. $\frac{d}{3} = -8$

7. $\frac{4}{9}h = \frac{2}{3}$

8. $\frac{2}{3}r + 9 = 75$

9. $4(t + 5) = -36$

10. $7g - 3g + 2 = 6$

11. $3(x - 4) = 2x + 1$

12. $q + 4.5 = 3q - 2.7$

Solve and graph each inequality.

13. $9 + x \leq 15$

14. $-g < 5$

15. $7y + 2 \geq -12$

16. $9h > -18$

17. $\frac{s}{5} \geq 7$

18. $4 - a \leq 9$

19. $-\frac{c}{4} < 7$

20. $-\frac{3v}{5} > -\frac{9}{10}$

21. $t - 5.3 < -3.3$

22. $4y - 9y > -55$

23. $-5w > 2w - 21$

24. $\frac{3c}{7} \leq -\frac{2}{3}$

Absolute Value Equations and Inequalities

To solve an absolute value equation, get the absolute value by itself on one side of the equation. Then use the definition of absolute value to write two equations.

1 EXAMPLE Solve $|x| + 3 = 11$.

$|x| + 3 = 11$ **Subtract 3 from each side.**
$|x| = 8$ **The value of x is either 8 or −8.**
$x = 8$ or $x = -8$

2 EXAMPLE Solve $|p - 20| = 4$.

$|p - 20| = 4$ **The value of the expression $p - 20$ is 4 or −4.**
$p - 20 = 4$ or $p - 20 = -4$ **Write two equations.**
$p = 24$ or $p = 16$ **Solve for p.**

To solve an absolute value inequality, write two inequalities. Join the inequalities with *and* when $|x| < c$. Join them with *or* when $|x| > c$.

3 EXAMPLE Solve $|x - 3| < 5$. Graph the solution.

$|x - 3| < 5$
$x - 3 < 5$ and $x - 3 > -5$ **Write two inequalities joined by *and*.**
$x < 8$ and $x > -2$ **The solutions are all numbers less than 8 *and* greater than −2.**

4 EXAMPLE Solve $|x + 2| \geq 4$. Graph the solution.

$|x + 2| \geq 4$
$x + 2 \geq 4$ or $x + 2 \leq -4$ **Write two inequalities joined by *or*.**
$x \geq 2$ or $x \leq -6$ **The solutions are all numbers less than or equal to −6 *or* greater than or equal to 2.**

EXERCISES

Solve each equation.

1. $|y| = 8$
2. $|a| + 4 = 7$
3. $|c + 4| = 9$
4. $3|r| = 18$

5. $|5x| = 35$
6. $-7|p| + 4 = -17$
7. $|w - 8| = 7$
8. $|3t - 2| = 8$

9. $\frac{|v|}{4} = 5$
10. $\left|h + \frac{1}{2}\right| = 5\frac{1}{2}$
11. $|n - 7| = 0$
12. $8|z + 3| = 24$

Solve each inequality. Graph the solution.

13. $|x - 6| \leq 9$
14. $|a + 3| > 7$
15. $|r| \geq 7$
16. $|3y| > 39$

17. $|5p| \leq 12$
18. $4|k| + 3 \leq 5$
19. $|7x + 4| < 10$
20. $7|w - 5| \geq 21$

Graphing Two-Variable Equations and Inequalities

An equation in the form $Ax + By = C$ represents a line. To graph the line, first find the x-intercept and the y-intercept.

1 EXAMPLE Graph $2x - 4y = 16$.

$2x - 4y = 16$
$2x - 4(0) = 16$ **To find the x-intercept,**
$2x = 16$ **replace y with 0.**
$x = 8$ **Solve for x.**

The x-intercept is $(8, 0)$.

$2x - 4y = 16$
$2(0) - 4y = 16$ **To find the y-intercept,**
$-4y = 16$ **replace x with 0.**
$y = -4$ **Solve for y.**

The y-intercept is $(0, -4)$.

Plot the points $(8, 0)$ and $(0, -4)$. Then draw a line through the points.

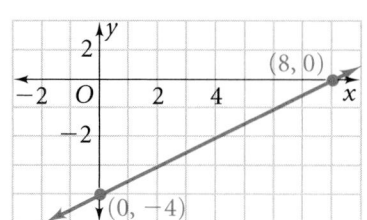

The equation $x = -3$ does not have a y-intercept. In this case, use *any* two points that lie on the line. For example, use $(-3, 1)$ and $(-3, 3)$.

A linear inequality describes a region of the coordinate plane that has a boundary line. Draw a dashed line when the inequality uses $<$ or $>$. Draw a solid line when the inequality uses $\leq$ or $\geq$.

2 EXAMPLE Graph $2x + y > 5$.

First, graph the boundary line $2x + y = 5$. Use the x-intercept $(2.5, 0)$ and the y-intercept $(0, 5)$. Since the inequality uses $>$, draw a dashed line.

Next, test a point. Use $(0, 0)$. $2x + y > 5$
$2(0) + 0 > 5$
$0 > 5$ **False**

The inequality is *false* for $(0, 0)$.
Shade the region that does *not* contain $(0, 0)$.

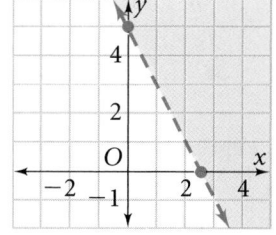

EXERCISES

Graph each equation or inequality.

1. $x + y = 6$

2. $2x + y = -4$

3. $x = 6$

4. $y = -3$

5. $3x - 2y = 12$

6. $x - 3y = -6$

7. $x - y = -3$

8. $y = x - 4$

9. $3x + 5y = 30$

10. $y = -4x + 5$

11. $2x - 5y = 20$

12. $4x + 7y = -21$

13. $y \geq -2$

14. $x + 2y < 8$

15. $4x - 4y > 8$

16. $x + 3y \leq 12$

17. $x - 5 < 0$

18. $7x - 4y > 12$

19. $y - 3x \leq 6$

20. $5x + 4y \geq 0$

21. $x + 5y \geq -8$

22. $y = \frac{2}{3}x + 2$

23. $\frac{2}{5}x - \frac{1}{2}y > 10$

24. $3y - x \leq 0$

Operations With Exponents

An exponent indicates how many times a number is used as a factor.

1 EXAMPLE Write using exponents.

a. $3 \cdot 3 \cdot 3 \cdot 3 \cdot 3 = 3^5$

      ↑

    five factors of 3

b. $a \cdot a \cdot b \cdot b \cdot b \cdot b = a^2 b^4$

      ↑   ↑

  two factors of *a*; four factors of *b*

$2^n = \square$	$10^n = \square$
$2^2 = 4$	$10^2 = 100$
$2^1 = 2$	$10^1 = 10$
$2^0 = 1$	$10^0 = 1$
$2^{-1} = \frac{1}{2}$	$10^{-1} = \frac{1}{10}$
$2^{-2} = \frac{1}{4}$	$10^{-2} = \frac{1}{100}$

The patterns shown at the right indicate that $a^0 = 1$ and that $a^{-n} = \frac{1}{a^n}$.

2 EXAMPLE Write each expression so that all exponents are positive.

a. $a^{-2}b^3 = \frac{1}{a^2} \cdot b^3 = \frac{b^3}{a^2}$

b. $x^3 y^0 z^{-1} = x^3 \cdot 1 \cdot \frac{1}{z} = \frac{x^3}{z}$

You can simplify expressions that contain powers with the same base.

3 EXAMPLE Simplify each expression.

a. $b^5 \cdot b^3 = b^{5+3}$ **Add exponents to multiply powers with the same base.**

      $= b^8$

b. $\frac{x^5}{x^7} = x^{5-7}$ **Subtract exponents to divide powers with the same base.**

      $= x^{-2} = \frac{1}{x^2}$

You can simplify expressions that contain parentheses and exponents.

4 EXAMPLE Simplify each expression.

a. $\left(\frac{ab}{n}\right)^3 = \frac{a^3 b^3}{n^3}$ **Raise each factor in the parentheses to the third power.**

b. $(c^2)^4 = c^{2 \cdot 4} = c^8$ **Multiply exponents to raise a power to a power.**

EXERCISES

Write each expression using exponents.

1. $x \cdot x \cdot x$

2. $x \cdot x \cdot x \cdot y \cdot y$

3. $a \cdot a \cdot a \cdot a \cdot b$

4. $\frac{a \cdot a \cdot a \cdot a}{b \cdot b}$

Write each expression so that all exponents are positive.

5. c^{-4}

6. $m^{-2}n^0$

7. $x^5 y^{-7} z^{-3}$

8. $ab^{-1}c^2$

Simplify each expression. Use positive exponents.

9. $d^2 d^6$

10. $n^4 n$

11. $r^3 \cdot r^2 \cdot s^7 \cdot s$

12. $x^5 y^2 \cdot xy^2 z^6$

13. $\frac{a^5}{a^2}$

14. $\frac{c^7}{c}$

15. $\frac{n^3}{n^6}$

16. $\frac{a^5 b^3}{ab^8}$

17. $(rt)^3$

18. $(3x)^2$

19. $\left(\frac{a}{b}\right)^4$

20. $\left(\frac{xz}{y}\right)^6$

21. $(c^3)^4$

22. $\left(\frac{x^2}{y^5}\right)^3$

23. $(u^4 v^2)^3$

24. $(p^5)^{-2}$

25. $\frac{(2a^4)(3a^2)}{6a^3}$

26. $(x^{-2})^3$

27. $(4a^2 b)^3 (ab)^2$

28. $(mg^3)^{-1}$

29. $g^{-3} g^{-1}$

30. $\frac{x^2 y^3 z^{-1}}{x^5 yz^3}$

31. $\frac{(3a^3)^2}{18a}$

32. $\frac{c^3 d^7}{c^{-3} d^{-1}}$

Factoring and Operations With Polynomials

When the terms of a polynomial are in descending order by degree and all like terms have been combined, the polynomial is in standard form.

1 EXAMPLE Perform each operation. Write in standard form.

a. $(3y^2 - 4y + 5) + (y^2 + 9y) = (3y^2 + y^2) + (-4y + 9y) + 5$ **To add, group like terms.**
$$= 4y^2 + 5y + 5$$ **Write in standard form.**

b. $8a^2(3a^2 - 5a - 2) = 8a^2(3a^2) + 8a^2(-5a) + 8a^2(-2)$ **To multiply, distribute $8a^2$.**
$$= 24a^4 - 40a^3 - 16a^2$$

c. $(n + 4)(n - 3) = n(n) + n(-3) + 4(n) + 4(-3)$ **Distribute n and 4.**
$$= n^2 - 3n + 4n - 12$$
$$= n^2 + n - 12$$

To factor a polynomial, first find the greatest common factor (GCF) of the terms. Then use the distributive property to factor out the GCF.

2 EXAMPLE Factor $6x^3 - 12x^2 + 18x$.

$6x^3 = 6 \cdot x \cdot x \cdot x; -12x^2 = 6 \cdot (-2) \cdot x \cdot x; 18x = 6 \cdot 3 \cdot x$ **List the factors of each term. The GCF is $6x$.**

$6x^3 - 12x^2 + 18x = 6x(x^2) + 6x(-2x) + 6x(3)$ **Use the distributive property to factor out $6x$.**
$$= 6x(x^2 - 2x + 3)$$

When a polynomial is the product of two binomials, you can work backward to find the factors.

$$x^2 + bx + c = (x + \blacksquare)(x + \blacksquare)$$

The *sum* of the numbers you use here must equal b.
The *product* of the numbers you use here must equal c.

3 EXAMPLE Factor $x^2 - 13x + 36$.

Choose numbers that are factors of 36. Look for a pair with the sum -13. The numbers -4 and -9 have a product of 36 and a sum of -13. The factors are $(x - 4)$ and $(x - 9)$. So, $x^2 - 13x + 36 = (x - 4)(x - 9)$.

Factors	Sum
$-6 \cdot (-6)$	-12
$-4 \cdot (-9)$	-13

EXERCISES

Perform the indicated operations. Write each answer in standard form.

1. $(x^2 + 3x - 1) + (7x - 4)$ **2.** $(5y^2 + 7y) - (3y^2 + 9y - 8)$ **3.** $4x^2(3x^2 - 5x + 9)$

4. $-5d(13d^2 - 7d + 8)$ **5.** $(x - 5)(x + 3)$ **6.** $(n - 7)(n - 2)$

Factor each polynomial.

7. $a^2 - 8a + 12$ **8.** $b^3 + 6b^2$ **9.** $n^2 - 2n - 8$ **10.** $x^2 + 5x + 4$

11. $3m^2 - 9$ **12.** $y^2 + 5y - 24$ **13.** $s^3 + 6s^2 + 11s$ **14.** $2x^3 + 4x^2 - 8x$

15. $y^2 - 10y + 25$ **16.** $3r^2 - 48$ **17.** $2x^2 + 5x - 12$ **18.** $4w^2 - 9$

Scientific Notation and Significant Digits

In *scientific notation*, a number has the form $a \times 10^n$, where n is an integer and $1 \leq a < 10$.

① EXAMPLE Write 5.59×10^6 in standard form.

$5.59 \times 10^6 = 5\,590\,000$ **A positive exponent indicates a value greater than 1.**
                                    Move the decimal point six places to the right.
           $= 5,590,000$

② EXAMPLE Write $0.000\,031\,8$ in scientific notation.

$0.0000318 = 3.18 \times 10^{-5}$ **Move the decimal point to create a number between 1 and 10 (five places to the right). Since the original number is less than 1, use a negative exponent.**

When a measurement is in scientific notation, all the digits of the number between 1 and 10 are *significant digits*. When you multiply or divide measurements, your answer should have as many significant digits as the least number of significant digits in any of the numbers involved.

③ EXAMPLE Multiply $\left(6.71 \times 10^8 \text{ mi/h}\right)$ and $\left(3.8 \times 10^4 \text{ h}\right)$.

$$\left(6.71 \times 10^8 \text{ mi/h}\right)\left(3.8 \times 10^4 \text{ h}\right) = (6.71 \cdot 3.8)(10^8 \cdot 10^4)$$ **Rearrange factors.**
$$= 25.498 \times 10^{12}$$ **Add exponents when multiplying powers of 10.**
$$= 2.5498 \times 10^{13}$$ **Write in scientific notation.**
$$\approx 2.5 \times 10^{13} \text{ mi}$$ **Round to two significant digits.**

    three significant digits   **two significant digits**

④ EXAMPLE Simplify $\dfrac{6.332 \times 10^5}{1.6 \times 10^{-2}}$.

$$\frac{6.332 \times 10^5}{1.6 \times 10^{-2}} = \frac{6.332}{1.6} \times 10^{5-(-2)}$$ **Subtract exponents when dividing powers of 10.**
$$= 3.9575 \times 10^7$$ **Simplify.**
$$\approx 4.0 \times 10^7$$ **Round to two significant digits.**

EXERCISES

Change each number to scientific notation or to standard form.

1. 1,340,000   **2.** 6.88×10^{-2} **3.** 0.000775   **4.** 0.0072   **5.** 1.113×10^5

6. 8.0×10^{-4} **7.** 1895   **8.** 2.3×10^3 **9.** 123,400   **10.** 7.985×10^4

Write each product or quotient in scientific notation. Round to the appropriate number of significant digits.

11. $\left(1.6 \times 10^2\right)\left(4.0 \times 10^3\right)$ **12.** $\left(2.5 \times 10^{-3}\right)\left(1.2 \times 10^4\right)$ **13.** $\left(4.237 \times 10^4\right)\left(2.01 \times 10^{-2}\right)$

14. $\dfrac{7.0 \times 10^5}{2.89 \times 10^3}$ **15.** $\dfrac{1.4 \times 10^4}{8.0 \times 10^2}$ **16.** $\dfrac{6.48 \times 10^6}{3.2 \times 10^5}$

17. $\left(1.78 \times 10^{-7}\right)\left(5.03 \times 10^{-5}\right)$ **18.** $\left(7.2 \times 10^{11}\right)\left(5 \times 10^6\right)$ **19.** $\left(8.90 \times 10^8\right) \div \left(2.36 \times 10^{-2}\right)$

20. $\left(3.95 \times 10^4\right) \div \left(6.8 \times 10^8\right)$ **21.** $\left(4.9 \times 10^{-8}\right) \div \left(2.7 \times 10^{-2}\right)$ **22.** $\left(3.972 \times 10^{-5}\right)\left(4.7 \times 10^{-4}\right)$

Operations With Radicals

To simplify a radical, remove all perfect square factors from the radicand.

1 EXAMPLE Simplify $\sqrt{75}$.

$\sqrt{75} = \sqrt{25 \cdot 3} = \sqrt{25} \cdot \sqrt{3} = 5\sqrt{3}$ **Use the property $\sqrt{ab} = \sqrt{a} \cdot \sqrt{b}$.**

2 EXAMPLE Simplify $\sqrt{18} - \sqrt{50} + \sqrt{27}$.

$$\sqrt{18} - \sqrt{50} + \sqrt{27} = \sqrt{9 \cdot 2} - \sqrt{25 \cdot 2} + \sqrt{9 \cdot 3} \quad \textbf{Simplify each radical.}$$
$$= 3\sqrt{2} - 5\sqrt{2} + 3\sqrt{3} \qquad\qquad \textbf{Use the distributive property}$$
$$= (3 - 5)\sqrt{2} + 3\sqrt{3} \qquad\qquad \textbf{to combine like terms.}$$
$$= -2\sqrt{2} + 3\sqrt{3}$$

To remove a radical from the denominator of a fraction, you *rationalize* the denominator. Make the denominator rational by multiplying by a form of 1.

3 EXAMPLE Simplify each expression.

a. $\dfrac{5}{\sqrt{3}} = \dfrac{5}{\sqrt{3}} \cdot \dfrac{\sqrt{3}}{\sqrt{3}}$ **Multiply the fraction by $\dfrac{\sqrt{3}}{\sqrt{3}}$ to make the denominator a rational number.**

$= \dfrac{5\sqrt{3}}{\sqrt{9}} = \dfrac{5\sqrt{3}}{3}$

b. $\dfrac{2}{\sqrt{3}} \cdot \sqrt{\dfrac{5}{6}} = \dfrac{2}{\sqrt{3}} \cdot \dfrac{\sqrt{5}}{\sqrt{6}}$ **Use the property $\sqrt{\dfrac{a}{b}} = \dfrac{\sqrt{a}}{\sqrt{b}}$.**

$= \dfrac{2\sqrt{5}}{\sqrt{18}}$ **Multiply radicals.**

$= \dfrac{2\sqrt{5}\sqrt{2}}{\sqrt{18}\sqrt{2}}$ **Multiply by $\dfrac{\sqrt{2}}{\sqrt{2}}$ to make the denominator a rational number.**

$= \dfrac{2\sqrt{10}}{\sqrt{36}}$

$= \dfrac{2\sqrt{10}}{6} = \dfrac{\sqrt{10}}{3}$

EXERCISES

Simplify each radical expression.

1. $\sqrt{36}$ **2.** $\sqrt{72}$ **3.** $\sqrt{18}$ **4.** $\sqrt{108}$ **5.** $\sqrt{54}$

6. $\sqrt{60}$ **7.** $\sqrt{300}$ **8.** $\sqrt{\dfrac{1}{2}}$ **9.** $\dfrac{2}{\sqrt{3}}$ **10.** $\dfrac{3}{\sqrt{5}}$

11. $\dfrac{\sqrt{2}}{\sqrt{5}}$ **12.** $\dfrac{\sqrt{3}}{\sqrt{8}}$ **13.** $\dfrac{1}{\sqrt{2}} \cdot \dfrac{\sqrt{3}}{\sqrt{2}}$ **14.** $\sqrt{\dfrac{2}{3}} \cdot \sqrt{\dfrac{5}{6}}$ **15.** $\dfrac{\sqrt{2}}{3} \cdot \sqrt{\dfrac{8}{5}}$

16. $\sqrt{\dfrac{2}{7}} \cdot \sqrt{\dfrac{8}{7}}$ **17.** $\dfrac{2}{\sqrt{2}} \cdot \sqrt{\dfrac{5}{3}}$ **18.** $\sqrt{2} + \sqrt{2}$

19. $3\sqrt{5} + 2\sqrt{5}$ **20.** $7\sqrt{7} - \sqrt{7}$ **21.** $4\sqrt{3} - 3\sqrt{3}$

22. $\sqrt{18} + \sqrt{98}$ **23.** $\sqrt{8} - \sqrt{50}$ **24.** $\sqrt{6} + \sqrt{24}$

25. $\sqrt{40} + \sqrt{90}$ **26.** $\sqrt{27} + \sqrt{75} - \sqrt{12}$ **27.** $\sqrt{45} + \sqrt{20} + \sqrt{5}$

28. $\sqrt{3} - \sqrt{75} + \sqrt{18}$ **29.** $\sqrt{98} + \sqrt{50} - \sqrt{5}$ **30.** $\sqrt{5} + \sqrt{3} - \sqrt{180}$

The Pythagorean Theorem and the Distance Formula

In a right triangle, the sum of the squares of the lengths of the legs is equal to the square of the length of the hypotenuse. Use this relationship, known as the Pythagorean Theorem, to find the length of a side of a right triangle.

The Pythagorean Theorem

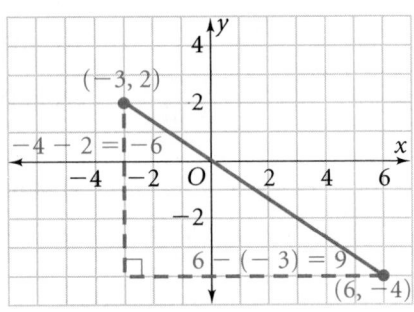

$a^2 + b^2 = c^2$

1 EXAMPLE Find m in the triangle below, to the nearest tenth.

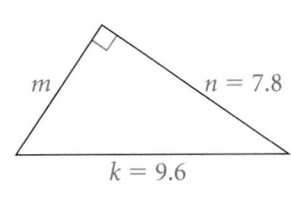

$$m^2 + n^2 = k^2$$
$$m^2 + 7.8^2 = 9.6^2$$
$$m^2 = 9.6^2 - 7.8^2$$
$$m^2 = 31.32$$
$$m = \sqrt{31.32}$$
$$\approx 5.6$$

● Thus, m is about 5.6 units.

To find the distance between two points on the coordinate plane, use the distance formula.

The distance d between any two points (x_1, y_1) and (x_2, y_2) is
$$d = \sqrt{(x_2 - x_1)^2 + (y_2 - y_1)^2}.$$

2 EXAMPLE Find the distance between $(-3, 2)$ and $(6, -4)$.

$$d = \sqrt{(6 - (-3))^2 + (-4 - 2)^2}$$
$$= \sqrt{9^2 + (-6)^2}$$
$$= \sqrt{81 + 36}$$
$$= \sqrt{117}$$
$$\approx 10.8$$

● Thus, d is about 10.8 units.

EXERCISES

In each problem, a and b are the lengths of the legs of a right triangle and c is the length of the hypotenuse. Find each missing length.

1. c if $a = 6$ and $b = 8$

2. a if $b = 12$ and $c = 13$

3. b if $a = 8$ and $c = 17$

4. c if $a = 10$ and $b = 3$

5. a if $b = 7$ and $c = 25$

6. b if $a = 24$ and $c = 40$

7. a if $b = 100$ and $c = 114$

8. b if $a = 12.0$ and $c = 30.1$

9. c if $a = 8.3$ and $b = 3.3$

Find the distance between each pair of points, to the nearest tenth.

10. $(0, 0), (4, -3)$

11. $(-5, -5), (1, 3)$

12. $(-1, 0), (4, 12)$

13. $(0, 15), (17, 0)$

14. $(-4, 2), (4, -2)$

15. $(-8, -8), (8, 8)$

16. $(-1, 1), (1, -1)$

17. $(-2, 9), (0, 0)$

18. $(-5, 3), (4, 3)$

19. $(-2, 1), (3, 4)$

20. $(3, -2), (3, 5)$

21. $(5, 4), (-3, 1)$

Bar and Circle Graphs

Sometimes you can draw different graphs to represent the same data, depending on the information you want to share. A *bar graph* is useful for comparing amounts; a *circle graph* is useful for comparing percents.

EXAMPLE Display the 1998 data on immigration to the United States in a bar graph and a circle graph.

Immigration to the United States, 1998

Place of Origin	Immigrants (1000's)
Africa	40.7
Asia	219.7
Europe	90.8
North America	253.0
South America	45.4

Source: U.S. Immigration and Naturalization Service.
Go to **www.PHSchool.com** for a data update.
Web Code: bbg-9041

To make a bar graph, place the categories along the bottom axis. Decide on a scale for the side axis. An appropriate scale would be 0–300, marked in intervals of 50. For each data item, draw a bar whose height is equal to the data value.

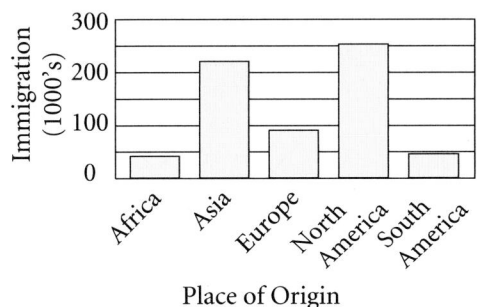

Immigration to the United States, 1998

To make a circle graph, first find the *percent* of the data in each category. Then express each percent as a decimal and multiply by 360° to find the size of each *central angle*.

Africa → total → $\frac{40.7}{649.6} \approx 0.06$ or 6%

$0.06 \times 360° \approx 22°$

Draw a circle and use a protractor to draw each central angle.

Immigration to the United States, 1998

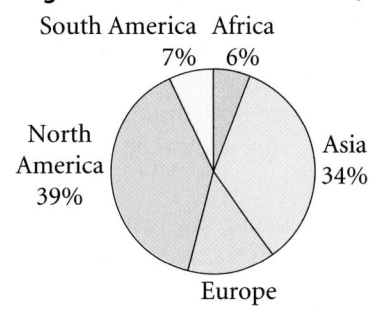

EXERCISES

Display the data from each table in a bar graph and a circle graph.

1.

NASA Space Shuttle Expenses, 2000

Operation	Millions of Dollars
Orbiter, integration	698.8
Propulsion	1,053.1
Mission, launch operations	738.8
Flight operations	244.6
Ground operations	510.3

Source: U.S. National Aeronautics and Space Administration.
Go to **www.PHSchool.com** for a data update.
Web Code: bbg-9041

2.

Cable TV Revenue, 1999

	Millions of Dollars
Advertising, programs	20,068
Basic service	26,890
Pay-per-view, premium services	6,324
Installation	765
Other	5,727

Source: U.S. Census Bureau. Go to **www.PHSchool.com** for a data update.
Web Code: bbg-9041

Descriptive Statistics and Histograms

For numerical data, you can find the *mean,* the *median,* and the *mode.*

Mean The sum of the data values in a data set divided by the number of data values

Median The middle value of a data set that has been arranged in increasing or decreasing order. If the data set has an even number of values, the median is the mean of the middle two values.

Mode The most frequently occurring value in a data set

1 EXAMPLE Find the mean, median, and mode for the following data set.
5   7   6   3   1   7   9   5   10   7

Mean $\dfrac{5 + 7 + 6 + 3 + 1 + 7 + 9 + 5 + 10 + 7}{10} = 6$

Median   5, 7, 6, 3, 1, 7, 9, 5, 10, 7 **Rearrange the numbers from least to greatest.**

1, 3, 5, 5, 6, 7, 7, 7, 9, 10 **The median is the mean of the two middle numbers, 6 and 7.**

The median is $\dfrac{6 + 7}{2} = 6.5$.

Mode   The most frequently occurring data value is 7.

The frequency of a data value is the number of times it occurs in a data set.
A *histogram* is a bar graph that shows the frequency of each data value.

2 EXAMPLE Use the survey results to make a histogram for the cost of a movie ticket at various theaters.

Survey of Movie Ticket Prices
$5 $6 $5 $7 $6 $7 $6 $8 $6

Movie Ticket Prices

EXERCISES

Find the mean, the median, and the mode of each data set.

1. −3 4 5 5 −2 7 1 8 9

2. 0 0 1 1 2 3 3 5 3 8 7

3. 2.4 2.4 2.3 2.3 2.4 12.0

4. 1 1 1 1 2 2 2 3 3 4

5. 1.2 1.3 1.4 1.5 1.6 1.7 1.8

6. −4 −3 −2 −1 0 1 2 3 4

Make a histogram for each data set.

7. 7 4 8 6 6 8 7 7 5 7

8. 73 75 76 75 74 75 76 74 76 75

Operations With Rational Expressions

A *rational expression* is an expression that can be written in the form $\frac{polynomial}{polynomial}$, where the denominator is not zero. A rational expression is in simplest form if the numerator and denominator have no common factors except 1.

1 EXAMPLE Write the expression $\frac{4x + 8}{x + 2}$ in simplest form.

$\frac{4x + 8}{x + 2} = \frac{4(x + 2)}{x + 2}$ **Factor the numerator.**

$= 4$ **Divide out the common factor $x + 2$.**

To add or subtract two rational expressions, use a common denominator.

2 EXAMPLE Simplify $\frac{x}{2y} + \frac{x}{3y}$.

$\frac{x}{2y} + \frac{x}{3y} = \frac{x}{2y} \cdot \frac{3}{3} + \frac{x}{3y} \cdot \frac{2}{2}$ **The common denominator of $3y$ and $2y$ is $6y$.**

$= \frac{3x}{6y} + \frac{2x}{6y}$

$= \frac{5x}{6y}$ **Add the numerators. Place the sum over the common denominator.**

To multiply rational expressions, first find and divide out any common factors in the numerators and the denominators. Then multiply the remaining numerators and denominators. To divide rational expressions, first use a reciprocal to change the problem to multiplication.

3 EXAMPLE Simplify $\frac{40x^2}{21} \div \frac{5x}{14}$.

$\frac{40x^2}{21} \div \frac{5x}{14} = \frac{40x^2}{21} \cdot \frac{14}{5x}$ **Change dividing by $\frac{5x}{14}$ to multiplying by the reciprocal, $\frac{14}{5x}$.**

$= \frac{{}^{8}40x^{2\,1}}{{}_{3}21} \times \frac{14^2}{{}_{1}5x}$ **Divide out the common factors 5, x, and 7.**

$= \frac{16x}{3}$ **Multiply the numerators ($8x \cdot 2$). Multiply the denominators ($3 \cdot 1$).**

EXERCISES

Write each expression in simplest form.

1. $\frac{4a^2b}{12ab^3}$

2. $\frac{5n + 15}{n + 3}$

3. $\frac{x - 7}{2x - 14}$

4. $\frac{28c^2(d - 3)}{35c(d - 3)}$

Perform the indicated operation.

5. $\frac{3x}{2} + \frac{5x}{2}$

6. $\frac{3x}{8} + \frac{5x}{8}$

7. $\frac{5}{h} - \frac{3}{h}$

8. $\frac{6}{11p} - \frac{9}{11p}$

9. $\frac{3x}{5} - \frac{x}{2}$

10. $\frac{13}{2x} - \frac{13}{3x}$

11. $\frac{7x}{5} + \frac{5x}{7}$

12. $\frac{5a}{b} + \frac{3a}{5b}$

13. $\frac{7x}{8} \cdot \frac{32x}{35}$

14. $\frac{3x^2}{2} \cdot \frac{6}{x}$

15. $\frac{8x^2}{5} \cdot \frac{10}{x^3}$

16. $\frac{7x}{8} \cdot \frac{64}{14x}$

17. $\frac{16}{3x} \div \frac{5}{3x}$

18. $\frac{4x}{5} \div \frac{16}{15x}$

19. $\frac{x^3}{8} \div \frac{x^2}{16}$

20. $\frac{3}{n^2} \div 9n^4$

Tables

Table 1 Measures

United States Customary	Metric

Length

$$12 \text{ inches (in.)} = 1 \text{ foot (ft)}$$
$$36 \text{ in.} = 1 \text{ yard (yd)}$$
$$3 \text{ ft} = 1 \text{ yd}$$
$$5280 \text{ ft} = 1 \text{ mile (mi)}$$
$$1760 \text{ yd} = 1 \text{ mi}$$

$$10 \text{ millimeters (mm)} = 1 \text{ centimeter (cm)}$$
$$100 \text{ cm} = 1 \text{ meter (m)}$$
$$1000 \text{ mm} = 1 \text{ meter}$$
$$1000 \text{ m} = 1 \text{ kilometer (km)}$$

Area

$$144 \text{ square inches (in.}^2) = 1 \text{ square foot (ft}^2)$$
$$9 \text{ ft}^2 = 1 \text{ square yard (yd}^2)$$
$$43{,}560 \text{ ft}^2 = 1 \text{ acre (a)}$$
$$4840 \text{ yd}^2 = 1 \text{ acre}$$

$$100 \text{ square millimeters (mm}^2) = 1 \text{ square centimeter (cm}^2)$$
$$10{,}000 \text{ cm}^2 = 1 \text{ square meter (m}^2)$$
$$10{,}000 \text{ m}^2 = 1 \text{ hectare (ha)}$$

Volume

$$1728 \text{ cubic inches (in.}^3) = 1 \text{ cubic foot (ft}^3)$$
$$27 \text{ ft}^3 = 1 \text{ cubic yard (yd}^3)$$

$$1000 \text{ cubic millimeters (mm}^3) = 1 \text{ cubic centimeter (cm}^3)$$
$$1{,}000{,}000 \text{ cm}^3 = 1 \text{ cubic meter (m}^3)$$

Liquid Capacity

$$8 \text{ fluid ounces (fl oz)} = 1 \text{ cup (c)}$$
$$2 \text{ c} = 1 \text{ pint (pt)}$$
$$2 \text{ pt} = 1 \text{ quart (qt)}$$
$$4 \text{ qt} = 1 \text{ gallon (gal)}$$

$$1000 \text{ milliliters (mL)} = 1 \text{ liter (L)}$$
$$1000 \text{ L} = 1 \text{ kiloliter (kL)}$$

Mass

$$16 \text{ ounces (oz)} = 1 \text{ pound (lb)}$$
$$2000 \text{ lb} = 1 \text{ ton (t)}$$

$$1000 \text{ milligrams (mg)} = 1 \text{ gram (g)}$$
$$1000 \text{ g} = 1 \text{ kilogram (kg)}$$
$$1000 \text{ kg} = 1 \text{ metric ton}$$

Temperature

$$32°F = \text{freezing point of water}$$
$$98.6°F = \text{normal body temperature}$$
$$212°F = \text{boiling point of water}$$

$$0°C = \text{freezing point of water}$$
$$37°C = \text{normal body temperature}$$
$$100°C = \text{boiling point of water}$$

Time	

$$60 \text{ seconds (s)} = 1 \text{ minute (min)}$$
$$60 \text{ minutes} = 1 \text{ hour (h)}$$
$$24 \text{ hours} = 1 \text{ day (d)}$$
$$7 \text{ days} = 1 \text{ week (wk)}$$
$$4 \text{ weeks (approx.)} = 1 \text{ month (mo)}$$

$$365 \text{ days} = 1 \text{ year (yr)}$$
$$52 \text{ weeks (approx.)} = 1 \text{ year}$$
$$12 \text{ months} = 1 \text{ year}$$
$$10 \text{ years} = 1 \text{ decade}$$
$$100 \text{ years} = 1 \text{ century}$$

Table 2 Math Symbols

$0.\overline{3}$	$0.333\ldots$	p. 5
$\ldots$	and so on	p. 5
π	pi, an irrational number, approximately equal to 3.14	p. 5
$\approx$	is approximately equal to	p. 6
$\cdot$	multiplication sign, times ($\times$)	p. 7
$(\ )$	parentheses for grouping	p. 7
$[\ ]$	brackets for grouping	p. 7
$\frac{1}{a}$	reciprocal of a, $a \neq 0$	p. 7
$\lvert a \rvert$	absolute value of a	p. 8
$\neq$	is not equal to	p. 12
$=$	equals	p. 18
$\stackrel{?}{=}$	Is the statement true?	p. 18
$a : b$	ratio of a to b	p. 20
$\circ$	degree(s)	p. 22
$\%$	percent	p. 22
$>$	is greater than	p. 26
$\leq$	is less than or equal to	p. 26
$\geq$	is greater than or equal to	p. 26
$<$	is less than	p. 26
AB	length of segment AB; distance between points A and B	p. 30
$\triangle ABC$	triangle ABC	p. 30
$P(\text{event})$	probability of the event	p. 40
(x, y)	ordered pair	p. 56
$\{\ \}$	set braces	p. 57
$f(x)$	f of x; the function value at x	p. 60
$\{x \mid x > 0\}$	the set of all x, such that x is greater than zero	p. 64
x_1, x_2, etc.	specific values of the variable x	p. 66
y_1, y_2, etc.	specific values of the variable y	p. 66
b	y-intercept of a linear function	p. 67
m	slope of a linear function	p. 67
$[x]$	greatest integer	p. 73
$\pm$	plus or minus	p. 96
$\begin{bmatrix} 1 & 2 \\ 3 & 4 \end{bmatrix}$	matrix	p. 172
a_{mn}	element in the mth row and nth column of matrix A	p. 173
A'	A prime	p. 196
A^{-1}	inverse of matrix A	p. 203
$\begin{vmatrix} a & b \\ c & d \end{vmatrix}$	determinant of a matrix	p. 204
$\det A$	determinant of matrix A	p. 204
$\sqrt{x}$	nonnegative square root of x	p. 270
i	the imaginary number $\sqrt{-1}$	p. 278
$n!$	n factorial	p. 351
$_nC_r$	combinations of n things taken r at a time	p. 352
$_nP_r$	permutations of n things taken r at a time	p. 352
a^n	nth power of a	p. 374
a^{-n}	$\frac{1}{a^n}$, $a \neq 0$	p. 374
$\sqrt[n]{a}$	the principal nth root of a	p. 376
$(g \circ f)(x)$	$g(f(x))$	p. 405
$*$	multiply (in a spreadsheet formula)	p. 408
$\wedge$	raised to a power (in a spreadsheet formula)	p. 408
$f^{-1}(x)$	the inverse of function f	p. 414
e	the number $2.71828\ldots$	p. 449
$\log_b x$	logarithm of x, base b	p. 455
$\ln x$	$\log_e x$	p. 478
$\sum\limits_{n=1}^{5}$	summation	p. 631
∞	infinity	p. 637
$P(A \mid B)$	probability of event A, given event B	p. 666
$\overline{x}$	mean of data values of x	p. 672
σ	sigma	p. 681
θ	theta, measure of an angle	p. 732
$\cos \theta$	cosine of θ	p. 732
$\sin \theta$	sine of θ	p. 732
$\tan \theta$	tangent of θ	p. 761
$\csc \theta$	cosecant of θ	p. 775
$\cot \theta$	cotangent of θ	p. 775
$\sec \theta$	secant of θ	p. 775
$\cos^{-1} x$	the angle whose cosine is x	p. 798
$\sin^{-1} x$	the angle whose sine is x	p. 798
$\tan^{-1} x$	the angle whose tangent is x	p. 798
$\angle A$	angle A	p. 806
$m\angle A$	measure of angle A	p. 807

Tables

Table 3 Squares and Square Roots

Number n	Square n^2	Positive Square Root $\sqrt{n}$	Number n	Square n^2	Positive Square Root $\sqrt{n}$	Number n	Square n^2	Positive Square Root $\sqrt{n}$
1	1	1.000	51	2601	7.141	101	10,201	10.050
2	4	1.414	52	2704	7.211	102	10,404	10.100
3	9	1.732	53	2809	7.280	103	10,609	10.149
4	16	2.000	54	2916	7.348	104	10,816	10.198
5	25	2.236	55	3025	7.416	105	11,025	10.247
6	36	2.449	56	3136	7.483	106	11,236	10.296
7	49	2.646	57	3249	7.550	107	11,449	10.344
8	64	2.828	58	3364	7.616	108	11,664	10.392
9	81	3.000	59	3481	7.681	109	11,881	10.440
10	100	3.162	60	3600	7.746	110	12,100	10.488
11	121	3.317	61	3721	7.810	111	12,321	10.536
12	144	3.464	62	3844	7.874	112	12,544	10.583
13	169	3.606	63	3969	7.937	113	12,769	10.630
14	196	3.742	64	4096	8.000	114	12,996	10.677
15	225	3.873	65	4225	8.062	115	13,225	10.724
16	256	4.000	66	4356	8.124	116	13,456	10.770
17	289	4.123	67	4489	8.185	117	13,689	10.817
18	324	4.243	68	4624	8.246	118	13,924	10.863
19	361	4.359	69	4761	8.307	119	14,161	10.909
20	400	4.472	70	4900	8.367	120	14,400	10.954
21	441	4.583	71	5041	8.426	121	14,641	11.000
22	484	4.690	72	5184	8.485	122	14,884	11.045
23	529	4.796	73	5329	8.544	123	15,129	11.091
24	576	4.899	74	5476	8.602	124	15,376	11.136
25	625	5.000	75	5625	8.660	125	15,625	11.180
26	676	5.099	76	5776	8.718	126	15,876	11.225
27	729	5.196	77	5929	8.775	127	16,129	11.269
28	784	5.292	78	6084	8.832	128	16,384	11.314
29	841	5.385	79	6241	8.888	129	16,641	11.358
30	900	5.477	80	6400	8.944	130	16,900	11.402
31	961	5.568	81	6561	9.000	131	17,161	11.446
32	1024	5.657	82	6724	9.055	132	17,424	11.489
33	1089	5.745	83	6889	9.110	133	17,689	11.533
34	1156	5.831	84	7056	9.165	134	17,956	11.576
35	1225	5.916	85	7225	9.220	135	18,225	11.619
36	1296	6.000	86	7396	9.274	136	18,496	11.662
37	1369	6.083	87	7569	9.327	137	18,769	11.705
38	1444	6.164	88	7744	9.381	138	19,044	11.747
39	1521	6.245	89	7921	9.434	139	19,321	11.790
40	1600	6.325	90	8100	9.487	140	19,600	11.832
41	1681	6.403	91	8281	9.539	141	19,881	11.874
42	1764	6.481	92	8464	9.592	142	20,164	11.916
43	1849	6.557	93	8649	9.644	143	20,449	11.958
44	1936	6.633	94	8836	9.695	144	20,736	12.000
45	2025	6.708	95	9025	9.747	145	21,025	12.042
46	2116	6.782	96	9216	9.798	146	21,316	12.083
47	2209	6.856	97	9409	9.849	147	21,609	12.124
48	2304	6.928	98	9604	9.899	148	21,904	12.166
49	2401	7.000	99	9801	9.950	149	22,201	12.207
50	2500	7.071	100	10,000	10.000	150	22,500	12.247

Table 4 Trigonometric Ratios

Angle	Sine	Cosine	Tangent	Angle	Sine	Cosine	Tangent
1°	0.0175	0.9998	0.0175	46°	0.7193	0.6947	1.0355
2°	0.0349	0.9994	0.0349	47°	0.7314	0.6820	1.0724
3°	0.0523	0.9986	0.0524	48°	0.7431	0.6691	1.1106
4°	0.0698	0.9976	0.0699	49°	0.7547	0.6561	1.1504
5°	0.0872	0.9962	0.0875	50°	0.7660	0.6428	1.1918
6°	0.1045	0.9945	0.1051	51°	0.7771	0.6293	1.2349
7°	0.1219	0.9925	0.1228	52°	0.7880	0.6157	1.2799
8°	0.1392	0.9903	0.1405	53°	0.7986	0.6018	1.3270
9°	0.1564	0.9877	0.1584	54°	0.8090	0.5878	1.3764
10°	0.1736	0.9848	0.1763	55°	0.8192	0.5736	1.4281
11°	0.1908	0.9816	0.1944	56°	0.8290	0.5592	1.4826
12°	0.2079	0.9781	0.2126	57°	0.8387	0.5446	1.5399
13°	0.2250	0.9744	0.2309	58°	0.8480	0.5299	1.6003
14°	0.2419	0.9703	0.2493	59°	0.8572	0.5150	1.6643
15°	0.2588	0.9659	0.2679	60°	0.8660	0.5000	1.7321
16°	0.2756	0.9613	0.2867	61°	0.8746	0.4848	1.8040
17°	0.2924	0.9563	0.3057	62°	0.8829	0.4695	1.8807
18°	0.3090	0.9511	0.3249	63°	0.8910	0.4540	1.9626
19°	0.3256	0.9455	0.3443	64°	0.8988	0.4384	2.0503
20°	0.3420	0.9397	0.3640	65°	0.9063	0.4226	2.1445
21°	0.3584	0.9336	0.3839	66°	0.9135	0.4067	2.2460
22°	0.3746	0.9272	0.4040	67°	0.9205	0.3907	2.3559
23°	0.3907	0.9205	0.4245	68°	0.9272	0.3746	2.4751
24°	0.4067	0.9135	0.4452	69°	0.9336	0.3584	2.6051
25°	0.4226	0.9063	0.4663	70°	0.9397	0.3420	2.7475
26°	0.4384	0.8988	0.4877	71°	0.9455	0.3256	2.9042
27°	0.4540	0.8910	0.5095	72°	0.9511	0.3090	3.0777
28°	0.4695	0.8829	0.5317	73°	0.9563	0.2924	3.2709
29°	0.4848	0.8746	0.5543	74°	0.9613	0.2756	3.4874
30°	0.5000	0.8660	0.5774	75°	0.9659	0.2588	3.7321
31°	0.5150	0.8572	0.6009	76°	0.9703	0.2419	4.0108
32°	0.5299	0.8480	0.6249	77°	0.9744	0.2250	4.3315
33°	0.5446	0.8387	0.6494	78°	0.9781	0.2079	4.7046
34°	0.5592	0.8290	0.6745	79°	0.9816	0.1908	5.1446
35°	0.5736	0.8192	0.7002	80°	0.9848	0.1736	5.6713
36°	0.5878	0.8090	0.7265	81°	0.9877	0.1564	6.3138
37°	0.6018	0.7986	0.7536	82°	0.9903	0.1392	7.1154
38°	0.6157	0.7880	0.7813	83°	0.9925	0.1219	8.1443
39°	0.6293	0.7771	0.8098	84°	0.9945	0.1045	9.5144
40°	0.6428	0.7660	0.8391	85°	0.9962	0.0872	11.4301
41°	0.6561	0.7547	0.8693	86°	0.9976	0.0698	14.3007
42°	0.6691	0.7431	0.9004	87°	0.9986	0.0523	19.0811
43°	0.6820	0.7314	0.9325	88°	0.9994	0.0349	28.6363
44°	0.6947	0.7193	0.9657	89°	0.9998	0.0175	57.2900
45°	0.7071	0.7071	1.0000	90°	1.0000	0.0000	

Table 5 Random Numbers

71133	15379	62220	83119	33872	80881	54263	35427
50631	71600	00133	22447	76212	94621	91026	89499
92641	47157	49324	27674	04501	30142	49180	17909
06747	85629	84240	41917	84067	44264	40953	20516
10967	26366	60323	55523	09686	47962	59778	99479
08945	67385	60015	91676	72694	49757	86540	32359
22437	77933	00815	21862	25049	30840	01760	60655
78658	17681	63881	99741	74067	35810	11989	68048
23006	64650	50777	06226	64703	73487	34815	35296
67218	66215	14219	61908	18165	17261	45017	29303
03020	75784	91506	02237	88056	15027	04040	96770
94965	75820	50994	31050	67304	16730	29373	96700
07845	69584	70548	52973	72302	97594	92241	15204
42665	29990	57260	75846	01152	30141	35982	96088
04003	36893	51639	65625	28426	90634	32979	05449
32959	06776	72420	55622	81422	67587	93193	67479
29041	35939	80920	31801	38638	87905	37617	53135
63364	20495	50868	54130	32625	30799	94255	03514
27838	19139	82031	46143	93922	32001	05378	42457
94248	29387	32682	86235	35805	66529	00886	25875
40156	92636	95648	79767	16307	71133	15714	44142
44293	19195	30569	41277	01417	34656	80207	33362
71878	31767	40056	52582	30766	70264	86253	07179
24757	57502	51033	16551	66731	87844	41420	10084
55529	68560	50069	50652	76104	42086	48720	96632
39724	50318	91370	68016	06222	26806	86726	52832
80950	27135	14110	92292	17049	60257	01638	04460
21694	79570	74409	95087	75424	57042	27349	16229
06930	85441	37191	75134	12845	67868	51500	97761
18740	35448	56096	37910	35485	19640	07689	31027
40657	14875	70695	92569	40703	69318	95070	01541
52249	56515	59058	34509	35791	22150	56558	75286
86570	07303	40560	57856	22009	67712	19435	90250
62962	66253	93288	01838	68388	55481	00336	19271
78066	09117	62350	58972	80778	46458	83677	16125
89106	30219	30068	54030	49295	48985	01624	72881
88310	18172	89450	04987	02781	37935	76222	93595
20942	90911	57643	34009	20728	88785	81212	08214
93926	66687	58252	18674	18501	22362	37319	33201
88294	55814	67443	77285	36229	26886	66782	89931
29751	08485	49910	83844	56013	26596	20875	34568
11169	15529	33241	83594	01727	86595	65723	82322
06062	54400	80649	70749	50395	48993	77447	24862
87445	17139	43278	55031	79971	18515	61850	49101
39283	22821	44330	82225	53534	77235	42973	60190

Properties and Formulas

Order of Operations
1. Perform any operation(s) inside grouping symbols.
2. Simplify any terms with exponents.
3. Multiply and divide in order from left to right.
4. Add and subtract in order from left to right.

Properties of Exponents
For any nonzero number a and any integers m and n:

$a^0 = 1, a \neq 0$ $\qquad a^m \cdot a^n = a^{m+n}$

$\dfrac{a^m}{a^n} = a^{m-n}$ $\qquad (a^m)^n = a^{mn}$

$a^{-n} = \dfrac{1}{a^n}$ $\qquad a^{\frac{1}{n}} = \sqrt[n]{a}$

$(ab)^n = a^n b^n$ $\qquad \left(\dfrac{a}{b}\right)^n = \dfrac{a^n}{b^n}$

Properties of Square Roots
For any numbers $a \geq 0$ and $b \geq 0$,
$\sqrt{ab} = \sqrt{a} \cdot \sqrt{b}$.
For any numbers $a \geq 0$ and $b > 0$,
$\sqrt{\dfrac{a}{b}} = \dfrac{\sqrt{a}}{\sqrt{b}}$.

The Pythagorean Theorem
In a right triangle, the sum of the squares of the lengths of the legs is equal to the square of the length of the hypotenuse.
$a^2 + b^2 = c^2$

The Converse of the Pythagorean Theorem
If a triangle has sides of lengths a, b, and c, and $a^2 + b^2 = c^2$, then the triangle is a right triangle with hypotenuse of length c.

The Distance Formula
The distance d between any two points (x_1, y_1) and (x_2, y_2) is $d = \sqrt{(x_2 - x_1)^2 + (y_2 - y_1)^2}$.

The Midpoint Formula
The midpoint M of a line segment with endpoints $A(x_1, y_1)$ and $B(x_2, y_2)$ is $\left(\dfrac{x_1 + x_2}{2}, \dfrac{y_1 + y_2}{2}\right)$.

Parent Function and Function Families
If a, k and h are positive numbers and $f(x)$ is a parent function, then
$f(x) + k$ shifts $f(x)$ up k units;
$f(x) - k$ shifts $f(x)$ down k units;
$f(x + h)$ shifts $f(x)$ left h units;
$f(x - h)$ shifts $f(x)$ right h units.
$af(x)$ stretches $f(x)$ vertically if $a > 1$
$af(x)$ shrinks $f(x)$ vertically if $0 < a < 1$
$-f(x)$ reflects $f(x)$ across the x-axis

Multiplication Counting Principle
If there are m ways to make a first selection and n ways to make a second selection, there are $m \times n$ ways to make the two selections.

Number of Permutations
The number of permutations of n items of a set arranged r items at a time is
$_nP_r = \dfrac{n!}{(n-r)!}$ for $1 \leq r \leq n$.

CHAPTER 1

The Identity Properties
For every real number a:
$a + 0 = a$ and $0 + a = a$
$a \cdot 1 = a$ and $1 \cdot a = a$

Closure
For all real numbers a and $b, a + b$ and $a \cdot b$ are real numbers.

The Commutative Properties
For all real numbers a and b:
$a + b = b + a$ and $a \cdot b = b \cdot a$

The Inverse Properties
For every real number a:
$a + (-a) = 0$ and $a \cdot \dfrac{1}{a} = 1$ $(a \neq 0)$

The Associative Properties
For all real numbers a, b, and c:
$(a + b) + c = a + (b + c)$
$(a \cdot b) \cdot c = a \cdot (b \cdot c)$

The Distributive Property
For all real numbers a, b, and c:
$a(b + c) = ab + ac$

Properties of Equality
Let a, b, and c represent real numbers.

Reflexive: $a = a$

Symmetric: If $a = b$, then $b = a$.

Transitive: If $a = b$ and $b = c$, then $a = c$.

Addition: If $a = b$, then $a + c = b + c$.

Subtraction: If $a = b$, then $a - c = b - c$.

Multiplication: If $a = b$, then $ac = bc$.

Division: If $a = b$ and $c \neq 0$, then $\dfrac{a}{c} = \dfrac{b}{c}$.

Substitution: If $a = b$, then b may be substituted for a in any expression to obtain an equivalent expression.

Properties of Inequality

Let a, b, and c represent real numbers.

Transitive: If $a \leq b$ and $b \leq c$, then $a \leq c$.

Addition: If $a \leq b$, then $a + c \leq b + c$.

Subtraction: If $a \leq b$, then $a - c \leq b - c$.

Multiplication:
If $a \leq b$ and $c > 0$, then $ac \leq bc$.
If $a \leq b$ and $c < 0$, then $ac \geq bc$.

Division:
If $a \leq b$ and $c > 0$, then $\frac{a}{c} \leq \frac{b}{c}$.
If $a \leq b$ and $c < 0$, then $\frac{a}{c} \geq \frac{b}{c}$.

CHAPTER 2

Slope Formula

$$\text{slope} = \frac{\text{vertical change (rise)}}{\text{horizontal change (run)}} = \frac{y_2 - y_1}{x_2 - x_1},$$
where $x_2 - x_1 \neq 0$.

Point-Slope Equation of a Line

The line through point (x_1, y_1) with slope m has the equation $y - y_1 = m(x - x_1)$.

CHAPTER 3

Vertex Principle of Linear Programming

If there is a maximum or a minimum value of the linear objective function, it occurs at one or more vertices of the feasible region.

CHAPTER 4

Matrix Addition

Let A, B, and C represent $m \times n$ matrices.

Closure: $A + B$ is an $m \times n$ matrix.

Commutative: $A + B = B + A$

Associative: $(A + B) + C = A + (B + C)$

Additive Identity: There exists a unique $m \times n$ matrix O such that $O + A = A + O = A$.

Additive Inverse: For each A, there exists a unique opposite $-A$ such that $A + (-A) = O$.

Matrix Subtraction

If two matrices A and B have the same dimensions, then $A - B = A + (-B)$.

Scalar Multiplication

Let A, B, and O represent $m \times n$ matrices, and let c and d represent scalars.

Closure: cA is an $m \times n$ matrix.

Associative: $(cd)A = c(dA)$

Distributive:
$c(A + B) = cA + cB$
$(c + d)A = cA + dA$

Multiplicative Identity: $1 \cdot A = A$

Zero: $0A = O$ and $cO = O$

Matrix Multiplication

Let A, B, and C represent $n \times n$ matrices.

Closure: AB is an $n \times n$ matrix.

Associative: $(AB)C = A(BC)$

Distributive:
$A(B + C) = AB + AC$
$(B + C)A = BA + CA$

Zero: $OA = AO = O$, where O has the same dimensions as A.

CHAPTER 5

Graph of a Quadratic Function in Standard Form

The graph of $y = ax^2 + bx + c$ is a parabola when $a \neq 0$.
When $a > 0$, the parabola opens up. When $a < 0$, the parabola opens down.
The axis of symmetry is the line $x = -\frac{b}{2a}$.
The x-coordinate of the vertex is $-\frac{b}{2a}$.
The y-coordinate of the vertex is the value of y when $x = -\frac{b}{2a}$, or $y = f\left(-\frac{b}{2a}\right)$.
The y-intercept is $(0, c)$.

Graph of a Quadratic Function in Vertex Form

The graph of $y = a(x - h)^2 + k$ is the graph of $y = ax^2$ translated h units horizontally and k units vertically.
When h is positive the graph shifts right; when h is negative the graph shifts left.
When k is positive the graph shifts up; when k is negative the graph shifts down.
The vertex is (h, k), and the axis of symmetry is the line $x = h$.
When $a > 0$, the parabola opens up. When $a < 0$, the parabola opens down.

Factoring Perfect Square Trinomials

$a^2 + 2ab + b^2 = (a + b)^2$

$a^2 - 2ab + b^2 = (a - b)^2$

Factoring a Difference of Two Squares

$a^2 - b^2 = (a + b)(a - b)$

Zero-Product Property

If $ab = 0$, then $a = 0$ or $b = 0$.

Example: If $(x + 3)(x - 7) = 0$, then $(x + 3) = 0$ or $(x - 7) = 0$.

Square Root of a Negative Real Number

For any positive real number a, $\sqrt{-a} = i\sqrt{a}$.

Example: $\sqrt{-4} = i\sqrt{4} = i \cdot 2 = 2i$

Note that $(\sqrt{-4})^2 = (i\sqrt{4})^2 = i^2\sqrt{4}^2 = -1 \cdot 4 = -4$ (not 4).

Quadratic Formula

The roots of $ax^2 + bx + c = 0$ are

$$x = \frac{-b \pm \sqrt{b^2 - 4ac}}{2a}.$$

The Discriminant

The standard form of a quadratic equation is $ax^2 + bx + c = 0$. The discriminant is the value of the expression $b^2 - 4ac$.

$b^2 - 4ac > 0 \Rightarrow$ two real solutions

$b^2 - 4ac = 0 \Rightarrow$ one real solution

$b^2 - 4ac < 0 \Rightarrow$ two complex solutions

CHAPTER 6

Factor Theorem

The expression $x - a$ is a linear factor of a polynomial if and only if the value a is a zero of the related polynomial function.

Remainder Theorem

If a polynomial $P(x)$ of degree $n \geq 1$ is divided by $(x - a)$, where a is a constant, then the remainder is $P(a)$.

Sum and Difference of Cubes

$a^3 + b^3 = (a + b)(a^2 - ab + b^2)$

$a^3 - b^3 = (a - b)(a^2 + ab + b^2)$

Rational Root Theorem

If $\frac{p}{q}$ is in simplest form and is a rational root of the polynomial equation

$a_n x^n + a_{n-1}x^{n-1} + \ldots + a_1 x + a_0 = 0$ with integer coefficients, then p must be a factor of a_0 and q must be a factor of a_n.

Irrational Root Theorem

Let a and b be rational numbers and let $\sqrt{b}$ be an irrational number. If $a + \sqrt{b}$ is a root of a polynomial equation with rational coefficients, then the conjugate $a - \sqrt{b}$ also is a root.

Imaginary Root Theorem

If the imaginary number $a + bi$ is a root of a polynomial equation with real coefficients, then the conjugate $a - bi$ also is a root.

Fundamental Theorem of Algebra

If $P(x)$ is a polynomial of degree $n \geq 1$ with complex coefficients, then $P(x) = 0$ has at least one complex root.

Corollary

Including imaginary roots and multiple roots, an nth degree polynomial equation has exactly n roots; the related polynomial function has exactly n zeros.

Binomial Theorem

For every positive integer n,

$(a + b)^n = {}_nC_0 a^n + {}_nC_1 a^{n-1}b + {}_nC_2 a^{n-2}b^2 + \ldots + {}_nC_{n-1}ab^{n-1} + {}_nC_n b^n.$

Chapter 7

nth Root of a^n

For any negative real number a, $\sqrt[n]{a^n} = |a|$ when n is even.

Multiplying Radical Expressions

If $\sqrt[n]{a}$ and $\sqrt[n]{b}$ are real numbers, then $\sqrt[n]{a} \cdot \sqrt[n]{b} = \sqrt[n]{ab}$.

Dividing Radical Expressions

If $\sqrt[n]{a}$ and $\sqrt[n]{b}$ are real numbers and $b \neq 0$, then

$$\frac{\sqrt[n]{a}}{\sqrt[n]{b}} = \sqrt[n]{\frac{a}{b}}.$$

Chapter 8

Properties of Logarithms

For any positive numbers, M, N, and $b, b \neq 1$:

$\log_b MN = \log_b M + \log_b N$

$\log_b \frac{M}{N} = \log_b M - \log_b N$

$\log_b M^x = x \log_b M$

Change of Base Formula

For any positive numbers, M, b, and c, with

$b \neq 1$ and $c \neq 1$, $\log_b M = \dfrac{\log_c M}{\log_c b}$.

Chapter 9

Probability of *A* and *B*
If *A* and *B* are independent events, then
$P(A \text{ and } B) = P(A) \cdot P(B)$.

Probability of *A* or *B*
If *A* and *B* are mutually exclusive events, then
$P(A \text{ or } B) = P(A) + P(B)$.
If *A* and *B* are not mutually exclusive events, then
$P(A \text{ or } B) = P(A) + P(B) - P(A \text{ and } B)$.

Chapter 10

Conic Section	Form of Equation
Parabola	vertex (h, k) $y = a(x - h)^2 + k$ $x = a(y - k)^2 + h$
Circle	center (h, k) $(x - h)^2 + (y - k)^2 = r^2$
Ellipse	center (h, k) $\dfrac{(x - h)^2}{a^2} + \dfrac{(y - k)^2}{b^2} = 1$ $\dfrac{(x - h)^2}{b^2} + \dfrac{(y - k)^2}{a^2} = 1$
Hyperbola	center (h, k) $\dfrac{(x - h)^2}{a^2} - \dfrac{(y - k)^2}{b^2} = 1$ $\dfrac{(y - k)^2}{a^2} - \dfrac{(x - h)^2}{b^2} = 1$

Chapter 11

Arithmetic Sequence Formulas
Recursive: $a_1 = $ a given value; $a_n = a_{n-1} + d$
Explicit: $a_n = a_1 + (n - 1)d$
In these formulas, a_n is the nth term, a_1 is the first term, n is the number of the term, and d is the common difference.

Geometric Sequence Formulas
Recursive: $a_1 = $ a given value; $a_n = a_{n-1} \cdot r$
Explicit: $a_n = a_1 \cdot r^{n-1}$
In these formulas, a_n is the nth term, a_1 is the first term, n is the number of the term, and r is the common ratio.

Sum of a Finite Arithmetic Series
The sum S_n of a finite arithmetic series
$a_1 + a_2 + a_3 + \ldots + a_n$ is $S_n = \frac{n}{2}(a_1 + a_n)$, where a_1 is the first term, a_n is the nth term, and n is the number of terms.

Sum of a Finite Geometric Series
The sum S_n of a finite geometric series
$a_1 + a_2 + a_3 + \ldots + a_n$ is $S_n = \frac{a_1(1 - r^n)}{1 - r}$, where a_1 is the first term, r is the common ratio, and n is the number of terms.

Sum of an Infinite Geometric Series
An infinite geometric series with $|r| < 1$ converges to the sum S given by the following formula:
$S = \frac{a_1}{1 - r}$

Chapter 12

Conditional Probability Formula
For any two events *A* and *B* from a sample space with $P(A) \neq 0$,
$$P(B \mid A) = \frac{P(A \text{ and } B)}{P(A)}$$

Margin of Error Formula
When a random sample of size *n* is taken from a large population, the sample proportion has a margin of error of approximately $\pm \frac{1}{\sqrt{n}}$.

Binomial Probability
For repeated independent trials, each with a probability of success *p* and a probability of failure *q* (with $p + q = 1$), the probability of *x* successes in *n* trials is $_nC_x p^x q^{n-x}$.

Chapter 13

Converting Between Radians and Degrees
To convert degrees to radians, multiply by $\frac{\pi \text{ radians}}{180°}$.
To convert radians to degrees, multiply by $\frac{180°}{\pi \text{ radians}}$.

Length of an Intercepted Arc
For a circle of radius *r* and a central angle of measure θ (in radians), the length *s* of the intercepted arc is $s = r\theta$.

Properties of Sine Functions
Suppose $y = a \sin b\theta$, with $a \neq 0, b > 0$, and θ in radians.
$|a|$ is the amplitude of the function.
b is the number of cycles in the interval from 0 to 2π.
$\frac{2\pi}{b}$ is the period of the function.

Properties of Cosine Functions

Suppose $y = a \cos b\theta$, with $a \neq 0$, $b > 0$, and θ in radians.

$|a|$ is the amplitude of the function.

b is the number of cycles in the interval from 0 to 2π.

$\frac{2\pi}{b}$ is the period of the function.

Properties of Tangent Functions

Suppose $y = a \tan b\theta$, with $b > 0$ and θ in radians.

$\frac{\pi}{b}$ is the period of the function.

One cycle occurs in the interval from $-\frac{\pi}{2b}$ to $\frac{\pi}{2b}$.
There are vertical asymptotes at each end of the cycle.

Translations of Sine and Cosine Functions

$y = a \sin b(x - h) + k$ and $y = a \cos b(x - h) + k$ represent translations of $y = a \sin bx$ and $y = a \cos bx$.

- $|a|$ = amplitude
- $\frac{2\pi}{b}$ = period (when x is in radians and $b > 0$)
- h = phase shift, or horizontal shift
- k = vertical shift

Cosecant, Secant, and Cotangent Functions

The cosecant (csc), secant (sec), and cotangent (cot) functions are defined using reciprocals. Their domains include all real numbers θ except those that make a denominator zero.

$$\csc\theta = \frac{1}{\sin\theta} \qquad \sec\theta = \frac{1}{\cos\theta} \qquad \cot\theta = \frac{1}{\tan\theta}$$

Chapter 14

Trigonometric Identities

Reciprocal Identities:

$$\csc\theta = \frac{1}{\sin\theta} \qquad \sec\theta = \frac{1}{\cos\theta} \qquad \cot\theta = \frac{1}{\tan\theta}$$

Tangent and Cotangent Identities:

$$\tan\theta = \frac{\sin\theta}{\cos\theta} \qquad \cot\theta = \frac{\cos\theta}{\sin\theta}$$

Pythagorean Identities:

$$\cos^2\theta + \sin^2\theta = 1$$
$$1 + \tan^2\theta = \sec^2\theta$$
$$1 + \cot^2\theta = \csc^2\theta$$

Trigonometric Ratios for a Right Triangle

In $\triangle ABC$ with $\angle C$ a right angle:

$$\sin A = \frac{\text{length of leg opposite } \angle A}{\text{length of hypotenuse}} = \frac{a}{c}$$

$$\cos A = \frac{\text{length of leg adjacent to } \angle A}{\text{length of hypotenuse}} = \frac{b}{c}$$

$$\tan A = \frac{\text{length of leg opposite } \angle A}{\text{length of leg adjacent to } \angle A} = \frac{a}{b}$$

$$\csc A = \frac{\text{length of hypotenuse}}{\text{length of leg opposite } \angle A} = \frac{c}{a}$$

$$\sec A = \frac{\text{length of hypotenuse}}{\text{length of leg adjacent to } \angle A} = \frac{c}{b}$$

$$\cot A = \frac{\text{length of leg adjacent to } \angle A}{\text{length of leg opposite } \angle A} = \frac{b}{a}$$

Law of Sines

In $\triangle ABC$, let a, b, and c represent the lengths of the sides opposite $\angle A$, $\angle B$, and $\angle C$, respectively.

Then $\frac{\sin A}{a} = \frac{\sin B}{b} = \frac{\sin C}{c}$.

You can use the Law of Sines to find missing measures of any triangle when you know the measures of two angles and any side, or two sides and the angle opposite one of them.

Law of Cosines

In $\triangle ABC$, let a, b, and c represent the lengths of the sides opposite $\angle A$, $\angle B$, and $\angle C$, respectively.

$$a^2 = b^2 + c^2 - 2bc \cos A$$
$$b^2 = a^2 + c^2 - 2ac \cos B$$
$$c^2 = a^2 + b^2 - 2ab \cos C$$

You can use the Law of Cosines to find missing parts of any triangle when you know the measures of two sides and the angle between them, or all three sides.

Angle Identities

Negative Angle Identities:

$$\sin(-\theta) = -\sin\theta$$
$$\cos(-\theta) = \cos\theta$$
$$\tan(-\theta) = -\tan\theta$$

Cofunction Identities:

$$\sin\left(\frac{\pi}{2} - \theta\right) = \cos\theta$$
$$\cos\left(\frac{\pi}{2} - \theta\right) = \sin\theta$$
$$\tan\left(\frac{\pi}{2} - \theta\right) = \cot\theta$$

Angle Difference Identities

$$\sin(A - B) = \sin A \cos B - \cos A \sin B$$
$$\cos(A - B) = \cos A \cos B + \sin A \sin B$$
$$\tan(A - B) = \frac{\tan A - \tan B}{1 + \tan A \tan B}$$

Angle Sum Identities

$$\sin(A + B) = \sin A \cos B + \cos A \sin B$$
$$\cos(A + B) = \cos A \cos B - \sin A \sin B$$
$$\tan(A + B) = \frac{\tan A + \tan B}{1 - \tan A \tan B}$$

Double Angle Identities

$$\sin 2\theta = 2 \sin\theta \cos\theta$$
$$\cos 2\theta = \cos^2\theta - \sin^2\theta$$
$$\cos 2\theta = 2 \cos^2\theta - 1$$
$$\cos 2\theta = 1 - 2 \sin^2\theta$$
$$\tan 2\theta = \frac{2 \tan\theta}{1 - \tan^2\theta}$$

Formulas from Geometry

You will use a number of geometric formulas as you work through your algebra book. Here are some perimeter, area, and volume formulas.

$P = 2\ell + 2w$
$A = \ell w$

Rectangle

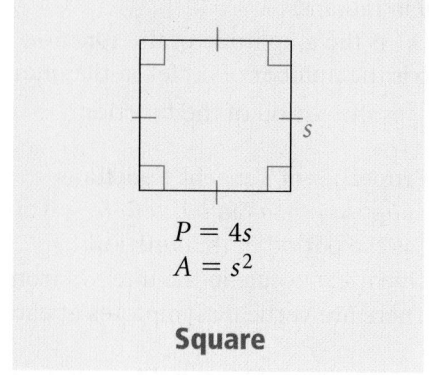

$P = 4s$
$A = s^2$

Square

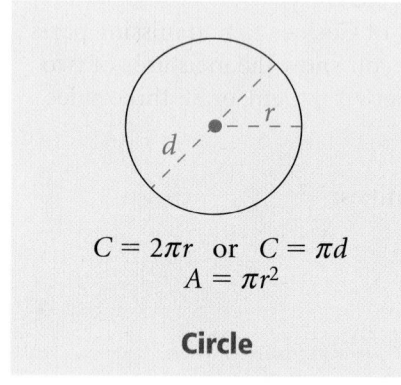

$C = 2\pi r$ or $C = \pi d$
$A = \pi r^2$

Circle

$A = \frac{1}{2}bh$

Triangle

$A = bh$

Parallelogram

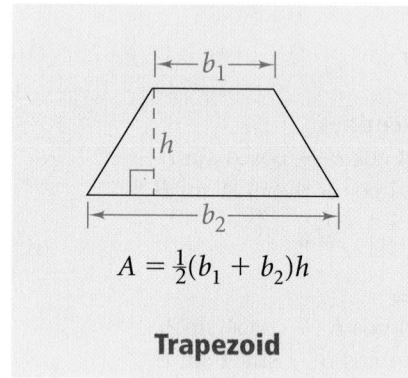

$A = \frac{1}{2}(b_1 + b_2)h$

Trapezoid

$SA = 2(\ell w + wh + h\ell)$
$V = Bh$
$V = \ell wh$

Rectangular Prism

$V = \frac{1}{3}Bh$

Pyramid

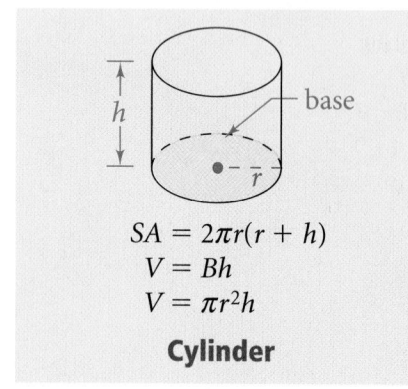

$SA = 2\pi r(r + h)$
$V = Bh$
$V = \pi r^2 h$

Cylinder

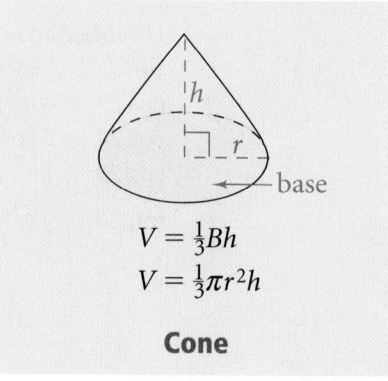

$V = \frac{1}{3}Bh$
$V = \frac{1}{3}\pi r^2 h$

Cone

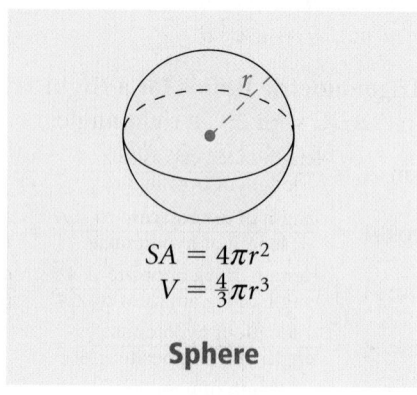

$SA = 4\pi r^2$
$V = \frac{4}{3}\pi r^3$

Sphere

English/Spanish Illustrated Glossary

A

Absolute value function (p. 90) A function of the form $f(x) = |mx + b| + c$, where $m \neq 0$, is an absolute value function.

$f(x) = |3x - 2| + 3$
$f(x) = |2x|$

Función de valor absoluto (p. 90) Una función de la forma $f(x) = |mx + b| + c$, donde $m \neq 0$, es una función de valor absoluto.

Absolute value of a complex number (p. 279) The absolute value of a complex number is its distance from the origin on the complex number plane. In general, $|a + bi| = \sqrt{a^2 + b^2}$.

$|3 - 4i| = \sqrt{3^2 + (-4)^2} = 5$

Valor absoluto de un número complejo (p. 279) El valor absoluto de un número complejo es la distancia a la que está del origen en el plano de números complejo. Generalmente, $|a + bi| = \sqrt{a^2 + b^2}$.

Absolute value of a real number (pp. 8, 33) The absolute value of a real number is its distance from zero on the number line. If $x \geq 0$, then $|x| = x$. If $x < 0$, then $|x| = -x$.

$|3| = 3$
$|-4| = 4$

Valor absoluto de un número real (pp. 8, 33) El valor absoluto de un número real es la distancia a la que el número se encuentra de cero en la recta numérica. Si $x \geq 0$, entonces $|x| = x$. Si $x < 0$, entonces $|x| = -x$.

Additive inverse (p. 7) The opposite or additive inverse of any number a is $-a$. The sum of opposites is 0.

$3 + (-3) = 0$
$5.2 + (-5.2) = 0$

Inverso aditivo (p. 7) El opuesto o inverso aditivo de cualquier número a es $-a$. La suma de los opuestos es 0.

Algebraic expression (p. 12) An expression that contains one or more variables is called an algebraic expression or a variable expression.

$2x + 3$
$z - y$

Expresión algebraica (p. 12) Una expresión que contiene una o más variables es llamada expresión algebraica o expresión variable.

Amplitude of a periodic function (p. 724) The amplitude of a periodic function is half the difference between the maximum and minimum values of the function.

The maximum and minimum values of $y = 4 \sin x$ are 4 and -4, respectively.
amplitude $= \dfrac{4 - (-4)}{2} = 4$

Amplitud de una función periódica (p. 724) La amplitud de una función periódica es la mitad de la diferencia entre los valores máximo y mínimo de la función.

English/Spanish Glossary

Arithmetic mean (p. 617) The arithmetic mean of any two numbers is their sum divided by two.

The arithmetic mean of 12 and 15 is $\frac{12 + 15}{2} = 13.5$.

Media aritmética (p. 617) La media aritmética de dos números cualesquiera es la suma de los números dividida por dos.

Arithmetic sequence (p. 616) In an arithmetic sequence, the difference between consecutive terms is constant. The constant is called the common difference.

The arithmetic sequence $1, 5, 9, 13, \ldots$ has a common difference of 4.

Progresión aritmética (p. 616) En una progresión aritmética la diferencia entre términos consecutivos es un número constante. El número constante se llama la diferencia común.

Arithmetic series (p. 630) An arithmetic series is a series whose terms form an arithmetic sequence.

$1 + 5 + 9 + 13 + 17 + 21$ is an arithmetic series with six terms.

Serie aritmética (p. 630) Una serie aritmética es una serie cuyos términos forman una progresión aritmética.

Asymptote (p. 441) An asymptote is a line that a graph approaches as x or y increases in absolute value.

The function $y = \frac{x + 2}{x - 2}$ has $x = 2$ as a vertical asymptote and $y = 1$ as a horizontal asymptote.

Asíntota (p. 441) Una asíntota es una recta a la cual se acerca una gráfica a medida que x o y aumentan de valor absoluto.

Augmented matrix (p. 226) An augmented matrix contains the coefficients and constants from a system of equations.

linear system augmented matrix

$$\begin{cases} x + 4 = 6 \\ -2x + 5y = 7 \end{cases} \qquad \begin{bmatrix} 1 & 4 & | & 6 \\ -2 & 5 & | & 7 \end{bmatrix}$$

Matriz aumentada (p. 226) Una matriz aumentada contiene los coeficientes y constantes de un sistema de ecuaciones.

Axis of symmetry (p. 243) The axis of symmetry is the line that divides a figure into two parts that are mirror images.

Eje de simetría (p. 243) El eje de simetría es la recta que divide una figura en dos partes que son imágenes una de la otra.

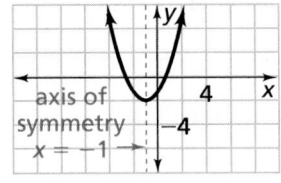

$y = x^2 + 2x - 1$

B

Bimodal (p. 672) A bimodal data set has two modes.

$\{1, 2, 3, 3, 4, 5, 6, 6\}$

mode = 3 and 6

Bimodal (p. 672) Un conjunto bimodal de datos tiene dos modas.

Binomial experiment (p. 697)   A binomial experiment is one in which the situation involves repeated trials. Each trial has two possible outcomes (success or failure), and the probability of success is constant throughout the trials.

Experimento binomial (p. 697)   Un experimento binomial es un experimento que requiere varios ensayos. Cada ensayo tiene dos resultados posibles (éxito o fracaso), y la probabilidad de éxito es constante durante todos los ensayos.

Binomial probability (p. 699)   In a binomial experiment with probability of success p and probability of failure q, the probability of x successes in n trials is given by $_nC_x\, p^x q^{n-x}$.

Probabilidad binomial (p. 699)   En un experimento binomial con una probabilidad de éxito p y una probabilidad de fracaso q, la probabilidad de x éxitos en n ensayos se expresa con $_nC_x\, p^x q^{n-x}$.

Suppose you roll a standard number cube and that you call rolling a 1 a success. Then $p = \frac{1}{6}$ and $q = \frac{5}{6}$. The probability of rolling nine 1's in twenty rolls is $_{20}C_9\left(\frac{1}{6}\right)^9\left(\frac{5}{6}\right)^{11} \approx 0.0022$.

Binomial Theorem (p. 360)   For every positive integer n,
$(a + b)^n = {}_nC_0 a^n + {}_nC_1 a^{n-1}b^1 + \ldots + {}_nC_{n-1}a^1 b^{n-1} + {}_nC_n b^n$. The numbers $_nC_0, {}_nC_1, \ldots, {}_nC_n$ are often called binomial coefficients.

Teorema binomial (p. 360)   Para todo número entero positivo n,
$(a + b)^n = {}_nC_0 a^n + {}_nC_1 a^{n-1}b^1 + \ldots + {}_nC_{n-1}a^1 b^{n-1} + {}_nC_n b^n$. Los números $_nC_0, {}_nC_1, \ldots, {}_nC_n$ a menudo se llaman coeficientes del binomio.

$$(2x - 3)^3 = {}_3C_0(2x)^3 + {}_3C_1(2x)^2(-3)^1$$
$$+ {}_3C_2(2x)^1(-3)^2 + {}_3C_3(-3)^3$$
$$= 8x^3 - 36x^2 + 54x - 27$$

Box-and-whisker plot (p. 674)   A box-and-whisker plot is a method of displaying data that uses quartiles to form the center box and the maximum and minimum values to form the whiskers.

Gráfica de cajas (p. 674)   Una gráfica de cajas es un método para mostrar datos que utiliza cuartiles para formar una casilla central y los valores máximos y mínimos para formar los conectores.

Branch (p. 503)   Each piece of a discontinuous graph is called a branch.

Rama (p. 503)   Cada segmento de una gráfica discontinua se llama rama.

Center of a circle (p. 571)   The center of a circle is the point that is the same distance from every point on the circle.

Centro de un círculo (p. 571)   El centro de un círculo es el punto que está situado a la misma distancia de cada punto del círculo.

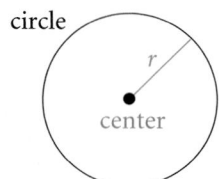

Center of rotation (p. 198)   The center of rotation is the fixed point of a rotation transformation.

Centro de rotación (p. 198)   El centro de rotación es el punto fijo de una transformación por rotación.

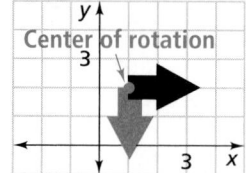

Central angle (p. 738)   A central angle of a circle is an angle whose vertex is at the center of a circle.

Ángulo central (p. 738)   El ángulo central de un círculo es un ángulo cuyo vértice está situado en el centro del círculo.

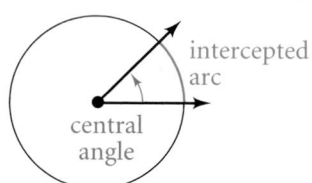

Change of Base Formula (p. 470) $\log_b M = \frac{\log_c M}{\log_c b}$, where M, b, and c are positive numbers, and $b \neq 1$ and $c \neq 1$.

$$\log_3 8 = \frac{\log 8}{\log 3} \approx 1.8928$$

Fórmula de cambio de base (p. 470) $\log_b M = \frac{\log_c M}{\log_c b}$, donde M, b y c son números positivos y $b \neq 1$ y $c \neq 1$.

Circle (p. 571)   A circle is the set of all points in a plane at a distance r from a given point. The standard form of the equation of a circle with center (h, k) and radius r is $(x - h)^2 + (y - k)^2 = r^2$.

Círculo (p. 571)   Un círculo es el conjunto de todos los puntos situados en un plano a una distancia r de un punto dado. La forma normal de la ecuación del círculo cuyo centro es (h, k) y cuyo radio es r es $(x - h)^2 + (y - k)^2 = r^2$.

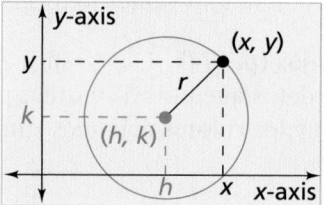

Circumscribed rectangles (p. 646)   When approximating the area under a curve, circumscribed rectangles are partially above the curve. Their combined area generally is greater than the area under the curve.

Rectángulos circunscritos (p. 646)   Al aproximar el área que queda dentro de una curva, los rectángulos circunscritos quedan parcialmente por fuera de la curva. Generalmente, su área total es mayor que el área dentro de la curva.

Coefficient (p. 13) The numerical factor in a term is the coefficient.

Coeficiente (p. 13) El factor numérico de un término es el coeficiente.

The coefficient of $-3k$ is -3.

Coefficient matrix (p. 218) When representing a system of equations with a matrix equation, the matrix containing the coefficients of the system is the coefficient matrix.

Matriz de coeficientes (p. 218) Al representar un sistema de ecuaciones con una ecuación de matriz, la matriz que contiene los coeficientes del sistema es la matriz de coeficientes.

$$\begin{cases} x + 2y = 5 \\ 3x + 5y = 14 \end{cases}$$

coefficient matrix $\begin{bmatrix} 1 & 2 \\ 3 & 5 \end{bmatrix}$

Combination (p. 352) Any unordered selection of r objects from a set of n objects is a combination. The number of combinations of n objects taken r at a time is $_nC_r = \frac{n!}{r!(n-r)!}$ for $0 \le r \le n$.

Combinación (p. 352) Cualquier selección no ordenada de r objetos tomados de un conjunto de n objetos es una combinación. El número de combinaciones de n objetos, cuando se toman r objetos cada vez, es $_nC_r = \frac{n!}{r!(n-r)!}$ para $0 \le r \le n$.

The number of combinations of seven items taken four at a time is

$$_7C_4 = \frac{7!}{4!(7-4)!} = 35.$$

There are 35 ways to choose four items from seven items without regard to order.

Combined variation (p. 498) When one quantity varies with respect to two or more other quantities, the relation is a combined variation.

Variación combinada (p. 498) Cuando una cantidad varía con respecto a otras dos o más cantidades, la relación es una variación combinada.

$y = kx^2\sqrt{z}$

$z = \frac{kx}{y}$

Common difference (p. 616) A common difference is the difference between consecutive terms of an arithmetic sequence.

Diferencia común (p. 616) La diferencia común es la diferencia entre los términos consecutivos de una progresión aritmética.

The arithmetic sequence $1, 5, 9, 13, \ldots$ has a common difference of 4.

Common logarithm (p. 455) A common logarithm is a logarithm that uses base 10. You can write the common logarithm $\log_{10} y$ as $\log y$.

Logaritmo común (p. 455) El logaritmo común es un logaritmo de base 10. El logaritmo común $\log_{10} y$ se expresa como $\log y$.

$\log 1 = 0$

$\log 10 = 1$

$\log 50 = 1.698970004\ldots$

Common ratio (p. 622) A common ratio is the ratio of consecutive terms of a geometric sequence.

Razón común (p. 622) Una razón común es el número que resulta al dividir términos consecutivos en una progresión geométrica.

The geometric sequence $2.5, 5, 10, 20, \ldots$ has a common ratio of 2.

Completing the square (p. 286) Completing the square is the process of finding the constant term of a perfect square trinomial.

Completar el cuadrado (p. 286) Completar el cuadrado es el proceso de hallar el término constante de un trinomio cuadrado perfecto.

$x^2 - 12x + \blacksquare$

$x^2 - 12x + \left(\frac{-12}{2}\right)^2$

$x^2 - 12x + 36$

English/Spanish Glossary

Complex conjugates (p. 280) Number pairs of the form $a + bi$ and $a - bi$ are complex conjugates.

The complex numbers $2 - 3i$ and $2 + 3i$ are complex conjugates.

Conjugados complejos (p. 280) Los pares de números de la forma $a + bi$ y $a - bi$ son conjugados complejos.

Complex fraction (p. 524) A complex fraction is a fraction that has a fraction in its numerator or denominator or in both its numerator and denominator.

$$\frac{\frac{2}{1}}{5}$$

$$\frac{\frac{2}{7}}{\frac{3}{2}}$$

Fracción compleja (p. 524) Una fracción compleja es una fracción que contiene otra fracción en el numerador o en el denominador, o en ambos.

Complex number plane (p. 279) You can use the complex number plane to represent a complex number geometrically. Locate the real part of the number on the horizontal axis and the imaginary part on the vertical axis.

Plano de números complejos (p. 279) Plano que sirve para representar geométricamente los números complejos. Se localiza la parte real del número en el eje horizontal y la parte imaginaria en el eje vertical.

Complex numbers (p. 279) Imaginary numbers and real numbers together make up the set of complex numbers. A complex number can be written in the form $a + bi$, where a and b are real numbers, including 0, and i is $\sqrt{-1}$.

$6 + i$

$7, 2i$

Números complejos (p. 279) Los números imaginarios y los números reales componen el conjunto de números complejos. Un número complejo es cualquier expresión de la forma $a + bi$, donde a y b son números reales, incluido 0, e i es $\sqrt{-1}$.

Composite function (p. 405) A composite function is a combination of two functions such that the output from the first function becomes the input for the second function.

$$f(x) = 2x + 1 \quad g(x) = x^2 - 1$$
$$(g \circ f)(5) = g(f(5)) = g(2(5) + 1)$$
$$= g(11)$$
$$= 11^2 - 1 = 120$$
$$(f \circ g)(5) = f(g(5)) = f((5)^2 - 1)$$
$$= f(24)$$
$$= 2(24) + 1 = 49$$

Función compuesta (p. 405) Una función compuesta es la combinación de dos funciones. La cantidad de salida de la primera función es la cantidad de entrada de la segunda función.

Compound inequality (p. 28) A compound inequality is a pair of inequalities joined by *and* or *or*.

$-1 < x$ and $x \le 3$

$x < -1$ or $x \ge 3$

Desigualdad compuesta (p. 28) Una desigualdad compuesta se forma con dos desigualdades enlazadas por medio de una *y* o una *o*.

Conditional probability (p. 666)   A conditional probability contains a condition that may limit the sample space for an event. The notation $P(B \mid A)$ is read "the probability of event B, given event A." For any two events A and B in the sample space,

$$P(B \mid A) = \frac{P(A \text{ and } B)}{P(A)}.$$

Probabilidad condicional (p. 666)   Una probabilidad condicional contiene una condición que puede limitar el espacio muestral de un suceso. La notación $P(B \mid A)$ se lee "la probabilidad del suceso B, dado el suceso A". Para dos sucesos cualesquiera A y B en el espacio muestral,

$$P(B \mid A) = \frac{P(A \text{ y } B)}{P(A)}.$$

Suppose that 83% of an airline's flights depart on schedule. Suppose also that 75% of its flights depart and arrive on schedule.

$P(\text{arrives on time} \mid \text{departs on time})$

$= \dfrac{P(\text{departs and arrives on time})}{P(\text{departs on time})}$

$= \dfrac{0.75}{0.83}$

≈ 0.9

Conic section (p. 557)   A conic section is a curve formed by the intersection of a plane and a double cone.

Sección cónica (p. 557)   Una sección cónica es una curva que se forma por la intersección de un plano con un cono doble.

ellipse   hyperbola

Conjugates (p. 343)   Number pairs of the form $a + \sqrt{b}$ and $a - \sqrt{b}$ are conjugates.

Conjugados (p. 343)   Los pares de números con la forma $a + \sqrt{b}$ y $a - \sqrt{b}$ son conjugados.

$5 + \sqrt{3}$ and $5 - \sqrt{3}$ are conjugates.

Constant matrix (p. 218)   When representing a system of equations with a matrix equation, the matrix containing the constants of the system is the constant matrix.

Matriz de constantes (p. 218)   Al representar un sistema de ecuaciones con una ecuación matricial, la matriz que contiene las constantes del sistema es la matriz de constantes.

$\begin{cases} x + 2y = 5 \\ 3x + 5y = 14 \end{cases}$

constant matrix $\begin{bmatrix} 5 \\ 14 \end{bmatrix}$

Constant of variation (pp. 74, 496, 498)   The constant of variation is the value of k in the direct variation $y = kx$ or the value of k in the indirect variation $xy = k$. A joint variation also has a constant of variation.

Constante de variación (pp. 74, 496, 498)   La constante de variación es el valor de k en una variación directa $y = kx$, o el valor de k en la variación indirecta $xy = k$. Una variación conjunta también tiene una constante de variación.

In $y = 3.5x$, the constant of variation k is 3.5. In $xy = 5$, the constant of variation k is 5.

Constraints (p. 141) Constraints are restrictions on the variables of the objective function in a linear programming problem. *See* **Linear programming.**

Restricciones (p. 141) Las restricciones son limitaciones a las variables de una función objetiva en un problema de programación lineal. *Ver* **Linear programming.**

Continuously compounded interest formula (p. 452) The formula for continuously compounded interest is $A = Pe^{rt}$.

Fórmula de interés compuesto continuo (p. 452) La fórmula para el interés compuesto continuo es $A = Pe^{rt}$.

Suppose that $P = \$1200, r = 0.05$, and $t = 3$. Then

$$A = 1200e^{0.05 \cdot 3}$$
$$= 1200(2.718\ldots)^{0.15}$$
$$\approx 1394.20$$

Converge (p. 637) An infinite geometric series converges when $|r| < 1$, where r is the common ratio of the related sequence.

Convergir (p. 637) Una serie geométrica infinita converge cuando $|r| < 1$, donde r es la razón común de la progresión.

$1 + \frac{1}{2} + \frac{1}{4} + \frac{1}{8} + \cdots$ converges.

Coordinate space (p. 148) Coordinate space is a three-dimensional space where each point is described uniquely using an ordered triple of numbers.

Espacio de coordenadas (p. 148) Un espacio de coordenadas es un espacio tridimensional en el cual cada punto es definido de manera única por una tripleta ordenada de números.

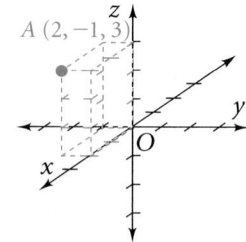

Cosecant function (p. 775) The cosecant (csc) function is the reciprocal of the sine function. For all real numbers θ except those that make $\sin \theta = 0$, $\csc \theta = \frac{1}{\sin \theta}$.

Función cosecante (p. 775) La función cosecante (csc) se define como el recíproco de la función seno. Para todos los números reales θ, excepto aquéllos para los que $\sin \theta = 0$, $\csc \theta = \frac{1}{\sin \theta}$.

If $\sin \theta = \frac{5}{13}$, then $\csc \theta = \frac{13}{5}$.

Cosine function (p. 753) The cosine function, $y = \cos \theta$, matches the measure θ of an angle in standard position with the x-coordinate of a point on the unit circle. This point is where the terminal side of the angle intersects the unit circle.

Función coseno (p. 753) La función coseno, $y = \cos \theta$, equivale a la medida θ de un ángulo en posición normal con la coordenada x de un punto en el círculo unitario. Este punto es el punto de intersección entre el lado terminal del ángulo y el círculo unitario.

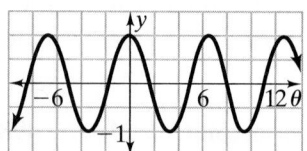

Cosine of θ (p. 732) The cosine of an angle measure θ ($\cos \theta$) is the x-coordinate of the point at which the terminal side of the angle intersects the unit circle.

Coseno de θ (p. 732) El coseno de un ángulo que mide θ ($\cos \theta$) es la coordenada x del punto de intersección del lado terminal del ángulo y el círculo unitario.

(Diagram: unit circle with point $P(\cos \theta, \sin \theta)$)

Cotangent function (p. 775) The cotangent (cot) function is the reciprocal of the tangent function. For all real numbers θ except those that make $\tan \theta = 0$, $\cot \theta = \frac{1}{\tan \theta}$.

Función cotangente (p. 775) La función cotangente (cot) es el recíproco de la función tangente. Para todos los números reales θ, excepto aquéllos para los que $\tan \theta = 0$, $\cot \theta = \frac{1}{\tan \theta}$.

If $\tan \theta = \frac{5}{12}$, then $\cot \theta = \frac{12}{5}$.

Coterminal angles (p. 731) Two angles in standard position are coterminal if they have the same terminal side.

Ángulos coterminales (p. 731) Dos ángulos que están en posición normal son coterminales si tienen el mismo lado terminal.

Angles that have measures 135° and −225° are coterminal.

Co-vertices (of an ellipse) (p. 578) The endpoints of the minor axis of an ellipse are the co-vertices of the ellipse.

Covértices (de una elipse) (p. 578) Los puntos de intersección entre una elipse y los ejes menores son los covértices de la elipse.

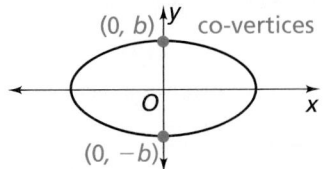

Cramer's Rule (p. 225) Cramer's Rule is a method of solving a system of linear equations using determinants. D is the determinant of the system's coefficient matrix. Form the determinants D_x and D_y by replacing the corresponding column of the coefficient matrix with the terms of the constant matrix.

Regla de Cramer (p. 225) La regla de Cramer es un método para resolver por medio de determinantes un sistema de ecuaciones lineales. D es el determinante de la matriz de coeficientes del sistema. Se forman los determinantes D_x y D_y reemplazando la columna correspondiente de la matriz de coeficientes con los términos de la matriz constante.

$$\begin{cases} x + 2y = 6 \\ -x + y = -6 \end{cases}$$

$$D = \begin{vmatrix} 1 & 2 \\ -1 & 1 \end{vmatrix} = 3$$

$$D_x = \begin{vmatrix} 6 & 2 \\ -6 & 1 \end{vmatrix} = 18$$

$$D_y = \begin{vmatrix} 1 & 6 \\ -1 & -6 \end{vmatrix} = 0$$

$$x = \frac{D_x}{D} = 6 \qquad y = \frac{D_y}{D} = 0$$

Cumulative probability (p. 660) Probability over a continuous range of events is cumulative probability.

Probabilidad acumulativa (p. 660) La probabilidad que existe a lo largo de una serie continua de sucesos es la probabilidad acumulativa.

Cycle (p. 723) A cycle of a periodic function is an interval of *x*-values over which the function provides one complete pattern of *y*-values.

Ciclo (p. 723) El ciclo de una función periódica es un intervalo de valores de *x* de los cuales la función produce un patrón completo de valores de *y*.

a cycle

Decay factor (p. 441) In an exponential function of the form $y = ab^x$, *b* is the decay factor if $0 < b < 1$.

Factor de decremento (p. 441) En una función exponencial de la forma $y = ab^x$, *b* es el factor de decremento si, $0 < b < 1$.

In the equation $y = 0.5^x$, 0.5 is the decay factor.

Degree of a polynomial (p. 313) The degree of a polynomial is the largest degree of any term of the polynomial.

Grado de un polinomio (p. 313) El grado de un polinomio es el grado mayor de cualquier término del polinomio.

$P(x) = x^6 + 2x^3 - 3$

degree 6

Degree of a term (p. 313) The exponent of the variable in a term determines the degree of the term.

Grado de un término (p. 313) El exponente de la variable de un término determina el grado del término.

$x^2 \leftarrow$ degree 2

$3y^3 \leftarrow$ degree 3

$-4a^{12} \leftarrow$ degree 12

Dependent events (p. 539) Two events are dependent if the occurrence of one event affects the probability of the second event.

Sucesos dependientes (p. 539) Cuando el resultado de un suceso influye en la probabilidad de que ocurra el segundo suceso, los dos sucesos son dependientes.

You have a bag with red and blue marbles. You draw one marble at random and then another without replacing the first. The colors drawn are dependent events. A red marble on the first draw changes the probability for each color on the second draw.

Dependent system (p. 122) A system of equations that does not have a unique solution is a dependent system.

Sistema dependiente (p. 122) Un sistema de ecuaciones es dependiente cuando no tiene una solución única.

$\begin{cases} y = 2x + 3 \\ -4x + 2y = 6 \end{cases}$ represents two equations for the same line, so it has many solutions. It is a dependent system.

Dependent variable (p. 64) If a function is defined by an equation using the variables *x* and *y*, where *y* represents output values, then *y* is the dependent variable.

Variable dependiente (p. 64) Si una función es definida por una ecuación que usa las variables *x* e *y*, donde *y* representa valores de salida, entonces *y* es la variable dependiente.

$y = 2x + 1$
y is the dependent variable.

Determinant (p. 204) The determinant of a square matrix is a real number that can be computed from its elements according to a specific formula.

The determinant of $\begin{bmatrix} 3 & -2 \\ 5 & 6 \end{bmatrix}$ is $3(6) - 5(-2) = 28.$

Determinante (p. 204) El determinante de una matriz cuadrada es un número real que se puede calcular a partir de sus elementos por medio de una fórmula específica.

Difference of cubes (p. 334) A difference of cubes is an expression of the form $a^3 - b^3$. It can be factored as $(a - b)(a^2 + ab + b^2)$.

$x^3 - 27 = (x - 3)(x^2 + 3x + 9)$

Diferencia de dos cubos (p. 334) La diferencia de dos cubos es una expresión de la forma $a^3 - b^3$. Se puede factorizar como $(a - b)(a^2 + ab + b^2)$.

Difference of two squares (p. 267) A difference of two squares is an expression of the form $a^2 - b^2$. It can be factored as $(a + b)(a - b)$.

$25a^2 - 4 = (5a + 2)(5a - 2)$
$m^6 - 1 = (m^3 + 1)(m^3 - 1)$

Diferencia de dos cuadrados (p. 267) La diferencia de dos cuadrados es una expresión de la forma $a^2 - b^2$. Se puede factorizar como $(a + b)(a - b)$.

Dilation (p. 196) A dilation is a transformation that can change the size of a figure. When the center of the dilation is the origin, you can use scalar multiplication to find the coordinates of the vertices of an image.

Dilatación (p. 196) Una dilatación es una transformación que puede cambiar el tamaño de una figura. Cuando el centro de dilatación está en el origen, se hallan las coordenadas de los vértices de la imagen por medio de la multiplicación de escalar.

Direct variation (p. 74) A linear function defined by an equation of the form $y = kx$, where $k \neq 0$, represents direct variation.

$y = 3.5x, y = 7x, y = -\frac{1}{2}x$

Variación directa (p. 74) Una función lineal definida por una ecuación de la forma $y = kx$, donde $k \neq 0$, representa una variación directa.

Directrix (p. 565) The directrix of a parabola is the fixed line used to define a parabola. Each point of the parabola is the same distance from the focus and the directrix.

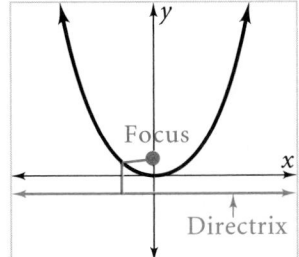

Directriz (p. 565) La directriz de una parábola es la recta fija con que se define una parábola. Cada punto de la parábola está a la misma distancia del foco y de la directriz.

Discriminant (p. 295) The discriminant of the quadratic trinomial $ax^2 + bx + c$ is $b^2 - 4ac$. The discriminant determines the number of real roots that the quadratic equation $ax^2 + bx + c = 0$ has. If $b^2 - 4ac < 0$, the equation has no real roots; if $b^2 - 4ac = 0$, the equation has one real root; if $b^2 - 4ac > 0$, the equation has two real roots.

$3x^2 - 6x + 1$

discriminant $= (-6)^2 - 4(3)(1)$

$= 36 - 12 = 24$

The equation has two real roots.

Discriminante (p. 295) El discriminante del trinomio cuadrático $ax^2 + bx + c$ es $b^2 - 4ac$. El discriminante determina la cantidad de raíces reales que tiene la ecuación $ax^2 + bx + c = 0$. Si $b^2 - 4ac < 0$, la ecuación no tiene raíces reales; si $b^2 - 4ac = 0$, la ecuación tiene una raíz real; si $b^2 - 4ac > 0$, la ecuación tiene dos raíces reales.

Diverge (p. 637) An infinite geometric series diverges when $|r| \geq 1$, where r is the common ratio of the related sequence.

$1 + 2 + 4 + 8 + \cdots$ diverges.

Divergir (p. 637) Una serie geométrica infinita diverge cuando $|r| \geq 1$, donde r es la razón común de la progresión relacionada.

Domain (p. 58) The domain of a relation is the set of all inputs, or x-coordinates, of the ordered pairs.

In the relation $\{(0, 1), (0, 2), (0, 3), (0, 4), (1, 3), (1, 4), (2, 1)\}$, the domain is $\{0, 1, 2\}$. In the function $f(x) = x^2 - 10$, the domain is all real numbers.

Dominio (p. 58) El dominio de una relación es el conjunto de todos los valores de entrada, o coordenadas x, de los pares ordenados.

Ellipse (p. 578) An ellipse is the set of points P in a plane such that the sum of the distances from P to two fixed points F_1 and F_2 is a given constant k. The standard form of the equation of an ellipse with its center at the origin is $\frac{x^2}{a^2} + \frac{y^2}{b^2} = 1$ if the major axis is horizontal and $\frac{x^2}{b^2} + \frac{y^2}{a^2} = 1$ if the major axis is vertical, where $a > b$.

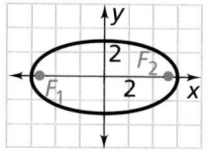

$\frac{x^2}{36} + \frac{y^2}{9} = 1$

$F_1 = (-3\sqrt{3}, 0), F_2 = (3\sqrt{3}, 0)$

Elipse (p. 578) Una elipse es el conjunto de puntos P situados en un plano tal que la suma de las distancias entre P y dos puntos fijos F_1 y F_2 es una constante dada k. La forma normal de la ecuación de una elipse con su centro en el origen es $\frac{x^2}{a^2} + \frac{y^2}{b^2} = 1$ si el eje mayor es horizontal y $\frac{x^2}{b^2} + \frac{y^2}{a^2} = 1$ si el eje mayor es vertical, donde $a > b$.

Equal matrices (p. 181) Equal matrices are matrices with the same dimensions and equal corresponding elements.

Matrices A and B are equal.

Matrices equivalentes (p. 181) Dos matrices son equivalentes si y sólo si tienen las mismas dimensiones y sus elementos correspondientes son iguales.

Equivalent systems (p. 129) Linear systems that have the same solution(s) are equivalent systems.

Sistemas equivalentes (p. 129) Sistemas lineales que tienen la misma solución o soluciones son sistemas equivalentes.

Evaluate (p. 12) To evaluate an expression, substitute numbers for the variables in the expression and then simplify the expression following the order of operations.

Evaluar (p. 12) Para evaluar una expresión, se sustituyen las variables de la expresión por números y luego se simplifica la expresión siguiendo el orden de las operaciones.

When $x = 2$ and $y = -1$,
$2x + 3y$ evaluates to 1.

Expand (p. 359) You expand a binomial raised to a power by multiplying and then writing the resulting polynomial in standard form.

Desarrollar (p. 359) Para desarrollar un binomio elevado a una potencia, se multiplica y luego se escribe el polinomio resultante en forma normal.

$$(x + 4)^3$$
$$= (x + 4)(x + 4)^2$$
$$= (x + 4)(x^2 + 8x + 16)$$
$$= x^3 + 8x^2 + 16x + 4x^2 + 32x + 64$$
$$= x^3 + 12x^2 + 48x + 64$$

Experimental probability (p. 40) The experimental probability of an event is the ratio

$$\frac{\text{number of times the event occurs}}{\text{number of trials}}.$$

Probabilidad experimental (p. 40) La probabilidad experimental de un suceso es la razón

$$\frac{\text{número de veces que el suceso ocurre}}{\text{número de ensayos}}.$$

Suppose a basketball player has scored 19 times in 28 attempts at a basket. The experimental probability of the player's scoring is $P(\text{score}) = \frac{19}{28} \approx 0.68$, or 68%.

Explicit formula (p. 612) An explicit formula expresses the nth term of a sequence in terms of n.

Fórmula explícita (p. 612) Una fórmula explícita expresa el n-ésimo término de una progresión en función de n.

Let $a_n = 2n + 5$ for positive integers n. If $n = 7$, then $a_7 = 2(7) + 5 = 19$.

Exponential equation (p. 469) An equation of the form $b^{cx} = a$, where the exponent includes a variable, is called an exponential equation. You can solve an exponential equation by taking the logarithm of each side of the equation.

Ecuación exponencial (p. 469) Una ecuación de la forma $b^{cx} = a$, donde el exponente incluye una variable, se llama ecuación exponencial. Dicha ecuación se resuelve hallando el logaritmo de cada lado de la ecuación.

$$5^{2x} = 270$$
$$\log 5^{2x} = \log 270$$
$$2x \log 5 = \log 270$$
$$2x = \frac{\log 270}{\log 5}$$
$$2x \approx 3.4785$$
$$x \approx 1.7392$$

English/Spanish Glossary

Exponential function (pp. 438, 449) The general form of an exponential function is $y = ab^x$, where x is a real number, $a \neq 0$, $b > 0$, and $b \neq 1$. When $b > 1$, the function models exponential growth with growth factor b. When $0 < b < 1$, the function models exponential decay with decay factor b.

Función exponencial (pp. 438, 449) La forma general de una función exponencial es $y = ab^x$, donde x es un número real, $a \neq 0$, $b > 0$ y $b \neq 1$. Cuando $b > 1$, la función representa un incremento exponencial con factor de incremento b. Cuando $0 < b < 1$, la función representa el decremento exponencial con factor de decremento b.

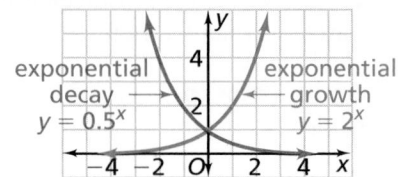

Extraneous solution (p. 34) An extraneous solution is a solution of an equation derived from an original equation but it is not a solution of the original equation.

Solución extraña (p. 34) Una solución extraña es una solución de una ecuación derivada de una ecuación dada, pero que no satisface la ecuación dada.

$$\sqrt{x - 3} = x - 5$$
$$x - 3 = x^2 - 10x + 25$$
$$0 = x^2 - 11x + 28$$
$$0 = (x - 4)(x - 7)$$
$$x = 4 \text{ or } 7$$

The number 7 is a solution, but 4 is not, since $\sqrt{4 - 3} \neq 4 - 5$.

Factor Theorem (p. 321) The expression $x - a$ is a linear factor of a polynomial if and only if the value a is a zero of the related polynomial function.

Teorema de factores (p. 321) La expresión $x - a$ es un factor lineal de un polinomio si y sólo si el valor a es un cero de la función del polinomio relacionada.

The value 2 makes the polynomial $x^2 + 2x - 8$ equal to zero. So, $x - 2$ is a factor of $x^2 + 2x - 8$.

Factoring (p. 263) Factoring is rewriting an expression as the product of its factors.

Descomposición factorial (p. 263) Descomponer en factores es convertir una expresión en el producto de sus factores.

expanded form   factored form
$x^2 + x - 56$ $(x + 8)(x - 7)$

Feasible region (p. 142) In a linear programming problem, the feasible region contains all the values that satisfy the constraints on the objective function.

Región factible (p. 142) En un problema de programación lineal, la región factible contiene todos los valores que satisfacen las restricciones de la función objetiva.

Focus (plural: foci) (pp. 565, 578, 585) The focus of a conic section is a point used to define a conic section.

A parabola is the set of all points that are the same distance from the parabola's focus and its directrix. An ellipse is the set of all points P such that the sum of the distances from each point P to the two foci of the ellipse is a constant. A hyperbola is the set of all points P such that the difference of the distances from each point P to the two foci of the hyperbola is a constant.

Foco (pp. 565, 578, 585) El foco de una sección cónica es el punto con el que se define una sección cónica.

Una parábola es el conjunto de todos los puntos que están a la misma distancia del foco y la directriz de la parábola. Una elipse es el conjunto de todos los puntos P tal que la suma de las distancias de cada punto P a los dos focos de la elipse es una constante. Una hipérbola es el conjunto de todos los puntos P tal que la diferencia de las distancias de cada punto P a los dos focos de la hipérbola es una constante.

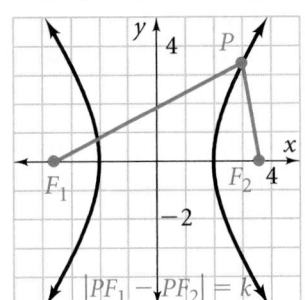

F_1 and F_2 are foci.

Frequency table (p. 660) A frequency table is a list of the outcomes in a sample space and the number of times each outcome occurs.

Tabla de frecuencias (p. 660) Una tabla de frecuencias es una lista de los resultados de un espacio muestral y el número de veces que cada resultado ocurre.

Roll	Freq.
1	5
2	9
3	7
4	8
5	8
6	3

Suppose that you roll a standard number cube 40 times and that each number occurs as often as shown in the table. The table is a frequency table and the diagram to its right is a frequency diagram, or histogram.

Function (p. 59) A function is a relation in which each element of the domain is paired with exactly one element of the range.

Función (p. 59) Una función es una relación que asigna exactamente un valor del dominio a cada valor del rango.

The relation $y = 3x^3 - 2x + 3$ is a function. $f(x) = 3x^3 - 2x + 3$ is the same relation written in function notation.

Function notation (p. 60) If f is the name of a function, the function notation $f(x)$ also indicates the function name, but also represents a range value for the domain value x. You read the function notation $f(x)$ as "f of x" or "a function of x." Note that $f(x)$ does *not* mean "f times x."

Notación de una función (p. 60) Si f es el nombre de una función, la notación de la función $f(x)$ indica el nombre de la función, pero también representa un rango de valores para el dominio de valores de x. La notación de una función $f(x)$ se lee "f de x" o "función de x". Hay que recordar que $f(x)$ no significa "f multiplicado por x".

When the value of x is 3, $f(3)$, read "f of 3," represents the value of the function at 3.

Fundamental Theorem of Algebra (p. 347) If $P(x)$ is a polynomial of degree $n \geq 1$ with complex coefficients, then $P(x) = 0$ has at least one complex root.

$P(x) = 3x^3 - 2x + 3$ is of degree 3, so $P(x) = 0$ has at least one complex root.

Teorema fundamental de álgebra (p. 347) Si $P(x)$ es un polinomio de grado $n \geq 1$ con coeficientes complejos, entonces $P(x) = 0$ tiene por lo menos una raíz compleja.

Geometric mean (p. 624) The geometric mean of any two positive numbers is the positive square root of the product of the two numbers.

The geometric mean of 12 and 18 is $\sqrt{12 \cdot 18} \approx 14.6969$.

Media geométrica (p. 624) La media geométrica de dos números positivos es la raíz cuadrada positiva del producto de los dos números.

Geometric sequence (p. 622) In a geometric sequence, the ratio of consecutive terms is constant. The constant is called the common ratio.

The geometric sequence $2.5, 5, 10, 20, 40, \ldots$ has a common ratio of 2.

Progresión geométrica (p. 622) En una progresión geométrica, la razón de términos consecutivos es un valor constante. La constante se llama razón común.

Geometric series (p. 636) A geometric series is the sum of the terms in a geometric sequence.

One geometric series with five terms is $2.5 + 5 + 10 + 20 + 40$.

Serie geométrica (p. 636) Una serie geométrica es la suma de términos en una progresión geométrica.

Greatest common factor (GCF) of an expression (p. 263) The greatest common factor (GCF) of an expression is the common factor of each term of the expression that has the greatest coefficient and the greatest exponent.

The GCF of $4x^2 + 20x - 12$ is 4.

Máximo factor común de una expresión (p. 263) El máximo común factor de una expresión es el factor común de cada término de la expresión que tiene el mayor coeficiente y el mayor exponente.

Growth factor (p. 438) In an exponential function of the form $y = ab^x$, b is the growth factor if $b > 1$.

In the exponential equation $y = 2^x$, 2 is the growth factor.

Factor de incremento (p. 438) En una función exponencial de la forma $y = ab^x$, b es el factor de incremento si $b > 1$.

Hyperbola (p. 585) A hyperbola is a set of points P in a plane such that the difference between the distances from P to the foci F_1 and F_2 is a given constant k. $|PF_1 - PF_2| = k$

The standard form of an equation of a hyperbola centered at $(0,0)$ is $\frac{x^2}{a^2} - \frac{y^2}{b^2} = 1$ if the transverse axis is horizontal and $\frac{y^2}{a^2} - \frac{x^2}{b^2} = 1$ if the transverse axis is vertical.

Hipérbola (p. 585) Una hipérbola es un conjunto de puntos P en un plano tal que la diferencia entre las distancias de P a los focos F_1 y F_2 es una constante k dada. $|PF_1 - PF_2| = k$

La forma normal de la ecuación de una hipérbola centrada en $(0,0)$ es $\frac{x^2}{a^2} - \frac{y^2}{b^2} = 1$, si el eje transversal es horizontal, y $\frac{y^2}{a^2} - \frac{x^2}{b^2} = 1$, si el eje transversal es vertical.

$$\frac{x^2}{5^2} - \frac{y^2}{3^2} = 1$$

***i* (p. 278)** The imaginary number i is the principal square root of -1. $i = \sqrt{-1}$ and $i^2 = -1$.

***i* (p. 278)** El número imaginario i es la raíz cuadrada principal de -1.

Image (p. 196) An image is a figure obtained by a transformation of a preimage.

Imagen (p. 196) Una imagen es la figura que resulta después de que la preimagen sufre una transformación.

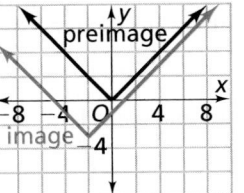

Imaginary number (p. 278) An imaginary number is any number of the form $a + bi$, where $b \neq 0$ and $i = \sqrt{-1}$. A number of the form bi is a pure imaginary number.

$2 + 3i$

$7i$

i

Número imaginario (p. 278) Un número imaginario es todo número de la forma $a + bi$, donde $b \neq 0$ e $i = \sqrt{-1}$. Un número de la forma bi es un número imaginario puro.

Imaginary Root Theorem (p. 344) If the imaginary number $a + bi$ is a root of a polynomial equation with real coefficients, then the conjugate $a - bi$ also is a root.

$2 + 3i$ is a root of $x^2 - 4x + 13 = 0$, so $2 - 3i$ is also a root.

Teorema de la raíz imaginaria (p. 344) Si el número imaginario $a + bi$ es la raíz de la ecuación de un polinomio con coeficientes reales, entonces el conjugado $a - bi$ también es una raíz.

Inconsistent system (p. 122)   A system of equations that has no solution is an inconsistent system.

Sistema incompatible (p. 122)   Un sistema incompatible es un sistema de ecuaciones para el cual no hay solución.

$\begin{cases} y = 2x + 3 \\ -2x + y = 1 \end{cases}$ is a system of parallel lines, so it has no solution. It is an inconsistent system.

Independent events (p. 539)   When the outcome of one event does not affect the probability of a second event, the two events are independent.

Sucesos independientes (p. 539)   Cuando el resultado de un suceso no altera la probabilidad de otro, los dos sucesos son independientes.

The results of two rolls of a number cube are independent. Getting a 5 on the first roll does not change the probability of getting a 5 on the second roll.

Independent system (p. 122)   A system of linear equations that has a unique solution is an independent system.

Sistema independiente (p. 122)   Un sistema de ecuaciones lineales que tenga una sola solución es un sistema independiente.

$\begin{cases} x + 2y = -7 \\ 2x - 3y = 0 \end{cases}$ has the unique solution $(-3, -2)$. It is an independent system.

Independent variable (p. 64)   If a function is defined by an equation using the variables x and y, where x represents input values, then x is the independent variable.

Variable independiente (p. 64)   Si una función es definida por una ecuación con las variables x e y, donde x representa los valores de entrada, entonces x es la variable independiente.

$y = 2x + 1$

x is the independent variable.

Index (p. 376)   With a radical sign, the index indicates the degree of the root.

Índice (p. 376)   Con un signo de radical, el índice indica el grado de la raíz.

index 2   index 3   index 4

$\sqrt{16}$ $\sqrt[3]{16}$ $\sqrt[4]{16}$

Initial side of an angle (p. 730)   When an angle is in standard position, the initial side of the angle is given to be on the positive x-axis. The other ray is the terminal side of the angle.

Lado inicial de un ángulo (p. 730)   Cuando un ángulo está en posición normal, el lado inicial del ángulo se ubica en el eje positivo de las x. El otro rayo, o semirrecta, forma el lado terminal del ángulo.

Inscribed rectangles (p. 645)   When approximating the area under a curve, inscribed rectangles are completely under the curve. Their combined area generally is less than the area under the curve.

Rectángulos inscritos (p. 645)   Cuando se aproxima el área situada dentro de una curva, los rectángulos inscritos quedan completamente contenidos en la curva. Generalmente, su área total es menor que el área dentro de la curva.

Intercepted arc (p. 738) An intercepted arc is the portion of a circle whose endpoints are on the sides of a central angle of the circle and whose remaining points lie in the interior of the angle.

Arco interceptado (p. 738) Un arco interceptado es la porción de un círculo cuyos extremos quedan sobre los lados de un ángulo central del círculo y cuyos puntos restantes quedan en el interior del ángulo.

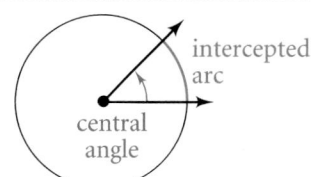

Interquartile range (p. 681) The interquartile range of a set of data is the difference between the third and first quartiles.

Intervalo intercuartil (p. 681) El rango intercuartil de un conjunto de datos es la diferencia entre el tercero y el primer cuartiles.

The first and third quartiles of the data set $\{2, 3, 4, 5, 5, 6, 7, 7\}$ are 3.5 and 6.5. The interquartile range is $6.5 - 3.5 = 3$.

Inverse functions (p. 415) If function f pairs a value b with a then its inverse, denoted f^{-1}, pairs the value a with b. If f^{-1} is also a function, then f and f^{-1} are inverse functions.

Funciones inversas (p. 415) Si la función f empareja un valor b con a, entonces su inversa, cuya notación es f^{-1}, empareja el valor a con b. Si f^{-1} también es una función, entonces f y f^{-1} son funciones inversas.

If $f(x) = x + 3$, then $f^{-1}(x) = x - 3$.

Inverse relation (p. 413) If a relation pairs element a of its domain with element b of its range, the inverse relation "undoes" the relation and pairs b with a. If (a, b) is an ordered pair of a relation, then (b, a) is an ordered pair of its inverse.

Relación inversa (p. 413) Si una relación empareja el elemento a de su dominio con el elemento b de su rango, la relación inversa "deshace" la relación y empareja b con a. Si (a, b) es un par ordenado de una relación, entonces (b, a) es un par ordenado de su inversa.

Inverse variation (p. 496) A relation represented by an equation of the form $y = \frac{k}{x}$ or $xy = k$, where $k \neq 0$, is an inverse variation with the constant of variation k.

Variación inversa (p. 496) Una relación representada por la fórmula $y = \frac{k}{x}$ o $xy = k$, donde $k \neq 0$, es una variación inversa con la constante de variación k.

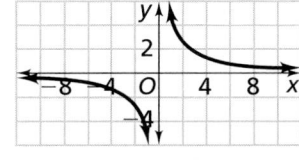

$xy = 5$, or $y = \frac{5}{x}$

Irrational Root Theorem (p. 343) Let a and b be rational numbers and let $\sqrt{b}$ be an irrational number. If $a + \sqrt{b}$ is a root of a polynomial equation with rational coefficients, then the conjugate $a - \sqrt{b}$ also is a root.

Teorema de la raíz irracional (p. 343) Sean a y b números racionales y sea $\sqrt{b}$ un número irracional. Si $a + \sqrt{b}$ es una raíz de una ecuación de un polinomio con coeficientes racionales, entonces el conjugado $a - \sqrt{b}$ también es una raíz.

$2 + \sqrt{3}$ is a root of $x^2 - 4x + 1 = 0$, so $2 - \sqrt{3}$ is also a root.

English/Spanish Glossary

Joint variation (p. 498) If one variable varies directly with respect to each of two or more other variables, the relation is a joint variation.

$$z = 8xy$$
$$T = kPV$$

Variación conjunta (p. 498) Si una variable varía directamente con respecto a cada una de dos o más variables, la relación es una variación conjunta.

Law of Cosines (p. 822) In $\triangle ABC$, let a, b, and c represent the lengths of the sides opposite $\angle A$, $\angle B$, and $\angle C$, respectively. Then

$$a^2 = b^2 + c^2 - 2bc \cos A,$$
$$b^2 = a^2 + c^2 - 2ac \cos B, \text{ and}$$
$$c^2 = a^2 + b^2 - 2ab \cos C$$

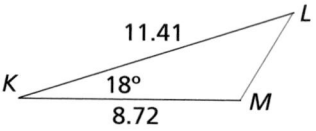

$$LM^2 = 11.41^2 + 8.72^2 - 2(11.41)(8.72) \cos 18°$$
$$LM^2 \approx 16.9754$$
$$LM \approx 4.12$$

Ley de cosenos (p. 822) En $\triangle ABC$, sean a, b y c las longitudes de los lados opuestos a $\angle A$, $\angle B$ y $\angle C$, respectivamente. Entonces

$$a^2 = b^2 + c^2 - 2bc \cos A,$$
$$b^2 = a^2 + c^2 - 2ac \cos B \text{ y}$$
$$c^2 = a^2 + b^2 - 2ab \cos C$$

Law of Sines (p. 815) In $\triangle ABC$, let a, b, and c represent the lengths of the sides opposite $\angle A$, $\angle B$, and $\angle C$, respectively. Then

$$\frac{\sin A}{a} = \frac{\sin B}{b} = \frac{\sin C}{c}.$$

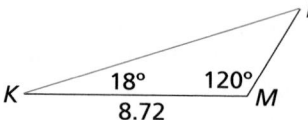

$$m\angle L = 180 - (120 + 18) = 42°$$
$$\frac{KL}{\sin 120°} = \frac{8.72}{\sin 42°}$$
$$KL = \frac{8.72 \sin 120°}{\sin 42°}$$
$$KL \approx 11.26$$

Ley de senos (p. 815) En $\triangle ABC$, sean a, b y c las longitudes de los lados opuestos a $\angle A$, $\angle B$ y $\angle C$, respectivamente. Entonces

$$\frac{\text{sen } A}{a} = \frac{\text{sen } B}{b} = \frac{\text{sen } C}{c}.$$

Like radicals (p. 386) Like radicals are radical expressions that have the same index and the same radicand.

$4\sqrt[3]{7}$ and $\sqrt[3]{7}$ are like radicals.

Radicales semejantes (p. 386) Los radicales semejantes son expresiones radicales que tienen el mismo índice y el mismo radicando.

Limits (p. 631) Limits in summation notation are the least and greatest integer values of the index n.

Límites (p. 631) Los límites en notación de sumatoria son el menor y el mayor valor del índice n en números enteros.

Linear equation (p. 64) A linear equation in two variables is an equation that can be written in the form $ax + by = c$. *See also* **Standard form of a linear equation.**

$y = 2x + 1$ can be written as $-2x + y = 1$.

Ecuación lineal (p. 64) Una ecuación lineal de dos variables es una ecuación que se puede escribir de la forma $ax + by = c$. *Ver también* **Standard form of a linear equation.**

Linear function (p. 64) A function whose graph is a line is a linear function. You can represent a linear function with a linear equation.

Función lineal (p. 64) Una función cuya gráfica es una recta es una función lineal. La función lineal se representa con una ecuación lineal.

Linear inequality (p. 103) A linear inequality is an inequality in two variables whose graph is a region of the coordinate plane that is bounded by a line. Each point in the region is a solution of the inequality. A sign of $\leq$ or $\geq$ indicates a solid boundary line. A sign of $<$ or $>$ indicates a dashed boundary line.

Desigualdad lineal (p. 103) Una desigualdad lineal es una desigualdad de dos variables cuya gráfica es una región del plano de coordenadas delimitado por una recta. Cada punto de la región es una solución de la desigualdad. El signo $\leq$ o $\geq$ denota que hay una recta de delimitación continua. El signo $<$ o $>$ denota que la recta de delimitación es punteada.

$y > x + 1$

Linear programming (p. 141) Linear programming is a technique that identifies the minimum or maximum value of some quantity. This quantity is modeled with an objective function. Limits on the variables in the objective function are constraints, written as linear inequalities.

Programación lineal (p. 141) La programación lineal es un método que permite identificar las condiciones que elevan al máximo o reducen al mínimo una cantidad. Se hace un modelo de esta cantidad con una función objetiva. Los límites de las variables en la función objetiva son restricciones, expresadas como desigualdades lineales.

Restrictions: $x \geq 0$, $y \geq 0$, $x + y \leq 7$, and $y \leq -2x + 8$

Objective function: $B = 2x + 4y$

Graph the restrictions to find the coordinates of each vertex.

Evaluate $B = 2x + 4y$ at each vertex.

The minimum value of B occurs when $x = 0$ and $y = 0$. The maximum value of B occurs when $x = 0$ and $y = 7$.

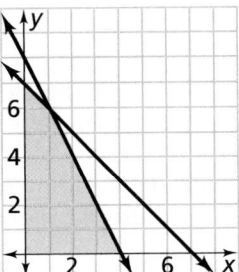

Linear system (p. 120) A linear system is a set of two or more linear equations that use the same variables.

Sistema lineal (p. 120) Un sistema lineal es un conjunto de dos o más ecuaciones lineales con las mismas variables.

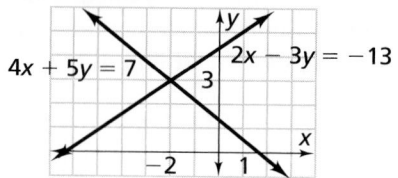

Logarithm (p. 455) A logarithm to the base b of a positive number y is defined as follows:
If $y = b^x$, then $\log_b y = x$.

Logaritmo (p. 455) El logaritmo de base b de un número positivo y se define así:
Si $y = b^x$, entonces $\log_b y = x$.

$$\log_2 8 = 3$$
$$\log_{10} 100 = 2$$
$$\log_5 5^7 = 7$$

Logarithmic equation (p. 471) An equation that includes a logarithmic expression is called a logarithmic equation.

Ecuación logarítmica (p. 471) Una ecuación que incluye una expresión logarítmica se llama ecuación logarítmica.

$$\log_3 x = 4$$

Logarithmic function (p. 456) A logarithmic function is the inverse of an exponential function.

Función logarítmica (p. 456) Una función logarítmica es la inversa de una función exponencial.

Major axis of an ellipse (p. 578) The major axis of an ellipse is the segment that contains the foci and has its endpoints on the ellipse. These endpoints are vertices of the ellipse.

Eje mayor de una elipse (p. 578) El eje mayor de una elipse es el segmento que contiene los focos y tiene los puntos extremos de la elipse. Los extremos son los vértices de la elipse.

Mapping diagram (p. 58) A mapping diagram describes a relation by linking elements of the domain with elements of the range.

Mapa (p. 58) Un mapa describe una relación al unir los elementos del dominio con los elementos del rango.

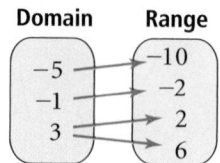

Margin of error (p. 691)   A sample proportion should be reported with an estimate of error, called the margin of error. When a random sample of size n is taken from a large population, the sample proportion has a margin of error of about $\pm\frac{1}{\sqrt{n}}$.

Margen de error (p. 691)   Una proporción muestral debe incluir una estimación del error, que se llama margen de error. Cuando se hace una muestra aleatoria de tamaño n de una población grande, la proporción muestral tiene un margen de error de aproximadamente $\pm\frac{1}{\sqrt{n}}$.

A set of 500 items is taken from a population for sampling. The margin of error for a sample proportion is about $\pm\frac{1}{\sqrt{500}} \approx \pm 0.045$.

Matrix (p. 172)   A matrix is a rectangular array of numbers written within brackets. A matrix with m horizontal rows and n vertical columns is an $m \times n$ matrix.

Matriz (p. 172)   Una matriz es un conjunto de números encerrados en corchetes y dispuestos en forma de rectángulo. Una matriz que contenga m filas y n columnas es una matriz $m \times n$.

$$A = \begin{bmatrix} 1 & -2 & 0 & 10 \\ 9 & 7 & -3 & 8 \\ 2 & -10 & 1 & -6 \end{bmatrix}$$

The number 2 is the element in the third row and first column. A is a 3×4 matrix.

Matrix addition (p. 178)   You add two matrices with the same dimensions by adding their corresponding elements.

Suma matricial (p. 178)   Para sumar dos matrices que tengan las mismas dimensiones se suman sus elementos correspondientes.

$$\begin{bmatrix} 2 & -3 \\ 0 & 4 \end{bmatrix} + \begin{bmatrix} -1 & 0 \\ 5 & -6 \end{bmatrix}$$
$$= \begin{bmatrix} 2 + (-1) & -3 + 0 \\ 0 + 5 & 4 + (-6) \end{bmatrix}$$
$$= \begin{bmatrix} 1 & -3 \\ 5 & -2 \end{bmatrix}$$

Matrix element (p. 173)   Every item listed in a matrix is an element of the matrix. An element is identified by its position in the matrix.

Elemento matricial (p. 173)   Cada cifra de una matriz es un elemento de la matriz. El elemento se identifica según la posición que ocupa en la matriz.

$$A = \begin{bmatrix} 1 & -2 & 0 & 10 \\ 9 & 7 & -3 & 8 \\ 2 & -10 & 1 & -6 \end{bmatrix}$$

Element a_{21} is 9, the element in the second row and first column.

Matrix equation (p. 180)   A matrix equation is an equation in which the variable is a matrix.

Ecuación matricial (p. 180)   Una ecuación matricial es una ecuación en que la variable es una matriz.

Solve $X + \begin{bmatrix} 3 & -2 \\ 5 & 1 \end{bmatrix} = \begin{bmatrix} 4 & 0 \\ 0 & 3 \end{bmatrix}$.

$$X + \begin{bmatrix} 3 & -2 \\ 5 & 1 \end{bmatrix} = \begin{bmatrix} 4 & 0 \\ 0 & 3 \end{bmatrix}$$

$$X = \begin{bmatrix} 4 & 0 \\ 0 & 3 \end{bmatrix} - \begin{bmatrix} 3 & -2 \\ 5 & 1 \end{bmatrix} = \begin{bmatrix} 1 & 2 \\ -5 & 2 \end{bmatrix}$$

English/Spanish Glossary

Matrix multiplication (p. 188) To find element c_{ij} of the product matrix AB, multiply each element in the ith row of A by the corresponding element in the jth column of B, and then add. If A is an $m \times n$ matrix and B is an $n \times p$ matrix, then the product matrix AB is an $m \times p$ matrix.

Multiplicación matricial (p. 188) Para encontrar el elemento c_{ij} del producto de la matriz AB, se multiplica cada elemento de la fila i de A por el elemento respectivo de la columna j de B y luego se suman. Si A es una matriz $m \times n$ y B es una matriz $n \times p$, entonces el producto de la matriz AB es una matriz $m \times p$.

$$\begin{bmatrix} 1 & 1 \\ 2 & 3 \\ 0 & 2 \end{bmatrix}\begin{bmatrix} 4 & 2 \\ 5 & 6 \end{bmatrix}$$

$$= \begin{bmatrix} (1)(4) + (1)(5) & (1)(2) + (1)(6) \\ (2)(4) + (3)(5) & (2)(2) + (3)(6) \\ (0)(4) + (2)(5) & (0)(2) + (2)(6) \end{bmatrix}$$

$$= \begin{bmatrix} 9 & 8 \\ 23 & 22 \\ 10 & 12 \end{bmatrix}$$

Mean (p. 672) The sum of the data values divided by the number of data values is the mean. *See also* **Arithmetic mean.**

Media (p. 672) La suma de los valores de datos dividida por el número de valores de datos sumados es la media. *Ver también* **Arithmetic mean.**

$\{1, 2, 3, 3, 6, 6\}$

$$\text{mean} = \frac{1 + 2 + 3 + 3 + 6 + 6}{6}$$

$$= \frac{21}{6} = 3.5$$

Measures of central tendency (p. 672) The mean, the median, and the mode are single, central values that help describe a set of data. They are called measures of central tendency.

Medidas de tendencia central (p. 672) La media, la mediana y la moda son los valores centrales únicos que permiten describir un conjunto de datos. Se llaman medidas de tendencia central.

$\{1, 2, 3, 3, 4, 5, 6, 8\}$

mean = 3.75

median = 3.5

modes = 3 and 6

Measures of variation (p. 681) Measures of variation, such as the range, the interquartile range, and the standard deviation, describe how the data in a data set are spread out.

Medidas de dispersión (p. 681) Las medidas de dispersión, tal como el rango, el intervalo intercuartil y la desviación típica, describen cómo se dispersan los datos en un conjunto de datos.

Median (p. 672) The median is the middle value in a data set. If the data set contains an even number of values, the median is the mean of the two middle values.

Mediana (p. 672) La mediana es el valor situado en el medio en un conjunto de datos. Si el conjunto de datos contiene un número par de valores, la mediana es la media de los dos valores del medio.

$\{1, 2, 3, 3, 4, 5, 6, 8\}$

$$\text{median} = \frac{3 + 4}{2} = \frac{7}{2} = 3.5$$

Minor axis of an ellipse (p. 578) The minor axis of an ellipse is the segment perpendicular to the major axis at its midpoint. The endpoints of the minor axis are on the ellipse and are the co-vertices of the ellipse.

Eje menor de una elipse (p. 578) El eje menor de una elipse es el segmento perpendicular al eje mayor en su punto medio. Los extremos del eje menor están en la elipse y son los covértices de la elipse.

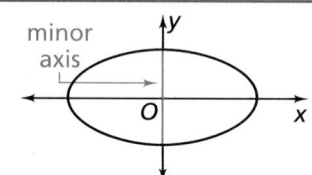

Mode (p. 672) The mode is the most frequently occurring value (or values) in a set of data.

$\{1, 2, 3, 3, 4, 5, 6, 6\}$
The modes are 3 and 6.

Moda (p. 672) La moda es el valor o valores que ocurren con mayor frecuencia en un conjunto de datos.

Monomial (p. 313) A monomial is either a real number, a variable, or a product of real numbers and variables with whole number exponents.

$1, x, 2z, 4ab^2$

Monomio (p. 313) Un monomio es un número real, una variable o un producto de números reales y variables cuyos exponentes son números enteros.

Multiple zero (p. 322) If a linear factor is repeated in the complete factored form of a polynomial, the zero related to that factor is a multiple zero.

The zeros of the function $P(x) = 2x(x - 3)^2(x + 1)$ are $0, 3,$ and $-1.$ Since $(x - 3)$ occurs twice as a factor, the zero 3 is a multiple zero.

Cero múltiplo (p. 322) Si un factor lineal se repite en la forma factorizada completa de un polinomio, el cero relacionado con ese factor es un cero múltiplo.

Multiplicative identity matrix (p. 203) For an $n \times n$ square matrix, the multiplicative identity matrix is an $n \times n$ square matrix $I,$ or $I_{n \times n},$ with 1's along the main diagonal and 0's elsewhere.

$$I_{2 \times 2} = \begin{bmatrix} 1 & 0 \\ 0 & 1 \end{bmatrix}$$

$$I_{3 \times 3} = \begin{bmatrix} 1 & 0 & 0 \\ 0 & 1 & 0 \\ 0 & 0 & 1 \end{bmatrix}$$

Matriz de identidad multiplicativa (p. 203) Para una matriz cuadrada $n \times n,$ la matriz de identidad multiplicativa es la matriz cuadrada I de $n \times n,$ o $I_{n \times n},$ con unos por la diagonal principal y ceros en los demás lugares.

Multiplicative inverse (p. 7) The multiplicative inverse, or reciprocal, of any nonzero number a is $\frac{1}{a}.$ The product of reciprocals is 1.

$5 \times \frac{1}{5} = 1$

Inverso multiplicativo (p. 7) El inverso multiplicativo, o recíproco, de todo número racional distinto de cero a es $\frac{1}{a}.$ El producto de números recíprocos es 1.

Multiplicative inverse of a matrix (p. 203) If A and X are $n \times n$ matrices, and $AX = XA = I,$ then X is the multiplicative inverse of $A,$ written $A^{-1}.$

$$A = \begin{bmatrix} 2 & 1 \\ 4 & 0 \end{bmatrix}$$

$$X = \begin{bmatrix} 0 & \frac{1}{4} \\ 1 & -\frac{1}{2} \end{bmatrix}$$

$$AX = \begin{bmatrix} 1 & 0 \\ 0 & 1 \end{bmatrix} = I, \text{ so } X = A^{-1}$$

Inverso multiplicativo de una matriz (p. 203) Si A y X son matrices $n \times n,$ y $AX = XA = I,$ entonces X es el inverso multiplicativo de $A,$ expresado como $A^{-1}.$

English/Spanish Glossary

Multiplicity (p. 322) The multiplicity of a zero of a polynomial function is the number of times the related linear factor is repeated in the factored form of the polynomial.

The zeros of the function $P(x) = 2x(x - 3)^2(x + 1)$ are $0, 3$, and -1. Since $(x - 3)$ occurs twice as a factor, the zero 3 has multiplicity 2.

Multiplicidad (p. 322) La multiplicidad de un cero de una función polinomial es el número de veces que el factor lineal relacionado se repite en la forma factorizada del polinomio.

Mutually exclusive events (p. 541) When two events cannot happen at the same time, the events are mutually exclusive. If A and B are mutually exclusive events, then $P(A \text{ or } B) = P(A) + P(B)$.

Rolling an even number E and rolling a multiple of five M on a standard number cube are mutually exclusive events.

$$P(E \text{ or } M) = P(E) + P(M)$$
$$= \frac{3}{6} + \frac{1}{6}$$
$$= \frac{4}{6}, \text{ or } \frac{2}{3}$$

Sucesos mutuamente excluyentes (p. 541) Cuando dos sucesos no pueden ocurrir al mismo tiempo, son mutuamente excluyentes. Si A y B son sucesos mutuamente excluyentes, entonces $P(A \text{ o } B) = P(A) + P(B)$.

n factorial (p. 351) For any positive integer n, n factorial (or $n!$) is $n(n - 1) \times \ldots \times 3 \times 2 \times 1. 0! = 1$.

$4! = 4 \times 3 \times 2 \times 1 = 24$

n factorial (p. 351) Para cualquier número entero positivo n, n factorial (o $n!$) es $n(n - 1) \times \ldots \times 3 \times 2 \times 1. 0! = 1$.

nth root (p. 375) For any real numbers a and b, and any positive integer n, if $a^n = b$, then a is an nth root of b.

$\sqrt[5]{32} = 2$ because $2^5 = 32$.

$\sqrt[4]{81} = 3$ because $3^4 = 81$.

raíz n-ésima (p. 375) Para todos los números reales a y b, y todo número entero positivo n, si $a^n = b$, entonces a es la n-ésima raíz de b.

Natural logarithmic function (p. 478) The function $y = \log_e x$ is the natural logarithmic function. It is the inverse of $y = e^x$. It is commonly written as $y = \ln x$.

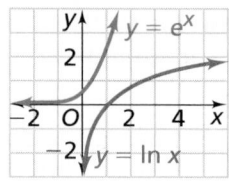

Función logarítmica natural (p. 478) La función $y = \log_e x$ es la función logarítmica natural. Es la inversa de $y = e^x$. Generalmente se expresa como $y = \ln x$.

$\ln e^3 = 3$

$\ln 10 \approx 2.3026$

$\ln 36 \approx 3.5835$

Normal distribution (p. 704) A normal distribution shows data that vary randomly from the mean in the pattern of a bell-shaped curve.

Distribución normal (p. 704) Una distribución normal muestra, con una curva en forma de campana, datos que varían alcatoriamente respecto de la media.

Distribution of Test Scores

In a class of 200 students, the scores on a test were normally distributed. The mean score was 66.5 and the standard deviation was 6.5. The number of students who scored greater than 73 was about 13.5% + 2.5% of those who took the test.

16% of 200 = 32

About 32 students scored 73 or higher on the test.

Objective function (p. 141) In a linear programming model, the objective function is a model of the quantity that you want to make as large or as small as possible. *See* **Linear programming**.

Función objetiva (p. 141) En un modelo de programación lineal, la función objetiva es un modelo de la cantidad que se quiere aumentar o disminuir cuanto sea posible. *Ver* **Linear programming**.

Opposite (p. 7) The opposite or additive inverse of any number a is $-a$. The sum of opposites is 0.

Opuesto (p. 7) El opuesto o inverso aditivo de todo número a es $-a$. La suma de dos opuestos es 0.

$3 + (-3) = 0$

$5.2 + (-5.2) = 0$

Ordered triples (p. 148) Ordered triples of the form (x, y, z) represent the location of a point in coordinate space.

Tripletas ordenadas (p. 148) Las tripletas ordenadas de la forma (x, y, z) representan la ubicación de un punto en el espacio de coordenadas.

$(2, 4, 5)$
$(0, 1, 2)$
$(0, 0, 0)$

Outlier (p. 676) An outlier is a data value that is substantially different from the other values in a data set.

Valor extremo (p. 676) Un valor extremo es un valor que difiere sustancialmente de los demás valores de un conjunto de datos.

The outlier in the data set $\{56, 64, 73, 59, 98, 65, 59\}$ is 98.

Parabola (pp. 243, 565) A parabola is the graph of a quadratic function. It is the set of all points P in a plane that are the same distance from a fixed point F, the focus, as they are from a line d, the directrix.

Parábola (pp. 243, 565) La parábola es la gráfica de una función cuadrática. Es el conjunto de todos los puntos P situados en un plano a la misma distancia de un punto fijo F, o foco, y de la recta d, o directriz.

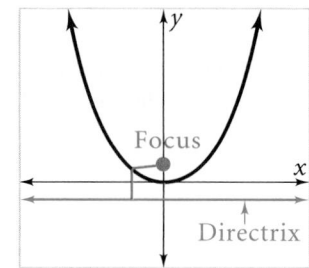

Parameter (p. 99) A parameter is a symbol, usually a letter, that represents a constant. In a function rule, a parameter helps describe a transformation of a function.

In $f(x) = a(x - h)^2 + k$, a, h, and k are parameters. x is the independent variable.

Parámetro (p. 99) Un parámetro es un símbolo, generalmente una letra, que representa una constante. En la regla de una función, el parámetro sirve para describir la transformación de la función.

Parent function (p. 95) A family of functions is a group of functions with common characteristics. A parent function is the simplest function with these characteristics.

$y = x$ is the parent function for the functions of the form $y = x + k$.

Función elemental (p. 95) Una familia de funciones es un grupo de funciones con características comunes. La función elemental es la función más simple que reúne esas características.

Pascal's Triangle (p. 359) Pascal's Triangle is a triangular array of numbers whose nth row contains the coefficients of the terms of the binomial expansion of $(a + b)^{n-1}$.

```
Pascal's Triangle      1
                      1   1
                    1   2   1
                  1   3   3   1
                1   4   6   4   1
              1   5  10  10   5   1
```

Triángulo de Pascal (p. 359) El triángulo de Pascal es una matriz triangular de números cuya fila n-ésima contiene los coeficientes de los términos del desarrollo del binomio $(a + b)^{n-1}$.

Percentile (p. 675) A percentile is a number from 0 to 100 that you can associate with a value in a data set to indicate the percent of the data that are less than or equal to it. If x is the 63rd percentile, then 63% of the data are less than or equal to x.

Percentil (p. 675) El percentil es un número del 0 al 100 que se puede asociar con un valor de un conjunto de datos para indicar el porcentaje de los datos que son menores que o iguales a él. Si x es el 63° percentil, entonces 63% de los datos son menores que o iguales a x.

Perfect square trinomial (p. 266) A perfect square trinomial is the product you obtain when you square a binomial.

$$\underset{\text{trinomial}}{\underset{\text{perfect square}}{}} \qquad \underset{\text{square}}{\underset{\text{binomial}}{}}$$
$$16x^2 - 24x + 9 = (4x - 3)^2$$

Trinomio cuadrado perfecto (p. 266) Un trinomio cuadrado perfecto se obtiene al elevar al cuadrado un binomio.

Period of a function (p. 723) The period of a periodic function is the horizontal length of one cycle.

Período de una función (p. 723) El período de una función periódica es el intervalo horizontal de un ciclo.

The periodic function $y = \sin x$ has period 2π.

Periodic function (p. 723) A periodic function repeats a pattern of y-values at regular intervals.

Función periódica (p. 723) Una función periódica repite un patrón de valores y a intervalos regulares.

$y = \sin x$

Permutation (p. 351) A permutation is an arrangement of items in a particular order. The number of permutations of n objects taken r at a time is $_nP_r = \frac{n!}{(n - r)!}$ for $1 \le r \le n$.

Permutación (p. 351) Una permutación es la disposición de objetos en un orden determinado. El número de permutaciones de n objetos seleccionados r veces es $_nP_r = \frac{n!}{(n - r)!}$ para $1 \le r \le n$.

$$_8P_5 = \frac{8!}{(8 - 5)!}$$
$$= \frac{8 \cdot 7 \cdot 6 \cdot 5 \cdot 4 \cdot 3!}{3!}$$
$$= 8 \times 7 \times 6 \times 5 \times 4$$
$$= 6720$$

Phase shift (p. 768) A horizontal translation of a periodic function is a phase shift.

Cambio de fase (p. 768) Una traslación horizontal de una función periódica es un cambio de fase.

$g(x)$: horizontal translation of $f(x)$
$g(x) = f(x - h)$

Point of discontinuity (p. 509) A point of discontinuity is the x-coordinate of a point where the graph of a function breaks into branches. A rational function has a point of discontinuity at $x = a$ if a is a number for which the denominator of the function is zero.

Punto de discontinuidad (p. 509) Un punto de discontinuidad es la coordenada x de un punto donde la gráfica de una función se divide en ramas. Una función racional tiene un punto de discontinuidad en $x = a$, si a es un número para el cual el denominador de la función es cero.

$f(x) = \frac{2}{x - 2}$ has a point of discontinuity at $x = 2$.

Point-slope form (p. 67) The point-slope form of an equation of a line is $y - y_1 = m(x - x_1)$, where m is the slope of the line and (x_1, y_1) is a point on the line.

Forma punto-pendiente (p. 67) La forma punto-pendiente de una ecuación lineal es $y - y_1 = m(x - x_1)$, donde m es la pendiente de la recta y (x_1, y_1) es un punto de la recta.

$y - 3 = 2(x - 1)$
$y + 4 = 5(x - 2)$
$y - 2 = 3(x + 2)$

Polynomial (p. 313) A polynomial is a monomial or the sum of monomials.

Polinomio (p. 313) Un polinomio es un monomio o la suma de dos o más monomios.

$3x^3 + 4x^2 - 2x + 5$

$8x$

$x^2 + 4x + 2$

Polynomial function (p. 313) $P(x) = a_n x^n + a_{n-1} x^{n-1} + \ldots + a_1 x + a_0$ is a polynomial function when n is a nonnegative integer and the coefficients $a_n, \ldots, a_0$ are real numbers.

Función polinomial (p. 313) $P(x) = a_n x^n + a_{n-1} x^{n-1} + \ldots + a_1 x + a_0$ es una función polinomial, donde n es un entero no negativo y los coeficientes $a_n, \ldots, a_0$ son números reales.

Preimage (p. 196) The preimage is the original figure before a transformation.

Preimagen (p. 196) La preimagen es la figura original antes de sufrir una transformación.

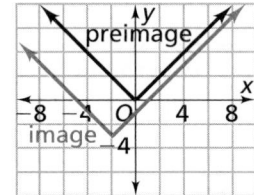

Principal root (p. 376) When a number has two real roots, the positive root is called the principal root. A radical sign indicates the principal root. The principal root of a negative number a is $i\sqrt{|a|}$.

Raíz principal (p. 376) Cuando un número tiene dos raíces reales, la raíz positiva es la raíz principal. El signo del radical indica la raíz principal. La raíz principal de un número negativo a es $i\sqrt{|a|}$.

The number 25 has two square roots, 5 and -5. The principal square root, 5, is indicated by the symbols $\sqrt{25}$ or $25^{\frac{1}{2}}$.

Probability distribution (p. 661) A probability distribution is a function that tells the probability of each outcome in a sample space.

Distribución de probabilidades (p. 661) Una distribución de probabilidades es una función que señala la probabilidad de que cada resultado ocurra en un espacio muestral.

Roll	Fr.	Prob.
1	5	0.125
2	9	0.225
3	7	0.175
4	8	0.2
5	8	0.2
6	3	0.075

The table and graph both show the experimental probability distribution for the outcomes of 40 rolls of a standard number cube.

Quadratic equation (p. 271) A quadratic equation is one that can be written in the standard form $ax^2 + bx + c = 0$, where $a \neq 0$.

Ecuación cuadrática (p. 271) Una ecuación cuadrática es una ecuación que se puede expresar en forma normal como $ax^2 + bx + c = 0$, donde $a \neq 0$.

$2x^2 + 3x + 1 = 0$

Quadratic Formula (p. 293) A quadratic equation written in standard form $ax^2 + bx + c = 0$, can be solved using the Quadratic Formula.

$$x = \frac{-b \pm \sqrt{b^2 - 4ac}}{2a}$$

Fórmula cuadrática (p. 293) Toda ecuación cuadrática $ax^2 + bx + c = 0$ escrita en forma normal se puede resolver por medio de la fórmula cuadrática.

$$x = \frac{-b \pm \sqrt{b^2 - 4ac}}{2a}$$

If $-x^2 + 3x + 2 = 0$, then

$$x = \frac{-3 \pm \sqrt{(3)^2 - 4(-1)(2)}}{2(-1)}$$

$$= \frac{-3 \pm \sqrt{17}}{-2}$$

Quadratic function (p. 242) A quadratic function is a function that can be written in the standard form $f(x) = ax^2 + bx + c$, where $a \neq 0$. Its graph is a parabola.

Función cuadrática (p. 242) Una función cuadrática se puede expresar con la forma normal $f(x) = ax^2 + bx + c$, donde $a \neq 0$. Su gráfica es una parábola.

$y = x^2 + 2x - 2$

Quartiles (p. 674) Quartiles are values that separate a finite data set into four equal parts. The second quartile (Q_2) is the median of the data. The first and third quartiles (Q_1 and Q_3) are the medians of the lower half and upper half of the data, respectively.

Cuartiles (p. 674) Los cuartiles son valores que separan un conjunto finito de datos en cuatro partes iguales. El segundo cuartil (Q_2) es la mediana de los datos. Los cuartiles primero y tercero (Q_1 y Q_3) son las medianas de la mitad superior e inferior de los datos, respectivamente.

$\{2, 3, 4, 5, 5, 6, 7, 7\}$
$Q_1 = 3.5$
$Q_2 \text{ (median)} = 5$
$Q_3 = 6.5$

R

Radian (p. 738) One radian is the measure of a central angle of a circle that intercepts an arc equal in length to a radius of the circle. You can use a proportion to convert an angle measure between different units.

$$\frac{\text{degree measure}}{180} = \frac{\text{radian measure}}{\pi}$$

Radián (p. 738) Un radián es la medida del ángulo central de un círculo que corta un arco de la misma longitud que el radio del círculo. Se puede usar una proporción para convertir la medida de un ángulo de una unidad de medida a la otra.

$$\frac{\text{medida en grados}}{180} = \frac{\text{medida de radián}}{\pi}$$

$60° \rightarrow \frac{60}{180} = \frac{x}{\pi}$

$x = \frac{60\pi}{180}$

$= \frac{\pi}{3}$

Thus, $60° = \frac{\pi}{3}$ radians.

Radical equation (p. 397)   A radical equation is an equation that has a variable in a radicand or has a variable with a rational exponent.

$(\sqrt{x})^3 + 1 = 65$

$x^{\frac{3}{2}} + 1 = 65$

Ecuación radical (p. 397)   La ecuación radical es una ecuación que contiene una variable en el radicando o una variable con un exponente racional.

Radical function (p. 421)   A radical function is a function that can be written in the form $f(x) = a\sqrt[n]{x - h} + k$, where $a \neq 0$. For even values of n, the domain of a radical function is the real numbers $x \geq h$. See also **Square root function.**

$f(x) = \sqrt{x - 2}$

Función radical (p. 421)   Una función radical es una función que puede expresarse como $f(x) = a\sqrt[n]{x - h} + k$, donde $a \neq 0$. Para n par, el dominio de la función radical son los números reales tales que $x \geq h$. Ver también **Square root function.**

Radicand (p. 376)   The number under a radical sign is the radicand.

The radicand in $3\sqrt[4]{7}$ is 7.

Radicando (p. 376)   La expresión que aparece debajo del signo radical es el radicando.

Radius (p. 571)   The radius r of a circle is the distance between the center of the circle and any point on the circumference.

Radio (p. 571)   El radio r de un círculo es la distancia entre el centro del círculo y cualquier punto de la circunferencia.

Random sample (p. 689)   In a random sample, each member of the population is as likely to be chosen for the sample as every other member.

Let the set of all females between the ages of 19 and 34 be the population. A random selection of 900 females between those ages would be a sample of the population.

Muestra aleatoria (p. 689)   En una muestra aleatoria es igualmente probable que cada miembro de la población sea escogido para la muestra.

Range (p. 58)   The range of a relation is the set of all outputs or y-coordinates of the ordered pairs.

In the relation $\{(0, 1), (0, 2), (0, 3), (0, 4), (1, 3), (1, 4), (2, 1)\}$, the range is $\{1, 2, 3, 4\}$. In the function $f(x) = |x - 3|$, the range is the set of real numbers greater than or equal to 0.

Rango (p. 58)   El rango de una relación es el conjunto de todas las salidas posibles, o coordenadas y, de los pares ordenados.

Range of a set of data (p. 681)   The range of a set of data is the difference between the greatest and least values.

The range of the set $\{3.2, 4.1, 2.2, 3.4, 3.8, 4.0, 4.2, 2.8\}$ is $4.2 - 2.2 = 2$.

Rango de un conjunto de datos (p. 681)   El rango de un conjunto de datos es la diferencia entre el valor máximo y el valor mínimo de los datos.

Rational exponent (p. 391) If the *n*th root of *a* is a real number and *m* is an integer, then $a^{\frac{1}{n}} = \sqrt[n]{a}$ and $a^{\frac{m}{n}} = \sqrt[n]{a^m} = \left(\sqrt[n]{a}\right)^m$. If *m* is negative, $a \neq 0$.

$$4^{\frac{1}{3}} = \sqrt[3]{4}$$
$$5^{\frac{3}{2}} = \sqrt{5^3} = \left(\sqrt{5}\right)^3$$

Exponente racional (p. 391) Si la raíz *n*-ésima de *a* es un número real y *m* es un número entero, entonces $a^{\frac{1}{n}} = \sqrt[n]{a}$ y $a^{\frac{m}{n}} = \sqrt[n]{a^m} = \left(\sqrt[n]{a}\right)^m$. Si *m* es negativo, $a \neq 0$.

Rational function (p. 509) A rational function $f(x)$ can be written as $f(x) = \frac{P(x)}{Q(x)}$, where $P(x)$ and $Q(x)$ are polynomial functions. The domain of a rational function is all real numbers except those for which $Q(x) = 0$.

Función racional (p. 509) Una función racional $f(x)$ se puede expresar como $f(x) = \frac{P(x)}{Q(x)}$, donde $P(x)$ y $Q(x)$ son funciones de polinomios. El dominio de una función racional son todos los números reales excepto aquéllos para los cuales $Q(x) = 0$.

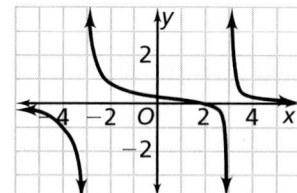

The function $y = \frac{x-2}{x^2-9}$ is a rational function with three branches separated by asymptotes $x = -3$ and $x = 3$.

Rational Root Theorem (p. 341) If $\frac{p}{q}$ is in simplest form and is a rational root of the polynomial equation $a_n x^n + a_{n-1} x^{n-1} + \ldots + a_1 x + a_0 = 0$ with integer coefficients, then *p* must be a factor of a_0 and *q* must be a factor of a_n.

The polynomial equation $10x^3 + 6x^2 - 11x - 2 = 0$ has leading coefficient 10 (with factors $\pm 1, \pm 2, \pm 5, \pm 10$) and constant term -2 (with factors ± 1 and ± 2). Its only possible rational roots are $\pm 1, \pm 2, \pm\frac{1}{2}, \pm\frac{1}{5}, \pm\frac{2}{5}, \pm\frac{1}{10}$.

Teorema de la raíz racional (p. 341) Si $\frac{p}{q}$ está en su forma más simple y es la raíz racional de la ecuación del polinomio $a_n x^n + a_{n-1} x^{n-1} + \ldots + a_1 x + a_0 = 0$ con números enteros como coeficientes, entonces *p* debe ser factor de a_0 y *q* debe ser factor de a_n.

Rationalize the denominator (p. 382) To rationalize the denominator of an expression, rewrite it so there are no radicals in any denominator and no denominators in any radical.

$$\frac{1}{\sqrt{2}} = \frac{1}{\sqrt{2}} \times \frac{\sqrt{2}}{\sqrt{2}} = \frac{\sqrt{2}}{2}$$

Racionalizar el denominador (p. 382) Para racionalizar el denominador de una expresión, ésta se escribe de modo que no haya radicales en ningún denominador y no haya denominadores en ningún radical.

Reciprocal (p. 7) The reciprocal or multiplicative inverse of any nonzero number *a* is $\frac{1}{a}$. The product of reciprocals is 1.

$$5 \times \frac{1}{5} = 1$$

Recíproco (p. 7) El valor recíproco, o inverso multiplicativo, de un número *a* cuyo valor no es cero es $\frac{1}{a}$. El producto de un número y su valor recíproco es 1.

Reciprocal function (p. 503) A reciprocal function is a function that can be written in the form $f(x) = \frac{a}{x-h} + k$, where $a \neq 0$. The domain of a reciprocal function is all real numbers except $x = h$.

$f(x) = \frac{1}{2x + 5}$

$p(v) = \frac{3}{v} + 5$

Función recíproca (p. 503) Una función recíproca es una función que puede expresarse como $f(x) = \frac{a}{x-h} + k$, donde $a \neq 0$. El dominio de una función recíproca son todos los números reales excepto aquéllos para los que se cumple que $x = h$.

Recursive formula (p. 612) A recursive formula defines the terms in a sequence by relating each term to the ones before it.

Let $a_n = 2.5a_{n-1} + 3a_{n-2}$.
If $a_5 = 3$ and $a_4 = 7.5$, then
$a_6 = 2.5(3) + 3(7.5) = 30$.

Fórmula recursiva (p. 612) Una fórmula recursiva define cada término de una progresión en función del término o términos precedentes.

Reflection (p. 194) A reflection, or flip, is a transformation that maps a point in the plane to its mirror image, using a specific line as the mirror.

preimage　　**image**

Reflexión (p. 194) Una reflexión es una transformación en la que se voltea una figura sobre una línea específica, que actúa a manera espejo.

Relation (p. 57) A relation is a set of pairs of input and output values.

$\{(0, 1), (0, 2), (0, 3), (0, 4), (1, 3)\}$

Relación (p. 57) Una relación es cualquier conjunto de pares ordenados de valores de entrada y valores de salida.

Relative maximum (minimum) (p. 321) The y-value of a point on the graph of a function that is higher (lower) than the nearby points of the graph is a relative maximum (minimum).

Máximo (mínimo) relativo (p. 321) El valor y de un punto en la gráfica de una función que es mayor (menor) que los de los puntos cercanos es un máximo (mínimo) relativo.

Remainder Theorem (p. 329) If a polynomial $P(x)$ of degree $n \geq 1$ is divided by $(x - a)$, where a is a constant, then the remainder is $P(a)$.

If $P(x) = x^3 - 4x^2 + x + 6$ is divided by $x - 3$, then the remainder is $P(3) = 3^3 - 4(3)^2 + 3 + 6 = 0$ (which means that $x - 3$ is a factor of $P(x)$).

Teorema del residuo (p. 329) Si un polinomio $P(x)$ de grado $n \geq 1$ se divide por $(x - a)$, donde a es una constante, el residuo es $P(a)$.

Root (p. 272) A root of a function is the input value for which the value of the function is zero. A root of an equation is a value that makes the equation true. *See also* **Zero of a function.**

-2 and 3 are roots of the function $f(x) = (x + 2)(x - 3)$ and the equation $(x + 2)(x - 3) = 0$.

Raíz (p. 272) La raíz de una función es el valor de entrada para el cual el valor de la función es cero. La raíz de una ecuación es un valor que hace verdadera la ecuación. *Ver también* **Zero of a function.**

Rotation (p. 198) A rotation is a transformation that turns a figure about a fixed point called the center of rotation.

Rotación (p. 198) Rotación es una transformación que hace girar una figura alrededor de un punto fijo llamado centro de rotación.

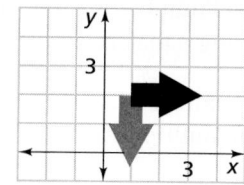

Row operations (p. 227) To solve a system of equations using an augmented matrix, you can use one or more of the following row operations:

- Switch any two rows.
- Multiply a row by a constant.
- Add one row to another.
- Combine one or more of these steps.

Operaciones de filas (p. 227) Para resolver un sistema de ecuaciones por medio de una matriz aumentada, se puede usar una o más de las siguientes operaciones de filas.

- Intercambiar dos filas.
- Multiplicar una fila por una constante.
- Sumar una fila a otra.
- Combinar uno o más de estos pasos.

Sample (p. 689) A sample is information gathered from only part of a population.

Muestra (p. 689) Una muestra contiene información reunida solamente de una parte de una población.

Let the set of all males between the ages of 19 and 34 be the population. A random selection of 900 males between those ages would be a sample of the population.

Sample proportion (p. 689) If an event occurs x times in a sample of size n, the sample proportion is $\frac{x}{n}$.

Proporción muestral (p. 689) Si un suceso ocurre x veces en un espacio muestral de tamaño n, la proporción de la muestra es $\frac{x}{n}$.

For a random selection of 900 males, 350 preferred red shirts to green shirts. The sample proportion would be $\frac{350}{900} = \frac{7}{18}$.

Sample space (p. 41) The set of all possible outcomes of an experiment is called the sample space.

Espacio muestral (p. 41) El espacio muestral es el conjunto de todos los resultados posibles de un suceso.

When you roll a number cube, the sample space is $\{1, 2, 3, 4, 5, 6\}$.

English/Spanish Glossary

Scalar (p. 186) A real number is called a scalar for certain special uses, such as multiplying a matrix. *See also* **Scalar multiplication.**

Escalar (p. 186) Un número real se llama escalar en ciertos casos especiales, como en la multiplicación de una matriz. *Ver también* **Scalar multiplication.**

$$2.5\begin{bmatrix} 1 & 0 \\ -2 & 3 \end{bmatrix} = \begin{bmatrix} 2.5(1) & 2.5(0) \\ 2.5(-2) & 2.5(3) \end{bmatrix}$$
$$= \begin{bmatrix} 2.5 & 0 \\ -5 & 7.5 \end{bmatrix}$$

Scalar multiplication (p. 186) Scalar multiplication is an operation that multiplies a matrix A by a scalar c. To find the resulting matrix cA, multiply each element of A by c.

Multiplicación escalar (p. 186) La multiplicación escalar es la que multiplica una matriz A por un número escalar c. Para hallar la matriz cA resultante, multiplica cada elemento de A por c.

$$2.5\begin{bmatrix} 1 & 0 \\ -2 & 3 \end{bmatrix} = \begin{bmatrix} 2.5(1) & 2.5(0) \\ 2.5(-2) & 2.5(3) \end{bmatrix}$$
$$= \begin{bmatrix} 2.5 & 0 \\ -5 & 7.5 \end{bmatrix}$$

Scatter plot (p. 82) A scatter plot is a graph that relates two different sets of data by plotting the data as ordered pairs. You can use a scatter plot to determine a relationship between the data sets.

Diagrama de puntos (p. 82) Un diagrama de puntos es una gráfica que relaciona dos conjuntos de datos presentando los datos como pares ordenados. El diagrama de puntos sirve para definir la relación entre conjuntos de datos.

Dollars Spent Per Capita on Entertainment

SOURCE: U.S. Bureau of Labor Statistics.
Go to **www.PHSchool.com** for a data update.

Secant (p. 775) The secant (sec) function is the reciprocal of the cosine function. For all real numbers θ except those that make $\cos \theta = 0$, $\sec \theta = \frac{1}{\cos \theta}$.

Secante (p. 775) La función secante (sec) es el recíproco de la función coseno. Para todos los números reales θ, excepto aquéllos para los que $\cos \theta = 0$, $\sec \theta = \frac{1}{\cos \theta}$.

If $\cos \theta = \frac{5}{13}$, then $\sec \theta = \frac{13}{5}$.

Sequence (p. 610) A sequence is an ordered list of numbers.

Progresión (p. 610) Una progresión es una sucesión de números.

$1, 4, 7, 10, \ldots$

Series (p. 629) A series is the sum of the terms of a sequence. The series is finite (infinite) if the corresponding sequence has finitely (infinitely) many terms..

Serie (p. 629) Una serie es la suma de los términos de una progresión. La serie es finita (infinita) si la progresión correspondiente tiene una cantidad finita (infinita) de términos.

The series $3 + 6 + 9 + 12 + 15$ corresponds to the sequence 3, 6, 9, 12, 15. The sum of the series is 45.

Shrink (p. 98) A vertical shrink of a function f by the factor a, $0 < a < 1$, is a transformation of f that multiplies all y-values by a.

$g(x) = \frac{1}{2}x^2$ is a vertical shrink of $f(x) = x^2$

Reducción (p. 98) La reducción vertical de una función f por el factor a, donde $0 < a < 1$, es una transformación de f que multiplica todos los valores de y por a.

Simplest form of a rational expression (p. 517) A rational expression is in simplest form when its numerator and denominator are polynomials that have no common divisors.

$\dfrac{x^2 - 7x + 12}{x^2 - 9} = \dfrac{(x - 4)(x - 3)}{(x + 3)(x - 3)}$
$= \dfrac{x - 4}{x + 3}$, where $x \neq -3$

Forma simplificada de una expresión racional (p. 517) Una expresión racional no se puede simplificar más cuando su numerador y su denominador son polinomios que ya no contienen factores comunes.

Simulation (p. 40) When actual trials are difficult to conduct, you can find experimental probability by using a simulation, which is a model of one or more events.

Suppose a weather forecaster predicts a 50% chance of rain for the next three days. You can use three coins landing heads up to simulate three days in a row of rain.

Simulación (p. 40) Cuando es difícil realizar los ensayos de un experimento, se puede determinar la probabilidad experimental por medio de una simulación, o modelo de uno o más sucesos del experimento.

Sine curve (p. 747) A sine curve is the graph of a sine function.

Sinusoide (p. 747) Sinusoide es la gráfica de la función seno.

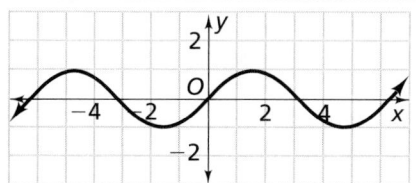

Sine function (p. 746) The sine function, $y = \sin \theta$, matches the measure θ of an angle in standard position with the y-coordinate of a point on the unit circle. This point is where the terminal side of the angle intersects the unit circle.

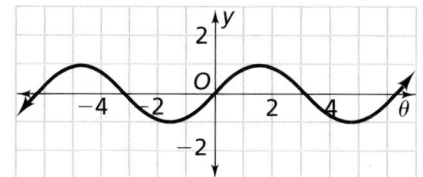

Función seno (p. 746) La función seno, $y = \text{sen } \theta$, equivale a la medida θ de un ángulo en posición normal con la coordenada y de un punto dado en el círculo unitario. Este punto es la intersección del lado terminal y el círculo unitario.

Sine of θ (p. 732) The sine of an angle measure θ ($\sin \theta$) is the y-coordinate of the point at which the terminal side of the angle intersects the unit circle.

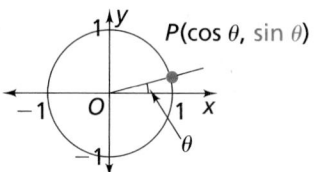

Seno de θ (p. 732) El seno de un ángulo que mide θ (sen θ) es la coordenada y del punto de intersección entre el lado terminal del ángulo y el círculo unitario.

English/Spanish Glossary

Slope of a line (p. 66) The slope of a non-vertical line is the ratio of the vertical change to a corresponding horizontal change. The slope of a vertical line is undefined.

$$\text{slope} = \frac{\text{vertical change}}{\text{horizontal change}} = \frac{y_2 - y_1}{x_2 - x_1}, \text{ where } x_2 - x_1 \neq 0$$

Pendiente de una recta (p. 66) La pendiente de una recta no vertical es la razón del cambio vertical y el cambio horizontal. La pendiente de una recta vertical no está definida.

$$\text{pendiente} = \frac{\text{cambio vertical}}{\text{cambio horizontal}} = \frac{y_2 - y_1}{x_2 - x_1}, \text{ donde } x_2 - x_1 \neq 0$$

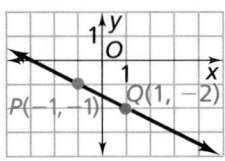

The slope of the line through points $(-1, -1)$ and $(1, -2)$ is

$$\frac{-2 - (-1)}{1 - (-1)} = \frac{-1}{2} = -\frac{1}{2}.$$

Slope-intercept form (p. 67) The slope-intercept form of an equation of a line is $y = mx + b$, where m is the slope and b is the y-intercept.

Forma pendiente-intercepto (p. 67) La forma pendiente-intercepto de una ecuación lineal es $y = mx + b$, donde m es la pendiente y b es el intercepto en y.

$y = 8x + 2$

$y = -x + 1$

$y = -\frac{1}{2}x - 14$

Solution of an equation (p. 18) A solution of an equation is a number that makes the equation true.

Solución de una ecuación (p. 18) Una solución de una ecuación es cualquier número que haga verdadera la ecuación.

The solution of $2x - 7 = -12$ is $x = -2.5$.

Square matrix (p. 204) A square matrix is a matrix with the same number of columns as rows.

Matriz cuadrada (p. 204) Una matriz cuadrada es la que tiene la misma cantidad de columnas y filas.

Matrix A is a square matrix.

$$A = \begin{bmatrix} 1 & 2 & 0 \\ -1 & 0 & -2 \\ 1 & 2 & 3 \end{bmatrix}$$

Square root equation (p. 397) A square root equation is a radical equation in which the radical has index 2.

Ecuación de raíz cuadrada (p. 397) Una ecuación de raíz cuadrada es una ecuación radical en la cual el radical tiene índice 2.

$\sqrt{x} = 4$

Square root function (p. 421) A square root function is a function that can be written in the form $f(x) = a\sqrt{x - h} + k$, where $a \neq 0$. The domain of a square root function is all real numbers $x \geq h$.

Función de raíz cuadrada (p. 421) Una función de raíz cuadrada es una función que puede ser expresada como $f(x) = a\sqrt{x - h} + k$, donde $a \neq 0$. El dominio de una función de raíz cuadrada son todos los números reales tales que $x \geq h$.

$f(x) = 2\sqrt{x - 3} + 4$

Standard deviation (p. 681)   Standard deviation is a measure of how much the values in a data set vary, or deviate, from the mean, $\overline{x}$. To find the standard deviation, follow five steps:

- Find the mean of the data set.
- Find the difference between each data value and the mean.
- Square each difference.
- Find the mean of the squares.
- Take the square root of the mean of the squares. This is the standard deviation.

$\{0, 2, 3, 4, 6, 7, 8, 9, 10, 11\}$

$\overline{x} = 6$

standard deviation $= \sqrt{12} \approx 3.46$

Desviación típica (p. 681)   La desviación típica denota cuánto los valores de un conjunto de datos varían, o se desvían, de la media, $\overline{x}$. Para hallar la desviación típica, se siguen cinco pasos:

- Se halla la media del conjunto de datos.
- Se calcula la diferencia entre cada valor de datos y la media.
- Se eleva al cuadrado cada diferencia.
- Se halla la media de los cuadrados.
- Se calcula la raíz cuadrada de la media de los cuadrados. Ésa es la desviación típica.

Standard form of a linear equation (p. 65)   The standard form of a linear equation is $Ax + By = C$, where A, B, and C are real numbers, and A and B are not both zero.

In standard form, the equation $y = \frac{4}{3}x - 1$ is $4x + (-3)y = 3$.

Forma normal de una ecuación lineal (p. 65)   La forma normal de una ecuación lineal es $Ax + By = C$, donde A, B, y C son números reales, y A y B son valores distintos de cero.

Standard form of an equation of a circle (p. 571)   *See* **Circle.**

Forma normal de la ecuación de un círculo (p. 571)   *Ver* **Circle.**

$(x - 3)^2 + (y - 4)^2 = 4$

Standard form of an equation of an ellipse (p. 578)   *See* **Ellipse.**

Forma normal de la ecuación de una elipse (p. 578)   *Ver* **Ellipse.**

$\frac{x^2}{5^2} + \frac{y^2}{3^2} = 1$

Standard form of an equation of a hyperbola (p. 585)   *See* **Hyperbola.**

Forma normal de la ecuación de una hipérbola (p. 585)   *Ver* **Hyperbola.**

$\frac{x^2}{5^2} - \frac{y^2}{3^2} = 1$

Standard form of a polynomial (p. 313)   The standard form of a polynomial has the terms in descending order by degree. A one-variable polynomial in standard form has no two terms with the same degree, since all like terms have been combined.

$2x^3 - 5x^2 - 2x + 5$

Forma normal de un polinomio (p. 313)   Un polinomio está en forma normal cuando sus términos están en orden descendente por grados. Un polinomio de una variable en forma normal no tiene dos términos del mismo grado puesto que todos los términos han sido combinados.

English/Spanish Glossary

Standard form of a quadratic equation (p. 271) *See* **Quadratic equation.**

$2x^2 + 5x + 2 = 0$

Forma normal de una ecuación cuadrática (p. 271) *Ver* **Quadratic equation.**

Standard form of a quadratic function (p. 242) The standard form of a quadratic function is $f(x) = ax^2 + bx + c$, where $a \neq 0$.

$f(x) = 2x^2 + 5x + 2$

Forma normal de una función cuadrática (p. 242) La forma normal de una función cuadrática es $f(x) = ax^2 + bx + c$, donde $a \neq 0$.

Standard normal curve (p. 705) The standard normal curve is a normal distribution centered on the y-axis. The mean of the standard normal curve is 0. The standard deviation is 1.

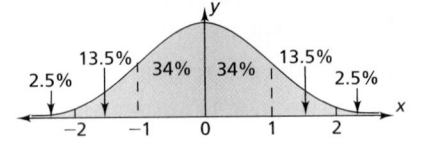

Curva normal en posición normal (p. 705) La curva normal es la distribución normal centrada en el eje y. La media de la curva normal es 0. La desviación normal es 1.

Standard position of an angle (p. 728) An angle is in standard position when the vertex is at the origin of a coordinate system and one ray is on the positive x-axis.

$x^3 + 27 = (x + 3)(x^2 - 3x + 9)$

Posición normal de un ángulo (p. 728) Un ángulo está en posición normal cuando su vértice está en el origen de un sistema de coordenadas y uno de sus lados está sobre el eje x positivo.

Stretch (p. 98) A vertical stretch of a function f by the factor a, $a > 1$, is a transformation of f that multiplies all y-values by a.

$g(x) = 2x^2$ is a vertical stretch of $f(x) = x^2$.

Ampliación (p. 98) Una ampliación vertical de una función f por el factor a, donde $a > 1$, es una transformación de f que multiplica todos los valores de y por a.

Sum of cubes (p. 334) The sum of cubes is an expression of the form $a^3 + b^3$. It can be factored as $(a + b)(a^2 - ab + b^2)$.

$x^3 + 27 = (x + 3)(x^2 - 3x + 9)$

Suma de dos cubos (p. 334) La suma de dos cubos es una expresión de la forma $a^3 + b^3$. Se puede factorizar como $(a + b)(a^2 - ab + b^2)$.

Synthetic division (p. 327) Synthetic division is a method of dividing polynomials in which you omit all variables and exponents and perform the division on the list of coefficients. You also reverse the sign of the divisor so that you can add throughout the process, rather than subtract.

-3	2	5	0	-2	-8
		-6	3	-9	33
	2	-1	3	-11	25

Divide $2x^4 + 5x^3 - 2x - 8$ by $x + 3$.

División sintética (p. 327) La división sintética es un método de dividir polinomios según el cual se omiten todas las variables y los exponentes y se hace la división con la lista de coeficientes. También se puede invertir el signo del divisor para sumar en vez de restar durante el proceso.

$2x^4 + 5x^3 - 2x - 8$ divided by $x + 3$ gives $2x^3 - x^2 + 3x - 11$ as quotient and 25 as remainder.

System of equations (p. 120) A system of equations is a set of two or more equations using the same variables.

$$\begin{cases} 2x - 3y = -13 \\ 4x + 5y = 7 \end{cases}$$

Sistema de ecuaciones (p. 120) Un sistema de ecuaciones es un conjunto de dos o más ecuaciones que contienen las mismas variables.

Tangent function (p. 761) The tangent function, $y = \tan \theta$, matches the measure θ of an angle in standard position with the y-coordinate of the point at which the line containing the terminal side of a central angle of the unit circle intersects the tangent line $x = 1$.

Función tangente (p. 761) La función tangente, $y = \tan \theta$, equivale a la medida θ de un ángulo en posición normal, con la coordenada y del punto donde la recta que contiene el lado terminal de un ángulo central del círculo unitario corta la tangente $x = 1$.

Tangent of θ (p. 761) The tangent of an angle measure θ (tan θ) is the y-coordinate of the point at which the line containing the terminal side of the angle intersects the tangent line $x = 1$.

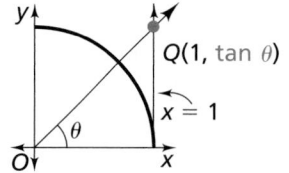

Tangente de θ (p. 761) La tangente de un ángulo que mide θ (tan θ) es la ordenada y del punto donde la recta que contiene el lado terminal del ángulo corta la tangente $x = 1$.

Term of a sequence (p. 610) Each number in a sequence is a term.

$1, 4, 7, 10, \ldots$

The second term is 4.

Término de una progresión (p. 610) Cada número de una progresión es un término.

Term of an expression (p. 13) A term is a number, a variable, or the product of a number and one or more variables.

The expression $4x^2 - 3y + 7.3$ has 3 terms.

Término de una expresión (p. 13) Un término es un número, una variable o el producto de un número y una o más variables.

Terminal side of an angle (p. 730) See *Initial side of an angle*.

Lado terminal de un ángulo (p. 730) *Ver Initial side of an angle*.

Theoretical probability (p. 41) If a sample space has n equally likely outcomes, and an event A occurs in m of these outcomes, then the theoretical probability of event A is $P(A) = \frac{m}{n}$.

Use the set $\{1, 4, 9, 16, 25, 36, 49, 64, 81, 100\}$. The probability that a number selected at random is greater than 50 is $P(A) = \frac{3}{10} = 0.3$.

Probabilidad teórica (p. 41) Si un espacio muestral tiene n resultados con la misma probabilidad de ocurrir, y ocurre un suceso A en m de estos resultados, entonces la probabilidad teórica del suceso A es $P(A) = \frac{m}{n}$.

Tolerance (p. 36) The difference between a desired measurement and its maximum and minimum allowable values is the tolerance. The tolerance equals one half of the difference between the maximum and minimum values.

A manufacturing specification calls for a dimension d of 10 cm with a tolerance of 0.1 cm. The allowable difference between d and 10 is less than or equal to 0.1.

Tolerancia (p. 36) La diferencia entre una medida deseada y sus valores máximo y mínimo permitidos es la tolerancia. La tolerancia equivale a la mitad de la diferencia entre los valores máximo y mínimo.

Trace (p. 150) If a plane in a three-dimensional xyz-coordinate system intersects the xy-, yz-, or xz-plane in a line, then that line is a trace of the given plane.

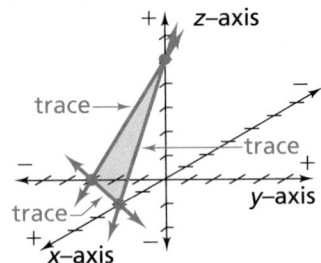

Trazo (p. 150) Si un plano en un sistema tridimensional de coordenadas xyz interseca el plano xy, yz o xz en una recta, entonces esa recta es una traza del plano dado.

Transformation (p. 195) A transformation of a function $y = af(x - h) + k$ is a change made to the value of at least one of the parameters a, h, and k.

$g(x) = 2(x - 3)^2$ is a transformation of $f(x) = x^2$.

Transformación (p. 195) Una transformación de una función $y = af(x - h) + k$ es un cambio en el valor de uno de los parámetros a, h y k.

Translation (p. 194) A translation is a transformation that slides a graph or figure horizontally, vertically, or both without changing the size or shape of the graph or figure.

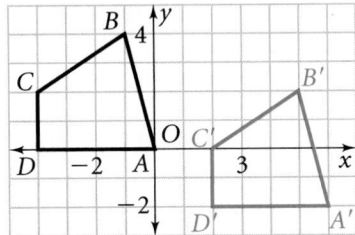

Traslación (p. 194) Una traslación es el proceso de deslizar una gráfica o figura horizontalmente, verticalmente, o en ambos sentidos, pero sin cambiar ni el tamaño ni la forma de la gráfica o figura.

Transverse axis of a hyperbola (p. 585) The transverse axis of a hyperbola is the segment that lies on the line containing the foci and has endpoints on the hyperbola. The endpoints are the vertices of the hyperbola.

Eje transversal de una hipérbola (p. 585) El eje transversal de una hipérbola es el segmento que pasa por la recta donde se encuentran los focos y que tiene los extremos sobre la hipérbola. Los extremos son los vértices de la hipérbola.

Trend line (p. 82) A trend line is a line that approximates the relationship between the data sets of a scatter plot. You can use a trend line to make predictions.

Línea de tendencia (p. 82) La línea de tendencia es una línea que aproxima la relación entre los conjuntos de datos en un diagrama de puntos. La línea de tendencia permite hacer predicciones.

Used Car Prices

Trigonometric identity (p. 792) A trigonometric identity is a trigonometric equation that is true for all values except those for which an expression on either side of the equal sign is undefined.

$$\tan \theta = \frac{\sin \theta}{\cos \theta}$$

Identidad trigonométrica (p. 792) Una identidad trigonométrica es una ecuación trigonométrica que satisface todos los valores excepto aquéllos para los cuales las expresiones a cada lado del signo igual no están definidas.

Trigonometric ratios for a right triangle (p. 806) The trigonometric ratios for a right triangle are the six different ratios of the sides of a right triangle. These ratios do not depend on the size of the right triangle. They depend only on the measures of the acute angles in the triangle. In a right triangle that has an acute $\angle A$, the ratios are defined as follows.

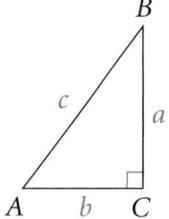

$\sin A = \dfrac{a}{c}$ $\qquad$ $\csc A = \dfrac{1}{\sin A} = \dfrac{c}{a}$

$\cos A = \dfrac{b}{c}$ $\qquad$ $\sec A = \dfrac{1}{\cos A} = \dfrac{c}{b}$

$\tan A = \dfrac{a}{b}$ $\qquad$ $\cot A = \dfrac{1}{\tan A} = \dfrac{b}{a}$

Razones trigonométricas para un triángulo rectángulo (p. 806) Las razones trigonométricas de un triángulo rectángulo son las seis razones de los lados de dicho triángulo. Esas razones no dependen del tamaño del triángulo rectángulo. Dependen sólo de la magnitud de los ángulos agudos del triángulo. En un triángulo rectángulo que tenga un ángulo agudo $\angle A$, las razones se definen así.

$\operatorname{sen} A = \dfrac{a}{c}$ $\qquad$ $\csc A = \dfrac{1}{\operatorname{sen} A} = \dfrac{c}{a}$

$\cos A = \dfrac{b}{c}$ $\qquad$ $\sec A = \dfrac{1}{\cos A} = \dfrac{c}{b}$

$\tan A = \dfrac{a}{b}$ $\qquad$ $\cot A = \dfrac{1}{\tan A} = \dfrac{b}{a}$

Unit circle (p. 732) The unit circle has a radius of 1 unit and its center is at the origin of the coordinate plane.

Círculo unitario (p. 732) El círculo unitario tiene un radio de 1 unidad y el centro está situado en el origen del plano de coordenadas.

Variable (p. 12) A variable is a symbol, usually a letter, that represents one or more numbers.

Variable (p. 12) Una variable es un símbolo, generalmente una letra, que representa uno o más valores.

x, a, k

Variable expression (p. 12) An expression that contains one or more variables is an algebraic expression, or a variable expression.

Expresión variable (p. 12) Una expresión que contenga una o más variables es una expresión algebraica o expresión variable.

$2x + 3, z - y$

Variable matrix (p. 218) When representing a system of equations with a matrix equation, the matrix containing the variables of the system is the variable matrix.

Matriz variable (p. 218) Al representar un sistema de ecuaciones con una ecuación de matricial, la matriz que contenga las variables del sistema es la matriz variable.

$$\begin{cases} x + 2y = 5 \\ 3x + 5y = 14 \end{cases}$$

variable matrix $\begin{bmatrix} x \\ y \end{bmatrix}$

Vertex form of a quadratic function (p. 256) The vertex form of a quadratic function is $f(x) = a(x - h)^2 + k$, where (h, k) are the coordinates of the vertex of the function.

Forma del vértice de una función cuadrática (p. 256) La forma del vértice de una función cuadrática es $f(x) = a(x - h)^2 + k$, donde (h, k) son las coordenadas del vértice de la función.

$f(x) = x^2 + 2x - 1 = (x + 1)^2 - 2$
The vertex is $(-1, -2)$.

Vertex of a function (p. 90) A vertex of a function is a point where the function reaches a maximum or a minimum value.

Vértice de una función (p. 90) El vértice de una función es el punto donde la función alcanza un valor máximo o mínimo.

Vertex of a parabola (p. 243) The vertex of a parabola is the point where the function for the parabola reaches a maximum or a minimum value. The parabola intersects its axis of symmetry at the vertex.

Vértice de una parábola (p. 243) El vértice de una parábola es el punto donde la función de la parábola alcanza un valor máximo o mínimo. La parábola y su eje de simetría se intersecan en el vértice.

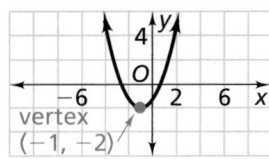

The vertex of the quadratic function $y = x^2 + 2x - 1$ is $(-1, -2)$.

Vertical-line test (p. 59) You can use the vertical-line test to determine whether a relation has at least one element of the domain paired with more than one element of the range. If a vertical line passes through two or more points on the graph, then the relation is *not* a function.

Prueba de la recta vertical (p. 59) La prueba de la recta vertical permite determinar si en una relación hay por lo menos un elemento del dominio al que corresponde más de un elemento del rango. Si una recta vertical del sistema de coordenadas pasa por dos o más puntos de la gráfica, quiere decir que la relación *no es* una función.

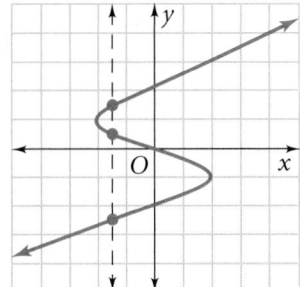

Vertices of a hyperbola (p. 585) The endpoints of the transverse axis of a hyperbola are the vertices of the hyperbola.

Vértices de una hipérbola (p. 585) Los dos puntos de intersección de la hipérbola y su eje mayor son los vértices de la hipérbola.

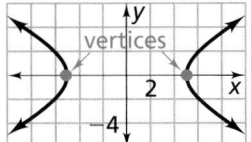

Vertices of an ellipse (p. 578) The endpoints of the major axis of an ellipse are the vertices of the ellipse.

Vértices de una elipse (p. 578) Los dos puntos de intersección de la elipse y su eje mayor son los vértices de la elipse.

x- and y-intercepts (p. 65) The point at which a line crosses the x-axis (or the x-coordinate of that point) is an x-intercept. The point at which a line crosses the y-axis (or the y-coordinate of that point) is a y-intercept.

Intercepto en x e intercepto en y (p. 65) El punto donde una recta corta el eje x (o la coordenada x de ese punto) es el intercepto en x. El punto donde una recta cruza el eje y (o la coordenada y de ese punto) es el intercepto en y.

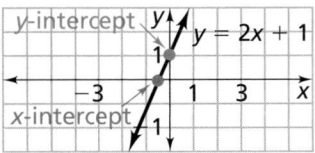

The x-intercept of $y = 2x + 1$ is $\left(-\frac{1}{2}, 0\right)$ or $-\frac{1}{2}$.
The y-intercept of $y = 2x + 1$ is $(0, 1)$ or 1.

Zero matrix (p. 179) The zero matrix O, or $O_{m \times n}$, is the $m \times n$ matrix whose elements are all zeros. It is the additive identity matrix for the set of all $m \times n$ matrices.

$$\begin{bmatrix} 1 & 4 \\ 2 & -3 \end{bmatrix} + O = \begin{bmatrix} 1 & 4 \\ 2 & -3 \end{bmatrix}$$

Matriz cero (p. 179) La matriz cero, O, o $O_{m \times n}$, es la matriz $m \times n$ cuyos elementos son todos ceros. Es la matriz de identidad aditiva para el conjunto de todas las matrices $m \times n$.

Zero of a function (p. 272) A zero of a function is any value of the variable for which the function is 0. On the graph of a function, each x-intercept represents a zero.

Cero de una función (p. 272) Un cero de una función es cualquier valor de la variable para el cual la función es 0. En la gráfica de una función, cada intercepto en x representa un cero.

The zeros of the function $P(x) = 2x(x - 3)^2(x + 1)$ are $0, 3$, and -1.

Zero-Product Property (p. 271) If the product of two or more factors is zero, then one of the factors must be zero.

$(x - 3)(2x - 5) = 0$

$x - 3 = 0$ or $2x - 5 = 0$

Propiedad del cero del producto (p. 271) Si el producto de dos o más factores es cero, entonces uno de los factores debe ser cero.

z-score (p. 683) The z-score of a value is the number of standard deviations that the value is from the mean.

$\{0, 2, 3, 4, 6, 7, 8, 9, 10, 11\}$

$\bar{x} = 6$

Puntaje z (p. 683) El puntaje z de un valor es el número de desviaciones normales que tiene ese valor de la media.

standard deviation $= \sqrt{12} \approx 3.46$

For 8, z-score $= \dfrac{8 - 6}{\sqrt{12}} \approx 0.58$.

Chapter 1

Check Your Readiness · p. 2

1. 0 **2.** −2 **3.** −2.09 **4.** 8.05 **5.** $-\frac{3}{4}$ **6.** $\frac{11}{12}$ **7.** $10\frac{7}{10}$
8. $3\frac{1}{2}$ **9.** −42 **10.** 72 **11.** 9 **12.** −9.8 **13.** $-3\frac{1}{3}$
14. $-5\frac{1}{2}$ **15.** $-4\frac{2}{3}$ **16.** $-\frac{3}{4}$ **17.** −21 **18.** 7.35
19. $-\frac{1}{6}$ **20.** $-\frac{3}{5}$ **21.** −20 **22.** 8 **23.** 0.97 **24.** −5
25. 55 **26.** 3

Lesson 1-1 · pp. 4–8

Check Skills You'll Need 1. 7.2 **2.** 4 **3.** −13.5 **4.** 6.8
5. −5 **6.** −1

CA Standards Check 1. rational numbers; rational numbers
2.

> number line with $-2\frac{1}{4}$, $-\sqrt{2}$, $0.\overline{3}$ marked; axis labeled −3 −2 −1 0 1 2 3

3. $-\sqrt{0.08} > -\sqrt{0.1}$, $-\sqrt{0.1} < -\sqrt{0.08}$
4a. $-400, \frac{1}{400}$ **b.** $-4\frac{1}{5}, \frac{5}{21}$ **c.** 0.002, −500
d. $\frac{4}{9}, -\frac{9}{4}$ $\left(\text{or } -2\frac{1}{4}\right)$ **5a.** Identity Prop. of Add.
b. Assoc. Prop. of Add. **6a.** 10, 1.5, 3 **b.** for values of x such that $x \le 0$

Lesson 1-2 · pp. 12–15

Check Skills You'll Need 1. 16 **2.** 6 **3.** $\frac{8}{3}$ **4.** 195 **5.** 21
6. −1

CA Standards Check 1a. $\frac{7}{2}$ **b.** 26 **c.** 4 **2a.** −16
b. −3 **c.** −69 **3a.** about 45%; about 43%
b. Answers may vary. Sample: Changing patterns in minority populations might lead to more voter turnout. Less stable international conditions might arouse voter concerns. **4a.** $-3x^2 + 6x$
b. $-4r - 4s$ **5a.** $10x$ **b.** $10c + 2d$

Lesson 1-3 · pp. 18–21, 24

Check Skills You'll Need 1. $-4x + 3$ **2.** $7x + 3y - 1$
3. $8g + 2h$ **4.** $\frac{x}{3}$ **5.** $2y$ **6.** $-3c + 1$

CA Standards Check 1a. −11 **b.** 2 **2a.** 35 **b.** 3
3. $b_1 = \frac{2A}{h} - b_2$ **4a.** $x = \frac{15}{a + b}, a \neq -b$
b. $x = \frac{a(d - b)}{2}, a \neq 0$ **5.** 8 cm wide; 16 cm long
6. 36 cm; 39 cm; 45 cm **7.** about 86.4 seconds, or 1 minute 26.4 seconds

Checkpoint Quiz 1 1. $-1, 0.3, \frac{2}{3}, 7$ **2.** Comm. Prop. of

Add., Assoc. Prop. of Add., Dist. Prop. **3.** $a + 2b$
4. $a^2 + a - 7$ **5.** 5 **6.** $\frac{3}{2}$, or $1\frac{1}{2}$ **7.** 2 **8.** $r = \frac{A - p}{pt}$,
$p \neq 0, t \neq 0$ **9.** $x = \frac{4b}{7a}, a \neq 0$ **10.** width = 76 yd, length = 236 yd

Lesson 1-4 · pp. 26–29

Check Skills You'll Need 1. true **2.** false **3.** false
4. false **5.** true **6.** true **7.** −6 **8.** 15

CA Standards Check
1a. $x < 11$

> number line 5 6 7 8 9 10 11 12 13, open circle at 11

b. $n \le -2$

> number line −6 −5 −4 −3 −2 −1 0 1 2, closed circle at −2

2a. All real numbers are solutions.

> number line −4 −3 −2 −1 0 1 2 3 4

b. no solutions

c. values of a less than or equal to 0; values of a greater than 0 **3.** at least $55,000
4.

> number line 2 3 4 5 6 7 8 9 10, open circles at 5 and 8, labeled z

5. $x < 4$ or $x > 5$

> number line −1 0 1 2 3 4 5 6 7, open circles at 4 and 5

6. by at least 0.03 in., but by no more than 0.43 in.

Lesson 1–5 · pp. 33–36, 38

Check Skills You'll Need 1. 14 **2.** 16 **3.** 2.3 **4.** $x > 3$
5. $a \ge 4$ **6.** $t < 9$

CA Standards Check 1. $\frac{5}{3}, -3$ **2.** $-\frac{13}{3}, 5$ **3a.** 1 **b.** no solutions **c.** Answers may vary; any positive real number. **4.** $x < -2$ or $x > 5$

> number line −3 −2 −1 0 1 2 3 4 5 6 7, open circles at −2 and 5

5. $-8\frac{4}{5} < z < 7\frac{3}{5}$

> number line −12 −10 −8 −6 −4 −2 0 2 4 6 8 10, open circles

6. $|C - 28.125| \le 0.375$

Checkpoint Quiz 2
1. $x \le 5$

> number line −2 −1 0 1 2 3 4 5 6 7, closed circle at 5

2. $x < 5\frac{4}{7}$

> number line −2 −1 0 1 2 3 4 5 6 7, open circle

3. $z > -1$

> number line −4 −3 −2 −1 0 1 2 3 4 5, open circle at −1

4. $w > 1$ or $w < -3$

> number line −6 −5 −4 −3 −2 −1 0 1 2 3 4, open circles at −3 and 1

5. $-15 \le x \le 7$

> number line −16 −14 −12 −10 −8 −6 −4 −2 0 2 4 6 8, closed circles

6. $x < -2$ or $x > 2$
-4-3-2-1 0 1 2 3 4

7. $-\frac{5}{2}, \frac{11}{2}$ **8.** $\frac{1}{6}$ **9.** $13 < 3n + 3 < 16, n = 4$

10. $PR - RQ < PQ < PR + RQ$; $4 < PQ < 26$

Lesson 1–6 pp. 39–42

Check Skills You'll Need **1.** 37.5% **2.** $183\frac{1}{3}\%$ **3.** 0.43%
4. 0.25% **5.** 104% **6.** 300%

CA Standards Check **1.** $\frac{29}{40}$, or 0.725, or 72.5% **2.** $\frac{3}{50}$, or 6% **3.** $\frac{1}{2}$, or 50% **4.** $\frac{1}{4}$, or 25% **5a.** $\frac{1}{16}$, or 6.25%
b. $\frac{5}{16}$, or 31.25%

Chapter 2

Check Your Readiness p. 52

1.
-2 0 2 4 6

2.
-4 -2 0 2

3. **4.** $6s$ **5.** $4a + b$
-2 0 2 4 6

6. $xy - y + x$ **7.** $1.5g$ **8.** 0 **9.** $3b - 2c - 2$
10. $6f - 5d$ **11.** $3h + 3g$ **12.** $-2z + 5$
13. $2g - 4dg - 12d$ **14.** $8v - 6$ **15.** $7t - 3st - 5s$
16. $-2 < x < 8$
-2 0 2 4 6 8

17. $a \leq 0$
-4 -2 0 2

18. $x > -1$
-2 0 2 4

19. $x < -4$ or $x > \frac{10}{3}$
-6 -4 -2 0 2 4 6

20. $-\frac{1}{2} \leq d \leq \frac{25}{4}$
-2 0 2 4 6 8

21. $-24 \leq f \leq 18$
-30 -20 -10 0 10 20 30 **22.** $\frac{15}{64}$ **23.** $\frac{1}{32}$

24. $\frac{11}{32}$ **25.** $\frac{13}{16}$ **26.** $\frac{27}{32}$ **27.** $\frac{13}{16}$

Lesson 2-1 pp. 57–63

Check Skills You'll Need

1. **2.** **3.**

---

4. 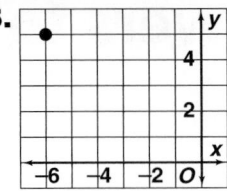 **5.**

6. 1, 2, 4, 7 **7.** 5, 3, −1, −7 **8.** 3, 1, 9, 51
9. 4, 3, 1, 2

CA Standards Check

1a. **b.**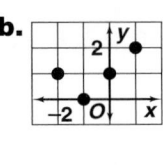

2a. domain {−3, 0, 2, 4}, range {2, 1, 4, −3}
b. domain {−3, −1, 1}, range {−4, −2, 1, 3}
3a. domain range **b.** domain range **4a.** function

 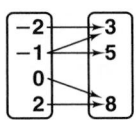

b. not a function **5a.** not a function **b.** function
c. not a function **6a.** −14, −5, 10 **b.** $-\frac{13}{4}, -1, \frac{11}{4}$
c. $\frac{6}{5}, \frac{3}{5}, -\frac{2}{5}$

Lesson 2-2 pp. 64–72

Check Skills You'll Need **1.** $\frac{17}{3}, 7, \frac{23}{3}, \frac{29}{3}$ **2.** $-\frac{16}{5}, -2, -\frac{7}{5}, \frac{2}{5}$
3. −5, 1, 4, 13 **4.** $-9, -8, -\frac{15}{2}, -6$

CA Standards Check

1a. **b.**

c. **2a.**

$y = 40 - x$, x-intercept (40, 0), y-intercept (0, 40).
When there are 0 children, the train holds 40 adults.
When there are 0 adults, the train holds 40
children. **b.** Answers may vary. Sample: Each
seat holds one person, whether adult or child.

3a. $\frac{2}{3}$ **b.** $-\frac{6}{7}$ **4a.** $2x - y = 10$ **b.** $\frac{5}{6}x - y = -\frac{11}{6}$
5a. $y - 0 = -\frac{1}{4}(x - 5)$ **b.** $y + 1 = -\frac{9}{4}(x + 2)$
c. $y - 1 = \frac{4}{9}(x - 5)$ **6a.** $-\frac{3}{2}$ **b.** $-\frac{4}{3}$ **c.** $-\frac{A}{B}, B \neq 0$,
undefined, $B = 0$
7a. $y = -\frac{1}{5}x + \frac{14}{5}$

b. $y = \frac{2}{3}x - \frac{1}{3}$

c. $x = 5$

Lesson 2-3   pp. 74–76, 79

Check Skills You'll Need 1. $y = \frac{x}{4}$ **2.** $y = \frac{5}{12}x$ **3.** $y = 20$
4. $y = 30x$ **5.** $y = 7$ **6.** true **7.** true **8.** false
9. true

CA Standards Check 1a. yes; $k = \frac{1}{3}$, $y = \frac{1}{3}x$ **b.** no
c. no **2a.** yes; $k = 0.5$ **b.** no **c.** yes; $k = \frac{5}{2}$ **d.** no
3a. π **b.** 33.4 cm **4a.** 8 **b.** 28 **c.** −0.6 **d.** 0.2

Checkpoint Quiz 1 1. (9, 0), (0, −3) **2.** $\left(-\frac{5}{7}, 0\right)$, (0, 5)

3. (0, 0), (0,0) **4.** $\left(-\frac{5}{2}, 0\right)$, (0, 10) **5.** $y = 2x - 9$
6. $y = 4x - 2$ **7.** $y = -\frac{3}{5}x - 2$ **8.** $y = -\frac{2}{3}x + 2$
9a. $y = 7x$ **b.**

Both intercepts are 0 when no one has bought
any tickets. **c.** Answers may vary. Sample: No; the
number of people must be a whole number. **10.** A

Lesson 2-4   pp. 80–86

Check Skills You'll Need 1. 3.6, −1.7 **2.** 1.5, −3.5
3. −1, $\frac{1}{10}$ **4.** −6, −2, −$\frac{4}{3}$ **5.** 6, $\frac{11}{2}$, 3

CA Standards Check 1a. $h = -20t + 1350$; the slope
is negative. **b.**

The h-intercept (0, 1350) represents the starting
height at time 0. **2a.** The candle is burning down
at the rate of $\frac{1}{4}$ inch per hour. **b.** the original

height of the candle **c.** $y = -2x + 9$ **3a.** $3\frac{1}{2}$ in.
b. $6\frac{1}{4}$ in. **c.** after 25 hours

4a.

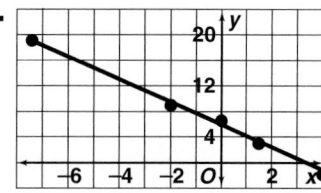

A linear model is reasonable; models may vary.
Sample: $y = -1.92x + 6$

b.

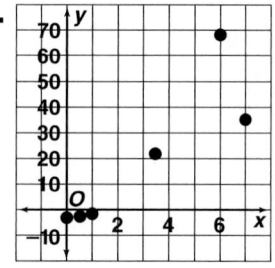

not reasonable

Lesson 2-5   pp. 90–92

Check Skills You'll Need

1. **2.** **3.**

CA Standards Check

1a. **b.**

2a.

b.

3a. **b.**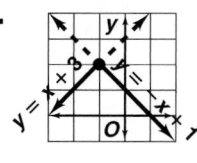

4a. The graph would stretch vertically by a factor of 3. **b.**

Lesson 2-6

pp. 95–99, 102

Check Skills You'll Need

1. **2.**

3. **4.**

5. **6.**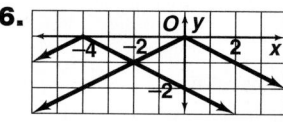

CA Standards Check 1a. $y = x + 1$ is $y = x$ shifted 1 unit up.

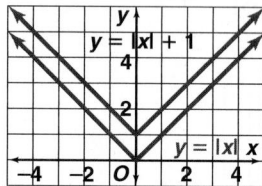

b. $y = |x| - \frac{1}{2}$; $y = |x| + 3.5$.

2a. $y = |x + \frac{3}{2}|$

b. The graph is translated 1 unit to the right.

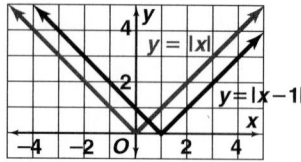

3. Answers may vary. Sample: 4.5 units right and 3 units up

4a. The graph is a vertical shrink by a factor of $\frac{1}{3}$.

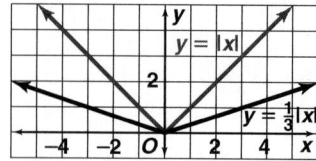

b. $y = 3|x|$

5. $y = -5|x|$

Checkpoint Quiz 2

1. **2.** **3.**

4. **5.**

6. 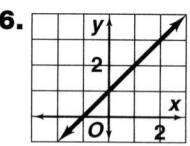 **7.** $y = x - 4$ **8.** $y = |x + 5| - 3$

9a. 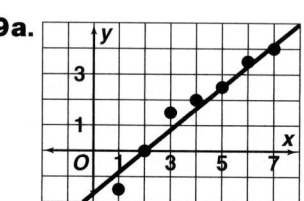 **b.** about 7 **10.** D

Lesson 2-7

pp. 103–106

Check Skills You'll Need

1. $p \le 1.25$

2. $t > 13$

3. $t \le -3$

4. $c = \pm 4.5$

5. $b = 2, 8$

6. $h \le -3.5$ or $h \ge 3.5$

CA Standards Check

1a. **b.** **c.**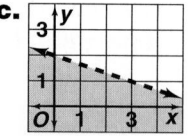

2a. at least 3; Answers may vary. Sample: (2, 5), (1, 6), (0, 7) **b.** $7x + 5y \ge 35, x > 0, y > 0$

3a. **b.**

4a. $y \le |x + 4| - 3$ **b.** $y \ge 2x + 5$

Chapter 3

Check Your Readiness
p. 118

1. $7x - 1$ **2.** $5 - p$ **3.** $-6z + 10$ **4.** $r - 4$

5. $a \leq \frac{3}{2}$

6. $b > 2$

7. $c < -12$

8. $d \leq -1$

9. **10.**

11. **12.**

13. **14.**

15. $y = 6x$ **16.**

17. **18.**

19.

Lesson 3-1
pp. 120–122

Check Skills You'll Need

1. **2.**

3.

4, 5, 6.

CA Standards Check

1. (1, 3)

2a. 2008—men: 43.63 s, women: 48.01 s, 2024—men: 43.34 s, women: 46.97 s **b.** It would mean that eventually the 400-m run would be run in zero seconds, and this could not happen.
3a. inconsistent **b.** dependent **c.** independent

Lesson 3-2
pp. 127–129

Check Skills You'll Need 1. -4 **2.** x **3.** $-5x$ **4.** $-8y$ **5.** 1
6. -2 **7.** $-\frac{1}{4}$

CA Standards Check 1.a. $(-6, -6)$ **b.** $(2, 6)$

2. $\begin{cases} c = 15.49x \\ c = 6 + 13.99x \end{cases}$ The number of CDs is 4.

3a. $(4, -1)$ **b.** $(-2, 1)$ **4.** Answers may vary.
Sample: Multiply (1) by -5. Multiply (2) by 3. Add equations together, solving for y. Substitute the value of y into either original equation and solve for x. **5a.** infinite number of solutions $\{(x, y)| -3x + 5y = 7\}$ **b.** no solution

Lesson 3-3 — pp. 135–137, 140

Check Skills You'll Need **1.** $x > \frac{33}{5}$ **2.** $y \le -14$ **3.** $x > -\frac{7}{5}$

4. **5.** **6.** **7.**

8. **9.**

CA Standards Check

1a. (0, 1), (1, 2), (2, 3), (3, 4), (4, 5), (5, 6), (6, 7)

1b. (1, 0), (2, 1), (2, 0), (3, 2), (3, 1), (3, 0), (4, 3), (4, 2), (4, 1), (4, 0), (5, 3), (5, 2), (5, 1), (5, 0), (6, 3), (6, 2), (6, 1), (6, 0), (7, 2), (7,1), (7,0), (8, 1), (8, 0), (9, 1), (9, 0), (10, 0)

2a. **b.** 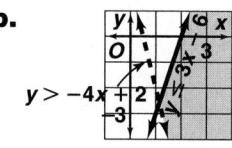 $y > -4x + 2$

3. $\begin{cases} 550 \le m \le 800 \\ v \le 800 \\ v + m \ge 1100 \end{cases}$

4a. 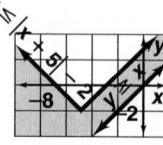 $y \le |x + 5|$ **b.** 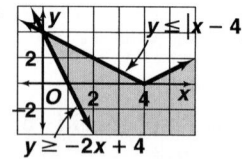 $y \le |x - 4|$ $y \ge -2x + 4$

Checkpoint Quiz 1 **1.** (4, −3) **2.** (7, 0) **3.** (2, −4) **4.** (1, 3)

5. $\begin{cases} 2n + 3m = 158 \\ 2n + 5m = 181 \end{cases}$ $61.75 cost per night, $11.50 cost per meal **6.** approximately 4.8 years

7a. $\begin{cases} h \ge 18 \\ s \ge 12 \\ s + h \le 35 \end{cases}$ **b.**

8. **9.**   **10.**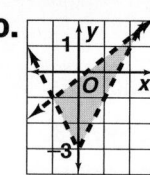

Lesson 3-4 — pp. 141–143

Check Skills You'll Need **1.** (2, −3) **2.** (1, 2) **3.** (1, 1)

4. **5.** 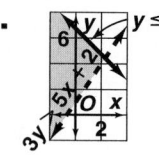 $y \le -x + 7$

6. $x + 3y$ $2x - 3y \le 4$

CA Standards Check **1.** $P = 2(0) + 3(0) = 0$, $P = 2(2) + 3(0) = 4$, $P = 2(4) + 3(3) = 17$, $P = 2(0) + 3(7) = 21$
When $x = 0$ and $y = 7$, P is maximized at 21.
When $x = 0$ and $y = 0$, P is minimized at 0.
2. Order 25 cases of mixed nuts and no cases of roasted peanuts.

Lesson 3-5 — pp. 148–150, 153

Check Skills You'll Need **1.** x: −3, y: 6 **2.** x: 18, y: 4
3. x: −8, y: 3 **4.** x: 10, y: −8

5. **6.** **7.** **8.**

CA Standards Check

1a. (0, −4, −2) **b.** (−1, 1, 3)

c. (3, −5, 2) **d.** (3, 3, −3)

2a. (0, 5, 0) **b.** outside the helmet, since the helmet is curved

3a.

b.

c.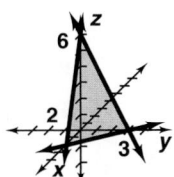

Checkpoint Quiz 2 1. p(5, 5) = 25 **2.** 300 acres corn and 100 acres soybeans

3. 3x + 2y + z = 6

4.   **5.**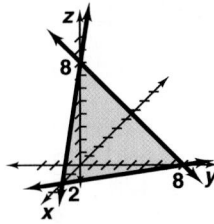

Lesson 3-6   pp. 154–158

Check Skills You'll Need 1. (3, −5) **2.** no solution

3. (1, −4) **4.** 1 **5.** 1 **6.** $\frac{1}{2}$ **7.** yes **8.** yes

CA Standards Check 1a. (1, 2, −1) **b.** (3, 3, 1) **c.** No; you wouldn't need to use any of the original equations twice. **2.** (2, −1, 1) **3a.** (4, 1, 5) **b.** (2, 0, −6) **4.** $1400 growth, $1100 income, and $700 money market

Chapter 4

Check Your Readiness   p. 170

1. 6 **2.** $\frac{1}{3}$ **3.** $-\frac{3}{8}$ **4.** $\frac{7}{12}$ **5.** $\frac{10}{3}$ **6.** −9 **7.** $-\frac{17}{4}$

8. all real numbers **9.** $t > -\frac{11}{4}$ **10.** $s < 2$

11.   **12.**   **13.**

14.   **15.**

16.   **17.**

18. **19.** $\left(\frac{1}{2}, -4\right)$ **20.** $\left(-\frac{2}{3}, -\frac{2}{3}\right)$ **21.** $\left(\frac{3}{4}, \frac{11}{4}\right)$
22. (7, 9, −6) **23.** (0, 0, 8)
24. (7, 5, 0)

Lesson 4-1   pp. 172–174

Check Skills You'll Need 1. 4.678 million units; 7.028 million units **2.** 2.35 million units **3.** 5.505 million units **4.** The export percent increase of 27.3% was smaller than the 43.9% increase for the imports.

CA Standards Check 1a. 2 × 3 **b.** 1 × 3 **c.** 3 × 2 **2a.** 15 **b.** 17 **c.** 10.4 **d.** 24

3a.

	China	Russia	United States
Production	42	46	71
Consumption	43	28	98

b. Add a new column for each additional country.
c. A $c \times d$ matrix has c rows and d columns, while a $d \times c$ matrix has d rows and c columns.

4a. $\begin{bmatrix} 9.725 & 9.700 & 9.587 & 9.137 & 9.837 & 9.837 \\ 9.650 & 8.537 & 9.712 & 9.412 & 9.775 & 9.725 \\ 9.512 & 9.650 & 9.725 & 9.700 & 9.712 & 9.475 \end{bmatrix}$

b. 9.837; Paul Hamm's score on the parallel bars

Lesson 4-2   pp. 178–181

Check Skills You'll Need 1. $\begin{bmatrix} 14 & 4 \\ 2 & -1 \end{bmatrix}$ **2.** $\begin{bmatrix} 3 & 1 \\ -3 & -2 \end{bmatrix}$

3. $\begin{bmatrix} 1 & -3 \\ -2 & -2 \end{bmatrix}$ **4.** $\begin{bmatrix} 4 & 13 \\ -2 & 12 \end{bmatrix}$ **5.** $\begin{bmatrix} 4 & -6 \\ 8 & -3 \end{bmatrix}$

6. $\begin{bmatrix} 6 & -2 \\ 1 & 7 \end{bmatrix}$

CA Standards Check 1a. $\begin{bmatrix} 4 & 7 & -3 \\ -6 & 1 & 19 \end{bmatrix}$

b. $\begin{bmatrix} -15 & 25 \\ -1 & 1 \\ -2 & 15 \end{bmatrix}$ 2a. $\begin{bmatrix} 0 & 0 \\ 0 & 0 \end{bmatrix}$ b. $\begin{bmatrix} -1 & 10 & -5 \\ 0 & 2 & -3 \end{bmatrix}$

3a. $\begin{bmatrix} 10 & -12 & 7 \\ -8 & -4 & -2 \end{bmatrix}$ b. $\begin{bmatrix} 0 & 4 \\ -3 & 14 \end{bmatrix}$ 4. $\begin{bmatrix} 11 & 7 \\ -6 & -1 \end{bmatrix}$

5a. no b. yes 6a. $x = 30, y = 2$
b. $x = -3, y = 7$

Lesson 4-3   pp. 186–190, 193

Check Skills You'll Need 1. $\begin{bmatrix} 9 & 15 \\ 6 & 24 \end{bmatrix}$ 2. $\begin{bmatrix} -20 \\ 35 \end{bmatrix}$

3. $\begin{bmatrix} -4 & 12 & 16 \\ 0 & -8 & -20 \end{bmatrix}$

CA Standards Check 1. $\begin{bmatrix} -45 & 36 & -30 & 0 \\ -60 & 30 & -21 & 0 \end{bmatrix}$

2a. $\begin{bmatrix} 7 & -12 & 58 \\ -9 & 24 & -10 \end{bmatrix}$ b. $\begin{bmatrix} 20 & 3 & 29 \\ -5 & 52 & 17 \end{bmatrix}$

3a. $\begin{bmatrix} 1 & 6 \\ 2 & 0 \end{bmatrix}$ b. $\begin{bmatrix} -1 & 0 & -3 \\ 7 & 5 & -2 \end{bmatrix}$

4a. $\begin{bmatrix} 12 & -12 \\ -5 & 0 \end{bmatrix}$ b. No; explanations may vary.
Sample: For the matrices in part (a),

$AB = \begin{bmatrix} 12 & -12 \\ -5 & 0 \end{bmatrix}$.

However, $BA = \begin{bmatrix} 3 & -3 \\ -29 & 9 \end{bmatrix}$, so $AB \neq BA$.

5a. [105] b. Product does not exist. 6a. *RS* is defined, but *SR* is undefined.

b. $RS = \begin{bmatrix} 28 & 10 & -6 & -16 \\ 32 & 20 & -9 & -32 \end{bmatrix}$

Checkpoint Quiz 1 1. 3 × 2; 1 2. 2 × 3; −2 3. 3 × 3; 5

4. $\begin{bmatrix} -2 & 4 \\ 6 & 16 \end{bmatrix}$ 5. $\begin{bmatrix} 1 & 5 \\ -4 & -7 \end{bmatrix}$ 6. $\begin{bmatrix} 4.5 & 6 \\ 27 & -18 \end{bmatrix}$

7. $\begin{bmatrix} 42 & 46 \\ 3 & 1 \end{bmatrix}$ 8. $\begin{bmatrix} 50 & 117 \\ 278 & 495 \end{bmatrix}$

9. Make sure that the number of columns in the first matrix is the same as the number of rows in the second matrix.

10. Answers may vary. Sample: 2X +
$\begin{bmatrix} 1 & 2 & 2 & 4 \\ 0 & 3 & 0 & 5 \end{bmatrix} = \begin{bmatrix} 25 & 16 & -4 & 20 \\ 18 & 3 & -22 & 7 \end{bmatrix}$

Lesson 4-4   pp. 195–199

Check Skills You'll Need

1.
$y = x + 6$

2.
$f(x) = \frac{1}{2}x + 7$

3.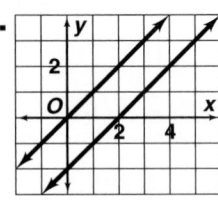
$g(x) = |x - 3|$

4.
$y = x - 2$

5.
$y = \frac{1}{3}|x - 3| - 2$

6.
$f(x) = |-2x + 4|$

CA Standards Check 1a. Subtract 6 from each x-coordinate and add 2 to each y-coordinate.

b. $\begin{bmatrix} -3 & -3 & -3 & -3 & -3 \\ 2 & 2 & 2 & 2 & 2 \end{bmatrix}$

c. $(-3, -3), (-4, 1), (-8, 2), (-2, 5), (1, 2)$

2a. $(-20, 0), (32, -4), (16, 20)$

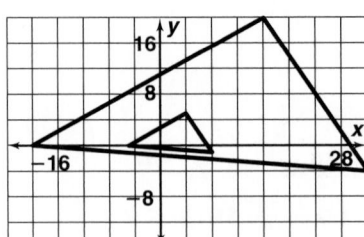

b. (−1, 0), (1.6, −0.2), (0.8, 1)

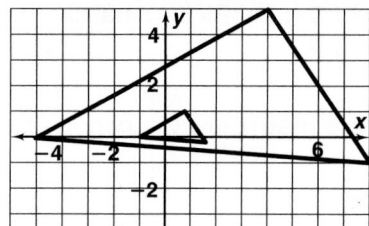

c. (7.5, 0), (−12, 1.5), (−6, −7.5)

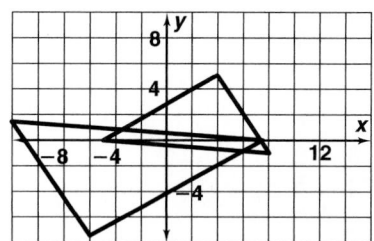

3a. $\begin{bmatrix} 3 & 4 & -1 \\ 0 & 4 & 1 \end{bmatrix}$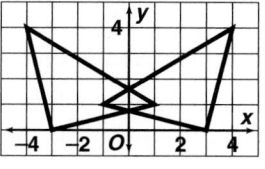

b. $\begin{bmatrix} -3 & -4 & 1 \\ 0 & -4 & -1 \end{bmatrix}$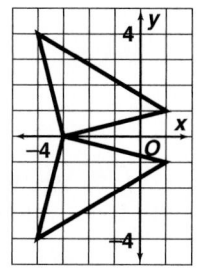

c. $\begin{bmatrix} 0 & 4 & 1 \\ -3 & -4 & 1 \end{bmatrix}$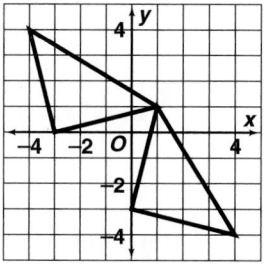

d. $\begin{bmatrix} 0 & -4 & -1 \\ 3 & 4 & -1 \end{bmatrix}$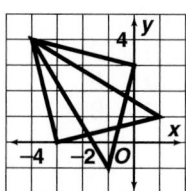

4a. $\begin{bmatrix} -1 & -1 & -4 & -3 \\ 1 & 3 & 6 & 1 \end{bmatrix}$

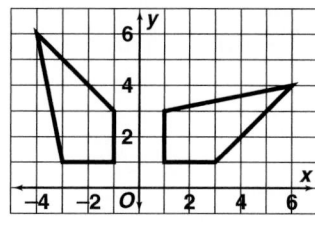

b. $\begin{bmatrix} -1 & -3 & -6 & -1 \\ -1 & -1 & -4 & -3 \end{bmatrix}$

c. $\begin{bmatrix} 1 & 1 & 4 & 3 \\ -1 & -3 & -6 & -1 \end{bmatrix}$

d. $\begin{bmatrix} 1 & 3 & 6 & 1 \\ 1 & 1 & 4 & 3 \end{bmatrix}$

Lesson 4-5   **pp. 203–207**

Check Skills You'll Need 1a. 12 **b.** 12 **c.** 0 **2a.** −12
b. −12 **c.** 0 **3a.** 12 **b.** −12 **c.** 24 **4a.** −12 **b.** 12
c. −24

CA Standards Check 1a. $\begin{bmatrix} 2 & 1 \\ 2.5 & 1 \end{bmatrix}\begin{bmatrix} -2 & 2 \\ 5 & -4 \end{bmatrix} =$

$\begin{bmatrix} 2(-2) + 1(5) & 2(2) + 1(-4) \\ 2.5(-2) + 1(5) & 2.5(2) + 1(-4) \end{bmatrix} = \begin{bmatrix} 1 & 0 \\ 0 & 1 \end{bmatrix}$

b. $\begin{bmatrix} -2 & -5 \\ -3 & -8 \end{bmatrix}\begin{bmatrix} -8 & 5 \\ 3 & -2 \end{bmatrix} =$

$\begin{bmatrix} -2(-8) + (-5)(3) & -2(5) + (-5)(-2) \\ -3(-8) + (-8)(3) & -3(5) + (-8)(-2) \end{bmatrix}$

$= \begin{bmatrix} 1 & 0 \\ 0 & 1 \end{bmatrix}$ **2a.** 0 **b.** 10 **c.** −9

3a. yes; $\begin{bmatrix} 1.5 & -2 \\ -0.5 & 1 \end{bmatrix}$ **b.** yes; $\begin{bmatrix} -\frac{24}{11} & \frac{23}{33} \\ \frac{10}{11} & \frac{-5}{33} \end{bmatrix}$

4a. $\begin{bmatrix} 0 & -2 \\ 0 & 4 \end{bmatrix}$ **b.** $\begin{bmatrix} -2 \\ 1 \end{bmatrix}$

5a. 43.3%, 62.0%, 70.3%; 73.9% **b.** about
11,829 people **c.** about 102 people

Lesson 4-6
pp. 210–212, 215

Check Skills You'll Need **1.** −24 **2.** 0 **3.** −24 **4.** 12 **5.** 12 **6.** 0

CA Standards Check **1a.** 27 **b.** 22 **c.** 0 **2.** −1087

3a. The matrices $\begin{bmatrix} 0 & 0 & 1 \\ 0.2 & -0.2 & 0 \\ 0 & -1 & 1 \end{bmatrix}$ and

$\begin{bmatrix} 1 & 5 & -1 \\ 1 & 0 & -1 \\ 1 & 0 & 0 \end{bmatrix}$ have a product of $\begin{bmatrix} 1 & 0 & 0 \\ 0 & 1 & 0 \\ 0 & 0 & 1 \end{bmatrix}$, so

they are inverses.

b. The matrices $\begin{bmatrix} 0 & 1 & 0 \\ 1 & 0 & 1 \\ 0 & 1 & 0 \end{bmatrix}$ and $\begin{bmatrix} 3 & 4 & 1 \\ -2 & 0 & 2 \\ 1 & 5 & 3 \end{bmatrix}$ have

a product of $\begin{bmatrix} -2 & 0 & 2 \\ 4 & 9 & 4 \\ -2 & 0 & 2 \end{bmatrix}$, so they are not

inverses.

4a. The matrices $\begin{bmatrix} 0 & 0 & 2 \\ 1 & 3 & -2 \\ 1 & -2 & 1 \end{bmatrix}$ and

$\begin{bmatrix} 0.1 & 0.4 & 0.6 \\ 0.3 & 0.2 & -0.2 \\ 0.5 & 0 & 0 \end{bmatrix}$ have a product of $\begin{bmatrix} 1 & 0 & 0 \\ 0 & 1 & 0 \\ 0 & 0 & 1 \end{bmatrix}$,

so they are inverses.

b. $\begin{bmatrix} 9 \\ -5 \\ 0 \end{bmatrix}$ **5.** POETRY

Checkpoint Quiz 2 **1.** $A'(-2, 8)$, $B'(-8, 0)$, $C'(2, -2)$
2. $A'(-4, 7)$, $B'(-7, 3)$, $C'(-2, 2)$ **3.** $A'(4, 1)$, $B'(0, 4)$,
$C'(-1, -1)$ **4.** $A'(-4, 1)$, $B'(0, 4)$, $C'(1, -1)$

5. $\begin{bmatrix} 2 & 3 \\ -4 & -5 \end{bmatrix}$ **6.** $\begin{bmatrix} 5 \\ 2 \\ 6 \end{bmatrix}$ **7.** $\begin{bmatrix} -2 \\ 8 \end{bmatrix}$ **8.** −10 **9.** 18

10. −71

Lesson 4-7
pp. 218–221

Check Skills You'll Need **1.** (2, 4) **2.** (0, 6, 3) **3.** (3, −3, 9)

CA Standards Check **1a.** $\begin{bmatrix} 3 & 2 \\ 0 & 1 \end{bmatrix}\begin{bmatrix} x \\ y \end{bmatrix} = \begin{bmatrix} 16 \\ 5 \end{bmatrix}$;

coefficient matrix is $\begin{bmatrix} 3 & 2 \\ 0 & 1 \end{bmatrix}$, variable matrix is $\begin{bmatrix} x \\ y \end{bmatrix}$,

constant matrix is $\begin{bmatrix} 16 \\ 5 \end{bmatrix}$.

b. $\begin{bmatrix} 1 & -1 & 1 \\ 1 & -2 & -1 \\ 2 & -1 & 2 \end{bmatrix}\begin{bmatrix} x \\ y \\ z \end{bmatrix} = \begin{bmatrix} 0 \\ 5 \\ 8 \end{bmatrix}$; coefficient matrix

is $\begin{bmatrix} 1 & -1 & 1 \\ 1 & -2 & -1 \\ 2 & -1 & 2 \end{bmatrix}$, variable matrix is $\begin{bmatrix} x \\ y \\ z \end{bmatrix}$, constant

matrix is $\begin{bmatrix} 0 \\ 5 \\ 8 \end{bmatrix}$. **2a.** (−1, 4) **b.** (−2, 8)

3a. $2(4) + (-10) + 3(1) \stackrel{?}{=} 1$
$8 - 10 + 3 \stackrel{?}{=} 1$
$1 = 1$
$5(4) + (-10) - 2(1) \stackrel{?}{=} 8$
$20 - 10 - 2 \stackrel{?}{=} 8$
$8 = 8$
$4 - (-10) - 9(1) \stackrel{?}{=} 5$
$4 + 10 - 9 \stackrel{?}{=} 5$
$5 = 5$

b. (1.25, 2.5, −1.75)

4. one large bead = $1.95, one small bead = $.55

5a. yes **b.** The graphing calculator indicates that there is a "singular matrix" error.

Lesson 4-8
pp. 225–229

Check Skills You'll Need **1.** −3 **2.** 1 **3.** 11 **4.** −18 **5.** 15
6. −35

CA Standards Check **1.** (1, 2) **2a.** In D, replace the coefficients of z with the constants. **b.** $y = 1$,
$z = 1$ **3a.** $\left[\begin{array}{cc|c} 1 & -5 & 15 \\ 3 & 3 & 3 \end{array}\right]$ **b.** $\left[\begin{array}{ccc|c} 1 & 2 & 3 & -4 \\ 0 & 1 & -2 & 8 \\ 0 & 0 & 1 & -3 \end{array}\right]$

4a. $\begin{cases} 5x + 7y = -3 \\ -8y = 6 \end{cases}$ **b.** $\begin{cases} -x + \quad 3z = -4 \\ 7x + 2y - z = \quad 0 \\ y + 2z = -3 \end{cases}$

5. (−15, 5)

6a. $3(4) - 2(1) + 4(0) \stackrel{?}{=} 10$
$12 - 2 + 0 \stackrel{?}{=} 10$
$10 = 10$ ✓
$4 + 4(1) - 2(0) \stackrel{?}{=} 8$
$4 + 4 - 0 \stackrel{?}{=} 8$
$8 = 8$ ✓

b. (−1, 2, 3)

Chapter 5

Check Your Readiness
p. 240

1. $4x^2 - 5x$ **2.** $\frac{11x^2}{30}$ **3.** $-7x^2 - 13x$ **4.** $\frac{2}{3}$ **5.** −1.8
6. 1

7. **8.** **9.**

10. **11.**

12. **13.**

Sample: $y = 3x + 12$

14.

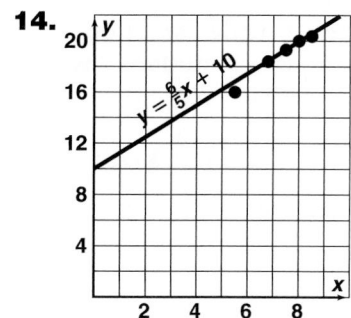

Sample: $y = \frac{6}{5}x + 10$

15. **16.** $y = |x|$

$v = 6s + 40$

Lesson 5-1 pp. 242–244

Check Skills You'll Need **1.** $-3, -1, 0, 1, 3$ **2.** $9, 1, 0, 1,$
9 **3.** $3, 1, 0, -1, -3$ **4.** $-9, -1, 0, -1, -9$ **5.** $3, \frac{1}{3},$
$0, \frac{1}{3}, 3$ **6.** $-3, -\frac{1}{3}, 0, -\frac{1}{3}, -3$ **7.** $y = -\frac{3}{4}x + 2$
8. $y = 2x + 7$ **9.** $y = -\frac{1}{6}x + 3$

CA Standards Check **1a.** linear; none, $5x$, none
b. quadratic; $3x^2, -16x, 5$ **c.** quadratic; $x^2, 3x,$
none **2a.** $(1, -1), x = 1; P'(3, 3), Q'(0, 0)$
b. $(-1, 2), x = -1; P'(0, 1), Q'(-3, -2)$
3. $y = -2x^2 + 3x - 1$ **4a.** 73 mm **b.** 39 mm
c. No; the tank is empty at 109 seconds.

Lesson 5-2 pp. 249–251

Check Skills You'll Need **1.** 3 **2.** -1 **3.** -4 **4.** $(0, 0)$
5. $\left(-\frac{3}{2}, 0\right)$ **6.** $\left(-\frac{7}{3}, 0\right)$

7. **8.** **9.**

CA Standards Check

1a. **b.** **c.** $(0, 0)$

2a. **b.**

3a. minimum: -9
b. none

4. \$10; \$500

Lesson 5-3 pp. 256–259, 262

Check Skills You'll Need
1. $y = x$ **2.** $y = |x|$

3. $y = |x|$

4. $y = x - 2$ **5.** $y = -|x + 1| - 1$

CA Standards Check

1a.

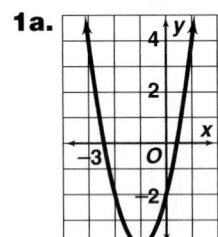

b. Check students' work.
2. $y = 2(x + 1)^2$ **3.** $y = 0.00015(x - 2000)^2$
4. $y = -3(x - 2)^2 + 17$

Checkpoint Quiz 1 **1.** $y = x^2 + 6x + 3$
2. $y = -2x^2 + 4x + 1$ **3.** $y = 5x^2 - 10x$

4. **5.**

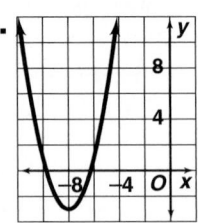

6.

7. max.; 14 8. min.; 7 9. $y = -3(x + 1)^2 - 5$;
$(-1, -5)$; $x = -1$ **10. Answers may vary.**
Sample: $y = (x - 3)^2 + 2$; $x = 3$; $(0, 11)$, $(6, 11)$

Lesson 5-4 pp. 263–267

Check Skills You'll Need **1.** $x^2 + 5x - 1$
2. $6x^2 - 10x - 3$ **3.** $4x^2 - x - 10$ **4.** $-2x^2 + 10x$
5. $4x^2 - 28x + 49$ **6.** $16x^2 - 9$

CA Standards Check **1a.** $3(3x^2 + x - 6)$ **b.** $7(p^2 + 3)$
c. $2w(2w + 1)$ **2a.** $(x + 2)(x + 4)$ **b.** $(x + 4)(x + 8)$
c. $(x + 4)(x + 10)$ **3a.** $(x - 2)(x - 4)$
b. $(x - 3)(x - 4)$ **c.** $(x - 3)(x - 8)$
4a. $(x + 2)(x - 16)$ **b.** $(x + 5)(x - 2)$

c. $(x + 5)(x - 1)$ **5a.** $(x + 4)(2x + 3)$
b. $(x + 1)(4x + 3)$ **c.** $(x - 2)(2x - 3)$
6a. $(x - 1)(2x + 9)$ **b.** $(x - 6)(3x + 2)$
c. $(x + 2)(4x - 3)$ **7a.** $(2x + 3)^2$ **b.** $(8x - 1)^2$
c. $(5x + 9)^2$ **8a.** $(x - 8)(x + 8)$ **b.** $(2a + 7)(2a - 7)$

Lesson 5-5 pp. 271–273

Check Skills You'll Need **1.** $(x + 7)(x - 2)$ **2.** $4x(x - 3)$
3. $(3x - 4)(3x + 4)$

4. **5.**

6.

CA Standards Check **1a.** $-9, 2$ **b.** $-3, 1$ **c.** $0, \frac{1}{2}$
2a. $-\frac{5}{2}, \frac{5}{2}$ **b.** $-2\sqrt{2}, 2\sqrt{2}$ **c.** $-\frac{1}{2}, \frac{1}{2}$ **3a.** 5 s
b. $t = 5$ or $t = -5$, and use positive solution
because it describes time; check students' work.
4. 4.56 **5a.** $-1.24, 3.24$ **b.** $-0.81, 0.31$

Lesson 5-6 pp. 278–281, 284

Check Skills You'll Need **1.** 5 **2.** $2\sqrt{17}$ **3.** 13 **4.** $2\sqrt{34}$
5. $x\sqrt{2}$ **6.** $5x$

CA Standards Check **1a.** $i\sqrt{2}$ **b.** $2i\sqrt{3}$ **c.** $6i$ **d.** $\sqrt{a^2}$
$= |a|$, $(\sqrt{a})^2 = a$ **2.** $7 + 3i\sqrt{2}$ **3a.** $2\sqrt{13}$ **b.** $\sqrt{29}$
c. 4 **4a.** $6 - i$ **b.** $4 - 2i$ **c.** $4 - 3i$ **5a.** -84
b. $9 - 38i$ **c.** $43 - 24i$ **6a.** $8i$ **b.** $\frac{-1 - 13i}{10}$ **c.** $\frac{5 + 5i}{4}$
7a. $\pm 4i$ **b.** $\pm i\sqrt{30}$ **c.** $\pm\frac{1}{2}i$ **8.** $-1 + i, -1 - i, -1$
$+ 3i$

Checkpoint Quiz 2 **1.** $(2x - 3)(x + 2)$ **2.** $5(x + 3)(x - 3)$
3. $(2x - 9)^2$ **4.** $-4, 1$ **5.** 1 **6.** $\pm 11i$ **7.** $\sqrt{29}$
8. $\sqrt{82}$ **9.** $\sqrt{65}$ **10. No; the graph does not
intersect the x-axis.**

Lesson 5-7 pp. 286–289

Check Skills You'll Need **1.** $x^2 - 6x + 9$ **2.** $4x^2 - 4x + 1$
3. $x^2 + 8x + 13$ **4.** ± 5 **5.** $\pm 4\sqrt{3}$ **6.** $\pm 2i$ **7.** $\pm\frac{3}{4}$
CA Standards Check **1.** $-2, 16$ **2.** $\frac{49}{4}$ **3a.** $-2 \pm 2\sqrt{2}$
b. $1 \pm \sqrt{2}$

4a. $x^2 - 8x + 36 = 0$; $(4 + 2i\sqrt{5})^2 - 8(4 + 2i\sqrt{5}) + 36 = 16 + 2(8i\sqrt{5}) + (2i\sqrt{5})^2 - 32 - 16i\sqrt{5} + 36 = (16 - 20 - 32 + 36) + (16i\sqrt{5} - 16i\sqrt{5}) = 0$; $(4 - 2i\sqrt{5})^2 - 8(4 - 2i\sqrt{5}) + 36 = 16 + 2(-8i\sqrt{5}) + (-2i\sqrt{5})^2 - 32 + 16i\sqrt{5} + 36 = 16 - 20 - 32 + 36 + (-16i\sqrt{5} + 16i\sqrt{5}) = 0$

b. The graph has no x-intercepts, so no real solutions. **c.** $-3 \pm 5i$ **5a.** $-2, \frac{3}{2}$ **b.** $\frac{3}{4} \pm \frac{i\sqrt{23}}{4}$

6a. $y = (x - 5)^2 - 27$ **b.** $y = \left(x + \frac{5}{2}\right)^2 - \frac{13}{4}$

7a. (280, 38,000) **b.** The coefficient of s^2 is negative, so the parabola opens downward.

Lesson 5-8   pp. 293–297

Check Skills You'll Need **1.** $y = -10x^2 + 8$ **2.** $y = x^2 + 4x + 3$ **3.** $y = -x^2 + 4x + 1$ **4.** $y = 8x^2 + 2x - 1$ **5.** 24 **6.** 84 **7.** −48 **8.** 89

CA Standards Check **1.** $-1, \frac{4}{3}$ **2a.** $-1 \pm \frac{i\sqrt{2}}{2}$

b.

The graph does not intersect the x-axis.
3a. $\frac{1}{2}, \frac{3}{2}$ **b.** $-2 \pm 3\sqrt{5}$; $-8.71, 4.71$
4a. one real solution **b.** two imaginary solutions
5. Yes; the discriminant is positive.

Chapter 6

Check Your Readiness   p. 310

1. $y = 2x^2 + 1$ **2.** $y = -\frac{1}{4}x^2 - 1$
3. $y = 3x^2 - 6x + 3$

4.

5.

6.

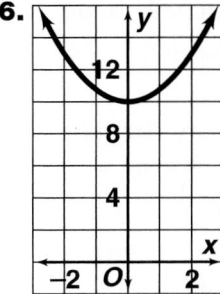

7. $x = -0.25, 1$
8. $x \approx -6.39, 4.39$
9. $x \approx -6.38, 0.38$
10. $x = -4, 9$

11. $x = 3, \frac{7}{2}$ **12.** $x = \frac{2 \pm \sqrt{13}}{3}$
13. 24; 2 real solutions **14.** 0; 1 real solution
15. 0; 1 real solution **16.** $\frac{50}{101}$

Lesson 6-1   pp. 312–315

Check Skills You'll Need **1.** x **2.** $3x^2y - 8xy^2$ **3.** $7x^2 - 3x$ **4.** 1 term **5.** 2 terms **6.** 3 terms

CA Standards Check **1a.** $-2x + 5$; linear binomial
b. $5x^3 + x^2 - 4x$; cubic trinomial **c.** $-2x^5 + 6$; quintic binomial **2.** Answers may vary. Sample: No; when $x = 25$ then, based on the cubic model, $y \approx 3.76$, but because of its turning points the cubic model is unreliable. **3.** 78.4 million troy oz

---

Lesson 6-2   pp. 319–322

Check Skills You'll Need **1.** $(x + 4)(x + 3)$ **2.** $(x + 10)(x - 2)$ **3.** $(x - 12)(x - 2)$ **4.** $x^2 + 4x$ **5.** $x^2 + 2x + 1$ **6.** $x^3 - 4x^2 - 3x + 18$

CA Standards Check **1.** $x^3 + 4x^2 + 5x + 2$
2. $3x(x - 4)(2x + 3)$ **3.** $V \approx 3014$ in.^{3}, depth 10.5 in., length 20.5 in., width 14 in. **4a.** 7, 5, 3

b.

5a. $y = x^3 + 5x^2 + 2x - 8$ **b.** $y = x^3 + 6x^2 + 8x$
c. Answers may vary. Sample: The zero at 0 can be from $x = 0$, $x^2 = 0$, $x^3 = 0$, and so on. Each power will lead to a different answer. **6a.** −1, multiplicity of 3 **b.** 2, multiplicity of 2

Lesson 6-3   pp. 326–29, 332

Check Skills You'll Need **1.** $x^2 - x - 10$ **2.** $2x^2 - 5x - 3$ **3.** $x^2 + 3x - 9$ **4.** $3x^2 + 9x - 30$ **5.** $4x^3 - 2x^2 + 5x + 9$; 4, −2, 5, 9 **6.** $5x^3 - 9x^2 + 10$; 5, −9, 0, 10 **7.** $-x^2 + 2x + 7$; −1, 2, 7 **8.** $-3x^4 + x^3 - 7x^2$; −3, 1, −7, 0, 0

CA Standards Check 1. $x + 1$, R 5 **2a.** yes **b.** no
3. $x^2 + 3x - 2$, R -4 **4a.** $x^2 - 4x + 3$
b. $(x + 2)(x - 3)(x - 1)$ **5.** -69

Checkpoint Quiz 1 1. Answers may vary. Sample:
$y = (x + 1)^2(x + 2)(x + 3)$ **2.** $-3x^3 + 5x + 6$;
degree 3, 3 terms **3.** $x^4 - 3x^2 + \frac{5}{2}x$; degree 4,
3 terms **4.** $3x^2 + 9x - 12$; degree 2, 3 terms
5. 1, 2 (mult. 2) **6.** $-\frac{1}{2}$, 4 **7.** 0 (mult. 3),
3, -1 (mult. 2) **8.** $x^2 + 2x + 1$ **9.** $2x^2 - 3x + 1$
10. 479

Lesson 6-4   pp. 333–336

Check Skills You'll Need

1. (1, 4) **2.** $\left(1, \frac{2}{3}\right)$

3. no points

4. $(x - 5)(x + 3)$ **5.** $(x - 7)(x - 2)$ **6.** $(x + 5)(x + 1)$

CA Standards Check

1. $x = -1$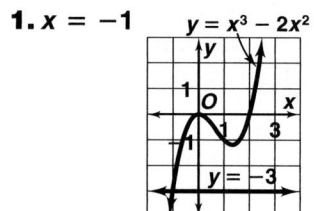

2. 22.7125 in., 25.7125 in., 20.7125 in.

3. $(2x - 1)(4x^2 + 2x + 1)$ **4a.** -2, $1 \pm i\sqrt{3}$ **b.** $\frac{1}{3}$,
$\frac{-1 \pm i\sqrt{3}}{6}$ **5a.** $(x^2 + 6)(x^2 + 1)$ **b.** $(x^2 - 5)(x^2 + 2)$
6. $3i$, $-3i$, $i\sqrt{2}$, $-i\sqrt{2}$

Lesson 6-5   pp. 341–344

Check Skills You'll Need 1. ±1, ±2, ±3, ±4, ±6, ±12
2. ±1, ±2, ±3, ±4, ±6, ±8, ±12, ±24 **3.** ±1, ±2,
±3, ±4, ±6, ±9, ±12, ±18, ±36 **4.** ±1, ±2, ±3,
±4, ±6, ±8, ±12, ±16, ±24, ±48
5. $x^3 - 5x^2 + 7x - 35$ **6.** $x^3 + 2x^2 - 3x - 6$

---

7. A rational number can be written as the
quotient of two integers $\frac{a}{b}$, where $b \neq 0$.
8. Irrational numbers cannot be written as
quotients of integers. **9.** An imaginary number is a
nonreal number of the form $a + bi$, where $b \neq 0$.

CA Standards Check 1. 4 **2a.** $\pm\sqrt{5}$, 2 **b.** -1, $\frac{1 \pm i\sqrt{2}}{3}$
3a. $2 + \sqrt{7}$, $-\sqrt{5}$ **b.** No; the Irrational Root
Theorem does not apply unless you know that all
of the coefficients of the polynomial are rational.
4a. $-3i$, $-2 - i$ **b.** 4 or greater
5a. $x^3 - 3x^2 + x + 5 = 0$ **b.** $x^4 + 5x^2 + 4 = 0$

Lesson 6-6   pp. 347–349

Check Skills You'll Need 1. 2 **2.** 3 **3.** 5 **4.** $\pm4i$
5. $1 \pm i\sqrt{2}$ **6.** $\frac{-5 \pm i\sqrt{7}}{4}$

CA Standards Check 1. 4 complex roots, number of
real roots: 0, 2, or 4, possible rational roots: ±1,
±3 **2a.** 2, $\pm2i$ **b.** You can verify the real zeros by
graphing the function. You can verify the complex
zeros by substituting the values into the function.

Lesson 6-7   pp. 351–353, 357

Check Skills You'll Need 1. 30, 240 **2.** $\frac{4}{5}$ **3.** 210 **4.** 42
5. 36 **6.** 60 **7.** 192

CA Standards Check 1. 720 **2.** 720 **3a.** 252 **b.** 28
c. 480,700 **4.** 77,520; 125,970 **5.** $\frac{1}{30}$

Checkpoint Quiz 2 1. 1, 3, -2 **2.** $\frac{1}{3}$, $\frac{-1 \pm i\sqrt{3}}{6}$ **3.** ±3,
$\pm i\sqrt{5}$ **4.** $\frac{1}{2}$, $\frac{-1 \pm i\sqrt{3}}{2}$ **5.** -2, 2, $-\frac{4}{3}$ **6a.** $3 + 5i$,
$-\sqrt{2}$ **b.** Degree must be ≥ 4. **7.** 5; by the
corollary to the Fundamental Theorem of Algebra
8a. 744 **b.** 10 **9a.** 21 **b.** 35 **c.** 35 **d.** 21
10. 5040

Lesson 6-8   pp. 359–361

Check Skills You'll Need 1. $x^2 + 4x + 4$ **2.** $4x^2 + 12x +$
9 **3.** $x^3 - 9x^2 + 27x - 27$ **4.** $a^4 + 4a^3b + 6a^2b^2 +$
$4ab^3 + b^4$ **5.** 1 **6.** 5 **7.** 10 **8.** 10 **9.** 5

CA Standards Check 1. $a^8 + 8a^7b + 28a^6b^2 +$
$56a^5b^3 + 70a^4b^4 + 56a^3b^5 + 28a^2b^6 + 8ab^7 + b^8$
2. $x^4 - 8x^3 + 24x^2 - 32x + 16$ **3a.** $v^9 + 9v^8w +$
$36v^7w^2 + 84v^6w^3 + 126v^5w^4 + 126v^4w^5 +$
$84v^3w^6 + 36v^2w^7 + 9vw^8 + w^9$ **b.** $c^5 - 10c^4 +$
$40c^3 - 80c^2 + 80c - 32$ **4a.** about 0.387
b. about 0.349

Chapter 7

Check Your Readiness   p. 372

1. $3y^2 - 14y + 8$ **3.** $x^3 + 4x^2 - 15x - 18$ **5.** $8b^3$
7. $6a^6$ **9.** $-2, 7$ **11.** $-4, \frac{2}{3}$ **15.** domain {1, 2, 3, 4},
range {2, 3, 4, 5} **17.** domain $\{x \mid x \in R\}$,
range $\{y \mid y \in R\}$

19. **21.**

Lesson 7-1   pp. 375–377

Check Skills You'll Need **1.** 5^2 **2.** 0.3^2 **3.** $\left(\frac{2}{7}\right)^2$ **4.** $(x^5)^2$
5. $(x^2y)^2$ **6.** $(13x^3y^6)^2$

CA Standards Check **1a.** 0; -1; 2 **b.** 0.01 and -0.01,
no real square root, $\frac{6}{11}$ and $-\frac{6}{11}$ **2a.** -3 **b.** 3 **c.** 7
3a. $2|x|y^2$ **b.** $-3c^2$ **c.** $x^2|y^3|$ **4a.** 2.29 in. **b.** 2.8 in.
c. 2.92 in.

Lesson 7-2   pp. 380–383

Check Skills You'll Need **1.** 6 **2.** 3 **3.** 3 **4.** x^2 **5.** ab
6. $5a^3b^4$

CA Standards Check **1a.** 6 **b.** -3 **c.** not possible
2. $5x^2\sqrt{2}$; $x\sqrt[3]{18x}$ **3.** $42x^3y\sqrt{3}$ **4a.** 3 **b.** $2x\sqrt{x}$
c. $4x^3\sqrt[4]{x^2}$ **5a.** $\frac{\sqrt{35}}{5}$ **b.** $\frac{x\sqrt{5y}}{5y}$ **c.** $\frac{\sqrt[3]{18x^2}}{3x}$ **6.** $t = \frac{\sqrt{da}}{a}$

Lesson 7-3   pp. 386–388, 390

Check Skills You'll Need **1.** $15x^2 + 2x - 8$
2. $-24x^2 + 71x - 35$ **3.** $x^2 - 16$ **4.** $16x^2 - 25$
5. $x^2 + 10x + 25$ **6.** $4x^2 - 36x + 81$

CA Standards Check **1a.** $5\sqrt{7}$ **b.** cannot combine
c. $9\sqrt{xy}$ **2.** $60\sqrt{2}$ in. or about 84.9 in. **3.** $2\sqrt{2}$
4. $5 - 2\sqrt{6}$ **5.** 3 **6.** $39 + 10\sqrt{15}$

Checkpoint Quiz 1 **1.** $|b|c^2$ **2.** xy^2 **3.** $-a$ **4.** $-y^2$
5. $8\sqrt{3} + 24$ **6.** $12x^3y\sqrt{35}$ **7.** $12\sqrt[3]{3} - 9\sqrt[3]{2}$
8. $\frac{4\sqrt{10x}}{45x}$ **9.** -7 **10.** $\frac{20\sqrt{7} - 25}{87}$

Lesson 7-4   pp. 391–394

Check Skills You'll Need **1.** $\frac{1}{16}$ **2.** $\frac{1}{9x^2}$ **3.** $\frac{1}{125x^6y^3}$ **4.** $\frac{1}{2}$
5. $\frac{16b^{12}}{a^8}$ **6.** $\frac{b^2}{16a^6}$

CA Standards Check **1a.** 2 **b.** 2 **c.** 4 **2a.** $\frac{1}{\sqrt[8]{y^3}}$, $\sqrt[5]{z^2}$
b. $x^{\frac{2}{3}}$, $y^{\frac{3}{2}}$ **c.** If m is negative, $a^{\frac{m}{n}} = \frac{1}{(\sqrt[n]{a})^m}$, and if
$a = 0$, then the denominator of the fraction would
be zero. Since this cannot happen, $a \neq 0$.
3. about 0.270 revolutions per second, or about
16 revolutions per minute **4a.** $\frac{1}{125}$ **b.** 8 **c.** 16
5. $\frac{1}{2x^5}$

Lesson 7-5   pp. 397–400

Check Skills You'll Need **1.** $-3, 2$ **2.** $-2, 7$ **3.** $1, -\frac{3}{2}$
4. $-\frac{1}{3}, 2$ **5.** $-\frac{5}{2}, \frac{1}{2}$ **6.** $-\frac{2}{3}, \frac{3}{2}$

CA Standards Check **1.** 7 **2.** 6 **3.** about 25.1 watts; it is
4 times the power of a 10-cm cell. **4.** 10 **5.** 5

Lesson 7-6   pp. 404–406, 410

Check Skills You'll Need **1.** D: {0, 2, 4}, R: {$-5, -3, -1$}
2. D: {$-1, 0, 1$}, R: 0 **3.** D: all real numbers, R: all
real numbers **4.** D: all real numbers, R: all real
numbers ≥ 0 **5.** 10 **6.** 28

CA Standards Check **1.** $(f + g)(x) = 5x^2 + x + 1$,
domain: all real numbers; $(f - g)(x) = 5x^2 - 9x - 1$,
domain: all real numbers **2.** $(f \cdot g)(x) = 12x^3 + 8x^2 -$
$17x + 5$, domain: all real numbers; $\left(\frac{f}{g}\right)(x) = 3x + 5$,
domain: all real numbers except $\frac{1}{2}$
3a. $(f \circ g)(x) = x^2 - 2$, $(f \circ g)(-5) = 23$ **b.** No; the
order in which operations are performed changes
between $(f \circ g)$ and $(g \circ f)$, which changes what
each composition equals. **4a.** Let $f(x) = 0.9x$ and
$g(x) = 0.75x$. Then $(g \circ f)(x) = g(0.9x) = 0.75(0.9x)$.
b. $(f \circ g)(x) = f(0.75x) = 0.9(0.75)x$. **c.** It makes no
difference.

Checkpoint Quiz 2 **1.** $81x^4$ **2.** $\frac{1}{4y^2}$ **3.** 5 **4.** $5, -\frac{29}{5}$
5. $-\frac{2}{3}, -1$ **6.** -2 **7.** $\frac{15}{4}$ **8.** 0 **9.** $\frac{7}{2}$ **10.** 43

Lesson 7-7   pp. 412–415

Check Skills You'll Need

1. **2.**

3.

4.

5.

6.

3.

4.

5.

6.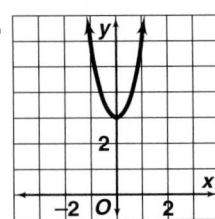

CA Standards Check **1a.** The line $y = x$ is the perpendicular bisector of each segment connecting a point in s to the corresponding point in the inverse of s. The graph of the inverse of s is a reflection in the line $y = x$ of the graph of s. **b.** yes; no **2a.** Yes; no; for every x-value except 3 in the domain of the inverse there are two y-values. **b.** $y = \frac{1}{3}x + \frac{10}{3}$; it is a function because for each value of x there is only one y-value.

3.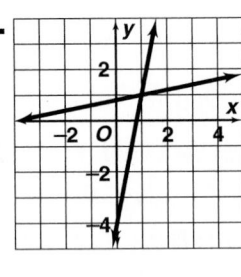

4a. D: all real numbers, R: all real numbers
b. $f^{-1}(x) = \frac{-x + 10}{3}$ **c.** D: all real numbers, R: all real numbers **d.** 3 **e.** 2 **5.** $v = 8\sqrt{d}$; ≈ 44 ft/s **6.** 777, −5802

CA Standards Check

1.

2.

3.

4.

5. about 60 m; it is about $\frac{1}{4}$ the height.
6. $y = 2\sqrt[3]{x - 3} + 3$; the graph is the graph of $y = 2\sqrt[3]{x}$ translated 3 units right and 3 units up.

Lesson 7-8 pp. 420–423

Check Skills You'll Need

1.

2.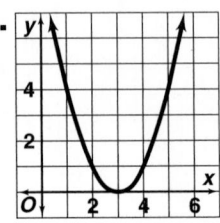

Chapter 8

Check Your Readiness p. 436

1. 0.1, 1, 10, 100, 1000 **2.** $\frac{4}{9}, \frac{2}{3}, 1, \frac{3}{2}, \frac{9}{4}$

3. 12, 0, 0, 0, 12

4a. $n = 3d$ **b.** 84 acorns **c.** The function would be $n = 9 + 3d$, and the graph would shift 9 units upward.

5. $y = x^2 - 4x$ **6.** $y = 3x^2 - 2x + 7$

7. $y = -x^2$ **8.** $y = 3x^2$

9.

10.

11.

Lesson 8-1   pp. 438–442

Check Skills You'll Need 1. 8 **2.** 16 **3.** 2 **4.** 9 **5.** 1 **6.** $\frac{1}{4}$

CA Standards Check

1a.   **b.**

 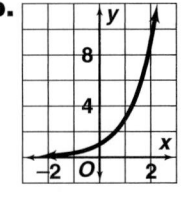

2a. about 338 million **b.** The growth factor may change. **c.** $y = 281(1.014)^x$; about 346 million
3. $y = 0.25(4)^x$

4a. exponential decay **b.** exponential growth
c. exponential decay

5a. $y = 0$ **b.** $y = 0$

 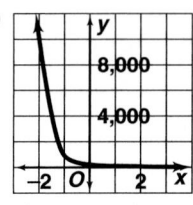

6. about $3900

Lesson 8-2   pp. 447–450, 453

Check Skills You'll Need 1. $y = |x + 2| + 1$
2. $y = -|x| - 2$ **3.** $y = (x - 1)^2 - 2$
4. $y = -(x + 1)^2 + 3$ **5.** $y = \frac{1}{x^5}$ **6.** $y = x$
7. $y = x^5$ **8.** $33

CA Standards Check

1a.   **b.**

2a.   **b.**

c.

3. $y = 90\left(\frac{1}{2}\right)^{\frac{2}{35}x}$; about 71 mg **4a.** 54.5982
b. 0.0498 **c.** 1.6487 **5.** $1479.00

Checkpoint Quiz 1 1. exponential growth; 45% increase **2.** exponential decay; 1% decrease
3. exponential growth; 70% increase
4. exponential decay; 20% decrease

5.   **6.**

7. 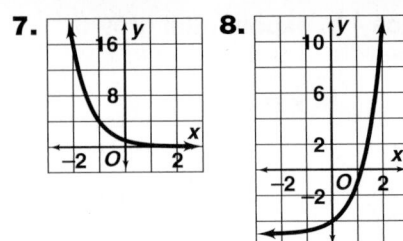 **8.**

9. Answers may vary. Sample: The population of Smallville was 1200 in 1990. It was growing at a rate of 1% per year. Find the population in 2010.
10. $y = 100\left(\frac{1}{2}\right)^{\frac{1}{30}x}$; about 9.9 mg

Check Skills You'll Need 1. 2 **2.** 16 **3.** 3 **4.** 2

5. **6.**

7. **8.**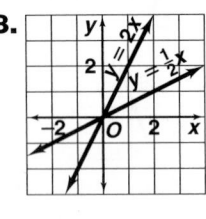

CA Standards Check 1. The earthquake in California released about 1265 times as much energy as the earthquake in Alabama. **2a.** $\log_3 729 = 6$
b. $3 = \log_{\frac{1}{2}}\left(\frac{1}{8}\right)$ **c.** $0 = \log_{10} 1$ **3a.** $-\frac{5}{6}$ **b.** $\frac{3}{2}$ **c.** 2
4. 3.2×10^{-9}

5. **6.**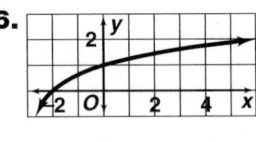

Check Skills You'll Need 1. 5 **2.** −1 **3.** $\frac{2}{3}$ **4.** 24 **5.** 2187
6. $\frac{1}{27}$ **7.** 36

CA Standards Check 1a. Product Property **b.** Power Property, Quotient Property **2a.** log 2 **b.** No; they do not have the same base. **3a.** $\log_2 7 + \log_2 b$
b. $2 \log y - 2 \log 3$ **c.** $3 \log_7 a + 4 \log_7 b$
4. about 6 decibels

Check Skills You'll Need 1. 1 **2.** 2 **3.** $\frac{4}{3}$ **4.** $\frac{1}{25}$

CA Standards Check 1a. 1.2619 **b.** 0.8496 **c.** 0.2009
2. 0.4634 **3.** 0.4634 **4.** 2068 **5a.** 3.7227, $\log_8 2301$
b. Sample: Use a calculator to raise 2 to the 2.465 power. **6.** 3.45 **7.** 200

Checkpoint Quiz 2

1. **2.**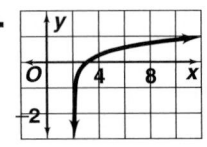

3. $3 \log s - 5 \log r$ **4.** $2 \log_6 3 + 2 \log_6 x + 2 \log_6 y$
5. $\log_6 4 + \frac{1}{2} \log_6 x$ **6.** 3 **7.** 20 **8.** 1000
9. $\log 2 \approx 0.3010$, $\log_3 2 \approx 0.6309$, $\log_2 3 \approx$
1.5850, $2^3 = 8$, $3^2 = 9$ **10.** Rewrite $\log_2 10$
as $\frac{\log 10}{\log 2}$ and evaluate it to get ≈ 3.322. Then set
$3.322 = \log_3 x$. Rewrite to get $3.322 = \frac{\log x}{\log 3}$ and
solve. Convert $\log x = 1.585$ to $10^{1.585} = x$ or
$x \approx 38.46$. So $\log_2 10 \approx \log_3 38.46$.

Check Skills You'll Need 1. 148.413 **2.** 40.171 **3.** 0.135
4. 0.368 **5.** 11.417 **6.** 81 **7.** $\frac{1}{2}$ **8.** 65,536

CA Standards Check 1a. $\ln 8$ **b.** $\ln x^3 y$ **c.** $\ln \sqrt[4]{3x}$
2a. ≈ 5.4 km/s; no **b.** One could increase its mass ratio or its exhaust velocity. **3a.** 1.105
b. 439,605,247.8 **c.** 488,262.4 **4a.** 2.401 **b.** 1.605
5. 6.5%

Chapter 9

1. $\frac{7}{27}$ **2.** $\frac{1}{3}$ **3.** $\frac{5}{9}$ **4.** $\frac{22}{27}$ **5.** $\frac{22}{27}$ **6.** $\frac{12}{27}$ **7.** $\frac{4}{3}$; −4 **8.** $-\frac{2}{3}$; 2
9. $-\frac{10}{3}$; 10 **10.** $-\frac{16}{7}$; $\frac{48}{7}$ **11.** $(x + 3)(x - 2)$
12. $(4x + 5)(x + 3)$ **13.** $(3x - 5)(3x + 5)$
14. $(x - 6)^2$ **15.** $(3x + 4)(x + 2)$ **16.** $(x - 3)(x - 2)$
17. 1, −8 **18.** −6, −8 **19.** 4, 2 **20.** 0, $-\frac{2}{3}$ **21.** 8, $\frac{1}{2}$
22. 15, −2

Check Skills You'll Need 1. 10 **2.** 15 **3.** 1.2

CA Standards Check 1. $y = \frac{0.42}{x}$ **2a.** inverse; $y = \frac{0.72}{x}$
b. neither **c.** direct; $y = 15x$
3a. about 5,000,000 min, or about 10 yr
b. about 27 beats per min

4. *A* varies jointly with the height and the sum of the bases. **5.** $V = \frac{\sqrt{2}}{6}e^3$

Check Skills You'll Need 1. 2 units up **2.** 2 units left **3.** 3 units down **4.** 3 units right **5.** 4 units left and 5 units down **6.** 10 units right and 7 units up

CA Standards Check

1.

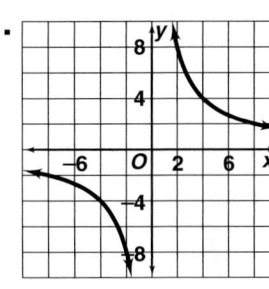

2. The graph of $y = \frac{2}{x}$ is a stretch of $y = \frac{1}{x}$ by the factor 2. The graph of $y = -\frac{2}{x}$ is the reflection of $y = \frac{2}{x}$ in the x-axis. The graph of $y = \frac{0.5}{x}$ is a shrink of $y = \frac{1}{x}$ by the factor 0.5. The graph of $y = -\frac{0.5}{x}$ is the reflection of $y = \frac{0.5}{x}$ in the x-axis.

3a. 2.28 ft, 1.81 ft, 1.52 ft **b.** As the pipe becomes very short, the pitch becomes very high (great frequency). As the pipe becomes very long, the pitch becomes low (frequency near 0).

4. $x = -7$ and $y = -3$

5a. $y = -\frac{1}{x + 4} + 5$ **b.**

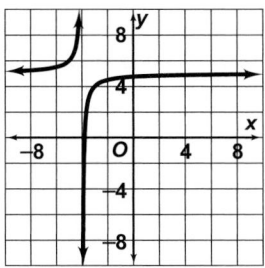

Check Skills You'll Need 1. $(x + 3)(x + 2)$
2. $(x - 4)(x - 2)$ **3.** $(x - 3)(x - 9)$
4. $(2x - 7)(x + 4)$ **5.** $(2x - 5)(x - 3)$
6. $(2x - 3)(x - 8)$ **7.** 3, −4 **8.** −4, 7 **9.** 3, 6

CA Standards Check 1a. −4, 4 **b.** none **c.** −4, 2
2a. Since 1 and −3 are the zeroes of the denominator and neither is a zero of the numerator, $x = 1$ and $x = -3$ are vertical asymptotes. **b.** The graph of this function is the

same as the graph of $y = \frac{1}{x + 3}$, except that it has a hole at $x = 2$. The vertical asymptote is $x = -3$.
c. The graph of this function is the same as the graph of $y = x - 1$, except that it has a hole at $x = -1$. **3a.** $y = -2$ **b.** $y = 2$

4.

5a. Answers may vary. Sample: Graph $y = 8$ and use the Intersection feature to find that the graphs intersect at $x = 16{,}103.2$. So the number of discs produced must be greater than 16,103.
b. $x = 100$; $y = 0.25$ **c.** Answers may vary. Sample: The vertical asymptote means that if you produce 100 or fewer discs you won't sell any, since the first 100 are samples. The horizontal asymptote means that the average cost will never go below $.25, since that is how much each disc costs to produce.

Checkpoint Quiz 1 1. $z = 5xy$ **2.** $z = \frac{20x}{y}$ **3.** $z = \frac{180}{xy}$
4. Answers may vary. Sample: Both have vertical asymptote $x = 0$ and horizontal asymptote $y = 0$. $y = \frac{4}{x}$ is closer to the axes. **5.** Answers may vary. Sample: $y_2 = \frac{1}{x} + 5$ is a vertical translation of $y_1 = \frac{1}{x}$ up 5 units. **6.** Answers may vary. Sample: $y_2 = \frac{1}{x - 1} + 2$ has vertical asymptote of $x = 1$ and horizontal asymptote $y = 2$. $y_2 = \frac{1}{x + 1} - 2$ has vertical asymptote $x = -1$ and horizontal symptote $y = -2$.

7.

8.

9.

10.

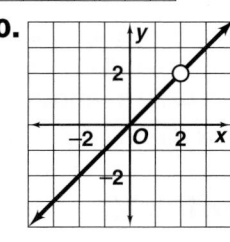

Check Skills You'll Need 1. $(2x - 1)(x - 1)$
2. $(2x + 3)(2x - 3)$ **3.** $(5x + 1)(x + 1)$

California Check System Answers

4. $10(x + 1)(x - 1)$ **5.** $\frac{5}{16}$ **6.** $\frac{1}{3}$ **7.** $\frac{1}{3}$ **8.** $\frac{6}{35}$ **9.** $\frac{5}{32}$
10. $\frac{3}{2}$ **11.** $\frac{3}{4}$ **12.** $\frac{2}{3}$

CA Standards Check 1a. $-\frac{3}{x}$; $x \neq 0$, $y \neq 0$
b. $\frac{-3(x + 2)}{(x - 2)(x - 4)}$; $x \neq 2$ or 4 **c.** $\frac{2x + 1}{x - 3}$; $x \neq 2$ or 3
2a. $\frac{2x^5y^5}{z}$ **b.** $x^2 - 2x + 4$ **c.** $\frac{b^7}{12a^2c^4}$
3. $\frac{a - 2}{a(a - 1)}$; $a \neq 0, 1, -1$, or -2 **4.** $\frac{3(a + 5)(a - 3)}{(a + 1)(a + 4)}$;
$a \neq -1, -4$, or 4

Lesson 9-5   **pp. 522–525, 528**

Check Skills You'll Need 1. 21 **2.** 30 **3.** 187 **4.** 210
5. $\frac{17}{38}$ **6.** $\frac{19}{75}$ **7.** $\frac{11}{72}$ **8.** $\frac{137}{180}$

CA Standards Check 1. 4 cm **2a.** $6(x - 5)(x + 5)(x + 2)$
b. $10(x + 2)(x - 2)(x + 1)$ **3.** $\frac{3x^2 - 18x + 4}{4(x - 6)(x + 2)}$
4a. $\frac{-3x^2 - 21x - 4}{6(x + 5)(x + 7)}$ **b.** $\frac{-x^2 + 5x + 2}{3(x - 1)(x - 2)(x + 2)}$ **5a.** $\frac{1}{xy}$
b. $\frac{6y}{2y - 1}$ **c.** $\frac{x^3 - 4x^2 + x + 2}{2x^2 + 4x}$

Checkpoint Quiz 2 1. $\frac{3(x - 8)}{25(x - 4)}$ **2.** $\frac{2}{3}$ **3.** 2 **4.** $\frac{y(y - 5)}{2(y + 4)}$
5. $\frac{4(6y^2 + x^2)}{9x^3y^3}$ **6.** $\frac{41}{15(y + 5)}$ **7.** $\frac{5xy - 12}{2y(y + 2)}$
8. $\frac{3x^3 - x^2 - 11x}{x^2 - 2}$ **9.** $\frac{2x}{y}$ **10.** $\frac{y(3x + 1)}{x(4y + 5)}$

Lesson 9-6   **pp. 530–532**

Check Skills You'll Need 1. $15t^2$ **2.** 8 **3.** $3h^3$
4. $(y + 2)(y - 1)$ **5.** $z(2z + 1)$ **6.** $(k + 2)(k - 2)$

CA Standards Check 1a. no solution **b.** $-3, 2$ **2.** 2,
-2 **3.** 10 mi/h downhill, 6 mi/h uphill **4a.** Maria:
6.75 h, Paco: 13.5 h **b.** Adrian: 4.5 h, Phillip: 9 h

Lesson 9-7   **pp. 539–542**

Check Skills You'll Need 1. $\frac{7}{36}$ **2.** $\frac{25}{36}$ **3.** $\frac{1}{2}$ **4.** 72

CA Standards Check 1. Independent; the number of
marbles is the same after the marble is replaced.
2a. $\frac{1}{25}$ or 4%; $\frac{1}{40}$ or 2.5% **b.** $\frac{1}{1000}$ or 0.1% **3a.** Not
mutually exclusive since 2 is both even and
prime. **b.** Mutually exclusive since no number is
both even and less than 2. **4a.** about 0.26 or
about 26% **b.** about 0.47 or about 47% **c.** about
0.79 or about 79% **5a.** $\frac{5}{9}$ **b.** $\frac{2}{3}$

Chapter 10

Check Your Readiness   **p. 554**

1. quadratic; $-x^2$, $6x$, 1 **2.** linear; none, $-12x$,
-18 **3.** linear; none, x, $-\frac{13}{2}$ **4.** quadratic; $-8x^2$,
$28x$, none **5.** quadratic; $-2x^2$, $-3x$, 6 **6.** linear;
none, $-x$, -10

7. **8.**

9. **10.**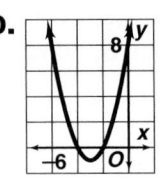

11. 16 **12.** $\frac{25}{4}$ **13.** 49
14. $y = (x + 3)^2 - 2$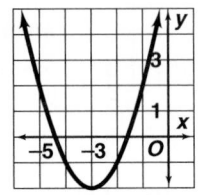

15. $y = 2(x - 1)^2 + 8$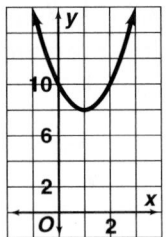

16. $y = -3\left(x - \frac{1}{6}\right)^2 + \frac{1}{12}$

17. $\frac{1}{2}, i\sqrt{5}, -i\sqrt{5}$ **18.** $\frac{1}{2}, 1$ **19.**

20. **21.**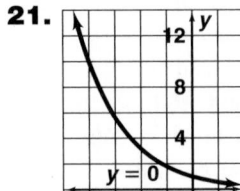

Lesson 10-1
pp. 557–560

Check Skills You'll Need 1. −2, 6 **2.** −3, −1.5 **3.** −4, 3 **4.** ±2, −4 **5.** 3, 9 **6.** ±0.5, 1

CA Standards Check

1a. 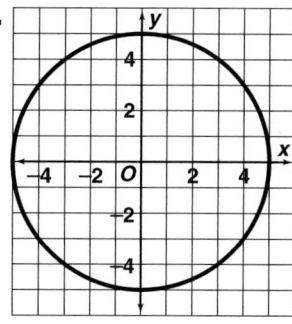 The graphs are the same.

b. Rewrite $x^2 + y^2 = 25$ as $y^2 = 25 − x^2$. Then take the square root of both sides, which gives you $y = ±\sqrt{25 − x^2}$. **c.** When $x = 6$, $25 − x^2 = −11$. $\sqrt{−11}$ is not a real number.

2a. 4 units; 3 units; an ellipse is oblong instead of round. It has 2 axes of symmetry rather than infinitely many. **b.** (1, −2.9), (−1, 2.9), (−1, −2.9)

c. 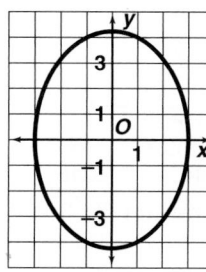 It is an ellipse with center (0, 0). The x-intercepts are 3 and −3 and the y-intercepts are $3\sqrt{2}$ and $−3\sqrt{2}$.

3a. No; there are vertical lines that intersect the graph in more than one point. **b.** Answers may vary. Sample: Solving $x^2 − y^2 = 9$ for y gives $y = ±\sqrt{x^2 − 9}$. For $−3 < x < 3$, the value of $x^2 − 9$ is negative and $\sqrt{x^2 − 9}$ is not a real number. **c.** $y = x$ and $y = −x$; asymptotes

4. center: (0, 0); no x-intercepts, y-intercepts: −4, 4; domain: all real numbers, range: all y such that $y ≥ 4$ or $y ≤ −4$ **5a.** Answers may vary. Sample: All equations have an x^2-term, a y^2-term, and no other terms on the left side. There is a positive constant term and nothing else on the right side. **b.** Answers may vary. Sample: The related domains and ranges are all different. The absolute values of the coefficients of x^2 and y^2 are equal for $x^2 − y^2 = 1$, but the signs of the coefficients are different. The absolute values of the coefficients of x^2 and y^2 are equal for $x^2 + y^2 = 16$, and the signs are the same. The absolute values of the coefficients of x^2 and y^2 are different for $9x^2 + 25y^2 = 225$, but the signs are the same.

Lesson 10-2
pp. 565–568

Check Skills You'll Need 1. 8 **2.** 4 **3.** 3 **4.** $\frac{1}{8}$ **5.** $2\sqrt{2}$ **6.** $\sqrt{65}$ **7.** $\sqrt{73}$

CA Standards Check 1. $x = \frac{1}{8}y^2$ **2.** $x = \frac{1}{2}y^2$ **3.** $y = \frac{1}{33}x^2$ **4.** (0, 3), $y = −3$ **5.** (−3, −1), (−3, −1.75), $y = −\frac{1}{4}$

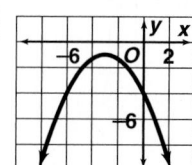

Lesson 10-3
pp. 571–574, 576

Check Skills You'll Need 1. 4 **2.** 7 **3.** $2\sqrt{5}$ **4.** $4\sqrt{3}$ **5.** $6\sqrt{2}$ **6.** 1 **7.** 4 **8.** 9

CA Standards Check 1. $(x − 5)^2 + (y + 2)^2 = 64$ **2a.** $(x + 5)^2 + (y + 3)^2 = 1$ **b.** $(x − 2)^2 + (y − 3)^2 = 9$ **3.** $x^2 + (y + 4)^2 = 1$ **4.** (−8, −3), 11

5.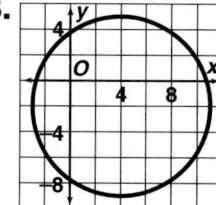

Checkpoint Quiz 1 1. (0, 0), $\left(0, \frac{1}{12}\right)$, $y = −\frac{1}{12}$;

2. (0, −2), $\left(\frac{1}{16}, −2\right)$, $x = −\frac{1}{16}$;

3. (3, −1), $\left(3, −\frac{3}{4}\right)$, $y = −\frac{5}{4}$;

4. $(x + 6)^2 + (y − 3)^2 = 64$ **5.** 4 units left and 6 units up

Lesson 10-4 pp. 578–580

Check Skills You'll Need 1. ±4 **2.** ±4√3 **3.** ±6 **4.** 34
5. −16 **6.** 7

CA Standards Check 1. $\frac{x^2}{9} + \frac{y^2}{36} = 1$ **2.** $\frac{x^2}{36} + \frac{y^2}{225} = 1$

3. $(2\sqrt{2}, 0), (-2\sqrt{2}, 0)$;

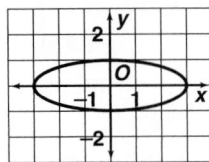

4. $\frac{x^2}{64} + \frac{y^2}{81} = 1$

Lesson 10-5 pp. 584–587, 590

Check Skills You'll Need 1. $y = -\frac{5}{2}x$ **2.** $y = \frac{1}{3}x$
3. $y = \pm 2\sqrt{x^2 - 4}$ **4.** $y = \pm\frac{3}{5}\sqrt{x^2 + 25}$
5. $y = \pm\frac{3}{2}\sqrt{x^2 - 36}$

CA Standards Check 1.

2. $(\sqrt{34}, 0), (-\sqrt{34}, 0)$;

3. $\frac{x^2}{4.770 \times 10^{12}} - \frac{y^2}{3.668 \times 10^{12}} = 1$

Checkpoint Quiz 2 1. $\frac{x^2}{25} + \frac{y^2}{16} = 1$ **2.** $\frac{x^2}{25} + \frac{y^2}{29} = 1$
3. $\frac{x^2}{100} + \frac{y^2}{149} = 1$ **4.** $(\sqrt{65}, 0), (-\sqrt{65}, 0)$

5. $(0, 2\sqrt{34}), (0, -2\sqrt{34})$

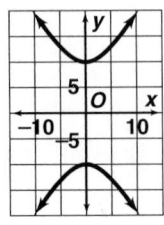

6. $(\sqrt{85}, 0), (-\sqrt{85}, 0)$

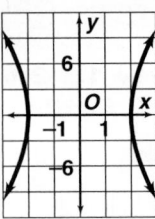

7. $(0, \sqrt{89}), (0, -\sqrt{89})$

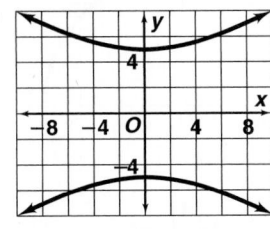

8. $\frac{x^2}{121} - \frac{y^2}{104} = 1$ **9.** $\frac{x^2}{16} - \frac{y^2}{9} = 1$
10. $\frac{y^2}{64} - \frac{x^2}{12.25} = 1$

Lesson 10-6 pp. 592–595

Check Skills You'll Need 1. $y = x^2$; 4 units up **2.** $y = x^2$;
3 units right and 2 units down **3.** $y = x^2$; 1 unit up
4. $y = x^2$; 5 units left, 6 units up
5. $y = (x - 3)^2 - 8$ **6.** $y = (x + 5)^2 - 32$
7. $y = 2(x + 2)^2 - 3$ **8.** $y = 4\left(x - \frac{3}{2}\right)^2 - 6$
CA Standards Check 1. $\frac{(x - 1)^2}{25} + \frac{(y + 4)^2}{4} = 1$
2. $\frac{(y - 3)^2}{16} - \frac{(x - 2)^2}{33} = 1$ **3.** $\frac{(x - 100)^2}{784} - \frac{y^2}{9216} = 1$
4. circle with center $(6, -2)$ and radius $4\sqrt{3}$;

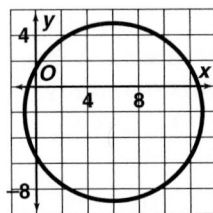

Chapter 11

Check Your Readiness pp. 608

1. 9, 11, 13, 15 **2.** 1, 6, 11, 16 **3.** 0.9, 1.1, 1.3, 1.5
4. −2, −7, −12, −17 **5.** $3\frac{1}{3}, 7\frac{1}{3}, 11\frac{1}{3}, 15\frac{1}{3}$
6. −12, −15, −18, −21 **7.**

8. **9.**

10. **11.** **12.**

13. 4 **14.** −4 **15.** 0.4 **16.** 50 **17.** $5x^2$
18. $-0.3y^4$ **19.** $|x^3y^5|$ **20.** $11y^{12}$ **21.** $\frac{4}{3}$ **22.** $\frac{3}{4}$
23. $\frac{5}{3}$ **24.** $\frac{5}{18}$

Lesson 11-1   pp. 610–612

Check Skills You'll Need 1. 13, 15; add 2. **2.** −14, −16; subtract 2. **3.** 3125, 15,625; multiply by 5. **4.** 20, 15; subtract 5. **5.** 8, 4; divide by 2. **6.** 20, 23; add 3. **7.** 128, 256; multiply by 2. **8.** −19, −23; subtract 4.

CA Standards Check 1a. Add 7; 55, 62, 69. **b.** Divide by 3; 3, 1, $\frac{1}{3}$. **2a.** 3.2 ft **b.** 10th bounce **3.** 22, 30 **4a.** 1, 4, 9, 16, 25, 36; 400 **b.** $a_n = n^2$ **c.** No; a_1 is not given.

Lesson 11-2   pp. 616–617

Check Skills You'll Need 1. Subtract 2. **2.** Add 17.
3. Add $\frac{3}{7}$. **4.** Subtract $\frac{1}{4}$.

CA Standards Check 1a. no **b.** yes; −3 **2a.** The first term in the sequence, 1100, was the amount of money with *no* participants, so there is one more term than the number of participants. **b.** 149
3a. 40.5 **b.** $\frac{a_6 + a_7}{2}$

Lesson 11-3   pp. 622–624, 627

Check Skills You'll Need 1. 16 **2.** 21 **3.** 1000 **4.** $\frac{100}{3}$

CA Standards Check 1a. 5, 15, 45, 135, 405, 1215, 3645, 10,935, 32,805, 98,415; the tenth term is the ninth term times 3. **b.** Geometric; the common ratio is −4. **c.** Arithmetic; the common difference is +12. **2a.** 4,261,625,379 **b.** −34 **3a.** 40 or −40 **b.** 7.5 or −7.5 **c.** 378 or −378

Checkpoint Quiz 1 1. arithmetic; 15 **2.** geometric; 3 **3.** arithmetic; −3 **4.** geometric; 0.5 **5.** geometric; −0.5 **6.** arithmetic; −2 **7.** 6.25 **8.** 82 **9.** 1 **10.** To find the arithmetic mean, add the terms and divide by 2. To find the geometric mean, multiply the terms and find the square root of the product.

Lesson 11-4   pp. 629–631

Check Skills You'll Need 1. 25 **2.** −42 **3.** $a_n = 2 + 2n$
4. $a_n = -2 + 3n$ **5.** $a_n = -11 - 6n$
6. $a_n = 19 - 9n$

CA Standards Check 1a. 0.3 + 0.6 + 0.9 + 1.2 + 1.5 + 1.8 + 2.1 + 2.4 + 2.7 + 3.0; 16.5
b. 100 + 125 + 150 + 175 + 200 + 225; 975
2a. 31 **b.** 252 **3a.** $\sum_{n=1}^{6} n$ **b.** $\sum_{n=1}^{9} (5n - 2)$
4a. 10, −2, 7; 25 **b.** 4, $\frac{3}{2}$, 3; 9 **c.** 4, 4, 25; 54

Lesson 11-5   pp. 636–638, 641

Check Skills You'll Need 1. $193\frac{3}{4}$ **2.** 120 **3.** −22 **4.** −75
5. $\frac{12}{5}$ **6.** $\frac{4}{3}$ **7.** $\frac{2}{3}$ **8.** $\frac{99}{16}$

CA Standards Check 1a. $a_1 = -45, r = -3, n = 5$; −2745 **b.** $a_1 = \frac{1}{3}, r = \frac{1}{3}, n = 4; \frac{40}{81}$ **2a.** To find the amount 20% larger than a given amount, multiply by 1.2, which is equivalent to 120%. **b.** The common ratio becomes 1.25. **c.** Yes; they will have $1407.35. **3a.** converges **b.** diverges **4.** a. 2 **b.** 2

Checkpoint Quiz 2 1. arithmetic; 900 **2.** geometric; 29,524 **3.** geometric; −7.9375 **4.** arithmetic; 1200 **5.** geometric; 239.0625 **6.** arithmetic; 6150 **7.** $\frac{15}{14}$ **8.** 4 **9.** Answers may vary. Sample: $\frac{1}{2} + \frac{1}{4} + \frac{1}{8}$ **10.** No; the common difference causes arithmetic series to diverge.

Lesson 11-6   pp. 645–647

Check Skills You'll Need 1. 4 ft^2 **2.** 2.75 m^2 **3.** 0.62 cm^2
4. $34\frac{7}{16}$ in.^{2}

CA Standards Check 1a. 1545; it is much larger. **b.** 1370; the mean is most accurate; it is between the other measures known to be smaller and larger than the actual value.

2a.

b. The left side values give the height of the circumscribed rectangles. **c.** 0.5(5) + 0.5(4.75) + 0.5(4) + 0.5(2.75) = 8.25 units²; it is greater than Example 2. **3a.** $4\frac{1}{3}$ **b.** $8\frac{2}{3}$ **c.** $5\frac{1}{4}$

Chapter 12

1. 120 **2.** 720 **3.** 144 **4.** 1 **5.** 6 **6.** 35 **7.** $a^5 + 5a^4b + 10a^3b^2 + 10a^2b^3 + 5ab^4 + b^5$ **8.** $j^3 + 9j^2k + 27jk^2 + 27k^3$ **9.** $m^2 + 1.4m + 0.49$ **10.** $0.000064 + 0.00192t + 0.024t^2 + 0.16t^3 + 0.6t^4 + 1.2t^5 + t^6$ **11.** ±0.1 **12.** ±0.071 **13.** ±0.063 **14.** ±0.051 **15.** ±0.048 **16.** ±0.036 **17.** 0.08 **18.** 0.125 **19.** 0.085 **20.** 0.865 **21.** 0.06

Lesson 12-1   **pp. 660–663**

Check Skills You'll Need   **1.** yes **2.** no **3.** no **4.** $\frac{1}{18}$ **5.** $\frac{1}{4}$ **6.** 1

CA Standards Check

1.

Type	Number
Acute	13
Right	7
Obtuse	5
Total	25

2. 0.857

3. Answers may vary. Sample:

Rolling One Number Cube

Numbers	1	2	3	4	5	6
Frequency	1	1	1	1	1	1
Probability	$\frac{1}{6}$	$\frac{1}{6}$	$\frac{1}{6}$	$\frac{1}{6}$	$\frac{1}{6}$	$\frac{1}{6}$

4a. The Plant Color Distribution would be most useful for avoiding white plants because it shows the total probability of growing green plants, which is the desired outcome.

b.

Genotype

Event	GG	Gw	ww
Frequency	1	2	1
Probability	$\frac{1}{4}$	$\frac{1}{2}$	$\frac{1}{4}$

Plant Color

Event	Green	White
Frequency	3	1
Probability	$\frac{3}{4}$	$\frac{1}{4}$

Lesson 12-2   **pp. 666–668**

Check Skills You'll Need   **1.** $\frac{1}{16}$ **2.** $\frac{1}{16}$ **3.** $\frac{3}{16}$ **4.** $\frac{9}{16}$ **5.** $\frac{7}{16}$ **6.** $\frac{9}{16}$

CA Standards Check   **1.** $\frac{7}{14}$ or $\frac{1}{2}$ **2.** about 0.021 or 2.1% **3.** 0.9 **4.** 0.33

Lesson 12-3   **pp. 672–676, 679**

Check Skills You'll Need

1. 0.2 0.3 0.6 0.7 0.8 0.9 1.2; 0.7 **2.** 11 15 17 18 21 21 23; 18 **3.** 2.6 3.9 7.8 9.1 10.4 11.7 15.6; 9.1

4. 76 80 82 84 86 86 89; 84

CA Standards Check   **1.** ≈ 3.6, 3.7, 2.8 **2.** ≈ 73.42; 73.5; 61, 70, 77, 83, 85

3.

25 30 35 40 45 50

4.

80 82 84 86 88 90

$Q_1 = 84$, $Q_2 = 85$, $Q_3 = 86$

5a. 21 **b.** 65 **c.** 71 **6a.** Yes; it is unlikely that the water temperature of a lake would change by 25°F. **b.** No; 98 would represent the busiest night of the week and it may relate to a weekly event.

Checkpoint Quiz 1

1.

2. 0.385 **3.** No; when $x = 1$, $P(x) = -\frac{1}{2}$, and probability is never negative. **4.** $\frac{12}{57}$ **5.** $\frac{5}{8}$ **6.** $\frac{23}{43}$ **7.** $\frac{45}{68}$ **8.** 5.69, 5, 4 **9.** 3.82, 2.85, no mode

Lesson 12-4   **pp. 680–684**

Check Skills You'll Need   **1.** 4.9 **2.** 2.5 **3.** 10.5 **4.** 9 **5.** 7 **6.** 8.03

CA Standards Check   **1a.** range: 14, interquartile range: 6
b. Yes; answers may vary.
  1   2   3   4   5   6   7   8   9   10
  1   1   1   1   1   10 10 10 10 10
c. Yes; sample:
  1   2   3   4   5   6   7   8   9   10
  3   3   3   5   5   6   6   8   8   8
2. 80, ≈ 18.7 **3.** 8, about 4.0 **4a.** 1 **b.** No; three standard deviations from the mean is 46.3, which is less than 48. **5.** 100

Lesson 12-5   **pp. 689–692**

Check Skills You'll Need   **1.** $\frac{1}{2}$ **2.** $-\frac{1}{3}$ **3.** $\frac{1}{6}$ **4.** $-\frac{1}{11}$ **5.** $\frac{\sqrt{2}}{10}$ **6.** $-\frac{1}{9}$

CA Standards Check   **1.** 52% **2a.** Yes; the sample is biased because it overrepresents students who live in a warm climate. **b.** Answers may vary. Sample: Every 10 years, the United States conducts a census of the population to find

exactly how many people live in the country.
3. B; a larger sample has less variation, which corresponds to a smaller standard deviation.
4a. 100 **b.** 625 **c.** 2500 **5.** 71%, ±9%, 62% to 80%

Lesson 12-6 pp. 697–700, 703

Check Skills You'll Need 1. 6 **2.** 1 **3.** 10 **4.** $x^3 + 6x^2 + 12x + 8$ **5.** $w^4 - 4w^3y + 6w^2y^2 - 4wy^3 + y^4$
6. $m^3 + 3m^2n + 3mn^2 + n^3$ **7.** $t^4 + 12t^3s + 54t^2s^2 + 108ts^3 + 81s^4$ **8.** $a^5 + 10a^4b + 40a^3b^2 + 80a^2b^3 + 80ab^4 + 32b^5$ **9.** $p^6 + 6p^5q + 15p^4q^2 + 20p^3q^3 + 15p^2q^4 + 6pq^5 + q^6$

CA Standards Check 2a. P (one prize) $= 3(0.4)^1(0.6)^2 = 0.432$; P(no prize) $= 1(0.6)^3 = 0.216$ **b.** 1
3a. 0.2637 **b.** 0.2335 **4.** 0.9933

Checkpoint Quiz 2 1. $33.8\overline{3}$, 20, 6.20 **2.** 11, 5, 1.63
3. 2.375, 4, 1.41 **4.** 228 **5a.** This survey may be biased because it overrepresents people who shop for CDs online and entirely misses those who do not have internet access. **b.** Answers may vary. Sample: Survey a random selection of students in homerooms for each grade level.
6a. $0.3441 \approx 34.4\%$ **b.** ±3.8% **c.** 30.6% to 38.2%
7. 25 **8.** 0.343 **9.** 0.4096 **10.** 0.0768

Lesson 12-7 pp. 704–706

Check Skills You'll Need 1. 8, 10, 14, 16 **2.** 14.7, 15.7, 17.7, 18.7 **3.** 4, 5.5, 8.5, 10 **4.** 18.6, 20.3, 23.7, 25.4 **5.** 15.7, 16.6, 18.4, 19.3 **6.** 30.7, 31.9, 34.3, 35.5

CA Standards Check 1a. 71% **b.** 88%

2.

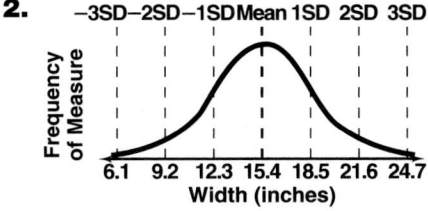

3a. 68 responses **b.** 13 or 14 responses
4a. 47 or 48 students **b.** 76 is about 1 SD above the mean. About 13.5% + 2.5% should receive grades above 76. 16% of 140 is about 22.

Chapter 13

Check Your Readiness p. 720

1. vertical asymptote $x = 3$ **2.** hole at $x = 1$
3. vertical asymptotes $x = -\frac{1}{2}$ and $x = 4$ **4.** $\frac{2b}{a}$
5. $\frac{55}{18}$ **6.** $\frac{3}{2(c + d)}$ **7.** $\frac{c}{16}$ **8.** $\frac{c + 4}{9}$ **9.** $\frac{16}{x}$ **10.** $\frac{15}{7}$ **11.** 6
12. $(x - 1)^2 + (y + 4)^2 = 16$;

13. $\frac{(x - 2)^2}{9} + \frac{(y - 5)^2}{4} = 1$;

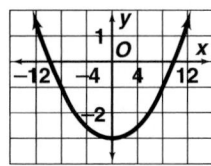

14. $y = \frac{1}{32} x^2 - 3$;

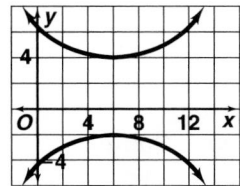

15. $\frac{(y - 1)^2}{9} - \frac{(x - 6)^2}{16} = 1$;

16. 4, 1; $a_n = 19 - 3n$, explicit; $a_1 = 16$, $a_n = a_{n-1} - 3$, recursive **17.** $-216, -343$; $a_n = -n^3$, explicit **18.** $\frac{1}{9}, \frac{1}{27}$; $a_n = 9\left(\frac{1}{3}\right)^{n-1}$, explicit; or $a_1 = 9$, $a_n = \frac{1}{3} \cdot a_{n-1}$, recursive

Lesson 13-1 pp. 722–725

Check Skills You'll Need 1. yes **2.** yes **3.** no **4.** yes **5.** no **6.** no **7.** yes **8.** yes

CA Standards Check 1a. from -3 to 1 or 0 to 4; 4 **b.** from -4 to -1 or 0 to 3; 3 **2a.** not periodic **b.** periodic; 4 **3a.** 1.5 **b.** 1.5

4.

1 unit on the x-axis is 0.001 s.

Lesson 13-2
pp. 730–734

Check Skills You'll Need

1. 2. 3.

4. 5. 6.

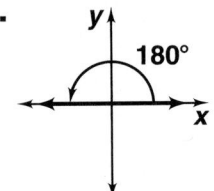

CA Standards Check **1.** 90°; 180°; 270°

2a. **b.**

c.

3a. 558° **b.** No; 40° is coterminal with 400° and 760°. **c.** Answers may vary. Sample: The difference between measures of two coterminal angles is a multiple of 360°.

4a. **b.**

$\frac{\sqrt{2}}{2} \approx 0.707$, $\frac{\sqrt{2}}{2} \approx 0.707$ $\frac{\sqrt{3}}{2} \approx 0.87$, 0.5

c.

-0.5, $\frac{\sqrt{3}}{2} \approx 0.87$

5a. -0.5, -0.87; the values are equal and are the rounded decimal values of $-\frac{1}{2}$ and $-\frac{\sqrt{3}}{2}$.
b. $-\frac{\sqrt{2}}{2}$, $\frac{\sqrt{2}}{2}$; ≈ -0.707, ≈ 0.707 **c.** $-\frac{\sqrt{3}}{2}$, $\frac{1}{2}$

Lesson 13-3
pp. 738–741, 745

Check Skills You'll Need **1.** 25.1 in. **2.** 219.9 m
3. 50.3 mi **4.** 10.7 ft **5.** 31.4 mm **6.** 19.8 cm

CA Standards Check **1a.** ≈ 1.48 radians **b.** $\approx 143.24°$
2a. 90° **b.** $\frac{5\pi}{4}$ radians **c.** $\approx 114.59°$ **d.** $\frac{5\pi}{6}$ radians

3a. 0.71, 0.71; these values are the rounded decimal equivalent of $\frac{\sqrt{2}}{2}$. **b.** π radians = 180°, so $\frac{\pi}{4}$ radians becomes $\frac{180°}{4}$, which is 45°. **4.** 6.3 in.
5a. ≈ 3.14 units **b.** ≈ 4.19 units **c.** ≈ 6.28 units
d. ≈ 10.47 units

Checkpoint Quiz 1 **1.** 5, 1 **2.** 4, 2 **3.** $-\frac{\sqrt{2}}{2}$, $\frac{\sqrt{2}}{2}$
4. $-\frac{1}{2}$, $-\frac{\sqrt{3}}{2}$ **5.** 0, -1 **6.** $\frac{1}{2}$, $\frac{\sqrt{3}}{2}$ **7.** $-\pi$ radians
8. $\frac{\pi}{5}$ radians **9.** 180° **10.** 240°

Lesson 13-4
pp. 746–750

Check Skills You'll Need **1.** 2 **2.** all real numbers **3.** 1
4. all real numbers between -1 and 1, inclusive

CA Standards Check **1a.** yes; at 450° **b.** Yes; the y-values repeat at regular intervals. **2a.** 1 **b.** 360°, 2π radians **c.** domain: all real numbers, range: all real numbers between -1 and 1, inclusive **3a.** 2π
b. $\frac{2\pi}{3}$ **4a.** 4 **b.** 3

5a. **b.** zero-min-zero-max-zero

c.

6a. **b.**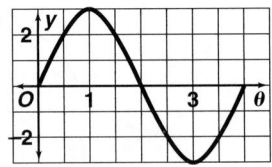

7. $y = \sin \frac{\pi}{320}\theta$, $y = \sin \frac{\pi}{285}\theta$

Lesson 13-5
pp. 755–757

Check Skills You'll Need **1.** 1 **2.** 0 **3.** -1 **4.** 0

CA Standards Check **1.** They are the same curve translated $\frac{\pi}{2}$ units horizontally.

2a.

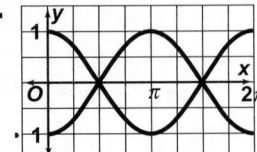

They are reflections of each other over the x-axis.

b. min-zero-max-zero-min

c.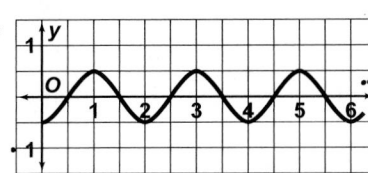

3a. $y = 4 \cos \frac{1}{3}\theta$ **b.** $y = 2.5 \cos \frac{\pi}{4}\theta$ **4a.** 1.2, 2.0, 4.3, 5.1 **b.** 2.2, 4.1 **c.** $0 \le \theta < 2.2$ and $4.1 < \theta \le 2\pi$; $2.2 < \theta < 4.1$

Lesson 13-6　　　　　　　　**pp. 761–763**

Check Skills You'll Need 1. ≈ 0.87, 0.5; ≈ 1.73
2. 0.5, ≈ 0.87; ≈ 0.58 **3.** 1, 0; undefined **4.** 0.5, ≈ -0.87; ≈ -0.58 **5.** 1, 0; undefined **6.** 0, 1; 0

CA Standards Check 1a. 0.4, -0.4 **b.** The terminal side of $\frac{\pi}{2}$ lies on the line $x = 0$, which cannot intersect $x = 1$.

2a. 　　　**b.**

3a. 46.6 ft **b.** 8°

Lesson 13-7　　　　　　**pp. 768–772, 774**

Check Skills You'll Need

1. 　　**2.**

　　vertical　　　　　　horizontal

3. 　　**4.**

　　vertical　　　　　　vertical

5. 　　**6.**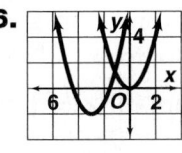

　　　　　　　　　　　　　diagonal

　diagonal

CA Standards Check 1a. 5; 5 units to the right
b. -3; 3 units to the left

2a. 　　**b.**

(b) is a phase shift.

3a. 　　**b.**

4a. 　　**b.**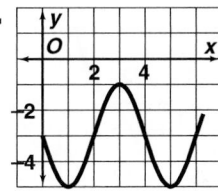

5a. $y = \cos x + \frac{\pi}{2}$ **b.** $y = 2 \sin\left(x - \frac{\pi}{4}\right)$
6a. 86.5° **b.** day 100

Checkpoint Quiz 2

1.

2.

3.

4.

5.

6.

7.

8.

9.

10.

| Lesson 13-8 | pp. 775–778 |

Check Skills You'll Need 1. $\frac{13}{9}$ **2.** $-\frac{8}{5}$ **3.** 2π
4. $\frac{15}{4m}$ **5.** $-\frac{t}{14}$

6. **7.**

8. **9.**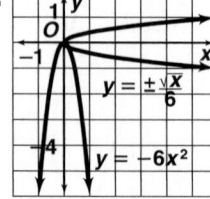

CA Standards Check 1a. $\frac{8}{15}$ **b.** ≈ 0.70 **2a.** 2 **b.** 1 **c.** 2
3a. -1.003 **b.** -2.403 **c.** undefined

4.

5. ≈ 1.4142 **6.** 6.9 ft; 8.5 ft; 68.8 ft

Chapter 14

| Check Your Readiness | p. 790 |

1. $\pm\frac{5}{2}$ **2.** $\pm\sqrt{23}$ **3.** $\pm\frac{4\sqrt{15}}{3}$ **4.** $\pm\frac{\sqrt{22}}{2}$ **5.** $\pm\sqrt{30}$
6. ± 2 **7.** Domain of f is $\{x \mid x \in R\}$, range of f is
$\{y \mid y \in R\}$; $f^{-1}(x) = \frac{x-2}{5}$, domain of f^{-1} is
$\{x \mid x \in R\}$, range of f^{-1} is $\{y \mid y \in R\}$. f^{-1} is a
function. **8.** Domain of f is $\{x \mid x \in R, x \geq -3\}$,
range of f is $\{y \mid y \in R, y \geq 0\}$; $f^{-1}(x) = x^2 - 3$,
$x \geq 0$, domain of f^{-1} is $\{x \mid x \in R, x \geq 0\}$, range
of f^{-1} is $\{y \mid y \in R, y \geq -3\}$. f^{-1} is a function.
9. Domain of f is $\left\{x \mid x \in R, x \geq \frac{4}{3}\right\}$, range of f is
$\{y \mid y \in R, y \geq 0\}$; $f^{-1}(x) = \frac{x^2 + 4}{3}$, $x > 0$, domain
of f^{-1} is $\{x \mid x \in R, x \geq 0\}$, range of f^{-1} is
$\left\{y \mid y \in R, y \geq \frac{4}{3}\right\}$. f^{-1} is a function. **10.** Domain
of f is $\{x \mid x \in R, x \neq 0\}$, range of f is $\{y \mid y \in R,$
$y \neq 0\}$; $f^{-1}(x) = \frac{5}{x}$, domain of f^{-1} is $\{x \mid x \in R,$
$x \neq 0\}$, range of f^{-1} is $\{y \mid y \in R, y \neq 0\}$. f^{-1} is a
function. **11.** Domain of f is $\{x \mid x \in R, x \neq 1\}$,
range of f is $\{y \mid y \in R, y \neq 0\}$; $f^{-1}(x) = \frac{10}{x} + 1$,
domain of f^{-1} is $\{x \mid x \in R, x \neq 0\}$, range of f^{-1} is
$\{y \mid y \in R, y \neq 1\}$. f^{-1} is a function. **12.** Domain of
f is $\{x \mid x \in R, x \neq 0\}$, range of f is $\{y \mid y \in R,$
$y \neq -1\}$; $f^{-1}(x) = \frac{10}{x+1}$, domain of f^{-1} is
$\{x \mid x \in R, x \neq -1\}$, range of f^{-1} is $\{y \mid y \in R,$
$y \neq 0\}$. f^{-1} is a function. **13.** -1.5 **14.** 0.002
15. ≈ 1.065 **16.** $\approx 18{,}257$ **17.** $\approx 3 \times 10^{-5}$ **18.** 5
19. 0.67, 0.74, 1.11 **20.** -0.26, -0.97, 3.73
21. 0.96, 0.28, 0.29 **22.** -0.87, 0.5, -0.58

| Lesson 14-1 | pp. 792–794 |

Check Skills You'll Need 1. Yes; $2x + 3x = (2 + 3)x$ by
the Dist. Prop. and $(2 + 3)x = 5x$ by addition.
2. Yes; $-(4x - 10) = -4x + 10$ by the Dist. Prop.,
and $-4x + 10 = 10 - 4x$ by the Comm. Prop.
3. No; for $x = 0$, $\frac{4x^2}{x}$ is not defined, but $4x = 0$.

4. No; for $x = 1$, $\frac{x^2+1}{x-1}$ is not defined, but
$x + 1 = 2$.

CA Standards Check **1.** $1 + \cot^2 \theta = 1 + \left(\frac{\cos \theta}{\sin \theta}\right)^2 =$
$1 + \frac{\cos^2 \theta}{\sin^2 \theta} = 1 + \frac{1 - \sin^2 \theta}{\sin^2 \theta} = 1 + \frac{1}{\sin^2 \theta} - \frac{\sin^2 \theta}{\sin^2 \theta} =$
$1 + \csc^2 \theta - 1 = \csc^2 \theta$ **2.** $\sec^2 \theta -$
$\sec^2 \theta \cos^2 \theta = \left(\frac{1}{\cos \theta}\right)^2 - \left(\frac{1}{\cos \theta}\right)^2 \cos^2 \theta =$
$\frac{1}{\cos^2 \theta} - \frac{1}{\cos^2 \theta} \cdot \cos^2 \theta = \frac{1}{\cos^2 \theta} - \frac{\cos^2 \theta}{\cos^2 \theta} =$
$\frac{1 - \cos^2 \theta}{\cos^2 \theta} = \frac{\sin^2 \theta}{\cos^2 \theta} = \tan^2 \theta$ **3.** $\csc \theta$

Lesson 14-2   pp. 797–800

Check Skills You'll Need **1.** $f^{-1}(x) = x - 1$
2. $f^{-1}(x) = \frac{x + 3}{2}$ **3.** $f^{-1}(x) = \pm\sqrt{x - 4}$
4. 0.5 **5.** $\frac{\sqrt{2}}{2}$ **6.** $-\frac{\sqrt{2}}{2}$ **7.** 0 **8.** -1 **9.** $-\frac{\sqrt{3}}{2}$

CA Standards Check **1.** none, $\frac{\pi}{2} + \pi n$, none
2a. $120° + n \cdot 360°$ and $240° + n \cdot 360°$
b. $150° + n \cdot 360°$ and $210° + n \cdot 360°$
c. $45° + n \cdot 360°$ and $315° + n \cdot 360°$
3a. $0.46 + 2\pi n$ and $2.69 + 2\pi n$

b. $-0.82 + 2\pi n$ and $3.96 + 2\pi n$ **4a.** $0.41 + 2\pi n$
and $3.56 + 2\pi n$ **b.** $-0.63 + 2\pi n$ and $2.51 + 2\pi n$
5. $\frac{11\pi}{6}$ and $\frac{7\pi}{6}$ **6.** $\frac{\pi}{2}$ and $\frac{3\pi}{2}$ **7a.** $\frac{1}{2}$ s; 3 s **b.** At 2 s;
the toy will reach a maximum at 4 in. and then
come back down, again hitting 2 in. at 2 s.
c. Let $y_1 = -4 \cos \frac{2\pi}{3} t$ and let $y_2 = 2$. Graph.
Trace and calculate the intersection.

Lesson 14-3   pp. 806–809, 813

Check Skills You'll Need **1.** s **2.** r **3.** a **4.** t

CA Standards Check **1.** 180 m

2.

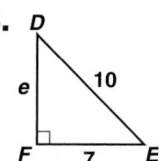
$\frac{3}{5} = 0.6, \frac{5}{3} \approx 1.67$

3a. Answers may vary. Sample: An advantage is
that simplification of the equation is easier. A
disadvantage is that you have to press an extra
button on the calculator to get the cotangent
function. **b.** ≈ 34.29 ft **4a.** $23.58°$ **b.** $56.25°$

5.

$e \approx 7.14; m\angle E \approx 45.6°, m\angle D \approx 44.4°$

Checkpoint Quiz 1 **1.** $\csc \theta$ **2.** $\tan^2 \theta$ **3.** $-\csc^2 \theta$
4. 2.25 **5.** 0.320 **6.** 1.345 **7.** $a \approx 7.7$,
$m\angle A \approx 29.0°, m\angle B \approx 61.0°$ **8.** $c \approx 10.0$,

$m\angle A \approx 51.9°, m\angle B \approx 38.1°$ **9.** $a \approx 19.6$,
$m\angle A \approx 34.0°, m\angle B \approx 56.0°$

Lesson 14-4   pp. 815–818

Check Skills You'll Need **1.** $\frac{1}{12}$ **2.** $\frac{\sqrt{2}}{8}$ **3.** $\frac{\sqrt{3}}{20}$ **4.** $\frac{1}{24}$ **5.** $\frac{\sqrt{2}}{16}$
6. $\frac{\sqrt{3}}{18}$ **7.** 6 cm² **8.** 45 in.² **9.** 32.8 mm²
10. 10.03 ft²

CA Standards Check **1.** 36.6 in.² **2.** 31.0 yd **3.** 68.4°
4. 56.4

Lesson 14-5   pp. 822–824

Check Skills You'll Need **1.** 26.2° **2.** 18.1 **3.** 52.1° or
17.9°

CA Standards Check **1.** 6.4 **2.** 75.3° **3.** 30.7°

Lesson 14-6   pp. 828–831, 834

Check Skills You'll Need **1.** $\sin \theta$ **2.** $\cos \theta$ **3.** $\tan \theta$ **4.** 1
5. $\sec^2 \theta$ **6.** $\csc^2 \theta$

CA Standards Check **1.** $\cos\left(\theta - \frac{\pi}{2}\right) =$
$\cos\left(-\left(\frac{\pi}{2} - \theta\right)\right) = \cos\left(\frac{\pi}{2} - \theta\right) = \sin \theta$
2. $0, \pi$ **3.** $\sec(90° - A) = \csc A$
4. $\frac{\sqrt{6} - \sqrt{2}}{4}$ **5.** $-2 - \sqrt{3}$

Checkpoint Quiz 2 **1.** 36.1 cm² **2.** 77.3 ft² **3.** 34.9 m²
4. 400.8 in² **5.** $a = 8.2$ ft, $m\angle B = 69.7°, m\angle C =$
$83.3°$ **6.** $m\angle D = 58.4°, m\angle E = 53.0°, m\angle F =$
$68.7°$ **7.** $\cos 80°$ **8.** $\sin 63°$ **9.** $\sin 80°$

Lesson 14-7   pp. 835–837

Check Skills You'll Need **1.** $\cos A \cos B + \sin A \sin B$
2. $\cos A \cos B - \sin A \sin B$ **3.** $\frac{\tan A - \tan B}{1 + \tan A \tan B}$
4. $\sin A \cos B - \cos A \sin B$ **5.** $\sin A \cos B +$
$\cos A \sin B$ **6.** $\frac{\tan A + \tan B}{1 - \tan A \tan B}$

CA Standards Check **1.** $\frac{\sqrt{3}}{2}$ **2.** $2 \cos 2\theta =$
$2(2 \cos^2 \theta - 1) = 4 \cos^2 \theta - 2$ **3a.** $\frac{1}{2}$ **b.** $-\frac{\sqrt{3}}{3}$
4. $-\frac{3}{5}, -\frac{4}{3}$

Selected Answers

Chapter 1

Lesson 1-1   pp. 8–10

EXERCISES 1. natural numbers, whole numbers, integers, rational numbers, real numbers **3.** irrational numbers, real numbers **5.** whole numbers, integers, rational numbers, real numbers **7.** rational numbers, real numbers **9.** whole numbers, rational numbers **11.** irrational numbers, rational numbers

13.   **15.**

17. > **19.** > **21.** < **23.** > **25.** $-\frac{1}{4} > -\frac{1}{3}, -\frac{1}{3} < -\frac{1}{4}$
27. $-2.\overline{3} < 2.\overline{1}, 2.\overline{1} > -2.\overline{3}$ **29.** $3.0\overline{4} < 3.4, 3.4 > 3.0\overline{4}$ **31.** $-4 < -\sqrt{4}, -\sqrt{4} > -4$ **33.** $-\sqrt{3} > -\sqrt{5}, -\sqrt{5} < -\sqrt{3}$ **35.** $-3\frac{3}{5}, \frac{5}{18}$ **37.** $\frac{7}{2}, -\frac{2}{7}$ **39.** $-2\pi; \frac{1}{2\pi}$
41. $3 - \pi; \frac{1}{\pi - 3}$ **43.** Comm. Prop. of Add.
45. Comm. Prop. of Mult. **47.** Inverse Prop. of Mult. **49.** 0.06 **51.** 1.6 **53.** 3 **55.** -2 **57.** $-3\frac{1}{2}$
59. $\frac{1}{2}$ **61.** $3\frac{1}{3}$ **63.** 4.8 **65.** natural numbers, whole numbers, integers, rational numbers, real numbers **67.** irrational numbers, real numbers **69.** irrational numbers, real numbers **71.** >
73. < **75.** < **77.** < **79.** Answers may vary. Sample: 4 is a whole number, but $\frac{1}{4}$ is not a whole number. **81.** 0 is a whole number, and since $-0 = 0$, the opposite of 0 is a whole number.
83. Answers may vary. Sample: $\sqrt{2}$ and $\sqrt{2}$ are irrational numbers, but their product (2) is a rational number. **85.** all except the Identity Prop. of Add. (since 0 is not in the set of natural numbers) and the inverse properties **87.** all except the Inverse Prop. of Mult. **89.** Comm., Assoc., and Distr. Prop. **91.** C **93.** C **95.** -3.8 **97.** 0 **99.** 7 **101.** $\frac{35}{3}$ or $11\frac{2}{3}$ **103.** 5 **105.** 45

Lesson 1-2   pp. 15–17

EXERCISES 1. -30 **3.** 368 **5.** -16 **7.** -70 **9.** 1 ft
11. 64 ft **13.** 0.013 mm **15.** 0.4 mm **17.** $1210
19. $1464.10 **21.** $4a$ **23.** $-9a + b$ **25.** $10r + 5s$
27. $2x^2 + x$ **29.** $-0.5x$ **31.** $10y + x - 4$
33. $-3a + 15b$ **35.** $-3x + 4y - z$ **37.** $4a$ **39.** 17
41. 66 **43.** $\frac{41}{4}$ **45.** -765 **47.** $-\frac{3}{4}a^2 + 2b^2$
49. $\frac{7y^2}{12} + \frac{2y}{15}$ **51.** $3x + 6y$ **53.** $-2x^2 + 2y^2$ **55.** C
57. G **59.** H **61.** I **63.** Assoc. Prop. of Add., Comm. Prop. of Add., Assoc. Prop. of Add., Identity Prop. of Mult., Dist. Prop. of Add., Simplify. **65.** Answers may vary. Sample: $x^3 + x^2 + x - x^3 - 2x, -x^2 + 2x^2 + 3x - 3x - x, x^2 - 5x + 4x - x^5 + x^5, 3x^2 - x^2 - x^2 + 7x - 8x$

67.a. 18 **b.** $2x^2$, 18 **c.** Properties of operations were used to simplify the original expression. Those properties convert one expression into an equivalent expression, and equivalent expressions have equal values for all replacements of their variables. **d.** No; explanations may vary. Sample: Students should check each step in the simplification; they also should substitute more than one value for x in the original and simplified expressions. **69.** A **71.** B **73.** $-1.5, -\sqrt{2}, -1.4, -0.5$ **75.** $-\frac{5}{6}, -\frac{3}{4}, -\frac{3}{8}, \frac{1}{2}$ **77.** > **79.** > **81.** <

Lesson 1-3   pp. 21–24

EXERCISES 1. 23 **3.** $\frac{17}{2}$ **5.** $\frac{7}{2}$ **7.** $\frac{17}{7}$ **9.** 8 **11.** 2
13. $-\frac{2}{3}$ **15.** 2 **17.** $h = \frac{2A}{b}$ **19.** $w = \frac{V}{lh}$ **21.** $r = \frac{S}{2\pi h}$
23. $x = \frac{c}{a + b}, a \neq -b$ **25.** $x = a(c - b)$ or $ac - ab, a \neq 0$ **27.** $x = 2(m + n) + 2$ or $2m - 2n - 2$ **29.** 4 h **31.** width = 4.5 cm, length = 7.5 cm **33.** 11 cm, 11 cm, 16.5 cm, 16.5 cm
35.a. $x + (x + 1) + (x + 2) = 90; 29, 30, 31$
b. $(x - 1) + x + (x + 1) = 90; 29, 30, 31$ **37.** 3
39. $\frac{3}{2}$ **41.** $\frac{79}{80}$ or 0.9875 **43.** $r_2 = \frac{Rr_1}{r_1 - R}$
45. $v = \frac{h + 5t^2}{t}$ **47.** $b_2 = \frac{2A}{h} - b_1$ **49.** 34°, 56°
51. ≈ 4.03 m **53.** 43, 45, 47, 49
55. $x = ab - b^2 - a, b \neq 0$ **57.** $x = \frac{b + d}{c - a}, a \neq c$
59. $x = \frac{3b + 2c - 5}{b - c}, b \neq c$ **61.** $x = \frac{4a - 3bc}{aq - 5bp}$,
$5bp \neq aq$ **63.** $x = \frac{10c}{a}, a \neq 0$ **65.a.** $t = \frac{s - 1055}{1.1}$
b. about 40.9°F **c.** $C = \frac{5}{9}(F - 32)$ **d.** about 4.9°C
67.a. If you solve $ax - b = c$ for x, you get $x = \frac{b + c}{a}$. Since b and c are integers, $b + c$ is an integer. But a is a nonzero integer. So $\frac{b + c}{a}$ is the quotient of two integers and hence, by the definition of a rational number, $\frac{b + c}{a}$ is a rational number. **b.** Solutions are rational when $\frac{c - b}{a} \geq 0$, $a \neq 0$, and $\frac{c - b}{a}$ is a perfect square (a whole number perfect square or, in simplest form, a fraction whose numerator and denominator are whole number perfect squares). Since $x^2 = \frac{c - b}{a}$, $(a \neq 0), x = \sqrt{\frac{c - b}{a}}$ or $x = -\sqrt{\frac{c - b}{a}}$. For $\sqrt{\frac{c - b}{a}}$ and $-\sqrt{\frac{c - b}{a}}$ to be rational $\frac{c - b}{a}$ must be nonnegative and also $\frac{c - b}{a}$ must be a perfect square. **69.** C **71.** -7 **73.** -20 **75.** $7x^2 - 2x$
77. $2y - 7x$ **79.** $-6x - s$

Lesson 1-4   pp. 29–31

EXERCISES 1. $x \leq -\frac{1}{2}$

3. $a > 11$

$\begin{array}{cccccccccc} 8 & 9 & 10 & 11 & 12 & 13 & 14 & 15 & 16 \end{array}$

5. $y \le -14$

$\begin{array}{ccccccccc} -17 & -16 & -15 & -14 & -13 & -12 & -11 & -10 & -9 \end{array}$

7. $x \le 8$

$\begin{array}{ccccccccc} 5 & 6 & 7 & 8 & 9 & 10 & 11 & 12 & 13 \end{array}$

9. $n > 8$

$\begin{array}{ccccccccc} 4 & 5 & 6 & 7 & 8 & 9 & 10 & 11 & 12 \end{array}$

11. All real numbers are solutions.

$\begin{array}{ccccccccc} -4 & -3 & -2 & -1 & 0 & 1 & 2 & 3 & 4 \end{array}$ **13.** no solutions

15. The longest side is less than 21 cm.

17. 40 students **19.** $-4 \le x \le 2$

$\begin{array}{cccccccccccc} -7 & -6 & -5 & -4 & -3 & -2 & -1 & 0 & 1 & 2 & 3 & 4 \end{array}$

21. $-5 < x \le 6$

$\begin{array}{cccccccccccccc} -6 & -5 & -4 & -3 & -2 & -1 & 0 & 1 & 2 & 3 & 4 & 5 & 6 & 7 \end{array}$

23. All real numbers are solutions.

$\begin{array}{ccccccccc} -4 & -3 & -2 & -1 & 0 & 1 & 2 & 3 & 4 \end{array}$

25. $x \le -3$ or $x \ge 9$

$\begin{array}{ccccccccccccccc} -4 & -3 & -2 & -1 & 0 & 1 & 2 & 3 & 4 & 5 & 6 & 7 & 8 & 9 & 10 \end{array}$

27. between $4\frac{1}{2}$ and $5\frac{1}{2}$ days

29. $z \ge 6$

$\begin{array}{cccccccc} 1 & 2 & 3 & 4 & 5 & 6 & 7 & 8 \end{array}$

31. $x \ge -48$

$\begin{array}{ccccc} -50 & -48 & -46 & -44 & -42 \end{array}$

33. no solutions **35.** Answers may vary. Sample: Mario has a coin collection that consists of dimes and nickels. There are half as many dimes as nickels. There are no more than 60 coins in the collection. Describe the collection. **37.a.** between $204,000 and $254,000 **b.** $y \le -20$ **39.** Dist. Prop.; arithmetic; Sub. Prop. of Inequality; Mult. Prop. of Inequality **41.** $-1 < x < 8$

$\begin{array}{cccccccccccc} -3 & -2 & -1 & 0 & 1 & 2 & 3 & 4 & 5 & 6 & 7 & 8 & 9 \end{array}$

43. no solutions **45.** All real numbers are solutions

$\begin{array}{ccccccccccc} -5 & -4 & -3 & -2 & -1 & 0 & 1 & 2 & 3 & 4 & 5 \end{array}$

47. All real numbers are solutions

$\begin{array}{ccccccccc} -4 & -3 & -2 & -1 & 0 & 1 & 2 & 3 & 4 \end{array}$

49. All real numbers are solutions

$\begin{array}{ccccccccc} -4 & -3 & -2 & -1 & 0 & 1 & 2 & 3 & 4 \end{array}$ **51.** Answers may vary.

Sample: $2x - 7 \ge -11$ **53.** Answers may vary. Sample: $-9 < 5x + 1 < 6$ **55.a.** no **b.** yes; values of a that are 8 or greater **c.** (a) yes; values of a that are less than 8, (b) no **57.** B **59.** 4 **61.** $\frac{9}{10}$ **63.** $7a + 5$ **65.** $\frac{1}{12}b + 1$

Lesson 1-5   pp. 36–38

EXERCISES 1. $-6, 6$ **3.** $-6, 12$ **5.** no solution **7.** $-18, 10$ **9.** $-7, 15$ **11.** $\frac{2}{3}$ **13.** $-4, 8$ **15.** 1 **17.** $x \le -3$ or $x \ge 13$

$\begin{array}{ccccccccccccc} -6 & -4 & -2 & 0 & 2 & 4 & 6 & 8 & 10 & 12 & 14 & 16 & 18 \end{array}$

19. All real numbers

$\begin{array}{ccccccccccc} -4 & -3 & -2 & -1 & 0 & 1 & 2 & 3 & 4 \end{array}$

21. $z < -4$ or $z > 4$

$\begin{array}{cc} -4 & 4 \end{array}$

23. $-2\frac{2}{3} < y < 3\frac{1}{3}$

$\begin{array}{cccccccccccc} -5 & -4 & -3 & -2 & -1 & 0 & 1 & 2 & 3 & 4 & 5 & 6 \end{array}$

25. no solution **27.** $-\frac{11}{15} \le t \le \frac{17}{15}$

$\begin{array}{ccccccccccc} -1\frac{12}{15} & -\frac{9}{15} & -\frac{6}{15} & -\frac{3}{15} & 0 & \frac{3}{15} & \frac{6}{15} & \frac{9}{15} & \frac{12}{15} & 1 & 1\frac{3}{15} & 1\frac{6}{15} \end{array}$

29. $|k - 50.5| \le 0.5$ **31.** $|b - 52.5| \le 2.5$

33. $|d - 0.11885| \le 0.00015$ **35.** $-\frac{3}{2}, -1$ **37.** $-\frac{1}{3}$

39. $\frac{5}{2}$ **41.** $-1, -3$ **43.** 2 **45.** $x \le -8$ or $x \ge 5$

$\begin{array}{cccccccccccc} -12 & -10 & -8 & -6 & -4 & -2 & 0 & 2 & 4 & 6 & 8 \end{array}$

47. $t < -\frac{3}{2}$ or $t > 2$

$\begin{array}{ccccccccc} -4 & -3 & -2 & -1 & 0 & 1 & 2 & 3 & 4 \end{array}$

49. $x < -\frac{1}{2}$ or $x > \frac{3}{2}$

$\begin{array}{ccccccccc} -4 & -3 & -2 & -1 & 0 & 1 & 2 & 3 & 4 \end{array}$

51. $-3.5 \le x \le 7.5$

$\begin{array}{cccc} -4 & 0 & 4 & 8 \end{array}$

53. $x < -32$ or $x > 22$

$\begin{array}{cccc} -40 & -20 & 0 & 20 \end{array}$

55. C **57.** Answers may vary. Sample: $|x - 1| \ge 0$; $|x| < -5$ **59.** $|x - 9.55| \le 0.02$, $9.53 \le x \le 9.57$ **61.** $-\frac{b + c}{a}, \frac{b + c}{a}, a \ne 0$; no solution, $b + c < 0$ **63.** $\frac{ac + d}{ab}, \frac{ac - d}{ab}, ab \ne 0$; no solution, $\frac{d}{a} < 0$ **65.**

$\begin{array}{cccccccc} -6 & -4 & -2 & 0 & 2 & 4 & 6 \end{array}$

$(x \le -6)$ or $(-5 < x < 5)$ or $(x \ge 6)$ **67.** B **69.** C **71.** $s > -\frac{7}{5}$ **73.** $x \le 12$ **75.** $t \le 7$ **77.** $-\frac{4}{15}$ **79.** Closure Prop. of Mult.

Lesson 1-6   pp. 42–45

EXERCISES 1. $\frac{161}{340}$ or about 47%; $\frac{179}{340}$ or about 53% **3.** Answers may vary. Sample: Generate random numbers between 0 and 1 using a graphing calculator. In each random number, examine the first five digits. Let even digits represent correct answers and odd digits incorrect answers. If there are two or more even digits, make a tally mark for that number. Do this 100 times. Find the total number of tally marks. This, as a percent, gives the experimental probability. The simulated probability should be about 80%. **5.** Answers may vary. Sample: Generate 100 random numbers with a calculator. Record the first five digits of each number. Let 0 and 1 represent correct answers and the other digits incorrect answers. Tally the recorded numbers with exactly one digit that represents a correct answer. Tally the recorded numbers with exactly two digits that represent correct answers. Tally the recorded numbers with exactly three digits that represent correct answers. The tally totals, as percents, give the experimental probabilities. They should be in the neighborhood of 40%, 20%, and 5%, respectively. **7.** $\frac{1}{2}$, or 50% **9.** $\frac{4}{5}$, or 80% **11.** $\frac{19}{125}$, or 15.2% **13.** $\frac{14}{25}$, or 56% **15.** {Gg, Gg, gg, gg}; $\frac{1}{2}$, or 50% **17.** $\frac{1}{16}$, or 6.25% **19.** $\frac{1}{4}$, or 25% **21.a.** 1 **b.** 0 **23.** Answers may vary. Sample: Let odd digits represent heads and even digits represent tails. Use the first 50 digits of the table. The experimental probability of heads is $\frac{1}{2}$. **25.** $\frac{52}{147}$, or 35.4% **27.** $\frac{31}{147}$, or 21.1% **29.** $\frac{1}{2}$ **31.** 0 **33.** 1 **35.** $\frac{4}{9}$ **37.** $\frac{4}{9}$ **39.** $\approx 6.4\%$ **41.** if there are any restrictions on the last digit of a ZIP code **43.a.** $\frac{a}{a+b}$ **b.** a to $b - a$ or $\frac{a}{b-a}$ **c.** A game where the probability of winning is $\frac{1}{2}$; when the odds of winning are $\frac{1}{2}$, the probability of winning is only $\frac{1}{3}$. **45.a.** about $\frac{1}{3}$ **b.** about $\frac{2}{3}$ **47.** A **49.** D **51.** $-\frac{5}{3}$, 5 **53.** -5, 9 **55.** $-\frac{12}{5}$, $\frac{24}{5}$ **57.** $-2 \leq x \leq 6$ **59.** $-5 < x < 1$ **61.** $-15 \leq x \leq -3$

Chapter Review   pp. 47–49

1. additive inverse **2.** sample space **3.** solution of an equation **4.** compound inequality **5.** reciprocal **6.** experimental probability **7.** theoretical probability **8.** extraneous solution **9.** simulation **10.** absolute value **11.** real numbers, irrational numbers **12.** real numbers, rational numbers, integers **13.** real numbers, rational numbers, integers, whole numbers, natural numbers **14.** real numbers, irrational numbers **15.** real numbers, rational numbers **16.** > **17.** > **18.** > **19.** <

20. 3.4; $-\frac{1}{3.4}$

21. $-4 - \pi$; $\frac{1}{4+\pi}$

22. $-1\frac{7}{8}$; $\frac{8}{15}$

23. $-\sqrt{12}$; $\frac{1}{\sqrt{12}}$ **24–28.** Answers may vary. Samples: **24.** $(x + 3)(1) = x + 3$ **25.** $(2x + 7) + 3y = 2x + (7 + 3y)$ **26.** $3(2x - 4) = 6x - 12$ **27.** $(5x)(3y) = (3y)(5x)$ **28.** $10z + 0 = 10z$ **29.** 4 **30.** 19 **31.** $5b$ **32.** 11 **33.** 10 **34.** 5 **35.** 4 **36.** -8 **37.** $\frac{b - a^2}{a}$, $a \neq 0$, $b \neq 0$ **38.** 10 cm, 6 cm **39.** 525 mi/h **40.** 70°, 110° **41.** $z \leq \frac{2}{5}$

42. $x > 2$

43. $y > 4.5$

44. $-1 \leq x \leq 1$

45. $x \leq \frac{3}{2}$ or $x > 6$

46. $y \geq \frac{5}{3}$

47. $\$155,850 \leq A \leq \$415,850$ **48.** 1 **49.** $\frac{1}{5}$, 9 **50.** no solutions **51.** $-\frac{1}{3} \leq x \leq \frac{5}{3}$

52. $y < 0$ or $y > 18$

53. $x < -4$ or $x > 6$

54. $|x - 43.6| \leq 0.1$ **55.** $\frac{1}{2}$ **56.** $\frac{5}{8}$ **57.** $\frac{1}{2}$ **58.** $\frac{3}{8}$ **59.** $\frac{5}{8}$ **60.** about 9%

CHAPTER 2

Lesson 2-1   pp. 61–63

EXERCISES

1. 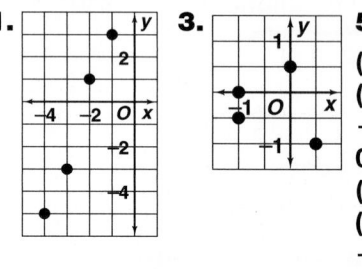 **3.** **5.** $(-2, -2)$, $(-1, 1)$, $(1, 1)$, $(1, 0)$, $(3, 3)$, $(3, -2)$; domain {-2, -1, 1, 3}, range {-2, 0, 1, 3} **7.** $(-2, 0)$, $(-1, 2)$, $(0, 3)$, $(1, 2)$, $(2, 0)$; domain {-2, -1, 0, 1, 2}, range {0, 2, 3}

9. **11.**

13. function **15.** function **17.** not a function **19.** function **21.** function **23.** 13, 7, -3.5, -14 **25.** -2, -4, -7.5, -11 **27.** -13, -9, -2, 5 **29.** $-\frac{23}{6}$, $-\frac{13}{6}$, $\frac{3}{4}$, $\frac{11}{3}$ **31.** $y = \frac{x}{39.37}$, where y is the number of meters and x is the number of inches; ≈ 1.50 m

33. domain {-4, -3, -2, -1}, range {1, 2, 3, 4}

35. domain $\left\{-\frac{3}{2}, \frac{1}{2}, \frac{3}{2}, \frac{5}{2}\right\}$, range $\left\{-\frac{1}{2}, \frac{1}{2}\right\}$

37. domain {-2, -1, 0, 9}, range {2, 5, 7}; not a function **39.** domain {$-3.2 \leq x \leq 3.2$}, range {$-1 \leq y \leq 1$}; not a function **41.** B **43.** yes **45.** no **47.** $v(r) = \frac{4}{3}\pi r^3$; about 4849 cm³ **49.** Check students' work. **51.** $-\frac{2}{3}$ **53.** 7 **55.** Yes; each x is paired with a unique y. **57.** Yes; each x is paired with a unique y. **59.** domain: {all integers}, range: {all even integers}; function,

each integer pairs to a unique even integer.
61. domain: {all integers}, range: {all even integers}; not a function, each nonzero integer pairs with a pos. and neg. even integer. **63.** A
65. $\frac{1}{11}$ **67.** $\frac{4}{11}$ **69.** $\frac{6}{11}$ **71.** $\frac{3}{11}$ **73.** $-2 \le b \le 2$

75. 11.1% increase **77.** 25% decrease

Lesson 2-2   pp. 69–72

EXERCISES

1. **3.** **5.** **7.**

9a. $y = 0.23x$, domain $\{x \mid x \in \mathbb{R}$ and $x \ge 0\}$, range $\{y \mid y \in \mathbb{R}$ and $y \ge 0\}$ **b.** x-intercept (0, 0), y-intercept (0, 0); when no miles have been driven, there is no cost.
c. 0.23 represents a cost of \$.23 per mile driven.
11. -1 **13.** 3 **15.** $-\frac{1}{5}$ **17.** undefined **19.** $\frac{17}{5}$
21. $\frac{5}{6}x - y = \frac{19}{3}$ **23.** $y = -2$ **25.** $5x - y = -2$
27. $y - 0 = \frac{5}{4}(x - 1)$ **29.** $y + 1 = -\frac{4}{3}(x - 0)$
31. $y - 9 = -\frac{7}{5}(x - 1)$ **33.** $\frac{3}{2}$ **35.** $-\frac{A}{B}$ **37.** 0
39. $y = \frac{5}{2}x + \frac{13}{2}$ 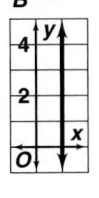 **41.** $x = 1$

43. **45.** **47.**

49. **51.** $\frac{1}{3}$ **53.** $-\frac{1}{4}$ **55.** -1; (0, 1000), (1000, 0) **57.** 54; (0, −1), $\left(\frac{1}{54}, 0\right)$
59. 0; (0, 0), all pts. on x-axis
61. $\frac{R}{S}$; $\left(0, -\frac{T}{S}\right)$, $\left(\frac{T}{R}, 0\right)$ **63.** $-\frac{5}{13}$ **65.** $-\frac{7}{10}$
67. $y = 3x + 2$ **69.** B
71. $y = -1$ **73.** $y = \frac{5}{6}x + \frac{10}{3}$
75. $3x - 2y = 2$ **77.** $3x + 12y = -4$
79. yes **81.** $y = 3x + 6$;
$y = -\frac{1}{3}x + \frac{8}{3}$; $\left(\frac{1}{2}, 2\frac{1}{2}\right)$

---

83. The slope of the line connecting (2, 5) to (4, 8) is $\frac{3}{2}$, (2, 5) to (5, 3) is $-\frac{2}{3}$, (4, 8) to (7, 6) is $-\frac{2}{3}$, and (5, 3) to (7, 6) is $\frac{3}{2}$. Since the adjacent sides' slopes are negative reciprocals they are perpendicular. By the def. of a rectangle, it is a rectangle. **85.** B
87. C **89.** domain {−2, 1, 2, 3, 4}, range {−2, −1, 2, 3}; not a function **91.** domain {−3, 0, 1, 7}, range {−10, −5, −1, 3}; not a function
93. multiplicative inverses **95.** additive inverses, additive identity

Extension   p. 73

1. **3.**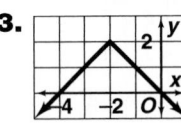

5. $f(x) = \begin{cases} -3x - 10, & \text{if } x \le -2 \\ \frac{1}{2}x - 3, & \text{if } -2 < x < 2 \\ 2x - 6, & \text{if } x \ge 2 \end{cases}$

Lesson 2-3   pp. 76–79

EXERCISES 1. yes; 2, $y = 2x$ **3.** no **5.** yes; $k = 7$, $y = 7x$ **7.** yes; $k = -2$, $y = -2x$ **9.** yes; $k = 12$
11. yes; $k = -2$ **13.** no **15.** yes; $k = 6$ **17.** $\frac{2}{7}$; $-\frac{10}{7}$
19. -1; 5 **21.** $k = -\frac{17}{4}$; $21\frac{1}{4}$ **23.a.** $k = \frac{13}{36}$
b. $s = \frac{13}{36}h$ **c.** $\approx$23 ft 1 in. **25.** 4 **27.** $\frac{5}{3}$ **29.** no
31. yes; $k = 1.3$, $y = 1.3x$ **33.** $y = 2x$ **35.** $y = -\frac{9}{2}x$
37. $y = \frac{3}{5}x$ **39.** $y = \frac{2}{7}x$ **41.** 9 **43.** 90 **45.** 1.2
47. Yes; $y = -\frac{5}{6}x$ contains the point $\left(15, -12\frac{1}{2}\right)$.
49. Answers may vary. Sample: $y = 0.5x$
51. Answers may vary. Sample: $y = -\frac{3}{4}x$
53. Answers may vary. Sample: No, the line $y = 0$ passes through the origin, but is not a direct variation. **55.** y is doubled. **57.** y is divided by 7.
59.a. $\frac{1}{2}$ **b.** 32 **c.** $z = kxy$, and $x = k_1w$, so $z = kk_1wy$, and z varies jointly with w and y. **61.** A

63. **65.** [graph]

67. domain {0, 1, −2, 3}, range {1, −3}

69. domain {1, 2, 4, 5};
range {−2, −1, 1, 2}

71. about 46.5%

Lesson 2-4 pp. 83–86

EXERCISES

1. $d = 62.5h + 15$

3. $h = 8x + 60$ 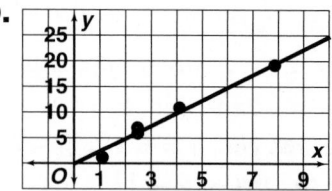 **5.** $y = 0.5x + 0.75$;

3.25 lb **7.** $y = 1.75x + 1.75$; $8.40

9. Linear model is

reasonable; models may vary. Sample:
$y = 2.6x − 0.6$ **11.** not reasonable

13a. Answers may vary.

Sample: $y = 110x + 1170$ **b.** 2930 Cal **c.** Answers
may vary. Sample: No; adults need fewer
Calories, not more. **15.** $y = −4x + 10$
17. $y = −7.5x − 2.5$ **19.a.** $y = 29.95$ **b.** $y = 2.95x$;
slope = 2.95; y-intercept = 0 **c.** Answers may
vary. Sample: Either way,

you will average the same costs over the long run.

21.a. population **b–c.**
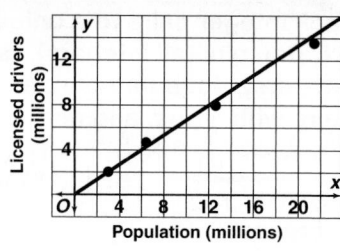

d. 7 million **e.** Answers may vary. Sample: Strong;
the points fall close to a straight line. **23.** 104.5
25. 13 **27.a.** $y = −\frac{17}{11}x + 14.27$ **b.** $y = −2x + 10$
c. Answers may vary. Sample: neither;
$y = −1.5x + 12$ **29.** A **31.** C **33.** A **35.** −3; 15
37. $\frac{42}{5}$; −42 **39.** {1, 3.5, 5, 6, 8}

41. $\left\{ −\frac{7}{2}, −\frac{5}{2}, −2, −\frac{5}{4}, \right\}$ **43.** {1, 6, 9, 11, 15}

Lesson 2-5 pp. 92–94

EXERCISES

1.

x	0	−1	1	−2	2
y	0	4	4	8	8

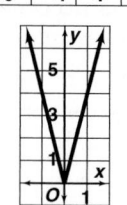

3.

x	−1	0	$\frac{1}{4}$	1	2
y	5	1	0	3	7

5.

x	−2	−1	0	1	2
y	8	5	2	5	8

7.

x	−2	−1	0	1	2
y	−4	−2	0	−2	−4

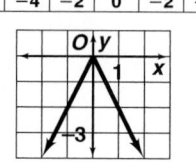

9.

x	−4	−3	$−\frac{5}{2}$	−1	0
y	−3	−1	0	−3	−5

11.

13. **15.** **17.**

19.

21.

23. **25.**

27. **29. B 31. A**

33. **35.** **37.**

39. **41.**

43. **45.** **47.**

49. **51. A 53.**

55. **57.**

59. Answers may vary. Samples: a. $y = |x|$, $y = -|x|$ **b.** $y = |x|$, $y = |x - 1| + 1$ **61. B 63. D**

65.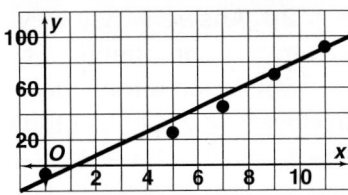

Yes, a linear model is reasonable. Equations may vary. Sample: $y = 8.7x - 10.9$

67.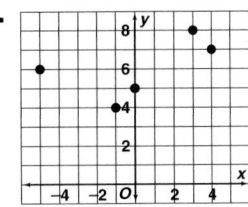

69. -3 **71.** $-\frac{1}{9}$ **73.** $-\frac{3}{2}$ **75.** $y = 18h$; linear
77. 9 **79.** 4

Lesson 2-6 pp. 99–102

EXERCISES 1. **3.**

5. $y = |x| - \frac{2}{3}$ **7.** $y = |x| + 2$
9. Translate $y = |x|$ **left 5 units;**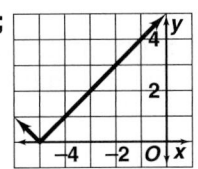

11. Translate $y = |x|$ **left 2 units;**

13. $y = |x - 3|$ **15. Answers may vary. Sample: 4.5 units to the left.**

17. **19.** **21.**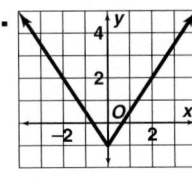

23. $y = 2|x|$ **25.** $y = \frac{2}{3}|x|$ **27.** $y = -\frac{1}{3}|x|$
29. vertical **31. horizontal**

33. vertical 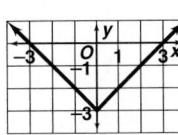 **35.** $y = |x - 2| - 2$

37. $y = -|x + 2| + 4$ **39.** Answers may vary.
Sample: Since a vert. translation affects only
y-values and a horiz. translation affects only
x-values, order is irrelevant. **41.** Check students'
work. **43.** $y = -|x| - 3$ **45.** $y = 2|x + 4| + 3$
47. $y = -|x - p| + q$

49. 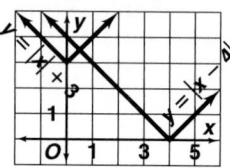 4 right, 3 down

51. 3 right, 3 up

53.a. **b.**

c. **d.**

55. C **57.** Answers may vary. Sample: $f(0) = 5$;
$f(1) = 4$; $f(2) = 3$; $f(3) = 2$; $f(-1) = 6$

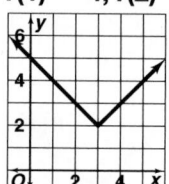

59. $f(x) = \frac{1}{3}|\frac{1}{3}x - 3|$ Answers may vary. Samples:
$f(0) = 1$; $f(1) = \frac{8}{9}$; $f(3) = \frac{2}{3}$; $f(-1) = \frac{10}{9}$; $f(-3) = \frac{4}{3}$

61. $a > 4.5$

63. $150 \cdot 75 \cdot x = 281{,}250$; 25 ft

Lesson 2-7 pp. 106–108

EXERCISES

1. **3.** **5.**

7. **9.** **11.**

13. **15.**

17. **19.**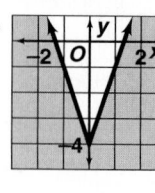

21. $5x + 3y \le 9$ **23.** **25.**

27. **29.**

31. **33.** **35.** Answers may vary.

Sample: $y \le -\frac{5}{3}x + \frac{95}{3}$ **37.** $y \le \frac{3}{2}x + 2$
39. $y \le |x + 2|$ **41.** $y > |x + 1| - 1$ **43.** Answers
may vary. Sample: when it lies on the boundary
line **45.** **47.** **49.** A

51. A **53.** **55.**

57. **59.** no **61.** yes; -5 **63.** yes; 3

65. yes; -10 **67.** $7800 **69.**

1. dependent 2. relations 3. sometimes
4. point-slope 5. sometimes 6. not a function;
domain: {1, 3, 5, 8}, range: {0, 1, 2, 3, 8}
7. function; domain: {−10, −6, 5, 6, 10}, range:
{2, 3, 4, 7} 8. not a function;

domain: $\left\{-2, -\frac{3}{2}, -1, \frac{1}{2}, 1, 2, 3\right\}$,

range: $\left\{-\frac{7}{2}, -\frac{1}{2}, 0, \frac{1}{2}, \frac{3}{2}, 2, \frac{5}{2}\right\}$

9. function; domain: {−4, −2, −1, 1, 3},
range: {−1, 2, 4} 10. function;

domain: $\left\{-2, -1, \frac{1}{2}, 3\right\}$, range: {2} 11. 6, 4.5, 1

12. $-3\frac{3}{4}, -3\frac{3}{16}, -1\frac{7}{8}$ 13. $2\frac{5}{6}, 2\frac{5}{24}, \frac{3}{4}$ 14. $3x + y = 12$

15. $2x - y = 1$ 16. $2, \left(\frac{3}{4}, 0\right), \left(0, -\frac{3}{2}\right)$

17. $\frac{M}{N}$; $\left(\frac{P}{M}, 0\right), \left(0, -\frac{P}{N}\right)$ 18. −1; (5, 0), (0, 5)

19a. $y = -\frac{1}{2}x + 7$ b. $y = 2x - 13$

c. 20. no 21. no 22. yes; 1;

$y = x$ 23. −4; 1.2 24. $\frac{10}{3}$; −1 25. $\frac{7}{2}$; $-1\frac{1}{20}$

26a and b.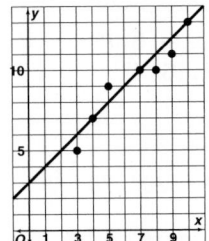

Answers may vary. Sample: $y = 2.5x + 21.5$
c. Answers may vary. Sample: about 96.5 million
27. Answers may vary.

Sample: reasonable; $y = x + 3$; 18
28.

Answers may vary. Sample: reasonable;
$y = -0.8x + 19.9$; 7.9
29. 30.

31. 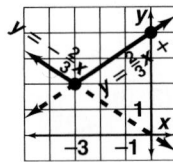 32. $y = |x - 2| + 4$

33. $y = |x + 3|$ 34. $y = |x - 5| + 2$
35. $y = |x - 4| + 1$ 36.

37. 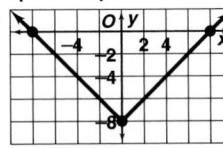 38.

39. 40.

41. 42. 43.

44. 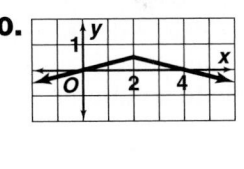 45.

46a. Answers may vary. Sample: $x + 3y \le 15$
b. Answers may vary. Sample: domain {1, 2, 3, 4, 5, 6, 7, 8, 9, 10, 11, 12, 13, 14, 15}, range {1, 2, 3, 4, 5}

c. 47. Answers may vary.

Sample: $y \le -|x| - 1$

Chapter 3

EXERCISES

1. (3, 1) **3.** (−2, 4)

5. no solution **7.** (3, 6)

9. (10, 20) **11.** Use 0 for 1970.

$$\begin{cases} y = 0.22x + 67.5 \\ y = 0.15x + 75.507 \end{cases}$$

about 2085

13. dependent

15. inconsistent

17. inconsistent **19.** dependent **21.** dependent
23 independent

25. infinite solutions   **27.** no solution

29. (2, −3)

31. $\left(\frac{16}{9}, -\frac{14}{9}\right) \approx (1.5, -1.5)$

33. infinite solutions

35. $\left(\frac{12}{7}, \frac{18}{7}\right) \approx (1.7, 2.6)$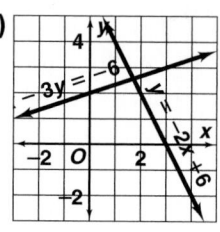

37.a. $\begin{cases} c = 3 + 0.40b \\ c = 9.00 \end{cases}$

b. (15, 9); the

point represents where the cost of using the bank
or online service would be the same. **c.** The local
bank would be cheaper if you only have 12 bills to
pay per month. **39.** dependent **41.** inconsistent
43. dependent **45.** x = minutes, y = flyers:

$$\begin{cases} y = 6x + 80 \\ y = 4x + 100 \end{cases}$$

After 10 minutes the numbers of flyers will
be equal. **47.** Answers may vary. Sample:
$y = -4x + 8$ **49.** No; they would be the same
line, and the system would be dependent and
consistent. **51.** Answers may vary. Sample:
$3x + 4y = 12$ **53.** Answers may vary. Sample:
$\begin{cases} -10x + 2y = 4 \\ 5x - y = -2 \end{cases}$ **55.a.** p: independent, n:
dependent **b.** $n = -1600p +$
14,800 **c.** $n = -6000 + 32,000$ **d.** About (3.91, 8545);
profits are maximized if about 8545 widgets are
sold for about \$3.91 each. **57.** C **59.** $y \le \frac{3}{4}x - 4$

 61. $x < -4$ **63.** $y = 4$

65. $y = \frac{1}{2}x - 5$ **67.** $\frac{3}{5}$ **69.** $\frac{4}{7}$ **71.** 1

EXERCISES 1. (0.5, 2.5) **3.** (20, 4) **5.** (10, −1)
7. $(a, b) = (0, 3)$ **9.** (−2, −5) **11.** (6, 4)

13.a. $\begin{cases} d = 0.50m \\ d = 15 \end{cases}$ **b.** 30 miles

15.a. $\begin{cases} p = 28 \\ p = 8 + 0.35d \end{cases}$ **b.** 58 **17.** 20°, 70°, 90°

19. (2, 4) **21.** (2, −2) **23.** $(u, v) = (4, 1)$ **25.** (6, 0)
27. (0, 3) **29.** $(r, s) = (2, -1)$ **31.** $\{(a, d) | -3a + d = -1\}$ **33.** no solution **35.** no solution **37.** (−3, 2)
39. (1, 3) **41.** $(m, n) = (1, -4)$ **43.** In determining
whether to use substitution or elimination to
solve an equation, look at the equations to
determine if one is solved or can be easily solved
for a particular variable. If that is the case,
substitution can easily be used. Otherwise,
elimination might be easier. **45.** $(m, n) = (4, -3)$

47. $(t, v) = (50, 750)$ **49.** $\left(\frac{3}{11}, -\frac{2}{11}\right)$ **51.** $(a, b) =$ $(-235, -5.8)$ **53.** A **55.** Substitution; the first equation is solved for y. **57.** Substitution; the second equation is solved for y. **59.** Elimination; substitution would be difficult since no coefficient is 1. **61.a.** $c = 9.95 + 2.25t$, $c = 2.95t$

b. **c.** about 14.2 h; it is where the graphs intersect. **d.** Answers may vary. Sample: Internet Action, because it would cost $4.05 less per month

63. yes; for -40 degrees **65.** 0 **67.** C **69.** B
71. $\{(x, y) \mid -9x - 3y = 1\}$ **73.** $y = (x + 3) - 4$ or $y = x - 1$ **75.** $y = 2(x - 1) - 4$ or $y = 2x - 6$
77. natural, whole, integer, rational

Lesson 3-3   pp. 138–140

EXERCISES 1. (0, 4), (0, 5), (0, 6), (0, 7), (0, 8)
3. (0, 7), (0, 6), (0, 5), (0, 4), (0, 3), (0, 2), (0, 1), (0, 0), (1, 6), (1, 5), (1, 4), (1, 3), (1, 2), (1, 1), (1, 0), (2, 5), (2, 4), (2, 3), (2, 2), (2, 1), (2, 0), (3, 4), (3, 3) **5.** no
7. **9.**

11. **13.** $y > -2x$ 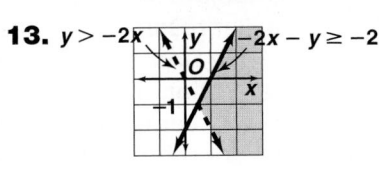 $-2x - y \geq -2$

15. $2x + y < 1$ $y + 3x < 1$

17. $\begin{cases} a + c \geq 40 \\ c \leq 30 \end{cases}$ **19.** $y > |2x| - 1$ $y < -\frac{1}{3}x + 1$

21. 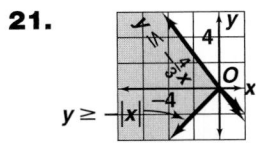 $y \geq -|x|$ **23.** $y \leq -|x - 3|$ $y > -2$

25. $y < |x + 3|$ 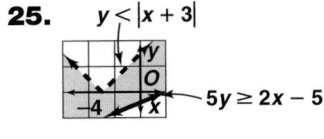 $-5y \geq 2x - 5$ **27.**

29. $y \leq x - 4$ **31.** A, B **33.** A, B **35.** B, C

37. A **39.** A **41.** Answers may vary. Sample:
$\begin{cases} x < 5 \\ y \geq 1 \end{cases}$ **43.** **45.**

47. 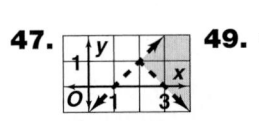 **49.** $\begin{cases} y \geq |x| - 2 \\ y \leq -|x| + 2 \end{cases}$

51. $\begin{cases} y \leq 4 \\ y \geq 0 \\ y \leq 2x \\ y \geq 2x - 8 \end{cases}$ **53.** B **55.** $(-9, -26)$

57. no solution **59.** $(-1, 2)$ **61.** 9 **63.** -8
65. $\frac{1}{2}, -\frac{11}{2}$ **67.** 8, 0 **69.** $-\frac{16}{3}, 4$

Lesson 3-4   pp. 144–146

EXERCISES 1. When $x = 4$ and $y = 2$, P is maximized at 16. **3.** When $x = 6$ and $y = 8$, C is minimized at 36.

5. 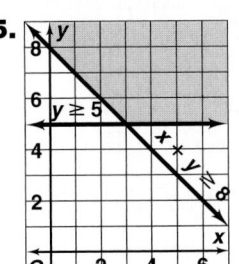 vertices: (3, 5), (0, 8); minimized at (0, 8)

7. vertices: (1, 5), (8, 5), (8, −2); minimized at (8, −2)

9. vertices: (2, 1), (6, 1), (6, 2), (2, 5), (3, 5); maximized at (6, 2)

11. 70 spruce; 0 maple **13.** A
15. vertices: (75, 20), (75, 110), $\left(25, 86\frac{2}{3}\right)$, (25, 110); minimized when $C = 633\frac{1}{3}$ at $\left(25, 86\frac{2}{3}\right)$

Selected Answers **995**

17. vertices: (0, 0), (150, 0), (100, 100), (0, 200); maximized when $P = 400$ at (0, 200)

19. 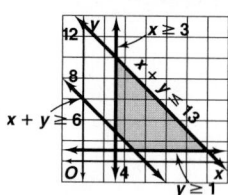 vertices: (3, 3), (3, 10), (5, 1), (12, 1); maximized when $P = 51$ at (12, 1)

21. vertices: (0, 60), $\left(23\frac{1}{3}, 13\frac{1}{3}\right)$, (50, 0); minimized when $x = 23\frac{1}{3}$ and $y = 13$ Round to (23, 14) and (24, 13); (24, 13) gives you a minimum C of 261. **23.** Answers may vary. Sample: (4, 6), (6, 5), (9, 3.5), (10, 3) **25.** B

27. **29.**

31. 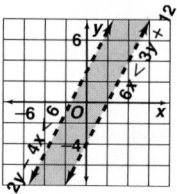 **33.** 1 **35.** −34 **37.** 24 **39.** $\frac{4}{3}$

Lesson 3-5 pp. 151–153

EXERCISES 1. 1 unit back, 5 units right **3.** 2 units forward, 5 units up

5. **7.**

9. **11.**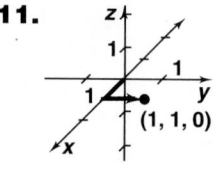

13. (0, 0, 0) **15.** (0, 40, 0) **17.** (0, 80, 100)

---

19. **21.**

23. **25.** Answers may vary Sample: Balcony represents vertical direction, row is backward or forward, and seat is left or right.

27. **29.** **31.**

33. xy-trace: $x + y = 6$
xz-trace: $x - 2z = 6$
yz-trace: $y - 2z = 6$

35. xy-trace: $-3x - 8y = 24$
xz-trace: $-x - 4z = 8$
yz-trace: $-2y - 3z = 6$

37. Mt. Kilimanjaro **39.** Valdivia Seamount **41.** Qattara Depression **43.** Jabal Toubkal **45.** Aswan High Dam **47.** The student is actually finding the equation of the yz-trace. If the student wants the x-intercept, the student should substitute 0 for both y and z in the equation of the plane. **49.a.** No, a plane that is parallel to two of the axes (and is therefore perpendicular to the third axis) has only two traces, which are perpendicular. **b.** No, a plane that intersects two of the axes and is parallel to the third axis has three traces, two of which are parallel.

51. **53.** D **55.** A

57. **59.**

Lesson 3-6 pp. 159–161

EXERCISES 1. (4, 2, −3) **3.** (2, 1, −5)
5. $(q, r, s) = \left(\frac{1}{2}, -3, 1\right)$ **7.** (1, −4, 3) **9.** (4, −1, 2)

11. $(a, b, c) = (2, 3, -2)$ **13.** $(5, 2, 2)$ **15.** $(4, 1, 6)$
17. $(1, -1, 2)$ **19.** \$220,000 was placed in short-term notes. \$440,000 was placed in government bonds. \$340,000 was placed in utility bonds.
21. 50 nickels, 10 dimes, and 15 quarters
23. one solution **25.** $(8, 1, 3)$ **27.** $\left(\frac{1}{2}, 2, -3\right)$
29. no solution **31.** $(6, 1.5, 3.2)$ **33.** $\left(-\frac{10}{13}, -\frac{2}{13}, \frac{4}{13}\right)$
35. $(-1, 2, 0)$ **37.** $\left(2, \frac{10}{3}, \frac{5}{3}\right)$ **39.** 75 apples; 25 pears
41. Answers may vary. Sample: When one of the equations can easily be solved for one variable, it is easier to use substitution.
43. $x + 2y = 180$
$y + z = 180$
$5z = 540$
$x = 36, y = 72, z = 108$
45. Let E, F, and V represent the numbers of edges, faces, and vertices, respectively. From the statement, "Every face has five edges, and the number of edges is 5 times the number of faces: $E = 5F$." But since each edge is part of two faces, this counts each edge twice. So $E = \frac{5}{2}F$. Since every face has five vertices and every vertex is shared by three faces, $3V = 5F$ or $V = \frac{5}{3}F$. Euler's formula: $V + F = E + 2$. Solving this system of three equations yields $E = 30$, $F = 12$, and $V = 20$. **47.** C **49.** B
51. **53.** **55.**

57. **59.**

61. **63.** $x \leq -18$

65. $x < 2$
67. $x \leq -2$

Chapter Review pp. 163–165

1. A **2.** D **3.** B **4.** E **5.** C **6.** $(-2, -3)$ **7.** $(2, 4)$
8. no solution **9.** $(-2, 0)$ **10.** $(3, 6)$ **11.** no solution **12.** consistent and dependent
13. consistent and independent **14.** inconsistent
15. 20 checks **16.** $(10, -4)$ **17.** $(0, 4)$ **18.** $(1, 9)$
19. $(3, 7)$ **20.** no solution **21.** $\left(\frac{7}{24}, \frac{1}{24}\right)$

22. 1 serving of roast beef and 2 servings of mashed potatoes
23. **24.**

25. **26.** Let r = number of gallons of regular coffee, and d = number of gallons of decaffeinated coffee. $r + d \geq 10$, $\frac{1}{3}r \geq d$

27.

vertices: $(0, 0)$, $(8, 0)$, $(8, 5)$, $(0, 5)$
$C = 0$ at $(0, 0)$

28. **29.**

vertices: $(4, 0)$ $(2, 3)$
$C = 11$ at $(2, 3)$

vertices: $(0, 0)$, $(4, 0)$, $(2, 3)$, $(0, 5)$ $P = 25$ at $(0, 5)$
30. 50 of each type

31. **32.** **33.**

34. **35.**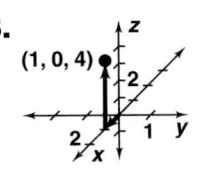

36. $(3, 3, 1)$ **37.** $(0, -2, 2)$ **38.** $(-2, 2, -1)$
39. $(0, 0, 3)$

40. **41.** **42.**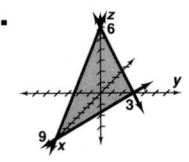

43. $(2, 5, 3)$ **44.** no solution **45.** $(6, 0, -2)$

Chapter 4

1. 3×3 **3.** 1×2 **5.** 4×1 **7.** -3 **9.** $\frac{1}{2}$ **11.** -1
13.

	Week 1	Week 2	Week 3	Week 4
Novels	175	154	201	180
Biogr.	100	93	110	92
Sci-Fi.	93	81	114	100
Nonfiction	100	104	103	110

15.

	1998	1999	2000	2001	2002	2003
CDs	847.0	933.9	942.5	881.9	803.3	745.9
DVDs	0.5	2.5	3.3	7.9	10.7	17.5

3.3, which represents 3.3 million DVDs shipped
in 2000 **17.** $2 \times 6, 6 \times 2$ **19.** You must include
what the columns and rows represent. **21.** 2×3; 1
23. 1×3; 12 **25.** 2×2; 8

27. a.

	Job	No Job
9th gr. boys	5	95
9th gr. girls	15	90

	Job	No Job
10th gr. boys	35	65
10th gr. girls	30	55

	Job	No Job
11th gr. boys	65	35
11th gr. girls	75	30

	Job	No Job
12th gr. boys	70	25
12th gr. girls	65	45

b. 175 **c.** 185 **d.** about 51.4%

29. Answers may vary. Sample:

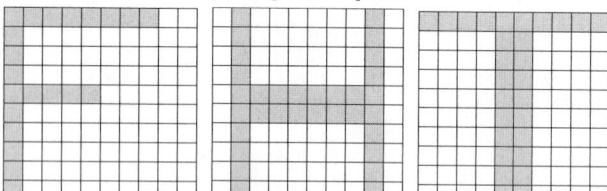

b.   Answers may vary. Sample:

$$F = \begin{bmatrix} 1&1&1&1&1&1&1&1&0&0 \\ 1&0&0&0&0&0&0&0&0&0 \\ 1&0&0&0&0&0&0&0&0&0 \\ 1&0&0&0&0&0&0&0&0&0 \\ 1&1&1&1&1&0&0&0&0&0 \\ 1&0&0&0&0&0&0&0&0&0 \\ 1&0&0&0&0&0&0&0&0&0 \\ 1&0&0&0&0&0&0&0&0&0 \\ 1&0&0&0&0&0&0&0&0&0 \end{bmatrix}$$

$$H = \begin{bmatrix} 0&1&0&0&0&0&0&0&1&0 \\ 0&1&0&0&0&0&0&0&1&0 \\ 0&1&0&0&0&0&0&0&1&0 \\ 0&1&0&0&0&0&0&0&1&0 \\ 0&1&1&1&1&1&1&1&1&0 \\ 0&1&1&1&1&1&1&1&1&0 \\ 0&1&0&0&0&0&0&0&1&0 \\ 0&1&0&0&0&0&0&0&1&0 \\ 0&1&0&0&0&0&0&0&1&0 \\ 0&1&0&0&0&0&0&0&1&0 \end{bmatrix}$$

$$T = \begin{bmatrix} 1&1&1&1&1&1&1&1&1&1 \\ 0&0&0&0&1&1&0&0&0&0 \\ 0&0&0&0&1&1&0&0&0&0 \\ 0&0&0&0&1&1&0&0&0&0 \\ 0&0&0&0&1&1&0&0&0&0 \\ 0&0&0&0&1&1&0&0&0&0 \\ 0&0&0&0&1&1&0&0&0&0 \\ 0&0&0&0&1&1&0&0&0&0 \\ 0&0&0&0&1&1&0&0&0&0 \\ 0&0&0&0&1&1&0&0&0&0 \end{bmatrix}$$

31. A **33.** $(1, -2, 4)$
35.

(3, 2) **37.**

$(-5, 2)$

39. -7 **41.** $\frac{5}{3}$ **43.** $\frac{27}{2}$

EXERCISES

1a.

Anita Allen	
Shoot	952
Fence	720
Swim	1108
Ride	1172
Run	1044

Mary Beth Iagorashvili	
Shoot	760
Fence	832
Swim	1252
Ride	1144
Run	1064

b. 4996; 5052

3. $\begin{bmatrix} 1 & 3 \\ 4 & 0 \end{bmatrix}$ **5.** $\begin{bmatrix} 0 & 0 \\ 0 & 0 \end{bmatrix}$ **7.** $\begin{bmatrix} 0 & -2 & 0 \\ -2 & 0 & -2 \end{bmatrix}$

9. $\begin{bmatrix} -6.8 & 1.3 \\ -2.1 & -1 \end{bmatrix}$ **11.** $\begin{bmatrix} -9 & -2 & 12 \\ -15 & 11 & -7 \end{bmatrix}$

13. $\begin{bmatrix} -4 & -1 \\ -1 & -2 \end{bmatrix}$ **15.** No; the matrices have different
dimensions. **17.** $x = 2, t = \frac{3}{5}$
19. B and D cannot be added because they do
not have the same dimensions.

21. $\begin{bmatrix} -6 & -3 \\ -4 & -2 \\ -2 & 5 \end{bmatrix}$ **23.** B **25.** $\begin{bmatrix} 9 & 62 \\ 125 & -11 \end{bmatrix}$

27.a.

	Plant 1		Plant 2	
	Plastic	Rubber	Plastic	Rubber
1-color	1000	1400	1200	3600
3-color	2600	3800	1800	4800

b.

	Plant 1 − Plant 2	
	Plastic	Rubber
1-color	−200	−2200
3-color	800	−1000

Plant 1; Plant 2

29. $a = 2, b = \frac{9}{4}, c = -1, d = 0, f = \frac{1}{2}, g = -4$
31. $c = \frac{5}{2}, d = \frac{2}{5}, f = 7, g = 5, h = -1$

33. Consider any two 2×2 matrices,

$A = \begin{bmatrix} a & b \\ c & d \end{bmatrix}$ and $B = \begin{bmatrix} w & x \\ y & z \end{bmatrix}$. By the def. of matrix addition and the Comm. Prop. of Add.,

$$A + B = \begin{bmatrix} a & b \\ c & d \end{bmatrix} + \begin{bmatrix} w & x \\ y & z \end{bmatrix} = \begin{bmatrix} a + w & b + x \\ c + y & d + z \end{bmatrix}$$

$$= \begin{bmatrix} w + a & x + b \\ y + c & z + d \end{bmatrix} = B + A$$ **35.** D **37.** C

39. Answers may vary. **41.** 2, −6 **43.** $-\frac{1}{2}$, −6

Lesson 4-3   pp. 190–193

1. $\begin{bmatrix} 9 & 12 \\ 18 & -6 \\ 3 & 0 \end{bmatrix}$ **3.** $\begin{bmatrix} -3 & -6 \\ 9 & -3 \end{bmatrix}$ **5.** $\begin{bmatrix} 9 & 2 \\ 2 & 6 \\ 3 & -10 \end{bmatrix}$

7. $\begin{bmatrix} 19 & 11 \\ -12 & 10 \end{bmatrix}$ **9.** $\begin{bmatrix} 8 & -2.5 \\ -1.5 & -1 \end{bmatrix}$ **11.** $\begin{bmatrix} 5 & -12 \\ 9 & -6 \end{bmatrix}$

13. $\begin{bmatrix} -8 & 0 \\ 0 & -8 \end{bmatrix}$ **15.** $[34 \ 0]$ **17.** $\begin{bmatrix} -15 & 0 \\ 25 & 0 \end{bmatrix}$

19a.

	Lilies	Carnations	Daisies
Arrangement 1	3	0	0
Arrangement 2	3	4	0
Arrangement 3	0	3	4

b.

	Cost
Lilies	2.15
Carnations	0.90
Daisies	1.30

c.

	Cost
Arrangement 1	6.45
Arrangement 2	10.05
Arrangement 3	7.90

21. defined **23.** undefined **25.** undefined

27. defined **29.** defined **31.** $\begin{bmatrix} -9 & 7 & 4 \\ 8 & 2 & -3 \end{bmatrix}$

33. $\begin{bmatrix} 1 & 0 & -1 \\ 0 & 1 & -1 \end{bmatrix}$ **35.** B

37. 4 × 4; $\begin{bmatrix} a & 0 & b & 0 \\ a - 2e & 0 & b & -2f \\ 2e & 0 & 0 & 2f \\ -a + e & 0 & -b & f \end{bmatrix}$ **39.** $\begin{bmatrix} 9 & -6 \\ 15 & -3 \\ -6 & -12 \end{bmatrix}$

41. $\begin{bmatrix} 17 & -24 \\ -33 & -7 \\ 69 & -18 \end{bmatrix}$ **43.** $\begin{bmatrix} 34 & -1 \\ 6 & -13 \\ -7 & 16 \end{bmatrix}$ **45.** $\begin{bmatrix} -90 & 0 \\ -78 & 42 \\ -30 & -30 \end{bmatrix}$

47. Answers may vary. Sample: Multiply the elements in each row of the first matrix by the elements in each column of the second matrix. Then add to get the corresponding entry in the resultant matrix. **49.** No; *AB* will be a 2 × 2 matrix and *BA* will be a 3 × 3 matrix, and equal matrices must have the same dimensions. Answers may vary. Sample: Let *A* be the matrix

$\begin{bmatrix} 0 & 1 & 2 \\ 3 & 0 & 0 \end{bmatrix}$, and let *B* be the matrix $\begin{bmatrix} 1 & 0 \\ 2 & 4 \\ 3 & 1 \end{bmatrix}$. Then

$AB = \begin{bmatrix} 8 & 6 \\ 3 & 0 \end{bmatrix}$ and $BA = \begin{bmatrix} 0 & 1 & 2 \\ 12 & 2 & 4 \\ 3 & 3 & 6 \end{bmatrix}$. **51.** *x* = −3,

---

y = −9 **53.** yes **55.** yes **57.** D **59.** $\begin{bmatrix} -33 & -12 \\ -6 & 27 \end{bmatrix}$

61. 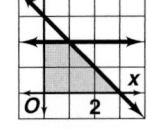 (0, 2), (0, 0), (1, 2), (3, 0); (1, 2)

63. **65.**

(0, 0), (5, 0), (4, 2), (0, 6); (5, 0)

Lesson 4-4   pp. 199–202

EXERCISES 1. $\begin{bmatrix} -2 & -2 & 2 & 2 \\ 2 & 6 & 6 & 2 \end{bmatrix}$

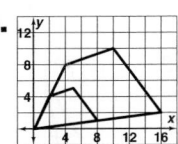

3. $\begin{bmatrix} -13 & -19 & 9 \\ 7 & a + 5 & 0 \end{bmatrix}$ **5.**

graph not possible

7. **9.**

11. **13.** $\begin{bmatrix} 3 & -3 & -3 & 3 \\ -3 & -6 & -3 & -6 \end{bmatrix}$

15. $\begin{bmatrix} 3 & 2 & 2 & 3 & 5 \\ 1 & 2 & 3 & 4 & 2.5 \end{bmatrix}$ **17.**

19.

21. $\begin{bmatrix} 0 & 4 & 8 & 6 \\ 0 & 4 & 4 & 2 \end{bmatrix}$

23. $\begin{bmatrix} -4 & 0 & 0 & -3 & -4 \\ 1 & 2 & 4 & 6 & 2 \end{bmatrix}$

25. $\begin{bmatrix} -8 & -5 & -2 & -5 \\ -8 & -5 & -8 & -11 \end{bmatrix}$

27. $\begin{bmatrix} -12 & 4 & -4 \\ 4 & 8 & 16 \end{bmatrix}$ **29.** $\begin{bmatrix} -1.5 & 0.5 & -0.5 \\ 0.5 & 1 & 2 \end{bmatrix}$

31. $\begin{bmatrix} -1 & -2 & -4 \\ -3 & 1 & -1 \end{bmatrix}$ **33.** $\begin{bmatrix} 3 & -1 & 1 \\ -1 & -2 & -4 \end{bmatrix}$ **35. A**

37.

39. *f*: $\begin{bmatrix} 1 & 2 & 4 & 5 & 2 \\ 2 & 1 & 2 & 5 & 4 \end{bmatrix}$, *g*: $\begin{bmatrix} 2 & 4 & 8 & 10 & 4 \\ 4 & 2 & 4 & 10 & 8 \end{bmatrix}$; dilation

41. *f*: $\begin{bmatrix} -5 & -2 & 1 \\ 3 & 0 & 3 \end{bmatrix}$, *g*: $\begin{bmatrix} -1 & 2 & 5 \\ 1 & -2 & 1 \end{bmatrix}$;

translation **43.**

45. a. Check students' work. **b.** Translate the vertices of *ABCD* down 12 units.
$\begin{bmatrix} 0 & 0 & 0 & 0 \\ -12 & -12 & -12 & -12 \end{bmatrix}$; coordinates of
pre-image: (5, 8), (6, 8), (6, 9), (5, 9), coordinates of image: (5, −4), (6, −4), (6, −3), (5, −3)

c. $\begin{bmatrix} 11 & 12 & 12 & 11 \\ 2 & 2 & 3 & 3 \end{bmatrix}$ **d.** Translate the vertices of

ABCD left 12 units. **47.** $\begin{bmatrix} 0 & 2 & 0 \\ -4 & -7 & -10 \end{bmatrix}$

49. $\begin{bmatrix} -3 & -1.5 & -2 & -4 \\ 3 & 4.5 & 5 & 3.5 \end{bmatrix}$ **51. B**

53. The product matrix is 2 × 3; $\begin{bmatrix} 2 & -1 & 33 \\ 4 & 4 & -50 \end{bmatrix}$

55. **57.**

59. no **61. no**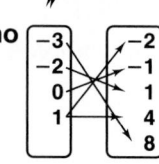

Lesson 4-5 pp. 207–209

EXERCISES 1. $\begin{bmatrix} 3 & 2 \\ 4 & 3 \end{bmatrix}\begin{bmatrix} 3 & -2 \\ -4 & 3 \end{bmatrix} =$

$\begin{bmatrix} 3(3) + 2(-4) & 3(-2) + 2(3) \\ 4(3) + 3(-4) & 4(-2) + 3(3) \end{bmatrix} = \begin{bmatrix} 1 & 0 \\ 0 & 1 \end{bmatrix}$

3. $\begin{bmatrix} \frac{1}{5} & -\frac{1}{10} \\ 0 & \frac{1}{4} \end{bmatrix}\begin{bmatrix} 5 & 2 \\ 0 & 4 \end{bmatrix} =$

$\begin{bmatrix} \frac{1}{5}(5) + (-\frac{1}{10})(0) & \frac{1}{5}(2) + (-\frac{1}{10})(4) \\ 0(5) + \frac{1}{4}(0) & 0(2) + \frac{1}{4}(4) \end{bmatrix} = \begin{bmatrix} 1 & 0 \\ 0 & 1 \end{bmatrix}$

5. 0 **7.** $-\frac{11}{40}$ **9.** 2 **11.** 13 **13.** −6 **15.** yes; $\begin{bmatrix} -1 & 3 \\ 1 & -2 \end{bmatrix}$

17. yes; $\begin{bmatrix} 0 & \frac{1}{2} \\ \frac{1}{3} & -\frac{1}{6} \end{bmatrix}$ **19.** yes; $\begin{bmatrix} -\frac{1}{8} & -\frac{1}{2} \\ \frac{3}{16} & \frac{1}{4} \end{bmatrix}$

21. yes; $\begin{bmatrix} 0 & \frac{1}{3} \\ -\frac{1}{2} & \frac{1}{6} \end{bmatrix}$ **23.** No solutions; the

determinant of $\begin{bmatrix} 0 & -4 \\ 0 & -1 \end{bmatrix}$ is 0.

25.a.

	From	
To	No Cable	Cable
No Cable	0.98	0.005
Cable	0.02	0.995

b. about 20,100 people **c.** about 19,897 people
27. −120 **29.** 2 **31.** yes **33.** No; answers may vary.

Sample: The product is $\begin{bmatrix} 0 & 1 \\ 1 & 0 \end{bmatrix}$. **35.** yes; $\begin{bmatrix} -5 & 7 \\ 3 & -4 \end{bmatrix}$

37. yes; $\begin{bmatrix} 0.5 & 0 \\ 0 & 0.5 \end{bmatrix}$ **39.** yes; $\begin{bmatrix} 0 & \frac{1}{2} \\ \frac{1}{3} & \frac{1}{6} \end{bmatrix}$ **41.** No; the

determinant is 0. **43.** $\begin{bmatrix} 8 & -2 \\ -6 & 1 \end{bmatrix}$

45. a.

	From	
	No DVD	DVD
No DVD	$\begin{bmatrix} 0.83 \end{bmatrix}$	0
To DVD	$\begin{bmatrix} 0.17 \end{bmatrix}$	$1 \end{bmatrix}$

b. about 10,910 people **c.** about 2289 people

d. The student used $\begin{bmatrix} 0.17 & 0 \\ 0.83 & 1 \end{bmatrix}$ for the transition

matrix. **47.** $\begin{bmatrix} -3 & 2 \\ -5 & 8 \end{bmatrix}$ **49.** Multiplicative inverses are only defined for square matrices because square matrices have an equal number of rows and columns. **51.a.** 6 units^2 **b.** 6; it is the same. **c.** They are the same. **d.** Check students' work.

53. B **55.** $\begin{bmatrix} 0 & 3 & 5 \\ -2 & -5 & 0 \end{bmatrix}$ **57.** $\begin{bmatrix} -6 & -4 & -2 \\ 8 & 2 & 10 \end{bmatrix}$

59. $\left(\frac{70}{11}, -\frac{10}{11}, \frac{50}{11}\right)$ **61.a.** $t = 40 - (w - 1)$, where t = number of minutes you walk and w = week number. **b.** No; if you continue to reduce your time by 1 minute every week, eventually you would reach 0.

Lesson 4-6   pp. 213–215

EXERCISES 1. 20 **3.** −14 **5.** 1 **7.** −7314.14

9. no **11.** $\begin{bmatrix} 5 \\ 8 \\ 2 \end{bmatrix}$ **13.** PORTRAIT **15.a.** $\begin{bmatrix} 1 & 1 & 1 \\ 0 & 1 & 1 \\ 0 & 0 & 1 \end{bmatrix}$

b. $\begin{bmatrix} 38 & 56 & 27 & 34 \\ 24 & 30 & 20 & 15 \\ 24 & 12 & 12 & 15 \end{bmatrix}$ **c.** Check students' work.

17. −3 **19.** 1 **21.** $\begin{bmatrix} 0.4 & 0.4 & 0.2 \\ -0.6 & -0.6 & 0.2 \\ -0.2 & 0.8 & 0.4 \end{bmatrix}$

23. no inverse **25.** MORNING GRACE

27. $\begin{bmatrix} 10 \\ 3 \\ -2 \end{bmatrix}$ **29.** D **31.** D **33.** no **35.** yes; $\begin{bmatrix} 0 & -1 \\ -1 & 0 \end{bmatrix}$

37. $\left(-\frac{13}{8}, \frac{69}{16}, -\frac{15}{16}\right)$

Extension   p. 217

1.

	N_1	N_2	N_3	N_4
N_1	0	1	0	1
N_2	1	0	1	1
N_3	0	1	0	1
N_4	1	1	1	0

3.

	V_1	V_2	V_3	V_4	V_5
V_1	0	1	0	0	0
V_2	1	0	1	0	0
V_3	0	1	0	1	1
V_4	0	0	1	0	1
V_5	0	0	1	1	0

5.

	A	B	C	D
A	0	1	0	0
B	0	0	0	0
C	0	1	1	1
D	1	1	0	1

7. **9.**

Lesson 4-7   pp. 221–223

EXERCISES 1. $\begin{bmatrix} 1 & 1 \\ 1 & -2 \end{bmatrix}\begin{bmatrix} x \\ y \end{bmatrix} = \begin{bmatrix} 5 \\ -4 \end{bmatrix}$; coefficient

matrix is $\begin{bmatrix} 1 & 1 \\ 1 & -2 \end{bmatrix}$, variable matrix is $\begin{bmatrix} x \\ y \end{bmatrix}$, constant

matrix is $\begin{bmatrix} 5 \\ -4 \end{bmatrix}$. **3.** $\begin{bmatrix} 3 & 5 \\ 1 & 1 \end{bmatrix}\begin{bmatrix} a \\ b \end{bmatrix} = \begin{bmatrix} 0 \\ 2 \end{bmatrix}$; coefficient

matrix is $\begin{bmatrix} 3 & 5 \\ 1 & 1 \end{bmatrix}$, variable matrix is $\begin{bmatrix} a \\ b \end{bmatrix}$, constant

matrix is $\begin{bmatrix} 0 \\ 2 \end{bmatrix}$. **5.** $\begin{bmatrix} 1 & -1 & 1 \\ 2 & 0 & 1 \\ 0 & 1 & 3 \end{bmatrix}\begin{bmatrix} r \\ s \\ t \end{bmatrix} = \begin{bmatrix} 150 \\ 425 \\ 0 \end{bmatrix}$;

coefficient matrix is $\begin{bmatrix} 1 & -1 & 1 \\ 2 & 0 & 1 \\ 0 & 1 & 3 \end{bmatrix}$, variable matrix

is $\begin{bmatrix} r \\ s \\ t \end{bmatrix}$, constant matrix is $\begin{bmatrix} 150 \\ 425 \\ 0 \end{bmatrix}$. **7.** (2, 1)

9. $\left(\frac{1}{2}, 20\right)$ **11.** (3, 2) **13.** (2, −1, 3) **15.** (1, 2, −2)

17. yes **19.** yes **21.** no **23.** $\begin{bmatrix} 6 \\ 2 \end{bmatrix}$ **25.** $\begin{bmatrix} 16 \\ -22 \end{bmatrix}$

27. (2, 4) **29.** (4, 1, 3) **31.** (−19, 22, 13) **33.** (2, −1, 3)
35. (2, 0, 2, 0) **37.** length = 280 ft, width = 140 ft
39. Answers may vary. Sample: 0, 0 **41.** The tea temperature was 126°F and the milk temperature was 36°F. **43.** A **45.** D **47.** −44 **49.** −218

51. $\begin{bmatrix} -1 & -4 & 3 \\ 6 & 2 & 4 \\ 26 & -7 & -3 \end{bmatrix}$ **53.** vertical

---

Lesson 4-8   pp. 228–231

EXERCISES 1. (2, 0) **3.** (3, 1) **5.** (3, −1, 2)

7. $\begin{bmatrix} 3 & -7 & 3 & | & -3 \\ 1 & 1 & 2 & | & -3 \\ 2 & -3 & 5 & | & -8 \end{bmatrix}$ **9.** $\begin{cases} 5x + y = -3 \\ -2x + 2y = 4 \end{cases}$

11. $\begin{cases} 2x + y + z = 1 \\ x + y + z = 2 \\ x - y + z = -2 \end{cases}$ **13.** (−2, −6)

15. $(6.25, -6.25)$ **17.** $\left(\frac{4}{3}, -\frac{1}{3}\right)$ **19.** $(3, 1, 1)$

21. no unique solution **23.** no unique solution
25. $(-3, 5)$ **27.** $(4, 8)$ **29.** $(1, 1, -1)$ **31.** $(4, 0, 1)$
33. C **35.** $(2, 0, 3)$ **37.** no unique solution **39.**
almonds: \$2/lb, pecans: \$4/lb, pistachios: \$6/lb
41. $(5, -10)$ **43.** $(0, 1, 0, 2)$ **45. a.** Let $x =$ the
width of the rectangle, let $y =$ the length of the
rectangle, and let $z =$ the length of the diagonal.

$$\begin{cases} 2x + 2y \quad\;\; = 28 \\ x + y + z = 24 \\ x \quad\quad - z = -2 \end{cases}$$ **b.** $\begin{cases} 2x + 2y = 28 \\ 2x + y = 22 \end{cases}$ **c.** $\begin{bmatrix} 2 & 2 & | & 28 \\ 2 & 1 & | & 22 \end{bmatrix}$

d. 6 cm $\times$ 8 cm **e.** 10 cm **47.** A **49.** $(1, -1, 2)$

51. Answers may vary. Sample:

53. $y = x + 5$ **55.** $y - 3 = \frac{-7}{5}(x + 9)$

Chapter Review   pp. 233–235

1. matrix **2.** transformations **3.** determinants
4. equal matrices **5.** zero matrix **6.** matrix
equation **7.** square matrix **8.** preimage **9.** scalar
product **10.** identity matrix **11.** 2×3; -7
12. 3×2; -5 **13.** 3×3; 78 **14.** 226 **15.** 50

16. about 9% **17.** $\begin{bmatrix} 1 & -8 & 12 \end{bmatrix}$ **18.** $\begin{bmatrix} t - 1 \\ 3 \end{bmatrix}$

19. $\begin{bmatrix} -3 & 10 \\ -3 & 3 \end{bmatrix}$ **20.** $\begin{bmatrix} 2 & 8 & 13 \\ 33 & 0 & -7 \end{bmatrix}$

21. $x = -2, w = 8, r = 4, t = -1$

22. $t = -4, y = \frac{11}{2}, r = 4, w = 5$

23. $\begin{bmatrix} 18 & 3 & 0 & 24 \\ -12 & 9 & 21 & 33 \end{bmatrix}$ **24.** $\begin{bmatrix} -9 & 7 \\ -8 & -8 \end{bmatrix}$

25. undefined **26.** $\begin{bmatrix} -6 & 10 & 21 & 41 \\ -28 & 10 & 28 & 28 \end{bmatrix}$

27. $\begin{bmatrix} -14 & -2 \\ 43 & -7 \end{bmatrix}$ **28.** $\begin{bmatrix} 4 & -1 & 2 \\ -1 & -2 & 3 \end{bmatrix}$

29. $\begin{bmatrix} 0 & -5 & -2 \\ 5 & 4 & 9 \end{bmatrix}$ **30.** $\begin{bmatrix} -3 & 2 & -1 \\ 1 & 0 & 5 \end{bmatrix}$

31. $\begin{bmatrix} 1 & 0 & 5 \\ 3 & -2 & 1 \end{bmatrix}$ **32.** $\begin{bmatrix} 1 & 0 & 5 \\ -3 & 2 & -1 \end{bmatrix}$

33. $\begin{bmatrix} 1.5 & -1 & 0.5 \\ 0.5 & 0 & 2.5 \end{bmatrix}$ **34.** $\begin{bmatrix} 6 & -4 & 2 \\ 2 & 0 & 10 \end{bmatrix}$

---

35. $\begin{bmatrix} -1 & 0 & -5 \\ 3 & -2 & 1 \end{bmatrix}$ **36.** 24; $\begin{bmatrix} \frac{1}{6} & -\frac{1}{24} \\ 0 & \frac{1}{4} \end{bmatrix}$

37. 0; does not exist **38.** 42; $\begin{bmatrix} \frac{5}{42} & -\frac{1}{42} \\ -\frac{4}{21} & \frac{5}{21} \end{bmatrix}$

39. 6; $\begin{bmatrix} \frac{1}{3} & -\frac{2}{3} & 0 \\ -\frac{1}{6} & \frac{1}{3} & -\frac{1}{2} \\ \frac{1}{3} & \frac{1}{3} & 0 \end{bmatrix}$ **40.** $\begin{bmatrix} 1 & 2 \\ -1 & 0 \end{bmatrix}$ **41.** $\begin{bmatrix} -4 \\ -7 \end{bmatrix}$

42. $\begin{bmatrix} 2 \\ 2 \end{bmatrix}$ **43.** $\begin{bmatrix} 2 & 1 \\ 3 & 2 \end{bmatrix}$ **44.** no unique solution

45. no unique solution **46.** 3 small canoes,
2 large canoes **47.** $(4, -7)$ **48.** $(6, 0, -2)$

Chapter 5

Lesson 5-1   pp. 245–247

EXERCISES 1. linear; none, x, 4 **3.** quadratic;
$3x^2$, $-6x$, none **5.** quadratic; x^2, $3x$, -10
7. quadratic; $6x^2$, none, 6 **9.** quadratic; $-2x^2$,
$-8x$, none **11.** $(-1, 0)$, $x = -1$ **13.** $P'(6, 9)$, $Q'(2, 1)$
15. $P'(-1, -1)$, $Q'(-4, -4)$ **17.** $y = x^2 - 5x + 2$
19. $y = x^2 + 2x$ **21.a.** $y = -16x^2 + 33x + 46$,
where x is the number of seconds after release
and y is the height in ft. **b.** 28.5 ft **23.** $y = 4x^2$
25. no **27.** $\left(-\frac{1}{2}, -\frac{1}{2}\right)$, $x = -\frac{1}{2}$ **29.** $\left(\frac{1}{2}, 0\right)$, $x = \frac{1}{2}$
31.a. $y = -0.0095x^2 + 1.12x + 14.83$ **b.** Answers
may vary. Sample: domain, whole numbers from 0
to 50; range, positive whole numbers to 50. **c.** 1992
d. Never; the quadratic model is reaches a
maximum of about 45 cents, so it is useful for only
a limited number of years. **33.** 8 **35.** $-\frac{11}{8}$ **37.** -10
39. Answers may vary. Sample: $y = -\frac{1}{25}x^2$,
$y = \frac{1}{25}x^2 - \frac{2}{5}x$, $y = \frac{1}{5}x^2 - \frac{6}{5}x$ **41.** Answers may
vary. Sample: They are similar in that both are
symmetric with respect to the y-axis, have only
non-negative y-values, lie in Quadrants I and II,
and have minimums at $(0, 0)$; they are different in
that the graph of $y = x^2$ rises more steeply, while
$y = |x|$ rises at a steady rate as $|x|$ increases.
43.a. You can find how high the arrow was when
it was released. **b.** The negative intercept tells
you how much earlier you would have to shoot
the arrow from height of zero for its height to be
described by the same function. The positive
intercept tells you how many seconds after the
release the arrow will take to hit the ground.
45. B **47.** $\begin{bmatrix} 3 & -1 & | & 7 \\ 2 & 2 & | & 10 \end{bmatrix}$; $(3, 2)$ **49.** $\begin{bmatrix} 0 & -4 & 17 & -4 \end{bmatrix}$
51. $(2, 5)$ **53.** $(-1, -1)$ **55.** $\frac{1}{2}$

EXERCISES

1.   **3.**   **5.**

7.   **9.**   **11.**

13.   **15.**   **17.**

19.   **21.**   **23.** min, $-\frac{10}{3}$

25. min, 2   **27.** min, 5

29. 2 s; 64 ft

31.   **33.**   **35.** 13, 13; 169

37. B **39.** A **41.** 2.25 ft by 2.25 ft; 5.0625 ft^2
43. length = 9 cm, width = 9 cm **45.** −3
47. 2 **49.** $y = -4x^2 - 3$ **51.** $y = 10x^2 - 1$
53. $y = 6x^2 + 8$ **55.** B **57.** $y = x^2 + 1$; up
59. $y = -\frac{1}{2}x^2 + 1$; down
61. $y = \frac{1}{3}x^2 + 1$; up **63.** $y = -\frac{1}{4}x^2 + 1$; down
65.a. $y = \frac{1}{14,400}x^2$ **b.** $y = \frac{1}{14,400}x^2 - \frac{1}{120}x$
c. $y = \frac{1}{14,400}x^2 + \frac{1}{120}x$ **67.** −6, 24 **69.** 3, −12
71. $10\frac{2}{3}$ square units **73.** $10\frac{2}{3}$ square units **75.** B

77. $\begin{bmatrix} 3 & -4 \\ 3 & 0 \end{bmatrix}$ **79.** Let x = amount of storage space
and y = amount of space to be covered by the
roof. $x \geq 40,000$ $y \leq 25,000$

EXERCISES

1. 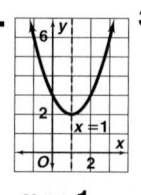 $x = 1$ **3.** $x = 2$ **5.** $x = -7$

7. $x = 5$ **9.** $x = 1$ **11.** $x = 7$

13. $y = \frac{1}{4}x^2$ **15.** $y = -(x - 2)^2$ **17.** $y = (x - 2)^2$
19. $y = 6(x + 3)^2 - 2$ **21.** (−20, 0), −600
23. (−5.5, 0), 726 **25.** (4, −25), −41
27. $y = (x - 2)^2 + 2$ **29.** $y = 6x^2 - 10$
31. $y = 4(x + \frac{7}{8})^2 - \frac{49}{16}$ **33.** $y = 4(x - \frac{5}{4})^2 - \frac{71}{8}$
35. $y = \frac{9}{4}(x + \frac{2}{3})^2 - 2$

37. $x = 2$ **39.** $x = 2$

41.   **43.** $y = -7(x - 1)^2 + 2$
45. $y = -\frac{1}{2}(x + 3)^2 + 6$
47. $y = 7(x + 1)^2 - 4$
49. $y = -10(x - \frac{1}{10})^2 - \frac{9}{10}$
51. $y = 25x^2 + 60x + 27$
53. $y = 2x^2 + 22x$

55. $y = -10x^2 - 40x - 40$ **57.a.** first: $x = 4$,
second: $x = 2.5$ **b.** For the first spreadsheet the
x_1-values 3 and 5 are equidistant from 4 and their
y_1-values are both −3. In the second spreadsheet,
the x_2-values 2 and 3 are equidistant from 2.5 and
their y_2-values are both 2. **c.** $y = -4(x - 4)^2 + 1$;

Selected Answers

$y = 4(x - \frac{5}{2})^2 + 1$ **59.** yes **61.** no; $y = -3(x + \frac{1}{3})^2 + \frac{4}{3}$ **63.** no; $y = (x + 1)^2 + 7$ **65.** no; $y = -4(x - \frac{3}{4})^2 + \frac{21}{4}$ **67.** no; $y = 100(x - \frac{1}{5})^2 + 6$ **69.** $a = 3$, $k = -1$ **71.** $a = \frac{1}{5}$, $k = 1$ **73.** $a = 1$, $k = -650$ **75.** Check students' work. **77.** Answers may vary. Sample: The graph of $y = (x - 6)^2 + 7$ is the graph of $y = (x + 6)^2$ translated right 12 units and up 7 units. **79.** $y = \frac{1}{4}x^2$ **81.** $y = -\frac{1}{4}(x - 3)^2$ **83.** $y = 2(x - 1)^2$ **85.** C **87.** B **89.** **91.** **93.** $\begin{bmatrix} -4 \\ 0 \end{bmatrix}$

Lesson 5-4   pp. 267–269

EXERCISES 1. $3; 3(a^2 + 3)$ **3.** $x; x(x - 2)$
5. $7y; 7y(2y + 1)$ **7.** $(x + 1)(x + 2)$ **9.** $(x + 2)(x + 5)$
11. $(y + 3)(y + 12)$ **13.** $(x - 1)(x - 2)$
15. $(r - 2)(r - 9)$ **17.** $(d - 3)(d - 9)$
19. $(x - 7)(x + 2)$ **21.** $(x - 8)(x + 5)$
23. $(x + 15)(x - 5)$ **25.** $(3x + 4)(x + 9)$
27. $(r + 2)(5r + 13)$ **29.** $(t + 4)(5t + 8)$
31. $(x + 4)(3x - 5)$ **33.** $(x - 2)(7x + 6)$
35. $(x + 4)(3x - 4)$ **37.** $(x + 1)^2$ **39.** $(x - 9)^2$
41. $(3x + 8)^2$ **43.** $(x + 2)(x - 2)$ **45.** $(3x + 1)(3x - 1)$
47. $5x - 1$ by $5x - 1$ **49.** $(x + y)^2 - y^2; x(x + 2y)$
51. $9(x + 2)(x - 2)$ **53.** $3(2y + 5)(2y - 5)$
55. $3(2x + 3)^2$ **57.** $2(a - 4)^2$ **59.** $2(3b - 1)(3b + 5)$
61. $3(y + 3)(y + 5)$ **63.** $2(x - 5)(2x - 1)$
65. $-6(z^2 + 100)$ **67.** $(x - 70)$ ft **69.** Check students' work. **71.** First factor out $4x^2$ to get $4x^2(x^2 + 6x + 8)$. To factor $x^2 + 6x + 8$, note that the numbers 2 and 4 have a product of 8 and a sum of 6. The complete factorization is $4x^2(x + 2)(x + 4)$. **73.** $100(9x - 10)(9x + 10)$
75. $(x + 12)(x - 3)$ **77.** $(2x + 9)(3x + 14)$ **79.** B
81. C **83.** $y = (x - 1)^2$ **85.** $y = 5x^2 - 1$ **87.** -29
89. penny: 2.5 g, nickel: 5 g, dime 2.3 g

Lesson 5-5   pp. 274–276

EXERCISES 1. $-4, -2$ **3.** $-1, \frac{3}{2}$ **5.** $-2, -1$ **7.** $-4, 4$
9. $-4, 4$ **11.** $-\sqrt{5}, \sqrt{5}$ **13.** $0, 4$ **15.** $-\frac{7}{2}, \frac{7}{2}$ **17.** $0, 4$
19.a. about 6.61 s **b.** about 6.89 s **21.** $-1.32, 8.32$
23. $-1.67, -1.5$ **25.** $-0.94, 2.34$ **27.** $-1, 0.25$
29. $-1.46, 5.46$ **31.** $-1.16, 2.16$ **33.** B **35.** 3ft
37. 3, 8 **39.** $-\frac{1}{2}, 3$ **41.** $-\frac{3}{2}, -\frac{2}{3}$ **43.** $-5.89, 5.89$
45. $-3.58, 3.58$ **47.** $1, 7$ **49.** $-10, -1$ **51.** $-6, 0$
53. $-4, 3.5$ **55.** $(0, -2), (2, 2)$ **57.** To find the x-coordinates, set the right side of the first equation equal to the right side of the second equation and solve for x. Then find the corresponding y-values by substituting each solution into the simpler of the two original

equations. **59.** Answers may vary. Sample: $x^2 + x - 6 = 0$ **61.** Answers may vary. Sample: $6x^2 - 7x + 2 = 0$ **63.** Answers may vary. Sample: If tables show same-sign values approaching 0, there likely is one solution. If same-sign values never approach 0, there likely are no solutions. **65.a.** 100 ft **b.** 5 s **67.** B **69.** C **71.** $(5z + 3)(5z - 3)$ **73.** $3 \times 3; 5$ **75.** $3 \times 3; 0$ **77.** Comm. Prop. of Add. **79.** Additive Inverse Prop.

Lesson 5-6   pp. 282–284

EXERCISES 1. $2i$ **3.** $i\sqrt{15}$ **5.** $5i\sqrt{2}$ **7.** $4i\sqrt{2}$
9. $-10i$ **11.** $2 + i\sqrt{3}$ **13.** $6 - 2i\sqrt{7}$ **15.** $7 - 5i$
17. $-2 - 5i\sqrt{2}$ **19.** 2 **21.** $2\sqrt{2}$ **23.** $3\sqrt{5}$ **25.** $1 - 7i$
27. $-2 - 3i$ **29.** $-7 - 10i$ **31.** $26 - 7i$ **33.** $9 - 23i$
35. $65 + 72i$ **37.** $\frac{12i}{3}$ **39.** $\pm 5i$ **41.** $\pm \frac{8i\sqrt{3}}{3}$ **43.** $\pm 6i$
45. $-i, -1 - i, i$ **47.** $1 - i, 1 - 3i, -7 - 7i$ **49.** $\pm 7i$
51. No; the test scores were real numbers. He added the scores and divided by the number of scores. The set of real numbers is closed with respect to addition and division so he should have gotten a real number **53.** B **55.** $288i$
57. $10 - 4i$ **59.** $-27 + 8i$ **61.** $\frac{-19 - 17i}{26}$
63. $\frac{-9 - 7i}{10}$ **65.** $x = -7, y = 3$ **67.** $x = -7, y = -3$
69. $0.383 + 0.11i, 0.517589 + 0.19426i$
71. $(3 + 4i)^1 = 3 + 4i$ and $3^2 + 4^2 = 25$;
$(3 + 4i)^2 = (3 + 4i)(3 + 4i) = 9 + 12i + 12i + 16i^2 = -7 + 24i$ and $(-7)^2 + (24)^2 = 25^2$; $(3 + 4i)^3 = (3 + 4i)(-7 + 24i) = -21 + 72i - 28i + 96i^2 = -117 + 44i$, and $(-117)^2 + (44)^2 = 25^3$; $(3 + 4i)^4 = (3 + 4i)(-117 + 44i) = -351 + 132i - 468i + 176i^2 = -527 - 336i$, and $(-527)^2 + (-336)^2 = 25^4$; $(3 + 4i)^5 = (3 + 4i)(-527 - 336i) = -1581 - 1008i - 2108i - 1344i^2 = -237 - 3116i$, and $(-237)^2 + (-3116)^2 = 25^5$ **73.** B **75.** $-2.351, 0.851$
77. $-5.562, -1.438$

79. **81.**

83.

Lesson 5-7   pp. 289–291

EXERCISES 1. $-4, -2$ **3.** $-1, 3$ **5.** $-4, 3$ **7.** 81
9. 144 **11.** $\frac{9}{4}$ **13.** $-4, 7$ **15.** $-3 \pm 4i\sqrt{2}$ **17.** $-1, 9$
19. $\pm 2i$ **21.** $1 \pm \sqrt{5}$ **23.** $2 \pm \frac{\sqrt{15}}{3}$ **25.** $-4, \frac{7}{2}$
27. $-\frac{3}{2}, \frac{1}{2}$ **29.** $y = -(x - 2)^2 + 3$

31. $y = (x + 2)^2 - 3$ **33.** $y = -(x + 1)^2 + 4$
35. $y = \frac{1}{2}(x - 5)^2 - \frac{1}{2}$; $\left(5, -\frac{1}{2}\right)$ **37.a.** (60, 5000)
b. positive rational numbers less than 130; whole numbers up to 5000 **c.** $60; $5000 **39.a.** (59, 36.81)
b. 36.81 ft **c.** 7.65 ft **d.** about 120 ft **e.** Answers may vary. Sample: The path is parabolic. Also, the linear model does not predict that the ball will eventually hit the ground. **41.** −20, 20 **43.** −16, 16 **45.** −10, 10 **47.** −12, 12 **49.** row 2: 47, 46, 45, 44, 43, 42, 41, 40 row 3: 96, 141, 184, 225, 264, 301, 336, 369, 400

a.

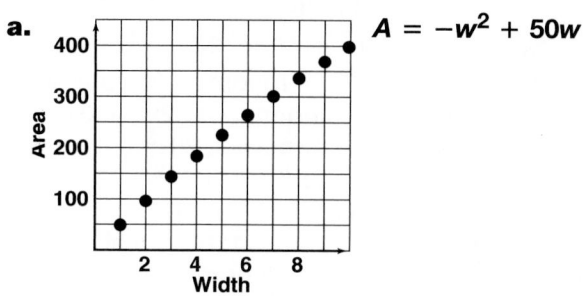

$A = -w^2 + 50w$

b. Check students' work. **c.** The numbers w such that $0 < w < 50$; since the perimeter is 100 the width would have to be less than 50, and since length can't be negative it would have to be greater than 0. **d.** 625 units^2; 25 units by 25 units **e.** $A = w(50 - w)$; yes; both equations are quadratic and model the same situation.
51. $-12 \pm 3\sqrt{17}$ **53.** $\frac{1}{4} \pm \frac{\sqrt{57}}{12}$ **55.** $\frac{1}{8} \pm \frac{\sqrt{5}}{8}$
57. $-\frac{3}{2}a, 2a$ **59.** $\frac{3}{a}, \frac{1}{a}, a \neq 0$ **61.** $3, -\frac{3a}{a + 3}, a \neq -3$
63. $-5 + 3\sqrt{2}, 5 + 3\sqrt{2}$ **65.** C **67.** $-2 + 2i$
69. $84 + 5i$ **71.** $y = -\frac{1}{2}x^2 + x + 2$ **73.** (2, 0)
75. (3, 1)

Lesson 5-8   pp. 297–299

EXERCISES 1. 1, 3 **3.** $-\frac{7}{2}, 1$ **5.** −5 **7.** $\frac{3 \pm \sqrt{5}}{2}$
9. $\frac{2 \pm \sqrt{10}}{3}$ **11.** 1, 4 **13.** $3 \pm i\sqrt{2}$ **15.** $-\frac{3}{2} \pm \frac{i\sqrt{11}}{2}$
17. $1 \pm i\sqrt{2}$ **19.** $\frac{5}{2} \pm \frac{i\sqrt{3}}{2}$ **21.** $-\frac{1}{15} \pm \frac{i\sqrt{14}}{15}$
23. $\frac{5}{3} \pm \frac{\sqrt{10}}{3}$; 0.61, 2.72 **25.** $-\frac{1}{6}, 1$ **27.** $-\frac{4}{5} \pm \frac{\sqrt{71}}{5}$;
−2.49, 0.89 **29.** $\frac{5}{4} \pm \frac{\sqrt{33}}{4}$; −0.19, 2.69 **31.** −4;
two, imaginary **33.** 0; one, real **35.** 169; two, real
37. 1; two, real **39.** 0; one, real **41.** 1,10 **43.** $-\frac{3}{2}$,
$\frac{1}{2}$ **45.** $1 \pm i$ **47.** −7, 7 **49.** $3 \pm i\sqrt{2}$ **51.** −1, 6
53.a. $w(18 - w) = 36$ **b.** 2.29 in. by 15.71 in.
55. Answers may vary. Sample: Assume the coefficients are real numbers. If the discriminant is negative, then there are 2 imaginary solutions. If the discriminant is 0, then there is 1 real solution. If the discriminant is positive, then there are 2 real solutions. **57.** two **59.** none **61.** two

63.a. 12 or −12 **b.** k such that $|k| < 12$ **c.** k such that $|k| > 12$ **65.** Imaginary solutions always come in pairs because they are the positive and negative solution of the square root of a negative number. **67.a.** $x^2 = 100\pi$ **b.** 17.72 cm
69. Answers may vary. Sample: $x^2 - 3x + 1 = 0$
71. Answers may vary. Sample: $x^2 - 5x + 7 = 0$
73. $\frac{5 \pm \sqrt{85}}{5a}$

75.a. $\frac{-b + \sqrt{b^2 - 4ac}}{2a} + \frac{-b - \sqrt{b^2 - 4ac}}{2a} = \frac{-2b}{2a} = \frac{-b}{a}$
b. $\left(\frac{-b}{2a} + \frac{\sqrt{b^2 - 4ac}}{2a}\right) \times \left(\frac{-b}{2a} - \frac{\sqrt{b^2 - 4ac}}{2a}\right) =$

$\left(\frac{-b}{2a}\right)^2 - \left(\frac{\sqrt{b^2 - 4ac}}{2a}\right)^2 = \frac{4ac}{4a^2} = \frac{c}{a}$

77. C **79.** $\frac{2 \pm \sqrt{2}}{2}$ **81.** $\begin{bmatrix} 5 & 6 & 2 \\ -7 & -1 & -2 \end{bmatrix}$

83. $\begin{bmatrix} 27 & -3 \\ -21 & 1 \end{bmatrix}$

Chapter Review   pp. 303–305

1. perfect square trinomial **2.** quadratic formula
3. vertex form of a quadratic function **4.** zero of a function **5.** discriminant **6.** quadratic; $-2x^2, 5x, 3$
7. quadratic; $-x^2, x, 3$ **8.** linear; none, $-4x, 3$
9. (0, −1), $x = 0$, (2, 3) and (−1, 0) **10.** (−2, 1), $x = -2$, (−2, 1) and (−4, 0) **11.** (1, −4), $x = 1$, (3, −1) and $\left(2, -3\frac{1}{4}\right)$ **12.a.** $y = 614x^2 - 342x + 4962$, where $x = 0$ corresponds to 1995 and y is in thousands. **b.** around 1999 **c.** $y = -25.5x^2 + 917.8x + 4776.7$ **d.** around 2007 **e.** $\approx 13{,}000{,}000$

13.

vertex (−1, −4),
y-intercept: −2; $x = -1$

14.

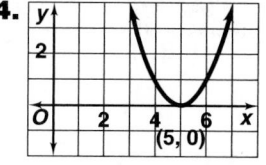

vertex (5, 0),
y-intercept: 25; $x = 5$

15.

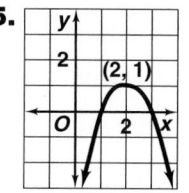

vertex (2, 1),
y-intercept: −3; $x = 2$

16.

vertex (0, 7),
y-intercept: 7; $x = 0$

17. $y = \left(x + \frac{1}{2}\right)^2 - 12\frac{1}{4}$; minimum: $-12\frac{1}{4}$
18. $y = -(x - 1)^2 + 3$; maximum: 3
19. $y = 2(x + 2)^2 - 11$; minimum: −11
20. $y = -0.5(x - 0)^2 + 5$; maximum: 5

21. $y = -\frac{1}{2}(x - 1)^2 + 2$; maximum: 2

22. $y = \frac{4}{9}(x - 3)^2 - 1$; minimum: -1

23. $y = \frac{1}{2}(x - 0)^2 - 2$; minimum: -2

24. 0, 7 **25.** -4, 2 **26.** -6, 0 **27.** $2 - 2\sqrt{2}$, $2 +$ $2\sqrt{2}$ **28.** -1, 4 **29.** -0.85, 5.85 or $\frac{5 \pm 3\sqrt{5}}{2}$

30. $\frac{2}{3}$, 4 **31.** -1, 4 **32.** -4 **33.** 3 **34.** $\frac{3}{2}$ **35.** -3, 3

36. $-\frac{1}{3}, \frac{5}{2}$ **37.** $-\frac{3}{2}, -\frac{1}{2}$ **38.** -2.61, 1.28 or $\frac{-2 \pm \sqrt{34}}{3}$ **39.** $5i$ **40.** $-1 + i\sqrt{2}$ **41.** $-4 - i$

42. $3i\sqrt{3}$ **43.** $4 + 8i\sqrt{2}$ **44.** $\sqrt{10}$ **45.** $\sqrt{13}$

46. 4 **47.** $-4 + 6i$ **48.** $51 + 21i$ **49.** $8 + 6i$

50. $2 + 16i$

51. $-2 + i$;   **52.** $4 - 3i$;

53. $7 + 4i$;   **54.** $2i$;

55. $-i\sqrt{2}, i\sqrt{2}$ **56.** $-i\sqrt{5}, i\sqrt{5}$ **57.** $-2i$, $2i$

58. $\frac{-i\sqrt{6}}{3}, \frac{i\sqrt{6}}{3}$ **59.** $-i, -1 - i, i$ **60.** $i, 1 + i, -i$

61. $-1, \frac{1}{3}$ **62.** $-\frac{3}{2} + \frac{i\sqrt{91}}{2}, -\frac{3}{2} - \frac{i\sqrt{91}}{2}$

63. $1 + i\sqrt{3}, 1 - i\sqrt{3}$ **64.** $\frac{1}{2} + \frac{3i\sqrt{3}}{2}, \frac{1}{2} - \frac{3i\sqrt{3}}{2}$

65. $-\frac{3}{4} + \frac{\sqrt{73}}{4}, -\frac{3}{4} - \frac{\sqrt{73}}{4}$ **66.** $-\frac{3}{4}, 1$

67. $y = \left(x + \frac{3}{2}\right)^2 - \frac{13}{4}; \left(-\frac{3}{2}, -\frac{13}{4}\right)$

68. $y = 2\left(x - \frac{1}{4}\right)^2 - \frac{9}{8}; \left(\frac{1}{4}, -\frac{9}{8}\right)$

69. $y = \left(x + \frac{1}{2}\right)^2 + \frac{7}{4}; \left(-\frac{1}{2}, -\frac{7}{4}\right)$ **70.** 2 real

solutions; $3 + \sqrt{7}, 3 - \sqrt{7}$ **71.** 2 imaginary

solutions; $\frac{7}{4} + \frac{i\sqrt{31}}{4}, \frac{7}{4} - \frac{i\sqrt{31}}{4}$ **72.** 2 real

solutions; $3 + \sqrt{5}, 3 - \sqrt{5}$

Chapter 6

Lesson 6-1   pp. 315–317

EXERCISES 1. $10x + 5$; linear binomial

3. $2m^2 + 7m - 3$; quadratic trinomial **5.** $2p^2 - p$;

quadratic binomial **7.** $-x^5$; quintic monomial **9.** $5x^3$;

cubic monomial **11.** $5x^2 + 4x + 8$; quadratic

trinomial **13.** $y = x^3 + 1$ **15.** $y = 1.5x^3 + x^2 - 2x + 1$

17.a. males: $y = 0.017857x^2 + 125571x + 66.337$

females: $y = -0.0022142857x^2 + 0.2575714x + 72.87714$ **b. males:** $y = -1.583\text{E}^{-4}x^3 + 0.0112857x^2 - 0.0010595x + 66.527$, **females:** $y = -0.00015x^3 + 0.006786x^2 + 0.12857x + 73.057$

c. For males, the models offer similar fit. For females, the cubic model is a better fit.

19. $y = x^3 - 10x^2$; 2023 **21.** $y = -0.03948x^3 + 2.069x^2 - 17.93x + 106.9$; 206.07 **23.** $y = 0.01002x^3 - 0.3841x^2 + 5.002x + 2.132$; 25.39 **25.** $x^3 + 4x$; cubic binomial **27.** 7; constant monomial

29. $x^4 + 2x^3$; quartic binomial **31.a.** $V = 10\pi r^2$

b. $V = \frac{2}{3}\pi r^3$ **c.** $V = \frac{2}{3}\pi r^3 + 10\pi r^2$ **33.** $-c^2 + 16$;

binomial **35.** $16x^2 - x - 5$; trinomial **37.** $a + 4b$;

binomial **39.** $8x^2 - 6y$; binomial **41.** $2x^3 + 9x^2 + 5x + 27$; polynomial of 4 terms **43.** $80x^3 - 109x^2 + 7x - 75$; polynomial of 4 terms **45.** $6a^2 + 3ab - 8$;

trinomial **47.** $30x^3 - 10x^2$; binomial **49.** $b^3 - 6b^2 + 9b$; trinomial **51.** $x^4 + 2x^2 + 1$; trinomial

53. $a^3 - a^2b - b^2a + b^3$; polynomial of 4 terms

55. $12s^3 + 61s^2 + 68s - 21$; polynomial of 4

terms **57.** $8c^3 - 26c + 12$; trinomial **59.a.** $y = 0.6877x + 47.97$, $y = 0.0007125x^3 - 0.06366x^2 + 2.1690x + 41.5929$, $y = -0.00005632x^4 + 0.005218x^3 - 0.1757x^2 + 3.0459x + 40.7482$

b.

Answers may vary. Sample: The quartic model fits best.

c. For sample in part (b). 71.68×10^{15} Btu

61.a. up 4 units **b.** $y = 4x^3$ is more narrow.

c. $y = x^3$ **63.** C **65.** B **67.** 2

69. $(5, -3)$

71. $\begin{bmatrix} -2 & -1 & -2 & -1 \\ -3 & -3 & -4 & -4 \end{bmatrix}$

Extension   p. 318

1. (↗,↗) **3.** (↗,↘) **5.** (↘,↗) **7.** (↗,↘) **9.** (↘,↘)

Lesson 6-2   pp. 323–325

EXERCISES 1. $x^2 + x - 6$ **3.** $x^3 - 7x^2 + 15x - 9$

5. $x^3 + 10x^2 + 25x$ **7.** $x(x - 6)(x + 6)$

9. $5x(2x^2 - 2x + 3)$ **11.** $x(x + 4)^2$ **13.** about 24.2, -1.4; 0, -5, 1 **15.a.** $h = x, \ell = 16 - 2x$,

$w = 12 - 2x$ **b.** $V = x(16 - 2x)(12 - 2x)$

c. 194 in.^{3}, 2.26 in.

17. 2, −9 **19.** −1, 2, 3

21. $y = x^3 - 18x^2 + 107x - 210$
23. $y = x^3 + 9x^2 + 15x - 25$
25. $y = x^3 + 2x^2 - x - 2$ **27.** $y = x^3 - 2x^2$
29. −3 (mult. 3) **31.** −1, 0, $\frac{1}{2}$ **33.** 4 (mult. 2)
35. $-\frac{3}{2}$, 1 (mult. 2) **37.** 2 x^3 blocks, 15 x^2 blocks,
31 x blocks, 12 unit blocks **39.** $V = 12x^3 - 27x$
41. $y = -2x^3 + 9x^2 - x - 12$
43. $y = 3x(x - 8)(x - 1)$ **45.** $y = x^2(x + 4)(x - 1)$
47. about 10.5, −7.1; $\frac{3}{2}$, 4, 6 **49.** about −2.98,
−6.17; 1.5 **51.** Answers may vary. Sample:
$y = x^3 - 3x^2 - 10x$ **53.** $y = x^4 - 4x^3 - 7x^2 +$
$22x + 24$ **55.** 0 (mult. 2), −1 (mult. 2)
57. Answers may vary. Sample: Write the
polynomial in standard form. The constant term
is the value of the *y*-intercept. **59.** Answers may
vary. Sample: $y = x^4 - x^2$, and zeros are 0, ±1.
61. $x + 2a$ **63.** Answers may vary. Sample:
$y = (x - 1)(x + 1)(x - i) (x + i); y = x^4 - 1$
65. B **67.** $-3x^5 + 3x^2 - 1$; quintic trinomial
69. $x^3 - 2$; cubic binomial **71.** $(x - 5)(x + 3)$
73. 8 **75.** 0

Lesson 6-3   pp. 330–332

EXERCISES 1. $x - 8$ **3.** $x^2 + 4x + 3$, R 5
5. $3x^2 - 7x + 2$ **7.** $x - 10$, R 40 **9.** no
11. yes **13.** $x^2 + 4x + 3$ **15.** $x^2 - 11x + 37$,
R −128 **17.** $x^2 - x - 6$ **19.** $x + 1$, R 4
21. $x^2 - 3x + 9$ **23.** $y = (x + 1)(x + 3)(x - 2)$
25. $\ell = x + 3$ and $h = x$ **27.** 0 **29.** 12 **31.** 10
33. 0 **35.** $x - 1$ is not a factor of $x^3 - x^2 - 2x$
because it does not divide into $x^3 - x^2 - 2x$
evenly. **37.** $x^2 + 4x + 5$ **39.** $x^4 - x^3 + x^2 - x + 1$
41. $x^3 - x^2 + 1$ **43.** yes **45.** no **47.** yes **49.** yes
51. no **53.** $x^3 - 2x^2 - 2x + 4$, R −35
55. $x^3 - 4x^2 + x$ **57a.** $x^2 - x + 1$
b. $x^4 - x^3 + x^2 - x + 1$
c. $x^6 - x^5 + x^4 - x^3 + x^2 - x + 1$
d. $(x + 1)(x^8 - x^7 + x^6 - x^5 + x^4 - x^3 + x^2 -$
$x + 1)$ **59.** $x + 2i$ **61.** *B* **63.** $y = x^2 + 2x - 15$
65. $y = x^3 - 6x^2 + 3x + 10$ **67.** 24 **69.** $23 - 11i$
71. none exists

Lesson 6-4   pp. 336–338

EXERCISES 1. −2, 1, 5 **3.** 0, 1 **5.** 0, −1, −2
7. 0, −0.5, 1.5 **9.** 1, 7 **11.** about 5.78 ft × 6.78 ft ×
1.78 ft **13.** $(x - 10)(x^2 + 10x + 100)$

15. 3, $\frac{-3 \pm 3i\sqrt{3}}{2}$ **17.** 5, $\frac{-5 \pm 5i\sqrt{3}}{2}$ **19.** $\frac{1}{2}$, $\frac{-1 \pm i\sqrt{3}}{4}$
21. $(x^2 - 7)(x - 1)(x + 1)$ **23.** $(x^2 - 3)(x - 2)(x + 2)$
25. $(x - 1)(x + 1)(x^2 + 1)$ **27.** ±3, ±1 **29.** ±4, ±2*i*
31. $\pm \sqrt{2}$, $\pm i \sqrt{6}$ **33.** 3.24, −1, −1.24 **35.** −3,
−2, 1, 2 **37.** 0, 1.54, 8.46 **39.** −1.04, 0, 6.04 **41.** D
43. $\frac{4}{3}$, $\frac{-2 \pm 2i\sqrt{3}}{3}$ **45.** ±5, $\pm i\sqrt{2}$ **47.** 0, ±2, ±1
49. 0, $\frac{1}{2} \pm \frac{\sqrt{265}}{10}$ **51.** 0, $3 \pm \sqrt{3}$ **53.** −1, 1, $\pm i\sqrt{5}$
55. −1, 3, 3 **57.** 0, 0, 1, 6 **59.** $\pm\sqrt{2}$, ±*i*
61. $V = x^2(4x - 2)$, 4 in. by 4 in. by 16 in.
63. $-\frac{5}{2}$, 1; $y = (2x + 5)(x - 1)$
65. −1, 2, 2; $y = (x + 1)(x - 2)^2$ **67.** −4, −1, 3;
$y = (x + 4)(x + 1)(x - 3)$ **69.a.** Answers may vary.
Sample: $x^4 - 9 = 0$, $\pm\sqrt{3}$, $\pm i\sqrt{3}$ **b.** No; two of
the roots are imaginary. **71.a.** *10* **b.** 8 and 12
73. B **75.** $2x^2 + x - 3$, R 2 **77.** ±6 **79.** $\begin{bmatrix} 0 \\ -5 \end{bmatrix}$

Lesson 6-5   pp. 345–346

EXERCISES 1. ±1, ±2; 1 **3.** ±1, ±2, ±4; −1
5. ±1, ±2, ±4, ±8, ±16; −2 **7.** 2, $\pm i\sqrt{5}$ **9.** −3, 1, $\frac{7}{2}$
11. $\pm\frac{1}{2}$, ±3 **13.** $-\sqrt{5}$, $\sqrt{13}$ **15.** $1 + \sqrt{10}$, $2 - \sqrt{2}$
17. $2 - 3i$, −6*i* **19.** $x^3 - x^2 + 9x - 9 = 0$ **21.** x^3
$- 2x^2 + 16x - 32 = 0$ **23.** $x^3 - 6x^2 + 4x - 24 = 0$
25. $\pm\frac{1}{12}$, $\pm\frac{1}{6}$, $\pm\frac{1}{4}$, $\pm\frac{1}{2}$, $\pm\frac{1}{3}$, $\pm\frac{2}{3}$, $\pm\frac{3}{4}$, ±1, $\pm\frac{3}{2}$, ±2,
±3, ±6; $\frac{1}{2}$, $\frac{3}{2}$, $\frac{2}{3}$ **27.** $\pm\frac{7}{3}$, $\pm\frac{1}{6}$, $\pm\frac{1}{2}$, $\pm\frac{1}{3}$, $\pm\frac{7}{6}$, ±1, $\pm\frac{3}{2}$,
±3, $\pm\frac{7}{2}$, ±7, $\pm\frac{21}{2}$, ±21; $\frac{1}{3}$, $-\frac{7}{2}$, 1, 3
29. $x^4 - 6x^3 + 14x^2 - 24x + 40 = 0$ **31.** $x^4 -$
$6x^3 + 2x^2 + 30x - 35 = 0$ **33.** Sometimes true;
since −2 is a factor of 8, −2 is a possible root of
the equation. **35.** Sometimes true; since $\sqrt{5}$ and
$-\sqrt{5}$ are conjugates, they can be roots of a
polynomial equation with integer coefficients.
37. D **39.** Answers may vary. Sample:
$x^4 - x^2 - 2 = 0$; roots are $\pm\sqrt{2}$ and ±*i*.
41. Answers may vary. Sample: You cannot use
the Irrational Root Theorem unless the equation
has rational coefficients. **43.a.–c.** Answers
may vary. Samples: **a.** $x - 1 - \sqrt{2} = 0$ **b.** $x^2 -$
$2(1 + \sqrt{2})x + (1 + \sqrt{2})^2 = 0$ **c.** −1
45. $-\frac{3}{2}$, $\frac{3 \pm 3i\sqrt{3}}{4}$ **47.** $\pm\sqrt{5}$, $\pm i\sqrt{5}$ **49.** $-2 \pm 2i$
51. (1, −4) **53.** (5, 0)

EXERCISES 1. 3 complex roots; number of real roots: 1 or 3; possible rational roots: ± 1 **3.** 4 complex roots; number of real roots: 0, 2, or 4; possible rational roots: 0 **5.** 7 complex roots number of real roots: 1, 3, 5, or 7 possible rational roots: ± 1, ± 3 **7.** 6 complex roots number of real roots: 0, 2, 4, or 6 possible rational roots: $\pm\frac{1}{2}$, ± 1, $\pm\frac{7}{2}$, ± 7 **9.** -1, $\frac{1 \pm i\sqrt{7}}{4}$ **11.** 4, $\frac{1 \pm i\sqrt{3}}{2}$

13. ± 2, $\pm\sqrt{2}$ **15.** 0, $\frac{3 \pm 3\sqrt{5}}{2}$ **17.** 4 complex roots; number of real roots: 0, 2, or 4; possible rational roots: $\pm\frac{1}{2}$, ± 1, ± 2, $\pm\frac{13}{2}$, ± 13, ± 26 **19.** 3 complex roots; number of real roots: 1 or 3; possible rational roots: $\pm\frac{1}{3}$, $\pm\frac{2}{3}$, ± 1, $\pm\frac{4}{3}$, ± 2, ± 3, ± 4, ± 6, ± 12 **21.** 4, $\pm 3i$ **23.** -6, $\frac{-1 \pm i}{2}$ **25.** $\frac{1}{2}$, $\pm 2i\sqrt{5}$

27. Answers may vary. Sample: $y = x^4 + 3x^2 + 2$

29. -3.24, 1.24 **31.** Yes;

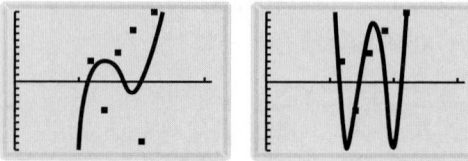

for example, $2x^2 - 11x + 5 = 0$ has roots 0.5 and 5. **33.** A **35.** 3 (mult. 2) **37.** $\frac{3 \pm i\sqrt{23}}{4}$ **39.** $f(x) = 2x^2 + 24x + 75$

EXERCISES 1. 120 **3.** 6,227,020,800 **5.** 665,280 **7.** 120 **9a.** 24 **b.** 120 **11.** 56 **13.** 1680 **15.** 120 **17.** 60 **19.** 4, 151, 347, 200 **21.** 15 **23.** 1 **25.** 35 **27.** 35 **29.** 4368 **31.** 2300 **33.** true because of the Assc. Prop. of Mult. **35.** False; answers may vary. Sample: $(3 \times 2)! = 720$ and $3! \times 2! = 12$ **37.** False; answers may vary. Sample: $(3!)^2 = 36$ and $(3)^{(2!)} = 9$ **39.** 60 **41.** $\frac{4}{19,393} \approx 0.000206$ **43.** $\frac{12}{49}$ **45.** permutation **47.** combination **49.** 330, 791, 175 **51.** 12, 650 **53.** 9504 **55.** 120 **57.** 360 **59.** 1680 **61.** 5040 **63–66.** Check students' work. **67. a.** 2048 **b.** Answers will vary. Sample: No, because there are too many possible solutions. **69.a.** 35 **b.** 6 **c.** $_7C_3 = \frac{7!}{3!\,4!}$, so, $_7C_3 = \frac{7!}{4!}$, which is the permutation formula for $_7P_3$. **71.** Answers may vary. Sample: 99 **73** D **75.** 3 complex roots number of real roots: 1 or 3 possible rational roots: $\pm\frac{1}{12}$, $\pm\frac{1}{6}$, $\pm\frac{1}{4}$, $\pm\frac{1}{3}$, $\pm\frac{1}{2}$, $\pm\frac{2}{3}$, ± 1, ± 2 **77.** $-x^3 - 3x^2 + 6$; cubic trinomial **79.** $5t^2 - 3t$; quadratic binomial **81.** $x^3 - 4x$; cubic binomial **83.** $4(x - 1)^2$ **85.** $3(x - 5)(x + 5)$ **87.** maximum; 4.125

EXERCISES 1. $a^3 + 3a^2b + 3ab^2 + b^3$ **3.** $a^4 + 4a^3b + 6a^2b^2 + 4ab^3 + b^4$ **5.** $a^6 - 6a^5b + 15a^4b^2 - 20a^3b^3 + 15a^2b^4 - 6ab^5 + b^6$ **7.** $x^8 + 8x^7y + 28x^6y^2 + 56x^5y^3 + 70x^4y^4 + 56x^3y^5 + 28x^2y^6 + 8xy^7 + y^8$ **9.** $x^3 - 9x^2 + 27x - 27$ **11.** $x^6 - 12x^5 + 60x^4 - 160x^3 + 240x^2 - 192x + 64$ **13.** $x^4 + 4x^3y + 6x^2y^2 + 4xy^3 + y^4$ **15.** $s^2 - 2st + t^2$ **17.** $x^4 - 4x^3y + 6x^2y^2 - 4xy^3 + y^4$ **19.** $x^5 - 15x^4 + 90x^3 - 270x^2 + 405x - 243$ **21a.** about 25% **b.** about 21% **c.** about 12% **23.** $x^7 + 7x^6y + 21x^5y^2 + 35x^4y^3 + 35x^3y^4 + 21x^2y^5 + 7xy^6 + y^7$ **25.** $81x^4 - 108x^3y + 54x^2y^2 - 12xy^3 + y^4$ **27.** $17,649 - 201,684x + 144,060x^2 - 54,880x^3 + 11,760x^4 - 1344x^5 + 64x^6$ **29.** $x^4 + 2x^2y^2 + y^4$ **31.** $x^6 + 6x^5 + 15x^4 + 20x^3 + 15x^2 + 6x + 1$ **33.** $x^5 + 10x^4 + 40x^3 + 80x^2 + 80x + 32$ **35.** $16x^4 + 96x^3y + 216x^2y^2 + 216xy^3 + 81y^4$ **37.** $64x^6 - 384x^5y + 960x^4y^2 - 1280x^3y^3 + 960x^2y^4 - 384xy^5 + 64y^6$ **39.** $32x^5 + 80x^4y + 80x^3y^2 + 40x^2y^3 + 10xy^4 + y^5$ **41.** $x^6 - 18x^5y + 135x^4y^2 - 540x^3y^3 + 1215x^2y^4 - 1458xy^5 + 729y^6$ **43a.** about 31% **b.** about 16% **c.** about 16% **45.** $_8C_4x^4y^4$ **47.** 7, $7r^6s$ **49.** $80x^2$ **51.** $264x^{10}$ **53.** $64y^6$ **55.** 314,928x^7 **57.** $1716x^{12}y^{14}$ **59a.** $(s + 0.5)^3$ **b.** $s^3 + 1.5s^2 + 0.75s + 0.125$ **61.** 13, d^{12}, $12d^{11}e$ **63.** 6, $32a^5$, $80a^4b$ **65.a.** -4 **b.** $(1 - i)^4 = 1 - 4i - 6 + 4i + 1 = -4 \checkmark$ **67.** Answers may vary. Sample: A coin is tossed five times with the probability of heads on each toss 0.5. Write an expression for the probability of exactly 2 heads being tossed. **69.** D **71.** 20 **73.** 35 **75.** 35 **77.** 20.75; -12.60; $-3,1,4$ **79.** $y = (x - 3)^2 - 7$ **81.** $y = -4(x - 0)^2 + 9$

1. degree **2.** standard form of a polynomial **3.** multiplicity **4.** complex conjugates **5.** combinations **6.** $3p^3 - 2p$; cubic binomial **7.** $-5x^9 + 3$; degree 9 binomial **8.** $-x^5 - x^3 + x$; quintic trinomial **9.** $4x^3 + 2x^2 + 2x$; cubic trinomial **10.** $x^7 + x^4 - x^2 + x + 5$; degree 7, 5 terms **11.** s; linear monomial **12.** cubic: $y = 62.2685x^3 - 303.194x^2 + 481.8148x - 248.522$; quartic: $y = 984.375x^4 - 6631.481x^3 + 16,498.68x^2 - 17,954.685x + 7208.88$;

The quartic model better fits the data.
13. $f(x) = x(x - 4)(x + 3)$; $-3, 0, 4$;

rel. max. ≈ 12.60, rel. min. ≈ −20.75 **14.** $g(x) =$ $(2 − x)(2 + x)$; −2, 2; rel. max. = 4
15. $y = x^3(x + 2)^4$; 0 (mult. 3), −2 (mult. 4); rel. max. = 0, rel. min. ≈ −1.07 **16.** $f(x) = x^4 + 3x^3 −$ $4x^2 − 12x$ **17.** $f(x) = x^3 − 4x^2 + 5x − 2$
18. $f(x) = x^4 + 2x^3 − 3x^2$ **19.** $f(x) = x^3 + 6x^2 +$ $12x + 8$ **20.** $x^2 + 5x + 8$, R 12; check students' work. **21.** $x^3 − x^2 + x − 2$, R 4; check students' work. **22.** $(x + 1)(x − 3)(x − 1)$ **23.** $(x − 3)^2(x + 2)$ **24.** 93 **25.** −30 **26.** 77 **27.** −9 **28.** −1, 1.38, 3.62 **29.** −1.78 **30.** 0 **31.** −1.52 **32.** −1.63 **33.** no real solution **34.** $(x − 2)(x^2 + 2x + 4)$; 2, $−1 ± i\sqrt{3}$
35. $t^4(2t − 1)(2t + 1)$; 0, $\frac{1}{2}$, $−\frac{1}{2}$
36. $(2x + 1)(4x^2 − 2x + 1)$; $−\frac{1}{2}$, $\frac{1 ± i\sqrt{3}}{4}$
37. $x(x − 4)(x − 1)$; 0, 1, 4 **38.** $x(x^2 − 2x − 5)$; 0, $1 ± \sqrt{6}$ **39.** $(x + 2)^2(x^2 − 2x + 4)^2$; −2, $1 ± i\sqrt{3}$ **40.** 3 complex roots; number of real roots: 3 or 1; possible rational roots: ±1, ±2, ±3, ±6; roots 1, 2, 3 **41.** 4 complex roots; number of real roots: 4, 2, or 0; possible rational roots: ±1, ±2, ±4, ±8, ±$\frac{1}{2}$, ±$\frac{1}{5}$, ±$\frac{2}{5}$, ±$\frac{4}{5}$, ±$\frac{8}{5}$, ±$\frac{1}{10}$; roots: −1, $−\frac{1}{2}$, $\frac{4}{5}$, 2 **42.** 4 complex roots; number of real roots: 4, 2, or 0; possible rational roots: ±1, ±7; roots: ±1.26, ±2.10 **43.** 4 complex roots; number of real roots: 4, 2, or 0; possible rational roots: ±1, ±2, ±4; roots: −1, −2 **44.** 3 complex roots; number of real roots: 3 or 1; possible rational roots: ±1, ±5; roots: −1, 2 ± i **45.** 4 complex roots; number of real roots: 4, 2, or 0; possible rational roots: ±1, ±2, ±3, ±6, ±9, ±18; roots: ±3, 1 ± i **46.** $x^3 − 2x^2 + x − 2 = 0$ **47.** $x^4 − 16x^3 +$ $91x^2 − 216x + 182 = 0$ **48.** $x^4 − 10x^3 + 39x^2 −$ $70x + 50 = 0$ **49.** $x^5 − 6x^4 + 11x^3 − 24x^2 +$ $28x = 0$ **50.** $x^4 − 8x^3 + 23x^2 − 42x + 30 = 0$
51. $x^4 − 12x^2 + 35 = 0$ **52.** 72 **53.** 24 **54.** 35 **55.** 30 **56.** 2 **57.** 120 **58.** $4320x^3y^3$ **59.** about 27%

Chapter 7

Lesson 7-1   pp. 378–379

EXERCISES 1. 15, −15 **3.** none **5.** −4 **7.** $−\frac{1}{2}$
9. 2, −2 **11.** 0.3, −0.3 **13.** 6 **15.** no real-number root **17.** −4 **19.** −3 **21.** $4|x|$ **23.** $x^4|y^9|$
25. −4a **27.** $x^2|y^3|$ **29.** 1.34 in. **31.** 0.48 cm
33. 10, −10 **35.** 0.5, −0.5 **37.** $\sqrt[3]{−64}$, $\sqrt[6]{64}$, $−\sqrt[3]{−64}$, $\sqrt{64}$ **39.** 0.5 **41.** 0.2 **43.** $2|c|$
45. $12y^2z^2|x|\sqrt{xy}$ **47.** $−y^4$ **49.** $−k^3$ **51.** $(x + 1)^2$
53. x^2 **55.** Answers may vary. Sample: $\sqrt[3]{−8x^6}$, $−\sqrt[4]{16x^8}$, $\sqrt[5]{−32x^{10}}$ **57.** Yes, because 10 is really 10^1. **59.** Some; true only for $x ≥ 0$. **61.** Some; true only for $x ≥ 0$. **63.** m^2 **65.** m^4 **67.** m^2 **69.** m^4 **71.** B

73. $x^5 − 5x^4y + 10x^3y^2 + 10x^2y^3 + 5xy^4 + y^5$
75. $729x^6 − 7290x^5 + 30,375x^4 − 67,500x^3 +$ $84,375x^2 − 56,250x + 15,625$ **77.** $y = x(2x − 7)$ $(2x + 7)$ **79.** $y = 9x(x + 1)^2$ **81.** $y = 3(x − 0)^2 − 7$
83. $y = \frac{1}{4}(x + 4)^2 − 5$

Lesson 7-2   pp. 383–385

EXERCISES 1. 16 **3.** −9 **5.** not possible **7.** −6
9. $2x\sqrt{5x}$ **11.** $5x^2\sqrt{2x}$ **13.** $3y^3\sqrt[3]{2y}$
15. $−5x^2y\sqrt[3]{2y^2}$ **17.** $2\sqrt[3]{12}$ **19.** $7x^3y^4\sqrt{6y}$
21. $30y^2\sqrt[3]{2y}$ **23.** 10 **25.** $2x^2y^2\sqrt{2}$ **27.** $\frac{\sqrt{2x}}{2}$
29. $\frac{\sqrt[3]{4x}}{2}$ **31.** $\frac{\sqrt[4]{250}}{5}$ **33.** $\frac{\sqrt{15y}}{5y}$ **35.** $r = \frac{\sqrt{Gm_1m_2F}}{F}$
37. $10\sqrt{2}$ **39.** $3x^6y^5\sqrt{2y}$ **41.** $10 + 7\sqrt{2}$
43. $5 + 5\sqrt{3}$ **45.** $3x^2\sqrt[3]{x}$ **47.** $\frac{5\sqrt{14x}}{21x}$ **49.** $\frac{2\sqrt[3]{25x}}{x}$
51. $\frac{\sqrt{33x}}{−4x}$ **53.** $\frac{3\sqrt{5} + 5}{5}$ **55.** about 212 mi/h greater
57. A product of two square roots can be simplified in this way only if the square roots are real numbers. $\sqrt{−2}$ and $\sqrt{−8}$ are not. **59.** For some values, it is easy to see that the equation is true if $x = 0$ or $x = 1$. But when $x < 0$, $\sqrt[3]{x^3}$ is not a real number, although $\sqrt[3]{x^2}$ is. **61.** $2xy$ **63.** $2\sqrt{5}$
65. $\frac{\sqrt[5]{yx}}{x}$ **67.** $a = −2c, b = −6d$ **69.** B **71.** C
73. $11|a^{45}|$ **75.** $−4a^{27}$ **77.** $0.5|x^3|$ **79.** $2|x^9|y^{24}$
81. $y^2 − 4y + 16$, R −128, not a factor
83. $3a^2 − 8a − 2$, R 6, not a factor **85.** 25 **87.** $\frac{121}{4}$
89. $\frac{1}{36}$ **91.** $\frac{9}{64}$

Lesson 7-3   pp. 388–390

EXERCISES 1. $6\sqrt{6}$ **3.** cannot combine
5. cannot combine **7.** $33\sqrt{2}$ **9.** $7\sqrt{2}$
11. $9\sqrt[3]{3} − 6\sqrt[3]{2}$ **13.** $8 + 4\sqrt{5}$ **15.** $63 − 38\sqrt{2}$
17. $49 + 12\sqrt{13}$ **19.** 14 **21.** −40 **23.** $−2 + 2\sqrt{3}$
25. $13 + 7\sqrt{3}$ **27.** $13\sqrt{2}$ **29.** $48\sqrt{2x}$ **31.** $33y\sqrt{6}$
33. $−11 + \sqrt{21}$ **35.** $17 + 31\sqrt{2}$ **37.** $x + 3\sqrt{3x} + 6$
39. $\frac{89 + 42\sqrt{3}}{−239}$ **41.** $\frac{\sqrt{3} − \sqrt{7}}{2}$ **43.** $\frac{x + 5\sqrt[4]{x^3}}{x}$
45. The reciprocal is $\frac{−1 + \sqrt{5}}{2}$, which is one less than $\frac{1 + \sqrt{5}}{2}$. **47.** Answers may vary. Sample: Without simplifying first, you must estimate three separate square roots, and then add the estimates. If they are first simplified, then they can be combined as $13\sqrt{2}$. Then only one square root need be estimated. **49.** Answers may vary.

Samples: $(\sqrt{7} + 2)(\sqrt{7} - 2)$; $(2\sqrt{2} + \sqrt{5})(2\sqrt{2} - \sqrt{5})$ 51. $-\frac{1}{2}$ 53. ($a = 0$ and $b \geq 0$) or ($b = 0$ and $a \geq 0$) 55. a. m and n can be any positive integers. b. m must be even or n must be odd. c. m must be even, and n can be any positive integer 57. B
59. C 61. $x\sqrt{15}$ 63. $\frac{\sqrt{93}}{3}$ 65. $7x^2\sqrt{2}$ 67. $\frac{\sqrt[3]{100x^2}}{5x}$
69. $-10, 5 \pm 5i\sqrt{3}$ 71. $\pm\sqrt{7}$ 73. $\pm\frac{i}{3}, \pm\frac{1}{3}$

Lesson 7-4   pp. 394–396

EXERCISES 1. 6 3. 7 5. -3 7. 8 9. 3 11. $\sqrt[5]{x}$
13. $\sqrt[5]{y^2}$ or $(\sqrt[5]{y})^2$ 15. $\frac{1}{\sqrt[4]{t^3}}$ or $\frac{1}{(\sqrt[4]{t})^3}$
17. $\sqrt[5]{y^6}$ or $(\sqrt[5]{y})^6$ 19. $7\frac{1}{2}x^{\frac{3}{2}}$ 21. $(7x)^{\frac{3}{2}}$ 23. $a^{\frac{2}{3}}$
25. $25x^2y^2$ 27. ≈15.1 m 29. ≈1.6 m 31. 16
33. 64 35. 8 37. 1000 39. $\frac{1}{x^4}$ 41. $\frac{5}{x^3}$ 43. $-2y^3$
45. $x^{\frac{13}{3}}$ 47. $\frac{y^2}{x^8}$ 49. $\frac{y^5}{x^{10}}$ 51. -3 53. 729
55. 1,000,000,000 or 10^9 57. $\frac{1}{8}$ 59. 16 61. 10
63. A 65. $x^{\frac{1}{2}}$ 67. $x^{\frac{1}{2}}$ 69. $x^{\frac{1}{6}}y^{\frac{1}{4}}$ 71. $\frac{4x^7}{9y^9}$ 73. $\frac{1}{x^{\frac{13}{36}}}$
75. $\frac{1}{x^{\frac{1}{3}}}$ 77. The cube root of -64 is -4, which equals $-(64)^{\frac{1}{3}}$. The square root of -64 is not a real number, but $-(64)^{\frac{1}{2}} = -\sqrt{64} = -8$. 79. Answers may vary. Sample: $4 - 5^{\frac{1}{2}}, 2(4 - 5^{\frac{1}{2}}), \frac{4 - 5^{\frac{1}{2}}}{2}$; no, if a is rational and the product is rational, then $4 + 5^{\frac{1}{2}}$ must be rational. 81. 49 83. $x^{2\pi}$ 85. $3^{\sqrt{2}}$
87. 33.13 mph 89. B 91. $4\sqrt[3]{3}$ 93. $1 + 3\sqrt{5}$
95. $\frac{4 + 6\sqrt{5} + 2\sqrt{10} + 15\sqrt{2}}{-41}$ 97. $4x(x^2 - 2x + 4)$
99. $(x - 9)^2$ 101. $(5x - 4y)^2$

Lesson 7-5   pp. 400–402

EXERCISES 1. 16 3. 22 5. 23 7. 3, -13 9. 18 11. 8
13. 30.6 ft 15. 3 17. -3, -4 19. 1 21. 3 23. 1
25. 2 27. 5 29. 5 31.a.

b. c.

d. The graph of each pair consists of two straight lines, one of which is horizontal. They intersect at different points, but these points have the same x-value, about 1.236. 33. B 35. 4 37. 23 39. 6.5

41. $\frac{81}{16}$ 43. 2 45. 2 47. 25 49. -1 51. $d = \frac{v^2}{64}$
53. 1 55. 2 57. Plan 1: Use a calculator to evaluate $\sqrt{2} + 2$ and store the result as x. Evaluate $\sqrt{x} + 2$ and store the result as x. Continue this procedure about seven times until it becomes clear that the values are approaching 2. Plan 2: The given equation is equivalent to $x = \sqrt{2 + x}$. Solve this equation to find that $x = 2$.
59. A 61. B 63. 125 65. $8\sqrt{5}$ 67. $\frac{1}{3}$ 69. 25
71. $\frac{1}{10^6}$ 73. 210 75. 1680 77. 10 79. 1 81. 7 83. 3, 5
85. $-2, -\frac{2}{3}$ 87. $-2, -\frac{3}{4}$

Lesson 7-6   pp. 406–410

EXERCISES 1. $x^2 + 3x + 5$ 3. $-x^2 + 3x + 5$
5. $\frac{3x + 5}{x^2}$ 7. $x^2 + 3x + 5$ 9. $x^2 - 3x - 5$
11. $\frac{3x + 5}{x^2}$ 13. $2x^2 + 2x - 4$; domain: all real numbers 15. $2x^2 - 2$; domain: all real numbers
17. $2x + 3$; domain: all real numbers except 1
19. $27x^2$, domain: all real numbers; 3, domain: all real numbers except 0 21. $x^2 + 5$; 14, 9 23. 104
25. 16 27. 10 29. 68 31. 1 33. -3 35. 9.25
37. 6.25 39. $c^2 - 6c + 9$ 41. $a^2 + 6a + 9$
43.a. $f(x) = 0.9x$ b. $g(x) = x - 2000$ c. \$14,200
d. \$14,400 45. $x^2 - x + 7$ 47. $x^2 - 5x - 3$
49. $-x^2 + 5x + 13$ 51. $-3x^2 + 2x + 16$, domain: all real numbers 53. $3x^3 + 8x^2 - 4x + 16$, domain: all real numbers 55. $3x - 4$, domain: all real numbers except -2 57. 7; answers may vary. Sample: First evaluate $f(3)$ since the expression is $(g \circ f)(3)$, and that means $g(f(3))$. Then evaluate $g(6)$. 59. -4 61. 2 63. $3x^2, 9x^2$ 65. $12x^2 + 2$, $6x^2 + 4$ 67. $-4x - 7, -4x - 28$ 69.a. Answers may vary. Sample: $g(x) = 0.12x$ b. $f(x) = 9.50x$
c. $(g \circ f)(x) = 1.14x$; your savings will be \$1.14 for each hour you work. 71.a. $P(x) = 5295x - 1000$
b. \$157,850
73. $(f + g)(x) = f(x) + g(x)$ Def. of Function Add.
     = $3x - 2 + (x^2 + 1)$ Substitution
     = $x^2 + 3x - 2 + 1$ Comm. Prop.
     = $x^2 + 3x - 1$ arithmetic
75. $(f \circ g)(x) = f(g(x))$ def. of comp. functions
     = $f(x^2 + 1)$ substitution
     = $3(x^2 + 1) - 2$ substitution
     = $3x^2 + 3 - 2$ Dist. Prop.
     = $3x^2 + 1$ arithmetic
77. $x^7 - x^6 - 16x^5 + 10x^4 + 85x^3 - 25x^2 - 150x$; domain: all real numbers 79. $\frac{x - 3}{x^2 + 2x}$; domain: all real numbers except 0, -2, $\sqrt{5}$, and $-\sqrt{5}$ 81. $\frac{1}{x}$
83. 2 85. B 87. D 89. -3 91. 3 93. 3

95. $x^6 + 6x^5y + 15x^4y^2$
$+ 20x^3y^3 + 15x^2y^4$
$+ 6xy^5 + y^6$

97. $128x^7 - 1344x^6y$
$+ 6048x^5y^2 - 15{,}120x^4y^3$
$+ 22{,}680x^3y^4 - 20{,}412x^2y^5$
$+ 10{,}206xy^6 - 2187y^7$

99. $1024x^5 - 1280x^4y$
$+ 640x^3y^2 - 160x^2y^3$
$+ 20xy^4 - y^5$

101. $x^{12} + 12x^{10}y^3 + 60x^8y^6$
$+ 160x^6y^9 + 240x^4y^{12}$
$+ 192x^2y^{15} + 64y^{18}$

103. $-2 + 19i\sqrt{2}$ **105.** $-8 - 36i$

Lesson 7-7   pp. 416–418

EXERCISES

1.

x	0	1	0	2
y	1	2	3	4

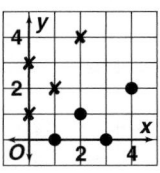

3.

x	0	1	4	9
y	0	1	2	3

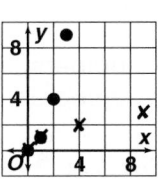

5. $y = \frac{1}{3}x - \frac{1}{3}$; yes **7.** $y = -\frac{1}{3}x + \frac{4}{3}$; yes

9. $y = \pm\sqrt{x - 4}$; no **11.** $y = \pm\sqrt{x - 1}$; no

13. $y = \pm\frac{\sqrt{x - 5} - 1}{2}$; no

15.   **17.**

19.   **21.**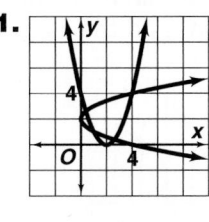

23. $f^{-1}(x) = \frac{x - 4}{3}$, and the domain and range for both f and f^{-1} are all real numbers; f^{-1} is a

function. **25.** $f^{-1}(x) = x^2 - 7, x \geq 0$, domain f: $\{x | x \geq -7\}$, range f: $\{y | y \geq 0\}$, domain f^{-1}: $\{x | x \geq 0\}$, and range f^{-1}: $\{y | y \geq -7\}$; f^{-1} is a function. **27.** $f^{-1}(x) = \pm\sqrt{\frac{x - 2}{2}}, x \geq 2$, domain of f: all reals, range f: $\{y | y \geq 2\}$, domain f^{-1}: $\{x | x \geq 2\}$, and range f^{-1}: all reals; f^{-1} is not a function.

29.a. $F = \frac{5}{9}(C - 32)$; yes **b.** $-3.89°F$

31. 10 **33.** 0.2 **35.** $f^{-1}(x) = \pm\sqrt{\frac{2x + 8}{3}}$; no

37. $f^{-1}(x) = \frac{x^2 - 6x + 10}{2}, x \geq 3$; yes

39. $f^{-1}(x) = \frac{1 \pm \sqrt{x}}{2}$; no **41.** $f^{-1}(x) = \sqrt[3]{x}$; yes

43. $f^{-1}(x) = \pm\sqrt{\frac{5x - 5}{2}}$; no **45.** The range of the inverse is the domain of f, which is $x \geq 1$.

47. $f^{-1}(x) = x^2, x \leq 0$, domain of f: $\{x | x \leq 0\}$, range of f: $\{y | y \geq 0\}$, domain of f^{-1}: $\{x | x \leq 0\}$, range of f^{-1}: $\{y | y \geq 0\}$, and f^{-1} is a function.

49. $f^{-1}(x) = 3 - x^2, x \geq 0$, domain of f: $\{x | x \leq 3\}$, range of f: $\{y | y \geq 0\}$, domain of f^{-1}: $\{x | x \geq 0\}$, range of f^{-1}: $\{y | y \leq 3\}$, and f^{-1} is a function.

51. $f^{-1}(x) = \pm\sqrt{2x}, x \geq 0$, domain of f: all real numbers, range of f: $\{y | y \geq 0\}$, domain of f^{-1}: $\{x | x \geq 0\}$, range of f^{-1}: all reals, and f^{-1} is not a function.

53. $f^{-1}(x) = \pm\sqrt{x} + 4, x \geq 0$ domain of f: all real numbers, range of f: $\{y | y \geq 0\}$, domain of f^{-1}: $\{x | x \geq 0\}$, range of f^{-1}: all reals, and f^{-1} is not a function.

55. $f^{-1}(x) = \pm\sqrt{\frac{1}{x}} - 1, x > 0$, domain of f: $\{x | x \neq -1\}$, range of f: $\{y | y > 0\}$, domain of f^{-1}: $\{x | x > 0\}$, range of f^{-1}: $\{y | y \neq -1\}$, and f^{-1} is not a function.

57. $f^{-1}(x) = \left(\frac{3}{x}\right)^2, x \geq 0$, domain of f: $\{x | x > 0\}$, range of f: $\{y | y > 0\}$, domain of f^{-1}: $\{x | x > 0\}$, range of f^{-1}: $\{y | y > 0\}$, and f^{-1} is a function.

59.a–b. Answers may vary. Sample:

a.   **b.**

61. $h = s\sqrt{2}$; $3\sqrt{2}$ in. ≈ 4.2 in. **63.** $f^{-1}(x) = \sqrt[3]{5x}$; yes **65.** $f^{-1}(x) = 27x^3$; yes **67.** $f^{-1}(x) = x^4$, $x \geq 0$; yes **69.** C **71.** A **73.** $2x + 7$ **75.** $x + 14$

77. $2x + 28 + |-2x + 4|$ **79.** -2 **81.** 3 **83.** -3

85. 30 **87.** $\pm1, \pm2, \pm3, \pm4, \pm6, \pm12,$
$\pm\frac{1}{2}, \pm\frac{3}{2}$; roots are $-\frac{3}{2}$,
±2.

89. $\pm1, \pm2, \pm3, \pm4, \pm6, \pm12,$
$\pm\frac{1}{3}, \pm\frac{2}{3}, \pm\frac{4}{3}$; roots are 1,
$-\frac{4}{3^3}, -3$.

91. $\pm1, \pm2, \pm3, \pm6$; roots are 1, 2, 3.

Lesson 7-8

pp. 423–425

EXERCISES

1.

3.

5.

7.

9.

11.

13.

15.

17.

19.

21.

23.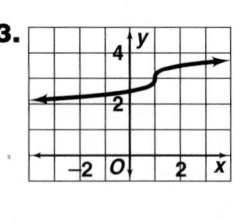

25. 147 **27.** −8.11 **29.** 5 **31.** $y = 3\sqrt{x - 1}$; the graph is the graph of $y = 3\sqrt{x}$ translated 1 unit to the right. **33.** $y = -14\sqrt{x + 1}$; the graph is the graph of $y = -14\sqrt{x}$ translated 1 unit to the left. **35.** $y = 8\sqrt{x - 2} - 3$; the graph is the graph of $y = 8\sqrt{x}$ translated 2 units to the right and 3 units down.

37.

39.

D: $x \geq 0$, R: $y \geq 7$ D: $x \geq 6$, R: $y \geq 0$

41.

43.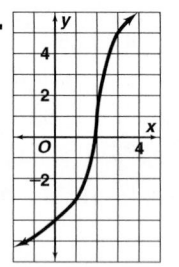

D: $x \geq 0$, R: $y \leq 0$ D: all real numbers, R: all real numbers

45.

47.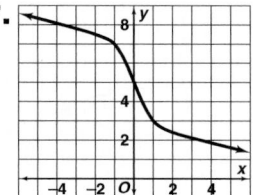

D: all real numbers, R: all real numbers   D: all real numbers, R: all real numbers

49.

51.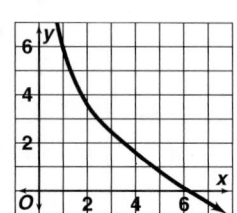

D: $x \geq -5$, R: $y \leq -1$ D: $x \geq \frac{3}{4}$, R: $y \leq 7$

53.a. **b.** D: $x \geq 2$, R: $y \geq -2$ **c.** (2, −2)

d. The domain is based on the x-coordinate of that point, and the range is based on the y-coordinate.

55.a.

b. Both domains are $x \geq 2$. The range of

$y = \sqrt{x - 2} + 1$ is $y \geq 1$. The range of
$y = -\sqrt{x - 2} + 1$ is $y \leq 1$.

57. $y = 6\sqrt{x + 3} + 4$; the graph is the graph
of $y = 6\sqrt{x}$ translated 3 units to the left and 4 up.
59. $y = \frac{1}{2}\sqrt{x - 1} - 2$; the graph is the same as

$y = \frac{1}{2}\sqrt{x}$ translated 1 unit right and 2 down.
61. $y = \frac{1}{3}\sqrt{x + 9} + 5$; the graph is the same
as $y = \frac{1}{3}\sqrt{x}$, translated 9 units to the left
and 5 up.

63.a. **b.** 20 in. **65.** $y = -\sqrt{2}$
$\sqrt{x + 4}$; the graph is the
graph of $y = -\sqrt{2x}$
translated 4 units to the
left; domain: $x \geq -4$,
range: $y \leq 0$.
67. $y = \sqrt{3} \cdot \sqrt{x - \frac{5}{3}} + 6$; the graph is the graph
of $y = \sqrt{3x}$ translated $\frac{5}{3}$ units to the right and
6 units up; domain: $x \geq \frac{5}{3}$, range: $y \geq 6$.

69.a.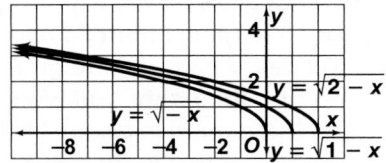

b. The graph of $y = \sqrt{h - x}$ is a reflection of
the graph of $y = \sqrt{x - h}$ in the line $x = h$.

71. C **73.** B **75.** $y = \frac{3(x + 3)}{2}$; yes

77. $y = (x + 4)^2 - 3$; yes **79.** $y = \sqrt[3]{\frac{x}{2}}$; yes

81. $\frac{\sqrt[3]{12xy^2}}{2y}$ **83.** $\frac{\sqrt[5]{48x^3y^4}}{2y}$ **85.** $\frac{-3 \pm 3\sqrt{5}}{2}$

87. $-5 \pm \sqrt{14}$ **89.** $\frac{5}{4}, -\frac{3}{2}$

Chapter Review pp. 429–431

1. radicand **2.** index **3.** rationalize the
denominator **4.** are not **5.** rational exponents
6. composite function **7.** rational exponents
8. inverse functions **9.** a radical equation
10. principal root **11.** 12 **12.** −0.4 **13.** 7 **14.** 0.5
15. −3 **16.** $7|xy^5|$ **17.** $-4y^3$ **18.** $(a - 1)^2$
19. $3x^3$ **20.** $(y + 3)^2$ **21.** $4x^4y^2\sqrt{2xy}$ **22.** 20
23. $6\sqrt[3]{2}$ **24.** $10x^2y\sqrt[3]{12y^2}$ **25.** $7x^2\sqrt{2}$
26. $15x^3y^2\sqrt{x}$ **27.** $6xy\sqrt[4]{2y}$ **28.** 4 **29.** $2y\sqrt[3]{y}$
30. $5x$ **31.** $6xy\sqrt{3x}$ **32.** $3a^2b\sqrt[3]{b}$ **33.** $\frac{2\sqrt{3}}{3}$
34. $\frac{x\sqrt{6x}}{4}$ **35.** $\frac{\sqrt[3]{5x^2}}{x^2}$ **36.** $\frac{a^3\sqrt{ab}}{4b}$ **37.** $\frac{y\sqrt[3]{150x}}{10x^2}$
38. $6\sqrt{3}$ **39.** $7 - 3\sqrt{3}$ **40.** 43 **41.** $2\sqrt{2x}$
42. $\frac{42 - 12\sqrt{3}}{37}$ **43.** $-\frac{\sqrt{2} + \sqrt{10}}{4}$ **44.** $\sqrt[5]{3}$ **45.** $\sqrt[3]{x^2}$

46. $\sqrt[4]{\frac{1}{8}}$ **47.** $\sqrt[5]{3}$ **48.** $\sqrt[4]{\frac{1}{p^9}}$ **49.** 81 **50.** 216 **51.** x

52. $x^{\frac{5}{6}}$ **53.** $\frac{y^4}{x^6}$ **54.** −42 **55.** 2 **56.** 121

57. $x^2 - x + 7$ **58.** $-x^2 + 5x + 3$

59. $2x^3 - x^2 - 11x + 10$ **60.** $x^2 - 5x - 3$

61. $\frac{x^2 - 3x + 2}{2x + 5}, x \neq -\frac{5}{2}$ **62.** 1 **63.** 25 **64.** 9 **65.** 1

66. $c^2 - 6c + 9$ **67.** $y = \frac{1}{6}x - \frac{1}{3}$; yes

68. $y = \left(\frac{x - 1}{2}\right)^{\frac{1}{3}}$; yes **69.** $y = \pm \sqrt[4]{x} + 2$; no

70. $y = x^2 - 2, x \geq 0$; yes **71.** 5 **72.** −5

73. 6 **74.** t

75. **76.**

77. **78.**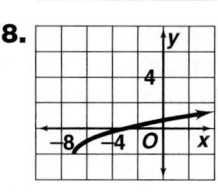

Chapter 8

Lesson 8-1 pp. 442–445

EXERCISES

1. **3.**

5. **7.**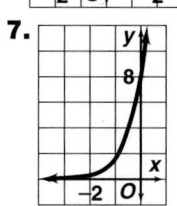

9.a. 1.0126 **b.** $y = 6.08(1.0126)^x$, where $x = 0$
corresponds to 2000 **11.** $y = 2.5(7)^x$
13. $y = 5(0.6)^x$ **15.** $y = 24(\frac{1}{3})^x$ **17.** exponential
decay **19.** exponential decay **21.** exponential
growth **23.** exponential decay

25. **27.**

29. **31.**

33. $y = 12{,}000(0.9)^x$; 6377 **35.a.** $y = 6500(0.857)^x$
b. \$4091.25 **37.** 30% increase **39.** 70% increase
41. 75% decrease **43.a.** about 5.6% **b.** about
0.0017%
45.a. $y = 80(0.965)^x$ **b.**

about 47 years

47. 6 **49.** 0.45 **51.** 0.999 **53.** 2 **55.** Check
students' work. **57.** C **59.a.** A negative growth
rate would be represented by adding the negative
rate to 1. **b.** Armenia: $y = 11.8(1.099)^x$, Canada:
$y = 958.7(1.017)^x$, Germany: $y = 2271(0.999)^x$,
Venezuela: $y = 117.9(0.908)^x$. x in each equation
represents the number of years since 2003.
c. Armenia: \$18.9 billion, Canada: \$1043 billion,
Germany: \$2260 billion, Venezuela: \$72.8 billion.
61. B **63.**

65. $6n^2\sqrt{5n}$ **67.** $\frac{2\sqrt{x}}{3x}$ **69.** $y = x^3 - 7x - 6$

71. $y = x^2 + 2$ **73.** $y = 2x^2 + 2$ **75.** $y = \frac{3}{2}x^2 + 2$
77. $y = -\frac{1}{2}x^2 + 2$

Lesson 8-2 pp. 450–452

EXERCISES 1. Asymptote is $y = 0$.

3.

5. **7.** **9.**

---

11. **13.**

15. $y = 50\left(\frac{1}{2}\right)^{\frac{1}{14.3}x}$; 0.85 mg **17.** $y = 24\left(\frac{1}{2}\right)^{\frac{1}{5730}x}$;
0.64 mg **19.** 403.4288 **21.** 1 **23.** 15.1543
25. \$448.30 **27.** 0 **29.** If $c < 0$, the graph models
exponential decay. If $c = 0$, the graph is a horizontal
line. If $c > 0$, the graph models exponential growth.
31.a. Answers may vary. Sample: $y = -2(1.3)^x$
b. Answers may vary. Sample: I am in debt for \$2
and my debt is growing at a rate of 30% per year.
c. The graph of exponential decay approaches
the asymptote $y = 0$ as x increases. The graph of
negative exponential growth approaches the
asymptote $y = 0$ as x decreases. **33.** $y = -3^x$;
$y = -3^{x-8} + 2$ **35.** $y = -3\left(\frac{1}{3}\right)^x$; $y = -3\left(\frac{1}{3}\right)^{x+5} - 1$
37. 8.7 yr **39.** B **41.** \$399.97 **43.** exponential
growth **45.** exponential growth **47.** exponential
growth **49.a.** about 10 names; about 24 names
b. Graphically, it will never happen; the graph has
$y = 30$ as an asymptote. (In reality, you would be
close to knowing all the names in about 21 days.)
c. Answers may vary. Sample: I learn names
pretty quickly; my learning rate might be 0.4.
51. A **53.** A **55.** $y = -2(4)^x$ **57.** $y = 8(0.5)^x$
59. $y = 10{,}000(0.8)^x$ **61.** $-\sqrt[3]{4}$ **63.** $2\left(\sqrt[4]{2} + \sqrt[4]{8}\right)$
65. $11\sqrt{7}$ **67.** $3 + \sqrt{5}$ **69.** $x^2 - x - 6$
71. $x^2 + x + 1$ **73.** $3x^2 - 7x + 2$ **75.** $x + y = -2$,
$x + 4z = -2$, $y + 4z = -2$ **77.** $x - y = 8$, $x + 2z =$
8, $-y + 2z = 8$ **79.** $-2x + y = 10$, $-2x - 5z = 10$,
$y - 5z = 10$

Lesson 8-3 pp. 457–460

EXERCISES 1. The earthquake in Missouri
released about 1.97 times more energy. **3.** The
earthquake in Missouri released about 8,759,310
times more energy. **5.** The earthquake in Alaska
released about 83 times more energy. **7.** $3 = \log$
1000 **9.** $\log \frac{1}{10} = -1$ **11.** $\log_{\frac{1}{2}} 4 = -2$ **13.** $-2 =$
$\log 0.01$ **15.** $\frac{1}{2}$ **17.** $\frac{3}{2}$ **19.** $\frac{1}{2}$ **21.** 2 **23.** 1 **25.** 3
27. 6.3×10^{-3} **29.** 7.9×10^{-4} **31.** 1.3×10^{-5}
33. 4.0×10^{-6} **35.** **37.**

39. 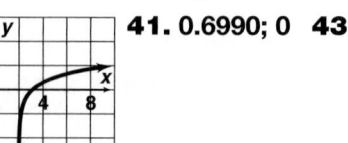 **41.** 0.6990; 0 **43.** -1.0969; -2

45. -0.7782; -1 **47.** 7.1139; 7 **49.** apple juice: 3.5, acidic; buttermilk: 4.6, acidic; cream: 6.6, acidic; ketchup: 3.9, acidic; shrimp sauce: 7.1, basic; strained peas: 6, acidic **51.** First rewrite $y = \log_1 x$ as $1^y = x$. For any real number y, $x = 1$.
53. $128 = 2^7$ **55.** $16{,}807 = 7^5$ **57.** $1 = 4^0$
59. $\frac{1}{2} = 2^{-1}$ **61.** $8192 = 2^{13}$ **63.** C **65.** $y = 0.5^x$
67. $y = 2^{x-1}$ **69.** $y = 10^{x-1}$ **71.** $y = 5^{\frac{x}{2}}$

73. **75.**

77. domain $\{x \mid x > 0\}$, range: all reals
79. domain $\{x \mid x > 0\}$, range: all reals
81. domain $\{x \mid x > -1\}$, range: all reals
83. domain $\{x \mid x > 0\}$, range: all reals **85.** 100
87. 60 **89.** 10 **91.** D **93.** B **95.** $y = 0$

97. $\sqrt[3]{t^2}$ **99.** $\sqrt[5]{z^8}$ **101.** $-2, -4$
103. $-1.217, 0, 8.217$ **105.** $\left(\frac{1}{2}b - 2\right)\left(\frac{1}{2}b + 2\right)$

Lesson 8-4 pp. 465–467

EXERCISES 1. Product Property **3.** Power Property **5.** Power Property, Quotient Property **7.** Power Property, Quotient Property **9.** Power Property, Quotient Property **11.** $\log 14$
13. $\log 972$ **15.** $\log \frac{m^4}{n}$ **17.** $\log_6 5x$ **19.** $3 \log x +$ $5 \log y$ **21.** $\log_4 5 + \frac{1}{2} \log_4 x$ **23.** $\log_5 r - \log_5 s$
25. $\log_3 7 + 2 \log (2x - 3)$ **27.** $\frac{1}{2} \log 2 + \frac{1}{2} \log x$ $- \frac{1}{2} \log y$ **29.** $\log s + \frac{1}{2} \log 7 - 2 \log t$ **31.** 9 dB
33. -2 **35.** 6 **37.** 2 **39.** 1 **41.** 1 **43.** Answers may vary. Sample: $\log 150 = \log 15 + \log 10$. **45.** 1.4772 **47.** 2.097 **49.** -0.0969 **51.** -1.398 **53.** -0.7782 **55.** 0.3495 **57.** 0.00001 **59.** False; $\frac{1}{2} \log_3 3$ $= \log_3 3^{\frac{1}{2}}$, not $\log_3 \frac{3}{2}$. **61.** False; the two logs have different bases. **63.** False; $\log_b \frac{x}{y} = \log_b x - \log_b y$. **65.** False; $\log_4 7 - \log_4 3 = \log_4 \frac{7}{3}$, not $\log_4 4$. **67.** False; the three logs have different bases. **69.** True; the left side equals $\log_b \left(\frac{1}{8} \cdot 4^3\right)$, which equals $\log_b 8$. **71.** No; the expression $(2x + 1)$ is a sum, so it is not covered by the Product, Quotient, or Power properties. **73.** $\log_3 \sqrt[4]{2x}$
75. $\log \frac{27}{2}$ **77.** $\log_b \frac{\sqrt[3]{x^2}\sqrt[4]{y^3}}{z^5}$ **79.** $3 \log 2 +$ $\frac{3}{2} \log x - 3 \log 5$ **81.** $\log 2 + \frac{1}{2} \log 4 + \frac{1}{2} \log r -$ $\log s$ **83.** $\frac{5}{2} \log_4 x + \frac{1}{2} \log_4 y - \log_4 z - 4 \log_4 w$
85. $\frac{1}{2} \log x + \frac{1}{4} \log 2 - \log y$ **87.** $\frac{1}{2} \log_7 (r + 9) - 2$

$\log_7 s - \frac{1}{3} \log_7 t$ **89.1.** $u = \log_b M$ (Given)
2. $b^u = M$ (Rewrite in exponential form.)
3. $(b^u)^x = M^x$ (Raise each side to x power.)
4. $b^{ux} = M^x$ (Power Property of exponents)
5. $\log_b b^{ux} = \log_b M^x$ (Take the log of each side.)
6. $ux = \log_b M^x$ (Simplify.) **7.** $\log_b M^x =$ $x \cdot \log_b M$ (substitution) **91.** D **93.** $\log_7 49 = 2$
95. $\log_8 \frac{1}{4} = -\frac{2}{3}$ **97.** $8, -8$ **99.** 2 **101.** $-4i$
103. $-\sqrt{2}, -i - 1$ **105.** $2i + 3, -i$

Lesson 8-5 pp. 472–476

EXERCISES 1. 1.5850 **3.** 2.7320 **5.** 3 **7.** 0.9534
9. 0.3579 **11.** 0.2720 **13.** 0.5690 **15.** 4.7027 **17.** 6
19. 0.64 **21.** -0.73 **23.** about 7.1 years
25. 3.1699; $\log_8 729$ **27.** 3.6309; $\log_8 1901.3$
29. 3.1827; $\log_8 748.56$ **31.** 3.8737; $\log_8 3149.6$
33. 0.05 **35.** 33 **37.** $\frac{1}{60}$, or ≈ 0.0167 **39.** $\sqrt{10}$, or $\approx$ 3.1623 **41.** 2 **43.** $100{,}000 \sqrt{5}$, or $\approx 223{,}606.8$
45. $\frac{1}{4}$ **47.** 7 **49.** 5.1 **51.** $2 = 10\left(\frac{1}{2}\right)^{\frac{x}{1.17}}$, about 2.7 min. **53.** -1 **55.** $\frac{1}{2}$ **57.** $\frac{1}{3}$ **59.** 3 **61.a.** Let x equal the number of years after 2000. Florida growth factor $= 1.0213$, $y = 15{,}982{,}378 \cdot (1.0213)^x$; New York growth factor $= 1.0054$, $y = 18{,}976{,}457 \cdot$ $(1.0054)^x$ **b.** 2011 **63.** Since Florida's growth rate is larger than Texas's growth rate, in theory, given constant conditions, Florida would exceed Texas in about 543 years. However, since no state has unlimited capacity for growth, it is unrealistic to predict over a long period of time. **65.** Answers may vary. Sample: $\log x = 1.6$, $10^{1.6} = x$, $x \approx 39.81$
67.a. $x = \frac{\log b}{\log a}$ **b.** $x = \log_a b = \frac{\log b}{\log a}$
c. Substituting the result from part (a) into the results from part (b), or vice versa, yields $\log_a b = \frac{\log b}{\log a}$. This justifies the Change of Base Formula. **69.** $\frac{\log 8}{\log 3}$ **71.** $\frac{\log 3.3}{\log 9}$ **73.** $\frac{\log (1 - x)}{\log 6}$
75. $\frac{\log (x + 1)}{\log x}$ **77.a.** top up: 10^{-5} W/m^2, top down: $10^{-2.5}$ W/m^2 **b.** 99.68% **79.** 2.9315 **81.** 0.6225
83. 2.3094 **85.** 0.8505 **87.** 7.4168 **89.** 2.9615
91. 1 **93.** 1.0451 **95.** 1.3063 **97.a.** bassoon, guitar, harp, violin, viola, cello **b.** bassoon, guitar, harp, cello, bass **c.** harp, violin **d.** harp, violin **99.** no; solving $0.65 = \frac{x}{(0.5)^{5730}}$ for x, the age in years of the sample, yields an age of about 3561 yrs.
101. $-4, 2$ **103.** 1 **105.a.** 91 hours or 4 days **b.** 0.928 mg or 1.061 mg **c.** Estimate in hours is more accurate; the days have a larger rounding error. **107.** C **109.** $\log 2 + 3 \log x - 2 \log y$
111. $3 \log_2 3 + 3 \log_2 x$ **113.** $\log_4 5 + \frac{1}{2} \log_4 x$
115. $x^2 + 3x - 1$ **117.** $3x^3 - 3x$ **119.** $\pm 2, \pm 2i$
121. $-2, -1, 3$ **123.** $\frac{679 + x}{6} = 133$; 119

EXERCISES 1. ln 125 **3.** ln 4 **5.** ln $\frac{1}{81}$ **7.** ln $\frac{m^5}{n^3}$

9. ln $\frac{a\sqrt{c}}{b^2}$ **11.** 24.13 **13.** 25 s **15.** 0.135

17. 1488.979 **19.** ±11.588 **21.** ±2.241 **23.** 2.890
25. 2.401 **27.** 1.242 **29.** 6 years **31.** 1 **33.** 10
35. 0 **37.** 1 **39.** 301 **41.** sometimes **43.** always
45. 19.8 h **47.** 3.6 **49.** 9.4 **51.** 13.9
53. 17.5 **55.** 542.31 **57.** 0.0794 **59.** 1.2639
61. 27,347.9 **63.** No; using the Change of Base
Formula would result in one of the log
expressions being written as a quotient of logs,
which couldn't then be combined with the other
expression to form a single logarithm.
65.a. about 43 min **b.** $t = \frac{-1}{0.041}$ ln $\left(\frac{T-72}{164}\right)$

1.7,   6.0,   11.3,   18.1,   27.6,   43.1,   97.6

67. C **69.** B **71.** 4 **73.** 0.272 **75.** 1.002
77. $y = \frac{x-7}{5}$; yes **79.** $y = \pm\sqrt{5-x}$; no

Chapter Review   pp. 487–489

1. growth factor **2.** common logarithm
3. asymptote **4.** logarithm **5.** exponential
equation
6. exponential   **7.** exponential
growth; 400%   growth; 300%

 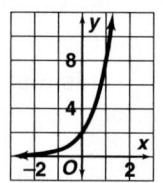

8. exponential   **9.** exponential
growth; 280%   decay; −75%

10. $y = \frac{25}{7}\left(\frac{7}{5}\right)^x$ **11.** $y = 0.0015(10)^x$
12. $y = 2.25\left(\frac{1}{3}\right)^x$ **13.** $y = \left(\frac{1}{3}\right)^x$

14. $y = 12{,}500(0.91)^x$; $7800 **15.** $y = 50(1.03)^x$; $58
16. $y = 1500(0.2)^x$; 2.4 **17.** $y = 2(1.4)^x$; 7.6832
18. $y = 3^x$ reflected over the x-axis
and translated up 1 unit

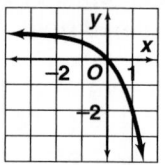

19. $y = 8^x$ translated   **20.** $y = 2(2)^x$ translated
down 1 unit   left 1 unit and up 3 units

21. $y = 2\left(\frac{1}{3}\right)^x$ reflected over the
x-axis and translated
right 2 units

22. $1100.76 **23.** $291.91 **24.** $645.23
25. 2.7183 **26.** 0.3679 **27.** 148.4132 **28.** 0.6065
29. $y = 3\left(\frac{1}{2}\right)^{\frac{x}{1620}}$; ≈2.937 mg **30.** 2.0×10^{-6}
31. 7 **32.** $2 = \log_6 36$ **33.** $-3 = \log_2 0.125$
34. $3 = \log_3 27$ **35.** $-3 = \log 0.001$ **36.** 6
37. −2 **38.** −5 **39.** 0

40.   **41.**

42.   **43.**

44. log 24 **45.** $\log_2 \frac{5}{3}$ **46.** $\log_3 7x^4$ **47.** $\log \frac{z}{y}$
48. $2\log_4 x + 3\log_4 y$; Product and Power
Properties **49.** $\log 4 + 4\log s + \log t$; Product
and Power Properties **50.** $\log_3 2 - \log_3 x$;
Quotient Property **51.** $2\log(x + 3)$; Power
Property **52.** 1.76 dB **53.** 2.38 **54.** 3.26 **55.** 4.65
56. 1.37 **57.** 1 **58.** ≈0.66 **59.** ≈0.67 **60.** ≈3.06
61. $\frac{10}{3}$ **62.** 8 **63.** 50 **64.** 7,625,597,484,987
65. $\log_5 91.68$ **66.** about 18.2 h **67.** 0.83 **68.** 2.26
69. 4.31 **70.** 0.00018 **71.** 3.77 **72.** 6.03 **73.** 3.4%

Chapter 9

Lesson 9-1 — pp. 499–501

EXERCISES **1.** $y = \frac{11}{x}$ **3.** $y = \frac{1}{x}$ **5.** $y = \frac{3.6}{x}$

7. direct; $y = 5x$ **9.** direct; $y = 2x$ **11.** inverse; $y = \frac{1}{x}$ **13.** $y = \frac{100}{x}$; 10 **15.** $y = -\frac{5}{3x}$; $-\frac{1}{6}$

17. A varies jointly with b and h. **19.** V varies jointly with B and h. **21.** h varies directly with V and inversely with the square of r. **23.** ℓ varies directly with V and inversely with the product of w and h. **25.** $z = 10xy$; 360 **27.** $z = \frac{4}{xy}$; $\frac{1}{9}$ **29.** 18

31. $\frac{1}{4}$ **33.** 9 **35.** 7200 rpm **37.** $18\frac{2}{3}$ **39.** 2 **41.** ≈ 4.277

43. 2.625 **45.** 8 **47.** 11.786 **49.** 32 **51.** $\frac{40}{3}$ **53.** 32

55. quartered; divided by 16 **57.** $x_1 y_1 = k$ and $x_2 y_2 = k$ def. of inverse variation $x_1 y_1 = x_2 y_2$ transitivity $\frac{x_1}{x_2} = \frac{y_2}{y_1}$ Divide both sides by $x_2 y_1$.

59. BMI $\approx \frac{705\,w}{h^2}$ **61.** D **63.** $3e^4 \approx 163.79$

65. $-90x\sqrt{x}$ **67.** $10x^2y^3\sqrt{2y}$ **69.** $-4ab^2$ **71.** $|x|$

Lesson 9-2 — pp. 506–508

EXERCISES 1. **3.**

5. 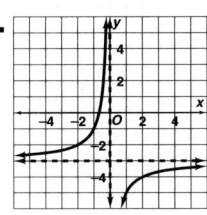 The graph is in Quadrant II and Quadrant IV. The graph is a reflection of the graph of $y = \frac{3}{x}$.

7. The graph is in Quadrant II and Quadrant IV. The graph is a reflection of the graph of $y = \frac{5}{x}$.

9. The graph is in Quadrant II and Quadrant IV. The graph is a reflection of the graph of $\frac{0.1}{x}$.

11. 7.67 ft **13.** 1.84 ft **15.**

17. **19.**

21. **23.** $y = \frac{2}{x + 2} + 3$

25.a. $c = \frac{750}{a}$ $a = 0,\ c = 0$

b. Answers may vary. Sample: If the number of awards is large, the amount of money available for each award approaches 0. If there are a small number of awards, then the amount of money available for each award gets larger. **27.** $y = \frac{0.5}{x}$
29. $y = -\frac{8.3}{x}$ **31.** $y = \frac{4}{x}$

33. **35.**

37.

39. Answers may vary. Sample: The graph of the translation looks similar to the graph of $y = \frac{k}{x}$, so knowing the asymptotes helps to position the translation; check students' work.
41. (3, 6)

43.

(−1.75, −4)

45.

(3.76, 4.2)

47.a. $m = \dfrac{10,000}{g}$

b. $m = \dfrac{10,000}{g - 50}$

c. 25 mi/gal, 28.57 mi/gal **49.** The branches of $y = \dfrac{1}{x^2}$ are in Quadrants I and II. The branches of $y = \dfrac{1}{x}$ are in Quadrants I and III. The graphs intersect at (1, 1). The graph of $y = \dfrac{1}{x^2}$ is closer to the x-axis for $x > 1$, and the graph of $y = \dfrac{1}{x}$ is closer to the y-axis for $0 < x < 1$. **51.** $y = \dfrac{16}{x}$, $y = -\dfrac{16}{x}$ **53.** C **55.** B **57.** B Varies directly with V and inversely with h. **59.** b varies directly with A and inversely with h. **61.** growth, 4
63. decay, 0.8 **65.** $79 - 2\sqrt{3}$ **67.** $50 + 35\sqrt{2}$

Lesson 9-3   pp. 513–516

EXERCISES 1. $x = 0, x = 2$ **3.** $x = 1, x = -1$
5. $x = -3$ **7.** $x = 2$ **9.** $x = -2.77, x = 1.277$
11. hole at $x = -5$ **13.** vertical asymptote at $x = -1$, hole at $x = 2$ **15.** none **17.** none
19. $y = 0$ **21.** $y = 1$ **23.** $y = 0$

25.

27.

29.

31.a. $y = \dfrac{0.19x + 210,000}{x - 500}$

b. $46.88; $14.68 **c.** more than 21,916 discs **d.** $x = 500, y = 0.19$ **33.** vertical asymptote at $x = -2$

35.

37.

39.

41. Answers may vary. Sample: There is no value of x for which the denominator equals 0.

43.a. $y = \dfrac{20,000x + 200,000}{x + 1}$

WINDOW FORMAT
Xmin=0
Xmax=40
Xscl=4
Ymin=0
Ymax=200000
Yscl=10000

b. $65,000; $25,806.45 **c.** Answers may vary. Sample: No; the president's salary throws off the average; the median or mode would be a better measure. **45.a.** The increase in production workers' average hourly wage is greater.

b. rational **c.** $R(x) = \dfrac{M(x)}{A(x)}$

d.

around the year 2106

47. D **49.** B; 90.00 **51.** vertical: $x = -3$, horizontal: $y = 0$ **53.** vertical: $x = 7$, horizontal: $y = -3$
55. vertical: $x = 5$, horizontal: $y = -6$
57. 3 units up

Lesson 9-4   pp. 519–521

EXERCISES 1. $\frac{1}{2x-1}$; $x \neq 0$ or $\frac{1}{2}$ **3.** a^3b; $b \neq 0$

5. $\frac{2}{x+5}$; $x \neq -5$ **7.** $\frac{7}{15x^2}$; $x \neq 0, y \neq 0$ **9.** $\frac{4}{3}$; $y \neq \frac{1}{2}$ or 3

11. $\frac{x-2}{x(x-1)}$; $x \neq 0, 1, -1,$ or -2 **13.** $\frac{2}{3x^2y^2}$;

$x \neq 0, y \neq 0$ **15.** $\frac{5(x+y)}{3}$; $x \neq y$ **17.** $\frac{x(x-1)}{3(x+1)}$;

$x \neq -1, 1,$ or 0 **19.** $\frac{(x-8)}{(x-10)}$; $x \neq -3$ or 10

21. $\frac{y(y+3)}{12(y+4)}$; $x \neq 0, y \neq -4$ or 3 **23.** The student
is not correct; $x = 2$ will make the denominator of
$\frac{x}{x-2}$ equal 0, so $x = 2$ is not a solution. **25.** The
numerator and the denominator have no common
factors; check students' work. **27.** $\frac{a+3}{(a-3)(a-3)}$;

$a \neq -4, -3,$ or 3 **29.** $\frac{4}{x}$; $x \neq 0, -5, 4,$ or 1

31. $\frac{x+1}{x-4}$; $x \neq -3, \frac{1}{2}, 2,$ or 4 **33.** $\frac{x(x-1)^3}{(x+4)}$, $x \neq -4,$

0, 1 **35.** $\frac{18x^5}{y^2}$, $y \neq 0$ **37a.** 1.2 m/s² **b.** 2.68 m/s²

39. $\frac{4x}{3y}$; $x \neq 0$ or $-1, y \neq 0$ **41.** $\frac{15}{4n^2}$; $m \neq 0$ or $-\frac{2}{3}n$,

$n \neq 0$ **43.** A **45.** hole at $x = 3$ **47.** hole at $x = 4$,
vertical asymptote at $x = -3$ **49.** -5 **51.** $\frac{3}{4}$
53. $x = 6$

Lesson 9-5   pp. 525–528

EXERCISES 1. $\frac{120}{59} \approx 2.03$ in. **3.** For distances
greater than 10 ft, d_i is nearly constant.
5. $(x-1)(x+1)(x+1)$ **7.** $18(2x-7)(x+3)$

9. $2(x+5)(x^2-32x-10)$ **11.** $\frac{2(d-2)}{2d+1}$

13. $\frac{7x^2+20x-18}{(x-3)(x+3)(x+4)}$ **15.** $\frac{5x^2+14x-12}{(x-3)(x+2)^2}$

17. $\frac{-3(2y+1)}{2y-1}$ **19.** $\frac{x^2-24}{3x(x+3)}$

21. $\frac{-2x(x+3)}{(x-2)(x-1)(x+1)}$ **23.** $\frac{15}{28}$ **25.** $\frac{b}{9}$ **27.** $\frac{3x}{2+xy}$

29. $\frac{3}{x-6}$ **31.** $\frac{3x-8}{4x^2}$ **33.** $\frac{2x^3-x^2+1}{x^2(x+1)(x-1)}$

37. $\frac{5x^2+6x+12}{(x-3)(x+2)^2}$ **39.** $\frac{4y^3+12y^2-y-2}{y(y+3)}$ **41.** Check
students' work. **43.** Answers may vary. Sample:
Substitute 0 for x in the three expressions, and
show that $\frac{4}{-9} + \frac{7}{3} \neq \frac{25}{-9}$. **45.** $\frac{2x-5y}{2(3x+2y)}$ **47.** x

49. $\frac{-5x+13}{2(x-4)}$ **51.** $x \neq -2, -3, -4$; those values
result in division by 0, which is undefined.
53.a. $\frac{24}{7}$ mi/h **b.** $\frac{24}{7}$ **c.** $\frac{400}{9}$ mi/h **d.** $\frac{2x(x+a)}{2x+a}$ mi/h

55. a. $f = \frac{d_i d_o}{d_i + d_o}$ **b.** $\frac{x(2x+1)}{3x+1} = f$ **57.** A **59.** C

61. $\frac{1}{4xy}$; $a \neq 0, b \neq 0, x \neq 0, y \neq 0$ **63.** $\frac{12x}{x+3}$;

$x \neq -3, 2,$ or 3 **65.** $\frac{3(x+1)}{2(x+3)}$; $x \neq 1, -1,$ or -3

67. $\log_{10} p^7 q$ **69.** 30 **71.** $\frac{15}{4}$

Lesson 9-6   pp. 532–535

EXERCISES 1. 5 **3.** 10 **5.** $\frac{4}{3}$ **7.** $\frac{7}{3}$ **9.** -1 **11.** 10

13. 2 **15.** -1 or 12 **17.** about -1.45 or 1.65 **19.** $-3, -2$
21. 1 **23.** passenger train: 112 mi/h, freight train:
92 mi/h **25.** $1\frac{5}{7}$ h **27.** $E = mc^2$ **29.** $c = \sqrt{a^2 - b^2}$

31. $B = \pm \frac{1}{r} \sqrt{\frac{2Vm}{q}}$ **33.** D **35.a.** $L = \pm \frac{24(R-r)}{T}$

b. 32 in., about 28.24 in., about 25.26 in.
37. Check students' work. **39.** 3 **41.** no solution
43. 5 **45.** no solution **47.** 21 **49.** no solution
51. 1, $-\frac{2}{3}$ **53.** $x \approx 4.5$ ft **55.a.** $t = \frac{d}{s}$ **b.** $\frac{35}{18}$ h **c.** $\frac{d}{t} + x$

d. $\frac{700}{360} + \frac{700}{360+x} = 3.5$; 90 mi/h **57.** about 44.44 mi/h

59. C **61.** A **63.** $\frac{5xy-12}{2y(y+2)}$ **65.** $x = -3$

67. $x = -0.999$ **69.** $y = \frac{5-x}{2}$; yes

71. $y = \sqrt[3]{x+4}$; yes

Lesson 9-7   pp. 542–545

EXERCISES 1. independent **3.** dependent **5.** $\frac{1}{6}$
7. 0.54 **9.** $\frac{9}{25}$ **11.** Mutually exclusive since if the
numbers are equal, then the sum is even.
13. 47% **15.** $\frac{14}{15}$ **17.** $\frac{26}{35}$ **19.** $\frac{1}{2}$ **21.** $\frac{5}{6}$ **23.** $\frac{5}{6}$ **25.** 1
27. $\frac{7}{12}$ **29.** $\frac{31}{56}$ **31.** 16% **33.** 86.9% **35.** 72.4%
37. $\frac{4}{15}$ **39.** $\frac{1}{15}$ **41.** $\frac{1}{11}$ **43.** $\frac{7}{15}$ **45a.** $\frac{1}{4}$ **b.** $\frac{1}{64}$
47. F and G are mutually exclusive so $P(F$ or $G) =$
$P(F) + P(G) \geq 0$ and $P(F$ and $G) = 0$. So $P(F$ or $G) \geq$
$P(F$ and $G)$. **49.** 6% **51.** $\frac{4}{9}$ **53.** C **55.** $\frac{3}{7}$ **57.** $\frac{1}{6}$ **59.** $\frac{e^6}{2}$
≈ 201.71 **61.** $\pm e^2 \approx \pm 7.39$ **63.** ln 12 ≈ 2.48
65. about ± 1.048

Chapter Review   pp. 547–549

1. mutually exclusive **2.** simplest form
3. independent events **4.** branch **5.** point of
discontinuity **6.** $y = \frac{150}{x}$; 30 **7.** $y = \frac{60}{x}$; 12
8. $y = \frac{180}{x}$; 36 **9.** $y = \frac{72}{x}$ **10.** not possible
11. $y = 6x$ **12.** $z = \frac{7}{4}xy$; 56 **13.** $z = \frac{4x}{y}$; 2
14. $z = \frac{x^3}{y}$; 8 **15.** R varies jointly with k, m and
the square of n. **16.** W varies inversely with the
square of d. **17.** P varies directly with x and
inversely with the product of z and the square of y.

18.

19.

20.

21.

22. $y = \frac{4}{x} + 3$ **23.** $y = \frac{4}{x-2} + 2$ **24.** $y = \frac{4}{x+3} - 4$

25. about 31,056 headsets

26. −7 vertical asymptote $x = -7$, horizontal asymptote $y = 0$

27. −2, 1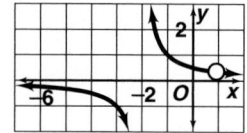

vertical asymptote $x = -2$, horizontal asymptote $y = 0$, hole at $x = 1$

28. 1, −1 vertical asymptote $x = -1$, hole at $x = 1$

29. no points of discontinuity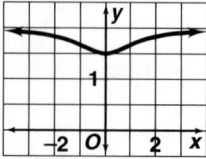

horizontal asymptote $y = 2$

30. $\frac{(x-1)(x+1)}{x+3}$; $x \neq -4, -3,$ or 6

31. $\frac{(2x-1)(x+1)}{x+4}$; $x \neq -4, -1,$ or 0 **32.** $\frac{r}{3}$

33. 12 cm **34.** $\frac{3(3x-4)}{(x-2)(x+2)}$

35. $\frac{-x^2+3x+2}{x(x+1)(x-1)(x+3)}$ **36.** $\frac{8}{15}$ **37.** $\frac{1}{4(x+y)}$

38. −1 **39.** no solution **40.** −12, 9 **41.** 7.5 h, 15 h **42.** dependent **43.** independent

44. not mutually exclusive **45.** not mutually exclusive **46.** $\frac{1}{3}$ **47.** $\frac{2}{3}$ **48.** $\frac{5}{6}$

Chapter 10

Lesson 10-1 pp. 560–563

EXERCISES 1.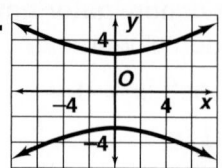

Hyperbola: center (0, 0), y-intercepts at $\pm\frac{5\sqrt{3}}{3}$, no x-intercepts, the lines of symmetry are the x- and y-axes; domain: all real numbers, range: $y \geq \frac{5\sqrt{3}}{3}$ or $y \leq -\frac{5\sqrt{3}}{3}$. **3.**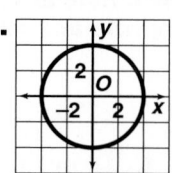

Circle: center (0, 0), radius 4, x-intercepts at ±4, y-intercepts at ±4, there are infinitely many lines of symmetry; domain: $-4 \leq x \leq 4$, range: $-4 \leq y \leq 4$. **5.** 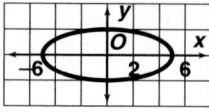 Ellipse: center (0, 0), y-intercepts at ±2, x-intercepts at ±5, the lines of symmetry are the x- and y-axes; domain: $-5 \leq x \leq 5$, range: $-2 \leq y \leq 2$.

7. Hyperbola: center (0, 0), y-intercepts at ±1, the lines of symmetry are the x- and y-axes; domain: all real numbers, range: $y \leq -1$ or $y \geq 1$.

9. 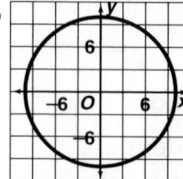 Circle: center (0, 0), radius 10, x- and y-intercepts at ±10, there are infinitely many lines of symmetry; domain: $-10 \leq x \leq 10$, range: $-10 \leq y \leq 10$.

11. Ellipse: center (0, 0), x-intercepts at ±4, y-intercepts at ±2, the lines of symmetry are the x- and y-axes; domain: $-4 \leq x \leq 4$, range: $-2 \leq y \leq 2$.

13. 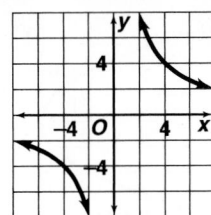 Ellipse: center (0, 0), x-intercepts at ± 1, y-intercepts at $\pm\frac{1}{3}$, the lines of symmetry are the x- and y-axes; domain: $-1 \le x \le 1$, range: $-\frac{1}{3} \le y \le \frac{1}{3}$.

15. Hyperbola: center (0, 0), y-intercepts at $\pm\frac{1}{2}$, the lines of symmetry are the x- and y-axes; domain: all real numbers, range: $y \le -\frac{1}{2}$ or $y \ge \frac{1}{2}$.

17. center (0, 0), x-intercepts at ± 3, y-intercepts at ± 2; domain: $-3 \le x \le 3$, range: $-2 \le y \le 2$
19. center (0, 0), x-intercepts at ± 3, no y-intercepts; domain: $x \le -3$ or $x \ge 3$, range: all real numbers **21.** center (0, 0), x-intercepts at ± 3, y-intercepts at ± 5; domain: $-3 \le x \le 3$, range: $-5 \le y \le 5$ **23.** 19 **25.** 18 **27.** 21
29. Hyperbola: center (0, 0), x-intercepts ± 4, the lines of symmetry are the x- and y-axes; domain: $x \le -4$ or $x \ge 4$, range: all real numbers.

31. Hyperbola: center (0, 0), y-intercepts at ± 2, the lines of symmetry are the x- and y-axes; domain: all real numbers, range: $y \le -2$ or $y \ge 2$.

33.a. Let the lamp sit in a normal, upright position, but close enough to the wall for the bottom rim of the shade to almost touch the wall. **b.** Hold the lamp so that the shade contacts the wall along a vertical line. **c.** Hold the lamp at an angle so that the light from the top of the shade gives a closed, curved oblong area of light on the wall. **d.** Hold the lamp so that the circular top rim of the shade is parallel to the wall.

35.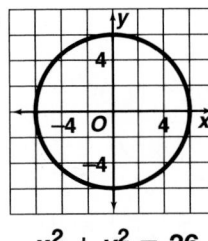
$$x^2 + y^2 = 36$$
37.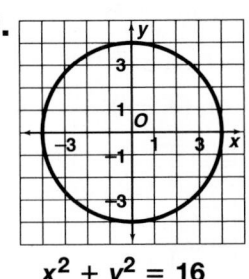
$$x^2 + y^2 = 16$$

39. D 41–43. Answers may vary. Samples are given. **41.** $(\sqrt{2}, 1)$ **43.** (2, 0) **45.** $(0, -\sqrt{7})$

47.a. **b.** hyperbola **c.** No intercepts, but $y = x$ and $y = -x$ are lines of symmetry. **d.** yes; $f(x) = \frac{16}{x}$

49. one branch of a hyperbola **51. A 53.** $\frac{1}{2}$ **55.** $\frac{1}{2}$
57. $z = -4xy$; 24 **59.** $y = \frac{1}{2}xy$; 3 **61.** $y = \frac{1}{2}(4)^x$
63. $y = \frac{1}{3}(3)^x$ **65.** $y = \frac{1}{4}(2)^x$ **67.** $p^6 + 6p^5q + 15p^4q^2 + 20p^3q^3 + 15p^2q^4 + 6pq^5 + q^6$
69. $243 - 405x + 270x^2 - 90x^3 + 15x^4 - x^5$

Lesson 10-2   **pp. 568–570**

EXERCISES 1. $y = \frac{1}{8}x^2$ **3.** $x = -\frac{1}{12}y^2$
5. $y = \frac{1}{8}x^2 + 2$ **7.** $x = \frac{1}{24}y^2$ **9.** $y = \frac{1}{28}x^2$
11. $x = \frac{1}{8}y^2$ **13.** $y = \frac{1}{6}x^2$ **15.** Answers may vary. Sample: $y = x^2$; The light produced by the bulb will reflect off the parabolic mirror in parallel rays.
17. $\left(0, \frac{1}{4}\right), y = -\frac{1}{4}$ **19.** $\left(\frac{1}{2}, 0\right), x = -\frac{1}{2}$
21. (9, 0), $x = -9$ **23.** $\left(0, -\frac{1}{8}\right), y = \frac{1}{8}$
25. (0, 0), (0, -1), $y = 1$

27. (0, 0), $\left(\frac{25}{4}, 0\right), x = -\frac{25}{4}$ **29.** (0, 0), (0, -1), $y = 1$

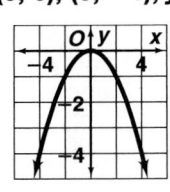

31. (0, 0), (-2, 0), $x = 2$

33. (-3, 0), $\left(-\frac{3}{2}, 0\right)$, $x = -\frac{9}{2}$ **35.** (3, -1), (6, -1), $x = 0$

37. $y = \frac{1}{400}x^2$ **39.** $x = -\frac{1}{28}y^2$ **41.** $y = -\frac{5}{56}x^2$

43. $x = -\frac{1}{8}y^2$ **45.** $x = y^2$ **47.**

49. **51.**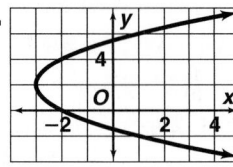

53. $x = -\frac{1}{2}(y - 1)^2 + 1$ **55.** Check students'
work. **57.** B **59.**

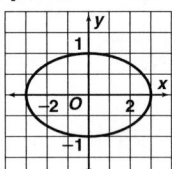

61.a. The vertex moves up, and the parabola
widens. **b.** The vertex moves down, and the
parabola narrows. **c.** The parabola would
degenerate into the ray with endpoint $(0, -2)$
that passes through the origin. **63.** D

65. **67.**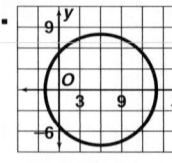

69. $x = 0$ and $y = 4$ **71.** $x = 1$ and $y = 0$
73. $x = 3$ and $y = -1$

Lesson 10-3   pp. 574–576

EXERCISES 1. $x^2 + y^2 = 100$ **3.** $(x - 2)^2 +$
$(y - 3)^2 = 20.25$ **5.** $(x - 1)^2 + (y + 3)^2 = 100$
7. $(x + 3)^2 + y^2 = 64$ **9.** $x^2 + (y + 1)^2 = 9$
11. $(x - 2)^2 + (y + 4)^2 = 25$ **13.** $x^2 + (y + 5)^2 = 100$
15. $(x + 6)^2 + (y - 1)^2 = 20$ **17.** $(x + 3)^2 +$
$(y - 4)^2 = 9$ **19.** $(1, 1), 1$ **21.** $(3, -1), 6$ **23.** $(0, -3),$
5 **25.** $(-2, -4), 16$

27. **29.**

31. **33.**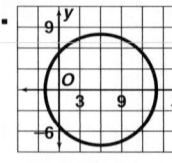

35. $x^2 + y^2 = 16$ **37.** $x^2 + y^2 = 25$ **39.** $x^2 + y^2 = 25$

---

41. $x^2 + y^2 = 169$ **43.** $x^2 + y^2 = 26$ **45.** $(x + 6)^2 +$
$(y - 13)^2 = 49$ **47.** $(x + 2)^2 + (y - 7.5)^2 = 2.25$
49. $(x - 2)^2 + (y - 1)^2 = 25$ **51.** $(x + 1)^2 + (y +$
$7)^2 = 36$ **53.** Check students' work. **55.** $(0, 0), \sqrt{2}$
57. $(0, 0), \sqrt{14}$ **59.** $(-5, 0), 3\sqrt{2}$ **61.** $(-3, 5), \sqrt{38}$
63. $(3, 1), \sqrt{6}$
65. circle; $(x - 4)^2 + (y - 3)^2 = 16$;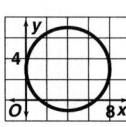

67. Let $P(x, y)$ be any point on the circle centered
at the origin and having radius r. If $P(x, y)$ is one
of the points $(r, 0)$, $(-r, 0)$, $(0, r)$, or $(0, -r)$,
substitution shows that $x^2 + y^2 = r^2$. If $P(x, y)$
is any other point on the circle, drop a
perpendicular $\overline{PK}$ from P to the x-axis (K on the
x-axis). $\triangle OPK$ is a right triangle with legs of
lengths $|x|$ and $|y|$ and with hypotenuse of
length r. By the Pythagorean Theorem,
$|x|^2 + |y|^2 = r^2$. But $|x|^2 = x^2$ and $|y|^2 = y^2$.
So $x^2 + y^2 = r^2$.
69.a.

1 Pluto
2 Mercury
3 Mars
4 Earth

b. Earth: $x^2 + y^2 = 15,705,369$, Mars: $x^2 + y^2 =$
$4,456,321$, Mercury: $x^2 + y^2 = 2,296,740$,
Pluto: $x^2 + y^2 = 511,225$ **71.** B **73.** $x = -\frac{1}{12}y^2$
75. $x = 2, x = 3$ **77.** 4 **79.** -3 **81.** $\frac{1}{2}$

Lesson 10-4   pp. 581–583

EXERCISES 1. $\frac{x^2}{16} + \frac{y^2}{9} = 1$ **3.** $\frac{x^2}{9} + y^2 = 1$
5. $\frac{x^2}{16} + \frac{y^2}{49} = 1$ **7.** $\frac{x^2}{81} + \frac{y^2}{4} = 1$ **9.** $\frac{x^2}{2.25} + \frac{y^2}{0.25} = 1$
11. $\frac{x^2}{36} + \frac{y^2}{100} = 1$ **13.** $\frac{x^2}{196} + \frac{y^2}{49} = 1$
15. $\frac{x^2}{256} + \frac{y^2}{56.25} = 1$ **17.** $x^2 + \frac{y^2}{6.25} = 1$

19. $(0, 4), (0, -4)$ **21.** $(8, 0), (-8, 0)$

          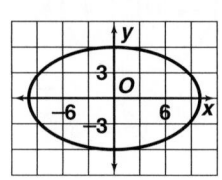

23. $(0, \sqrt{6})$, $(0, -\sqrt{6})$ **25.** $(9, 0)$, $(-9, 0)$

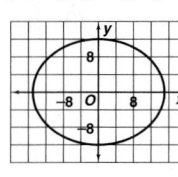

27. $\dfrac{x^2}{100} + \dfrac{y^2}{64} = 1$ **29.** $\dfrac{x^2}{89} + \dfrac{y^2}{64} = 1$ **31.** $\dfrac{x^2}{245} + \dfrac{y^2}{49} = 1$

33. $(\sqrt{5}, 0)$, $(-\sqrt{5}, 0)$ **35.** $(0, 4\sqrt{2})$, $(0, -4\sqrt{2})$

37. $(0, 2\sqrt{7})$, $(0, -2\sqrt{7})$ **39.** $(-3, 8)$, $(-3, 2)$

41.a. 0.9; **b.** 0.1;

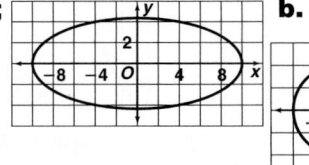

c. The shape is close to a circle. **d.** The shape is close to a line segment. **43.a.** Since $c^2 = a^2 - b^2$, if the foci are close to 0, c^2 will be close to 0 and a^2 will be close to b^2. This means a will be close to b and hence the ellipse will be close to a circle. **b.** If F_1 and F_2 are considered distinct pts., then a circle is not an ellipse. If F_1 and F_2 are the same pt., then a circle is an ellipse. **45.** $\dfrac{x^2}{16} + y^2 = 1$ **47.** $\dfrac{x^2}{4} + \dfrac{y^2}{16} = 1$

49. Check students' work. **51.** $\dfrac{x^2}{25} + \dfrac{y^2}{4} = 1$

53. $\dfrac{x^2}{702.25} + \dfrac{y^2}{210.25} = 1$ **55.** $\dfrac{x^2}{256} + \dfrac{y^2}{324} = 1$

57. $\dfrac{x^2}{400} + \dfrac{y^2}{100} = 1$ **59.** $\dfrac{x^2}{16} + \dfrac{y^2}{25} = 1$ **61.** $\dfrac{x^2}{36} + \dfrac{y^2}{27} = 1$

63. $\dfrac{x^2}{18} + \dfrac{y^2}{20} = 1$ **65.** When c is close to 0, the values of a and b are almost the same, and πab is close to πa^2, that is, close to the area of a circle of radius a. **67.** area of blue region = 3(area of white region) **69.** D **71.** $(x - 2)^2 + (y + 3)^2 = 36$

73. $\dfrac{1}{2x - 3x^4}$; $x \ne 0$, $\dfrac{\sqrt[3]{2}}{3}$ **75.** $\dfrac{x - 5}{x^2 - 2x + 4}$; $x \ne -2$

77. $\log_3 6$ **79.** $\log 320$ **81.** $\log \dfrac{5^k}{4}$

Lesson 10-5   **pp. 588–590**

EXERCISES 1.   **3.**

5.   **7.**

9. 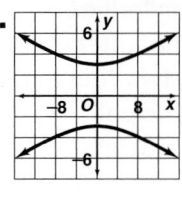 **11.** $(0, \sqrt{113})$, $(0, -\sqrt{113})$;

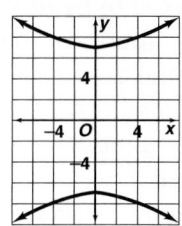

13. $(10, 0)$, $(-10, 0)$; **15.** $(\sqrt{205}, 0)$, $(-\sqrt{205}, 0)$

17. $(2\sqrt{11}, 0)$, $(-2\sqrt{11}, 0)$

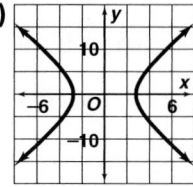

19. $\dfrac{x^2}{69,169} - \dfrac{y^2}{96,480} = 1$ **21.** $\dfrac{x^2}{192,432,384} -$

$\dfrac{y^2}{170,203,465} = 1$ **23.** $\dfrac{x^2}{9} - \dfrac{y^2}{16} = 1$ **25.** $y^2 - \dfrac{x^2}{3} = 1$

27.   **29.**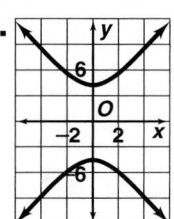

31. $\dfrac{y^2}{9} - x^2 = 1$

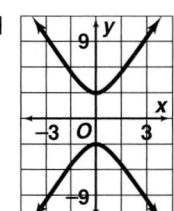

33. $y = \pm\dfrac{1}{2}\sqrt{2x^2 - 8}$; $(2, 0)$, $(-2, 0)$

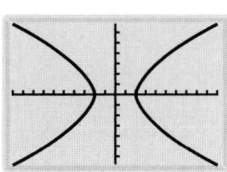

35. $y = \pm\sqrt{3x^2 - 2}$; $(-0.816, 0)$, $(0.816, 0)$

  37. Check students' work.

39. Answers may vary. Sample: Similarities— Both have two axes of symmetry that intersect at the center of the figure. Both have two foci that lie on the same line as the two "principal" vertices. Differences—An ellipse consists of points whose distances from the foci have a constant sum, but a hyperbola consists of points whose distances from the foci have a constant difference. An ellipse is a closed curve, but a hyperbola is not and has two separate branches that do not touch. Hyperbolas have asymptotes, but ellipses do not. An ellipse intersects both its axes of symmetry, but a hyperbola intersects only one of its axes of symmetry. **41.** $(\pm 1, 0)$, $y = \pm\frac{1}{3}x$ **43.** $(\pm 5, 0)$, $y = \pm\frac{4}{5}x$ **45.** $(\pm 7, 0)$, $y = \pm\frac{5}{7}x$

47.a. your airport **b.** 30 km **c.** $\frac{x^2}{225} - \frac{y^2}{351} = 1$

d. the branch that contains the vertex closest to your airport

49. A **51.** C **53.** $(\pm\sqrt{34}, 0)$, $(0, \pm 5)$ **55.** $(0, \pm 10)$, $(\pm 8, 0)$ **57.** $\frac{2x^2 - x - 7}{x^3 + x^2 - 9x - 9}$ **59.** $\frac{1}{3}$ **61.** 6

Lesson 10-6   pp. 595–598

EXERCISES 1. $\frac{(x + 2)^2}{9} + \frac{(y - 1)^2}{4} = 1$

3. $\frac{x^2}{36} + \frac{(y + 4)^2}{25} = 1$ **5.** $\frac{(x + 3)^2}{16} - \frac{(y + 3)^2}{9} = 1$

7. $\frac{(x + 1)^2}{9} - \frac{(y - 2)^2}{40} = 1$ **9.** $\frac{(y - 1)^2}{9} - \frac{x^2}{16} = 1$

11. $\frac{(x - 175)^2}{1936} - \frac{y^2}{28,689} = 1$

13. $(x + 6)^2 + y^2 = 81$; circle, center $(-6, 0)$, radius 9

15. $(x - 1)^2 + (y + 3)^2 = 13$; circle, center $(1, -3)$, radius $\sqrt{13}$

17. $\frac{(x - 1)^2}{4} - (y + 1)^2 = 1$; hyperbola, center $(1, -1)$, foci $(1 \pm \sqrt{5}, -1)$

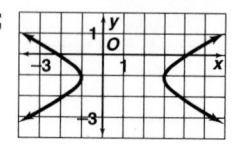

19. $x - 3 = \frac{1}{2}(y - 2)^2$; parabola, vertex (3, 2)

21. $(x + 3)^2 - (y - 5)^2 = 1$; hyperbola, center $(-3, 5)$, foci $(-3 \pm \sqrt{2}, 5)$

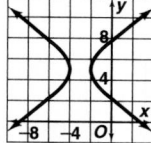

23. $\frac{x^2}{4} - \frac{(y + 3)^2}{9} = 1$; hyperbola, center $(0, -3)$, foci $(\pm\sqrt{13}, -3)$

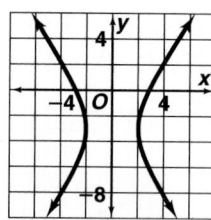

25.a. hyperbola **b.** line **27.** The hyperbola originally had center (0, 0) and a horizontal or vertical transverse axis. If the new center is (h, k), then the equations of the new asymptotes are obtained by replacing x with $x - h$ and y with $y - k$ in the equations of the original asymptotes.

29. $(x + 6)^2 + (y - 9)^2 = 81$

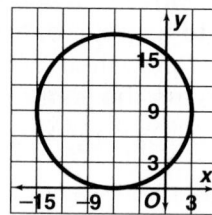

31. $y = \frac{1}{20}(x - 2)^2 - 3$

33. $\frac{(x - 1)^2}{9} + \frac{(y + 1)^2}{16} = 1$

35. $(x + 4)^2 + (y + 4)^2 = 25$

37. $(x - 8)^2 + (y - 2)^2 = 4$

39. $y - 5 = 4(x - 3)^2$ **41.** $\frac{(x - 5)^2}{36} - \frac{(y - 8)^2}{25} = 1$

43. $\frac{(x - 2)^2}{16} + \frac{(y - 7)^2}{9} = 1$

45. $\frac{(x - 4)^2}{16} - (y - 9)^2 = 1$ **47.** $\frac{x^2}{16} + \frac{(y - 10)^2}{25} = 1$

49.   ellipse, $\frac{x^2}{9} + \frac{y^2}{36} = 1$

51.   hyperbola, $\frac{y^2}{36} - \frac{x^2}{9} = 1$

53. 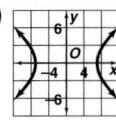 ellipse, $\frac{x^2}{36} + \frac{y^2}{9} = 1$

55. Check students' work. **57.a.** $A = B$; $A \neq B$ and A and B have the same sign; A and B have opposite signs; $A = 0$ or $B = 0$, but not both A and B are zero. **b.** No; answers may vary. Sample: If $C = D = E = 0$, then the graph will be the single point $(0, 0)$. **c.** two intersecting lines ($y = x$ and

$y = -x$). **61.** $(\sqrt{85}, 0), (-\sqrt{85}, 0)$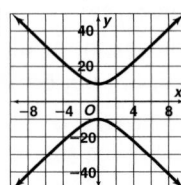

63. $(0, 2\sqrt{26}), (0, -2\sqrt{26})$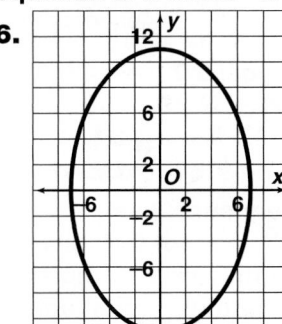

65. 5 **67.** 1 **69.** 3

Chapter Review   pp. 601–603

1. directrix **2.** major axis **3.** standard form of an equation of a circle **4.** radius **5.** transverse axis

6. 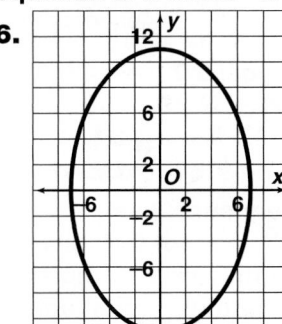 ellipse; x-axis and y-axis; domain: $-7 \leq x \leq 7$ range: $-11 \leq y \leq 11$

7. 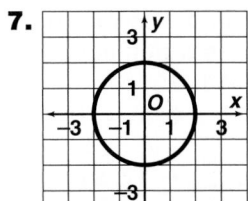 circle; every line through the center; domain: $-2 \leq x \leq 2$ range: $-2 \leq y \leq 2$

8. 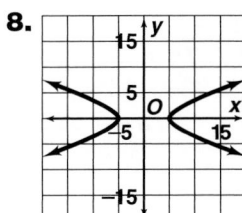 hyperbola; x-axis and y-axis; domain: $x \leq -5$ or $x \geq 5$ range: all real numbers

9. parabola; x-axis; domain: $x \geq 5$, range: all real numbers **10.** center $(0, 0)$; $(\pm 4, 0)$; domain: $x \geq 4$ or $x \leq -4$, range: all real numbers **11.** center $(0, 0)$; $(0, \pm 2)$, $(\pm 3, 0)$; domain: $-3 \leq x \leq 3$, range: $-2 \leq y \leq 2$

12. $y = \frac{1}{8}x^2 + 1$ **13.** $x = -\frac{1}{12}y^2 + 1$

14. $x = \frac{1}{20}y^2$ **15.** $y = -\frac{1}{20}x^2$ **16.** $y = \frac{1}{24}x^2$

17. $y = \frac{1}{10}x^2$ **18.** $y = 3x^2$

19. $\left(0, \frac{1}{20}\right), y = -\frac{1}{20}$ **20.** $\left(\frac{1}{8}, 0\right), x = -\frac{1}{8}$

21. $(-2, 0), x = 2$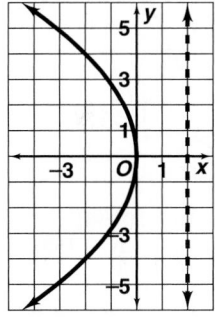

22. $x^2 + y^2 = 16$ **23.** $(x - 8)^2 + (y - 1)^2 = 25$

24. $(x + 3)^2 + (y - 2)^2 = 100$ **25.** $(x - 5)^2 + (y + 3)^2 = 64$ **26.** $(x - 3)^2 + (y - 1)^2 = 9$

27. $(x + 1)^2 + y^2 = 4$

28. center $(1, 0)$, radius 8

29. center $(-7, -3)$, radius 7

 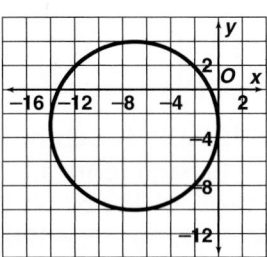

30. $\frac{x^2}{17} + \frac{y^2}{16} = 1$ **31.** $\frac{x^2}{25} + \frac{y^2}{29} = 1$ **32.** $\frac{x^2}{9} + \frac{y^2}{10} = 1$

33. $\frac{x^2}{40} + \frac{y^2}{36} = 1$ **34.** $\frac{x^2}{64} + \frac{y^2}{16} = 1$

35. **36.**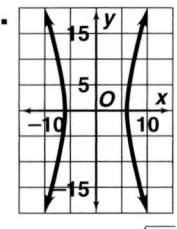

foci $(0, \pm\sqrt{5})$ foci $(\pm 3\sqrt{29}, 0)$

37.

foci $(0, \pm\sqrt{569})$

38.

foci $(\pm\sqrt{202}, 0)$

39. $\dfrac{x^2}{1.148 \times 10^{10}} - \dfrac{y^2}{3.395 \times 10^{10}} = 1$

40. $\dfrac{(x-3)^2}{4} + \dfrac{(y+2)^2}{9} = 1$ **41.** $\dfrac{(x-6)^2}{9} - \dfrac{(y-3)^2}{16} = 1$

42. $\dfrac{(x-77.5)^2}{1640.25} - \dfrac{y^2}{4366} = 1$

43. hyperbola; center $(0, -2)$, foci $(0, -2 \pm 2\sqrt{10})$

44. circle, center $\left(-\frac{3}{2}, 2\right)$, radius $\dfrac{\sqrt{61}}{2}$

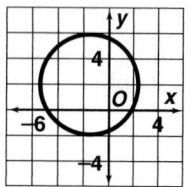

45. parabola; vertex $\left(-\frac{1}{2}, -\frac{169}{4}\right)$

46. ellipse; center $(1, -2)$, foci $\left(\dfrac{3 \pm \sqrt{51}}{3}, -2\right)$

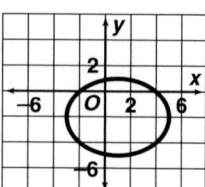

Chapter 11

Lesson 11-1 pp. 613–615

EXERCISES 1. Subtract 3; 65, 62, 59. **3.** Add one more to each term (add 3, add 4, add 5, etc.); 25, 33, 42. **5.** Divide by 10; 0.001, 0.0001, 0.00001. **7.** Multiply by -2; -128, 256, -512. **9.** Every odd-numbered term is 0, and every even-numbered term is $\dfrac{1}{n-1}$; 0, $\frac{1}{7}$, 0.

11.

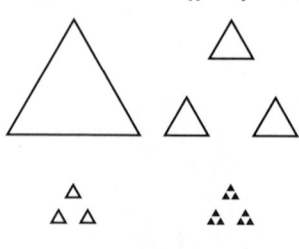

13. $a_n = a_{n-1} - 2$, $a_1 = 43$; 33 **15.** $a_n = a_{n-1} - 5$, $a_1 = 6$; -14 **17.** $a_n = a_{n-1} \cdot \frac{1}{2}$, $a_1 = \frac{1}{2}$; $\frac{1}{64}$
19. $a_n = \dfrac{1}{n+1}$; $\frac{1}{13}$ **21.** $a_n = 4n - 1$; 47
23. $a_n = n^2 + 1$; 145 **25.** explicit; 0, 1, 3, 6, 10
27. recursive; -2, 6, -18, 54, -162 **29.** explicit; 3, 9, 19, 33, 51 **31.** recursive; 340, 323, 306, 289, 272 **33.** 20, 23; $a_n = 3n + 2$; explicit or $a_n = a_{n-1} + 3$, $a_1 = 5$; recursive **35.** 216, 343; $a_n = n^3$; explicit **37.** 144, 169; $a_n = (n + 6)^2$; explicit OR $a_{n+1} = a_n + 2n + 13$; $a_1 = 49$; recursive
39. -1, $-\frac{1}{2}$; $a_n = \dfrac{a_{n-1}}{2}$, $a_1 = -16$; recursive OR $a_n = \dfrac{-32}{2^n}$; explicit **41.** -11, -19; $a_n = a_{n-1} - 8$; $a_1 = 21$; recursive OR $a_n = 29 - 8n$; explicit
43. Answers may vary. Sample: A recursive formula requires that the previous term be known to find a given term. An explicit formula only requires the number of the term. **45.** 28, 53, 89, 138 **47.** 25, 36, 49, 64 **49.** $\frac{16}{5}$, $\frac{25}{6}$, $\frac{36}{7}$, $\frac{49}{8}$ **51a.** 25 boxes **b.** 110 boxes **c.** 9 levels
53. $a_n = -n - 4$ **55.** $a_n = 1 + 4(n - 1)$
57.a. 15, 21 **b.** $a_n = a_{n-1} + n$, $a_1 = 1$ **c.** Yes; the formula yields the same value as the recursive formula. **59.** C **61.** $\dfrac{(x+1)^2}{36} + \dfrac{(y+2)^2}{36} = 1$
63. $xy = 10$ **65.** $xy = 27$ **67.** $xy = 72$ **69.** $xy = 100$

Lesson 11-2 pp. 618–620

EXERCISES 1. no **3.** no **5.** yes; 3 **7.** yes; 4 **9.** no
11. 127 **13.** 12.5 **15.** 225 **17.** -59 **19.** -146
21. -7.5 **23.** 13 **25.** -7 **27.** 7.5 **29.** a_{11} **31.** 4
33. 13 **35.** -19.5 **37.** -1 **39.** $\dfrac{r+s}{2}$ **41.** 0 **43.** The student assumed that the sequence was $a_n = 2^{n-1}$. However, $a_1 = 2^0 = 1$, not 0 as given in the problem. **45.** Answers may vary. Sample: An advantage of a recursive formula is that only the preceding term must be known to find the next term; a disadvantage is that many calculations may be required to find a term. An advantage of an explicit formula is that it is easy to find any term. **47.** 15 **49.** 22 **51.** 29
53. $a_n = 0 + 6(n - 1)$, $a_n = a_{n-1} + 6$, $a_1 = 0$
55. $a_n = -4 - 4(n - 1)$, $a_n = a_{n-1} - 4$, $a_1 = -4$
57. $a_n = 27 - 12(n - 1)$; $a_n = a_{n-1} - 12$, $a_1 = 27$
59. $a_n = -32 + 12(n - 1)$; $a_n = a_{n-1} + 12$, $a_1 = -32$ **61.** $a_n = \frac{1}{8}(n - 1)$; $a_n = a_{n-1} + \frac{1}{8}$, $a_1 = 0$ **63.** -4, -10, -16 **65.** -8, -17, -26
67. 17, 17, 17 **69.** -12.5, -8, -3.5 **71.a.** \$20, \$45, \$75, \$110, \$150, \$195, \$245, \$300, \$360, \$425, \$495 **b.** $a_n = a_{n-1} + \$20 + \$5(n - 1)$, $a_1 = \$20$

c. $495 **73.**

75. 54 **77.** 21st term **79.** $a_1 = -1, d = 3$
81. $a_1 = 52, d = -10$ **83.** $a_1 = -100.5, d = 22$
85. $9k + 32$ **87.** B **89.** B **91.** explicit; 6, 18, 36, 60,
90 **93.** recursive; $-121, -108, -95, -82, -69$
95. $(-4\sqrt{2}, 0)$ and $(4\sqrt{2}, 0)$ **97.** $(1 + \sqrt{39}, 3)$ and
$(1 - \sqrt{39}, 3)$

Extension p. 621

1.a. fifth **b.** seventh **c.** sixth **d.** fourth **3.a.** 1, 1,
2, 3, 5, 8, 13, 21, 34, 55 **b.** 143; 13; the answer is
the seventh term. **c.** Check students' work; the
answer is the seventh term. **d.** It will be 11 times
the seventh term.

Lesson 11-3 pp. 624–627

EXERCISES 1. yes; 2; 16, 32 **3.** yes; -2; 16, -32
5. yes; 0.4; 0.256, 0.1024 **7.** yes; $-\frac{1}{3}; \frac{2}{9}, -\frac{2}{27}$ **9.** yes;
1.5; 50.625, 75.9375 **11.** yes; 6; $-1296, -7776$
13. $a_n = 5 \cdot (-3)^{n-1}$; 5, -15, 45, -135, 405
15. $a_n = \frac{1}{2}\left(\frac{2}{3}\right)^{n-1}; \frac{1}{2}, \frac{1}{3}, \frac{2}{9}, \frac{4}{27}, \frac{8}{81}$
17. $a_n = 100(-20)^{n-1}$; 100, -2000, 40,000,
$-800,000$, 16,000,000 **19.** $a_n = 1024(0.5)^{n-1}$;
1024, 512, 256, 128, 64 **21.** $a_n = 10(-1)^{n-1}$; 10,
-10, 10, -10, 10 **23.** 1530 or -1530 **25.** 1.5 or -1.5
27. 6 or -6 **29.** arithmetic; 125, 150 **31.** arithmetic;
50, 55 **33.** geometric; 0.125, 0.0625 **35.** either; 2, 2
37. 6561, 2187, 729, or -6561, 2187, -729
39. 10, 8, 6.4, or -10, 8, -6.4 **41a–d.** Answers
may vary. Sample: **a.** 3 and 12; 6 **b.** 3, 6, 12; 2
c. 768 **d.** 48; 5th term **43.** 12,288 **45.** 201,326,592
47. $3(4^{n-1})$ **49.** 16 **51.** 10 **53.** $-\frac{2}{3}$ **55.** $142.79,
$613.59, $28.62, $58.92, $105.82, $262.94 **57.** Both
arithmetic and geometric sequence explicit
formulas use the first term $a_1, n - 1$, and a
common term. The recursive formulas both use
a_{n-1} and a common term. **59.** 7 **61.** B **63.** D
65. $a_n = -6 + 3n; a_n = a_{n-1} + 3; a_1 = -3$
67. $a_n = 9 - 11n; a_n = a_{n-1} - 11, a_1 = -2$
69. $(x + 3)^2 + (y - 1)^2 = 25$

71. $x = -3$ **73.** $x = 0, 1$

Lesson 11-4 pp. 632–634

EXERCISES 1. $21 + 18 + 15 + 12 + 9 + 6 + 3$;
84 **3.** $100 + 99 + 98 + 97 + 96 + 95$; 585 **5.** 17.3
$+ 19.6 + 21.9 + 24.2 + 26.5$; 109.5 **7.** 32 **9.** 264
11. 4292 **13.** $\sum_{n=1}^{4} 2n$ **15.** $\sum_{n=1}^{7} (n + 4)$ **17.** $\sum_{n=1}^{15} 7n$
19. 5, 1, 9; 25 **21.** 6, 4, -1; 9 **23.** $9, \frac{8}{3}, \frac{40}{3}$; 72
25. sequence; infinite **27.** series; finite
29. sequence; infinite **31.a.** 270 chairs on each
side, 390 chairs middle, 930 chairs total **b.** each
side: $\sum_{n=1}^{20} (n + 3)$; middle: $\sum_{n=1}^{20} (n + 9)$ **c.** $46,950
33.a. 91 **b.** 83 **35.** 110 **37.** 5150 **39.** -0.6
41.a. No; $75 + 25(6) = 225$, which is less than
500. **b.** Answers may vary. Sample: Pro:
spreading the cost over several years, con:
calculators purchased first may be outdated by
the time 500 calculators have been purchased;
check student's work. **43.** 300 **45.** 34
47. $10x + 45y$ **49.** B **51.** D **53.** $a_n = 5^{n-1}$; 1, 5, 25
55. $a_n = 3\left(\frac{3}{2}\right)^{n-1}; 3, \frac{9}{2}, \frac{27}{4}$ **57.** $a_n = 20(-0.5)^{n-1}$;
20, -10, 5 **59.** hyperbola: x- and

y-axes; domain: $x \le -5$ or $x \ge 5$; range:
$-\infty \le y \le \infty$ **61.** $\frac{x + 3}{x - 4}$ **63.** $\frac{z^2 + 12z + 20}{z - 1}$

Lesson 11-5 pp. 638–641

EXERCISES 1. 255 **3.** 381 **5.** $-10,235$ **7.** $\frac{255}{256}$
9. converges; has a sum **11.** converges; has a
sum **13.** diverges; no sum **15.** diverges; no sum
17. diverges; no sum **19.** 1 **21.** $\frac{9}{2}$ **23.** $\frac{9}{5}$
25. arithmetic; 420 **27.** geometric; ≈ 96.47
29. geometric; ≈ 121.5 **31.a.** 20, 18, 16.2, 14.58
b. ≈ 198.59 **c.** $S = \frac{20}{1 - 0.9} = 200$ **d.** Check
students' work. **33.** 4 **35.** no sum **37.** no sum
39. Check students' work. **41.** $\frac{7}{8}$ **43.** (b); (a)
yields $26,000; using the formula for finding the
sum of a finite geometric series, (b) yields
$1,342,177.26. **45.** converges; 1 **47.** converges;
≈ 2.718 **49.a.** $S = \frac{0.142857}{1 - 0.000001} = \frac{0.142857}{0.999999} = \frac{1}{7}$
b. $\frac{3}{7}$ **51.** B **53.** C **55.** -825
57. $(0, 4), y = -4$; **59.** $\left(0, -\frac{9}{4}\right), y = \frac{9}{4}$;

61. $\frac{10(2y + 3)}{(y + 3)(y - 3)}$ **63.** $\frac{-3(5d + 16)}{(d + 3)(d - 3)}$

Extension
p. 643

1. $1 + 3 + 5 + 7 + 9 + 11 \stackrel{?}{=} 6^2$, $36 = 36$; $1 + 3 + 5 + 7 + 9 + 11 + 13 \stackrel{?}{=} 7^2$, $49 = 49$; $1 + 3 + 5 + 7 + 9 + 11 + 13 + 15 \stackrel{?}{=} 8^2$, $64 = 64$
3. For $n = 1$, $\frac{1}{1(1 + 1)} = \frac{1}{1 + 1}$
Assume
$\frac{1}{1 \cdot 2} + \frac{1}{2 \cdot 3} + \frac{1}{3 \cdot 4} + \ldots + \frac{1}{k(k + 1)} = \frac{k}{k + 1}$
Prove
$\frac{1}{1 \cdot 2} + \frac{1}{2 \cdot 3} + \frac{1}{3 \cdot 4} + \ldots + \frac{1}{k(k + 1)} + \frac{1}{(k + 1)((k + 1) + 1)} = \frac{k + 1}{(k + 1) + 1}$
Proof
$\frac{1}{1 \cdot 2} + \frac{1}{2 \cdot 3} + \frac{1}{3 \cdot 4} + \ldots + \frac{1}{k(k + 1)} + \frac{1}{(k + 1)((k + 1) + 1)} = \frac{k}{k + 1} + \frac{1}{(k + 1)((k + 1) + 1)} = \frac{k(k + 2)}{(k + 1)(k + 2)} + \frac{1}{(k + 1)((k + 1) + 1)} = \frac{k(k + 2) + 1}{(k + 1)((k + 1) + 1)} = \frac{k^2 + 2k + 1}{(k + 1)((k + 1) + 1)} = \frac{(k + 1)^2}{(k + 1)((k + 1) + 1)} = \frac{k + 1}{(k + 1) + 1}$

Lesson 11-6
pp. 647–649

EXERCISES 1. total produced **3.** miles **5.** total price **7.** 100 units^2 **9.** $A = \sum\limits_{n=1}^{2} 1f(a_n)$ **a.** 0.5 units^2
b. 2.5 units^2 **11.** $A = \sum\limits_{n=1}^{2} 1g(a_n)$ **a.** 3 units^2
b. 7 units^2 **13.** $A = \sum\limits_{n=1}^{2} 1f(a_n)$ **a.** $10\frac{2}{3}$ units^2
b. $13\frac{1}{3}$ units^2 **15.** $A = \sum\limits_{n=1}^{2} 1f(a_n)$ **a.** 6.75 units^2
b. 7.75 units^2 **17.** $A = \sum\limits_{n=1}^{2} 1f(a_n)$ **a.** 5 units^2
b. 9 units^2 **19.** 2.5 units^2 **21.** 3.3 units^2
23. 3.25 units^2
25.
43 units^2
27.
50 units^2
29.
19.5 units^2
31.a. Answers may vary. Sample: ≈ 0.37 mile

b. Answers may vary. Sample: Using inscribed rectangles will result in an estimate smaller than the actual number.
Xmin:0   Ymin:0
Xmax:200   Ymax:70
Xscl:25   Yscl:10

33. 7.5 units^2 **35.** ≈ 3.46 units^2 **37.** 9.75 units^2
39. 2.5 units^2 **41.** Check students' work.
43.a.   **b.** The area under both curves is the same, 3 units^2, over the interval $-1.5 \le x \le 1.5$; this is true because the amount of area *above* $y = \frac{1}{4}x^3 + 1$ and *below* $y = 1$ on the left side of the y-axis is equal to the area *below* $y = \frac{1}{4}x^3 + 1$ and *above* $y = 1$ on the right side of the y-axis. **45.a.** $y = \sqrt{9 - \frac{9x^2}{25}}$
b. ≈ 23.56 units^2
c. ≈ 47.12 units^2 **d.** Check students' work. **47.** A
49. has a sum
51. $\frac{x^2}{16} - \frac{y^2}{9} = 1$;   **53.** $\frac{x^2}{10} - \frac{y^2}{16} = 1$;

55. $\frac{3}{14}$

Chapter Review
pp. 651–653

1. limits **2.** circumscribed rectangles
3. sequence **4.** converges **5.** common ratio
6. $a_n = a_{n-1} + 17$, $a_1 = 5$; 73, 90, 107
7. $a_n = -7a_{n-1}$, $a_1 = 1$; 2401; $-16{,}807$; 117,649
8. $a_n = a_{n-1} + 9$, $a_1 = -2$; 34, 43, 52
9. $a_n = 3n - 2$; 34 **10.** $a_n = 2^n$; 4096
11. $a_n = 6n^2 - 30$; 834 **12.** Answers may vary.
Sample: If the formula uses the previous term, then it is recursive; otherwise it is explicit. **13.** no
14. yes; $d = 15$; $a_{32} = 468$ **15.** yes; $d = 3$; $a_{32} = 100$ **16.** 5 **17.** 101.5 **18.** -4.9 **19.** 5 **20.** -10.5, -8, -5.5 **21.** 1.4, 0.8, 0.2 **22.** 11 **23.** 0.5 **24.** If the terms of the sequence have a common difference, then the sequence is arithmetic.
25. yes; $r = \frac{1}{2}$, $a_n = 1\left(\frac{1}{2}\right)^{n-1}$, $\frac{1}{16}$, $\frac{1}{32}$ **26.** no
27. yes; $r = 1.2$, $a_n = 3(1.2)^{n-1}$, 6.2208, 7.46496
28. 6 **29.** 20 **30.** 0.04 **31.** -10, -5, -2.5 **32.** $\pm\frac{1}{3}$, $-\frac{2}{3}$, $\pm\frac{4}{3}$ **33.** $3\frac{1}{2}$, $12\frac{1}{4}$, $42\frac{7}{8}$ **34.** $\sum\limits_{n=1}^{5} 13 - 3n$; 20
35. $\sum\limits_{n=1}^{7} 45 + 5n$; 455 **36.** $\sum\limits_{n=1}^{11} 4.6 + 1.4n$; 143

37. $\sum_{n=1}^{8} 23 - 2n$; 112 **38.** 3, −8, 26; 27 **39.** 9, 4, 8;
54 **40.** 11, $-\frac{10}{3}$, −10; $-\frac{220}{3}$ **41.** No; she will have
only 1150 available by the end of the fifth year.
42. $4\frac{121}{243}$ **43.** 31 **44.** 53.125 **45.** $14\frac{7}{18}$
46. converges; $S = 187.5$ **47.** diverges; no sum
48. diverges; no sum **49.** converges; $S = 2$
50. $A = \sum_{n=1}^{2} 1 \cdot f(a_n)$ **a.** 1 unit^2 **b.** 5 units^2

c. $\frac{8}{3}$ units^2 **51.** $A = \sum_{n=1}^{2} 1 \cdot f(a_n)$ **a.** 3 units^2

b. 11 units^2 **c.** 6 units^2 **52.** $A = \sum_{n=1}^{2} 1 \cdot f(a_n)$

a. 6 units^2 **b.** 14 units^2 **c.** $10.\overline{6}$ units^2

53. $A = \sum_{n=1}^{2} 1 \cdot f(a_n)$ **a.** 7 units^2

b. 9 units^2 **c.** 8 units^2

54. $A = \sum_{n=1}^{2} 1 \cdot f(a_n)$ **a.** 9 units^2 **b.** 17 units^2

c. 12 units^2 **55.** $A = \sum_{n=1}^{2} 1 \cdot f(a_n)$ **a.** 7 units^2

b. 11 units^2 **c.** $8\frac{2}{3}$ units^2

Chapter 12

Lesson 12-1   pp. 663–665

EXERCISES

1.

Object	Frequency
Rock	11
Paper	10
Scissors	15
Total	36

3. 0.11 **5.** 0.53

7. Number of Days Per Month

Days	28	29	30	31
Frequency	3	1	16	28
Probability	$\frac{3}{48}$	$\frac{1}{48}$	$\frac{16}{48}$	$\frac{28}{48}$

9.

11. Answers may vary. Sample design: Use
random numbers. Assign numbers 1 to 1000 to
each event, based on its probability.

Type	Prob.	Cum. Prob.	Assigned Numbers
Luxury	0.165	0.165	1–165
Large	0.076	0.241	166–241
Midsize	0.527	0.768	242–768
Small	0.232	1	769–1000

Random numbers generated: 612, 904, 249, 194,
435, 772, 93, 236, 80, 370, 849, 468, 819, 800, 371,
14, 396, 278, 303, 662, 637, 572, 700, 196, 810, 314,
496, 408, 737, 624
Results of simulation: 3 luxury cars, 3 large cars,
18 midsize cars, and 6 small cars
13.

15. Check students' work.

17. Answers may vary. Sample: Suppose the
events in a probability distribution are *not* equally
likely. By assigning the appropriate number of
equally likely outcomes to each event, you can
design a simulation that reflects the actual
probabilities expected. **19.** Answers may vary.
Sample: **a.**

Calls	$P(c)$	Cum. Prob.	Assigned #s
0	0.21	0.21	1–21
1	0.30	0.51	22–51
2	0.18	0.69	52–69
3	0.13	0.82	70–82
4	0.09	0.91	83–91
5	0.05	0.96	92–96
6	0.03	0.99	97–99
7	0.01	1.00	100

b. There were six hours in which 3 calls were
received, and two in which 4 calls were received.
A total of ten callers would have to wait. **c.** $\frac{10}{47}$
d. An additional response team would reduce the
probability of having to wait from $\frac{10}{47}$ to $\frac{2}{47}$, a
considerable improvement. **21.** C **23.** 3 units^2
25. 2 units^2 **27.**

29. independent

Lesson 12-2   pp. 668–670

EXERCISES 1. 0.9 **3.** $0.\overline{6}$ **5.** ≈0.406
7. ≈0.562 **9.** ≈45%

11.

0.1, 0.114

13.a. 0.15 **b.** 0.60 **c.** $P(A)$ is equal to $P(A|B)$
d. The fact that $P(A) = P(A|B)$ illustrates that the probability of A is the same, regardless of the occurrence of B. **14–18.** Check students' work.
19. $P(C)$ **21.** $P(R|W)$ **23.a.** The four right branches represent probabilities conditional upon the person being an adult or a minor. For example, the top branch represents the probability that a person is licensed given that he or she is an adult. **b.** No; the probability of a minor being licensed is not the same as the probability of an adult being licensed. **c.** Check students' work. **25.** C **27.** D

29.

31. center (0, 0); x-intercepts: (2, 0); (−2, 0); y-intercepts: (0, 4), (0, −4); domain: $\{x \,|\, -2 \le x \le 2\}$; range: $\{y \,|\, -4 \le y \le 4\}$

33. 0.830 **35.** 3.465
37. 3.162

Extension   **p. 671**

1. 0.9508 **3.** 0.9998 **5.** $\frac{2}{3}$ or about 67% **7.** 0.08
9. 0.84

Lesson 12-3   **pp. 676–679**

EXERCISES 1. $4.\overline{36}$, 3, 1 **3.** 600.3, 535.5, 499

5.

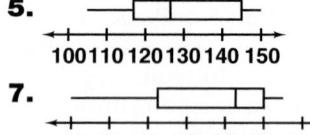

7.

9. 6, 18 **11.** 0 **13.a.**

b. 37, 39

c. The main effect of removing the outlier is a shortening of the long whisker. The median decreases from 8.5 to 8. **15.** 381; this value raises the mean. **17.** 60th **19.a.** 18.9, 19 **b.** No; none of the values is significantly less or greater than the

others. **c.** Recent earthquakes have been more consistent in their numbers, with fewer light years as well as fewer extremely heavy years; this is indicated by the shorter whiskers on the box-and-whisker plot for 1991 through 2000.

21.a.

b. Answers may vary. Sample: The range for women's shot put is greater than men's. The men are more consistent, as indicated by the shorter box and whiskers. Overall the men tend to throw farther. **23.** D **25.** C; $\ell = 4w$, $2(\ell + w) = 15$
27. ≈0.56 **29.** yes; 17
31. yes; 0 **33.**

Lesson 12-4   **pp. 684–686**

EXERCISES 1. 5, 2.5 **3.** 704, 461 **5.** 15.1, 3.5
7. 10,259.18; 300.28 **9.** 3 standard deviations
11. −1.4 **13.** 0 **15.** 14.6, 52.3; the bird speeds are more spread out than the cat speeds.
17. 2001: ≈6707; 2002: ≈6738 **19.** 2678.9, 2759.0; The incomes in 2001 clustered more tightly around the mean. **21.a.** 53.8, ≈3.4 **b.** 7; 9; 10
23. ≈75.8; ≈8.7 **25.** ≈0.007; ≈0.08 **27.** Minh; one standard deviation encompasses all values within one standard deviation above and below the mean. The graph actually shows that all values are within 3 standard deviations of the mean.
29.a. men: 14; 22.9; 3.2 women: 12; 25.9; 3.8 **b.** No; the men's team has a broader range of ages, but a smaller standard deviation than the women's team. **31.** B

33.

35. 16 **37.** 43.5 **39.**

Lesson 12-5   **pp. 692–695**

EXERCISES 1. 73% **3.** 92% **5.** very little bias
7. C; this sample has the smallest standard deviation, which most likely indicates a larger sample. **9.** ±7% **11.** ±3% **13.** 400 **15.** ±4%; 55% to 63% **17.a.** 63% **b.** ±5% **c.** 58% to 68%

19.a. 94% **b.** ±18% **c.** 76% to 100% **21.** Check students' work. **23.** Check students' work. **25.** This method is biased because it overrepresents people who respond to the online advertisement. A less biased method could involve surveying a group of people selected at random. **27.** 31%, ±13% **29.** 63%, ±5% **31.a.** There is an 8% margin of error; the candidate should be aware that 52% of the voters could actually prefer the opponent. **b.** The candidate should feel more confident after the second poll; it has a margin of error of only 4%, which means this candidate is preferred by at least 51% of voters. **33.** D **35.** C **37.** ≈6.6, ≈5.1

39. $\sum_{n=1}^{8} (49 - 8n)$ **41.** $\sum_{n=1}^{10} (-33 + 6n)$

43. $\frac{x^2}{25} + \frac{y^2}{36} = 1$

Lesson 12-6 pp. 700–703

EXERCISES 1. Each guess is a trial. There are 5 trials. Each correct answer is a success. The probability of a success on a single trial is 0.5. Check students' designs and simulations. **3.** Each shift is a trial. There are 3 trials. Not experiencing a breakdown is a success. The probability of a success on a single trial is 0.9. Check students' designs and simulations. **5.** 25% **7.** 0% **9.** 0.1361 **11.** 0.0015

13. $P(0) = 0.0156$ $P(1) = 0.0938$ $P(2) = 0.2344$ $P(3) = 0.3125$ $P(4) = 0.2344$ $P(5) = 0.0938$ $P(6) = 0.0156$

15. 0.2824 **17.** 0.1109 **19.** 0.2051 **21.** Each term of a binomial expansion $(p + q)^n$ involves a power of p times a power of q. The coefficient of each term is the number of times that combination of powers results when $(p + q)^n$ is expanded. In a binomial experiment of n trials, each trial results in success or failure, with probabilities p and q. The probability of each outcome contains n factors, each of which is either p or q. The coefficient of each term is the number of ways that outcome can be achieved. **23.** Check students' work.

25.a. $_{40}C_3 \cdot \left(\frac{1}{7}\right)^3 \left(\frac{6}{7}\right)^{37} \approx 0.0960 = 9.6\%$
b. Answers may vary. Sample: Generate 40 numbers ranging from 1 to 7. Let the number 4 represent Wednesday birthdays. Repeat 10 times. Count the number of runs that 4 came up exactly 3 times; divide that number by 10 to get the probability that exactly 3 of 40 people will have Wednesday birthdays. Check students' work for probability. **c.** 10 runs is too few to get an accurate probability.

27. Getting 5 or more items right by guessing would be statistically rare. The probability of getting 10, 9, 8, 7, or 6 correct is each less than 1%. The probability of getting 5 right is 2.6%. The probability of getting 4 right is 8.8%. **29.a.** The graph is symmetrical about the line $x = 3.5$.

b.

x	y
0	0.0078
1	0.0547
2	0.1641
3	0.2734
4	0.2734
5	0.1641
6	0.0547
7	0.0078

c. No; the bulge in the graph has shifted right.

31. B **33.** Sample B was larger because it had a smaller standard deviation. **35.** ≈18.18 **37.** 85.3125 **39.** $\frac{x^2}{400} - \frac{y^2}{441} = 1$ **41.** $(x + 3)(x - 2)$ **43.** $3(x + 1)(x + 3)$ **45.** $5(x - 1)(x + 2)$

Lesson 12-7 pp. 707–710

EXERCISES 1. 43% **3.** 43 men
5. **7.**

9. 79.1 **11.** 68% **13.** 50% **15.** 32% **17.a.** set 2
b&c

19. 2.5% **21.** 100% **23.** 50% **25.** 97.5%
27.a. 209 **b.** 41 **c.** 127 – 250 **29.** Elena scored within the top 10% of her group. Her score is 2.75 std. dev. above the mean, which places her in the top 1%. Jake did not score in the top 10%. His score is 1.16 std. dev. above the mean, or at the 88th percentile. **31.a.** 162 balls **b.** 930 balls **c.** Check students' work. **33.** A **35.** A **37.** total garbage generated over x years **39.** $(x - 4)^2 + (y + 5)^2 = 49$ **41.** Answers may vary. Sample:
$\frac{x^2}{4} - \frac{y^2}{4} = 1$ **43.** $y = -\frac{10}{x}$ **45.** $y = -\frac{125}{x}$
47. $y = \frac{375}{x}$

Chapter Review pp. 713–715

1. sample **2.** outlier **3.** probability distribution **4.** binomial experiment **5.** measures of variation

6.a.

Winner	Freq.
Player 1	8
Player 2	4
Ties	3
Total	15

b. $P(\text{Player 2 wins}) = \frac{4}{15}$

9. $\frac{3}{14}$ **10.** $\frac{3}{5}$ **11.**

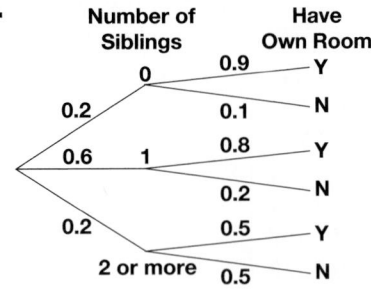

12. 0.9 **13.** 0.2 **14.** 14.4; 14; 12, 13, 14

15.

$0 \le x \le 20$
$0 \le y \le 10$

16. 20th percentile = 13, 90th percentile = 18
17. 53rd percentile **18.** 8 **19.** 6 **20.** 0.26 **21.** 2
22. ≈1.56 **23.a.** 76% **b.** ±14% **c.** from 62% to
90% **24.** Answers may vary. Sample: Each guess
is a trial. There are 4 trials. Since there are 2
equally likely answers, the probability of success
is 0.5. Let 1 represent a correct response and 2
an incorrect response. Generate 4 random
numbers, either 1 or 2, 10 times. The probability
is one tenth the number of times there are exactly
three 1's. **25.** 0.137

27.

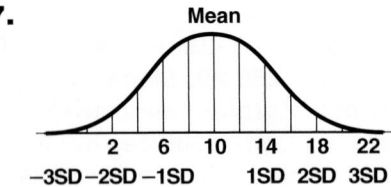

Mean

2   6   10   14   18   22
−3SD −2SD −1SD   1SD 2SD 3SD

Chapter 13

Lesson 13-1 pp. 725–728

EXERCISES 1. $x = -2$ to $x = 3$, $x = 2$ to $x = 7$; 5
3. $x = 0$ to $x = 4$, $x = 2$ to $x = 6$; 4 **5.** periodic; 12
7. not periodic **9.** periodic; 7 **11.** 3 **13.** 2

15.

1 unit on the x-axis is 0.001 s.

17. Answers may vary. Sample: Yes; average

monthly temperatures for three years should be
cyclical due to the variation of the seasons.
19. Answers may vary. Sample: Yes; traffic that
passes through an intersection should be at the
same levels for the same times of day for two
consecutive work days. **21.a.** 1 s **b.** 1.5 mV
23. 3, −3, 4;

25. 4, −4, 8;

27. 2 weeks **29.** 1 hour **31.** 2, 2, 2

33.a.

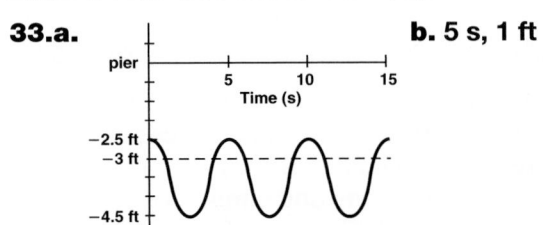

b. 5 s, 1 ft

c. Answers may vary. Sample: about $1\frac{1}{3}$ s **35.** B
37. C **39.**

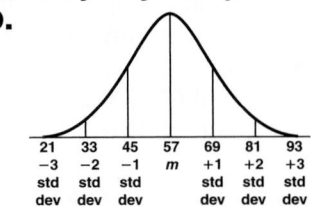

21	33	45	57	69	81	93
−3 std dev	−2 std dev	−1 std dev	m	+1 std dev	+2 std dev	+3 std dev

41. 14, 16; $a_n = 2n + 2$, explicit OR $a_1 = 4$,
$a_n = a_{n-1} + 2$; explicit **43.** $(x + 3)^2 = 20(y - 2)$

45. $\dfrac{(x + 2)^2}{16} + \dfrac{(y - 1)^2}{4} = 1$

Lesson 13-2 pp. 734–736

EXERCISES 1. −315° **3.** 240° **5.** −110°

7. **9.** **11.**

40°   −270°   95°

13. 215° **15.** 4° **17.** 150° **19.** 180° **21.** $\frac{1}{2}$, $-\frac{\sqrt{3}}{2}$; 0.50, −0.87 **23.** $\frac{\sqrt{3}}{2}$, $-\frac{1}{2}$; 0.87, −0.50 **25.** $\frac{\sqrt{3}}{2}$, $\frac{1}{2}$; 0.87, 0.50 **27.** $\frac{\sqrt{3}}{2}$, $-\frac{1}{2}$; 0.87, −0.50 **29.** 1.00, 0.00 **31.** 0.71, −0.71 **33.** −0.09, −1.00 **35.** −0.90, 0.44 **37–39.** Answers may vary. Samples: **37.** 405°, −315° **39.** 45°, −315° **41.** 275°, −445° **43.** 573°, −147° **45.** II **47.** negative *x*-axis **49.** positive *x*-axis **51a.** 0.77, 0.77, 0.77 **b.** The cosines of the three angles are equal because the angles are coterminal. **53.**

$\frac{1}{2}$, $\frac{\sqrt{3}}{2}$

55.

$-\frac{\sqrt{2}}{2}$, $-\frac{\sqrt{2}}{2}$

57.

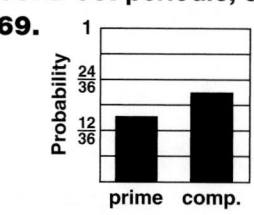

$\frac{\sqrt{2}}{2}$, $-\frac{\sqrt{2}}{2}$ **59.** $\left(-\frac{\sqrt{2}}{2}, \frac{\sqrt{2}}{2}\right)$

61. No; yes; if the sin θ and cos θ are both negative, θ is in Quadrant III. −120° is in Quadrant III.

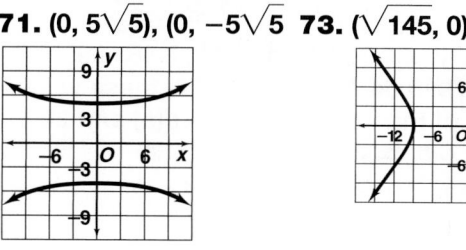

63. B **65.** periodic; 3 **67.** periodic; 6

69.

Probability

prime   comp.

71. (0, 5√5), (0, −5√5) **73.** (√145, 0), (−√145, 0)

Lesson 13-3   pp. 741–745

EXERCISES 1. $-\frac{5\pi}{3}$, −5.24 **3.** $-\frac{\pi}{2}$, −1.57 **5.** $\frac{8\pi}{9}$, 2.79 **7.** 540° **9.** −120° **11.** 90°

13.

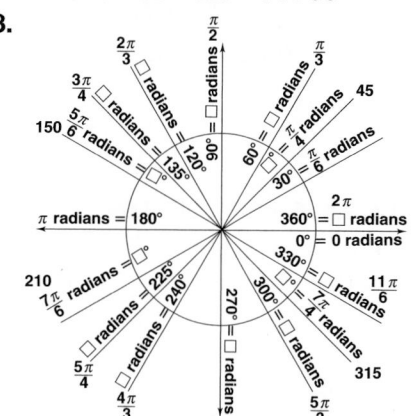

15. $\frac{1}{2}$, $\frac{\sqrt{3}}{2}$ **17.** $-\frac{1}{2}$, $\frac{\sqrt{3}}{2}$ **19.** 0, −1 **21.** 10.5 m **23.** 25.1 in. **25.** 43.2 cm **27.** ≈32 ft **29.** ≈42.2 in. **31.** III **33.** positive *y*-axis **35.** negative *x*-axis

37.

0.71, −0.71

39.

41.

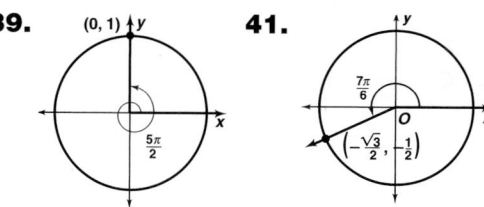

0.00, 1.00

−0.87, −0.50

43.a-b.

c. All five triangles are congruent by SSS. All have a hypotenuse of 1 unit, a long leg of 0.81 unit, and a short leg of 0.59 unit.

$\cos \frac{\pi}{5} \approx 0.81$, $\sin \frac{\pi}{5} \approx 0.59$;

$\sin \frac{3\pi}{10} \approx 0.81$, $\cos \frac{3\pi}{10} \approx 0.59$;

$\cos \frac{4\pi}{5} \approx -0.81$, $\sin \frac{4\pi}{5} \approx 0.59$;

$\cos \frac{6\pi}{5} \approx -0.81$, $\sin \frac{6\pi}{5} \approx -0.59$;

$\cos \frac{9\pi}{5} \approx 0.81$, $\sin \frac{9\pi}{5} \approx -0.59$

45. ≈11 radians **47.** ≈798 ft; 55°, −665° **49.** If two angles measured in radians are coterminal, the difference of their measures will be evenly divisible by 2π. **51.** ≈ 4008.7 mi **53.** $-\frac{11\pi}{3}$ radians **55.** $\frac{35\pi}{6}$ radians **57.a.** 0.5017962; 0.4999646; the first four terms **b.** $1 - \frac{x^2}{2!} + \frac{x^4}{4!} - \frac{x^6}{6!} + \frac{x^8}{8!} - \ldots$ **c.** ≈ 0.951; 18° **59.** A **61.** B **63.**

c. When either a or b is replaced by its opposite, the graph is a reflection of the original graph in the x-axis. **43.a.** $\frac{1}{440}$ **b.** 0.001 **c.** 880π

45. $\frac{2\pi}{5}$, 3.5

65.

67. 9.1, 5.41 **69.** 30, 8.09
71. $x^2 + (y + 5)^2 = 16$
73. $(x + 8)^2 + (y - 4)^2 = 9$

47. 1, 2 **49.** 6, 0.5

51. Check students' work. **53.** $y = \sin 60\pi\theta$
55. $y = \sin 240{,}000\pi\theta$ **57.** 2π, 1

Lesson 13-4 pp. 750–753

EXERCISES 1. $\frac{1}{2}$ **3.** ≈ 0.9 **5.** ≈ -0.9 **7.** 1 **9.** ≈ -0.8
11. -1 **13.** 3; 2, $\frac{2\pi}{3}$ **15.** 2; 3, π

17.

$y = \frac{1}{3} \sin 2\theta$

19.

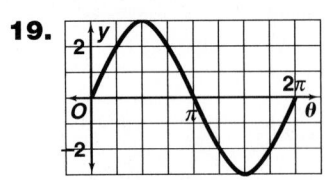

$y = 3 \sin \theta$

21.

$y = 1.5 \sin \frac{2\pi}{3} \theta$

23.

25.

27.

29. 2π; $y = -3 \sin \theta$

31. $\frac{\pi}{3}$; $y = \frac{1}{2} \sin 6\theta$ **33.** 4; $y = 3 \sin \frac{\pi}{2}\theta$ **35.** 5; 1, $\frac{2\pi}{5}$
37. 1; 3, 2π **39.** 2π; 5, 1
41.a.

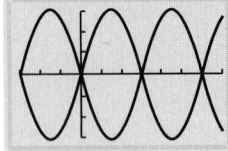

They are reflections of each other in the x-axis.

b.

They are reflections of each other in the x-axis.

59.a. days from spring equinox, hours of sunlight
b. $\frac{23}{12}$ h, about 365 days **c.** $y = \frac{23}{12} \sin \frac{2\pi x}{365}$ **d.** 1.1 h
e. Check students' work. **61.** B **63.** $\frac{5\pi}{6}$ radians, 2.62 radians **65.** $\frac{16\pi}{9}$ radians, 5.59 radians
67. $\approx 49\%$ **69.** $a_n = 12 + 3n$; 57

Lesson 13-5 pp. 758–760

EXERCISES 1. 2π, 3; max: 0, 2π; min: π, zeros: $\frac{\pi}{2}$, $\frac{3\pi}{2}$
3. π, 1; max: 0, π, 2π; min: $\frac{\pi}{2}$, $\frac{3\pi}{2}$; zeros: $\frac{\pi}{4}$, $\frac{3\pi}{4}$, $\frac{5\pi}{4}$, $\frac{7\pi}{4}$
5. **7.**

9. **11.** $y = \frac{\pi}{2} \cos \frac{2\pi}{3}\theta$

13. $y = -3 \cos 2\theta$ **15.** $y = 4 \cos \frac{2\pi}{3}\theta$ **17.** 1.98, 4.30 **19.** 2.52 **21.** 0.86, 5.14 **23.** π, $-1 \le y \le 1$, 1
25. 4π, $-\frac{1}{3} \le y \le \frac{1}{3}$, $\frac{1}{3}$ **27.** $\frac{2\pi}{3}$, $-\frac{1}{2} \le y \le \frac{1}{2}$, $\frac{1}{2}$
29. 2, $-0.7 \le y \le 0.7$, 0.7 **31.** 1.83, 2.88, 4.97, 6.02 **33.a.** 3.79, 5.64 **b.** 10.07, 11.92; these values are the sums of the values from part (a) and 2π.
35.a. 5.5 ft; 1.5 ft **b.** about 12 h 22 min
c. $y = 1.5 \cos \frac{2\pi t}{742}$ **d.** 12:17 A.M.–7:49 A.M., 12:39 P.M.–8:11 P.M.

37.a. shift of $\frac{\pi}{2}$ units to the right

b. They are the same. **c.** To write a sine function as a cosine function, replace sin with cos and replace θ with $\theta - \frac{\pi}{2}$.

39. On the unit circle, the x-values of $-\theta$ are equal to the x-values of θ, so $\cos(-\theta) = \cos\theta$. $-\cos\theta$ is the opposite of $\cos\theta$, so these graphs are reflections of each other over the x-axis.

41. D **43.** $y = \frac{5}{2}\sin 2\theta$

45. about 1111 **47.** about 83 **49.** $a_n = 10 \cdot 3^{n-1}$; 10, 30, 90, 270, 810

Lesson 13-6   pp. 763–766

EXERCISES 1. 0 **3.** -1 **5.** 1 **7.** 1 **9.** π **11.** $\frac{\pi}{5}, \theta = -\frac{\pi}{10}, \frac{\pi}{10}$ **13.** $\frac{\pi}{4}, \theta = -\frac{\pi}{8}, \frac{\pi}{8}$

15. **17.**

19. 50, undefined, -50

21. $\approx 51.8, 125, \approx 301.8$

23. 6

25. $\frac{2\pi^2}{3}$ 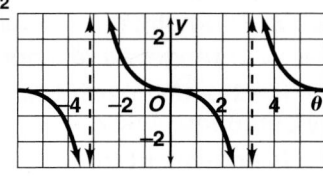 **27.** 2.03, 5.18

29.a. **b.** Check students' work; doubling the coefficient of the tangent function also doubles the output.

c. Answers may vary. Sample: the values of $y = 600\tan x$ will be three times greater than the values of $y = 200\tan x$. **31.** Check students' work. **33.** 200 **35.** 135 **37.** 70 **39.** $y = -\tan\left(\frac{1}{2}x\right)$ **41.** $y = \tan(2x)$ **43.a.** **b.** ≈ 130 ft

c. $\approx 61{,}500$ ft^2 **45.** Answers may vary. Sample: Triangles OAP and OBQ both share the angle θ and each triangle has a right angle, so they are

similar by AA. $\frac{\sin\theta}{\cos\theta} = \frac{AP}{OA} = \frac{BQ}{OB} = \frac{\tan\theta}{1}$. Thus $\frac{\sin\theta}{\cos\theta} = \tan\theta$. **47.** D **49.** C **51.** 1.77, 4.51

53. 6.15 **55.** 0.44, 1.56, 2.44, 3.56, 4.44, 5.56 **57.** 42.6, 42, 42 **59.** 83 **61.** 66 **63.** 145

Lesson 13-7   pp. 772–774

EXERCISES 1. -1; 1 unit to the left **3.** 1.6; 1.6 units to the right

5. $-\pi$; π units to the left

7. **9.**

11. **13.**

15. **17.** 3, 2π; 1 unit up

19. 1, 2π; $\frac{\pi}{2}$ units left and 2 units up

21. **23.**

25. **27.**

29. 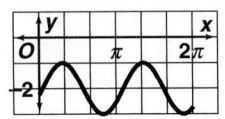 **31.** $y = \sin(x + \pi)$

33. $y = \sin x + 3$ **35.** $y = \cos\left(x + \frac{3}{2\pi}\right)$

37a.

b. $y = 8.5 \cos \frac{2\pi}{365}(x - 228) + 77.5$

39. $y = \cos(x + 3) + \pi$ **41.** $y = 2 \cos\left(x - \frac{\pi}{3}\right) - 1$;
$y = 2 \sin\left(x + \frac{\pi}{6}\right) - 1$ **43.a.** $\frac{\pi}{2}$; $\sin x = \cos\left(x - \frac{\pi}{2}\right)$
b. $-\frac{\pi}{2}$; $\cos x = \sin\left(x + \frac{\pi}{2}\right)$ **45.a.** Check students'
work. **b.** $g(x) = f(x + 4) - 3$ **47.**

49. **51.**

53. **55.** C **57.** $\frac{\pi}{6}$; $\theta = -\frac{\pi}{12}, \frac{\pi}{12}$

59. $\frac{2\pi}{3}$; $\theta = -\frac{\pi}{3}, \frac{\pi}{3}$ **61.** 0.0064 **63.** ≈0.136 **65.** 62

67. −335,923

Lesson 13-8   **pp. 778–781**

EXERCISES 1. 1.02 **3.** −0.70 **5.** $\frac{3}{4}$ **7.** $-\frac{5}{3}$ **9.** $\sqrt{2}$
11. 0 **13.** undefined **15.** undefined **17.** undefined
19. 2 **21.** −7.02 **23.** 1 **25.** −1.25 **27.** 1.73

29. **31.**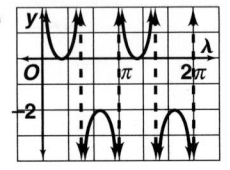

---

33. 1.1547 **35.** −2.9238 **37.** 1.0642 **39.** 1.7321
41.a. **b.** ≈28.3 ft **c.** ≈23.1 ft **d.** ≈20.7 ft
43. $\frac{2\sqrt{3}}{3}$; 1.15 **45.** −1

47. **49.**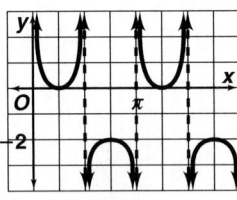

51. C **53.** D **55.a.** Reciprocals have the same
sign. **b.** The reciprocal of −1 is −1. **57.** sec 90° is
undefined because cos 90° is 0 and sec $\theta = \frac{1}{\cos \theta}$.
59.a. **b.** 63.9 ft **c.** 69.3 ft
d. ≈41.4°; 60.9 ft

61. **63.**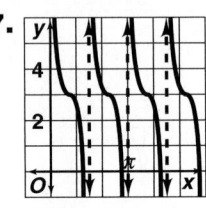
3 units up   1 unit down

65. 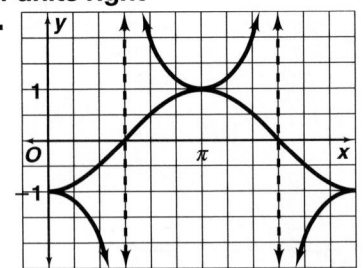 **67.**
π units left, 3 units up
4 units right

69.a.

b. $y = -\cos x$—domain: all real numbers; range:
all real numbers between −1 and 1, inclusive;
period: 2π; $y = -\sec x$—domain: all real numbers
except odd multiples of $\frac{\pi}{2}$; range: all real numbers
except those between −1 and 1; period: 2π
c. Multiples of π; by definition, sec $x = \frac{1}{\cos x}$,
so $-\cos x = -\sec x$ is equivalent to
$-\cos x = -\frac{1}{\cos x}$, or $(\cos x)^2 = 1$. The solutions of

$(\cos x)^2 = 1$ are the values of x for which $\cos x = 1$ or $\cos x = -1$. These values are the multiples of π. **d.** Answers may vary. Sample: The graphs have the same period and their signs are always the same. However, they have no range values in common except 1 and -1. **e.** The signs of $-\sec x$ and $-\cos x$ are the same because reciprocals have the same sign.
71. $y = \sec x$ and $y = \csc x$ are not parabolas because parabolas are not restricted by asymptotes, whereas the branches of $y = \sec x$ and $y = \csc x$ are between asymptotes.

73.a. **b.** Answers may vary. Sample: Given $y = \cot bx$, as $|b|$ decreases, the period increases; as $|b|$ increases, the period decreases.
If $b < 0$, $y = \cot bx$, $\cot x$ begins each branch with negative y-values and ends with positive y-values; the opposite is true for $b > 0$. **75.** C
77. 2, 2π; 5 units down **79.** 3, 2π; $\frac{\pi}{6}$ units left, 4 units up **81.**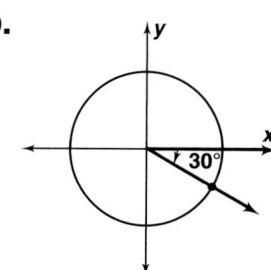

83.a. $1(0) + 1(0) + 1(3)$, 3 units^2 **b.** $1(3) + 1(3) + 1(12)$, 18 units^2 **85.a.** $1(3) + 1(3) + 1(0)$, 6 units^2 **b.** $1(4) + 1(4) + 1(3)$, 11 units^2

Chapter Review   pp. 783–785

1. period **2.** unit circle **3.** tangent function
4. phase shift **5.** secant function **6.** periodic; 4, 2
7. Answers may vary. Sample:

[graph]

8. $-225°$

9.

[graph with 30° angle]

10. $240°$ **11.** $\left(\frac{\sqrt{2}}{2}, -\frac{\sqrt{2}}{2}\right)$; $(0.71, -0.71)$ **12.a.** $\frac{\pi}{3}$
b. $\frac{1}{2}, \frac{\sqrt{3}}{2}$ **13.a.** $-\frac{\pi}{4}$ **b.** $\frac{\sqrt{2}}{2}, -\frac{\sqrt{2}}{2}$ **14.a.** π **b.** $-1, 0$
15.a. $360°$ **b.** 1, 0 **16.a.** $150°$ **b.** $-\frac{\sqrt{3}}{2}, \frac{1}{2}$

17.a. $-135°$ **b.** $-\frac{\sqrt{2}}{2}, -\frac{\sqrt{2}}{2}$ **18.** 26.2 ft
19.

20. [graph] **21.** [graph]

22. 3 cycles; 1, $\frac{2\pi}{3}$; $y = -\sin 3\theta$ **23.** $y = 4 \sin 4\theta$
24. $y = 3 \cos 2\theta$ **25.** $y = 2 \cos 2\theta$ **26.** 3.92, 5.51
27. 0.16, 1.84, 4.16, 5.84 **28.** 0.58, 1.00, 2.15, 2.57, 3.72, 4.14, 5.29, 5.71

29. [graph] **30.** [graph]

0.41, 1 -1, undefined

31. [graph] **32.** [graph]

2, undefined

33. [graph]

35. $y = \sin\left(x - \frac{\pi}{4}\right)$ **36.** $y = \cos x - 2$ **37.** $\sqrt{2}$
38. $-\frac{\sqrt{3}}{3}$ **39.** 2 **40.** [graph]

41. [graph] **42.** [graph]

Selected Answers

Chapter 14

EXERCISES 1. $\cos \theta \cot \theta = \cos \theta \left(\frac{\cos \theta}{\sin \theta} \right) =$
$\frac{1 - \sin^2 \theta}{\sin \theta} = \frac{1}{\sin \theta} - \sin \theta$ **3.** $\cos \theta \tan \theta =$
$\cos \theta \left(\frac{\sin \theta}{\cos \theta} \right) = \sin \theta$ **5.** $\cos \theta \sec \theta = \cos \theta \left(\frac{1}{\cos \theta} \right)$
$= 1$ **7.** $\sin \theta \csc \theta = \sin \theta \left(\frac{1}{\sin \theta} \right) = \frac{\sin \theta}{\sin \theta} = 1$ **9.** 1
11. $\tan^2 \theta$ **13.** $\csc \theta$ **15.** $\cos \theta$ **17.** $\sin \theta$ **19.** 1
21. $\sec \theta$ **23.** $\sec^2 \theta$ **25.** $\cot \theta$ **27.** $-\tan^2 \theta$
29. $\sec \theta$ **31.** $\sin^2 \theta$ **33.** $\sin \theta$ **35.** $\sec \theta \csc^2 \theta$
37. 1 **39.** $\pm\sqrt{1 - \cos^2 \theta}$ **41.** $\frac{\pm\sqrt{1 - \sin^2 \theta}}{\sin \theta}$
43. $\pm\sqrt{\csc^2 \theta - 1}$ **45.** $\sin^2 \theta \tan^2 \theta = \sin^2 \theta$
$\left(\frac{\sin^2 \theta}{\cos^2 \theta} \right) = (1 - \cos^2 \theta) \left(\frac{\sin^2 \theta}{\cos^2 \theta} \right)$
$= \frac{\sin^2 \theta - \sin^2 \theta \cos^2 \theta}{\cos^2 \theta} = \frac{\sin^2 \theta}{\cos^2 \theta} - \frac{\sin^2 \theta \cos^2 \theta}{\cos^2 \theta} =$
$\tan^2 \theta - \sin^2 \theta$ **47.** $\sin \theta \cos \theta (\tan \theta + \cot \theta) =$
$\sin \theta \cos \theta \left(\frac{\sin \theta}{\cos \theta} + \frac{\cos \theta}{\sin \theta} \right) = \frac{\sin^2 \theta \cos \theta}{\cos \theta} + \frac{\cos^2 \theta \sin \theta}{\sin \theta}$
$= \sin^2 \theta + \cos^2 \theta = 1$
49. $\frac{\sec \theta}{\cot \theta + \tan \theta} = \frac{\frac{1}{\cos \theta}}{\frac{\cos \theta}{\sin \theta} + \frac{\sin \theta}{\cos \theta}} \cdot \frac{\sin \theta \cos \theta}{\sin \theta \cos \theta} =$
$\frac{\sin \theta}{\cos^2 \theta + \sin^2 \theta} = \frac{\sin \theta}{1} = \sin \theta$ **51.** $\frac{1 - \sin^2 \theta}{\sin^2 \theta}$
53. Check students' work. 55. $1 + \sec \theta =$
$1 + \frac{1}{\cos \theta} = \frac{1}{\cos \theta} + \frac{\cos \theta}{\cos \theta} = \frac{1 + \cos \theta}{\cos \theta}$ **57.** $\frac{\cot \theta \sin \theta}{\sec \theta}$
$+ \frac{\tan \theta \cos \theta}{\csc \theta} = \frac{\left(\frac{\cos \theta}{\sin \theta} \right) \sin \theta}{\frac{1}{\cos \theta}} + \frac{\left(\frac{\sin \theta}{\cos \theta} \right) \cos \theta}{\frac{1}{\sin \theta}} = \frac{\cos \theta}{\frac{1}{\cos \theta}}$
$+ \frac{\sin \theta}{\frac{1}{\sin \theta}} = \cos^2 \theta + \sin^2 \theta = 1$ **59.** 1 **61.** If $n_2 > n_1$,
then $\theta_1 > \theta_2$; if $n_2 < n_1$, then $\theta_1 < \theta_2$; if $n_2 = n_1$,
then $\theta_1 = \theta_2$ **63. D 65.**

67.

69.

71. 45° **73.** 211° **75.** 79° **77.** 111°
79.

EXERCISES 1. $-\frac{\pi}{2} + 2\pi n$ **3.** $\frac{\pi}{2} + 2\pi n$ **5.** 30° +
$n \cdot 360°$ and 210° + $n \cdot 360°$, or 30° + $n \cdot 180°$
7. 120° + $n \cdot 360°$ and 300° + $n \cdot 360°$, or 120° +
$n \cdot 180°$ **9.** $0.38 + 2\pi n$ and $2.76 + 2\pi n$
11. $1.89 + \pi n$ **13.** no solution **15.** $0.95 + 2\pi n$
and $5.33 + 2\pi n$ **17.** $\frac{\pi}{6}, \frac{11\pi}{6}$ **19.** $\frac{\pi}{4}, \frac{3\pi}{4}$ **21.** 0.46,
3.61 **23.** 2.11, 5.25 **25.** $\frac{4\pi}{3}, \frac{5\pi}{3}$ **27.** $\frac{\pi}{2}, \frac{3\pi}{2}$ **29.** $\frac{\pi}{4}, \frac{3\pi}{4}, \frac{5\pi}{4},$
$\frac{7\pi}{4}$ **31.** 0, π **33.** $\frac{7\pi}{6}, \frac{11\pi}{6}$ **35.** 30° + $n \cdot 360°$ and
150° + $n \cdot 360°$ **37.** 210° + $n \cdot 360°$ and 330° +
$n \cdot 360°$ **39.** $\frac{3\pi}{2}$ **41.** 0.34, 2.80 **43.** 0 **45.a.** 30° +
$n \cdot 360° \leq x \leq 150° + n \cdot 360°$ **b.** 150° + $n \cdot 360° \leq$
$x \leq 390° + n \cdot 360°$ **c.** Find the values of x where
the graphs intersect, and then choose the
appropriate interval. **47.** $\frac{\pi}{2} + 2\pi n, \frac{3\pi}{2} + 2\pi n$
49. $\frac{\pi}{4} + \frac{\pi}{2} n$ **51.** $0 + 2\pi n, \pi + 2\pi n, 1.25 + 2\pi n,$
$4.39 + 2\pi n$ **53.** $\frac{\pi}{6} + \pi n, \frac{5\pi}{6} + \pi n$ **55.** $1.107 + \pi n,$
$\frac{3\pi}{4} + \pi n$ **57.** The student divided both sides of the
equation by $\sin \theta$, which in the given interval can
be equal to zero. Since division by zero is not
possible, this is where the error was. **59.** $0.79 +$
$\pi n, 2.36 + \pi n$ **61.** $0.79 + \pi n, 2.36 + \pi n$ **63.** 2.09
$+ 2\pi n, 4.19 + 2\pi n$ **65.** $\frac{3\pi}{2} + 2\pi n$ **67.** $\sin^{-1}\left(\frac{y}{2} \right)$
69. $\sin^{-1}\left(\frac{y}{3} \right) - 2$ **71.** $\cos^{-1}(y - 1)$
73.a. $K = 1250(\theta - \sin \theta)$ ft² **b.** ≈ 2.08 **75.** C
77. $\cot \theta$ **79.** 1 **81.** $\sin \theta$ **83.** $4 \cos \frac{\pi}{4} \theta$
85. $y = 3\pi \cos 2\pi\theta$ **87.** about 0.91

EXERCISES 1.a. ≈ 8333 ft **b.** ≈ 8824 ft

3.a.

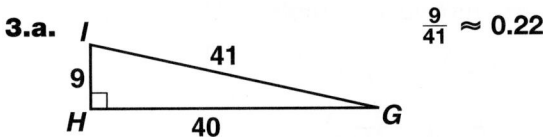

$\frac{9}{41} \approx 0.22$

b. $\frac{40}{41} \approx 0.98$ **c.** $\frac{40}{9} \approx 4.44$ **d.** $\frac{41}{9} \approx 4.56$
e. $\frac{9}{41} \approx 0.22$ **f.** not defined **5.** 41.8 **7.** 10.6
9. 45.0° **11.** 48.6° **13.** 19.6° **15.** 74.3° **17.** 68.0°
19. $c \approx 7.8, m\angle A \approx 39.8°, m\angle B \approx 50.2°$
21. $c \approx 10.2, m\angle A \approx 52.6°, m\angle B \approx 37.4°$
23. $b \approx 14.0, m\angle A \approx 50.6°, m\angle B \approx 39.4°$
25. $\cos \theta = \frac{\sqrt{55}}{8}, \tan \theta = \frac{3\sqrt{55}}{55}, \csc \theta = \frac{8}{3},$
$\sec \theta = \frac{8\sqrt{55}}{55}, \cot \theta = \frac{\sqrt{55}}{3}$ **27.** $\sin \theta = \frac{2\sqrt{6}}{5},$
$\tan \theta = 2\sqrt{6}, \csc \theta = \frac{5\sqrt{6}}{12}, \sec \theta = 5, \cot \theta = \frac{\sqrt{6}}{12}$
29. $\sin \theta = \frac{4}{7}, \cos \theta = \frac{\sqrt{33}}{7}, \tan \theta = \frac{4\sqrt{33}}{33},$
$\sec \theta = \frac{7\sqrt{33}}{33}, \cot \theta = \frac{\sqrt{33}}{4}$ **31.** $\sin \theta = \frac{4\sqrt{41}}{41},$
$\cos \theta = \frac{5\sqrt{41}}{41}, \tan \theta = \frac{4}{5}, \csc \theta = \frac{\sqrt{41}}{4},$

$\sec \theta = \frac{\sqrt{41}}{5}$ **33.** $\sin \theta \approx 0.192$, $\cos \theta \approx 0.981$, $\tan \theta \approx 0.196$, $\sec \theta \approx 1.019$, $\cot \theta \approx 5.103$
35. $a = 15$, $m\angle A \approx 61.9°$, $m\angle B \approx 28.1°$
37. $a \approx 7.9$, $b \approx 6.2$, $m\angle B = 38°$ **39.** $a \approx 26.8$, $c \approx 28.1$, $m\angle A = 72.8°$ **41.** $35.5°$ **43.** 20.3 m^2
45.a. 12 **b.** 12 **47.**

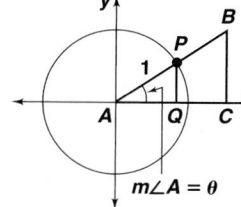

Since $\triangle APQ$ and $\triangle ABC$ are similar triangles, $\frac{AQ}{AP} = \frac{AC}{AB}$. So, $\cos \theta = AQ = \frac{AQ}{1} = \frac{AQ}{AP} = \frac{AC}{AB} =$

$\cos A$. **49.** $\sec A \stackrel{?}{=} \frac{1}{\cos A}$, $\frac{c}{b} \stackrel{?}{=} \frac{1}{\frac{b}{c}}$, $\frac{c}{b} = \frac{c}{b}$

51. $\cos^2 A + \sin^2 A \stackrel{?}{=} 1$, $\left(\frac{b}{c}\right)^2 + \left(\frac{a}{c}\right)^2 \stackrel{?}{=} 1$, $b^2 + a^2 \stackrel{?}{=} c^2$, $c^2 = c^2$ **53.a.** 72° **b.** 19.0 cm **55.** D **57.** C
59. no solution **61.** $0 + n \cdot 360°$ and $180° + n \cdot 360°$
63. **65.**

67. $P(0) \approx 0.016796$ $P(1) \approx 0.089580$

$P(2) \approx 0.209019$ $P(3) \approx 0.278692$ $P(4) \approx 0.232243$

$P(5) \approx 0.123863$ $P(6) \approx 0.041288$ $P(7) \approx 0.007864$

$P(8) \approx 0.000655$

Lesson 14-4 · pp. 817–820

EXERCISES 1. 18.7 cm^2 **3.** 81.9 m^2 **5.** 10.9
7. 7.4 **9.** 10.7 m **11.** 33.5° **13.** 27.0° **15.** 28.8°
17. $m\angle D = 100°$, $e = 22.3°$, $f = 34.2$ **19.** $m\angle T = 29.3°$, $m\angle R = 26.7°$, $r = 8.3$ **21.** $m\angle C = 40°$, $b = 10$, $c = 6.8$ **23.** $m\angle F = 72°$, $e = 20$ in., $f = 23.5$ in. **25.a.** when $m\angle C = 50°$ **b.** when $m\angle C = 50°$ **c.** 90°; a right triangle has the greatest height. **27.** 7.5 mi, 7.9 mi **29.** 66
31. 44.4 **33.** 49.4 **35.** 0.3 **37.** 0.9 **39.** 28.0 ft
41. 4.0 cm **43.** 2.4 miles **45.a.** 56.4° **b.** 93.6°, 26.4°
c. No; $\triangle EFG$ could be congruent to $\triangle ABC$ instead of $\triangle ABD$. **47.** C **49.** 53.1° **51.** 38.7°
53. $a = 3$, $m\angle A = 36.9°$, $m\angle C = 53.1°$
55. $c = 11.2$, $m\angle A = 41.8°$, $m\angle C = 45°$
57. $c = 8.5$, $m\angle A = 63.3°$, $m\angle C = 64.1°$

59. **61.**

Extension · p. 821

1. 70.4 and 47.6°, or 109.6° and 8.4° **3.** 87.3° and 44.7°, or 92.7° and 39.3° **5.** 44.0° and 112.4°, or 136.0° and 20.4°

Lesson 14-5 · pp. 824–827

EXERCISES 1. 37.1 **3.** 13.7 **5.** 10.0 cm **7.** 47.3°
9. 125.1° **11.** 83.3° **13.** 60.5° **15.** 71.7° **17.** 35.5°
19. $c^2 = a^2 + b^2 - 2ab \cos C$ **21.** $\frac{\sin A}{a} = \frac{\sin B}{b}$
23. $a^2 = b^2 + c^2 - 2bc \cos A$ **25.** $m\angle A = 50.1°$,
$m\angle B = 56.3°$, $m\angle C = 73.6°$ **27.** $m\angle A = 90°$,
$m\angle B = 36.9°$, $m\angle C = 53.1°$ **29.** $m\angle A = 56.1°$,
$m\angle B = 70°$, $m\angle C = 53.9°$ **31.** 46 ft **33.** 77.2°
35. 56.6° **37.** 8.8 cm **39.** 117.3° **41.** 32.6°
43. 67.2° **45.** 64.0° **47.** 109 cm **49.** Yes; since
$\cos 90° = 0$, $c^2 = a^2 + b^2 - 2ab \cos C$ reduces
to $c^2 = a^2 + b^2$. **51.a.** 2.1 m **b.** 9.8 m^2 **53.** B **55.**
17.1 in. **57.** 26.3 in. **59.** $2\pi y = \tan 0.5 \theta$ **61.** $\frac{\pi}{3}$,
$x = \pm \frac{\pi}{6}$ **63.**

x	P(x)
2	0.016
3	0.031
4	0.047
5	0.063
6	0.078
7	0.094
8	0.109
9	0.125
10	0.109
11	0.094
12	0.078
13	0.063
14	0.047
15	0.031
16	0.016

Lesson 14-6 · pp. 832–834

EXERCISES 1. $\csc \left(\theta - \frac{\pi}{2}\right) = \frac{1}{\sin \left(\theta - \frac{\pi}{2}\right)} =$

$\frac{1}{\sin \left(-\left(\frac{\pi}{2} - \theta\right)\right)} = \frac{1}{-\sin \left(\frac{\pi}{2} - \theta\right)} = \frac{1}{-\cos \theta}$

$= -\sec \theta$ **3.** $\cot \left(\frac{\pi}{2} - \theta\right) = \frac{\cos \left(\frac{\pi}{2} - \theta\right)}{\sin \left(\frac{\pi}{2} - \theta\right)} = \frac{\sin \theta}{\cos \theta}$

$= \tan \theta$ **5.** $\tan \left(\theta - \frac{\pi}{2}\right) = \tan \left(-\left(\frac{\pi}{2} - \theta\right)\right) =$
$-\tan\left(\frac{\pi}{2} - \theta\right) = -\cot \theta$ **7.** $\frac{\pi}{2}, \frac{3\pi}{2}$ **9.** $\frac{\pi}{4}, \frac{3\pi}{4}, \frac{5\pi}{4}, \frac{7\pi}{4}$
11. π **13.** $\frac{\pi}{2}, \frac{3\pi}{2}$ **15.** $\sec A$ **17.** 0 **19.** -1
21. $\frac{\sqrt{2} - \sqrt{6}}{4}$ **23.** $2 - \sqrt{3}$ **25.** $\frac{\sqrt{6} - \sqrt{2}}{4}$ **27.** $-\frac{\sqrt{2}}{2}$
29. $\frac{\sqrt{2} - \sqrt{6}}{4}$ **31.** $-2 + \sqrt{3}$ **33.** $-\frac{1}{2}$ **35.** $\frac{1}{2}$

37. $\sin (A - B) = \sin (A + (-B)) = \sin A \cos (-B) + \cos A \sin (-B) = \sin A \cos B - \cos A \sin B$
39. $\cos (A + B) = \cos (A - (-B)) = \cos A \cos (-B) + \sin A \sin (-B) = \cos A \cos B - \sin A \sin B$
41. $\sin \left(x + \frac{\pi}{3}\right) + \sin \left(x - \frac{\pi}{3}\right)$

$= \sin x \cos \frac{\pi}{3} + \cos x \sin \frac{\pi}{3}$
$\quad + \left[\sin x \cos \frac{\pi}{3} - \cos x \sin \frac{\pi}{3}\right]$
$= \sin x \cos \frac{\pi}{3} + \cos x \sin \frac{\pi}{3}$
$\quad + \sin x \cos \frac{\pi}{3} - \cos x \sin \frac{\pi}{3}$
$= 2 \sin x \cos \frac{\pi}{3} = 2 \sin x \cdot \frac{1}{2} = \sin x$

43. Answers may vary. Sample:
$\sin (30° + 60°) \overset{?}{=} \sin 30° + \sin 60°$,
$\sin (90°) \overset{?}{=} \sin 30° + \sin 60°$, $1 \neq \frac{1}{2} + \frac{\sqrt{3}}{2}$
45. $\sin 5\theta$ **47.** $\cos 5\theta$ **49.** $\tan 2\theta$
51. $(5 \cos \theta - 5\sqrt{3} \sin \theta, 5 \sin \theta + 5\sqrt{3} \cos \theta)$
53. $\cos (\pi - \theta) = \cos \pi \cdot \cos \theta + \sin \pi \sin \theta$
$= \cos \pi \cos \theta = -\cos \theta$ **55.** $\sin (\pi + \theta)$
$= \sin \pi \cdot \cos \theta + \cos \pi \sin \theta = -\sin \theta$
57. Given a parallelogram with adjacent sides x_1 and x_2 and diagonals of d_1 and d_2, then by the Law of Cosines:
$$d_1{}^2 + d_2{}^2 = x_1{}^2 + x_2{}^2 - 2x_1x_2 \cos \theta$$
$$\quad + [x_1{}^2 + x_2{}^2 - 2x_1x_2 \cos(\pi - \theta)]$$
$$= 2x_1{}^2 + 2x_2{}^2 - 2x_1x_2 \cos \theta - 2x_1x_2$$
$$\quad [\cos \pi \cos \theta + \sin \pi \sin \theta]$$
$$= 2x_1{}^2 + 2x_2{}^2 - 2x_1x_2 \cos \theta - 2x_1x_2$$
$$\quad [-\cos \theta]$$
$$= 2x_1{}^2 + 2x_2{}^2 - 2x_1x_2 \cos \theta + 2x_1x_2 \cos \theta$$
$$= 2x_1{}^2 + 2x_2{}^2 = 2(x_1{}^2 + x_2{}^2)$$

59. D **61.** 9.8 ft **63.** 21.1 mm **65.** $\frac{4\pi}{9}$ and 1.40
67. $-\frac{\pi}{12}$ and -0.26 **69.** $\frac{19\pi}{18}$ and 3.32 **71.** 45.2
73. 57.6

Lesson 14-7   pp. 838–839

EXERCISES 1. $-\frac{\sqrt{3}}{2}$ **3.** $-\sqrt{3}$ **5.** $-\frac{1}{2}$ **7.** $-\frac{1}{2}$
9. $\sin 2\theta = \sin (\theta + \theta) = \sin \theta \cos \theta + \cos \theta \cdot \sin \theta = 2 \sin \theta \cos \theta$ **11.** $\frac{\sqrt{2 + \sqrt{3}}}{2}$
13. $\frac{\sqrt{2 - \sqrt{3}}}{2}$ **15.** $\frac{\sqrt{2 + \sqrt{2}}}{2}$ **17.** 0 **19.** $\frac{3\sqrt{10}}{10}$
21. 3 **23.** $\frac{4\sqrt{17}}{17}$ **25.** -4 **27.** $\sin 2R =$
$2 \sin R \cos R = 2\frac{r}{t} \cdot \frac{s}{t} = \frac{2rs}{t^2}$ **29.** $\sin 2S =$
$2 \sin S \cos S = 2 \cdot \frac{s}{t} \cdot \frac{r}{t} = \frac{2sr}{t^2} = 2 \sin R \cos R =$

$\sin 2R$ **31.** $\tan \frac{R}{2} = \sqrt{\frac{1 - \cos R}{1 + \cos R}} = \sqrt{\frac{1 - \frac{s}{t}}{1 + \frac{s}{t}}}$

$= \sqrt{\frac{t - s}{t + s} \cdot \frac{t + s}{t + s}} = \sqrt{\frac{t^2 - s^2}{(t + s)^2}} = \sqrt{\frac{r^2}{(t + s)^2}} = \frac{r}{t + s}$

33. No; since the sine function is periodic, A and B can have many different values. **35.** $-\frac{7}{25}$

37. $-\frac{25}{24}$ **39.** $-\frac{2\sqrt{5}}{5}$ **41.** -2 **43.** $\sin \theta (4 \cos \theta - 3)$
$= 0; 0, \pi, 0.723, 5.560$ **45.** $4 \cos^2 \theta - 1 = 0; \frac{\pi}{3}, \frac{2\pi}{3}$,

---

$\frac{4\pi}{3}, \frac{5\pi}{3}$ **47.** $-\cos \theta$ **49. Answers may vary. Sample:**
a. $\sin 60° = \frac{\sqrt{3}}{2}$, $\cos 60° = \frac{1}{2}$ **b.** $\sin 120° = \frac{\sqrt{3}}{2}$
c. $\cos 30° = \frac{\sqrt{3}}{2}$ **51–55. Answers may vary.**
51. $4 \sin \theta \cos \theta (\cos^2 \theta - \sin^2 \theta)$
53. $\frac{4 \tan \theta (1 - \tan^2 \theta)}{\tan^4 \theta - 6 \tan^2 \theta + 1}$ **55.** $\pm\sqrt{\frac{1}{2} \pm \frac{1}{2}\sqrt{\frac{1}{2} + \frac{1}{2} \cos \theta}}$

57. $\tan \frac{A}{2} = \pm\sqrt{\frac{1 - \cos A}{1 + \cos A}} = \pm\sqrt{\frac{1 - \cos A}{1 + \cos A}} \cdot$

$\sqrt{\frac{1 + \cos A}{1 + \cos A}} = \pm\sqrt{\frac{1 - \cos^2 A}{(1 + \cos A)^2}} = \pm\sqrt{\frac{\sin^2 A}{(1 + \cos A)^2}}$
$= \frac{\sin A}{1 + \cos A}$; **Since $\tan \frac{A}{2}$ and $\sin A$ always have the same sign, only the positive sign occurs.**

b. $\tan \frac{A}{2} = \pm\sqrt{\frac{1 - \cos A}{1 + \cos A}} = \pm\sqrt{\frac{1 - \cos A}{1 + \cos A}} \cdot$

$\sqrt{\frac{1 - \cos A}{1 - \cos A}} = \pm\sqrt{\frac{(1 - \cos A)^2}{1 - \cos^2 A}} = \pm\sqrt{\frac{(1 - \cos A)^2}{\sin^2 A}}$

$= \frac{1 - \cos A}{\sin A}$; **Since $\tan \frac{A}{2}$ and $\sin A$ always have the same sign, only the positive sign occurs.**
59. D **61.** $\frac{\sqrt{2}}{2}$ **63.** $\sqrt{3}$ **65.** 4, 2

Chapter Review   pp. 841–843

1. Law of Sines 2. trigonometric ratios for a right triangle 3. Law of Cosines 4. trigonometric identity 5. Law of Sines 6. $\sin \theta \tan \theta = \frac{\sin^2 \theta}{\cos \theta} =$
$\frac{1 - \cos^2 \theta}{\cos \theta} = \frac{1}{\cos \theta} - \frac{\cos^2 \theta}{\cos \theta} = \frac{1}{\cos \theta} - \cos \theta$
7. $\cos^2 \theta \cot^2 \theta = (1 - \sin^2 \theta) \cot^2 \theta =$
$\cot^2 \theta - \sin^2 \theta \cot^2 \theta = \cot^2 \theta - \sin^2 \theta \cdot \frac{\cos^2 \theta}{\sin^2 \theta} =$
$\cot^2 \theta - \cos^2 \theta$ **8.** $\cos^2 \theta$ **9.** 1 **10.** 1 **11.** $-60°$
12. 60° **13.** $-30°$ **14.** 30° **15.** $0.34 + 2\pi n$,
$2.80 + 2\pi n$ **16.** $-1.11 + 2\pi n$, $2.03 + 2\pi n$
17. $2.27 + 2\pi n$, $4.02 + 2\pi n$ **18.** $0.20 + 2\pi n$,
$6.08 + 2\pi n$ **19.** $\frac{\pi}{3}, \frac{5\pi}{3}$ **20.** $\frac{\pi}{6}, \frac{7\pi}{6}$ **21.** $0, \frac{\pi}{2}, \pi$
22. $\frac{3}{5}$, 0.6 **23.** $\frac{4}{5}$, 0.8 **24.** $\frac{3}{4}$, 0.75 **25.** $3\sqrt{10}$, 18.4°,
71.6° **26.** 16, 36.9°, 53.1° **27.** 37.7, 43.3°, 46.7°
28. 13.14 m² **29.** 92.12 ft² **30.** 57.81 m²
31. 7.1 in. **32.** 54.3° or 125.7° **33.** 21.4 ft
34. 43.9° **35.** 52.2° **36.** $\cos \left(\theta + \frac{\pi}{2}\right)$
$= \cos \theta \cdot \cos \left(\frac{\pi}{2}\right) - \sin \theta \cdot \sin \left(\frac{\pi}{2}\right) = \cos \theta \cdot 0$
$- \sin \theta \cdot 1 = -\sin \theta$ **37.** $\sin^2 \left(\theta - \frac{\pi}{2}\right) =$
$\sin^2 \left(-\left(\frac{\pi}{2} - \theta\right)\right) = \left(-\sin \left(\frac{\pi}{2} - \theta\right)\right) \cdot$
$\left(-\sin \left(\frac{\pi}{2} - \theta\right)\right) = (-\cos \theta)(-\cos \theta) = \cos^2 \theta$
38. $\frac{\pi}{2}$ and $\frac{3\pi}{2}$ **39.** 0 **40.** $\frac{\sqrt{3}}{2}$ **41.** 0 **42.** $-\sqrt{3}$
43. -1 **44.** $\sqrt{3}$ **45.** $\frac{\sqrt{3}}{2}$

Extra Practice

CHAPTER 1

1. > **3.** > **5.** = **7.** > **9.** $-102, \frac{1}{102}$ **11.** $-2\frac{3}{4}, \frac{4}{11}$

13. $-\sqrt{2}, \frac{\sqrt{2}}{2}$ **15.** $\frac{8}{5}, -\frac{5}{8}$ **17.** $-\frac{6}{7}, \frac{7}{6}$ **19.** -0.0001, 10,000 **21.** 28 **23.** 14 **25.** 2

27. -11 **29.** $\frac{33}{20}$ **31.** $t \le -1$

33. $a < -\frac{7}{2}$

35. $y < 10$

37. $-2 \le z < 1$

39. $x < -2, x > 8$

41. $p > -5$

43. $-11, 15.5$ **45.** $-5, 9$

47. $-\frac{23}{2}, \frac{17}{2}$

49. $t \le -5.5, t \ge -1.5$

51. $-11 \le w \le -1$

53. $-\frac{7}{2} \le z \le -\frac{3}{2}$

55. 1 **57.** $\frac{4}{9}$ **59.** $\frac{4}{9}$ **61.** \$500 **63.** $3\frac{2}{3}$ **65.** \$11,500
67. less than 8 h **69.** $\frac{3}{38}$ **71.** $\frac{2}{5}$

CHAPTER 2

1. Yes; each x-value has exactly one y-value.
3. No; the x-value 1 has two y-values.
5. No; the x-values 3 and 6 have two y-values.

7. **9.**

11. **13.**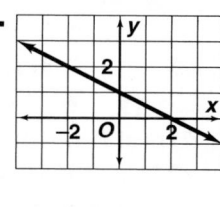

15. $3x - y = -7$ **17.** $3x - 4y = -26$
19. $8x - 3y = -16$ **21.** $y - 2 = -1(x - 0)$
23. $y - 0 = \frac{1}{2}(x - 3)$ **25.** $y - 6 = -2(x + 5)$
27. 2, -5, 2.5 **29.** 0, 4, none **31.** $\frac{1}{3}$, -15, 45
33. -6, 0, 0 **35.** $3x - y = -9$ **37.** $8x - 2y = 7$
39. $3x + 12y = 24$ **41.** $x + y = 8$ **43.** $y = \frac{7}{3}x$
45. $y = 2.5x$ **47.** $y = -x$ **49.** $y = \frac{2}{3}x$

51. **53.**

55. **57.**

59. **61.**

63. **65.**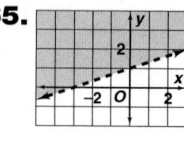

67. $A(h) = 21h$; 798 ft^2 **69.** $y - 3 = -\frac{4}{3}(x - 4)$
71.a. $f(x) = |x - 100|$ **b.** $g(x) = |x - 300|$

c. $h(x) = |x - 300| + 200$

d. They are translations of each other. **73.** $y = 75x - 18,000$; the y-intercept, $-18,000$, represents the initial investment; the x-intercept, 240, represents the days needed for the company to break even; the slope, 75, is the rental income per day.

CHAPTER 3

1. **3.**

5. no solution **7.** (1, 4) **9.** (6, -3)

11. $\left(-\frac{1}{3}, \frac{13}{3}\right)$ **13.** **15.**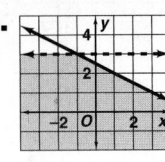

17. (0, 0) **19.** 50 chef's salads and 50 Caesar salads

21–23. **29.**

31. **33.**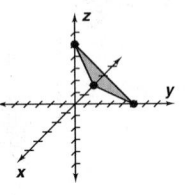

35. (2, 1, 3) **37.** (2, 3, −6) **39.** 4.5 mi/h **41.** $4.70 per lb of cheese, $5.65 per lb of chicken loaf

43.a.
$$\begin{cases} 5x + 8y \le 400 \\ 2.5x + 2y \le 120 \\ x \ge 0 \\ y \ge 0 \end{cases}$$
b.

45. first chef: $3\frac{1}{3}$ h; second chef: $8\frac{1}{3}$ h

47. Student: $6; Adult: $15; Senior: $8

CHAPTER 4

1. 2 × 3; 6 **3.** 2 × 3; −83 **5.** 1 × 2; $\frac{3}{8}$ **7.** $\begin{bmatrix} 4 & 67 \\ 12 & 18 \end{bmatrix}$

9. $\begin{bmatrix} -6 & -1 & 0 \\ 17 & -11 & -8 \end{bmatrix}$ **11.** $\begin{bmatrix} -62 & 121 \\ 43 & -54 \end{bmatrix}$

13. $\begin{bmatrix} 5 & -7 & 7 \\ 2 & 1 & -2 \end{bmatrix}$ **15.** $\begin{bmatrix} -26 & 7 & 5 \\ -4 & -7 & 25 \end{bmatrix}$

17. $\begin{bmatrix} 16 & 2 \\ -4 & 10 \end{bmatrix}$ **19.** product undefined

21. $\begin{bmatrix} 1.6 & 0.2 \\ -0.4 & 1 \end{bmatrix}$ **23.** $\begin{bmatrix} 45 & 20 \\ 25 & 5 \\ 10 & 0 \end{bmatrix}$

25. $\begin{bmatrix} 0.5 & 3.5 & 1.5 \\ 4 & 5 & -1 \end{bmatrix}$ **27.** $\begin{bmatrix} 5 & 10 & 20 \\ 25 & -5 & 15 \end{bmatrix}$

29. $\begin{bmatrix} 3 & 4 & 6 \\ -2 & -8 & -4 \end{bmatrix}$ **31.** $\begin{bmatrix} \frac{68}{15} & -\frac{34}{15} \\ -\frac{16}{15} & \frac{83}{15} \end{bmatrix}$ **33.** $\begin{bmatrix} 2 \\ 7 \end{bmatrix}$

35. (9, 1) **37.a.** machine 1 $\begin{bmatrix} 13 & 22 \\ 22 & 37 \end{bmatrix}$
machine 2

b. the total number of gals. of chocolate and vanilla yogurt made by each machine in the A.M. and P.M.

39. $\begin{bmatrix} \frac{\sqrt{3}-1}{2} & \frac{\sqrt{3}-2}{2} & \frac{5\sqrt{3}-4}{2} \\ \frac{\sqrt{3}+1}{2} & \frac{2\sqrt{3}+1}{2} & \frac{4\sqrt{3}+5}{2} \end{bmatrix}$

41. $\begin{bmatrix} 1 & 1 & 1 \\ 1 & 1 & -1 \\ -1 & 1 & 0 \end{bmatrix} \begin{bmatrix} x \\ y \\ z \end{bmatrix} = \begin{bmatrix} 249 \\ 95 \\ 6 \end{bmatrix}$; $x = 83, y = 89, z = 77$

43. $\begin{bmatrix} 2 & 1 \\ 3 & 2 \end{bmatrix} \begin{bmatrix} x \\ y \end{bmatrix} = \begin{bmatrix} 10 \\ 17.25 \end{bmatrix}$; $x = 2.75, y = 4.50$

45. orchestra: $25; balcony: $15

CHAPTER 5

1. linear; none, 3x, 4
3. linear; none, $-\frac{3}{2}x, \frac{1}{2}$ **5.** quadratic; $-x^2$, none, 3

7. **9.**

11. **13.**

15. (x + 9)(x − 6) **17.** (x − 6)(x + 6) **19.** (x − 8)(x − 7) **21.** (7x + 1)(x − 3) **23.** $\frac{1}{4}$(x − 4)(x + 4)

25. 4(x^2 + 3x + 10) **27.** 0.24, −4.24 **29.** 0.41, −2.41 **31.** −7, 5 **33.** 0, −4 **35.** 8 − 3i **37.** 1 − 3i

39. 8 + 4i **41.** ±4i **43.** $\pm i\sqrt{10}$ **45.** $\pm i\frac{\sqrt{10}}{2}$

47. −i, −1 − i, i **49.** −1, −4 **51.** $\frac{5}{4} \pm \frac{\sqrt{17}}{4}$ **53.** $2 \pm 2i\sqrt{2}$ **55.** −2 **57.** $-4 \pm \sqrt{33}$ **59.** −7; 2, imaginary **61.** 25; 2, real **63.** −16; 2, real **65.** 0; 1, real **67.a.** 30 ft by 20 ft **b.** 300 ft² **69.** 19 years old; 24 years old **71.a.** 625 bulldozers; $781,250 **b.** x ≥ 0; P(x) ≤ $781,250 **c.** 500 ≤ x ≤ 750 **73.** 12; 20 in. **75.a.** The archer releases the arrow 5 ft above the ground. **b.** 402 ft

CHAPTER 6

1. $-4a^2 + 3a$; quadratic binomial **3.** $-2n^3 + 3n^2 - n - 3$; cubic polynomial of 4 terms **5.** $-2c^2 - 4c + 7$; quadratic trinomial **7.** $y = x^3 - 4x^2 + x + 6$ **9.** $y = x^3 + 2x^2 - x - 2$ **11.** $y = x^3 - x^2 - 17x - 15$ **13.** $y = x^4 - 3x^3 - 2x^2 + 12x - 8$

15. $x^2 - 2x - 2$ **17.** $2x^2 + 2x$ **19.** $x - 2$, R -2
21. $0, -2, 5$ **23.** 2 **25.** $\pm 3, \pm 2$ **27.** $-2, \pm i\sqrt{3}$
29. $-1, \frac{-5 \pm \sqrt{13}}{6}$ **31.** $-2, -\frac{2}{5}, \frac{1}{3}$ **33.** 720 **35.** 210
37. 6720 **39.** 15 **41.** 35 **43.** 42
45. permutation; 60,480 orders **47.** combination;
6 ways **49.** $81x^4 + 216x^3 + 216x^2 + 96x + 16$
51. $16x^4 + 160x^3y + 600x^2y^2 + 1000xy^3 + 625y^4$
53. $x^7 + 14x^6y + 84x^5y^2 + 280x^4y^3 + 560x^3y^4 + 672x^2y^5 + 448xy^6 + 128y^7$ **55.** $x^4 - 16x^3y^3 + 96x^2y^6 - 256xy^9 + 256y^{12}$ **57.a.** Answers may
vary. Sample: $P(N) = (N - 1)N(N + 1) = N^3 - N$
b. 5, 6, 7 **59.** 14 in. by 14 in. by 14 in. **61.** 455
ways **63.** 255 kinds of pizza **65.** 100,947 ways

CHAPTER 7

1. $6x^2$ **3.** $3|x^3|$ **5.** $-2k$ **7.** $m^4n^2\sqrt{m}$ **9.** $6x^3\sqrt{2x}$
11. $10a^2$ **13.** $3x^2\sqrt{y}$ **15.** $5\sqrt{7}$ **17.** $3\sqrt{7x}$ **19.** $7\sqrt{3}$
21. $\frac{y^9}{x^{20}}$ **23.** $\frac{y^3}{2x^5}$ **25.** $-\frac{2y^3}{x^2}$ **27.** $\frac{3y^4}{2x^3}$
29. no real solution **31.** 3, 7 **33.** 3, 11 **35.** 1
37. 64 **39.** 1 **41.** 4 **43.** 40 **45.** $f^{-1}(x) = x^2 - 4$,
$x \geq 0$; domain of f: $\{x \geq -4\}$, range of f: $\{y \geq 0\}$,
domain of f^{-1}: $\{x \geq 0\}$, range of f^{-1}: $\{y \geq -4\}$; f^{-1}
is a function. **47.** $f^{-1}(x) = -\frac{x^2 - 2}{5}$, $x \geq 0$; domain
of f: $\{x \leq \frac{2}{5}\}$, range of f: $\{y \geq 0\}$, domain of f^{-1}:
$\{x \geq 0\}$, range of f^{-1}: $\{y \leq \frac{2}{5}\}$; f^{-1} is a function.
49. $f^{-1}(x) = \pm\sqrt{2 - x}$; domain of f: all real numbers,
range of f: $\{y \leq 2\}$, domain of f^{-1}: $\{x \leq 2\}$, range of
f^{-1}: all real numbers; f^{-1} is not a function.

51. **53.**

55. **57.**

59. 7.3 ft **61.** $d = \frac{v^2}{64}$ **63.a.** $g(p) = 106p + 500$
b. $(f \circ g \circ g)(p)$; $2282.82
65.a. $t(h) = 2 \pm \frac{1}{4}\sqrt{64 - h}$; no; for each height
$h < 64$, there are two times when the rocket
passes that height. **b.** $t(h) = 2 - \frac{1}{4}\sqrt{64 - h}$

CHAPTER 8

1. $y = 4(2.5)^x$ **3.** $y = \frac{2}{3}(3)^x$ **5.** $y = 32(2)^x$
7. exponential growth **9.** exponential decay
11. exponential growth **13.** exponential decay
15. exponential growth

17. **19.**

21. **23.**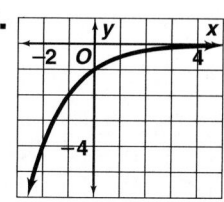

25. $\log_9 729 = 3$ **27.** $\log_{\frac{1}{2}} \frac{1}{16} = 4$ **29.** $\log_{\frac{1}{3}} 27 = -3$
31. $\log_2 \frac{1}{32} = -5$

33. **35.**

37. **39.**

41. $\log 24$ **43.** $\log x^7$ **45.** $\log\left(\frac{rs^2}{t}\right)$ **47.** $\log_b 2 + 2 \log_b x + 3 \log_b y$ **49.** $5(\log_b 4 + \log_b m + \log_b n)$
51. $4(\log_b x + \log_b y) - \log_b 2$ **53.** ± 8 **55.** 50,000
57. 1.609 **59.** 4386.533 **61.** 400 **63.** 2
65. $3745.32 **67.** $1214.87 **69.** 1432 yr **71.** 2399
species **73.a.** -0.042 **b.** 48.5°F **c.** 69.5 min **d.** No;
$e^{kt} > 0$ for all t, so $T(t) > T_r = 38°F$.

CHAPTER 9

1. $y = \frac{6}{x}$ **3.** $y = \frac{40}{x}$ **5.** $y = \frac{-24}{x}$

7. **9.**

11. **13.**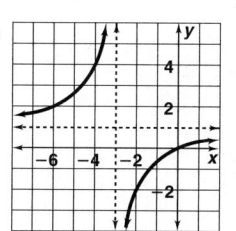

15. 0 **17.** $-2, 1$ **19.** $0, \pm\sqrt{2}$ **21.** 7 **23.** $x + 3; x \neq -6$
25. $x + 2; x \neq -3, 4$ **27.** $\frac{(x + 2)^2}{(x^2 - 6x - 6)(2x + 3)}$;
$x \neq -\frac{1}{3}, -\frac{3}{2}, 3 \pm \sqrt{15}, -2$

29. $\dfrac{14x - 3}{2(x + 2)}$ **31.** $\dfrac{8x - 3}{x(x + 3)}$ **33.** $\dfrac{-3x^2 + 5}{x^2 - 1}$

35. -4 **37.** $-5, 4$ **39.** 20

41. independent **43.** dependent **45.** about 0.26 tons

47. $f(x) = \dfrac{0.658x + 7}{x + 9}$ **49.** 2.4 mi/h **51.** about 16 h

53. $\dfrac{10}{22}$

CHAPTER 10

1. 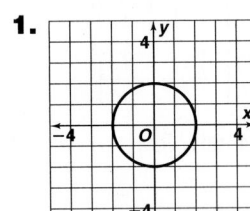 Circle; every line through $(0, 0)$ is a line of symmetry, radius 2; domain: $-2 \le x \le 2$, range: $-2 \le y \le 2$.

3. ellipse; $x = 0, y = 0$; domain: $-3 \le x \le 3$, range: $-2 \le y \le 2$

5. circle; every line through $(0, 0)$ is a line of symmetry, radius 2; domain: $-2 \le x \le 2$, range: $-2 \le y \le 2$

7. $y = \frac{1}{12}x^2$ **9.** $y = -\frac{1}{8}x^2$ **11.** $y = \frac{1}{4}x^2$

13. $y = -\frac{1}{12}x^2$ **15.** $x = \frac{1}{6}y^2$

17. $(4, 0), x = -4$; **19.** $(2, 0), x = -2$;

21. $(5, 0), x = -5$;

23. $\left(0, -\frac{1}{2}\right), y = \frac{1}{2}$;

25. $(x + 4)^2 + (y + 6)^2 = 4$ **27.** $(x - 1)^2 + (y -$

$4)^2 = 25$ **29.** $x^2 + (y + 3)^2 = 1$ **31.** $(-6, -9), 12$

33. $(-8, 1), 10$ **35.** $(7, 2), 9$

37. $(\pm 4\sqrt{2}, 0)$ **37.** $(\pm 4\sqrt{2}, 0)$

39. $(\pm\sqrt{17}, 0)$ **41.** $(\pm\sqrt{3}, 0)$

43. **45.**

47.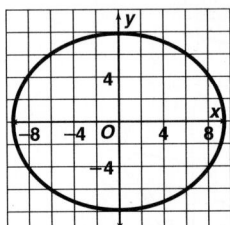

49. ellipse; center $(0, 0)$, foci $(\pm 3\sqrt{3}, 0)$

51. parabola; vertex $\left(-\frac{7}{4}, \frac{3}{2}\right)$

53. parabola; vertex $(1, 13)$

 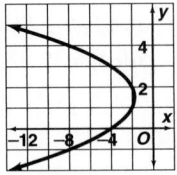

55. 8 in. **57.** $(x - 4.5)^2 + (y - 7)^2 = 1.5^2$

59. hyperbola

CHAPTER 11

1. explicit; 5, 8, 11, 14, 17 **3.** explicit; 15, 40, 75, 120, 175 **5.** explicit; 5, 23, 53, 95, 149 **7.** 9, 11, 13;

$a_n = 2n + 1; a_1 = 3, a_n = a_{n-1} + 2$ **9.** $-7.5, -6,$
$-4.5; a_n = -13.5 + 1.5n; a_1 = -12, a_n = a_{n-1} +$
1.5 **11.** $-62, -75, -88; a_n = -13n - 10; a_1 =$
$-23, a_n = a_{n-1} - 13$ **13.** 15 **15.** -4.5

17. $a_n = -27\left(\frac{1}{3}\right)^{n-1}; -27, -9, -3, -1, -\frac{1}{3}$

19. $a_n = -5(3)^{n-1}; -5, -15, -45, -135, -405$

21. $a_n = 500(0.2)^{n-1}; 500, 100, 20, 4, 0.8$

23. $\sum_{n=1}^{10} (3n + 1); 175$ **25.** $\sum_{n=1}^{20} (-n + 98); 1750$

27. $6, 2, -3; -3$ **29.** $8, 4, 25; 116$ **31.** $\frac{9}{4}$ **33.** 1

35. $\frac{10}{9}$ **37.** geometric; 3069 **39.** arithmetic;
-1110 **41.** $0 + 1 = 1; 1 + 8 = 9$ **43.** $3 + 4 = 7;$
$4 + 5 = 9$ **45.a.** 23 cm, 17.6 cm, 13.5 cm, 10.4 cm,
8.0 cm **b.** $a_n = 30\left(\frac{23}{30}\right)^n$ **47.a.** 47 **b.** 761 seats

49. 45 ft **51.a.** 44.49 m^2 **b.** 53.86 m^2 **c.** 49.18 m^2

CHAPTER 12

1.
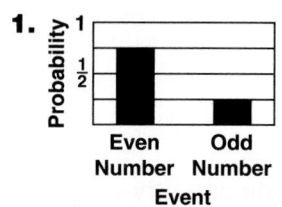

3. $\frac{39}{80}$ **5.** $\frac{25}{80}$ or $\frac{5}{16}$ **7.** $\frac{25}{41}$ **9.** 25.8, 21, 24 **11.** 4.8,
4.2, 6.1 **13.** 25.429, 11, 8, 3.81 **15.** 99.71, 5, 3, 1.578
17. ±6% **19.** ±3% **21.** ±1% **23.** $0.2787 \approx 28\%$
25. $0.0003 \approx 0.03\%$ **27.** $0.0710 \approx 7\%$
29. $P(k = 0) = 0.0467$ $P(k = 1) = 0.1866$
$P(k = 2) = 0.3110$ $P(k = 3) = 0.2765$
$P(k = 4) = 0.1382$ $P(k = 5) = 0.0369$
$P(k = 6) = 0.0041$

31. $P(k = 0) = 0.4096$ $P(k = 1) = 0.4096$
$P(k = 2) = 0.1536$ $P(k = 3) = 0.0256$
$P(k = 4) = 0.0016$

33. $P(k = 0) = 0.000064$
$P(k = 1) = 0.001536$ $P(k = 2) = 0.01536$
$P(k = 3) = 0.08192$ $P(k = 4) = 0.24576$
$P(k = 5) = 0.393216$ $P(k = 6) = 0.262144$

35.

37.

39. $\frac{3}{4}$ **41.a.** 79.95; 82; 84 **b.** 70th percentile

c.
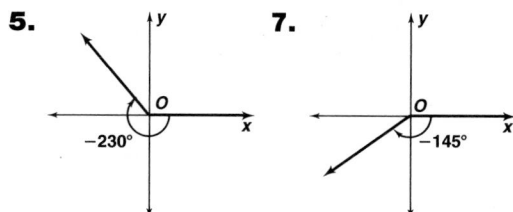

**d. Answers may vary. Sample: None; all the
scores are reasonably close to each other.**
43.a. about 5% **b.** 102 to 141 students **45.** 2.5%

CHAPTER 13

1. $4, 1\frac{1}{2}$ **3.** 4, 2

5.

7.

9.

11. $\frac{3\pi}{2}, 4.71$ **13.** $\frac{-55\pi}{18}, -9.60$ **15.** $\frac{\pi}{18}, 0.17$ **17.** $-115°$

19. $-540°$ **21.** $516°$ **23.** $1, \frac{\pi}{2}$ **25.** $2, 8\pi$ **27.** $\frac{1}{9}, \frac{2\pi}{5}$

29. **31.**

33.

35. **37.**

39. −1.5299 **41.** −1 **43.** $\sqrt{2} \approx 1.4142$ **45.** −0.4577
47. 50°F; 2 min **49.a.** 2:00. 10:00 **b.** 4:00, 8:00
51. $y = -2.7 \cos\left(\frac{\pi}{6}x\right) + 12$

53. $y = \sin\left(\frac{2\pi}{7}\right) + 7.5$

55.a. Answers may vary. Sample: the height of
the tower, 30 cm, is the scale factor that gives the
length of the cable when multiplied by csc x.
b. Explanations may vary. Sample: 30 to about
85.5 cm; the length of the cable is at least 30 cm,
and the longest cable must still be attached to
the bridge. So the longest cable is at most

$\sqrt{30^2 + \left(\frac{160}{2}\right)^2} \approx 85.44$ cm long. **c.** $\frac{\pi}{6}$ radians or 30°

CHAPTER 14

1. $60° + n \cdot 360°$ and $120° + n \cdot 360°$ **3.** $60° +$
$n \cdot 360°$ and $240° + n \cdot 360°$ **5.** no solution **7.** 1.313
9. no solution **11.** $\pi \approx 3.142$ **13.** $\frac{3\pi}{2}$ **15.** $0, \pi,$
$2.6779, 5.8195, 2\pi$ **17.** $0, \pi$ **19.** $b = 5.7, \angle A =$
$51.1°, \angle B = 38.9°$ **21.** $c = 4.5, \angle A = 26.6°, \angle B =$
$63.4°$ **23.** $a = 6.2, \angle B = 38.7°, \angle A = 51.3°$ **25.** $\frac{12}{13},$
0.923 **27.** $\frac{12}{5}, 2.4$ **29.** 11.3 **31.** 46.3

33. $\frac{\sqrt{6} - \sqrt{2}}{4}$ **35.** $\frac{\sqrt{3}}{2}$ **37.** 1 **39.** 1 **41.** −1 **43.** $-\frac{1}{2}$

45. $\frac{\sqrt{6} - \sqrt{2}}{4}$ **47.** $\frac{\sqrt{2 + \sqrt{2}}}{2}$ **49.** $\frac{\sqrt{2 + \sqrt{2 + \sqrt{3}}}}{2}$

51. 140 ft, 229 ft **53.** 246.6 ft² **55.** 2.36 mi
57. 76°, 115.3°, 78.7°, 90°

Skills Handbook

p. 876 1. $\left(13, 6\frac{1}{2}\right)$ **3.**

p. 877 1. 23 pigs and 17 ducks **3.** 45 mi

5. **7.** 19.6

p. 878 1. ten of each coin
3.a.

Rectangle Perimeter

		length						
		1	2	3	4	5	6	7
width	1	4	6	8	10	12	14	16
	2	6	8	10	12	14	16	18
	3	8	10	12	14	16	18	20
	4	10	12	14	16	18	20	22
	5	12	14	16	18	20	22	24
	6	14	16	18	20	22	24	26
	7	16	18	20	22	24	26	28

Rectangle Area

		length						
		1	2	3	4	5	6	7
width	1	1	2	3	4	5	6	7
	2	2	4	6	8	10	12	14
	3	3	6	9	12	15	18	21
	4	4	8	12	16	20	24	28
	5	5	10	15	20	25	30	35
	6	6	12	18	24	30	36	42
	7	7	14	21	28	35	42	49

b. yes **5.** 11 ways if you include one fifty-cent
coin **7.** 6 ways
p. 879 1. 12 slices **3.** 204 squares **5.a.** 90 games
b. $s(s - 1)$ games
p. 880 1. Leon **3.** 15 students **5.** Luis: editor;
Marisa: surgeon; Neil: florist; Ophelia: baker
p. 881 1. $85\frac{1}{3}$ cm

3.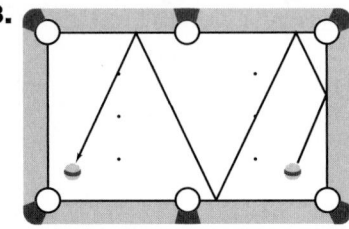

5. 23 **7.** 1011 mi

p. 882 1. 46% **3.** 29.4% **5.** 0.7% **7.** 25% **9.** 66.7%
11. 115% **13.** 0.4 **15.** 1.5 **17.** 1.035 **19.** 12.5
21. 75 **23.** 20 **25.** $600
p. 883 1. $1\frac{2}{5}$ **3.** $6\frac{5}{6}$ **5.** $10\frac{3}{20}$ **7.** $\frac{5}{21}$ **9.** $7\frac{3}{10}$ **11.** $\frac{3}{8}$
13. 38 **15.** $38\frac{1}{4}$ **17.** 2 **19.** $2\frac{1}{2}$ **21.** $11\frac{1}{4}$ **23.** $\frac{2}{9}$ **25.** $4\frac{13}{16}$
27. $2\frac{1}{6}$ **29.** $6\frac{7}{33}$ **31.** $\frac{7}{12}$
p. 884 1. 3 to 4 **3.** 9.5 g/oz **5.** $\frac{14}{5}$ **7.** 8 **9.** 1.8
11. 1.95 **13.** 45.5 **15.** ±6 **17.** 227.5 calories
p. 885 1. 1 **3.** −38 **5.** −17 **7.** 8 **9.** −14 **11.** 28
13. −12 **15.** −90 **17.** 12 **19.** 15 **21.** −18 **23.** 0
25. 49 **27.** −10 **29.** 1 **31.** 18
p. 886 1. 14.4 **3.** 84 **5.** 21 **7.** 4.6 **9.** 55 **11.** 528.6
13. $\ell = \frac{P}{2} - w$ **15.** $b = c - 2a$ **17.** $x = 2y$

19. $m = q - (n + p)$ **21.** $m = \frac{q}{np}$ **23.** $r = \frac{1 - 3s}{2}$
25. $b = \frac{2A}{h}$ **27.** $b = \pm\sqrt{c^2 - a^2}$ **29.** $\ell = \frac{2V}{A_1 + A_2}$;
24.2 ft

p. 887 **1.** 14 m^2 **3.** 30 cm^2 **5.** 91.1 ft^3
7. 314.2 in.^{3} **9.** 110.5 in.^{2} **11.** 121.5 ft^2

p. 888 **1.** I **3.** IV **5.** III

7–12.

13. $\frac{3}{4}$ **15.** 0 **17.** $\frac{1}{5}$ **19.** $\left(5, -\frac{3}{2}\right)$ **21.** $\left(\frac{5}{2}, -1\right)$

p. 889 **1.** −1 **3.** 6 **5.** 40 **7.** 1.5 **9.** −14 **11.** 13

13. $x \le 6$

15. $y \ge -2$

17. $s \ge 35$ **19.** $c > -28$

21. $t < 2$ **23.** $w < 3$

p. 890 **1.** 8, −8 **3.** 5, −13 **5.** 7, −7 **7.** 1, 15
9. 20, −20 **11.** 7

13. $-3 \le x \le 15$ **15.** $r \le -7$ or $r \ge 7$

17. $-2.4 \le p \le 2.4$ **19.** $-2 < x < \frac{6}{7}$

p. 891

1. **3.**

5. **7.**

9. **11.**

13. **15.**

17. **19.**

21. **23.**

  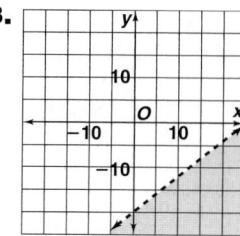

p. 892 **1.** x^3 **3.** a^4b **5.** $\frac{1}{c^4}$ **7.** $\frac{x^5}{y^7z^3}$ **9.** d^8 **11.** r^5s^8

13. a^3 **15.** $\frac{1}{n^3}$ **17.** r^3t^3 **19.** $\frac{a^4}{b^4}$ **21.** c^{12} **23.** $u^{12}v^6$

25. a^3 **27.** $64a^8b^5$ **29.** $\frac{1}{g^4}$ **31.** $\frac{a^5}{2}$

p. 893 **1.** $x^2 + 10x - 5$ **3.** $12x^4 - 20x^3 + 36x^2$
5. $x^2 - 2x - 15$ **7.** $(a - 6)(a - 2)$ **9.** $(n - 4)(n + 2)$
11. $3(m^2 - 3)$ **13.** $s(s^2 + 6s + 11)$ **15.** $(y - 5)^2$
17. $(2x - 3)(x + 4)$

p. 894 **1.** 1.34×10^6 **3.** 7.75×10^{-4} **5.** 111,300
7. 1.895×10^3 **9.** 1.234×10^5 **11.** 6.4×10^5 **13.**
$\approx 8.52 \times 10^2$ **15.** $\approx 1.8 \times 10^1$ **17.** $\approx 8.95 \times 10^{-12}$
19. $\approx 3.77 \times 10^{10}$ **21.** $\approx 1.8 \times 10^{-6}$

p. 895 **1.** 6 **3.** $3\sqrt{2}$ **5.** $3\sqrt{6}$ **7.** $10\sqrt{3}$ **9.** $\frac{2\sqrt{3}}{3}$ **11.** $\frac{\sqrt{10}}{5}$

13. $\frac{\sqrt{3}}{2}$ **15.** $\frac{4\sqrt{5}}{15}$ **17.** $\frac{\sqrt{30}}{3}$ **19.** $5\sqrt{5}$ **21.** $\sqrt{3}$ **23.** $-3\sqrt{2}$

25. $5\sqrt{10}$ **27.** $6\sqrt{5}$ **29.** $12\sqrt{2} - \sqrt{5}$

p. 896 **1.** 10 **3.** 15 **5.** 24 **7.** ≈ 54.7 **9.** ≈ 8.9 **11.** 10

13. 22.7 **15.** 22.6 **17.** 9.2 **19.** 5.8 **21.** 8.5

p. 897

1.

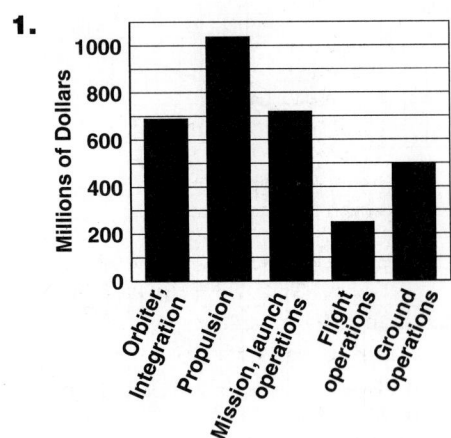

p. 898 1. 3.8, 5, 5 **3.** 4.0, 2.4, 2.4 **5.** 1.5, 1.5, no mode

7.

p. 899 1. $\frac{a}{3b^2}$ **3.** $\frac{1}{2}$ **5.** $4x$ **7.** $\frac{2}{h}$ **9.** $\frac{x}{10}$ **11.** $\frac{74x}{35}$ **13.** $\frac{4x^2}{5}$

15. $\frac{16}{x}$ **17.** $\frac{16}{5}$ **19.** $2x$

Index

A

Abscissa, 56

Absolute value, 33
  of complex number, 279, 305
  of real number, 8, 33

Absolute value equations, 33–34, 49, 892

Absolute value function, 90–92, 113

Absolute value inequalities, 35–36, 105–106

Absolute value symbols, 377

Absolute value systems of inequalities, 137

ACT preparation. *See* Test Prep

Active Math Online, 6, 28, 42, 59, 91, 97, 104, 120, 129, 137, 143, 179, 197, 251, 257, 273, 296, 322, 329, 377, 423, 442, 448, 456, 497, 505, 512, 568, 574, 580, 587, 616, 624, 646, 675, 699, 747, 756, 762, 770, 793, 831

Activity. *See also* Data analysis, Technology
  Adding Fractions–Extended, 522
  Analyzing Data Spread, 680
  Analyzing Graphs, 120
  Analyzing Hyperbolas, 584
  Angles in a Circle, 732
  Arithmetic Series, 629
  Binomial Probability, 697
  Checking for Extraneous Solutions, 400
  Counting Zeros, 347
  Estimating Square Roots, 4
  Factoring, 263
  Finding a Minimum Value, 141
  Finding the Line of Best Fit, 88
  Generating a Pattern, 610
  Geometric Sequences, 622
  Graphs of Polynomial Functions, 312
  Hands-On, 39, 539
  Inverses, 412
  Linear Inequalities, 103
  Periodic Cycles, 722
  Point-Slope Form, 66
  Properties of Logarithms, 462
  Right Triangle Ratios, 806
  Technology, 120, 312, 400, 592, 792
  Tournament Play, 440
  Translating a Geometric Figure, 195
  Translating Conic Sections, 592
  Trigonometric Identities, 792
  Using Matrices, 188
  Using the Line of Best Fit to Estimate, 89
  Using the Line of Best Fit to Predict, 88
  Vertex Form, 256

Activity Lab
  Area Under a Curve, 711
  Completing the Square, 285
  Conic Sections, 556

Continuous Probability, 688
Deriving Summation Formulas, 644
Exponential and Logarithmic Inequalities, 484–485
Extraneous Solutions, 529
Fibonacci Sequence, 621
Finding a Line of Best Fit, 88–89
Fitting Exponential Curves to Data, 446
Geometry and Infinite Series, 635
Graphing calculator, 126, 147, 248, 300–301, 419, 426–427, 446, 477, 484–485, 502, 536–537, 564, 577, 599, 644, 711, 754, 805
Graphing Conic Sections, 564
Graphing Inverses, 419
Graphing Rational Functions, 502
Graphing Trigonometric Functions, 754
Hands-On, 285, 556, 737
Judging the Validity of an Argument, 468
Linear and Exponential Models, 477
Linear Programming, 147
Lissajous Figures, 805
Measuring Radians, 737
Modeling Using Residuals, 248
Parametric Equations, 126
Pascal's Triangle, 358
Quadratic Inequalities, 300–301
Radical Inequalities, 426–427
Rational Inequalities, 536–537
Solving Quadratic Systems, 599
Solving Systems Using Tables, 134
Spreadsheets, 25
Technology, 25, 88–89, 126, 147, 185, 248, 300–301, 419, 426–427, 446, 477, 484–485, 502, 536–537, 564, 577, 599, 644, 711, 754, 805
Using Parametric Equations, 577
Working with Matrices, 185
Writing Equations From Roots, 277
Writing Expressions From Tables, 11

Addition. *See also* Summation
  of complex numbers, 280
  of fractions, 522–523
  of functions, 404
  of matrices, 178–179, 185, 195–196, 234
  of polynomials, 895
  of radical expressions, 386–387
  of rational expressions, 523

Addition property
  of equality, 18
  of inequality, 26

Additive identity matrix, 179

Additive inverse
  of complex number, 283
  of matrix, 179
  opposites, 7, 47–48

Algebra at Work. *See also* Careers
  acoustical physicist, 827
  demographer, 418
  economist, 545

landscape architect, 255
market researcher, 695
miniaturist, 79
quality control engineer, 332
radiologist, 153
wildlife biologist, 24

Algebra 1 Review
  Coordinate Plane, 56
  Properties of Exponents, 374
  Square Roots and Radicals, 270

Algebra tiles, 264, 285

Algebraic expressions, 12–14, 48

Ambiguous Case, (Law of Sines), 821

Amplitude
  of cosine function, 756
  defined, 724, 783
  of periodic function, 724–725, 747–751, 783
  of sine curve, 748

Amplitude modulation (AM) radio, 724

Analyzing data. *See* Data analysis

And (compound inequality), 28, 48–49

Angle(s)
  central, 738, 784, 899
  in a circle, 732
  congruent, 821
  cosine of, 732–734, 740, 783, 798, 841–842
  coterminal, 731, 783
  initial side of, 731, 783
  measuring, 730–731, 737, 809, 823, 824
  radian measure, 737, 738–741, 784
  sine of, 732–734, 740, 783
  in standard position, 730–731, 783
  tangent of, 761, 785
  terminal side of, 730, 783, 837
  of triangle, 816
  in unit circle, 732–734, 783

Angle difference identities, 830–831, 843

Angle identities, 828–831, 843

Angle sum identities, 830, 831, 843

Applications. *See* Algebra at Work, Careers, Point in Time, Real-World Connections

Arc
  finding length of, 740–741
  intercepted, 738, 740, 784

Area
  under curve, 645–647, 653, 711
  formulas for, 815, 912
  Law of Sines and, 815–816, 842
  of triangle, 815–816

Arithmetic mean, 617, 651

Arithmetic sequences
  defined, 616, 651
  formulas for, 617
  identifying and generating, 616–617, 652

Arithmetic series, 629–631, 652

Assessment. *See also* California Mathematics Content Standards, California Multiple Choice

Index

transforming into linear functions, 477
writing, 440

Exponential growth, 438–440, 487

Exponential inequalities, 484–485

Exponential models, 477

ExpReg feature, of graphing calculator, 470

Expressions
algebraic, 12–14, 48
equivalent, 13
evaluating, 12–13, 48
logarithmic, 454–456, 462–463, 489
quadratic. *See* Quadratic expressions
radical. *See* Radical expressions
rational. *See* Rational expressions
simplifying, 12–14, 48
terms of, 13, 242, 313
trigonometric, 794
variable, 12
writing from tables, 11

Extension
The Ambiguous Case, 821
Comparing Conditional Probabilities, 671
End Behavior, 318
The Fibonacci Sequence, 621
Mathematical Induction, 642–643
Networks, 216–217
Piecewise Functions, 73

Extra Practice, 850–875

Extraneous solution, 34, 48, 399, 400, 529

Extrapolate, 316

F _____

Factor(s)
common, 263
decay, 441, 487
defined, 263
greatest common factor (GCF), 263, 304
growth, 438, 487
linear, 319
of polynomial function, 321–322
prime, 319

Factor Theorem, 321, 366

Factor trees, 319

Factorial notation, 351, 367

Factoring
defined, 263
difference of cubes, 334, 366
difference of two squares, 267, 304
greatest common factor, 263, 304
perfect square trinomial, 266, 304
polynomials, 319–322, 326–329, 334–336, 366, 893
quadratic expressions, 263–266
quadratic trinomial, 264–266
solving polynomial equations by, 334–336
solving quadratic equations by, 271, 297, 304
solving trigonometric equations by, 800
sum of cubes, 334, 366

Family(ies)
of conic sections, 593
of exponential functions, 447–449
of functions, 95–99
of logarithmic functions, 457
of quadratic functions, 257
of radical functions, 421
of reciprocal functions, 503–506
of sine and cosine functions, 770

Feasible region, 142, 164

Fibonacci sequence, 621

Finite graph, 216–217

Finite sequences, 629

Finite series, 629–631, 636–637, 644, 652

Flip. *See* Reflections

Focus (foci)
of ellipse, 578, 580, 602
of hyperbola, 585, 586–587
of parabola, 565, 567–568, 601

FOIL, 242, 430

Formulas
for area, 815, 910
for arithmetic sequences, 617
for binomial probability, 699
Change of Base, 470–471
for conditional probability, 667
for continuously compounded interest, 449, 488
for converting between radians and degrees, 739
for distance, 571
evaluating, 886
explicit, 612, 617, 623, 651
generating mathematical patterns with, 612
for geometric sequences, 623
for geometric series, 636
Law of Cosines, 822
Law of Sines, 816
for length of intercepted arc, 740
for margin of error, 691
Quadratic, 293–295, 297, 305
radical expressions in, 403
recursive, 612, 617, 623, 651
slope, 66, 888
solving for one variable, 19
spreadsheet, 25
for standard deviation, 681
for sum of arithmetic series, 630, 644
for sum of geometric series, 638, 644
for volume, 498

Fractal, 281, 283

Fractal geometry, 613

Fractions
adding, 522–523
complex, 524–525, 548
dividing, 883
multiplying, 883
subtracting, 883

Frequency table, 660–661, 713, 714

Function(s). *See also* Equations, Graph(s)
absolute value, 90–92, 113
adding, 404
amplitude of, 724–725, 748, 756, 783
composite, 405, 431

composition of, 405–406
continuous, 59
cosecant, 775, 785
cosine. *See* Cosine functions
cotangent, 775, 785
cube root, 422
cubic, 313, 334
defined, 59, 111
discrete, 59
dividing, 404, 405
domain of, 404
exponential. *See* Exponential functions
family of, 95–99
identifying, 59–60
inverse, 412–415, 419, 420–421, 431
linear, 64, 112, 242, 477
logarithmic, 454–457, 488
maximum and minimum values of, 141–142, 251, 321, 366
multiplying, 404, 405
natural logarithmic, 478–480, 489
objective, 141, 164
operations with, 404–405, 431
parent. *See* Parent function
period of, 747, 767, 783
periodic. *See* Periodic functions
piecewise, 73
polynomial. *See* Polynomial functions
quadratic. *See* Quadratic functions
radical, 420–423
range of, 404
rational, 502, 509–513, 548
reciprocal, 503–506
reciprocal trigonometric, 775–778
secant, 775, 785
sine. *See* Sine functions
square root, 421–422, 431
step, 73
subtracting, 404
tangent, 761–763, 785
translations. *See* Translations
trigonometric. *See* Trigonometric functions
truth, 427
vertical-line test, 59–60
zeros of. *See* Zeros of functions

Function notation, 60, 111

Function rules, 60, 749

Fundamental Theorem of Algebra, 347–349, 367

G _____

Gauss, Carl Friedrich, 347

GCF (greatest common factor), 263, 304

Geometric mean, 624, 652

Geometric probability, 42, 49

Geometric sequences, 622–624
defined, 622, 652
formulas for, 623
graph of, 624
identifying, 623

Geometric series
defined, 636, 653
finite, 636–637, 644

Index

664, 669, 677, 685, 693, 701, 708, 726, 735, 743, 751, 759, 765, 773, 779, 795, 802, 811, 819, 825, 832, 838

Horizontal asymptotes, 512, 548

Horizontal line, 68

Horizontal translation, 96–97, 256, 421, 768–770, 785

Hyperbola, 560
 analyzing, 584
 axes of, 585, 603
 branches of, 558, 585
 center of, 558, 585
 defined, 585, 603
 equation of, 585, 587, 593, 594
 focus of, 585, 586–587
 graphing, 558–559, 586
 moiré pattern, 560
 translations, 594, 603
 vertices of, 585, 603

I

i, **imaginary number,** 278–279, 305

Identities, trigonometric. *See* Trigonometric identities

Identity matrix
 additive, 179
 multiplicative, 203, 235

Identity property, 7, 179, 187

Image, 196, 234

Imaginary axis, 279

Imaginary number(s), 278–279, 305. *See also* Complex number(s)

Imaginary Root Theorem, 344, 367

Inclusive events, 541

Inconsistent system, 122, 163

Independent events, 539–540, 549

Independent system, 122, 163

Independent variable, 64, 112

Index of radical, 376, 429

Indirect measurement, 778, 779, 780, 810, 811, 814

Induction, mathematical, 642–643

Inequalities
 absolute value, 35–36, 105–106, 137
 compound, 28–29, 36, 48
 equivalent compound, 36
 exponential, 484–485
 graphs of, 26–28
 linear. *See* Linear inequalities
 logarithmic, 484–485
 properties of, 26
 quadratic, 300–301
 radical, 426–427
 rational, 536–537
 simplified compound, 36
 solutions of, 26–28
 systems of, 135–137, 164
 writing, 106

Infinite geometric series, 635, 637–638

Infinite sequences, 629

Infinite series, 629, 635, 637–638

Initial side of angle, 730, 783

Inscribed rectangles, 645, 653

Intercepted arc, 738, 740, 784

Interdisciplinary Connections
 archaeology, 395, 450, 459, 475
 architecture, 201, 291, 518, 632
 art, 4, 60, 273, 274, 295
 astronomy, 475, 583, 598, 753, 792, 828
 biology, 41, 452, 481, 489, 705, 707, 760
 botany, 450
 chemistry, 63, 453, 456, 458, 461, 475, 488
 civil engineering, 258
 ecology, 144
 economics, 125, 251, 407, 445
 electrical engineering, 15
 engineering, 15, 258, 811
 geography, 152, 743, 744
 geology, 677
 geometry, 14, 15, 20, 22, 30, 32, 38, 42, 43, 48, 62, 64, 71, 75, 78, 85, 102, 130, 139, 152, 160, 161, 195, 196, 200, 201, 222, 231, 246, 268, 290, 299, 317, 323, 324, 330, 336, 337, 355, 362, 368, 378, 384, 408, 411, 416, 417, 432, 452, 498, 612, 614, 615, 620, 635, 743, 765, 766, 780, 811, 812, 819, 826
 history, 160, 236, 254, 597, 731
 language arts, 727
 literature, 212, 213, 214, 353
 medicine, 448, 704
 meteorology, 37, 677
 microbiology, 145
 music, 141, 189, 475, 504, 527, 744, 752
 oceanography, 444, 673, 675
 physics, 15, 222, 245, 252, 253, 275, 299, 306, 383, 384, 389, 395, 402, 451, 482, 488, 490, 498, 500, 520, 527, 624, 640, 654, 786, 796, 800, 801, 826
 psychology, 138, 452
 science, 81
 seismology, 454, 457, 473, 708
 social science, 661
 social studies, 85
 sociology, 701
 statistics, 178, 543, 702
 weather, 132, 396, 664, 668, 669, 676, 700
 zoology, 444, 470, 474, 497

Interest, 25, 449–450, 480, 488

Internet Links. *See* Active Math Online, Homework Video Tutor, Lesson Quiz Online, California Standards Tutorials Online, Video Tutor Help Online, Vocabulary Quiz Online

Interpolate, 316

Interquartile range, 681, 715

Intersect feature, of graphing calculator, 757

Inverse
 additive, 7, 47–48, 179, 280
 finding, 7
 multiplicative, 7, 47–48, 414
 of trigonometric functions, 797–799, 841–842

Inverse function, 412–415, 419, 420–421, 431

Inverse matrix
 additive, 179
 of coefficient matrix, 219, 220, 235
 encoding and decoding messages, 212
 multiplicative, 179, 203, 204, 211, 235
 solving matrix equations, 205–207, 212, 218–221
 solving systems of equations, 218–221

Inverse properties of real numbers, 7

Inverse relations, 412–415, 431

Inverse trigonometric function, 797–799, 841–842

Inverse variations, 496–497, 503, 547, 548

Irrational numbers, 5

Irrational Root Theorem, 343, 367

Isosceles triangle, 660

J

Joint variation, 498

Justifying Steps, 16, 30, 50

K

Koch snowflake, 611

L

Law of Cosines, 822–824, 843

Law of Large Numbers, 690

Law of Sines, 815–817, 822, 842

Least common denominator, 531

Least common multiple, 523

Least squares method, 89

Left end behavior, 318

Lesson Quiz Online, 9, 17, 23, 31, 37, 45, 63, 71, 77, 85, 93, 101, 107, 125, 131, 139, 145, 151, 161, 177, 183, 193, 201, 209, 213, 223, 231, 247, 253, 261, 269, 275, 283, 291, 299, 317, 325, 331, 337, 345, 349, 357, 363, 379, 385, 389, 395, 401, 409, 417, 425, 445, 453, 459, 467, 475, 481, 501, 507, 515, 521, 527, 535, 543, 561, 569, 575, 583, 589, 597, 615, 619, 625, 633, 641, 649, 665, 669, 679, 685, 693, 703, 709, 727, 735, 745, 753, 759, 765, 773, 781, 795, 803, 813, 819, 825, 833, 839

Like radicals, 386, 430

Like terms, combining, 14

Limits, 631, 652

Line(s). *See also* Linear equations, Linear inequalities, Linear systems
 horizontal, 68
 parallel, 68
 perpendicular, 68, 69
 slope of, 66–68, 112
 vertical, 68, 112
 x-intercept, 65
 y-intercept, 65

MODE feature, of graphing calculator, 502, 754

Models and modeling. *See* Mathematical modeling, Simulations

Modem, 768

Moiré pattern, 560

Monomial, 264

Multiple, least common, 523

Multiple Choice. See also California Multiple Choice Practice, California Standards Mastery Cumulative Practice

examples, 14, 29, 98, 106, 121, 142, 181, 226, 267, 296, 334, 353, 398, 415, 439, 480, 498, 542, 566, 595, 600, 611, 638, 666–667, 676, 750, 776, 798, 823

exercises, 107, 145, 183, 191, 200, 213, 261, 283, 337, 345, 354, 395, 401, 443, 451, 459, 473, 533, 537, 561, 569, 575, 581, 600, 821

Multiple events, probability of, 539–542

Multiple zero, 322, 366

Multiplication

of binomial radical expressions, 387
of binomials, 895
of complex numbers, 280
of conjugates, 387, 430
of fractions, 885
of functions, 404, 405
of matrices, 188–190, 234
of radical expressions, 380–381
of rational expressions, 518
scalar, 186–187, 234
simplifying algebraic expressions, 13
of square roots, 270

Multiplication Counting Principle, 351, 352

Multiplication property

of equality, 18
of inequality, 26
simplifying algebraic expressions, 13
of square roots, 270

Multiplicative identity matrix, 203, 235

Multiplicative identity property of scalar multiplication, 187

Multiplicative inverses

of matrices, 203, 204, 211, 235
reciprocals, 7, 47–48

Multiplicative Property of Zero

matrix multiplication, 190
real number multiplication, 13
scalar multiplication, 187

Multiplicity, 322, 366

Mutually exclusive events, 541

N

n **factorial,** 351, 367

Natural logarithm, 478–480, 489

Natural logarithmic equation, 479

Natural logarithmic function, 478–480, 489

Natural numbers, 5

Negative angle identities, 829, 843

Negative square root, 5

Networks, 216–217

New Vocabulary, 4, 12, 18, 26, 33, 39, 57, 64, 74, 80, 90, 95, 103, 120, 127, 141, 148, 172, 178, 186, 195, 203, 218, 225, 242, 256, 263, 271, 278, 286, 293, 312, 319, 326, 333, 341, 347, 351, 359, 375, 380, 386, 391, 397, 404, 412, 420, 438, 447, 454, 469, 478, 496, 503, 509, 517, 522, 539, 557, 565, 571, 578, 584, 610, 616, 622, 629, 636, 645, 660, 666, 672, 680, 689, 697, 704, 722, 730, 738, 746, 755, 761, 768, 775, 792, 806, 815, 822

Non-mutually exclusive events, 541

Normal curves, 705–706, 715

Normal distributions, 704–706, 715

Notation

factorial, 351, 367
function, 60, 111
scientific, 896
summation, 631, 652

*n***th root,** 375, 376

Number(s)

complex. *See* Complex number(s)
imaginary, 278–279, 305
irrational, 5
natural, 5, 279
random, 40, 43, 663, 906
rational, 5, 279
real. *See* Real numbers
roots of. *See* Roots of numbers
simplifying, 278, 279, 393
whole, 5, 279

Number cubes, 539, 549, 563, 664, 713

Number line, 6

Number of combinations, 352

Number of permutations, 352

O

Objective function, 141, 164

Oblique triangle, 815

Odds, 664

Online. *See* Active Math Online, Homework Video Tutor Online, Lesson Quiz Online, California Standards Tutorials Online, Video Tutor Help Online, Vocabulary Quiz Online

Open-Ended, 9, 16, 23, 31, 37, 44, 48, 50, 71, 77, 84, 93, 100, 107, 109, 113, 114, 124, 131, 145, 160, 166, 177, 184, 192, 193, 194, 195, 209, 213, 222, 229, 236, 246, 253, 261, 262, 268, 274, 275, 298, 306, 315, 324, 331, 337, 338, 346, 349, 355, 378, 384, 389, 395, 402, 408, 417, 424, 432, 444, 451, 452, 453, 458, 465, 474, 482, 490, 500, 507, 520, 526, 534, 535, 544, 550, 562, 575, 577, 582, 597, 604, 614, 618, 621, 622, 625, 633, 639, 641, 648, 649, 679, 701, 709, 710, 716, 726, 735, 743, 752, 765, 773, 786, 795, 803, 805, 811, 813, 819, 825, 833, 838, 844

Open-ended questions, answering, 840

Operations

order of, 885
row, 227, 235

Opposites

additive inverse, 7, 47–48
additive inverse matrices, 179
simplifying algebraic expressions, 13

Or (compound inequality), 28, 48

Order of operations, 885

Ordered pairs, 56–58

Ordered triples, 148, 165

Ordering, real numbers, 6

Ordinate, 56

Origin, 56, 148

Oscilloscope, 725

Outlier, 676, 714

P

Parabolas, 565–568

axis of symmetry, 243, 303, 565
conic sections, 557, 565–568
defined, 243, 565
directrix, 565, 567–568, 601
equation of, 257–258, 565–567, 568, 593
focus of, 565, 567–568, 601
graphing, 249–250, 257, 567–568
maximums and minimums, 251
points on, 243
properties of, 250
transformations, 256–259
vertex of, 243, 303

Parabolic solar mirrors, 567

Parallel lines, 68

Parameters, 99

Parametric equations, 126, 419, 577, 805

Parent function, 95–97, 99, 113

exponential, 447–449, 503–505
quadratic, 257
reciprocal, 503–506
trigonometric, 770

Pascal, Blaise, 359

Pascal's Triangle, 358, 359–360, 367, 621

Paths, finite graphs, 216–217

Patterns. *See also* Sequences, Series

exercises that use, 256, 277
formulas to generate, 612
mathematical, 610–612
moiré, 560
Test-Taking Tip, 334

Percent, 882

Percentile, 675, 714

Perfect square trinomial, 266, 286, 304

Perimeter, 14

Period

of cosine function, 756
defined, 723, 783
of function, 747, 767, 783
of sine curve, 747–748
of tangent function, 762

Index

solving by tables, 273, 297
solving using discriminant, 295–296, 297, 305
solving using Quadratic Formula, 293–295, 297, 305
standard form of, 271, 304
types of solutions, 297
writing from roots, 277
Zero Product Property, 271, 304, 321

Quadratic expressions
difference of squares, 267, 304
factoring, 263–266
factoring by using, 335
factoring trinomials, 264–266
perfect square trinomials, 266

Quadratic Formula, 293–295, 297, 305

Quadratic functions
classifying, 242
defined, 242
family of, 257
graphs of, 243, 249–250, 303
maximums and minimums, 251
modeling with, 244, 248, 314
perfect square trinomials, 286
properties of, 250
rewriting by completing the square, 288–289
standard form of, 242, 250, 303
transformations, 256–259
vertex form of, 256–259, 288–289, 304
zeros of functions, 272, 304

Quadratic inequalities, 300–301

Quadratic systems, 599

Quadratic term, 242

Quadratic trinomials, 264–266

QuadReg feature, of graphing calculator, 244, 248, 303, 314

QuarticReg feature, of graphing calculator, 314–315

Quartile, 674, 714

Quick Check. *See* California Check System

Quotient Property of Logarithms, 462–463

R

Radian(s)
comparing graphs in, 754
converting to and from degrees, 739, 784
defined, 738, 784
evaluating reciprocal trigonometric functions, 776
measuring in, 737, 738–741, 784

Radian feature, of graphing calculator, 577

Radical conjugates, 387–388

Radical equations, 397–399, 431

Radical expressions
adding, 386–387
binomial, 387–388
conjugates, 387, 430
converting to and from radical form, 392
dividing, 381–383

in formulas, 403
index of, 376, 429
like radicals, 386, 430
multiplying, 380–381
principal root, 376, 429
radicand, 376, 429
rational exponents and, 391–394, 430
rationalizing denominator, 382–383, 388, 429, 897
simplifying, 270, 377, 381, 387, 897
square roots, 270
subtracting, 386–387

Radical functions, 420–423

Radical inequalities, 426–427

Radical symbol, 270

Radicand, 376, 429

Radius
of circle, 571, 573–574, 602
of cylinder, 737

Random numbers, 40, 43, 663, 906

Random sample, 689–690, 715

Range
of functions, 404
interquartile, 681, 715
of relations, 58, 111
of set of data, 681, 715

Rate, 886

Ratio
common, 622, 652
golden, 273, 295, 389
for right triangle, 806–808, 842
trigonometric, 732–734, 842, 905
using, 20

Rational equations, 530–532

Rational exponents, 391–394, 399, 430

Rational expressions
adding, 523
complex fractions, 524–525, 548
dividing, 519
least common multiples, 523
multiplying, 518
operations with, 901
simplest form of, 517, 548
simplifying, 517–518, 548–549
subtracting, 524

Rational functions. *See also* Inverse variations
defined, 509
graphing, 502, 512–513
horizontal asymptotes, 512, 548
point of discontinuity, 509–511, 548
properties of, 509–512
vertical asymptotes, 511, 548

Rational inequalities, 536–537

Rational numbers, 5, 279

Rational Root Theorem, 341–343, 367

Rationalizing denominators, 382–383, 388, 429, 895

Reading Comprehension. *See* Assessment

Real numbers, 5–8
absolute value of, 8, 33
graphing, 6
ordering, 6
properties of, 7–8, 278

as solutions of inequalities, 27
square root of, 278
subsets of, 5

Real-World Connections. *See also* Algebra at Work, Careers, Point in Time
acoustics, 474, 583
advertising, 124, 357
aerodynamics, 531, 579
aeronautics, 21
agriculture, 153, 268, 423, 708
air pollution, 298
air quality, 145
air traffic control, 589
automobiles, 82, 298, 415, 534, 743
aviation, 79
banking, 124, 163, 625
baseball, 812
basketball, 36, 514
boats, 352, 378
break-even point, 132
budgeting, 506
business, 123, 184, 191, 192, 220, 229, 260, 298, 443, 513, 514, 543, 653
calendar, 727
carpentry, 324
ceramics, 764
circular dwellings, 571
circus, 424
classroom management, 135
coins, 269
college admissions, 137
college enrollment, 541
colors, 230
commission, 72, 108
communications, 206–207, 245, 444, 639
computer use, 694
construction, 20, 30, 254, 466, 500, 670, 765, 809, 811
consumer issues, 355, 406
consumer spending, 703
cooking, 106, 145
cost analysis, 69
crafts, 630
cryptography, 212, 213
custom tailoring, 289
data collection, 62, 444, 664, 686, 693, 701
depreciation, 442
design, 97, 149, 159, 268, 520, 534, 560, 623, 735, 743, 763
discounts, 432
dog grooming, 124
earnings, 166, 686
education, 633, 706
Egyptology, 807
Eiffel Tower, 68
Einstein's formula, 383
elections, 13, 16, 131, 133, 353, 694
electricity, 9, 752, 802
electronics, 424
energy, 173, 398, 682, 683, 685, 687
entertainment, 84, 104, 208, 613
environment, 77
estimation, 9, 176, 246, 403, 772, 773
exercise, 209
fabric design, 97

Acknowledgments

Staff Credits

The people who made up the California Mathematics team—representing design services, editorial, editorial services, education technology, image services, marketing, market research, production services, publishing processes, and strategic markets—are listed below. Bold type denotes the core team members.

Dan Anderson, **Scott Andrews,** Carolyn Artin, Judith D. Buice, Kerry Cashman, Sarah Castrignano, Allison Cook, Carl Cottrell, Bob Craton, Patrick Culleton, Sheila DeFazio, Kathleen J. Dempsey, Frederick Fellows, **Suzanne Finn,** Patricia Fromkin, David J. George, **Patricia K. Gilbert,** Sandy Graff, **Ellen Welch Granter,** Richard Heater, Jayne Holman, Jennifer King, Betsy Krieble, Christopher Langley, Lisa LaVallee, Christine Lee, **Elizabeth Lehnertz,** Catherine Maglio, Cheryl Mahan, **Ann Mahoney,** Constance McCarty, **Carolyn McGuire,** Anne McLaughlin, Richard McMahon, Eve Melnechuk, Terri Mitchell, Michael Oster, Jeffrey Paulhus, Marcy Rose, Rashid Ross, Siri Schwartzman, Vicky Shen, **Dennis Slattery,** Nancy Smith, Mark Tricca, Paula Vergith, Teresa Whitney, Merce Wilczek, Joe Will, Kristin Winters, Heather Wright, Helen Young

Additional Credits: J. J. Andrews, Sarah J. Aubry, Deborah Belanger, Beth Blumberg, Casey Clark, Patty Fagan, Tom Greene, Karmyn Guthrie, Gillian Kahn, Jonathan Kier, Mary Landry, Mary Beth McDaniel, Anakin Steuart Michele, Hope Morley, Carol Roy, Jewel Simmons, Ted Smykal, Richard Sullivan, Dan Tanguay, Steve Thomas, Michael Torocsik, Alwyn Velasquez, Allison Wyss

Cover Design

Nancy Smith

Cover Photos

Subway station, David Sailors/Corbis; Sand dunes, Picture Partners/SuperStock, Inc.

Technical Illustration

Argosy Illustration; Nesbitt Graphics, Inc.

Illustration

Argosy Illustration: 91
Kenneth Batelman: 75, 143, 179, 212, 240, 308, 350, 431, 507b, 663, 751
Jim DeLapine: 507
GeoSystems Global Corporation: 150
John Edwards Inc.: 79, 187, 226 b, 473, 651, 674 tl
Dennis Harms: 174, 182, 352, 385, 649 b
Lois Leonard Stock: 190
Seymour Levy: 141, 149
Ron Magnes: 202, 203, 204
Steve McEntee: 661
Jim Nuttle: 56
Brucie Rosch: 9, 156, 169, 188, 351, 370, 456, 652, 681 t, 761
Gary Torrisi: 208, 573, 603 b, 604 l, 716, 805 t

J/B Woolsey Associates: 171, 226 t, 317 mr, 318, 331, 348, 371, 553 br, 654, 665, 679, 696 b, 759
XNR Productions: 566

Photo Research

Sharon Donahue

Photography

Front Matter: Page CA7, Liane Caryl/SuperStock; **CA8,** Bruno Perousse/Age Fotostock; **CA10,** David Weintraub/Stock Boston; **CA11,** Andrew Syred/Science Photo Library/Photo Researchers, Inc.; **CA12,** SuperStock, Inc.; **CA13,** ©2000 by Consumers Union of the United States, Inc., Yonkers, New York 10703-1057, a nonprofit organization. Reprinted with permission from the March 2000 issue of Consumer Reports, for educational purposes only; **CA14,** Getty Images, Inc.; **CA15,** NASA; **CA16,** Getty Images, Inc.; **CA17,** Getty Images, Inc.; **CA18,** Getty Images, Inc.; **CA19,** Raymond Gehman/Corbis; **CA20,** Lawrence Migdale/Photo Researchers, Inc.; **CA21,** Chris Bensley/Stock Boston; **CA35,** AP Photo/Ben Margot; **CA36,** Jeff Foott/Getty Images; **CA37,** David McNew/Getty Images; **CA39,** National Geographic Images.

Chapter 1: Pages 2, 3, Ambient Images Inc./Alamy; **4,** Art Institute of Chicago, Illinois/Lauros-Giraudon, Paris/SuperStock, Inc.; **6,** Jeff Greenberg/PhotoEdit; **13,** Charles Gupton/Stock Boston; **15,** Bob Daemmrich Photography, Inc.; **16,** Jonathan Nourock/Getty Images, Inc.; **20,** Bob Daemmrich/Stock Boston; **21,** SuperStock, Inc.; **22,** Bruno Perousse/Age Fotostock; **24,** Jeff Henry/Peter Arnold, Inc.; **28,** Bob Daemmrich/Stock Boston; **30,** Jon Riley; **36,** AP Photo/Donna McWilliam; **37,** Northeast River Forecast Center/NOAA; **39 l,** Richard Haynes; **39 m, r,** Ken O'Donoghue; **41,** Ken O'Donoghue; **44,** Tim Davis/Allstock/PictureQuest.

Chapter 2: Pages 54, 55 Terje S. Johansen/Norwegian Leonardo Project; **57,** Richard Megna/Fundamental Photographs; **60,** Dirk Weisheit/DDB Stock Photo; **63,** Bob Rowan/Corbis; **65,** Figaro Magazine/Getty Images, Inc.; **66 t,** Patrick Ingrand/Getty Images, Inc.; **67 b,** Pearson Education, Inc.; **71,** Texas Instruments; **78,** Vanessa Vick/Photo Researchers, Inc.; **79 l,** Stacy Pick/Stock Boston; **79 r,** George A. Robinson/Getty Images, Inc.; **80,** AP Photo/Brietling Orbiter; **82,** Getty Images, Inc.; **84,** PhotoDisc, Inc./Getty Images, Inc.; **92,** Martin Rogers/Stock Boston/PictureQuest; **93,** Russ Lappa; **96,** Bill Aron/PhotoEdit; **97,** The British Museum; **99 both,** ©The Design Library, New York; **104 t,** Joe Sohm/Stock Boston; **104 b,** M. Grecco/Stock Boston.

Chapter 3: Pages 118, 119, Simon Jauncey/Getty Images; **121,** AP Photo/Thomas Kienzle; **123 l,** PhotoDisc, Inc./Getty Images, Inc.; **123 m,** Corbis; **123 r,** Getty Images, Inc.; **124,** David Young-Wolff/PhotoEdit; **128,** PhotoDisc, Inc./Getty Images, Inc.; **134,** Russ Lappa; **135,** Stock Boston; **137,** Bob Daemmrich/Stock Boston; **143 both,** Mark Thayer; **145,** Bob Daemmrich Photography, Inc.; **148,** David Weintraub/Stock Boston; **149,** Mark Thayer; **151,** Zigy Kaluzny/Getty Images, Inc.; **153 l,** Jose L. Pelaze/Corbis; **153 r,** 1992 SIU Biomed Comm/Custom Medical Stock Photo; **155,** Pearson Education; **159,** AP Photo/Paul Sakuma; **160,** Getty Images, Inc.

Chapter 4: Pages 170, 171, Peter Ginter/Getty Images; **173,** Michael Newman/PhotoEdit; **174,** AP Photo/L.G. Patterson; **178,** Frank Siteman/Stock Boston; **183,** AP Photo/John Bazemore;

186, Jeff Greenberg/Omni-Photo Communications, Inc.; **189 both,** Andrew Syred/Science Photo Library/Photo Researchers, Inc.; **192,** Atlantic Feature ©1996 by Mark Parisi; **197,** Russ Lappa; **197 inset,** William Taufic/Corbis; **199,** George Holton/Photo Researchers, Inc.; **201,** Jerry Clapsaddle; **206,** The New York Times; **215,** ©1976-2002 Photos courtesy of SPARC; **220,** Russ Lappa; **222,** David Simson/Stock Boston.

Chapter 5: Pages 240, 241, Pearson Education/Prentice Hall College Division; **243,** Jon Chomitz; **246,** U.S. Postal Service; **251,** Marty Katz/The Image Works; **253,** Michael Newman/PhotoEdit; **254,** James L. Stanfield/National Geographic Image Collection; **255,** Michael Epstein/PhotoEdit; **258,** SuperStock, Inc.; **267,** Doug Menuez/PhotoDisc, Inc./Getty Images, Inc.; **268,** Jeff Greenberg/Visuals Unlimited; **272,** Mike McMillan/Spotfire Images; **273,** Portrait of a Man, 1773-1775, 12" x 16 1/4", Museo De Zaragoza; **274,** Asian Art Museum of San Francisco, The Avery Brundage Collection, B60 M427; **281,** Prentice Hall; **282,** © Robotman reprinted by permission of Newspaper Enterprise Association, Inc.; **283,** Prentice Hall; **285,** Jon Chomitz; **287,** Courtesy of Craig Smorynski; **290,** Prentice Hall; **291,** Petyer Pearson/Getty Images, Inc.; **292,** Prentice Hall; **295,** Getty Images, Inc.; **296,** Reuters New Media Inc./Corbis; **298,** AP/Wide World Photos.

Chapter 6: Pages 310, 311, AP Photo/Eric Risberg; **314,** National Geographic Society; **320,** Spencer Grant/Stock Boston; **323,** Greg Pease/Getty Images, Inc.; **324,** Bob Daemmrich/Stock Boston/PictureQuest; **328,** Museo Archeologico, Florence, Italy/Art Resource, New York; **332,** Corbis; **334,** Nik Kleinberg/Stock Boston; **337,** James A. Sugar/Corbis; **340,** Craig Smorynski; **347,** C. Marvin Lang; **352,** Getty Images, Inc.; **355 t,** ©2000 by Consumers Union of the United States, Inc., Yonkers, New York 10703-1057, a nonprofit organization. Reprinted with permission from the March 2000 issue of Consumer Reports, for educational purposes only; **355b,** Peanuts reprinted by permission of United Feature Syndicate, Inc.; **359,** Jean-Loup Charmet/Photo Researchers, Inc.; **361,** Andy Lyons/Allsport/Getty Images, Inc.; **362,** Getty Images, Inc.

Chapter 7: Pages 372, 373, U.S. Space & Rocket Center; **378,** Getty Images, Inc.; **383,** Sidney Harris; **384,** PhotoDisc, Inc./Getty Images, Inc.; **389,** Judy Canty/Stock Boston; **392,** Jason Grow/Corbis; **395,** An Keren/Sovfoto/Eastfoto/PictureQuest; **398,** Jean-Claude LeJeune/Stock Boston; **401,** Russ Lappa; **406,** Robert Brenner/PhotoEdit; **407 l,** Amy C. Etra/PhotoEdit; **407 r,** Robert Fried/Stock Boston; **409,** Stone/Getty Images, Inc.; **415,** AP Photo/The Saginaw News, Bernie Eng; **417,** Tony Freeman/PhotoEdit; **418,** Bob Daemmrich/The Image Works; **424,** Ringling Bros. and Barnum & Bailey Combined Shows, Inc.

Chapter 8: Pages 436, 437, Craig Tuttle/Corbis; **439,** Spencer Grant/PhotoEdit; **440,** AP Photo/University of Illinois, Mark Jones; **444,** AP Photo/Bob Care; **448,** Peter Berndt, MD/Custom Medical Stock Photo; **451,** Bill Aron/PhotoEdit; **452,** Laura Dwight/Omni-Photo Communications, Inc.; **454,** AP Photo/Lauren McFalls; **456,** L.S. Stepanowicz/Bruce Coleman, Inc.; **459,** James King-Holmes/Science Photo Library/Photo Researchers, Inc.; **464,** John Neubauer/PhotoEdit; **466,** Reuters NewMedia Inc./Corbis; **470,** Jeff Greenberg/PhotoEdit; **473,** Andrew Rafkind/Getty Images, Inc.; **474,** Catherine Karnow/Corbis; **475,** Andy Sacks/Getty Images, Inc.; **479,** NASA; **482,** David Young-Wolff/PhotoEdit; **483,** NASA; **483 inset,** NASA/Bruce Coleman, Inc.; **484,** The British Museum/HIP/The Image Works; **485,** ABPL/Daryl Balfour/Animals Animals.

Chapter 9: Pages 494, 495, David Breashears /Arcturus Motion Pictures; **497,** Kevin Dodge/Masterfile; **500,** Bob Daemmrich/Stock Boston; **504,** Robert Freck/Getty Images, Inc.;

507, Comstock Images; **513,** Dennis O'Clair/Getty Images, Inc.; **518,** Tom Dietrich/Getty Images, Inc.; **520,** 1992 Jeffrey Muir Hamilton/Stock Boston; **522 both,** Mark Thayer; **527,** Bob Daemmrich Photography, Inc.; **531,** Courtesy of Lightning Cycle Dynamics, Inc.; **534 t,** Reprinted with special permission of King Features Syndicate.; **534 b,** Morton Beebe/Corbis; **539 t,** Jon Chomitz; **539 b,** Jon Chomitz; **540,** Mark C. Burnett/Stock Boston; **542,** Prentice Hall; **545,** H. Dratch/The Image Works.

Chapter 10: Pages 554, 555, Richard Cummins/Corbis; **557,** Jeff Smith; **558 both,** Jeff Smith; **561,** Richard Pasley/Stock Boston; **563,** Painting by Ken Marschall from Titanic: an Illustrated History ©1992, A Madison Press Book; **567,** Getty Images, Inc.; **569 t,** Prentice Hall; **569 b,** Woody Woodworth/SuperStock, Inc.; **571,** Molly & Georg Gerster/Comstock Images; **573,** Michael Rosenfeld/Getty Images, Inc.; **575,** Susan Van Etten/Stock Boston; **579,** NASA Langley Research Center; **582,** Ken O'Donoghue; **589,** Ed Young/Science Photo Library/Photo Researchers, Inc.; **597,** Collection of the Lowe Art Museum, University of Miami. Museum Purchase in memory of Shelia Natasha Simrod Friedman, #92.0094.

Chapter 11: Pages 608, 609, Doug Wechsler/Vireo; **610 t,** Bob Daemmrich/The Image Works; **610 m,** Laura Dwight/PhotoEdit; **610 b,** Will & Deni McIntyre/Photo Researchers, Inc.; **611,** Prentice Hall; **613,** AP/Wide World Photos; **614,** From Not Strictly By The Numbers ©Carolina Mathematics/Carolina Biological Supply Company; **616,** Arthur Tilley/Getty Images, Inc.; **617,** AP Photo/Michael Tweed; **619,** James Lamb/Getty Images, Inc.; **621 l,** Jane Grushow/Grant Heilman Photography, Inc.; **621 ml,** Ed Reschke/Peter Arnold, Inc.; **621 mr,** Joy Spurr/Bruce Coleman, Inc.; **621 r,** Ed Reschke/Peter Arnold, Inc.; **622,** Ken O'Donoghue; **623,** Cindy Charles/PhotoEdit; **624,** Paul Barton/Corbis; **626,** Corel Corp.; **627 both,** China Stock; **630 t,** Russ Lappa; **630 b,** Prentice Hall; **632,** The Image Works; **633,** Russ Lappa; **638,** Scott Camazine/Photo Researchers, Inc.; **640,** Leonard Lessin/Peter Arnold, Inc.; **645,** Doug Wechsler/Vireo.

Chapter 12: Pages 658, 659, Getty Images, Inc.; **662,** P. Dumas/Eurelios/Science Photo Library/Photo Researchers, Inc.; **665,** Tony Freeman/PhotoEdit; **668,** AP Photo/Don Heupel; **678,** Corbis; **681,** AP Photo/Michael Gallacher; **683,** AP Photo/Jim McKnight; **685,** Corbis; **690 t,** Michael Newman/PhotoEdit; **690 b,** Anthony Wood/Stock Boston; **691,** Corel Corp.; **692,** Courtesy, The Southpaw Shoppe, San Diego; **694,** Raymond Gehman/Corbis; **695,** Spencer Grant/Stock Boston; **698,** Comstock Images; **700,** AP Photo/Ronald Martinez; **701,** Mark Richards/PhotoEdit; **704,** Bob Daemmrich Photography, Inc.; **705,** Chuck Davis/Getty Images, Inc.; **707 both,** PhotoDisc, Inc./Getty Images, Inc.

Chapter 13: Pages 720, 721, Novastock/PhotoEdit; **722,** Lawrence Migdale/Stock Boston; **725 l,** Lawrence Migdale/Photo Researchers, Inc.; **725 r,** Lester V. Bergman/Corbis; **726,** David Young-Wolff/PhotoEdit; **728,** PhotoDisc, Inc./Getty Images, Inc.; **731 l,** Kenneth Garrett/National Geographic Image Collection; **731 r,** Victor R. Boswell, Jr./National Geographic Image Collection; **734,** PhotoDisc, Inc./Getty Images, Inc.; **735,** Dale O'Dell/Corbis; **738,** Jo Prater/Visuals Unlimited; **741,** John Elk III/Stock Boston; **742 l,** Jean Kugler/Getty Images, Inc.; **742 r,** John Cancalosi/Stock Boston; **743 l,** Frank Cezus/Getty Images, Inc.; **743 r,** David Young-Wolff/PhotoEdit; **744,** Foxtrot ©Bill Amend. Reprinted with permission of Universal Press Syndicate. All rights reserved.; **747,** Russ Lappa; **750,** Getty Images, Inc.; **752,** Francene Keery/Stock Boston; **755,** Michael Newman/ PhotoEdit; **757,** Mark Gibson/ImageQuest/Visuals Unlimited; **759,** Tom Walker/Stock Boston; **760,** Mark Thayer; **764,** PhotoDisc, Inc./Getty Images, Inc.; **768,** Corbis; **777,** Richard Haynes; **778,** Vanessa Vick/Photo Researchers, Inc.; **780,** Visuals Unlimited.

Chapter 14: Pages 790, 791, Peter Sterling/Getty Images, Inc.; **792,** Frank Zullo/Photo Researchers, Inc.; **800,** Russ Lappa; **802,** Lincoln Electric Co.; **803,** Spencer Grant/Index Stock Imagery, Inc.; **807,** Chris Bensley/Stock Boston; **808,** Corbis; **809,** Michael Newman/PhotoEdit; **811,** Fotostock/Getty Images, Inc.; **812,** John de Visser/Masterfile Corporation; **817,** Tom Prettyman/ PhotoEdit; **823,** Matthew J. Atamian/GettyImages, Inc.; **836,** Jeff Greenberg/PhotoEdit; **827,** Volker Steger/Science Photo Library/Photo Researchers, Inc.; **828,** The Granger Collection, New York; **833,** "Watch", 1925 by Gerald Murphy. Dallas Museum of Art ©2004 Estate of Honoria Murphy Donnelly.

Acknowledgments